MICROECONOMICS

CANADIAN EDITION

B. Douglas Bernheim
Stanford University

Michael D. Whinston
Northwestern University

Patrick M. Martin
University of Guelph

McGraw-Hill Ryerson
Connect. Learn. Succeed.

The McGraw-Hill Companies

McGraw-Hill Ryerson
Connect. Learn. Succeed.™

Microeconomics
Canadian Edition

The Internet addresses listed in the text were accurate at the time of publication. The inclusion of a Web site
does not indicate an endorsement by the authors or McGraw-Hill Ryerson, nor does McGraw-Hill Ryerson
guarantee the accuracy of information presented at these sites.

ISBN-13: 978-0-07-096927-8
ISBN-10: 0-07-096927-2

1 2 3 4 5 6 7 8 9 0 DOW 1 9 8 7 6 5 4 3 2 1

Printed and bound in the United States.

Care has been taken to trace ownership of copyright material contained in this text; however, the publisher
will welcome any information that enables them to rectify any reference or credit for subsequent editions.

Vice-President and Editor-in-Chief: *Joanna Cotton*
Executive Sponsoring Editor: *Leanna MacLean*
Sponsoring Editor: *James Booty*
Executive Marketing Manager: *Joy Armitage Taylor*
Developmental Editor: *Rachel Horner*
Supervising Editor: *Kara Stahl*
Senior Editorial Associate: *Stephanie Hess*
Copy Editor: *Judy Sturrup*
Manager, Production Services: *Yolanda Pigden*
Cover and Interior Design: *Valid Design & Layout/Dave Murphy*
Cover Image Credit: © *Chad Baker/Getty Images (RF)*
Page Layout: *Aptara, Inc.*
Printer: *R.R. Donnelly*

Library and Archives Canada Cataloguing in Publication

Bernheim, B. Douglas
    Microeconomics / B. Douglas Bernheim, Michael D. Whinston, Patrick Martin.—Canadian ed.
        Includes index.
    ISBN 978-0-07-096927-8
    1. Microeconomics—Textbooks. I. Whinston, Michael Dennis II. Martin, Patrick III. Title.
HB172.B486 2010
338.5

                                                                C2010-903254-3

ABOUT THE AUTHORS

B. DOUGLAS BERNHEIM graduated with an A.B. in Economics from Harvard University, summa cum laude and Phi Beta Kappa, in 1979. He entered graduate study at M.I.T. under a National Science Foundation Graduate Fellowship and completed his Ph.D. three years later. He began his academic career at Stanford University and taught there from 1982 to 1987. He left Stanford in 1988 to assume an endowed chair in the Department of Finance at Northwestern University's J.L. Kellogg Graduate School of Management. In 1990 he moved to Princeton University, where he held an endowed chair in the Department of Economics and also served as the co-director of the Center for Economic Policy Studies. He returned to Stanford in 1994 and is now the Edward Ames Edmonds Professor of Economics.

Professor Bernheim's work has spanned a number of fields, including public economics, political economy, game theory, contract theory, behavioural economics, industrial organization, and financial economics. He is a research associate of the National Bureau of Economic Research, a Senior Fellow of the Stanford Institute for Economic Policy Research (SIEPR), and co-director of SIEPR's Tax and Budget Policy Program. He is also a former director of the Stanford Institute for Theoretical Economics and co-editor of the *American Economic Review.*

Professor Bernheim's teaching has included principles of economics, intermediate micro-economics, public economics, microeconomic theory, industrial organization, behavioural economics, and insurance and risk management.

MICHAEL D. WHINSTON is the Robert E. and Emily H. King Professor of Business Institutions in the Department of Economics at Northwestern University. He also holds appointments at Northwestern's School of Law and its Kellogg Graduate School of Management. Whinston received his B.S. and M.B.A. from the Wharton School at the University of Pennsylvania and his Ph.D. from M.I.T. He taught at Harvard from 1984 to 1997 before moving to Northwestern. His research has covered a variety of topics in microeconomics, including game theory, the design of contracts and organizations, firm behaviour in oligopolistic markets, antitrust, and law and economics. He has also conducted empirical research on the airline and pharmaceutical industries, and served as a consultant—for private parties, the government, and the courts—in various antitrust cases. Whinston is a co-author of the leading graduate textbook in microeconomics, *Microeconomic Theory* (Oxford University Press, 1995), and is also the author of *Lectures on Antitrust Economics* (MIT Press, 2006). He and Bernheim have collaborated since 1983, and are excited about this opportunity to produce an innovative new microeconomics text for undergraduates.

PATRICK M. MARTIN received a B.A. in Economics from the University of California at Irvine, an M.A. in Economics from Cornell University, and a Ph.D. in Economics from the University of Guelph. He joined the Department of Economics at the University of Guelph in 1999 where he still teaches today.

His research has included work in a several areas of applied microeconomics, and he has published research on environmental and resource economics and economic development. He has been fortunate enough to put "theory into practice" by serving as both a principal investigator and as a member of research projects in India funded by the Canadian Development Agency and the Shastri Indo Canadian Institute. He has also consulted for various government agencies including the Department of Fisheries and Oceans and the U.S. Forest Service.

Professor Martin's teaching has included introductory and intermediate microeconomics and macroeconomics, advanced microeconomics, and topics in microeconomics. He has also taught a variety of field courses on topics such as international trade, environmental economics, and economic development.

BRIEF CONTENTS

CONTENTS

part Markets

PREFACE

All of us confront an endless variety of economic choices. Some of those choices involve such personal matters as financing the purchase of a new car, borrowing for university, or saving for retirement. Some involve such business matters as cost-effective production techniques or investment in new product development. Some involve matters of public policy, such as whether to vote for a candidate who advocates reductions in personal income taxes or a candidate who promotes stronger environmental regulations. Sometimes good economic decision making is just a matter of common sense. But in many situations, a command of basic microeconomic principles helps us to understand the consequences of our choices and make better decisions. In effect, microeconomics has evolved into the study of decision making.

In this Canadian edition of *Microeconomics* we have tried to include applications that are as diverse as our students. Our hope is that the Canadian edition stimulates interest in a subject that provides the foundation for continued study in all areas of economics and commerce, introduces the tools of the discipline, and encourages students to "think like an economist." Most students will not become economists, but an education in microeconomics can be invaluable in endeavours that range from making business decisions to helping design public policies, and simply managing their own money.

Microeconomics is intended to be an effective resource for both business-oriented and policy-oriented courses, providing students with a basic knowledge of essential microeconomic principles. While many fine microeconomics texts are available, *Microeconomics* offers instructors and students some distinct advantages.

MICROECONOMICS

A STRATEGY FOR LEARNING

Canadian examples and applications. The inclusion of specific Canadian examples and applications is important for students, as they relate to Canadian practices and policy-making. The Canadian edition has been adapted to fit the needs of both students and instructors in Canada, incorporating recent, relevant, and current events in Canada. For example, Chapter 15 illustrates market interventions by incorporating specific examples of how Canadian marketing boards intervene in agricultural markets. Chapter 19 explores oligopoly and includes a history and summary of Canadian competition law. Examples scattered throughout this chapter highlight mergers (Suncor and Petro-Canada), locational predation (Safeway in Edmonton and Calgary), predatory pricing (Air Canada's attempt to drive newcomer WestJet from their markets), strategic entry (Bombardier's entry into the small commercial airline market), and the deregulation of electricity in Canada. Throughout the text, Canadian applications are incorporated to highlight the usefulness of modelling in microeconomics.

Some examples include:

- The price of Sidney Crosby rookie cards on eBay before and after his winning goal in the 2010 Olympic hockey final. This application provides a demonstration of supply and demand in Chapter 2. Also illustrated is the impact of the Great Ice Storm of 1998 on the price of maple syrup.

- Tax credits at the provincial and federal levels, and tiered rate structures at the Ontario Energy Board provide examples of kinked budget constraints as we discuss consumer choice in Chapter 5.

- The discussion of production in Chapter 8 shows how vertical integration at Molson and Coor's was a factor in their emergence as market leaders before their recent merger. Purolator's expansion into international markets highlights the discussion of economics of scope.

- The Canada–U.S. Softwood Lumber Agreement appears in several chapters as a starting point for discussions on profit maximization, tariffs, and market supply.

- In Chapter 10, the discussion of present value is expanded upon by applications on topics as diverse as the Western Canada Lottery Corporation's Millionaire Life contest and Human Resources and Skills Development Canada studies on the increased earnings associated with higher levels of educational attainment.

- In Chapter 20, the discussion of externalities and public goods includes examples such as the deadweight loss in Canada from the overuse of antibiotics resulting in drug resistance, Transport Canada estimates of congestion costs on Canadian highways, and public financing of CBC radio and television.

Calculus and Non-Calculus Flexibility. *Microeconomics* requires no knowledge of calculus; however, an instructor who wishes to teach a calculus-based course using this book can easily do so. For the most important points, explanations involving calculus appear in optional margin boxes, footnotes, appendices, and certain Add-Ons. In addition, the book includes a large number of quantitative worked-out problems and exercises. Where calculus would ordinarily be required, we simply supply the student with a derivative—for example, a formula for the marginal rate of substitution between goods or for the marginal product of an input. In the context of consumer theory, the marginal rate of substitution is actually a more natural starting point for analysis than the utility function; after all, the marginal rate of substitution is observable, whereas a utility function is not. For a calculus-based course, an instructor can ask students to verify the derivatives. Supplying the derivatives cleanly separates the calculus portion of problem-solving from the "economic" portion and prevents the calculus from interfering with students' understanding of the economics.

Clarity. Students face enough challenges while learning microeconomics without having to slog through opaque explanations. We have worked hard to make sure that the writing in *Microeconomics* is transparent, the explanations are clear and intuitive, and the graphs lead students naturally through the key ideas.

Current information. This book covers exciting recent developments in microeconomics, drawing on game theory, information economics, and behavioural economics. Equally important, it offers cutting-edge coverage of traditional core topics, including marginal analysis, consumer theory, producer theory, monopoly, and oligopoly. Applications of theory include discussions of current events and issues.

Accuracy. Sometimes textbooks stretch the truth a bit to make a point seem more obvious to students. We believe that such stretches are rarely desirable. Nor are they necessary, provided adequate attention is given to the development of clear explanations. *Microeconomics* strives to "tell no lies" while ensuring that its explanations are understandable.

Usefulness. Many students who use books that don't require calculus or minimize the use of mathematics often learn to do little more than draw pictures to illustrate solutions (for example, of a consumer's choice from a budget constraint). This does a disservice to students with less mathematical training. In fact, if students are given the right starting points, they can solve a wide range of quantitative problems using only simple algebra. By combining this innovative approach with worked-out problems and in-text exercises, *Microeconomics* allows students of varying mathematical backgrounds to solve problems using microeconomic tools.

Relevance. Students should always understand why they are studying topics. Other texts sometimes assure students that new concepts will be useful in contexts where their usefulness is not at all obvious to the average person. We believe that students learn better if they have immediate answers to the questions "Why should I care?" and "What do I gain from learning this?" We also underscore the relevance of the material by featuring fact-based applications (as opposed to hypothetical discussions), which relate directly to one or more of the central aspects of the theory being discussed.

A STRATEGY FOR TEACHING

True-to-Discipline Organization

The organization of *Microeconomics* is slightly unconventional for an undergraduate micro-economics text. As a discipline, microeconomic theory begins by examining the behaviour of individuals in their roles as either consumers or managers of firms. On this foundation, it builds a theory of aggregate economic outcomes, with an emphasis on market equilibrium. Logically, it therefore makes sense to study the theory of decision making before diving into an analysis of how markets operate. *Microeconomics* follows the logical structure of the discipline more closely than other texts by clearly distinguishing the study of individual decision making from the analysis of markets.

- **Part I** contains three introductory chapters. The first introduces the field of micro-economics. The second reviews the basic principles of supply and demand. The third elaborates on a central theme of microeconomic reasoning: how to find a decision that maximizes the difference between total benefits and total costs by equating marginal benefits to marginal costs. We invoke this principle repeatedly throughout the rest of the book.

- **Part II** focuses on individuals' economic decisions. Three chapters on consumer theory and three on producer theory are followed by three chapters covering decisions involving time, uncertainty, and strategy/game theory. An additional chapter examines behavioural perspectives on economic decision making.

- **Part III** concerns markets. To begin, three chapters cover competitive markets, includ-ing one on partial equilibrium theory, one on the analysis of government interventions, and one on general equilibrium. We then turn to market failures, including three chapters on monopoly and oligopoly, one on externalities and public goods, and one on asymmetric information (available online).

Flexible Organization

While the organization of the book emphasizes the distinction between topics concern-ing decision making and topics concerning markets, we recognize that instructors may not wish to teach the material in that order. For example, some instructors may wish to jump directly from basic producer theory to competitive equilibrium, returning to the additional topics on decision making as time allows. *Microeconomics* provides instructors with this flexibility.

Alternative Course Designs

Instructors who use this book can organize their courses in a variety of ways. A basic **one-semester or one-quarter course** might cover the core (non-optional) sections of Chapters 1–9, 14–15, 17, 18.1–18.3, 19, and 20. A more ambitious course or a **two-term course** might cover some optional material from those chapters and parts of Chapters 10–13 (additional topics on decision making), 16 (general equilibrium), the remainder of 18 (price discrimination through self-selection and bundling), and 21 (asymmetric information). Instructors adopting this more ambitious approach may choose to assign Chapters 2 and 3, which largely contain review material from introductory microeconomics, as independent reading. As we've noted, the material on decisions involving time, uncertainty, and strategy/ game theory in Chapters 10–12 could be covered immediately after covering consumer and producer theory, or delayed until later in the course.

Business-oriented courses, on the other hand, might reduce to some degree their coverage of consumer theory (Chapters 4–6) and externalities and public goods (Chapter 20) in favour of covering choices involving time (Chapter 10) and risk (Chapter 11), game theory (Chapter 12), and all of Chapter 18 on pricing policies. More **policy-oriented courses** might skip Chapter 18 entirely in favour of covering general equilibrium (Chapter 16).

This book is one of the few that devotes a separate chapter to behavioural economics (Chapter 13). This material is entirely compartmentalized, and any instructor who wishes to teach a conventional course on intermediate microeconomics can simply skip the chapter. For those who are interested in introducing behavioural perspectives, we have designed the chapter with a modular structure, so that it can be used in one of two different ways. Most obviously, an instructor can introduce behavioural economics as a stand-alone topic, covering all or part of the chapter. Alternatively, an instructor can integrate behavioural perspectives with traditional perspectives, for example, covering Sections 13.1 and 13.2 after basic consumer theory (Chapters 4 through 6), Section 13.3 after discussions involving time (Chapter 10), Section 13.4 after discussions involving uncertainty (Chapter 11), and Section 13.5 after discussions involving strategy (Chapter 12).

Optional Material

Microeconomics contains both core material and optional material. The optional material takes three easy-to-use forms. First, we have identified certain sections of the text as optional by placing an asterisk (*) in front of the section heading. Second, some advanced or specialized topics are covered in chapter appendices. Third, instructors who wish to delve into particular topics more deeply, or to introduce additional topics that enrich and extend the core material, may wish to incorporate one or more of the book's Add-Ons, which can be downloaded online. Each Add-On is listed in the Table of Contents following the chapter with which it is associated, and readers are referred to these Add-Ons within the text. As we receive feedback on the book, we expect to write additional Add-Ons, which will also be available online.

A STRATEGY FOR UNDERSTANDING

Microeconomics strives to present economics clearly and logically, helping instructors make the topic more accessible to students and giving students insight into the world around them.

Instructor Supplements—*Microeconomics* offers a range of materials written to integrate seamlessly with the text, providing extra practice for students and additional resources for instructors.

Instructor's Manual and Solutions

The instructor's manual provides chapter overviews, outlines, and a discussion of how the core principles apply to each chapter. It also addresses concepts students often find difficult and includes suggestions for alleviating confusion. Solutions to the problems are give at the end of each chapter of the instructor's manual.

Computerized Test Bank

Adapted by Lee Bailey, University of Toronto, and screened by teaching assistants to ensure accuracy, instructors have access to over 1200 questions. The computerized test bank is available through EZ Test Online, a flexible and easy-to-use electronic testing program, which allows instructors to create tests from book-specific items. EZ Test accommodates a wide range of question types and allows instructors to add their own questions. Test items are also available in Microsoft Word® (Rich Text Format). For secure online testing, exams created in EZ Test can be exported to WebCT and Blackboard. EZ Test Online is supported at www.mhhe.com/eztest where users can download a Quick Start Guide, access FAQs, or request help with specific issues.

Microsoft® PowerPoint® Slides

Prepared by Maria Sabourin-Jovel, Carleton University, the slides outline the main points in each chapter and reproduce major graphs and charts.

Connect[TM]

Connect is a web-based assignment and assessment platform that gives students the means to better connect with their coursework, with their instructors, and with the important concepts that they will need to know for success now and in the future. *Connect* embraces diverse study behaviours and preferences with breakthrough features that help students master course content and achieve better results. The powerful course management tool in *Connect* also offers a wide range of exclusive features that help instructors spend less time managing and more time teaching.

With *Connect*, you can deliver assignments, quizzes, and tests online. A robust set of questions and problems are presented and tied to the textbook's learning objectives. Track individual student performance—by question, assignment, or in relation to the class overall—with detailed grade reports. Integrate grade reports easily with Learning Management Systems (LMS) such as WebCT and Blackboard. And much more.

Connect helps you teach for today's needs:

Unlimited Practice, Instant Feedback
Provide instant feedback to unlimited textbook practice problems, acknowledging correct answers and pointing to areas that need more work.

Automatic Grading
Focus on teaching instead of administrating with electronic access to the class roster and gradebook, which easily sync with your school's course management system.

Direct Textbook and Test Bank Questions
Assign students online homework and test and quiz questions with multiple problem types, algorithmic variation, and randomized question order.

Integrated eBooks
Connect directly integrates the McGraw-Hill textbooks you already use into the engaging, easy-to-use interface.

Dedicated Canadian Support and Training
The Connect development team and customer service groups are located in our Canadian offices and work closely together to provide expert technical support and training for both instructors and students.

Connect^{TM} **for Students**
Connect provides students with a powerful tool for improving academic performance and truly mastering course material, plus 24/7 online access to an interactive and searchable eBook. *Connect* allows students to practise important skills at their own pace and on their own schedule. Importantly, students' assessment results and instructors' feedback are all saved online—so students can continually review their progress and plot their course to success.

McGraw-Hill Ryerson offers a range of flexible integration solutions for **WebCT** and **Blackboard** platforms. Please contact your local McGraw-Hill Ryerson *i*Learning Sales Specialist for details.

E-STAT is an educational resource designed by Statistics Canada and made available to Canadian educational institutions. Using 450 000 current CANSIM (Canadian Socio-economics Information Management System) Time Series and the most recent—as well as historical—census data, E-STAT lets you bring data to life in colourful graphs and maps. Access to E-STAT is made available to purchasers of this book by special agreement between McGraw-Hill Ryerson and Statistics Canada.

McGraw-Hill's **Create Online** places the most abundant resource at your fingertips—literally. With a few mouse clicks, you can create customized learning tools simply and affordably. McGraw-Hill Ryerson has included many of its market-leading textbooks within Create Online for e-book and print customization, as well as many licensed readings and cases. For more information, please visit www.mcgrawhillcreate.com.

CourseSmart brings together thousands of textbooks across hundreds of courses in an eTextbook format providing unique benefits to students and faculty. By purchasing an eTextbook, students can save up to 50 percent off the cost of a print textbook, reduce their impact on the environment, and gain access to powerful Web tools for learning, including full text search, notes and highlighting, and email tools for sharing notes among classmates. For faculty, CourseSmart provides instant access to review and compare textbooks and course materials in their discipline area without the time, cost, and environmental impact of mailing print examination copies. For further details, contact your *i*Learning Sales Specialist or visit www.coursesmart.com.

ACKNOWLEDGEMENTS

Many people have made important contributions to the development of the first Canadian edition of *Microeconomics*. First I would like to thank the team at McGraw-Hill Ryerson. James Booty and Rachel Horner kept the book on schedule and helped make important decisions along the way. Judy Sturrup and Kara Stahl helped with the editing of the manuscript, and their assistance led to major improvements in the book's exposition. For their contributions early on, I thank Andria Fogarty and especially Daphne Scriabin, who made various contributions to moving the project forward. I would especially like to thank Bruce McIntosh for first asking if I would be interested in working on the Canadian edition of *Microeconomics*. He couldn't have picked a book that was more aligned with my own teaching approach. It was the enthusiasm I felt when first reviewing the text that led me to believe that working on the Canadian edition was a worthwhile endeavour.

I would also like to thank my colleagues at the University of Guelph who alerted me to research, both new and old, that could be used in writing many of the applications. I must also thank my students, for whom this book was written, for providing a sounding board for helping me to separate explanations and approaches that work from those that do not.

I would also like to thank the reviewers who helped shape this book:

Kurt Annen, University of Guelph
Lee Bailey, University of Toronto, Mississauga
Stephan Dodds, Carleton University
Ida Ferrara, York University
Bernard Lebrun, York University
Leigh MacDonald, University of Western Ontario
Maria Sabourin-Jovel, Carleton University

Finally, I would like to thank my wife Nancy, and my children, Tim, Peter, and Elena, for their patience these past several years. Vacations invariably became working vacations, and evening and weekend time with the family was less than I would have enjoyed and they deserved. Nancy was always willing to look over the manuscript when asked and her involvement led to numerous improvements, both technical and expository. I would also like to thank my father, Alfred Martin, for first telling me that "you go to university to learn how to think." That insight has helped to guide and motivate me throughout my education, and it is an approach that I try to pass on to my students.

Patrick M. Martin

Introduction

Part I The first three chapters of this book lay the groundwork for all the material that follows. In Chapter I we'll provide a brief overview of microeconomics, previewing the types of questions it addresses, the tools it employs, the themes it emphasizes, and its uses in personal decision making, business, and public policy. In Chapter 2 we'll review some basic concepts that are typically covered in introductory economics courses, including demand, supply, market equilibrium, and elasticity. In Chapter 3 we'll study some basic principles of good decision making, and develop useful tools for identifying the choice that strikes the best balance between benefits and costs.

Preliminaries

LEARNING OBJECTIVES

After reading this chapter, students should be able to

LO1 Describe the scope of microeconomics and understand that it concerns the allocation of scarce resources.

LO2 Explain how economists apply the scientific method to common economic questions.

LO3 Identify recurring economic themes within the field.

LO4 Recognize a variety of situations where economic ideas can be applied.

LO5 Explain the goals of microeconomic inquiry.

It is often said that money can't buy happiness. Yet, undeniably, people derive both sustenance and pleasure from material goods. Some of those goods, like clean water or a quiet spot on the beach, are found in nature. Others, like automobiles and television sets, are produced from natural resources. All these goods, whether natural or manufactured, have one important characteristic: their supplies are limited, or scarce.

Scarcity forces societies to confront three critical issues. First, each society must decide *what to produce*. All societies convert natural resources, like land, minerals, and labour, into the various things that people want, like food, clothing, and shelter. When we produce more of one good, we use up scarce resources, and this reduces our ability to produce other goods. For example, if a farmer uses an acre of land to produce wheat, he can't use the same acre to grow corn or tomatoes, or to graze livestock. He can't use it as the site for a manufacturing plant or a housing development. Since resources are scarce, every society must develop procedures for determining what is and is not produced.

Second, a society must decide *how to produce goods*. There is usually more than one way to produce a good. For example, if a farmer uses more fertilizer per acre, he can grow the same amount of wheat on less land. This decision frees up scarce land, which then becomes available for other purposes, such as housing or manufacturing. But fertilizer is also scarce. If farmers use more of it to grow wheat, less will remain for other crops. Since different methods of production consume different resources, every society must develop procedures for determining how goods are produced.

Finally, a society must determine *who gets what.* Every society produces goods so that people can eat, wear, use, or otherwise consume them. In some cases, a small number of individuals receive a large share of the goods. In Canada, for example, the richest 100 individuals accounted for more than one quarter of one percent of the nation's wealth in 2008. Individuals such as David Thomson (publishing), and members of the Irving (energy), Rogers (communications), and Weston (retailing) families are able to buy a great deal more than the rest of us. In other cases, goods are distributed more equally. Every society must develop procedures for allocating goods among consumers.

The field of economics examines the ways in which societies address these three issues. In other words, it concerns the allocation of scarce resources. If everyone could have whatever they wanted whenever they wanted it, there would be no need for economics.

In this introductory chapter, we'll cover four main topics concerning microeconomics.

1. *What is microeconomics?* The field of microeconomics concerns decision making by individuals—typically consumers and the managers of firms—and how their decisions determine the allocation of a society's scarce resources. As we'll see, microeconomists address a wide range of issues related to individual and social behaviour.

2. *Tools of microeconomics.* Microeconomists try to understand the allocation of scarce resources by applying the scientific method. We'll summarize the main principles of this method and describe its application to economic questions.

3. *Themes of microeconomics.* As you read through this book, you'll notice that some themes come up over and over again. We'll preview the most important ones.

4. *Uses of microeconomics.* Microeconomics can help with the decisions we make in our personal lives and in business. It also provides some useful tools for evaluating the effects and desirability of public policies. We'll briefly describe several problems to which microeconomic principles have been usefully applied.

1.1 WHAT IS MICROECONOMICS?

There are two main branches of economics, microeconomics and macroeconomics. While microeconomics concerns individual decision making and its collective effect on the allocation of a society's scarce resources, macroeconomics concerns aggregate phenomena. Booms and busts (recessions), the pace of economic growth, and the rate of unemployment are all macroeconomic topics. Much of modern macroeconomics involves applications of microeconomics, in the sense that explanations for aggregate outcomes are often rooted in theories of decision making by consumers and firms.

Institutions for Allocating Resources

Microeconomic analysis begins with an understanding of the institutions, including the laws and customs, that define a society's procedures for allocating resources. Those procedures empower various people to make decisions, but they also constrain their choices. For example, in most Western economies consumers are free to spend their money as they choose, but they can't spend more than they can earn, accumulate, or borrow. Even an absolute dictator is constrained by the scarcity of a country's total resources.

Decentralization versus Centralization   In some societies, most economic decisions are decentralized. Capitalism involves a high degree of decentralization. A **capitalist economy** is one in which the means of production are mostly owned and controlled by and for the benefit of private individuals, and the allocation of resources is governed by voluntary trading among businesses and consumers. Typically, this trading is organized into markets, which we discuss below. In capitalist economies, production takes place in thousands of independent firms, which are free to produce whatever their owners and managers choose. Likewise, consumers are free to spend their money as they please.

In some societies, many economic decisions are centralized. Communism involves a high degree of centralization. A **communist economy** is one in which the state owns and controls the means of production and distribution.[1] Government officials decide what to produce, how to produce it, and who gets it. In the former Soviet Union, for example, the managers of manufacturing plants received their production targets and other instructions from government ministries. Government officials also decided who would receive coveted consumer items, such as washing machines and automobiles.

No economy is completely centralized or decentralized. Every society takes a hybrid approach. While there is no foolproof way to measure a society's degree of economic centralization, it is possible to get a general idea by examining statistics on the size of government. Figure 1.1 shows total government spending on goods and services (also known as *government consumption*) and total government expenditure (which includes both consumption and transfer payments like social security and welfare), expressed as

A **capitalist economy** is one in which the means of production are mostly owned and controlled by and for the benefit of private individuals, and the allocation of resources is governed by voluntary trading among businesses and consumers.

A **communist economy** is one in which the state owns and controls the means of production and distribution.

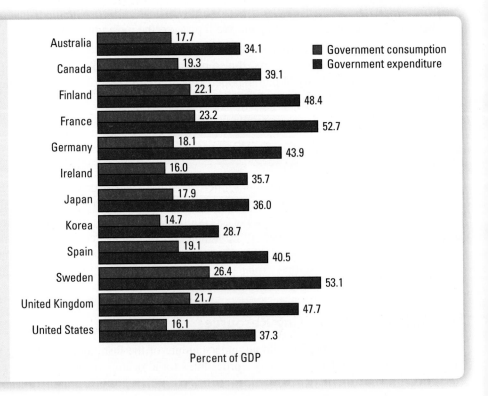

Figure 1.1
Relative Economic Centralization. For each of the 12 countries in this figure, the lengths of the bars show total government spending on goods and services (also known as *government consumption*) and total government expenditure as fractions of gross domestic product (GDP) in 2008.

Source: *OECD in Figures, 2009 Edition,* OECD Publications, 2009.

Country	Government consumption	Government expenditure
Australia	17.7	34.1
Canada	19.3	39.1
Finland	22.1	48.4
France	23.2	52.7
Germany	18.1	43.9
Ireland	16.0	35.7
Japan	17.9	36.0
Korea	14.7	28.7
Spain	19.1	40.5
Sweden	26.4	53.1
United Kingdom	21.7	47.7
United States	16.1	37.3

Percent of GDP

---

[1]This definition is not intended to encompass the meaning of communism as a political philosophy. The ownership and control of the means of production and distribution are also substantially centralized in socialist economies. As this book is primarily concerned with the operation of capitalist economies, we will not delve into the economic, political, and philosophical distinctions between the various forms of communism and socialism.

Application 1.1

A Pain in the Neck

Canada spends 12 percent of its GDP on health care while other developed nations spend as much as 17.3 percent (the United States) of their GDPs on health care.[2,3] How is the allocation of resources to health care determined? In most countries, even those with capitalist economies, decisions that affect medical expenditures are both centralized and decentralized.

Suppose you have severe neck pain and need a strong painkiller. Who picks your medication? To some extent, you are free to purchase the painkiller of your choice. However, your decision is also constrained by government policy. In Canada, Health Canada regulates pharmaceutical products like painkillers. Before bringing a new drug to market, the manufacturer must first demonstrate to Health Canada that it is both effective and reasonably safe. Consumers are not permitted to choose drugs that haven't received Health Canada approval. For example, in early 2007 doctors were free to prescribe a painkiller called lumiracoxib in Australia,

Canada, and the United Kingdom, but not in the United States. By the end of the year the drug was withdrawn from Canada and other countries.[4] Newly approved drugs are usually dispensed only on a prescription basis, according to the judgment of physicians. Prescription painkillers include codeine and morphine. Ultimately, Health Canada approves many drugs for over-the-counter (OTC) use. Consumers can purchase and use OTC drugs without a doctor's consent. OTC painkillers include aspirin, acetominophen, ibuprofen, and naproxen. In 2002 Claritin (loratadine), an antihistamine, was sold over the counter in Canada but not in the United States. In late 2002 the FDA followed Canada's lead and permitted Claritin to be sold as a OTC drug in the U.S.

In short, the choice of a pain killer depends not only on voluntary transactions between consumers and producers, but also on the decisions of health care providers and government regulators. Therefore, the allocation of pain killers is decentralized in some ways, and centralized in others.

---

percentages of gross domestic product, or GDP (a measure of national economic activity), for 12 countries as of 2008. According to these measures, resource allocation is centralized to a significant degree in all 12 countries. Sweden has the most centralized economy of the twelve: 26.4 percent of GDP goes to government consumption and 53.1 percent to government expenditure. South Korea's economy is the least centralized: there, only 14.7 percent of GDP goes to government consumption and 28.7 percent to government expenditure. Canada lies in the middle of this spectrum, with slightly higher centralization than the United States, Australia, and Japan, and slightly less than the United Kingdom, France, and Finland.

Sometimes, a country centralizes certain aspects of resource allocation, like spending on national defense, and decentralizes others, like spending on breakfast cereal. (We'll see in Chapter 20 why this can make sense.) However, as Application 1.1 illustrates, there are also situations in which the decisions that affect the allocation of particular goods are both centralized and decentralized.

Markets The most common form of economic decentralization involves markets. **Markets** are economic institutions that provide people with opportunities and procedures for buying and selling goods and services. The procedures are sometimes defined by

> **Markets** are economic institutions that provide people with opportunities and procedures for buying and selling goods and services.

---

[2]Canadian Institute for Health Information, *National Health Expenditure Trends, 1975 to 2009* (Ottawa, Ont.: CIHI, 2009); http://www.cbc.ca/health/story/2009/11/19/health-care-spending-canada.html; http://www40.statcan.gc.ca/l01/cst01/ECON04-eng.htm, accessed July 12, 2010.

[3]https://www.cms.gov/NationalHealthExpendData/25_NHE_Fact_Sheet.asp, accessed July 12, 2010.

[4]http://www.hc-sc.gc.ca/ahc-asc/media/advisories-avis/_2007/2007_141-eng.php, accessed July 12, 2010.

explicit rules, sometimes by custom. Compare, for example, the strict rules and procedures governing the sale and purchase of corporate stock on the Toronto Stock Exchange, with the loose customs that prevail in an open bazaar.

In microeconomic analysis, each market is associated with a single group of closely related products that are offered for sale within particular geographic boundaries. For example, an economist might examine the retail market for ice cream in Vancouver. Often, it is difficult to say exactly what constitutes an appropriate group of products or geographic boundaries. For example, should we consider a narrower product category, like chocolate ice cream, or a broader one that includes sorbet and frozen yogurt? Similarly, should we consider a smaller geographic area like the West End, or a larger one like British Columbia?

Economists think of products as belonging to the same market when they are highly interchangeable. If consumers freely substitute sorbet for ice cream and vice versa, an economist would group those goods into a single market. Likewise, if the consumers who frequent ice cream parlours in the West End and Granville Island are happy to consider alternatives in the other neighbourhood, an economist would group those Vancouver neighbourhoods into a single market. In cases in which any seller can serve any customer regardless of location, the market is worldwide.

In contrast to economists, most people associate markets with specific physical locations where trading takes place. Picture, for example, a flea market, a farmer's market, or the electronic market of the Toronto Stock Exchange. To an economist, a flea market doesn't qualify as a market for two reasons. First, a flea market offers a wide variety of goods, from socks to sofas. An economist would distinguish between a sock market and a sofa market. Second, flea market customers can usually buy most of the same goods at other local stores. To an economist, the sock market would include other sources of socks for the flea market's customers, such as local clothing and department stores, and possibly companies that sell socks over the Internet.

In many markets, the sellers are companies and the buyers are individuals. The markets for most consumer products fall into this category. For example, a consumer can buy ice cream from a Loblaws supermarket and televisions from the Future Shop. But there are also markets in which companies are buyers: Loblaws buys ice cream from Breyer's, and Future Shop buys televisions from Sony. And there are markets in which individuals are sellers: employees sell their labour services to Loblaws and Future Shop. In some markets, buyers and sellers both include mixes of companies and individuals. Think about markets for used cars. You can buy a used car from, or sell one to, either a company or another individual.

In modern markets, trade is usually governed by prices. A **price** is the rate at which someone can swap money for a good. In the markets for many consumer products, each seller establishes a non-negotiable price at which it is willing to sell the good. For example, a Loblaws supermarket offers containers of Breyer's chocolate ice cream to all customers at a fixed price. In other markets, sellers negotiate different prices with different customers. For instance, while new car dealers set prices for the automobiles in their inventories, most are willing to haggle.

To function, markets require institutions that establish and protect private property rights. A **property right** is an enforceable claim on a good or resource. The notion of property rights is closely related to the idea of ownership. When we say that someone owns an object, we mean that she holds the only enforceable claim on it—in other words, she owns the property rights. If sellers lacked property rights, they would have nothing of value to offer buyers. (That's why you can't sell the CN Tower!)

Trade can occur only if property rights are **transferrable**, in the sense that the current owner of a good can reassign those rights to another consenting party. When you buy a

A flea market located in a large city in North America.

A **price** is the rate at which someone can swap money for a good.

A **property right** is an enforceable claim on a good or resource.

Property rights are **transferrable** if the current owner of a good can reassign those rights to another consenting party.

used car, for example, the previous owner transfers the car's title into your name. When property rights aren't transferrable, markets can't operate. For example, though many workers in Canada have rights to pension benefits, those rights aren't legally transferrable, so there's no market for them. You can't buy the rights to someone else's pension benefits.

Nations that allocate scarce resources primarily through markets are said to have **market economies**. Governments can play either large or small roles in market economies. In a **free market system**, the role of government is rather limited. Government enforces and protects property rights but otherwise mostly allows markets to operate as they will, with little regulation or other intervention. Most people equate capitalism with the free market system.

> A **market economy** allocates scarce resources primarily through markets. In a **free market system**, the government mostly allows markets to operate as they will, with little regulation or other intervention.

There are, of course, ways to decentralize economic decision making without using markets. For example, many resources, like space on the beach, are allocated on a first-come, first-served basis. Others, like seats in an oversubscribed college or university class, may be allocated by lottery.

One of the main objectives of microeconomics is to determine when each method of allocating scarce resources performs well and when it performs poorly. This knowledge allows us to judge whether specific economic decisions should be centralized or decentralized. In particular, it tells us whether markets are preferable to other economic institutions for allocating specific resources.

Economic Motives

By studying economic institutions, we learn about the constraints people face when they make choices that affect the allocation of resources. To determine which choices they will make, we need to understand their motives.

Microeconomists assume that people are motivated by material self-interest—that is, by the desire for goods and services. Throughout this book (except where we explicitly state otherwise), we'll assume that material self-interest is the *only* motive for behaviour. Microeconomic theory can, however, accommodate a broader view of human motivations, including the possibility that someone might care about someone else's well-being.

The procedures used to allocate scarce resources create incentives for people to engage in certain activities and to avoid others. In market economies, people respond to material incentives in a variety of different ways, depending on whether they act as *consumers*, *employees*, or *owners of firms*.

In deciding how to spend their resources, self-interested consumers try to choose the mix of goods and services that provides the highest possible level of personal satisfaction. They respond to incentives created by the prices of those goods and services. Ordinarily, a high price discourages the consumption of a good, while a low price encourages it. The rapid increase in the price of oil in the past several years saw a dramatic reduction in the demand for SUVs and increased demand for high-efficiency furnaces by homeowners.

In deciding how to spend their time, self-interested employees try to choose the mix of work and leisure that provides the highest possible level of personal satisfaction. They respond to monetary incentives provided by their employers. For example, if an employer pays a fixed wage for each hour of work, that decision affects the relative attractiveness of work and leisure to the employee. Many sales jobs are structured so that commissions constitute a large portion of the employee's income. This induces employees to work harder and allows the employer to reduce the cost of monitoring workers' efforts.

In directing production, the owners of firms are motivated by material self-interest to choose the mix of inputs and outputs that provides the highest possible level of profit. Because owners can exchange profits for goods and services, higher profits permit greater consumption and greater material satisfaction. Thus, owners respond to incentives created by the prices of inputs and outputs. For inputs, high prices discourage their use. For outputs, high prices encourage their production.

In other institutional settings, the quest for either material self-interest or broader notions of personal satisfaction motivates different types of activities. For example, children respond to incentives to study hard at school, politicians respond to incentives to promote policies that increase the likelihood of their re-election, and military officers respond to incentives to behave in ways that increase the likelihood of promotion. Microeconomic analysis can help us to understand how people respond to incentives in a wide range of settings, not just in economic markets.

Positive versus Normative Analysis

One of the main objectives of microeconomists is to address factual questions, also known as **positive questions**, usually concerning choices or market outcomes. This activity is known as **positive economic analysis**.[5] The truth of every possible answer to a positive question is potentially testable—the relevant facts, once known, must either confirm or contradict it.

> **Positive economic analysis** addresses factual questions, also known as **positive questions**, usually concerning choices or market outcomes. It concerns what did, will, or would happen.

All positive questions concern what *did* happen, what *will* happen, or what *would* happen. In addressing what *did* happen, economists provide a factual account of the past—for example, how the distribution of wealth among Canadian households changed between 1900 and 2000. In addressing what *will* happen, they forecast the future—for example, how the average interest rate charged on home mortgages will change over the next year. In addressing what *would* happen, they describe the likely consequences of a course of action, based on an understanding of cause and effect.

While historical fact-finding and forecasting are certainly important branches of economics, the cause-and-effect analysis of actions and their consequences is the bread and butter of microeconomics. Here are some examples of questions that address what *would* happen:

- If Dell were to reduce the price of notebook computers by 10 percent, how many more notebooks would the company sell? Would the increase in the sale of notebooks cut into the sales of Dell's desktop computers? If so, by how much?

- If Ford were to launch an advertising campaign to promote its new line of cars, would Toyota respond by advertising more? By lowering prices? By changing how it markets some models?

- Newfoundland's minimum wage is $8.50, but the province plans to increase it to $10.00 sometime in 2010. How would this change effect employment? Would businesses hire fewer workers? Would firms relocate to other provinces?

To answer positive questions accurately, economists must stick to objective facts and avoid value judgments. Sometimes, the facts aren't what we would like them to be. In such cases, positive economic analysis can at times seem callous, insensitive, or politically incorrect.

In 2001, for example, economist Steven Levitt and legal scholar John Donohue teamed up to study the important positive question of whether unwanted children are more likely to commit crimes when they become teenagers and adults.[6] After examining

---

[5]The word *positive* does *not* mean that the answer admits no doubt. On the contrary, all answers—particularly those involving predictions—involve *some* degree of uncertainty. Rather, in this context, *positive* simply means that the prediction concerns a factual matter.

[6]John Donohue and Steven Levitt, "The Impact of Legalized Abortion on Crime," *Quarterly Journal of Economics* 166, May 2001, pp. 379–420.

variations in crime statistics across the United States and across time, they concluded that the legalization of abortion—which presumably reduced the number of unwanted children—led to lower crime rates among teenagers and young adults roughly 20 years later. The study touched off a firestorm of controversy. The authors received stacks of hate mail; some critics accused them of encouraging genocide. Yet the study drew no implications concerning the desirability of abortion. Its purpose was to investigate the positive, cause-and-effect relationship between neglect and subsequent criminal behaviour. Professor Levitt sees a less controversial implication of the study: "We should do the best we can to try to make sure kids who are born are wanted and loved."

The other main objective of microeconomists is to address questions that involve value judgments, also known as **normative questions**, concerning the allocation of resources. This activity is known as **normative economic analysis**. Normative questions concern what ought to happen, rather than what did, will, or would happen. Here are some examples:

* Is society better off with free trade between countries or with barriers to free trade?
* Which is better, taxing income from labour or income from capital?
* Will a merger between two large firms that produce similar goods benefit society?

Since value judgments are subjective, particular answers to normative questions are neither right nor wrong, and their validity isn't testable. Consider, for example, the following normative statement: "Economic inequality is evil." This statement is a value judgment, and people are free to disagree with each other about it, even when they agree about the objective facts.

If all normative statements are subjective, how can an economist usefully conduct normative analysis? Typically, economists rely on a single overarching value judgment, known as the principle of **individual sovereignty**, which holds that each person knows what's best for him or her. This principle requires us to avoid paternalistic judgments, like the notion that classical music is "better for you" than hip hop. If you choose hip hop, then hip hop must be better for you. Economists apply the same principles to policy questions. If, *with full knowledge of all consequences*, someone would choose trade barriers over free trade, we conclude that he's better off with trade barriers than with free trade. In this way, economists turn normative questions into positive questions. To determine whether a consumer would be better or worse off with one of two alternatives, they predict which one the consumer would choose, given full and correct information about the effects of each alternative. This type of normative analysis obviously requires accurate positive analysis, both to forecast the consequences of the alternatives and to predict the consumer's choice.

Unfortunately, the interests of different people often conflict. A policy that benefits one person may hurt another. This conflict requires us to weigh one person's gain against another's loss. For example, suppose we must choose between two policies, one that benefits person A at the expense of person B, and another that benefits person B at the expense of person A. If person A is poor and person B is wealthy, most people would probably lean toward the first policy. But what if the benefit to A was small, while the cost to B was large? What if the policy involved taking money away from someone who works hard and giving it to someone who makes no effort?

Neither the principle of individual sovereignty nor any other economic principle can help us to decide whether the gain to one person outweighs the loss to another, or vice versa. However, if someone supplies a subjective criterion, normative economic analysis can identify the best policy. For example, suppose someone believes that, from a social perspective, extra dollars in the hands of person A are worth twice as much as extra dollars in the hands

Normative economic analysis addresses questions that involve value judgments, also known as **normative questions**. It concerns what ought to happen rather than what did, will, or would happen.

The principle of **individual sovereignty** holds that each person knows what's best for him or her.

of person B (possibly because person A is poor relative to person B). If positive economic analysis reveals that a policy is likely to raise person A's income by $80 and lower person B's income by $100, then *according to this criterion*, the policy will be beneficial.

The Scope of Microeconomics

Microeconomics isn't just about money. When economists speak of the allocation of resources, they often have in mind a broad definition of resources. Suppose, for example, that you're scheduled to take a test and have only a limited amount of time to study. Since your time is a scarce resource, its allocation between studying, sleep, and recreation is an economic issue.

Virtually every human decision involves the use of some scarce resource. As a result, micreconomists study an extremely broad range of topics, including marriage, crime, addiction, and suicide. In effect, microeconomics has evolved into the study of decision making, the ways in which decisions by many individuals combine to produce social outcomes, and the desirability of those outcomes.

Application 1.2

For Richer or Poorer

Though we make many important decisions over the course of our lives, few affect our happiness as profoundly as the choice of a spouse. Do economists have anything to say about who pairs up with whom?

In the past, the motivation for marriage was often explicitly economic. Betrothals were arranged to advance families' material interests, and marriages were treated as financial transactions. In some cultures, the groom's family made a substantial payment to the bride's family. Called a *bride price*, it was intended as compensation for the costs of the bride's upbringing and the loss of her services to her parents. In other cultures, the bride's family made a substantial payment to the groom's. Such "dowries" were particularly common in societies in which an unmarried adult daughter was considered a burden or an embarrassment to her parents. As in any economic market, the magnitude of the bride price or the dowry reflected the forces of supply and demand (see Chapter 2).

In contemporary western societies, we frown on "gold-diggers" who place financial concerns before romance. According to custom, we choose our spouses based on love. Does that mean that our choice of a spouse is not an economic decision? Not at all. From an unmarried woman's

point of view, appropriate mates are scarce—indeed, it's often said that a good man is hard to find. The same principle holds for unmarried men. Potential spouses are a scarce resource, the allocation of which is governed by the customs and institutions associated with dating and marriage.

A skeptic might argue that love is irrational, that it defies logical analysis. But an economist doesn't need to explain why Bob is more attracted to Sally than to Sue, any more than she needs to explain why Bob likes pizza more than popcorn. Rather, an economist tries to explain Bob's *choices*, taking his likes and dislikes, as well as the intensity of those feelings, as givens.

While economists can't predict who will fall in love with whom, they can (and do) investigate the types of traits that men and women value in potential mates. By examining who chooses whom, they can also determine the typical person's willingness to trade off one desirable characteristic, like financial success, for another, like an aspect of physical attractiveness. In one study, economist Raymond Wolff found that where marriage is concerned, income is the most important determinant of a man's desirability to women, while slimness is the most important determinant of a woman's desirability to men.[7] While many people might find

[7]Raymond Alfred Wolff, "The Relationship between Child Support and Remarriage for Divorced and Separated Women and Men," Ph.D. dissertation, Stanford University, 2000.

these conclusions somewhat offensive, it is important to remember that Wolff was describing tendencies, not universal truths, and that he was engaged in *positive* analysis. That is, his objective was to discover the facts, not to make judgments.

Why then does marriage fall within the scope of microeconomics? Economists study how the allocation of scarce resources (including spouses with desirable characteristics) depends on institutions and customs (including those governing who meets whom) given the objectives that motivate choices (including the desire for a wealthy or attractive mate). Equipped with an understanding of the traits that people value in spouses, an economist could, for example, predict how a change in the social customs and institutions that determine who meets whom—resulting perhaps from a technological development like the Internet, which makes it easier to meet potential mates with particular characteristics—will tend to affect the standards applied in evaluating potential mates, the length of time spent searching for mates, and the types of people who ultimately pair up. These effects may lead to further consequences of economic interest. For example, a reduction in the tendency for people to marry spouses with similar social and economic backgrounds will reduce the likelihood that differences in income and wealth will persist across generations.

1.2 TOOLS OF MICROECONOMICS

Economics is a social science—social in the sense that it concerns human behaviour, and a science in the sense that, when studying behaviour, economists follow the scientific method. In practice, what does that method involve?

The Scientific Method

How do scientists uncover the truth about the world? How do they learn about the characteristics, causes, and effects of observed phenomena? Though the details differ from one discipline to another, all scientists follow a common approach known as the **scientific method**, which consists of the following five steps.

Step 1: Initial observation Scientific inquiry starts with the observation of an unexplained phenomenon. Think of Sir Isaac Newton, who wondered why objects (like apples) tend to fall toward the earth rather than away from it. Observation also motivates economic questions. An economist might wonder why water, which is essential to life, costs far less per ounce than diamonds, which are not.

"I'm a social scientist, Michael. That means I can't explain electricity or anything like that, but if you ever want to know about people I'm your man."

Step 2: Theorizing After observing an unexplained phenomenon, a scientist tries to come up with a possible explanation, known as a **theory**. To account for the behaviour of falling objects, Newton proposed the theory of gravity. Likewise, to account for differences between the prices of goods like water and diamonds, economists developed the theory of supply and demand (which we'll review in the next chapter).

Step 3: Identification of additional implications It isn't enough for a theory to explain the observation that motivated its creation. Good theorizing requires the scientist to "stick her neck out." Having formulated a theory, she must look for additional implications that can either be verified or refuted. Virtually every scientific theory implies that there are circumstances under which a phenomenon will reoccur. For example, according to

The **scientific method** is the general procedure used by scientists to learn about the characteristics, causes, and effects of natural phenomena.

A **theory** is a possible explanation for a natural phenomenon.

Newton's theory of gravity, apples should *always* fall when separated from their branches. Sometimes a theory's additional implications are more subtle. Newton's theory implies that in a vacuum, all objects should fall at precisely the same rate, regardless of their weight or size. Similarly, the theory of supply and demand implies that prices should rise following an increase in production costs.

Step 4: Further observation and testing To determine whether a theory is valid, scientists make further observations, gathering data that will allow them to test the theory's additional implications. A physicist might test the theory of gravity by designing an experiment to determine whether different objects do, in fact, fall at the same rate in a vacuum. An economist might gather the data needed to determine whether prices do, in fact, rise following an increase in production costs.

Step 5: Refinement of the theory Sometimes a scientist's further observations are inconsistent with some or all of a theory's additional implications. In some cases, the rebuttal of the theory is so complete that scientists must go back to the drawing board. In other instances, they can account for the new observations by modifying the theory. In either case, after further theorizing, they return to step 3, identify additional implications of the new or modified theory, and put those to the test.

This process never truly ends. Though a scientist may have enormous confidence in a thoroughly tested theory, she never treats it as absolute truth. Scientists are free to examine and re-examine the validity of any theory, no matter how well-established.

Some theories are more useful than others. A useful theory is both broadly applicable and specific in its implications. The theory of gravity is extremely useful both because it applies to all physical objects and because it has very specific implications about the rate at which any two objects will move toward each other. In contrast, the theory that "anything can happen, anytime, anywhere" may be broadly applicable, but it has no specific implications. Likewise, a theory that explains only why a particular leaf on a particular tree fell at a particular moment may have very specific implications, but isn't useful because it isn't broadly applicable.

Models and Mathematics

A **model** is a simplified representation of a phenomenon.

Scientists usually express their theories through *models*. A **model** is a simplified representation of a phenomenon—a story or analogy that explains how part of the world works. Typically, a model provides an account of cause and effect.

Without realizing it, all of us use simple models in our daily lives. For example, when you get into a car and step on the gas, you expect the car to move forward, because you have in your mind a model of how the car works. If you're not mechanically inclined, your model may be no more complicated than the idea that pressing on the accelerator makes the car move forward. Even so, it's still a model.

Newton's model of gravity starts with a simple principle, that every object pulls every other object toward it. The complete theory adds numerous details. For example, it maintains that the pull between two objects depends on their masses and the distance between them. Since Newton was interested in quantitative questions—for instance, how fast an object moves or how far it travels—the theory involves a great deal of mathematics.

A model needn't be mathematical, however. Take the following statement: "If you study longer for a microeconomics exam, you'll receive a higher grade." This qualitative model is certainly useful, though not as useful as a good quantitative model. For example, if you knew that another hour of studying would improve your numerical score on an exam by 10 percent, you could better assess whether additional studying is worth the time and effort.

Economists usually work with mathematical models. Why? Because most economic choices are quantitative, most of the economic questions raised in business and government call for precise answers. Mathematical models can provide precision, qualitative theories cannot. In addition, mathematical modeling imposes intellectual discipline. It forces us to be specific about our assumptions and prevents us from relying on loose or incomplete reasoning.

In Chapter 2, we'll explore one important economic model in some detail: the model of supply and demand. Economists often use that model qualitatively—for example, to understand whether the price of a good will rise or fall after an increase in production costs. However, by using a mathematical model of supply and demand, they can also say, with some precision, how much the price will rise for a given change in cost.

"Duh!"

Simplifying Assumptions

There's a famous joke about an economist and two scientists stranded on a desert island with a great deal of canned food, but no can opener. The scientists suggest various methods for opening the cans, which the economist dismisses out of hand. When they ask irritably what he would suggest, he smiles and replies, "Assume a can opener."

Though the joke implies otherwise, all scientists—not just economists—make assumptions that are not literally true. By their nature, models are *simplified* representations of the real world. Simplification allows us to wrap our minds around phenomena that might otherwise be too complex to understand.

In formulating a model, scientists often concentrate on the *most important* explanations for a phenomenon. For example, to describe how quickly a paper clip falls from a tabletop to the floor, a scientist might focus exclusively on gravity, using a simple theory that near the earth's surface, objects accelerate downward at the rate of 9.8 metres/sec^2. This model isn't literally correct. Among other things, air resistance affects the rate of descent. Should the scientist factor in air pressure, wind speed, humidity, surface imperfections on the paper clip, and other factors that could in principle affect its speed? The answer depends on her need for precision. In this context, her simple model of acceleration is reasonably accurate and hard to improve on, even though it is literally false.

Economists do much the same thing. Since the social phenomena they study are extremely complex, they must make many simplifying assumptions. Typically, some of those assumptions are easy to criticize. In evaluating economic models, then, we must remember that no model is literally true. The real test of a good model is its usefulness. A model that contributes to our understanding of social phenomenon and does a reasonably good job of predicting outcomes is certainly useful, even if it isn't entirely realistic.

It follows that the same simplifying assumption can be reasonable in one context but unreasonable in another. For example, in studying patterns of household spending on consumption goods like food, clothing, and shelter, it's probably reasonable to assume that people care only about their material self-interest. But in studying charitable contributions, that certainly is *not* a good assumption.

CALVIN AND HOBBES © 1995 Watterson. Dist. By UNIVERSAL PRESS SYNDICATE. Reprinted With Permission. All Rights Reserved.

Data Analysis

The scientific method requires us to test our theories by confronting them with data. Sources of economic data fall into three main categories: records, surveys, and experiments.

Records   Most companies maintain detailed business records, including financial accounts, personnel records, and client or customer databases. Many companies employ in-house economists to analyze these data, and some companies share their data with independent economists. Other companies compile data for the express purpose of selling it to others. For example, they track the prices of stocks, bonds, and various commodities. Both companies and households are required to supply information to the government, which is, in some cases, available to the public. For example, the Canadian Securities Commissions require publicly traded companies to disclose certain financial information. In some cases, economists can also obtain limited access to confidential data, like individual income tax returns and social security records.

Surveys   A survey can be used to collect data on virtually anything, including topics for which there are no records, such as the amount of time people devote to work, housekeeping, leisure, and sleep. The Canadian government sponsors many large-scale surveys that collect data on a wide range of topics. The Survey on Labour and Income Dynamics (SLID), for instance, tracks the well-being of Canadian families over time by collecting data on employment, education, income, and government transfers. Companies, too, sponsor surveys for business purposes and sometimes turn to economists for analyses of the resulting data. In some cases, they provide that data to independent economists, either for a fee or free of charge. In a pinch, an economist can even design and field her own survey.

Experiments   Natural scientists routinely test their theories by conducting controlled experiments. Though economics is not primarily an experimental science, over the past two or three decades economic experiments have become increasingly common. To test theories of consumer behaviour, economists present experimental subjects with options and then observe their choices. To test market theories, economists set up experimental markets and study their operation.

Through controlled experiments, scientists can determine the causal relationship between circumstances and outcomes. For example, if a medical researcher wants to know whether a new drug will prevent a disease, he randomly assigns subjects to a "treatment group," which will receive the drug, and a "control group," which will receive a placebo (an inactive substance known to have no therapeutic effect). He then attributes any differences in the health outcomes of the two groups to the drug. Experimental economists try to isolate causal relationships in a similar way.

Outside the laboratory, however, there are few controlled experiments. How do economists determine cause and effect using data obtained from the real world? Sometimes, the circumstances of otherwise identical people differ entirely by chance. In those cases, economists can attribute the differences in the average outcomes for different groups of people to the differences in their circumstances, just as in the laboratory. This approach is known as a **natural experiment**.

For example, suppose we want to measure the effect of military service on an individual's later earnings as a civilian. The Vietnam draft lottery in the United States, which resulted in the migration of many American youth to Canada, provides an opportunity for a natural experiment. Since the lottery drawings were entirely random, we can focus on those men who were eligible for the draft and compare the subsequent earnings of those who were drafted and those who were not.[8]

When the circumstances of different people differ entirely by chance, as in a controlled laboratory or natural experiment, we can be reasonably confident that other factors do not explain any observed differences in outcomes. However, in the real world, the circumstances of different people usually do not differ by chance. Those who find themselves in one circumstance are often systematically different from those who find themselves in another. Economists must then control for those differences statistically, rather than experimentally. Suppose, for instance, that we're interested in learning whether men and women prefer to spend their money on different goods. Merely observing differences in their spending patterns won't settle the issue. Why not? Among other reasons, men tend to have higher incomes than women. Before attributing gender differences in spending habits to preferences, then, we need to remove differences that are attributable to income. Statistical methods allow us to adjust data on spending by men and women to reflect a common level of income. The application of statistical methods to empirical questions in economics is known as **econometrics**.

> In a **natural experiment**, the circumstances of otherwise identical people differ entirely by chance. An economist attributes differences in the average outcomes for those people to the differences in their circumstances.

> **Econometrics** is the application of statistical methods to empirical questions in the field of economics.

Why Economists Sometimes Disagree

Though good economists use the scientific method, as in all sciences there is still room for disagreement. In economics, it's important to distinguish between disagreements that concern positive matters and those that concern normative matters.

Disagreements about positive matters usually reflect differences in scientific judgment. Sometimes, two economists look at the same evidence and come to different conclusions. For example, based on the available studies, some economists think that an increase in the minimum wage would significantly reduce employment, and others believe that the effect on employment would be relatively minor. These types of disputes aren't unique to economics. Indeed, most of the leading theories in the natural sciences were at one time controversial.

When two scientists reach different positive conclusions based on the same evidence, it's a safe bet that they've started from different assumptions. For example, what

---

[8]In contrast, a comparison of earnings for people with and without military service would not be as informative, because the decision to enlist is not the result of chance. On the contrary, it is related to personal characteristics (like self-discipline) that can affect job performance.

conclusions follow from the observation that college and university graduates earn more money than high school graduates? If we assume that university attendance is unrelated to ability, then we may conclude that university teaches valuable skills. But if we assume that university teaches nothing of practical value, then we may conclude that university students are more capable to begin with. Fortunately, most assumptions are testable, so we can, at least in principle, resolve such disputes by analyzing additional data. In practice, nailing down all the relevant facts can be difficult and time-consuming. As the evidence accumulates, judgments converge, and a scientific consensus emerges.

Through decades of research and stacks of studies, economists have reached a degree of consensus on a number of important issues.[9] However, even when there's widespread agreement about a particular issue, there are usually a few dissenters, who sometimes receive disproportionate attention from the media, particularly when their views are helpful to powerful political interests. While economists do disagree about many things, the extent of this disagreement is therefore often exaggerated.

While the accumulation of scientific evidence can resolve positive disagreements, it can't resolve normative disputes arising from differences in values. For example, it can't tell us whether one person's gain is more or less important than another person's loss. As a result, even when economists reach the same positive conclusions, they may disagree about the desirability of a particular public policy. Two economists may agree that an increase in the minimum wage leads to a moderate reduction in employment, benefiting those who receive higher wages at the expense of those who lose their jobs. Yet they may disagree on whether helping the first group justifies hurting the second. Careful positive inquiry allows us to measure the size of the two effects, but it can't tell us which is more important.

1.3 THEMES OF MICROECONOMICS

Judging by the length and content of this book, microeconomists have a lot to say about a wide range of topics. Still, as you progress through the book, you'll notice that a number of themes come up over and over again. Here we'll preview some of the most important ones.

Decisions: Some Central Themes

The following four themes, which concern decision making, are featured in Chapters 3 through 13.

Theme 1: Trade-offs are unavoidable. Economists like to remind us that there's no such thing as a free lunch. Simply put, scarcity forces us to confront trade-offs. To get something we want, we must usually give up something else.

Every choice involves trade-offs. In selecting one alternative, you forgo others. If you want to get good grades, you have to study, but since your time is scarce, you socialize less. Likewise, when a consumer spends an extra dollar on food, she has one less dollar to spend on other goods like clothes and housing. And when a company decides to shut down, it saves money, but gives up the chance to earn revenue.

---

[9]See Richard M. Alston, J. R. Kearl, and Michael B. Vaughan, "Is There Consensus among Economists in the 1990s?" *American Economic Review* 82, May 1992, pp. 203–209.

Recognizing trade-offs is an essential part of good decision making. When we ignore trade-offs, we risk giving up something we value highly for something that is less important, and we tend to regret our choices. If you pretend that socializing doesn't cut into your study time, you're likely to be disappointed with your grades. Similarly, if a consumer ignores trade-offs, he risks spending his money on the wrong things. When a company ignores trade-offs, it risks the loss of profit opportunities.

Theme 2: Good choices are usually made at the margin. While some decisions have an all-or-nothing quality, most are matters of degree. For example, registering for a course in microeconomics is an all-or-nothing choice, but preparing for a test is not—a student can devote as much or as little time to studying as she likes. Likewise, a consumer's decision to purchase 40 litres of gasoline rather than 42 is a matter of degree, as is a company's decision to produce 20,000 units of a good rather than 21,000.

For decisions involving matters of degree, microeconomic principles teach us to think "on the margin." To determine whether a particular choice is best, we ask whether a small adjustment of the choice—also known as a **marginal change**—will lead to improved results. The typical adjustment has both benefits and costs. If the benefits exceed the costs, then the decision maker will be better off; if the costs exceed the benefits, then he will be worse off. If a marginal change makes the decision maker better off, then the original choice obviously wasn't the best one.

> A **marginal change** is a small adjustment of a choice.

Suppose, for example, that a student plans to spend five hours studying for her mid-term, which she knows is better than not studying at all. But is it her *best* choice? Thinking on the margin requires her to ask whether she would be better off studying a little bit more—say, an extra 15 minutes—or a little bit less. The answer depends on many factors: how well she knows the material, how much she expects to accomplish in 15 minutes, and the relative importance of other activities.

Thinking on the margin sometimes leads to surprising conclusions. Imagine that you have arranged to stage a play at a 1000-seat theater at a cost of $15,000. Since the average cost per seat is $15, you might hesitate to sell any tickets for less than $15 a piece. But suppose that just before show time there are still some empty seats, and you believe you can fill some of them by dropping the ticket price to $5. Doing so is clearly worth your while, even though the marginal customer doesn't pay enough to cover the average cost per seat.

The principle of thinking on the margin is so important that we'll devote an entire chapter to it (Chapter 3). In Part II, we'll apply the principle to decisions involving consumption and production.

Theme 3: People respond to incentives. To determine whether an action is desirable, a good decision maker carefully weighs benefits and costs. Benefits provide incentives to take the action; costs provide disincentives. The action becomes more attractive when benefits rise or costs fall, and less attractive when benefits fall or costs rise. So any development that changes benefits or costs has the potential to alter behaviour.

Imagine that it's Friday, and you have a microeconomics exam the next Monday. If a friend decides to throw a party over the weekend, you'll probably spend less time studying than you planned. The prospect of missing the party makes studying more costly, creating a disincentive to hit the books. But what if your professor announces that the exam will count for 40 percent of your final grade instead of 15 percent, as you had expected? In that case, you'll probably study more than you planned. The professor's decision raises the benefits of studying, creating an incentive to hit the books.

Most public policies provide people with incentives to take certain actions and avoid others. Unfortunately, lawmakers often fail to think through all those incentives. As a result, their policies sometimes have unintended and unfortunate consequences.

In most developed economies governments provide payments to workers who have become unemployed while they search for another job. This policy, which is designed to allow unemployed workers a period of time to better match their skills with an employer's needs, is not immune from strategic manipulation on the part of workers. An investigation of Canadian labour markets in the late 1980s found that Unemployment Insurance (UI) benefits affected job duration. The authors of the study found that a significant number of jobs terminated after the length of employment needed to receive unemployment benefits were reached.[10]

In 1994 the state of Texas adopted a new system for financing public primary and secondary schools. Among other features, the system provided school districts with extra funds for each child with a qualifying disability. Texas lawmakers were surprised to discover that the fraction of Texas schoolchildren classified as disabled leapt upward by roughly 20 percent between 1992 and 1997, creating an unanticipated strain on the state's financial resources. Little consideration had been given to the possibility that schools might strategically reclassify students with marginal disabiliies in order to obtain additional resources. Yet it appears that is precisely what happened. Indeed, many schools hired consultants to help them get the most out of the system.[11]

Theme 4: Prices provide incentives. The costs of buying goods and the benefits of selling them depend on their prices. An increase in the price of a good provides a disincentive to buy, because it raises the costs of buying. It also provides an incentive to sell because it raises the benefits of selling. Conversely, a reduction in the price of a good provides an incentive to buy, because it reduces the costs of buying. It also provides a disincentive to sell, because it reduces the benefits of selling.

Since people respond to incentives, changing prices tend to change people's choices. A price increase tends to reduce the amount people want to buy, and increase the amount they want to sell. A price reduction has the opposite effect. These relationships form the basis for supply and demand curves, which we'll review in the next chapter.

Markets: Some Central Themes

The following four themes, which concern markets, are featured in Part III (Chapters 14 through 21).

Theme 5: Trade can benefit everyone. **Trade** occurs whenever two or more people exchange valuable goods or services. Think about what life would be like if you were unable to trade with others. How would you eat? What would you wear? What would you use for shelter? Even if you had the skills needed to survive on your own, your life would be primitive. All of the conveniences and luxuries that we associate with modern life, such

Trade occurs whenever two or more people exchange valuable goods or services.

---

[10]See Louis N. Christofides and C. J. McKenna, "Unemployment Insurance and Job Duration in Canada," *Journal of Labor Economics* 14, April 1996, pp. 286–312.

[11]According to one study, the financial incentives embedded in the state's new school financing system accounted for 40 percent of the growth in student disability rates. See Julie Berry Cullen, "The Impact of Fiscal Incentives on Student Disability Rates," *Journal of Public Economics* 87, August 2003, pp. 1557–1589.

as cars, airplanes, cell phones, computers, air conditioning, and television, are available to you only because people trade with each other.

Through trade, someone who owns a good that is of relatively little value to him, but of substantial value to another, can exchange it for something he values more highly. Trade also frees him from the need to produce everything he needs or wants. Instead, he can focus on producing a single good or service that has value to others. By specializing in something that he does well, he can become even more skilled and productive. Talented carpenters can focus on building, talented chefs on cooking, and talented scientists on research. Society ends up with better goods and services, and more of them.

Theme 6: The competitive market price reflects both value to consumers and cost to producers. In a market, every buyer requires a seller, and every seller requires a buyer. The market price adjusts to balance supply and demand, falling when supply exceeds demand and rising when demand exceeds supply. As a result, the market price reflects both demand and supply.

In a competitive market, consumers balance the benefits of a good against the cost of acquiring it (namely, its price). On the margin, those benefits and costs must be equal. Otherwise, the consumer would benefit by consuming a little bit more (if the benefits exceed the costs) or a little bit less (if the costs exceed the benefits). Thus, a good's market price is equal to the value consumers place on an extra unit.

Similarly, competitive firms balance the revenue they receive from selling another unit of a good (once again, its price) against the cost of producing it. At the margin, those benefits and costs must be equal. Otherwise, the firm could earn a higher profit by producing more (if the revenue exceeds the cost) or less (if the cost exceeds the revenue). Thus, a good's competitive market price is equal to the cost of producing an extra unit.

Theme 7: Compared to other methods of resource allocation, markets have advantages. The Cold War, which lasted from the end of World War II in 1945 to the fall of the Berlin Wall in 1989, was in large part a struggle between two competing economic systems, capitalism and communism. Ultimately, the communist economies were unable to keep pace with the capitalist economies. Economic pressures caused the collapse of the Soviet Union and forced other communist countries, like the People's Republic of China, to adopt market reforms.

Why do market economies perform so well, even though individuals pursue their own narrow self-interests? How do they manage to achieve such high levels of productivity and growth with so little centralized coordination? The answer to both these questions is that market prices coordinate our activities, providing us with incentives to expend our effort and resources in pursuits that others value.

True, companies usually don't try to advance social goals; instead, they seek profit. But in deciding whether to produce a good, they look to its price, which reflects its value to consumers at the margin. Similarly, most consumers are concerned primarily with their own satisfaction. But in deciding whether to purchase a good, they consider its price, which reflects its cost to firms at the margin. Thus, market prices cause self-interested producers and consumers to consider the costs and benefits that their actions create for other members of society.

For example, suppose new medical research identifies important health benefits from eating peaches. In response, a knowledgeable and well-intentioned central planner would presumably shift social resources toward peach production. Yet without any centralized decision making, free markets can and do accomplish exactly the same thing. Learning of the research, consumers demand more peaches. With no change in the price of peaches, demand will exceed supply, so the price must rise. (We'll explain why in Chapter 2.) The higher price then encourages farmers to produce more peaches.

Theme 8: Sometimes, government policy can improve on free-market resource allocations. Though market economies have many advantages, they aren't perfect. There are some legitimate concerns about the way in which markets allocate scarce resources. In many instances, there are potential justifications for government intervention in markets.

In some situations, the market price of a good doesn't accurately reflect its costs and benefits to all consumers and producers, on the margin. When that occurs, markets may fail to allocate resources to their best uses. There are several types of market failure. In some cases, the failure is associated with insufficient competition among producers. If, for example, only one company can provide telephone service, it may set the price of a minute of service well above cost. Consumers react to the high price by using their telephones less often than they would if they had to pay only the true cost. In other cases, markets fail because transactions affect uninvolved third parties. Take gasoline, for example. The market price of gasoline reflects the production costs incurred by gasoline producers. It does not, however, reflect the costs associated with polluting the environment, which fall on the general population. As a result, consumers use more gasoline than they would if its price reflected all the social costs. In still other cases, markets fail because different people have access to different information. For example, potential used car buyers may worry that sellers will try to unload lemons. That fear may prevent a buyer and a seller from consummating a mutually beneficial deal.

When a market fails, government intervention may be beneficial. In the case of the telephone company with no competition, there may be some justification for regulating prices. In the case of gasoline, a tax that reflects the costs of pollution may induce consumers to take those costs into account. In the case of used cars, laws requiring the full and truthful disclosure of a car's history of accidents and repairs may allay the fears of potential buyers. However, it's important to remember that government policy making is imperfect, and that interventions can also fail. Sometimes the cure is worse than the disease. Many forms of government intervention can prevent the economy from performing as well as it might.

Finally, free markets can produce a great deal of inequality across consumers. Some people can afford private jets, while others whose skills are not highly valued, at least on the margin, struggle to make ends meet. Concerns about equity can justify government policies that redistribute resources from the haves to the have-nots.

1.4   USES OF MICROECONOMICS

Why study microeconomics? The simple answer is that microeconomics is extremely useful. It can help us to make important decisions, and it provides tools for understanding and evaluating the effects of public policies.

In terms of decision making, microeconomics offers a wide variety of helpful principles. For example, it stresses the importance of approaching every decision in terms of the trade-offs implied. It also trains us to search for our best choice by thinking on the margin.

In some cases, the principles of economics involve little more than common sense. For example, if your old car requires $3000 worth of engine work, after which it will be worth only $2000, it's ready for the junk heap. This conclusion holds even if you've just sunk $1200 into a complete tune-up and new brakes. Economic principles discourage you from throwing good money after bad.

Other decisions are much more complex, so that common sense takes us only so far. In such cases, the careful application of microeconomic principles guides us toward good choices. Here are two examples:

1. *Business Investments.* Suppose a company is considering investing $10 million to build a new manufacturing plant. It expects the plant to generate a net profit of $1.5 million per year for 20 years, at which point it will have a scrap value of $1 million. Is this investment worthwhile? Upon what does the answer depend? Does it matter that the investment doesn't break even until the seventh year? (We explain how to evaluate business investments in Section 10.3.)

2. *Portfolio management.* Most people try to save money for retirement. Should a particular individual accumulate her savings in bank accounts? Should she buy corporate stocks? Corporate bonds? Government bonds? Mutual funds? Upon what does the answer depend? Should she behave differently if she's cautious than if she's a risk-taker? If so, how? (We discuss some basic principles behind portfolio allocation in Section 11.4 and Add-On 11A.)

Microeconomic tools are also indispensable to the analysis and evaluation of public policy. Those who stand to gain from a public policy often exaggerate its benefits and downplay its costs, while those who stand to lose do the opposite. And as we've seen, sometimes even well-intentioned policymakers overlook important effects of policy changes on incentives. Careful microeconomic analysis can identify beneficial policies and provide reliable, objective measures of the costs and benefits. Here's an example:

Environmental policy. Coal-fired electric plants and metal smelters emit sulfur dioxide (SO_2), which is the main cause of acid rain in Canada and the United States. However the two countries have taken different approaches in reducing SO_2 emissions both before and after the signing of the Canada–United States Air Quality Agreement in 1991. Canada adopted the more traditional approach of regulating emissions by mandating the use of pollution control equipment and using low sulphur fuels. This approach has been successful in reducing emissions well below the current national cap on SO_2 emissions. At the urging of economists, the United States government adopted a new approach. The idea is to provide each plant with permits that allow them to emit certain amounts of SO_2 and then allow them to trade those permits. This policy created a market for SO_2 emission permits in 1990, thereby ensuring that plants with low abatement costs would trade them to plants with high abatement costs. By harnessing the power of markets, the policy is estimated to have reduced abatement costs by $225 to $375 million per year. (We elaborate on this policy in Section 14.5.) In Canada, it wasn't until May of 2008 that the first environmental market was established. The Montreal Climate Exchange allows trading of greenhouse gas emissions and was established in anticipation of the creation of industrial carbon emission allowances in North America.

Application 1.3 describes one setting in which microeconomic analysis has had an enormous influence, both on major business decisions and on policy making. Throughout this book, you'll find many other applications to important problems confronting households, companies, and public officials.

Application 1.3

Allocating the Airwaves

Wireless electronics, like cell phones, television, and radio, all make use of "the airwaves"—technically, the electromagnetic spectrum. Doing so requires coordination. If different service providers tried to use the same portion of the spectrum, their signals would overlap, rendering certain frequencies virtually useless. Governments usually solve this problem by assigning different services and service providers to different frequencies within the spectrum.

Advances in communications technologies have forced governments to re-evaluate the allocation of the electromagnetic spectrum. Industry Canada recently began to use auctions to allocate spectrum bandwidth. These auctions have been very lucrative. In Canada's first spectrum auction, which occurred during a 39-day period in 2008, 15 bidders paid more than $4.25 billion for spectrum licences. The first spectrum auctions were conducted in the United States. In August 1993, President Bill Clinton signed legislation authorizing the Federal Communications Commission (FCC) to assign spectrum licences through auctions. The legislation required the FCC to develop auction rules and conduct the first spectrum auction within one year.

The FCC found itself in a rather difficult position. While the government had used auctions for a variety of other purposes, spectrum licences are rather special. Since wireless telecommunications providers require multiple licences for geographically contiguous areas, the value of any one licence to a given company depends critically on the combination of licences it succeeds in acquiring. The FCC's technical staff understood that traditional auction structures are not well suited to auctioning off multiple licences with these types of interdependencies.

The most obvious possibility would have been to auction off the licences one at a time in succession, each to the highest bidder. The main problem with this approach is that the value to a bidder of a licence that is auctioned off early depends on the prices it will have to pay for other licences to be auctioned off later. Bidders in the early auctions must therefore guess the prices that will emerge from the later When bidders actually participate in a sequence of auctions, they often guess wrong and make poor decisions in the early rounds.[12]

Hoping to discover some new procedure that would allocate spectrum to its most valuable uses while generating substantial revenue for the government, the FCC sought suggestions from interested parties. In response, several economists—most notably Paul Milgrom and Robert Wilson, acting as consultants for what was then Pacific Bell, and Preston McAfee, acting as a consultant for what was then Airtouch—proposed a completely novel auction structure, called the *simultaneous ascending auction*. The rules of the new auction are complex. However, the basic idea is to auction off all licences at the same time. That way, as the auction proceeds, bidders gradually learn what the prices of *all* licences will be, and they can make their final decision about each licence based on accurate knowledge concerning the prices of other licences, rather than on guesses. Milgrom, Wilson, and McAfee argued that the new auction structure was therefore more likely to promote good decisions and allocate spectrum to its most valuable uses.

The FCC's staff was understandably reluctant to approve a new auction structure with no track record, particularly since the proposed rules were significantly more complicated than those of any auction with which they were familiar. FCC Chairman Reed Hunt made it clear to the staff that he feared a fiasco, and that the FCC's spectrum auctions were far too important to serve as an economic "beta test site."

Despite these obstacles, the FCC staff eventually became convinced that the basic ideas behind the proposed auction were sound. However, the elegance of the underlying theory was not in itself sufficient to carry the day. The staff insisted on hard evidence. So several economists, including Charles Plott (working for what was then PacTel), turned to experiments. The experimental evidence confirmed that the new auction performed considerably better than traditional alternatives.

The FCC opened its first spectrum auction, based primarily on the economists' proposal, on July 25, 1994. To the surprise of many observers, it ran smoothly and was a great success, generating far more revenue for the U.S. government than anyone had expected, as well as prices that were indicative of more informed decision making on the part of bidders.[13] The FCC was so satisfied with the results that it decided to use the same basic procedures for later spectrum auctions.

As we'll see in later chapters, microeconomic principles have important implications not only for auction design, but for effective bidding strategies. Not surprisingly, when the stakes are high, bidders often turn to economic consultants for advice and guidance.

---

[12]For example, virtually identical objects sometimes sell for radically different prices in early rounds versus later rounds.

[13]For example, licences that were roughly interchangeable sold for similar prices.

1. **What is microeconomics? (LO1)**

   a. Microeconomics is the study of decision making by individuals, usually consumers or managers of firms. It is also the study of how the separate decisions of many individuals combine to determine the allocation of scarce resources.

   b. Societies differ with respect to their relative centralization or decentralization of economic decision making.

   c. The most common form of economic decentralization involves markets. Economists usually define markets by focusing on one product and place at a time.

   d. Economists often assume that people are motivated by material self-interest. Self-interest leads to different choices in different societies, depending on the procedures used to allocate scarce resources.

   e. In a market economy, people make decisions that affect resource allocation in three main ways: as consumers, as employees, and as owners of firms.

   f. A positive economic statement concerns factual matters and is testable (the facts either confirm or contradict it). A normative economic statement involves value judgments and is not testable.

   g. The scope of microeconomics is extremely broad, encompassing most of human decision making.

2. **Tools of microeconomics (LO2)**

   a. In studying human behaviour, economists employ the scientific method.

   b. Economists usually express their theories through mathematical models.

   c. Models are simplified representations of the real world. As a result, they rely on assumptions that are not literally true.

   d. A useful model captures the most important factors that contribute to an economic phenomenon, advances our understanding of it, and leads to reasonably accurate predictions.

   e. Sources of economic data fall into three main categories: records, surveys, and experiments.

   f. When controlling for multiple factors that contribute to a phenomenon isn't possible through laboratory or natural experiments, economists control for those factors statistically, using econometrics.

   g. Economists sometimes disagree about both positive and normative matters. They have achieved a reasonable degree of consensus with respect to a number of positive issues through the accumulation of evidence. However, factual evidence cannot resolve normative disputes.

3. **Themes of microeconomics (LO3)**

   a. Major themes concerning decision making include the following: trade-offs are unavoidable, good choices are usually made on the margin, people respond to incentives, and prices provide incentives.

   b. Major themes concerning markets include the following: trade can benefit everyone; the competitive market price reflects both value to consumers and cost to producers; compared to other methods of resource allocation, markets have advantages; and sometimes government policy can improve on free-market resource allocation.

4. **Uses of microeconomics (LO4)**

   a. Microeconomics offers a wide variety of principles that can help us make decisions.

   b. Microeconomic tools are indispensable to the analysis and evaluation of public policy.

Exercise 1.1: Name three examples of each of the following (other than those given in the text): (LO1)

a. Goods that are provided centrally, by the government.

b. Goods that are provided by firms operating in decentralized markets.

c. Goods that are provided *both* centrally by the government and by firms operating in decentralized markets.

d. Goods that are provided through some decentralized procedure other than markets.

Exercise 1.2: Which of the following statements are positive and which are normative? Why? (LO1)

a. The Canadian government should eliminate the goods and services tax.

b. The income tax causes people to work less.

c. Public education improves the well-being of the average citizen.

d. Exercise lowers the risk of heart disease.

e. Exercise is good for you.

f. Most people would choose pizza over tacos.

g. Most people are better off with pizza than with tacos.

Exercise 1.3: Every decision involves costs and benefits. As a result, some economists believe that the methods of economic analysis can and should be applied to *all* human decision making. Do you agree or disagree? Are there certain types of decisions that economists shouldn't study? Justify your answer. (LO1)

Exercise 1.4: Peter believes that people are irrational, that each person is irrational in his or her own special way, and that the nature of a person's irrationality sometimes changes from one moment to the next. Is her belief a theory? Does it have implications that can be verified or falsified? Is it a useful theory? (LO2)

Exercise 1.5: Which of the following are models? Explain.

a. Red sky at night, sailors' delight. Red sky at morning, sailors take warning. (LO2)

b. Let sleeping dogs lie.

c. What goes around comes around.

d. Cleanliness is next to godliness.

e. Absence makes the heart grow fonder.

Exercise 1.6: Economists often assume that most people are motivated only by their own material self-interest. Is this assumption always, usually, sometimes, rarely, or never a good one? Give examples to justify your answer. (LO2)

Exercise 1.7: Which of the following is a natural experiment? Which is more likely to produce a reliable answer? Explain. (LO2)

a. Elena wants to determine whether rain causes people to drive less. To do so, she compares the amount of gasoline sold on an average day in March in Seattle, Washington (where it rains a great deal), and in Los Angeles, California (where there is much less rainfall).

b. Annika also wants to determine whether snow causes people to drive less. To do so, she compares the amount of gasoline sold on an average snowy day in March and on an average sunny day in March in Winnipeg, Manitoba.

Exercise 1.8: Going to university involves trade-offs. What are they? Make your list as complete as possible. (LO3)

Exercise 1.9: Give some examples of how thinking on the margin is important to making good decisions. Are there times when thinking *only* on the margin can lead to mistakes? Give an example. (LO3, 4)

Exercise 1.10: Give three examples in which you or someone you know has responded to an economic incentive. (LO3, 4)

Supply and Demand

When Hurricane Katrina made landfall near New Orleans on August 29, 2005 the results were devastating to residents of the Crescent City and many other communities along the Gulf Coast. The world was shocked to see a major U.S. city flooded, its residents struggling for survival. Less than a month later, on September 24, Hurricane Rita made landfall near Houston. Together, the two storms disabled a large portion of the coast's oil refineries, representing a significant fraction of the nation's gasoline production capacity. By early October roughly 30 percent of U.S. refining capacity had been shut down by the two storms.

Even though Canada is an oil exporter the disruption in production in along the Gulf Coast of the United States also affected prices in Canada. At the beginning of September the average Canadian price surged to nearly $1.24 per litre from a pre-Katrina average of around $1 although by the start of November the average Canadian price had fallen back to below $0.88 per litre. In the United States gasoline prices followed a similar pattern. These price spikes occurred despite the fact that on world markets the price of crude oil (the key input in gasoline) had barely changed as a result of the hurricane.

During the Great Ice Storm of 1998 economic activity in south-eastern Ontario and southern Quebec came to a halt as a layer of ice up to 120 mm thick covered the provinces

Quebec after the 1998 ice storm

and northern New England. One of the most seriously affected agricultural sectors was the maple syrup industry. Quebec alone produces roughly 70 percent of the world's maple syrup and it was estimated that up to 22 percent of Canada's maple syrup trees were covered in a thick layer of ice. The Ontario Maple Syrup Producers Association predicted it could take up to 40 years for production to return to normal. Yet the price of maple syrup barely budged after the ice storm.

Why did the price of gasoline rise so dramatically while the price of maple syrup did not? How much would the price of gasoline have fallen if half of the sidelined capacity had quickly come back on line? If consumers did not have alternative sweeteners that they could purchase would the impact on maple syrup prices have been different? To answer questions such as these, economists often use a model of supply and demand. If you've taken an introductory economics course before, you're no doubt familiar with this model. In that case, this chapter should mostly help to refresh your memory. If you've never taken an economics course, this chapter will provide an introduction to a simple but important economic model, along with some examples of its usefulness. As you study this book, you'll learn more about the building blocks of supply and demand, as well as about other economic models.

This chapter covers four topics:

1. *Demand.* To analyze a market using a model of supply and demand, we first need to determine the demand for the product. We'll see how demand curves and demand functions summarize this information.

2. *Supply.* The next step is to determine the supply of the product. We'll see how supply curves and supply functions summarize this information.

3. *Market equilibrium.* The price of a product tends to adjust to balance supply and demand. We'll see how to find the equilibrium price and the amount bought and sold. We'll also see how changes in demand or supply can alter those outcomes.

4. *Elasticities of demand and supply.* One factor that affects how changes in demand or supply alter the price and amount bought and sold is the responsiveness of demand and supply to changes in price. We'll see how economists measure that responsiveness, as well as the responsiveness to changes in other economic variables.

2.1 DEMAND

To analyze a market using a model of supply and demand, we first need to determine the demand for the product that is sold in that market. As a general matter, that product could be a manufactured good, a raw material, or a service. We can represent its demand in two ways: graphically, as a demand curve, or mathematically, as a demand function.

Demand Curves

A product's **demand curve** shows how much buyers of the product want to buy at each possible price, holding fixed all other factors that affect demand. Figure 2.1(a) shows a (hypothetical) demand curve for the Canadian corn market. The vertical axis shows the price of a bushel of corn. The horizontal axis shows the annual demand for corn, measured

A product's **demand curve** shows how much buyers of the product want to buy at each possible price, holding fixed all other factors that affect demand.

Figure 2.1

The Demand Curve for Corn. Figure (a) shows the demand curve for corn, which depicts the amount of corn consumers and firms want to buy at each possible price, holding fixed all other factors that affect demand. Figure (b) shows that when the price of potatoes rises, the demand for corn increases at each price, shifting the demand curve to the right.

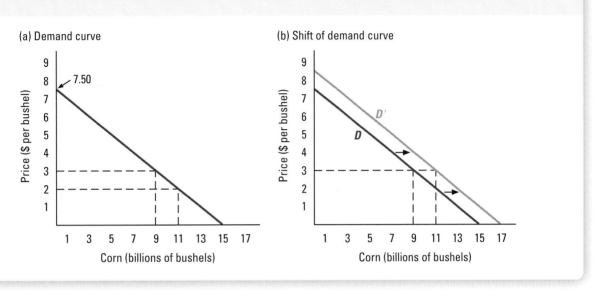

in billions of bushels. For example, when the price of corn is $3 a bushel, buyers demand nine billion bushels per year.

The demand for corn comes from a number of sources. Consumers buy corn to include in their meals. Food processors use corn as an ingredient in chowder and soup. Farmers use corn to feed their livestock. A number of companies use corn to make ethanol, which is then mixed into gasoline.

Note that the demand curve in Figure 2.1(a) is downward sloping: the higher the price, the less corn consumers and firms want to buy. For example, if the price is $2 per bushel, the amount demanded is 11 billion bushels per year, two billion bushels more than if the price is $3 per bushel. Almost all demand curves slope downward. Intuitively, we know that when the price is higher, buying a product is less attractive than when the price is lower. As a result, some potential purchasers will decide to spend their money on other products. In Chapters 5, 6, 8, and 9, we'll discuss this relationship more fully.

Implicitly, a demand curve holds all factors other than the product's price constant. Some other factors that can affect the demand for a product include population growth, consumer tastes and incomes, the prices of other products, and in some cases, government taxes or regulations. Consider the demand for corn. If a popular diet recommends a low intake of carbohydrates, consumers' desire for corn will decrease and they will purchase less at any given price. If vegetarianism becomes more popular, consumers' desire for corn will increase, and they will purchase more at any given price. If the price of potatoes—an alternative source of starch—rises, consumers are likely to buy fewer potatoes and more corn at any given price of corn. Potatoes and corn are **substitutes**—all else equal, an increase in the price of one of these products causes buyers to demand more of the other

Two products are **substitutes** if, all else equal, an increase in the price of one of the products causes buyers to demand more of the other product.

product. If the price of butter—which consumers like to spread on corn—rises, the demand for corn is likely to decrease at any given price of corn because the total cost of a corn-with-butter meal will have increased. Butter and corn are **complements**—all else equal, an increase in the price of one of these products causes buyers to demand less of the other product. Finally, if consumers' incomes rise, they are likely to buy more corn at any given price.

A change in one of these other factors will cause the entire demand curve to *shift*. Figure 2.1(b) shows how the demand curve for corn shifts outward (to the right) when the price of potatoes rises. At each price of corn, buyers demand more corn. For example, the figure shows that the amount of corn demanded at a price of $3 per bushel increases from nine billion bushels per year to 11 billion bushels per year.

As we have seen, either a change in the price of a product or a change in some other factor can change the amount of the product that buyers demand. However, Figure 2.1(a) and (b) illustrate an important distinction: A change in the price of a product causes a *movement along* its demand curve, whereas a change in some other factor *shifts* the product's demand curve. Accordingly, economists differentiate between a *change in the quantity (or amount) demanded* (which occurs when a change in a product's price produces a movement along its demand curve), and a *change in demand* (which occurs when a change in some other factor shifts a product's demand curve).

> **Movements Along versus Shifts of the Demand Curve**   A change in the price of a product causes a *movement along* its demand curve, resulting in a *change in the quantity (or amount) demanded*. A change in some other factor (such as consumer tastes or income, or the prices of other products) causes a *shift* of the entire demand curve, known as a *change in demand*.

Demand Functions

We can represent the demand for a product mathematically as well as graphically. A product's **demand function** is a formula of the form *Quantity Demanded = D(Price, Other factors)*. It describes the amount of the product that buyers demand for each possible combination of its price and other factors. For example, if the demand for corn is affected by three factors other than its price—the price of potatoes, the price of butter, and consumers' income—then the demand function for corn might take the form

$$Q^d_{corn} = 5 - 2P_{corn} + 4P_{potatoes} - 0.25P_{butter} + 0.0003M \qquad (1)$$

where Q^d_{corn} is the amount of corn demanded per year in billions of bushels; P_{corn} is the price of corn per bushel; $P_{potatoes}$ and P_{butter} are the price of potatoes and butter per kilogram, respectively; and M is consumers' average annual income. According to this demand function, increases in the prices of corn and butter will decrease the amount that buyers demand (because P_{corn} and P_{butter} are multiplied by negative numbers), while increases in the price of potatoes and consumer income will increase the amount that buyers demand (because $P_{potatoes}$ and M are multiplied by positive numbers).

The demand curve in Figure 2.1(a) shows the relationship between the amount of corn demanded and its price based on the demand function in formula (1) when potatoes cost $0.50 per kilogram, butter costs $4 per kilogram, and consumers' average annual

---

Two products are **complements** if, all else equal, an increase in the price of one of the products causes consumers to demand less of the other product.

A product's **demand function** describes the amount of the product that is demanded for each possible combination of its price and other factors.

income is $30,000. Substituting those values into formula (1), the demand function for corn becomes $Q^d_{corn} = 15 - 2P_{corn}$. According to this formula, for example, if corn were free (that is, if $P_{corn} = 0$), the amount demanded would be 15 billion bushels per year. Graphically, this means that the demand curve in Figure 2.1(a) hits the horizontal axis at 15 billion bushels per year. If the price of corn rose to $7.50 per bushel (or higher), the amount demanded would fall to zero [since $15 - 2(7.50) = 0$]. At that price, the demand curve in Figure 2.1(a) hits the vertical axis. The same information about the relationship between quantity demanded and price can in conveyed if we rewrite the demand function as $P_{corn} = 15/2 - (1/2) Q^d_{corn}$. This representation of the demand function is referred to as the **inverse demand function** and it will often be used in place of the demand function in this and later chapters. (The inverse demand function will be explained in Chapter 9.)

The inverse demand function for a firm's product describes how much the firm must charge to sell any given quantity of its product. It takes the form *Price = P(Quantity demanded).*

The shift in the demand curve shown in Figure 2.1(b) corresponds to a change in the price of potatoes from $0.50 to $1 per kilogram. That $0.50 increase in the price of potatoes changes the demand function to $Q^d_{corn} = 17 - 2P_{corn}$. (You can check, for example, that when the price of corn is $3 per bushel, the amount demanded is nine billion bushels a year if the price of potatoes is $0.50, versus 11 billion bushels a year if the price of potatoes is $1.)

Economists determine the demand function for a product by applying statistical techniques to historical data. The appendix to this chapter provides an intuitive and non-technical summary of these techniques.

WORKED-OUT PROBLEM 2.1

The Problem Suppose that the demand function for corn takes the form in formula (1), that potatoes cost $0.50 per kilogram, that butter costs $4 per kilogram, and that consumers' average annual income is $30,000. At what price of corn will consumers demand eight billion bushels per year? How does your answer change if the price of potatoes rises from $0.50 to $1 per kilogram?

The Solution We've seen that when potatoes cost $0.50 per kilogram, butter costs $4 per kilogram, and the average annual income is $30,000, the demand function for corn is $Q^d_{corn} = 15 - 2P_{corn}$. We want to find the price at which

$$15 - 2P_{corn} = 8$$

Solving this expression for P_{corn}, we find that

$$P_{corn} = 3.50$$

So demand is eight billion bushels per year when the price of corn is $3.50 a bushel.

If the price of potatoes rises to $1 per kilogram, the demand function for corn becomes $Q^d_{corn} = 17 - 2P_{corn}$, so we must find the price at which $17 - 2P_{corn} = 8$. The solution is $4.50 per bushel.

IN-TEXT EXERCISE 2.1 Suppose that the demand function for corn is $Q^d_{corn} = 20 - 4P_{corn} + 8P_{potatoes} - 0.50P_{butter}$. Potatoes cost $0.25 per kilogram and butter costs $2 per kilogram. At what price of corn will consumers demand eight billion bushels per year? How does your answer change if the price of butter rises to $4 per kilogram?

2.2 SUPPLY

The second step in analyzing a market using a model of supply and demand is to determine the supply of the product. We can represent supply in two ways: graphically, as a supply curve, or mathematically, as a supply function.

Supply Curves

A product's **supply curve** shows how much sellers of a product want to sell at each possible price, holding fixed all other factors that affect supply.

A product's **supply curve** shows how much sellers of a product want to sell at each possible price, holding fixed all other factors that affect supply. Figure 2.2(a) shows a (hypothetical) supply curve for corn in Canada. The vertical axis shows the price of a bushel of corn; the horizontal axis shows the annual supply of corn, measured in billions of bushels. For example, when the price of corn is $3 per bushel, the amount supplied is nine billion bushels per year. That supply includes the production of many farmers.

Note that the supply curve in Figure 2.2(a) is upward sloping: the higher the price, the more corn farmers want to sell. For example, when the price is $2 per bushel, the amount supplied is four billion bushels per year, five billion less than when the price is $3 per bushel. Intuitively, when the price of corn is higher, producing and selling corn is more profitable. At a higher price, farmers will find it profitable to plant more of their land with corn rather than other crops, such as wheat or soybeans, and fewer farmers will sell their land to real estate developers. In Chapter 9, we'll discuss these trade-offs more fully.

A supply curve holds all factors other than the product's price constant. Many other factors can affect the supply of a product: technology, the prices of inputs, the prices of other possible outputs, and in some cases, government taxes or regulations. Consider the supply of corn.

Figure 2.2

The Supply Curve for Corn. Figure (a) shows the supply curve for corn, which depicts the amount of corn farmers want to produce and sell at each possible price, holding fixed all other factors that affect supply. Figure (b) shows that when the prices of diesel fuel and soybeans fall, the supply of corn increases at each price, shifting the supply curve to the right.

(a) Supply curve

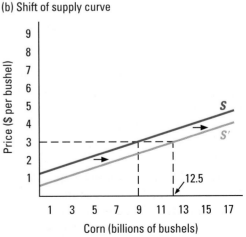

(b) Shift of supply curve

When a new disease-resistant corn hybrid becomes available, farmers can produce more corn using the same quantities of inputs. That lowers the cost of producing corn, making corn more attractive to produce and sell at any given price. Reductions in the price of fertilizer or diesel fuel also lower the cost of production and increase the amount supplied at any given price. On the other hand, increases in the price of other crops that farmers can plant instead of corn, such as soybeans, lower the amount of corn supplied at any given price of corn.

A change in one of these other factors will cause the supply curve for corn to *shift*. Figure 2.2(b) shows how the supply curve for corn shifts outward (to the right) when the prices of diesel fuel and soybeans fall. At each price of corn, the amount supplied increases.

Figures 2.2(a) and (b) illustrate the important distinction between movements along and shifts of supply curves: A change in the price of a product causes a *movement along* its supply curve, whereas a change in some other factor *shifts* the product's supply curve. Accordingly, economists differentiate between a *change in the quantity (or amount) supplied* (which occurs when a change in a product's price produces a movement along its supply curve), and a *change in supply* (which occurs when a change in some other factor shifts a product's supply curve).

> **Movements Along versus Shifts of the Supply Curve**   A change in the price of a product causes a *movement along* its supply curve, resulting in a *change in the quantity (or amount) supplied.* A change in *some other factor* (such as technology or input prices) causes a *shift* of the entire supply curve, known as a *change in supply.*

Supply Functions

We can represent the supply of a product mathematically by means of a **supply function**, a formula of the form *Quantity Supplied = S(Price, Other Factors)*. It describes the amount of the product supplied for each possible combination of its price and other factors. For example, if the supply of corn is affected by only two factors other than its price—the price of diesel fuel and the price of soybeans—then the supply function for corn might take the form

$$Q^s_{corn} = 9 + 5P_{corn} - 4P_{fuel} - 1.25P_{soybeans} \tag{2}$$

*A product's **supply function** describes the amount of the product that is supplied for each possible combination of its price and other factors. [Quantity Supplied = S(Price, Other factors)]*

where Q^s_{corn} is the amount of corn supplied per year in billions of bushels; P_{corn} is the price of corn per bushel; P_{fuel} is the price of diesel fuel per litre; and $P_{soybeans}$ is the price of soybeans per bushel. According to this supply function, the amount of corn supplied will increase if the price of corn rises, and fall if the prices of fuel and soybeans rise.

The supply curve shown in Figure 2.2(a) shows the relationship between the price of corn and the amount of corn supplied based on the supply function in formula (2) when diesel fuel costs $1.25 a litre and soybeans sell for $8 a bushel. Substituting those values into formula (2), the supply function for corn becomes $Q^s_{corn} = 5P_{corn} - 6$. For example, if the corn price is $1.20 (or less), the amount supplied falls to zero [since $5(1.20) - 6 = 0$]. At that price, the supply curve in Figure 2.2(a) hits the vertical axis. Just as we can rewrite the demand function with price viewed as the independent variable on the left hand side of the equation, we can also define an *inverse* supply function. The inverse supply function in our example would be $P_{corn} = 6/5 + (1/5)Q^s_{corn}$.

The shift in the supply curve shown in Figure 2.2(b) corresponds to a fall in the price of diesel fuel from $1.25 to $1 per litre, combined with a fall in the price of soybeans from \$8 to \$6 per bushel. Those price reductions change the supply function to $Q^s_{corn} = 5P_{corn} - 2.5$ (you should check this). For example, if the price of corn is \$3 per bushel, the amount of corn supplied is nine billion bushels per year when diesel fuel costs \$1.25 per litre and soybeans cost \$8 per bushel, versus 12.5 billion bushels per year when diesel fuel costs \$1 per litre and soybeans cost \$6 per bushel.

As with demand functions, economists determine the supply function for a product by applying statistical techniques to historical data—a topic discussed in the appendix.

2.3 MARKET EQUILIBRIUM

The **equilibrium price** is the price at which the amounts supplied and demanded are equal.

Once we know the demand and supply for a product, the next step is to determine the **equilibrium price**. That is the price at which the amounts supplied and demanded are equal. Graphically, it's the price at which the supply and demand curves intersect. The market "clears" at the equilibrium price, with buyers and sellers making all their desired purchases and sales.

Figure 2.3 shows the equilibrium price of corn. That price, \$3 per bushel, is the price at which the demand and supply curves intersect. At that price, the amount that buyers wish to buy, nine billion bushels, exactly equals the amount that sellers wish to sell.

Market prices tend to adjust so that the amount supplied equals the amount demanded. Suppose, for example, that the price of corn is \$2 per bushel. According to Figure 2.3, there is excess demand; the amount demanded exceeds the amount supplied. In that case, some buyers won't be able to purchase as much of the product as they would like at the prevailing price. They'll have an incentive to offer a slightly higher price to acquire their desired amounts. These offers will push the market price upward; reducing buyers' demands and increasing sellers' supply until supply and demand are once more in balance.

Now suppose that the price of corn is \$4 per bushel. According to Figure 2.3, there is excess supply: the amount supplied exceeds the amount demanded. In that case, some sellers won't be able to sell as much as they would like at the prevailing price. They'll have an incentive to lower their prices a little to boost sales. These price reductions will

Figure 2.3

Equilibrium in the Corn Market. The price of corn adjusts to equate the amounts supplied and demanded, which occurs when the price of corn is \$3 per bushel. At that price there is no excess demand or supply and no pressure for the price to rise or fall. The amount bought and sold at the equilibrium price is nine billion bushels per year.

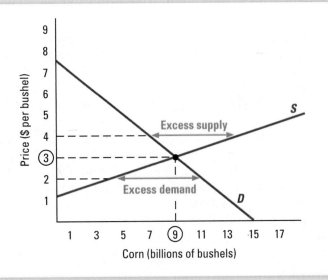

push the market price downward, increasing buyers' demands and reducing sellers' supply until supply and demand are once more in balance.

When the price is such that the amounts supplied and demanded are equal, there is neither excess supply nor excess demand. Since everyone can buy or sell as much as they like at the prevailing price, there is no pressure for the market price to rise or fall.

Worked-out problem 2.2 shows how to find the equilibrium price using supply and demand functions and a bit of algebra.

WORKED-OUT PROBLEM   2.2

The Problem   Suppose the demand function for corn is $Q^d_{corn} = 15 - 2P_{corn}$ and the supply function is $Q^d_{corn} = 5P_{corn} - 6$. What is the equilibrium price of corn? What are the amounts bought and sold?

The Solution   The equilibrium price in the corn market, which equates the amounts supplied and demanded, is the solution to the equation $Q^d_{corn} = Q^s_{corn}$, or equivalently

$$15 - 2P_{corn} = 5P_{corn} - 6$$

The equilibrium price of corn is therefore $P_{corn} = \$3$. We can derive the amount bought and sold from either the demand or supply function, by substituting \$3 for the price: $Q^d_{corn} = 15 - 2(3) = 9$ or $Q^s_{corn} = 5(3) - 6 = 9$.

IN-TEXT EXERCISE 2.2   Suppose the demand function for corn is $Q^d_{corn} = 20 - 2P_{corn}$ and the supply function is $Q^s_{corn} = 1.6P_{corn} - 7$. What is the equilibrium price of corn? What is the amount of corn bought and sold?

Application 2.1

Market Equilibrium from Alfred Marshall to Vernon Smith's Laboratory

Economists' use of supply and demand curves to study and predict market equilibrium originated with the publication in 1890 of Alfred Marshall's *Principles of Economics*. Marshall, a professor at Cambridge University in England, was the first to show how the market price is determined as an equilibrium, equating the amount sellers wish to sell with the amount buyers wish to buy. Since then, economists have used Marshall's theoretical framework to analyze a wide variety of markets.

Alfred Marshall (1842–1924)

Marshall's simple framework yielded predictions that matched observed outcomes well. Still, something was missing. Since economists can never *directly* observe a supply or demand curve, how can they be sure that Marshall's theory is right? One sleepless night in 1955, economist Vernon Smith had an idea: perhaps he might see how well supply and demand theory worked by bringing economics into the laboratory.[1]

Smith began to run experiments using students at Purdue University in Indiana as

---

[1]In the appendix to this chapter we discuss how economists can infer supply and demand curves through their observations of historical market outcomes. However, those methods typically *assume* that markets clear, so that the observed amounts bought and sold reflect buyers' and sellers' desired purchases and sales. This assumption is exactly what Smith wanted to test.

his subjects. In the early experiments, he tried to create an environment similar to the setting in a stock or commodity market by splitting the students into buyers and sellers. Each buyer received a card listing a value for a unit of the hypothetical product. Each seller received a card listing the cost of producing a unit. The students, who observed only their own cards, were told that they could not buy at a price above their value or sell at a price below their cost. Other than that, they should try to buy or sell at the best price possible. In this way, Smith created an experimental market. Since he created the market conditions, he could easily compare what actually happened with what supply and demand analysis would predict.

The trading process involved students calling out or accepting offers to buy or sell. For example, a buyer holding a card that said $2.50 might raise her hand and shout "Buy at $1." Any seller was then free to accept her offer or shout out a counteroffer to sell (for example, "Sell at $3.60"). The process continued until no further trades occurred. Then Smith would start the process all over again, to simulate what would happen over time in a market with stable supply and demand conditions.

Figure 2.4 shows the theoretical supply and demand curves from one of Smith's experiments in which there were 11 buyers and 11 sellers. The highest buyer value was $3.25, the lowest was $0.75. The lowest seller cost was $0.75, the highest $3.25. Supply and

Vernon Smith (left) accepting the Nobel Prize from the King of Sweden.

demand analysis would predict that the equilibrium price in this market should be $2 and that either five or six units should be traded. In principle, however, many other outcomes were possible. Indeed, if higher-value sellers were to trade with higher-value buyers (for example, the buyer with a value of $3.25 buying from the seller with a cost of $3.25), up to 11 voluntary trades could occur in this market.

Smith found that Marshall's theoretical framework worked remarkably well in practice.[2] Since neither buyers nor sellers knew the market conditions, initial trades sometimes took place at prices far from equilibrium. But prices generally converged to the equilibrium level over time, often very rapidly. For example, Smith ran his experiment with the market shown in Figure 2.4 five times for the same group of subjects (who traded in five separate "market periods").

The results are shown on the right-hand side of the figure. In the first period, the average price was $1.80, but by the third market period and thereafter, it had risen to within a few pennies of the predicted price. The amount bought and sold was always close to the predicted number of trades.

Smith made a number of interesting observations about factors that affect the speed of convergence to market equilibrium. His experiment started an entire new subfield within economics: the experimental study of economic institutions. In 2002 he was awarded the Nobel Prize in Economics for his pioneering work.

Changes in Market Equilibrium

Market conditions often change. Supply can increase or decrease, as can demand. Consider again the corn market. If the price of diesel fuel falls from $1.25 to $1 per litre and the price of soybeans falls from $8 to $6 per bushel, the supply curve of corn will shift outward as Figure 2.5 shows. After the supply curve shifts, the market is no longer in equilibrium at the original price of $3 per bushel. Instead there is excess supply; the buyers still demand nine billion bushels, but sellers now wish to sell 12.5 billion bushels. Some sellers won't be able to sell their corn at $3 per bushel and will accept a lower price. As a result, the price will fall to bring supply and demand into balance once more. Figure 2.5 shows that the new price of corn will be $2.50 per bushel, and that 10 billion bushels of corn will be bought and sold.

---

[2]V. L. Smith, "An Experimental Study of Competitive Market Behavior," *Journal of Political Economy* 70, April 1962, pp. 111–137.

Figure 2.4

Results of Vernon Smith's Experimental Market. The figure at left shows the supply and demand curves in Smith's experimental market. Supply and demand analysis would predict that five or six units would be traded at a price of $2. The table on the right shows the results in each of five market periods. The number of units traded was always close to the predicted number, and by the third period, the average price was within pennies of the predicted price.

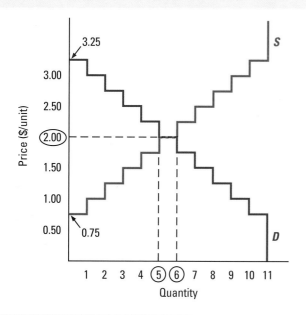

Market Period	Average Price ($)	Quantity Traded
1	1.80	5
2	1.86	5
3	2.02	5
4	2.03	7
5	2.03	6

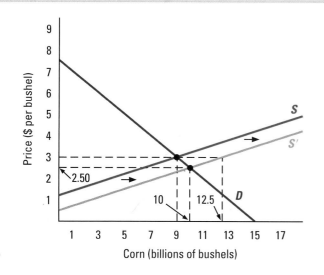

Figure 2.5

A Change in Market Equilibrium. When the price of diesel fuel falls from $2.50 to $2 per litre and the price of soybeans falls from $8 to $6 per bushel, the supply of corn increases, shifting the supply curve to the right. At the original price of $3 per bushel, there is an excess supply of corn: farmers want to sell 12.5 billion bushels but consumers and firms want to buy only nine billion bushels. This imbalance puts downward pressure on the market price. The equilibrium price falls to $2.50, and the amount bought and sold increases to 10 billion bushels per year.

Just as in worked-out problem 2.1, we can also find the new price of corn using algebra. When the prices of diesel fuel and soybeans fall, the market supply function becomes $Q^s_{corn} = 5P_{corn} - 2.5$. Since the demand function is unchanged, the new equilibrium price solves the equation

$$15 - 2P_{corn} = 5P_{corn} - 2.5$$

The solution is $P_{corn} = \$2.50$. Using the supply and demand functions, we can see that 10 billion bushels of corn will be bought and sold at that price: $Q^s_{corn} = 15 - 2(2.50) = 10$ and $Q^s_{corn} = 5(2.50) - 2.5 = 10$.

Figure 2.6 shows the four possible ways in which either demand or supply curves can shift. Demand can increase or decrease, as in panels (a) and (b) where in each case the initial demand curve is D and the new curve is D'. Alternatively, supply can increase or decrease, as in panels (c) and (d) where in each case the initial supply curve is S and the new curve is S'. Figure 2.6(a) shows the effects of an increase in demand: a rise in the price and the amount bought and sold. Figure 2.6(b) shows that when demand decreases, shifting to the left, the opposite happens: the price and the amount bought and sold fall. Figure 2.6(c) shows that when supply increases, the price falls but the amount bought and sold rises (just as we saw in Figure 2.5). Figure 2.6(d) shows that when supply decreases,

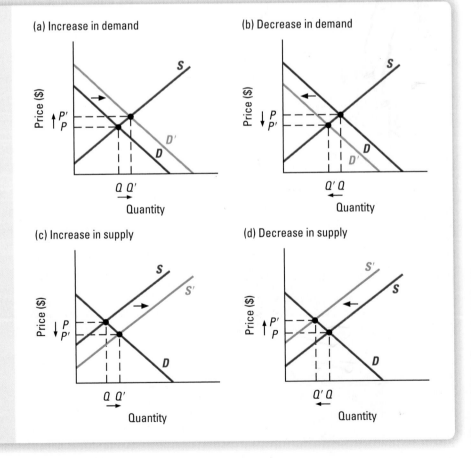

Figure 2.6

The Effects of Shifts in Demand or Supply on Market Equilibrium. The four figures show the effects of various shifts in either demand or supply on price and the amount bought and sold.

Table 2.1

Effects of Changes in Demand or Supply

Source of Change	Effect on Price	Effect on Amount Bought/Sold
Increase in demand	Rises	Rises
Decrease in demand	Falls	Falls
Increase in supply	Falls	Rises
Decrease in supply	Rises	Falls

the opposite happens: the price rises and the amount bought and sold falls. Table 2.1 summarizes these conclusions. Applications 2.2 and 2.3 discuss some practical examples of such changes.

Application 2.2

A Room with a View (and Its Price)

Sooke Harbour House on the southern coast of Vancouver Island overlooks the Strait of Juan de Fuca and the mountainous Olympic peninsula in the state of Washington. On Conde Nast's 2009 Gold List, it is one of the most well known, and expensive, small inns in Canada.[3] At the height of the summer tourist season, the inn's rooms cost over $450 per night. Unfortunately, those same tourists have little interest in visiting during the cold and grey winter months. By then, they're thinking of Caribbean beaches or the ski slopes at one of the many resorts in British Columbia or Alberta.

As a result, the price of hotel rooms at Sooke Harbour House, and many other inns on Vancouver Island, which together make up the supply in this market, varies from season to season. As Figure 2.7 shows, the supply curve for hotel rooms in Sooke is the same in December as in July.[4] The quantity $\bar{Q}$ is the total number of rooms. At high prices, innkeepers want to rent all those rooms, but at low prices, they withdraw some rooms from the supply, since the price no longer compensates them for the expense and effort of serving customers. (In the dead of winter, some inn owners close temporarily and take a vacation.) The demand in the two months is very different, however, so that the price in December (P_{Dec}) is much lower than the price in July (P_{July}).

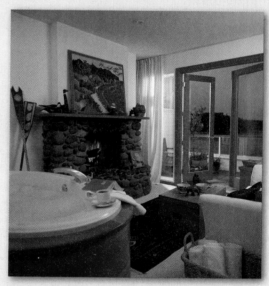

Sooke Harbour House

In 2009, for example, tourists paid $650 a night to stay in the Sooke Harbour House's best room during July, but only $340 a night to stay in the same room during December.[5]

---

[3]http://www.concierge.com/tools/travelawards/goldlist/2009/regions/northamerica/canada/.

[4]In reality, the supply curve is not exactly the same in all seasons. Utility costs and wage rates, for example, may vary by season, causing the supply curve to shift a bit. We draw it as unchanging here for simplicity. The important point is that the supply curve does not shift very much compared to the shift in the demand curve.

[5]Sooke Harbour House in Canada Hotels on Concierge.com. (n.d.). Concierge.com. Retrieved June 22, 2010, from http://www.concierge.com/travelguide/canada/hotels/500557; http://www.sookeharbourhouse.com/images/rates2010_11-temp.html.

Figure 2.7

Changes in the Market Equilibrium for Rooms at the Sooke Harbour House. This figure shows the demand curve for the Sooke Harbour House's rooms in July (D_{July}) and December (D_{Dec}). Because of the lower demand in December, the price of a room in December ($340) is much lower than in July ($650).

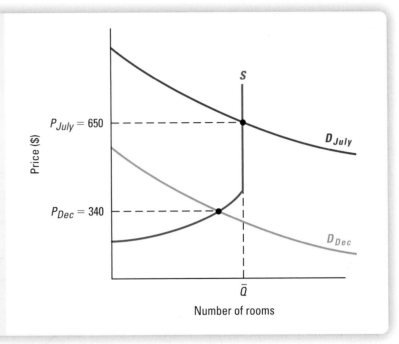

Application 2.3

Tourism in Toronto Gets Sick

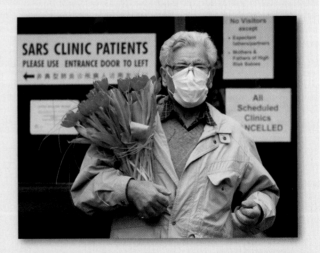

The severe acute respiratory syndrome (SARS) outbreak was a near pandemic that originated in China in 2002. By the summer of 2003 the disease had infected over 8000 people in 37 countries, killing 774. In Canada, a woman returning to Toronto from Hong Kong in February 2003 became the first recognized case in Canada. Over the next several months 367 cases of SARS in Ontario were recorded and of those 33 people died. On April 22 the World Health Organization recommended that travel to Toronto be limited. The impact of the economy of Ontario was immediate and devastating. By the end of May 2003 the Conference Board of Canada estimated that SARS had cost the Canadian economy $1.5 billion or 0.15 percent of GDP. The impact on Toronto was particularly severe. In the second quarter of 2003 overseas travel to Toronto fell by 40 percent and economic activity at Pearson International airport fell by over $400 million. During the last week in April revenue at downtown Toronto hotels was down 75 percent and for the entire month of April tourism revenue declined 45 percent. Over one third of the city's 95,000 hospitality workers were laid off. The occupancy rate in downtown Toronto's 12,000 hotel rooms fell from 64 percent (7680 rooms) in the first six months of 2002 to 52 percent (6240 rooms)

over the same time period in 2003. The average room rate in 2002 was $159 compared with $141 in 2003.[6]

Figure 2.8 illustrates the shift in demand that occurred between the first half six months of 2002 and the first six months of 2003. The downward shift in demand from D_{2002} to D_{2003} resulted in a reduction in both the average room rate and the number of occupied rooms.

Sometimes, changes in market conditions involve shifts in *both* demand and supply. The effects of such changes are a combination of the separate effects of changes in demand and supply. Suppose, for example, that demand and supply both increase. For example, over time the number of hotel rooms in Toronto has gradually increased despite fluctuations in demand such as those observed during the SARS outbreak. We've just seen that both these changes lead to increases in the amount bought and sold, so we can safely say that the amount bought and sold will increase.

What about the effect on price? The increase in demand alone would make the price rise, but the increase in supply alone would cause the price to fall. Because these effects work in opposite directions, we can't be sure which way the price will change.

Figure 2.9 illustrates this point. In Figure 2.9(a), demand increases a lot but supply increases only a little. These changes move the market equilibrium from point A to B, which brings a higher price. In Figure 2.9(b), demand increases a little but supply increases a lot. These changes move the market equilibrium from point C to E, which brings a lower price. In both cases, the amount bought and sold rises.

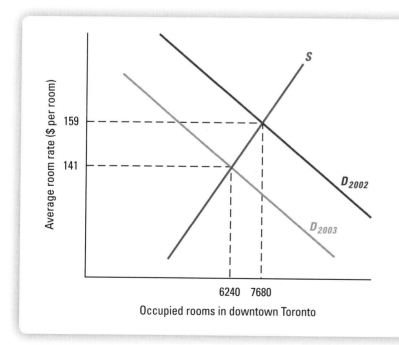

Figure 2.8

The Effect of SARS on Market Equilibrium. Figure 2.8 shows the effects of SARS on the number of hotel rooms occupied and the average room rate during 2003 and 2004.

---

[6]Information about the SARS outbreak in Toronto was obtained from a variety of industry and government sources.

Figure 2.9

The Effects of an Increase in Both Demand and Supply. When both demand and supply increase, the amount bought and sold necessarily increases, but the effect on price is ambiguous. Figure (a) shows that when demand increases a lot but supply increases only a little, the price rises. Figure (b) shows that when supply increases a lot but demand increases only a little, the price falls.

In general, when separate shifts in demand and supply each individually move the price in the same direction, the equilibrium price will definitely move in that direction. When separate shifts in supply and demand move the price in opposite directions, the equilibrium price can move in either direction, depending on the relative sizes of the changes. This principle applies as well to effects on the amount bought and sold. Table 2.2 summarizes the effects on price and the amount bought and sold from simultaneous changes in demand and supply. Application 2.4 presents a real-world example of a shift in both demand and supply. (See Add-On 2A for another example.)

Table 2.2

Effects of Simultaneous Changes in Demand and Supply

Source of Change	Effect on Price	Effect on Amount Bought/Sold
Demand increases/supply increases	Ambiguous	Rises
Demand decreases/supply decreases	Ambiguous	Falls
Demand increases/supply decreases	Rises	Ambiguous
Demand decreases/supply increases	Falls	Ambiguous

Application 2.4

Hockey Card Prices and the 2010 Vancouver Olympics

After 7 minutes and 40 seconds of overtime in the Olympic gold medal men's hockey game between Canada and the United States on February 28, 2010, Sidney Crosby took a pass from Jarome Iginla and slid a shot under the pads of Ryan Miller to win the game 3–2. For the Canadian men's hockey team this was a must-win game on home soil after not even medalling in the 2006 Olympic games in Torino, Italy. For Sidney Crosby it was another incredible accomplishment to go along with his first Stanley Cup victory with the Pittsburgh Penguins in the 2008–2009 season. Since being drafted first overall in the 2005 NHL draft Crosby has consistently been among the top scorers in the league and one of the most popular young Canadian-born players.

Sidney Crosby celebrates after scoring the goal that clinched Canada's gold medal in the 2010 Vancouver Olympic Games.

The Olympic victory made a lot of Canadian fans happy. It also increased their desire to own the trading cards of one their favourite Canadian players. Of particular interest are Sidney Crosby's rookie cards. After the gold medal game the number of Sidney Crosby rookie cards listed on eBay skyrocketed. Table 2.3 shows the number of new listing of Sidney Crosby rookie cards over a one week period centred

on the day of the gold medal game itself. In the three and a half days leading up to the gold medal game, 97 rookie cards were listed. Within the first hour after Crosby's winning goal 22 additional cards were listed, and over the next three and a half days an additional 321 rookie cards were put up for auction.[7]

We can understand these changes using supply and demand analysis, as illustrated in Figure 2.10. At any given point in time, the total number of rookie cards for a particular player is fixed. People who don't own the cards can buy them at the market price; people who do own the cards can either sell them or buy more at the market price. At any point in time, these various individuals differ in their willingness to pay to own a particular player's card. Some may be rabid hockey fans while others just like collecting; some may feel a strong affinity for the player, while others may actively dislike him; and some may be wealthy, while others are strapped for cash.

As a general matter, though, an increase in the price of the card increases the willingness of current owners to sell it and reduces the willingness of others to buy it. The supply curve for a given card, such as such as one of Sidney Crosby's rookie cards, therefore slopes upward, and the demand curve slopes downward, as shown in Figure 2.10. When the price is low, no current owners want to sell their cards; they think the value of each card exceeds the price they can get for it. As the price increases, more and more owners become willing to sell. When the price becomes high enough, the existing owners will want to sell all of their cards. Since the number of cards is fixed, higher prices cannot bring forth additional supply, so the supply curve becomes perfectly vertical at a quantity equal to the number of existing cards (labelled $\bar{Q}$ in Figure 2.10). The demand curve reflects the behaviour of potential purchasers of the cards. As the card's price rises, fewer and fewer of them will think that the card is desirable enough to justify its purchase.

Table 2.3

eBay Listings of Sidney Crosby Rookie Cards over a One-Week Period Centred on February 28, 2010

Date	Number of Listings
February 25	21
February 26	26
February 27	41
February 28, before game time	9
February 28, 1st hour after game	22
February 28, last part of day	46
March 1–3	275

---

[7] A "rookie card" is a player's first card as a major leaguer, and usually the most valuable of a player's trading cards. Card-buying guides report a range of prices and many cards are actively traded on eBay. Searching for "Sidney Crosby hockey card" on eBay picked up over 1000 listings in the first week of March 2010.

By scoring the winning goal in arguably the most important game ever played in Canada, the win made owning the cards more desirable both to current owners and to potential buyers. At any given price, buyers became more willing to buy (shifting the demand curve outward from D_{Before} to D_{After}) and sellers became less willing to sell (shifting the supply curve inward from S_{Before} to S_{After}). These shifts in both demand and supply raised the equilibrium prices of the cards. Sidney Crosby's Upper Deck Young Gun rookie card of 2005 is one of the most desirable hockey cards of any current player. The average selling price of the 11 cards sold on eBay two days prior to the game was $244.81 USD with a range of $191.38 to $355.03. The average selling price of the 24 cards sold during the 10 days after the gold medal game was $344.44 with a range of $200 to $1087.[8]

The Size of Changes in Market Equilibrium

Our discussion so far has focused only on the *direction* of changes in the price and the amount bought and sold following shifts in the demand and/or supply curves. We learned, for example, that an increase in demand increases a product's equilibrium price, while an increase in supply lowers it. Often, though, we want to know *how much* the price or amount bought and sold will change. What factors determine the *size* of the price change?

Certainly the size of the change in demand or supply matters. The larger the shift in the demand or supply curve, the larger the effect on price. Perhaps less obviously, the size of the changes in the price and the amount bought and sold also depend on the *steepness* (that is, the slope) of the curve that does *not* shift. Consider an increase in supply. As Figure 2.5 (page 35) showed, when the supply curve shifts outward, the market equilibrium shifts, moving along the fixed demand curve. How much the price and the amount

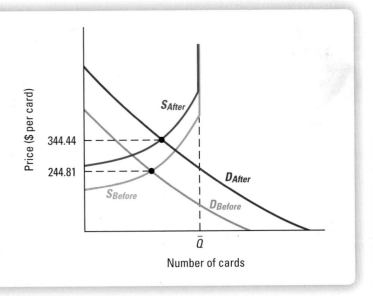

Figure 2.10
Changes in the Market Equilibrium for a Sidney Crosby Rookie Card. The figure shows the changes in demand and supply for a Sidney Crosby rookie card from before his winning goal in the 2010 Olympic Men's Gold Medal game (curves D_{Before} and S_{Before}) to after (curves D_{After} and S_{After}). Winning the gold increased the quantity demanded and reduced the quantity supplied at any given price. This led the equilibrium price to increase.

[8]For a card as valuable as this particular rookie card, condition has a large impact on price. Part of the increase in price might be attributed to the sale of cards after the gold medal game that were in better condition then those sold before the game. Graded cards in mint condition garner the highest prices. For the 35 cards studied here, the seven non-graded cards sold after the gold medal game all fetched more than the average card price before the game.

Figure 2.11

Changes in Market Equilibrium for Two Extreme Demand Curves. Figure (a) shows that when the demand curve is perfectly horizontal, an increase in supply has no effect on the product's price but increases the amount bought and sold. Figure (b) shows that when the demand curve is perfectly vertical, an increase in supply has no effect on the amount bought and sold but decreases the product's price.

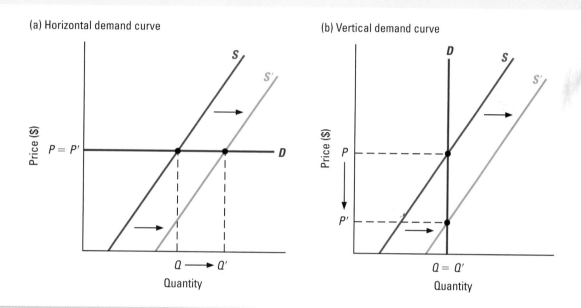

(a) Horizontal demand curve

(b) Vertical demand curve

bought and sold will change depends on the steepness of the demand curve. That steepness reflects the responsiveness of buyers' demands to the price. For example, if the demand curve is perfectly horizontal as in Figure 2.11(a), the amount demanded is extremely responsive to price. In that case, when the supply curve shifts outward the amount bought and sold increases from Q to Q', but the price does not change at all. In contrast, if the demand curve is perfectly vertical as in Figure 2.11(b), the amount demanded is completely unresponsive to the price. In that case, when the supply curve shifts outward the price falls from P to P', but the amount bought and sold does not change at all.

Typically, when the supply curve shifts outward, *both* the price and the amount bought and sold will change. However, the steeper the demand curve—the less responsive the amount demanded is to price—the more the price changes and the less the amount bought and sold changes. Figure 2.12 illustrates this point using two demand curves that differ in steepness labelled D_1 and D_2. Suppose that the supply curve is initially the dark red curve labelled S. For both demand curves the initial equilibrium price is P^* and the amount bought and sold is Q^*. Now suppose the supply curve shifts outward to the light red curve, labelled S'. The steeper demand curve (labelled D_1) results in a *larger* reduction in price than the flatter one (labelled D_2). On the other hand, the steeper demand curve results in a *smaller* increase in the amount bought and sold. (The prices and amounts bought and sold after the change in supply are labelled with the subscripts 1 and 2, corresponding to demand curves D_1 and D_2 respectively.)

Figure 2.12

Changes in Market Equilibrium for Two Demand Curves. The closer the demand curve is to being vertical, the larger the decrease in the product's price and the smaller the increase in the amount bought and sold when supply increases from S to S'.

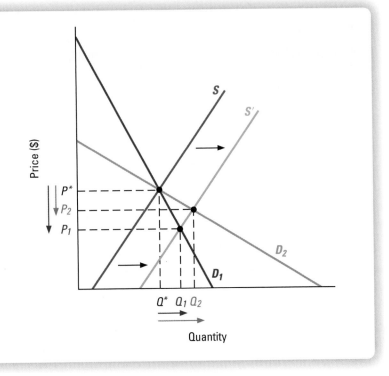

A similar point holds for shifts in demand. In that case, the sizes of the price and quantity changes depend on the steepness (that is, the slope) of the supply curve. Figure 2.13(a) shows the extreme case of a perfectly horizontal supply curve, for which the amount supplied is extremely responsive to the price. When the demand curve shifts outward, there is an increase in the amount bought and sold but no change in price. Figure 2.13(b) shows a perfectly vertical supply curve, for which the amount supplied is completely unresponsive to the price. In that case an outward shift in the demand curve increases the price but has no effect on the amount bought and sold. Figure 2.14 shows two intermediate cases. For the dark blue curve labelled D, the two supply curves (labelled S_1 and S_2) result in the same initial equilibrium price P^* and amount bought and sold Q^*. What happens when the demand curve shifts outward to the light blue curve labelled D'? The steeper supply curve, S_1, results in a larger increase in price and a smaller increase in the amount bought and sold than the flatter one, S_2.

In-text exercise 2.3 asks you to confirm that similar effects arise for inward shifts of the demand or supply curves (reductions in demand or supply).

IN-TEXT EXERCISE 2.3   **Draw a picture similar to Figure 2.12 to show that the steeper the demand curve (the less responsive the amount demanded is to price), the larger the change in price and the smaller the change in the amount bought and sold when the supply curve shifts inward. Draw a picture similar to Figure 2.14 to show that the steeper the supply curve (the less responsive the amount supplied is to price), the larger the change in price and the smaller the change in the amount bought and sold when the demand curve shifts inward.**

Figure 2.13

Changes in Market Equilibrium for Two Extreme Supply Curves. Figure (a) shows that when the supply curve is perfectly horizontal, an increase in demand has no effect on the product's price but increases the amount bought and sold. Figure (b) shows that when the supply curve is perfectly vertical, an increase in demand has no effect on the amount bought and sold but increases the product's price.

(a) Horizontal supply curve

(b) Vertical supply curve

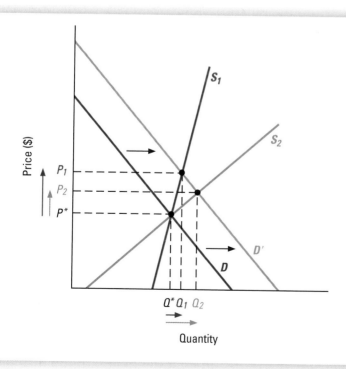

Figure 2.14

Changes in Market Equilibrium for Two Supply Curves. The steeper the supply curve, the larger the increase in the product's price and the smaller the increase in the amount bought and sold when demand increases.

We can summarize these findings as follows:

> ### Changes in Market Equilibrium and the Price Responsiveness of Demand and Supply
>
> 1. The demand curve shifts: the steeper the supply curve (the less responsive the amount supplied is to price), the larger the price change and the smaller the change in the amount bought and sold.
>
> 2. The supply curve shifts: the steeper the demand curve (the less responsive the amount demanded is to price), the larger the price change and the smaller the change in the amount bought and sold.

Short-Run and Long-Run Changes in Market Equilibrium   The responsiveness of a product's demand or supply to its price, and therefore the slopes of supply and demand curves, can depend on the time horizon. For example, once farmers plant their fields, they may be unable to produce much more corn in the short run if the price of corn rises. But in the long run they can plant more of their land with corn and even acquire additional land.

Because the steepness of supply and demand curves can depend on the time horizon, long-run changes in the equilibrium price and the amount bought and sold resulting from a shift in supply or demand can differ from short-run changes. For example, suppose the corn market is in equilibrium at price P^* in Figure 2.14, and the demand curve suddenly shifts from D to D'. The steeper supply curve, S_1, might represent the short-run supply curve, while the flatter one, S_2, might represent the long-run supply curve. If so, then as the figure shows, the price will rise sharply to P_1 in response to the increase in demand, but over time it will fall back toward its original level, eventually reaching P_2 in long-run equilibrium. The amount bought and sold, on the other hand, will increase only to Q_1 at first, but will continue to increase over time, eventually reaching Q_2 in long-run equilibrium.

2.4 ELASTICITIES OF DEMAND AND SUPPLY

In Section 2.3 we saw that changes in market equilibrium depend on the responsiveness of the amounts demanded and supplied to changes in price. How can we measure that responsiveness?

One possibility is to do as we did in Section 2.3, and describe the responsiveness to price changes in terms of the steepness (or slope) of the demand and supply curves. This measure has one problem, though: it depends on the units we use to measure both the amount of the good and its price. For example, if someone says that the demand curve for apple cider has a slope of -200, what does that mean? It might mean that when the price of apple cider rises by a penny per litre, 200 fewer litres are sold. But it might instead mean that when the price of apple cider rises by a dollar per four-litre container, 200 fewer containers are sold. To know which it is we would have to be careful to specify exactly how we are measuring both the units of the good and the price. Doing so every time we want to measure the responsiveness of demand would be cumbersome and inconvenient.

Economists get around this problem by measuring the responsiveness of one variable to changes in another variable using the concept of *elasticity*. Suppose that a change in X causes a change in Y. The **elasticity** of Y with respect to X, denoted E_X^Y, equals the percentage change in Y divided by the percentage change in X

$$E_X^Y = \frac{\% \text{ change in } Y}{\% \text{ change in } X}$$

For example, if a two percent increase in X causes a four percent increase in Y, then $E_X^Y = 2$. This value tells us that Y increases by two percent for each one percent increase in X. If the change in X instead causes Y to *fall*, then the elasticity will be negative. For example, if the two percent increase in X causes Y to fall by four percent, then $E_X^Y = -2$. This value tells us that Y falls by two percent for each one percent increase in X. Elasticities are "unit-free measures": for example, if someone tells you the elasticity of demand for a good with respect to some variable X, you can understand what it means without knowing the units in which they were measuring the quantity demanded and the variable X.

Negative-elasticity measures sometimes confuse students. An important point to remember is that, for both positive *and* negative elasticities, values that are further from zero indicate greater responsiveness. For example, suppose that initially a two percent increase in X causes Y to fall by four percent, but due to some new development, Y becomes more responsive to X—a two percent increase in X now causes Y to fall by six percent. Then the elasticity of Y with respect to X would change from $E_X^Y = -2$ to $E_X^Y = -3$. Because the new elasticity is further from zero, we would say that Y has become *more elastic* with respect to changes in X. We would say the same thing if the elasticity instead changed from $E_X^Y = 2$ to $E_X^Y = 3$.

Let's take a closer look at how economists use elasticity to measure the responsiveness of the amount of a product demanded or supplied to its price.

> The **elasticity** of Y with respect to X, denoted E_X^Y, equals the percentage change in Y divided by the percentage change in X, or equivalently, the percentage change in Y for each one percent increase in X.

> *Optional* Suppose that Y can be written as a function of X. The **elasticity** of Y with respect to X, denoted E_X^Y, can be found using calculus and is given by
>
> $$E_X^Y = \frac{dy}{dx}\frac{x}{y}$$
>
> The expression is evaluated at the initial values for x and y.

The (Price) Elasticity of Demand

First, let's consider the elasticity of demand for a product with respect to its price. Economists use this particular elasticity so often that they usually refer to it simply as the elasticity of demand (omitting the reference to price), writing it as E^d rather than E_p^d. A product's **(price) elasticity of demand** equals the percentage change in the amount demanded divided by the percentage change in the price, or equivalently, the percentage change in the amount demanded for each one percent increase in the price.

Since the quantity demanded typically decreases when the price increases, we expect the elasticity of demand to be a negative number. Products tend to have more elastic demands when they have closer substitutes to which consumers can switch in response to a price increase. The reason that the price of maple syrup did not increase significantly after the Great Ice Storm of 1998 discussed at the beginning of this chapter was due in part to the availability of maple syrup substitutes. Demand will also be more elastic when the potential buyers of the product regard it as a discretionary (luxury) purchase, rather than as a necessity. On the other hand, if the potential buyers are all very wealthy and are relatively insensitive to price, the demand will be less elastic than if the potential buyers are strapped for cash.

In general, the elasticity of demand can differ at different points on the demand curve (we'll see an example of this soon). For example, at high prices consumers may respond differently to a two percent price increase than they would at low prices. So, when economists

> The **(price) elasticity of demand** at price P, denoted E^d, equals the percentage change in the amount demanded for each one percent increase in the price.

measure the elasticity of demand they usually measure it separately at each possible initial price. To do this, they also focus on the responsiveness of demand to *small* price changes so that they are getting a measure of responsiveness close to the initial price.

Let's be more specific about this. Suppose the price changes from P to P', causing the amount demanded to change from Q to Q'. The change in price is $(P' - P)$. For convenience, we'll call this $\Delta P = (P' - P)$. (Mathematicians use the Greek letter Δ, "delta," to represent the *change* in a variable, so ΔP represents a change in price.) The percentage change in price is $100 \times (\Delta P/P)$. (For example, if the initial price P is \$100, and the new price P' is \$101, then $\Delta P = 1$ and the percentage change is $100 \times (1/100) = 1\%$.) The change in the amount demanded is $Q' - Q$; we'll call this ΔQ. The percentage change in Q is $100 \times (\Delta Q/Q)$. So the elasticity of demand at price P is[9]

$$E^d = \frac{\% \text{ change in amount demanded}}{\% \text{ change in price}} = \frac{100 \times (\Delta Q/Q)}{100 \times (\Delta P/P)} = \frac{(\Delta Q/Q)}{(\Delta P/P)} \qquad (3)$$

Application 2.5

Elasticities of Demand for New Cars

The elasticity of demand for a product at a given price depends on how readily consumers will switch to other products if the product's price increases a little. That depends in turn on the prices and characteristics of the other available products. In the new car market, consumers who are considering lower-price cars, such as the Nissan Sentra, can choose from among many fairly similar alternatives. Those consumers also tend to keep a close eye on their budgets. So we'd expect the elasticity of demand for these cars to be high. In contrast, those who are considering certain luxury cars, such as the BMW 7 Series, have fewer alternatives and are less concerned about their budgets. Each of those luxury cars also has a distinctive cachet that inspires strong loyalty among some buyers. As a result, we'd expect the elasticities for these cars to be relatively low.

The Nissan Sentra

The BMW 750Li

In a study of the demand for cars from 1970 to 1990, economists Steven Berry, James Levinsohn, and Ariel Pakes estimated the elasticities of demand for various models.[10] For low-priced cars like the Nissan Sentra, Mazda 323, and Ford Escort, elasticities of demand were roughly −6. That is, a one percent increase in price would cause them to lose about six percent of their sales. In contrast, the BMW 735i and Lexus LS400 had demand elasticities of roughly −3. This value implies that they would suffer much smaller percentage reductions in sales in response to a one percent increase in price. Between these two extremes were cars like the Honda Accord (with an elasticity of (−4.8), the Ford Taurus (with an elasticity of (−4.2), and the Lincoln Town Car (with an elasticity of (−4.3).

---

[9]You might wonder why we calculate the percentage change in the elasticity formula relative to the initial price and quantity demanded, P and Q, and not the final price and quantity demanded, P' and Q'. The answer is that for small price changes these values will be very close to each other, so it doesn't matter which we use. Sometimes, though not often, economists calculate the elasticity for a *large* price change using a measure called the *arc elasticity of demand*. This measure replaces P and Q in formula (3) with the average price and average quantity demanded, $\bar{P} = (P + P')/2$ and $\bar{Q} = (Q + Q')/2$. For small price changes, the arc elasticity is approximately equal to the elasticity measure in expression (3) (which is sometimes called the *point elasticity*), because $\bar{P}$ will be close to P, and $\bar{Q}$ will be close to Q.

[10]Steven Berry, James Levinsohn, and Ariel Pakes, "Automobile Prices in Market Equilibrium," *Econometrica* 63, July 1995, pp. 841–90.

Elasticities for Linear Demand Curves   Let's examine the elasticity of demand for linear demand curves; that is, demand curves that are straight lines, such as the one shown in Figure 2.1(a) (page 27). Linear demand curves correspond to demand functions of the form $Q^d = A - BP$, where A and B are positive numbers. For example, we've seen that the demand curve in Figure 2.1(a) corresponds to the demand function $Q^d_{corn} = 15 - 2P_{corn}$, so in that case $A = 15$ and $B = 2$.

To calculate the elasticity of demand for a linear demand curve, we rewrite the elasticity formula (3) as follows.[11]

$$E^d = \left(\frac{\Delta Q}{\Delta P}\right)\left(\frac{P}{Q}\right) \tag{4}$$

The first term in parentheses is the change in the amount demanded for each dollar that the price increases (when prices are measured in dollars). For a linear demand curve, that just equals $-B$. (To verify this, observe that for any change in price, ΔP, the change in demand is $\Delta Q = -B(\Delta P)$; dividing both sides by P implies that $(\Delta Q/\Delta P = -B)$.) The second term in parentheses in formula (4) is just the initial price divided by the initial quantity. Thus, the elasticity of demand for a linear demand curve starting at price P and quantity Q is

$$E^d = -B(P/Q) \tag{5}$$

Figure 2.15 reproduces the linear demand curve for corn from Figure 2.1(a), $Q^d_{corn} = 15 - 2P_{corn}$, and indicates the elasticity of demand at three prices along this demand curve: $6, $3.75, and $1.50. For example, when $P = 3.75$, the amount demanded is $Q = 7.5$. Since $B = 2$, that means the elasticity of demand at $P = 3.50$ is $E^d = -2(3.75/7.5) = -1$. Similar calculations imply that when $P = 6$, the elasticity is $E^d = -4$ and that when $P = 1.50$, the elasticity is $E^d = -1/4$.

More generally, formula (5) tells us that, for a linear demand curve, demand is more elastic at higher prices than at lower prices, since then P is larger and Q is smaller. For

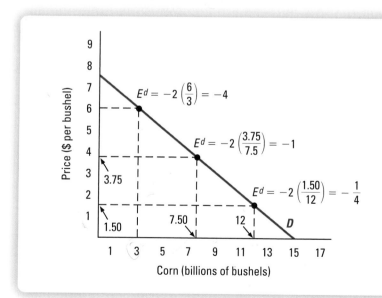

Figure 2.15

Elasticities along a Linear Demand Curve. When the demand curve is linear, the price elasticity of demand, which equals $-B(P/Q)$, is different at different points on the curve. This figure shows elasticities for the demand curve for corn from Figure 2.1(a).

---

[11]We derive formula (4) by rewriting formula (3) in the following way.

$$E^d = \frac{(\Delta Q/Q)}{(\Delta P/P)} = \left(\frac{\Delta Q}{Q}\right)\left(\frac{P}{\Delta P}\right) = \left(\frac{\Delta Q}{\Delta P}\right)\left(\frac{P}{Q}\right)$$

example, in Figure 2.15, the demand elasticity is less than -1 ($E^d < -1$) at prices above $3.75, and greater than -1 ($E^d > -1$) at prices below $3.75.

When the elasticity of demand is less than -1, economists say that demand is **elastic**, which means that the percentage change in the amount demanded is larger (in absolute value) than the percentage change in the price. When the elasticity of demand is greater than -1 (that is, between -1 and 0), economists say that demand is **inelastic**, which means that the percentage change in the amount demanded is smaller (in absolute value) than the percentage change in the price.

Another useful way to write the elasticity of demand comes from dividing the numerator and denominator of the first term in formula (4) by ΔQ.

$$E^d = \left(\frac{1}{(\Delta P/\Delta Q)}\right)(P/Q) \tag{6}$$

The denominator of the first term in formula (6), $(\Delta P/\Delta Q)$, is the change in the price divided by the change in quantity. For a linear demand curve, $(\Delta P/\Delta Q)$ is exactly the demand curve's slope (its vertical rise divided by its horizontal run between any two points on the line), which equals $-(1/B)$.[12] For example, the slope of the demand curve in Figure 2.15, the graph of the demand function $Q^d_{corn} = 15 - 2P_{corn}$ (for which $B = 2$), is $-(1/2)$.

Figure 2.11 (page 43) depicted two extreme cases of demand elasticity. The horizontal demand curve in Figure 2.11(a) has a slope of zero: $(\Delta P/\Delta Q) = 0$. Applying formula (6), we therefore conclude that the elasticity of demand at price P equals minus infinity: $E^d = -\infty$. When a demand curve is horizontal, we say that demand is **perfectly elastic**.

The vertical demand curve in Figure 2.11(b) is one for which any price change, ΔP, produces no change in the amount demanded, so $(\Delta Q/\Delta P) = 0$. Applying formula (4), we see that the elasticity of demand is zero: $E^d = 0$. When a demand curve is vertical, we say that demand is **perfectly inelastic**.

WORKED-OUT PROBLEM   2.3

The Problem   Consider the linear demand curve for corn in Figure 2.5 (page 35). What is the elasticity of demand at a price of $2.50 per bushel? What about at $3? Is demand elastic or inelastic?

The Solution   First, we need to determine the value of B, which we can compute from the changes in the market equilibrium in Figure 2.5 using this formula.[13]

$$B = -\frac{\Delta Q}{\Delta P} = -\frac{(10 - 9)}{(2.50 - 3.00)} = 2$$

Thus, the elasticity of demand at $2.50 per bushel is

$$E^d = -B\left(\frac{P}{Q}\right) = -2\left(\frac{2.50}{10}\right) = -0.50$$

Similarly, the elasticity of demand at $3 per bushel is -0.67. Demand is inelastic at both prices.

---

[12] Substituting $-(1/B)$ for $(\Delta P/\Delta Q)$ in formula (6) gives formula (5) again.

[13] Alternatively, we can find the value of both A and B by solving the two equations, $A - B(2.51) = 395$ and $A - B(2.92) = 365$. The solution is $B = 73.17$ and $A = 578.66$.

IN-TEXT EXERCISE 2.4 **Consider the linear demand curve for corn in Figure 2.5. What is the elasticity of demand at a price of $5 per bushel? At a price of $3.75 per bushel?**

Elasticities for Nonlinear Demand Curves Calculating the elasticity of demand at a particular price is a little more complicated for demand curves that are not linear, such as the one in Figure 2.16. To consider this issue, recall the way we expressed the elasticity in formula (6).

$$E^d = \left(\frac{1}{\Delta P/\Delta Q}\right)(P/Q)$$

We already saw that for a linear demand curve, $(\Delta P/\Delta Q)$ is exactly the demand curve's slope. What about for a nonlinear demand curve? In that case, for very small price changes starting at the initial price P, $(\Delta P/\Delta Q)$ equals the slope of the black line in Figure 2.16 that is touching the demand curve at the point corresponding to price P, labelled point A.

Figure 2.16 shows why that is so. Consider, for example, a price change from P to P' that is not tiny, that produces a movement along the demand curve from point A to point C, with the amount purchased changing from Q to Q'. The changes in the price and quantity demanded between points A and C, $\Delta P'$ and $\Delta Q'$, are shown along the axes in the figure. The ratio $\Delta P'/\Delta Q'$ equals the slope of the light grey line connecting points A and C, since

Figure 2.16

Slope of the Demand Curve at Price P. For the large price change from P to P', the light grey line connecting points C and A has the slope $(\Delta P'/\Delta Q')$. For the smaller price change from P to P'', the medium grey line connecting points B and A has the slope $(\Delta P''/\Delta Q'')$. As the price change grows smaller and smaller, the slope of the lines connecting the new and old demand points comes closer to the slope of the black line that is touching the demand curve at point A, known as the tangent line at point A. Thus, for small price changes, $(\Delta P/\Delta Q)$ comes to equal the slope of that tangent line, which is also called simply the *slope of the demand curve* at point A.

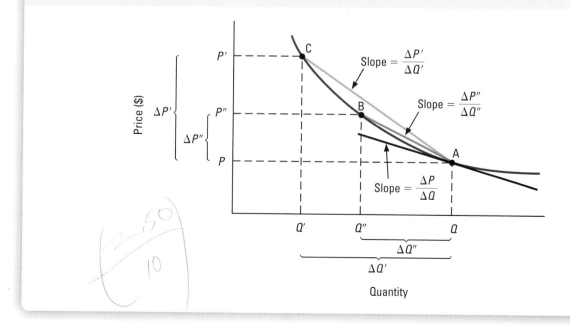

the line's rise is $\Delta P'$ and its run is $\Delta Q'$. Now consider a smaller price change, from P to P'', that produces a movement along the demand curve from point A to point B, with the amount purchased changing from Q to Q''. Again, the changes in price and quantity demanded between points A and B, $\Delta P''$ and $\Delta Q''$, are shown along the axes in the figure. The ratio $\Delta P''/\Delta Q''$ equals the slope of the medium-grey line connecting points A and B. This line is steeper than the black line, but less steep than the line connecting points A and C. As the figure suggests, if we were to consider smaller and smaller price changes, the slopes of the corresponding lines would eventually become very close to the slope of the black line that touches the demand curve at point A. That black line is said to be *tangent* to the demand curve at point A.[14]

Optional The slope of the line tangent to a point on a curve is the derivative of the curve at that point.

A common shorthand expression says that the slope of the tangent line to a curve at a point is the "slope of the curve" at that point. Using this language, we can restate our conclusion as follows: *for small price changes starting at price P, the ratio $\Delta P/\Delta Q$) equals the slope of the demand curve at point A.*[15]

A **constant elasticity** (or **isoelastic**) **demand curve** has the same elasticity at every price.

Economists sometimes work with demand curves for which the demand elasticity is the same at every price. Those curves, known as **constant elasticity** (or **isoelastic**) **demand curves**, correspond to demand functions of the form $Q^d = A(P^{-B})$, where A and B are positive numbers. For these demand functions, the elasticity of demand is $E^d = -B$.[16] Figure 2.17 shows the demand curve for the constant elasticity demand function $Q^d = 100/P$ [or, equivalently, $Q^d = 100(P^{-1})$], which has an elasticity of $E^d = -1$ at

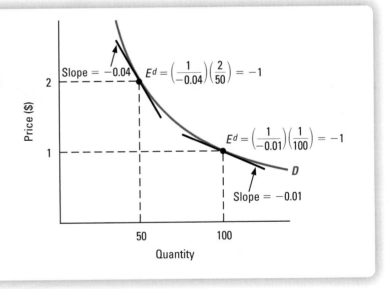

Figure 2.17

A Constant-Elasticity Demand Curve. This figure shows the curve for the demand function $Q^d = 100/P$. At every price P, the elasticity of demand is equal to -1.

Slope $= -0.04$ $E^d = \left(\frac{1}{-0.04}\right)\left(\frac{2}{50}\right) = -1$

$E^d = \left(\frac{1}{-0.01}\right)\left(\frac{1}{100}\right) = -1$

Slope $= -0.01$

---

[14]In mathematics, a line is said to be tangent to a curve at a point if its slope equals the rise over the run for very small changes along the curve starting at the point.

[15]If you know calculus, you may want to look at Add-On 2B, which discusses elasticities in terms of calculus.

[16]Add-On 2B shows this result using calculus. If you don't know calculus, you can see it another way: Suppose that the price increases from P to αP, where $\alpha > 1$. Then formula (3) tells us that

$$E^d = \frac{\left(\dfrac{A(\alpha P)^{-B} - AP^{-B}}{AP^{-B}}\right)}{\left(\dfrac{\alpha P - P}{P}\right)} = \left(\dfrac{\alpha^{-B} - 1}{\alpha - 1}\right)$$

For very small price changes in which α is very close to 1, this expression equals approximately $-B$ in value. For example, if B equals 5, this expression equals -4.853 when $\alpha = 1.01$; -4.985 when $\alpha = 1.001$; and -4.999 when $\alpha = 1.0001$.

every price P. As shown in the figure, a constant elasticity demand curve gets steeper as the price increases. Why? Looking at formula (6), we see that as P increases (and Q decreases), P/Q increases. For the elasticity to remain constant, the slope of the demand curve, $(\Delta P/\Delta Q)$ must increase too, as shown in the figure.

Total Expenditure and the Elasticity of Demand   The elasticity of demand for a product tells us how buyers' total expenditure on the product changes when the price increases and we move along the demand curve. That expenditure equals $P \times Q$, the product of the price and the total amount demanded. *Total expenditure will increase with a small increase in price when demand is inelastic and decrease when demand is elastic.* Since sellers' total revenue always equals buyers' total expenditure, the same is true for sellers' revenue.

Why does this relationship hold? Suppose that a one-percent price increase causes the quantity demanded to fall by one percent. With no change in quantity, the one-percent increase in price would cause total expenditure to rise by one percent. With no change in price, the one-percent drop in quantity would cause total expenditure to fall by one percent. So, intuitively, the one-percent increase in price and the one-percent decline in quantity offset one another, leaving total expenditure unchanged. If a one-percent price increase causes a less than one-percent decline in quantity, total expenditure will rise, and if it causes a more than one-percent decline in quantity, total expenditure will fall. (For a demonstration of this result using algebra, see Add-On 2C.)

Let's look at a couple of examples. First consider constant elasticity demand curves. For the demand function $Q^d = 100/P$ depicted in Figure 2.17, which has an elasticity of -1, total expenditure equals \$100 at every price. This follows from the fact that $P \times (100/P) = 100$. More generally, if $Q^d = A(P^{-B})$ (for which $E^d = -B$), then the total expenditure at price P is $P \times (A \times P^{-B}) = A(P^{1-B})$. Accordingly, a price increase raises total expenditure if $B < 1$ (which implies that E^d is between -1 and 0) and reduces total expenditure if $B > 1$ (which implies that E^d is less than -1).

Now consider linear demand curves. Figure 2.18 graphs the relationship between the total expenditure on corn and its price for the linear demand curve shown in Figure 2.15. The formula for total expenditure is $P_{corn} \times Q_{corn} = P_{corn} \times (15 - 2P_{corn}) = 15P_{corn} - 2(P_{corn})^2$. Recall that this demand curve is inelastic for prices below \$3.75 per bushel, and elastic for

Figure 2.18

The Relationship between Price and Total Expenditure. This figure shows the total expenditure on corn for the demand curve in Figure 2.15. Total expenditure increases when the price rises for prices below \$3.75, where demand is inelastic. It falls when the price rises for prices above \$3.75, where demand is elastic. It is largest when the price is \$3.75, where $E^d = -1$.

prices above \$3.75 per bushel. As the figure shows, a price increase raises total expenditure when the initial price is below this threshold (so that demand is inelastic) and reduces total expenditure when the initial price is above this threshold (so that demand is elastic).

At what price is total expenditure largest? That must be a price at which the elasticity of demand equals -1. Why? If demand was inelastic (an elasticity between zero and -1), a small increase in price would increase the total expenditure. If it was elastic (an elasticity less than -1), a small decrease in price would raise total expenditure. If expenditure is at its largest possible value, neither a small increase nor a small decrease can increase total expenditure; demand must therefore be neither elastic nor inelastic, so its elasticity must equal -1. In Figure 2.18, for example, the price that maximizes total expenditure is \$3.75 per bushel—the same price for which the elasticity of demand is -1.

To summarize:

Total Expenditure and the Elasticity of Demand   A small increase in price causes total expenditure to increase if demand is inelastic, and decrease if demand is elastic. Total expenditure is largest at a price for which the elasticity equals -1.

WORKED-OUT PROBLEM 2.4

The Problem   Consider the linear demand curve for hotel rooms in 2003 in Figure 2.8 (page 39). Suppose that the demand function for that curve is $Q^d_{2003} = 11880 - 40P$. At what price will total expenditure on hotel rooms be largest?

The Solution   Recall that the elasticity of the linear demand function $Q^d = A - BP$ at price P is $E^d = -B(P/Q)$, where Q is the amount demanded at that price. Substituting for Q, we can rewrite this formula as

$$E^d = -B\left(\frac{P}{A - BP}\right)$$

We know that the largest total expenditure occurs at a price for which the elasticity of demand equals -1. Since $B = 40$, that value of P will solve the equation

$$-40\left(\frac{P}{11880 - 40P}\right) = -1$$

Multiplying both sides by $-(11880 - 40P)$, we can rewrite this equation as

$$40P = 11880 - 40P$$

Solving for P, we find that total expenditure is largest at a price of \$148.50 per room.

IN-TEXT EXERCISE 2.5   **Suppose the linear demand function for hotel rooms the year before the SARS outbreak shown in Figure 2.8 (page 39) is $Q^d_{2002} = 14040 - 40P$. At what price will the total expenditure on hotel rooms be largest?**

Application 2.6

Hurricane Ike Blows a Hole in Consumers' Pockets

In September of 2008 Hurricane Ike roared through the Gulf of Mexico and threatened to disrupt oil production and distribution as Hurricane Katrina did three years earlier. Just the expectation of a reduction in the supply of gasoline led to a spike in gasoline prices in Canada. As the hurricane approached the Texas and Louisiana coasts refineries shut down and off-shore oil production in the path of the hurricane was curtailed. In the United States the average price of gasoline jumped the equivalent of about three cents a litre. In Canada the price increase was approximately eight cents a litre and in Toronto the price increase was closer to 15 cents a litre. In fact, the hurricane did little damage to the refineries along the gulf coast and prices settled back to their pre-hurricane levels within a week in most regions. The large increase in the price of gasoline occurred, in part, because the demand for gasoline is very inelastic. In a report prepared for Transport Canada in 1999 it was estimated that gasoline's short-run elasticity of demand was between -0.10 and -0.20. Even the perception that the supply of gasoline would be disrupted was enough to cause gasoline prices to increase

Prime Minister Harper asked if Canadian oil companies used the threat of hurricane damage to Gulf refineries as an excuse to raise gasoline prices.

more than 10 percent in some cities in Canada. Some, including Prime Minister Harper, suggested that Canadian oil companies used the hurricane as a pretext for raising prices in anticipation of a supply shortfall that never did materialize.[17]

The (Price) Elasticity of Supply

Economists also use elasticities to measure the responsiveness of supply to a product's price. The basic ideas are the same as for demand. For example, the **(price) elasticity of supply** at price P, denoted E^s, equals the percentage change in the amount supplied for each one percent increase in the price,

$$E^s = \frac{\% \text{ change in amount supplied}}{\% \text{ change in price}} = \left(\frac{\Delta Q/Q}{\Delta P/P}\right) = \left(\frac{\Delta Q}{\Delta P}\right)\left(\frac{P}{Q}\right) \qquad (7)$$

> The **(price) elasticity of supply** at price P, denoted E^s, equals the percentage change in the amount supplied for each one percent increase in the price.

where Q is now the amount *supplied* at price P and $\Delta Q/\Delta P$ is the change in the amount supplied for each dollar the price increases (when prices are measured in dollars). Since supply usually increases as the price increases, we expect the elasticity of supply to be a positive number. In parallel with our discussion of demand elasticities, we can also express the elasticity of supply as

$$E^s = \left(\frac{1}{\Delta P/\Delta Q}\right)(P/Q) \qquad (8)$$

where $\Delta P/\Delta Q$ is the slope of the supply curve.

[17]Sarah Schmidt, "Soaring Gas Prices Bring Storm of Debate," Canwest News Service, September 12, 2008; Vancouver Sun. (September 13, 2008). "Canada's gas prices expected to soar." *Canada.com.* Retrieved June 22, 2010, from http://www.canada.com/vancouversun/news/story.html?id=6de62424-09e6-49c3-ba44-7d41f6f0edde; Yutangco, P. (September 14, 2008). "Gasoline prices should ease." *thestar.com.* Retrieved June 22, 2010, from http://www.thestar.com/news/canada/article/499145; Competition Bureau—Competition Bureau Concludes Examination Into Gasoline Price Spike Following Hurricane Katrina. (March 30, 2006). *Competition Bureau—Home.* Retrieved June 22, 2010, from http://www.competitionbureau.gc.ca/eic/site/cb-bc.nsf/eng/02047.html.

The horizontal supply curve in Figure 2.13(a) (page 45) has a slope of zero, so applying formula (8) the elasticity of supply at price P is infinite: $E^s = +\infty$. This supply curve is **perfectly elastic**. In contrast, the vertical supply curve in Figure 2.13(b) is one for which any price change, ΔP, produces no change in the amount supplied, so $\Delta Q = 0$. For this supply curve, $(\Delta Q/\Delta P)$ equals 0, so [applying formula (7)] the elasticity of supply is zero: $E^s = 0$. This supply curve is **perfectly inelastic**.

In general, supply curves with an elasticity of supply between zero and one are referred to as **inelastic**; when the elasticity of supply is greater than one they are referred to as **elastic.** With an inelastic supply curve, the percentage increase in the amount supplied is less than the percentage increase in price. With an elastic supply curve, the opposite is true.

Supply is **perfectly inelastic** when the supply curve is vertical so that the price elasticity of supply is zero, and **perfectly elastic** when the supply curve is horizontal so that the price elasticity of supply is infinite.

Supply is **elastic** at price P when the elasticity of supply is greater than one, and **inelastic** when the elasticity of supply is between zero and one.

The Size of Changes in Market Demand, Revisited

We've said that elasticities of demand and supply are a more convenient way to measure price responsiveness than is the steepness (or slope) of the demand and supply curves. In Section 2.3 we related the steepness of the demand and supply curves to the size of the change in the market price and the amount bought and sold when, respectively, the supply or demand curve shifts. Let's go back to that discussion to see how it relates to elasticities.

Figure 2.12 (page 44), for example, showed that the price changed more and the amount bought and sold changed less in response to a shift of the supply curve with the steeper demand curve, D_1, than the flatter curve, D_2. How is the steepness of those two demand curves related to their elasticities? When two different demand curves coincide at a particular price, the steeper one is always less elastic at that price. For example, both demand curves in Figure 2.12 run through the initial market equilibrium point, with price P^* and quantity Q^*. Since the slope $(\Delta P/\Delta Q)$ is closer to zero for the flatter curve and the value of P^*/Q^* is the same for both curves at the point of intersection, formula (6) implies that the flatter curve is more elastic at price P^*. Thus, for small shifts in the demand and supply curves, we can restate the conclusion from our discussion in Section 2.3 as follows:

Changes in Market Equilibrium and the Elasticity of Demand and Supply

1. When the demand curve shifts: the less elastic the supply curve at the initial equilibrium price, the larger the price change and the smaller the change in the amount bought and sold.

2. When the supply curve shifts: the less elastic the demand curve at the initial equilibrium price, the larger the price change and the smaller the change in the amount bought and sold.

Other Elasticities

As we explained in Sections 2.1 and 2.2, the demand and supply for a product are affected by factors other than its price. We can use the concept of elasticity to measure the responsiveness of demand and supply to those other factors as well. For example, the elasticity of demand with respect to income (denoted by M), usually called the **income elasticity of demand**, equals the percentage change in the amount demanded divided by the percentage change in income, or equivalently, the percentage change in the amount demanded for each one percent increase in income.

$$E_M^d = \frac{(\Delta Q/Q)}{(\Delta M/M)}$$

The **income elasticity of demand** equals the percentage change in the amount demanded for each one percent increase in income.

If an increase in income raises the demand for a product, the income elasticity is positive, and we say that the product is a **normal good**. Sometimes, an increase in income reduces the demand for a product. This usually occurs when the product is of low quality, and higher incomes cause consumers to substitute toward higher quality alternatives. In that case, the income elasticity is negative, and we say that the product is an **inferior good**. We'll discuss these concepts further in Chapter 5.

If the demand for a product increases when income grows larger, the product is called a **normal good**. If it instead decreases, it is called an **inferior good**.

Economists also frequently measure the elasticity of demand for a product with respect to the price of another product, known as the first product's **cross-price elasticity** with the second product. Let Q denote the demand for the first product and P_O the price of the second "other" product. Then this elasticity equals the percentage change in the amount demanded of the product divided by the percentage change in the price of the other product, or equivalently, the percentage change in the amount demanded for each one percent increase in the price of the other product.

The **cross-price elasticity of demand** with another product equals the percentage change in the amount demanded of the product for each one percent increase in the price of the other product.

$$E_{P_O}^d = \frac{(\Delta Q/Q)}{(\Delta P_O/P_O)}$$

With products that are substitutes (see Section 2.1), the cross-price elasticity is positive. With products that are complements, it is negative. If the two goods may be unrelated, the cross-price elasticity is 0.

In a similar fashion, we can measure the elasticities of supply for a product with respect to other factors, such as the prices of inputs or other outputs.

Application 2.7

Cross-Price Elasticities for the Honda Accord

The similarity of substitute products affects not only a product's elasticity of demand with respect to its own price, but also its cross-price elasticities with other products. Recall from Application 2.5 that the elasticity of demand for a Honda Accord was −4.8: when its price went up by one percent, it experienced a 4.8 percent reduction in sales. What happened to the sales of other cars? According to economists Berry, Levinsohn, and Pakes, the Nissan Sentra, Ford Escort, and Ford Taurus—relatively similar cars to the Accord—all had cross-price elasticities with the Accord of about 0.2. That is, each experienced roughly a 0.2 percent increase in sales when the price of a Honda Accord rose one percent. In contrast, the much more upscale BMW 735i and Lexus LS400 experienced almost no change in their sales—their cross-price elasticities with the Honda Accord were essentially zero.

The Honda Accord

1. **Demand (LO1, 2)**

   a. The first step in a demand-and-supply analysis of the market for a product is to determine the demand for the product.

   b. A product's demand curve shows how much of the product consumers and firms want to buy at each possible price, holding fixed all other factors that affect demand.

   c. The demand function for a product is a formula of the form *Quantity Demanded = D(Price, Other Factors)*. It gives the total demand for the product at every possible combination of its price and other factors.

   d. A change in a product's price leads to a movement along its demand curve. A change in other factors leads to a shift in the entire demand curve.

2. **Supply (LO1, 2)**

   a. The second step in a demand-and-supply analysis of the market for a product is to determine the supply of the product.

   b. A product's supply curve shows how many units sellers of the product want to sell at each possible price, holding fixed all other factors that affect supply.

   c. The supply function for a product is a formula of the form *Quantity Supplied = S(Price, Other Factors)*. It gives the total supply of the product at every possible combination of its price and other factors.

   d. A change in a product's price leads to a movement along its supply curve. A change in other factors leads to a shift in the entire supply curve.

3. **Market equilibrium (LO3, 4)**

   a. Once we know the demand and supply in a market, the next step is to determine the equilibrium price—the price at which the demand and supply curves intersect, so that the amounts supplied and demanded are equal. That price can be found graphically or algebraically.

   b. Market prices tend to adjust to equate the amounts demanded and supplied. If there is excess demand then some buyers will have an incentive to raise the price they offer in order to acquire their desired quantity. If there is excess supply, then some sellers will have an incentive to lower the price in order to sell their desired quantity. These processes tend to restore the balance between supply and demand.

   c. To determine how a change in market conditions, such as a change in the price of an input or a shift in consumer preferences, will change the price and the amount bought and sold, we solve for the market equilibrium before and after the change.

   d. Changes that increase demand (shifting the demand curve to the right) raise the price and the amount bought and sold; changes that decrease demand lower them. In contrast, changes that increase supply (shifting the supply curve to the right) raise the amount bought and sold but lower the price; changes that decrease supply have the opposite effect.

   e. If both the demand curve and supply curve shift and each would individually increase the price, the overall effect is to increase the price. If the two effects work in opposite directions, the overall effect is ambiguous. The same principle applies to changes in the amount bought and sold.

   f. When demand or supply increases, shifting the demand or supply curves, the size of the change in price and the amount bought and sold depends on how much the curve shifts and on the steepness of the non-shifting curve. The steeper the non-shifting curve, the greater the change in the equilibrium price and the smaller the change in the amount bought and sold.

4. **Elasticities of supply and demand (LO5)**

   a. The elasticity of one variable, Y, with respect to another, X, measures how responsive Y is to a change in X. It equals the percentage change in Y divided by the percentage change in X, or equivalently, the percentage change in Y for each one percent increase in X.

   b. The (price) elasticity of demand at a given price P, denoted E^d, measures the percentage change in the amount demanded for each one percent increase in its price, for small price changes. The elasticity of demand is typically a negative number.

   c. The elasticity of demand is calculated using the formula $E^d = (P/Q)/(\Delta P/\Delta Q)$. For a linear demand curve of the form $Q^d = A - BP$, $(\Delta P/\Delta Q)$ equals $-(1/B)$, the slope of the demand curve. For a nonlinear demand curve, it equals the slope of the demand curve at the particular price P (which equals the slope of the line that is tangent to the curve at that point).

   d. Demand is inelastic at price P when the elasticity of demand is closer to zero than -1 ($E^d > -1$). It is elastic at price P when the elasticity of demand at that price is further from zero than -1 ($E^d < -1$). It is perfectly inelastic when the price elasticity of demand is zero, and perfectly elastic when the price elasticity of demand equals negative infinity.

   e. When demand is elastic, a small price increase causes total expenditure to fall. When demand is inelastic, a small price increase causes total expenditure to rise. Total expenditure is largest at a price at which the elasticity of demand equals -1.

   f. The price elasticity of supply at a given price P, denoted E^s, measures the percentage change in supply for each one percent increase in price.

g. Supply is inelastic when the price elasticity of supply is closer to zero than one ($E^s < 1$). It is elastic when the price elasticity of supply is further from zero than one ($E^s > 1$). Supply is perfectly inelastic when the elasticity of supply is zero, and perfectly elastic when the elasticity of supply is infinite.

h. For small shifts in the demand curve, the less elastic the supply curve at the equilibrium price, the larger the price change and the smaller the change in the amount bought and sold. For small shifts in the supply curve, the less elastic the demand curve at the initial equilibrium price, the larger the price change, and the smaller the change in the amount bought and sold.

i. Economists also study elasticities of a product's demand or supply with respect to other factors, such as income (for demand), the prices of other products (for demand and supply), and input prices (for supply).

ADDITIONAL EXERCISES

Exercise 2.1: Consider again the demand function for corn in formula (1). Graph the corresponding demand curve when potatoes and butter cost $0.75 and $4 per kilogram, respectively, and average income is $40,000 per year. At what price does the amount demanded equal 15 billion bushels per year? Show your answer using algebra. (LO1)

Exercise 2.2: Consider again the supply function for corn in formula (2). Graph the corresponding supply curve when diesel fuel costs $1.00 per litre and the price of soybeans is $12 per bushel. At what price does the amount supplied equal 21 billion bushels per year? Show your answer using algebra. (LO1)

Exercise 2.3: What is the equilibrium price for the demand and supply conditions described in exercises 2.1 and 2.2? How much corn is bought and sold? What if the price of diesel fuel increases to $1.875 per litre? Show the equilibrium price before and after the change in a graph. (LO1, 2)

Exercise 2.4: Consider again the demand and supply functions in worked-out problem 2.2 (page 33). Suppose the government needs to buy 3.5 billion bushels of corn for a third-world famine relief program. What effect will the purchase have on the equilibrium price of corn? How will it change the amount of corn that consumers and firms buy? (LO3, 4)

Exercise 2.5: After terrorists destroyed the World Trade Center and surrounding office buildings on September 11, 2001, some businesspeople worried about the risks of remaining in Manhattan. What effect would you expect their concern to have in the short run (before any of the destroyed office buildings are rebuilt) on the price of office space in Manhattan? What factors does your answer depend on? What about the effect over the long run? Suppose the area around the former World Trade Center is made into a park, so that the destroyed office buildings are never rebuilt. Economically, who would gain and who would lose from such a plan? (LO4)

Exercise 2.6: If imports of Canadian beef were to be banned by the United States for reasons unrelated to health concerns, what would be the effect on the price of beef in the United States? How would the typical American's diet change? What about the

typical Canadian's? What if the ban suggested to consumers that there might be health risks associated with beef? (LO4)

Exercise 2.7: Suppose that the U.S. demand for Canadian maple syrup, in thousands of litres per year, is $Q^d = 1500 - 30P$. What is the elasticity of demand at a price of $20 per litre? (LO5)

Exercise 2.8: Consider again exercise 2.7. At what price is the expenditure on maple syrup by U.S. consumers highest? (LO5)

Exercise 2.9: Suppose the demand function for jelly beans in Calgary is linear. Two years ago, the price of jelly beans was $4 per kilogram, and consumers purchased 100,000 kilograms of jelly beans. Last year the price was $6, and consumers purchased 50,000 kilograms of jelly beans. No other factors that might affect the demand for jelly beans changed. What was the elasticity of demand at last year's price of $6? At what price would the total expenditure on jelly beans have been largest? (LO5)

Exercise 2.10: Consider again the demand and supply functions in in-text exercise 2.2 (page 33). At the equilibrium price, what are the elasticities of demand and supply? (LO5)

Exercise 2.11: Last September, the price of gasoline in Hamilton was $1 a litre, and consumers bought 50 million litres. Suppose the elasticity of demand in September at a price of $1 was -0.5, and that the demand function for gasoline that month was linear. What was that demand function? At what price does consumers' total expenditure on gasoline reach its largest level? (LO5)

Exercise 2.12: Suppose the annual demand function for the Honda Accord is $Q^d = 430 - 10P_A + 10P_C - 40P_G$, where P_A and P_C are the prices of the Accord and the Toyota Camry respectively (in thousands), and P_G is the price of gasoline (per litre). What is the elasticity of demand of the Accord with respect to the price of a Camry when both cars sell for $20,000 and fuel costs $0.75 per litre? What is the elasticity with respect to the price of gasoline? (LO2, 5)

Exercise 2.13: The demand for a product is $Q^d = A - BP$, where P is its price and A and B are positive numbers. Suppose that when the price is $1 the amount demanded is 60 and the elasticity of demand is -1. What are the values of A and B? Find A and B if the elasticity of demand is -3. (LO1, 3, 5)

APPENDIX

ESTIMATING DEMAND AND SUPPLY CURVES

To answer many questions in economics and business, we need to measure the relationships between the amount demanded and supplied and various factors, including the product's price. We've already seen that we need to know the demand and supply functions to predict market prices. Later in this book, we'll see that this same knowledge is useful for such diverse purposes as evaluating the effects of a tax and determining a firm's profit-maximizing price. The process of learning about demand and supply is known as *demand and supply function estimation*. For the sake of simplicity, and because the issues are very similar, we'll focus here primarily on the estimation of demand functions.

How can we determine the demand function for a product? There are various approaches to this problem. One is to ask buyers about their willingness to buy the product at different prices. Marketing specialists have developed survey methods for this purpose. But while surveys can provide useful information, they suffer from some shortcomings. Consumers may have difficulty providing accurate responses about what they would do in hypothetical situations. And since their well-being doesn't depend on their answers, they may not give these questions much thought.

Given these problems, economists usually take a different approach: they try to learn about demand by studying consumers' *actual behaviour.*

The "Ideal Experiment"

Suppose we're interested in estimating the weekly demand function for hot dogs in Winnipeg, Manitoba. To start, we'll assume for simplicity that this demand depends only on the price of a hot dog. Suppose the demand function is linear, so that it takes the form $Q^d = A - BP$. We don't know the values of A (the intercept term) and B (which determines how much the amount demanded changes when the price changes). In what follows we will be graphing the inverse demand curve, $P = A/B - (1/B)Q^d$.

How can we learn these values? First let's think about an ideal experiment in which we present consumers with different prices in different weeks and observe their demand. Figure 2.19 shows the amounts demanded at two different prices, $P = \$1$ and $P = \$2$, as black dots. We can find the demand curve, labelled D, by drawing a line through these dots, as in the figure. The value A is the quantity at which this line hits the horizontal axis (corresponding to the amount demanded when hot dogs are free). The demand curve hits the vertical axis at a height equal to A/B. So the value of B equals the horizontal intercept of the demand curve divided by the vertical intercept. [This is also equal to $-(1/\text{demand curve slope})$].

If the demand function isn't linear, we would usually need to observe the demand at more than two prices to trace out the demand curve. And if observable factors other than the price affect demand, such as the season (summer versus non-summer), we would need to perform a similar experiment in each season.

In reality, if we were to present consumers with a price of $1 in some weeks and $2 in other weeks, we would find that the quantities demanded would differ even across weeks in which the price was the same. Variation in other unobserved factors creates this pattern. For example, in some weeks the local university may hold home hockey games, the youth soccer league may hold a "SoccerFest," or a large church may have a potluck dinner, significantly increasing the demand for hot dogs.

Let's imagine that half the time the demand is high, which we represent by the curve labelled D^H in Figure 2.20, and half the time it is low, which we represent by the demand curve D^L in that figure. In that case, for any given price we face the consumer with ($1 or $2), half of the time the amount demanded corresponds to the black dot on D^H, and half of the time to the black dot on D^L. Though we can't determine the demand curve with

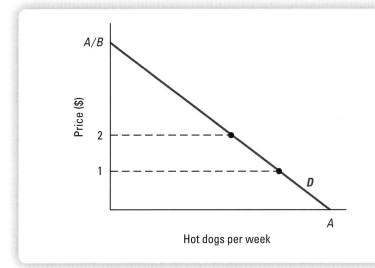

Figure 2.19
Estimating the Demand Curve through an "Ideal Experiment." If consumers face different prices in different weeks within each season, their choices will reveal the market demand curve.

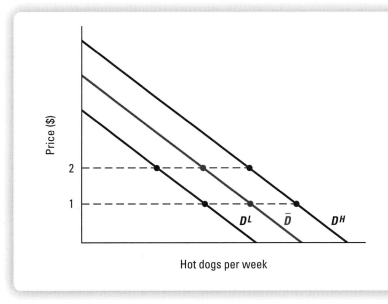

Figure 2.20
Estimating the (Average) Demand Curve, Given Unobservable Factors. When unobservable factors affect demand, the quantity demanded will differ from week to week even when consumers face the same price. In such cases, we can learn how the average demand varies with the price.

certainty, we *can* learn about the *average* demand curve, which tells us how many hot dogs consumers would demand, on average, at each possible price. To do so, we would calculate the average demand when the price is $1 and the average demand when the price is $2, shown as the two blue dots in Figure 2.20. We could then draw a line through those two dots to obtain an estimate of the average demand curve, labelled $\overline{D}$ in the figure.

Economists who specialize in a field called *econometrics* study how best to use such data to derive estimates of average demand. One such method, known as *linear regression*, involves minimizing the sum of the squared distances between the estimated demand curve and the observed demand. In econometrics, the variable whose movements we are trying to explain is called the **dependent variable**. The variables that explain the changes in the dependent variable are called the **explanatory variables**.

In econometrics, the variable whose movements we are trying to explain is called the **dependent variable**. The variables that explain the changes in the dependent variable are called the **explanatory variables**.

Using Actual Market Data

If economists could easily conduct the ideal experiment, our discussion of demand estimation would be complete. Unfortunately, they rarely can perform such experiments. Instead, they must typically use actual market data. To see why doing so creates problems, look at Figure 2.21. The figure shows the same two demand curves as in Figure 2.20, but now also includes a supply curve labelled *S*. When we look at market data, we see the equilibrium prices and amounts demanded. These equilibria correspond to the two black dots, where the demand curves intersect the supply curve.

Like our ideal experimental data, these market data tell us how much consumers purchased at two different prices. Suppose we treat these data the same way as we did in Figure 2.20, drawing a line to connect the two dots. That line, labelled $\hat{D}$, is upward sloping and doesn't look at all like the actual demand curves. Why isn't our method working? The answer is that we're no longer performing the ideal experiment. In the ideal experiment, the price that consumers faced was unrelated to the unobserved factors that affect demand. In Figure 2.20, for example, we presented consumers with prices of $1 and $2 every other week. But when we look at real market data, as in Figure 2.21, *the price we observe is affected by the unobserved factors that influence demand*. The market price

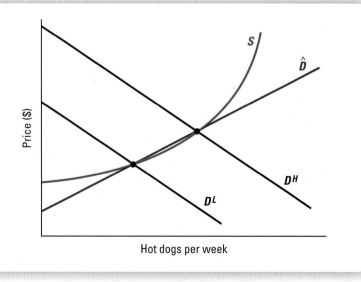

Figure 2.21
The Effect of Unobservable Factors on Estimated Demand. This figure shows two different demand curves, a variation in demand that is caused by unobserved factors. Because the equilibrium price is higher when unobserved factors increase demand, demand appears to be higher when the price is higher.

tends to be high precisely when unobserved factors shift the demand curve outward, which in turn increases the amount bought and sold. As a result, we tend to underestimate how much an increase in price reduces demand. In fact, in Figure 2.21, a higher price always goes hand-in-hand with a higher quantity, because both result from an outward shift of the demand curve.

Is there some way to determine the true average demand curve? The answer is "maybe," but it depends on our ability to observe a factor that shifts the *supply* curve while leaving the demand curve unaffected.[18]

Imagine, for instance, that the price of hot dog meat rises, increasing a hot dog vendor's cost by $1 per hot dog. The cost increase shifts the supply curve for hot dogs to the left (reducing supply). In Figure 2.22, these two supply curves are labelled S (before the increase in the cost of meat) and S' (after the increase). Suppose we compare the prices and quantities demanded when the meat price is high and when it is low. With the higher meat cost, hot dog prices tend to be higher because of the reduced supply. The hot dog prices and quantities we observe correspond to points A and B. When the price of meat is low, the hot dog prices and quantities we observe correspond to points C and D. The blue dots labelled E and F show the *average* price and *average* demand when the cost of meat is high (E) and when it is low (F). If we connect those blue dots by drawing the blue line labelled $\hat{D}$, we see that the line is downward sloping. In fact, it gives us a reliable estimate of the average demand curve.

What's going on here? We would like to perform the ideal experiment in which we face consumers with different prices while holding all other factors that affect demand fixed and estimate the demand curve by plotting the average demand at those prices. We can't do that, because the price consumers actually pay in a market equilibrium depends on unobserved factors that also affect demand. Instead, we perform a different experiment: we

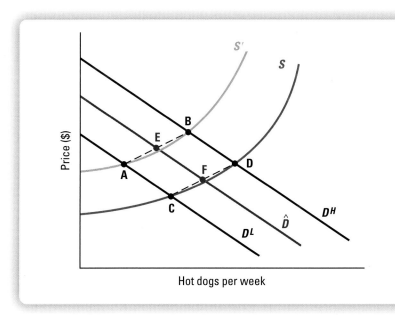

Hot dogs per week

Figure 2.22
Using a Supply-Shifter to Estimate the (Average) Demand Curve. This figure shows two supply curves, one with a low price of hot dog meat (S) and the other with a high cost of meat (S'). Point E is the average of the market equilibria with a high cost of meat; point F is the average with a low cost of meat. These two points allow us to estimate the (average) demand curve, shown in blue.

---

[18]In econometrics, an observed factor that shifts the *other* curve (here the supply curve) rather than the one we are estimating (here the demand curve) is known as an *instrumental variable*.

compare the average prices and quantities demanded in periods when supply is high to those when supply is low, in this case due to the differences in the price of meat. By computing the average difference in the amount demanded between these two situations, and comparing it to the average difference in the price, we can estimate the average relationship between the price and the quantity demanded. This gives us an estimate of the demand curve.

In fact, we've already put this idea to work in worked-out problem 2.4 (see also in-text exercise 2.5). There we used information about the price and number of hotel rooms rented before and after the SARS outbreak in Toronto, which affected the demand for hotel rooms but left the supply largely unchanged, to learn about the revenue-maximizing price of a hotel room.

The methods for estimating the supply curve parallel those used to estimate demand curves. The main difference is that, when estimating the supply curve, we need to observe factors that shift demand. For example, if we want to estimate the supply curve for hot dogs, we might compare the average prices and amounts sold in summer weeks versus winter weeks. Since the demand is greater in the summer, the price will tend to be higher during summer weeks, and we can use market data to determine how the amount supplied responds to that price difference.

Balancing Benefits and Costs

LEARNING OBJECTIVES

After reading this chapter, students should be able to

LO1 Understand the concept of maximizing benefits less costs.

LO2 Describe what it means to think on the margin.

LO3 Explain the concepts of marginal benefit and marginal cost.

LO4 Use marginal analysis to identify best choices.

LO5 Understand why sunk costs can be ignored in making economic decisions.

Last week your 1998 Honda Civic broke down for the second time in a month, jeopardizing your after-school pizza delivery job. You and your "Civ" have been through some good times together, but you've reluctantly concluded that it's time to replace it with another car. Before you sell it, however, you may want to spend some money to fix it up.

Think about the benefits of having a mechanic work on your car: The more problems you fix, the more money you'll get for it. Some things that don't cost that much to fix can greatly increase its resale value. A broken turn signal, streaky windshield wipers, and a cracked windshield strike most car buyers as bad signs. Careful buyers might also discover that your brake pads are worn and your muffler has holes. But fixing your car also has costs. Your mechanic's time isn't cheap, and neither are the parts she uses. While the car is in the repair shop, you won't be able to do your delivery job. Making the right decision involves balancing these benefits and costs.

Many decisions we will study in this book involve such a trade-off. A decision maker is confronted with various options and needs to find the best choice. Doing so means balancing benefits and costs. In this chapter, we'll see how economists think about such problems. We'll use the tools we develop here over and over again throughout the book. The chapter can be studied at the start of a course, or used as a reference while reading later chapters. It covers three topics:

1. *Maximizing benefits less costs.* Economic decisions generate both benefits and costs. We'll discuss how the best choice maximizes benefits less costs.

2. *Thinking on the margin.* Economists often think about a choice in terms of its marginal benefits and marginal costs, which capture its incremental benefits and costs. We'll define these concepts and examine their relationships to best choices.

3. *Sunk costs and decision making.* In some situations, a decision is associated with costs that the decision maker has already incurred or to which she has previously committed. Economists call such costs *sunk costs.* We'll see that a decision maker can always make the right choice simply by ignoring sunk costs.

3.1   MAXIMIZING BENEFITS LESS COSTS

Let's take a closer look at your car repair decision. For the sake of simplicity, we'll assume that your mechanic charges for her time in one-hour increments, so that the amount of time you choose must be a whole number, like two hours or four hours, but not two-and-one-half hours. Also for the sake of simplicity, we'll assume your mechanic has at most six hours of available time.

We'll focus first on the benefits. Table 3.1 shows how much more money you will get for your car per each hour your mechanic works on it. Notice that the more repair time, the more your car is worth. For example, your car will be worth $1150 more if the mechanic works on it for two hours, and $1975 more if she works on it for four hours.

Now let's think about the costs. First, you'll have to pay for your mechanic's time and the parts she uses. For example, Table 3.2 shows that the cost of two hours of repair work is $355. Second, you won't be able to work at your pizza delivery job while your car is being repaired. For example, Table 3.2 shows that you will earn $25 less if you miss two hours of work, but will earn $75 less if you miss four hours of work. (Your boss will be more annoyed if you miss four hours of work and will reassign you to a delivery route in a less wealthy part of town, where tips are lower.)

Table 3.2 also shows the total cost for each number of repair hours you could choose. Notice that the costs of repairing your car are of two different types. When you hire your mechanic and buy parts, you incur an out-of-pocket cost in the sense that you have to take money out of your pocket (or bank account) to pay her. But when repairing your car

Table 3.1
Benefits of Repairing Your Car Repair Time (Hours) Total Benefit

Repair Time (Hours)	Total Benefit
0	$0
1	615
2	1,150
3	1,600
4	1,975
5	2,270
6	2,485

Table 3.2
Costs of Repairing Your Car

Repair Time (Hours)	Cost of Mechanic and Parts	Lost Earnings from Pizza Delivery Job	Total Cost
0	$0	$0	$0
1	140	10	150
2	355	25	380
3	645	45	690
4	1,005	75	1,080
5	1,440	110	1,550
6	1,950	150	2,100

Table 3.3
Total Benefit and Total Cost of Repairing Your Car

Repair Time (Hours)	Total Benefit	Total Cost	Net Benefit
0	$0	$0	$0
1	615	150	465
2	1,150	380	770
3	1,600	690	910
4	1,975	1,080	895
5	2,270	1,550	720
6	2,485	2,100	385

Best choice → (3) (910)

forces you to skip your pizza delivery job, the cost is of a different nature. You hand no money to others; instead, you forgo the opportunity to have others hand money to you. That type of cost is known as an opportunity cost. In general, an **opportunity cost** is the cost associated with forgoing the opportunity to employ a resource in its best alternative use.[1] Here, you forgo the opportunity to use your car to deliver pizzas.

> An **opportunity cost** is the cost associated with forgoing the opportunity to employ a resource in its best alternative use.
>
> **Net benefit** equals total benefit less total cost.

To make the right decision, you need to find the number of repair hours that maximizes your **net benefit**—the total benefit you derive less the total cost you incur. Table 3.3 shows the total benefit, total cost, and net benefit for each of your possible choices. The best choice is three hours, which has a net benefit of $910.

Figure 3.1 graphs the total benefits and total costs from Table 3.3. The horizontal axis measures the number of repair hours and the vertical axis measures total benefit and total cost. The figure shows the total benefit for each number of hours in blue and the total cost in red. At the best choice of three hours, the vertical distance between the blue total benefit point and red total cost point is larger than at any other number of hours.

In practice, managers often construct benefit and cost tables using a computer. By entering the various benefits and costs into a spreadsheet program and then using it to calculate the net benefit of each possible choice, they can identify the best choice.

> **IN-TEXT EXERCISE 3.1** **Suppose your mechanic lowers the amount she charges by $25 an hour. The total benefits are the same as in Table 3.1. What is your best choice?**

Maximizing Net Benefits with Finely Divisible Actions

Many choices involve actions that are finely divisible, that is, that can be adjusted in arbitrarily small increments. Consider again your decision about how much repair time to invest in your Honda Civic. Originally, we assumed that you had to hire your mechanic in

---

[1]As a general matter, the cost you incur in paying your mechanic could also be viewed as an opportunity cost since when you hand over your money you forgo the opportunity to spend that money on something else. However, we will typically reserve the term *opportunity cost* for implicit or hidden costs such as your lost pizza delivery income, and not direct out-of-pocket expenses.

Figure 3.1

Total Benefit and Total Cost of Repairing Your Car. This figure shows the total benefits from Table 3.3 in blue and the total costs in red. The best choice is three hours, which results in a net benefit of $910. That is the number of hours at which the vertical distance between the blue and red dots is greatest.

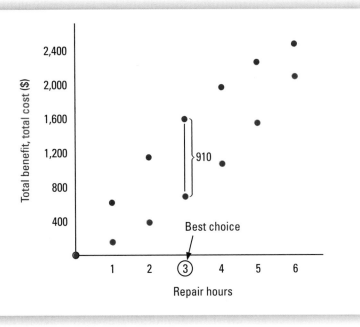

one-hour increments. But what if your mechanic charged by the quarter-hour, or even the minute? And what if you were doing the repair work yourself? Then you could even choose the number of seconds.

When a decision maker's choices are finely divisible, we can use total benefit and total cost curves to find the best choice. Figure 3.2(a) shows the total benefit curve for your car repair decision. The horizontal axis measures hours of your mechanic's time. The vertical axis measures in dollars the total benefit you derive (the increase in your car's value). To draw the figure, we assume that the total benefit with H hours of repair work is described by the function $B(H) = 654H - 40H^2$. (The total benefits in Table 3.1 correspond to the values of this function, rounded to the nearest $5.) Note that the total benefit increases as the amount of repair work rises from zero to six hours.

Figure 3.2(b) shows the total cost curve. Here, we assume that the total cost of H hours of repair work is described by the function $C(H) = 110H + 40H^2$. (The total costs in Table 3.2 correspond to the values of this function, rounded to the nearest $5.) In this case, the horizontal axis again measures repair hours and the vertical axis measures total cost in dollars. Just like total benefit, total cost increases as the amount of repair work rises from zero to six hours.

Figure 3.2(c) combines these two curves and identifies the best choice. The vertical axis measures total benefit and total cost in dollars. The best choice gives you the largest possible net benefit (total benefit less total cost). Graphically, that point is the number of hours at which the vertical distance between the total benefit and total cost curves is largest. In Figure 3.2(c), your best choice turns out to be 3.4 hours, at which point total benefit is $1761.20 and total cost is $836.40. The difference between total benefit and total cost at 3.4 hours is $924.80, the largest possible net benefit. With any other choice, the net benefit would be smaller.[2]

---

[2]This net benefit is larger than the largest net benefit in Table 3.3 and Figure 3.1, where repair hours could only be chosen in increments of an hour. Having more flexibility (the ability to hire your mechanic in finer increments) allows you to do better.

(a) Total benefit

(b) Total cost

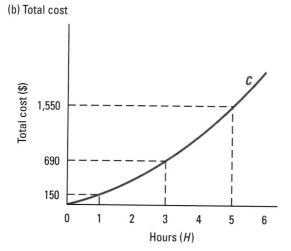

(c) Total benefit versus total cost

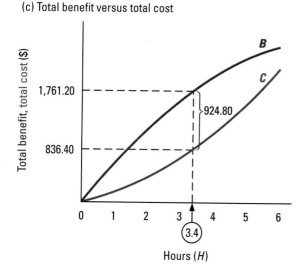

Figure 3.2

Total Benefit and Total Cost Curves When Repair Time Is Finely Divisible. The blue curve in (a) shows the total benefit from repairing your car for each amount of repair work between zero and six hours. It represents the total benefit function $B(H) = 654H - 40H^2$. The red curve in (b) shows the total cost of repairing your car for each amount of repair work between zero and six hours. It represents the total cost function $C(H) = 110H + 40H^2$. The two curves are combined in (c), which shows that the net benefit (which equals the vertical distance between the two curves at any given number of hours) is largest at a choice of 3.4 hours. In this case, total benefit is $1761.20, total cost is $836.40, and net benefit is $924.80.

Figure 3.3 shows the net benefit, $B - C$, in the form of a curve (the horizontal axis again measures the number of repair hours, while the vertical axis now measures the net benefit, the difference between the total benefit and total cost). The best choice of 3.4 hours leads to the highest point on the curve.

Figure 3.3
Net Benefit When Repair Time Is Finely Divisible. This figure shows the difference between the total benefit and total cost curves in Figure 3.2. Note that the curve is highest at a choice of 3.4 hours, the point where total benefit exceeds total cost by $924.80.

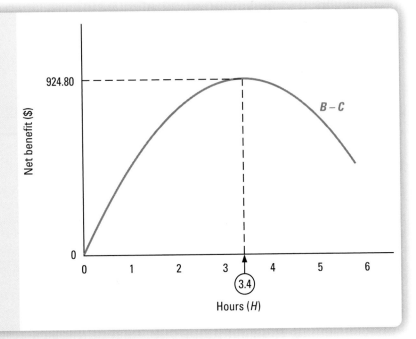

Application 3.1

Benefits and Costs of a University Degree

What do Wayne Gretzy and Jim Carrey have in common, aside from being rich and famous? The answer is that neither got a university degree or even finished high school (although both have since received *honorary* doctorates.)

Each year millions of high school students decide to go on to university. Is a university degree a good investment for the typical student? The answer involves a comparison of the benefits and costs. While a university education has many benefits (for example, you will become a much more interesting dinner companion), we'll look only at its effects on earnings.

A recent study by McMaster economists John Burbidge, Lionel Magee, and Leslie Robb document how the wage premium for different levels of educational attainment has changed during over the past several decades.[3] Table 3.4 illustrates the median weekly earnings of males for different

What do Wayne Gretzky and Jim Carrey have in common?

[3]J. B. Burbidge, L. Magee, and A. L. Robb, "The Education Premium in Canada and the United States," *Canadian Public Policy*, June 2002, pp. 203–217.

Table 3.4

Median Weekly Earnings by Education for Males (1997 dollars)

Year	Elementary School	Some High School	High School Degree	University Degree
1981	$683	$738	$794	$1063
1985	666	714	783	1051
1990	676	688	738	1019
1995	599	684	715	984
2000	572	600	687	936

levels of educational attainment obtained from two surveys of households; the Canadian Survey of Consumer Finances (SCF) and the Survey of Labour and Income Dynamics (SLID). Not surprisingly weekly earnings increase by level of educational attainment during the reported years. The authors of the study also find the same trend among women albeit with lower median weekly earnings than their male counterparts.

Another study by Ana Ferrer (Calgary) and Craig Riddell (UBC) study the role of educational credentials and document the impact on earnings when graduating from high school or university. They find that the "sheepskin" effect of an university degree explains up to half of the return to university education.[4]

But what about the costs of attending university? One obvious cost is tuition, which varies tremendously. The average undergraduate tuition paid across all disciplines in Canada in 2008–2009 was $4734. The least expensive undergraduate tuition amount was for education ($3666) while the most expensive annual tuition amount was for dentistry ($12,906).

But tuition and books are *not* the only costs of going to university. There's also an important opportunity cost: while you're in university you probably can't hold a full-time job. According to Table 3.4, for an average high school graduate in 2000 this cost is roughly $572 per week (or approximately $30,000 per year) which even after tax far exceeds tuition costs. Even if one were to look at average annual incomes of university-age students with a high school degree the lost income might still exceed $20,000 per year. On an after-tax basis, this opportunity cost raises the cost of a university education to roughly $100,000. (If you can still work at a part-time job, that would reduce the opportunity cost below this amount.)

With a total benefit of approximately $750,000 (the difference between weekly earning with a university degree and a high school degree over a 45-year working lifetime) and a total cost of about $100,000 going to university looks like a good decision![5, 6]

What about Wayne Gretzky and Jim Carrey? In some cases, the opportunity costs of going to university are so great that getting a degree doesn't make sense, at least not from the perspective of maximizing lifetime earnings. On January 26, 1979 Wayne Gretzky turned 18 and celebrated by signing a 10-year deal with the Edmonton Oilers for $3 million. He only completed half of his grade 12 year in high school. Jim Carrey when he was already a fixture on the comedy scene while in grade 10. He was a top act at Yuk Yuks in Toronto before moving to Los Angeles to work at the Comedy Store. For both Wayne Gretzky and Jim Carrey, the opportunity costs of completing high school, or enrolling in university, were just too high relative to the benefits.[7]

The decision to go to university is a discrete decision, either you go or you don't, at least if you want to get the degree that comes with completing university. But university students make other, finely divisible decisions about their education nearly every day. For example, is it worthwhile studying another 15 minutes for next week's microeconomics test? Doing so has benefits (a better grade, better future job prospects, and greater understanding of the world) but also costs (less time for that pizza delivery job, sleep, or socializing). Making those decisions correctly involves a balancing of benefits and costs.

---

[4]Ana M. Ferrer and W. Craig Riddell, "The role of credentials in the Canadian labour market," *Canadian Journal of Economics*, November 2002, pp. 879–905.

[5]In Chapter 10 we explain how to calculate the value of an income stream that is spread out over time. In doing so the total benefit from having a university degree over a high school degree would be less than $750,000 but would still be substantially greater than the $100,000 cost.

[6]These estimates of the effect of a college degree on lifetime earnings have two shortcomings. First, the average income in Table 3.4 for a university graduate is the average for those individuals who have only a university degree, not a more advanced degree. As such, it overlooks the fact that getting a universtiy degree gives you the option to get a more advanced degree that could further increase your lifetime earnings—and therefore it understates the true effect of a university degree on your lifetime earnings. On the other hand, it may also overstate the true increase in earnings that comes with a university degree. If smart people tend to get more education, and employers like to hire smart employees, part of the extra salary that university graduates earn may be due to their intelligence rather than to the extra time they spent in the classroom.

[7]While Wayne Gretzy's future was secure as soon as he signed with the Edmonton Oilers, Jim Carrey's future earnings from his decision to drop out of high school were uncertain. In Chapter 11, we'll discuss how to evaluate uncertain returns.

3.2 THINKING ON THE MARGIN

Another way to approach the maximization of net benefits involves thinking in terms of *marginal effects*. In fact, this is one of the most important ways in which you can learn to "think like an economist." In this section, we'll introduce the basic ideas behind marginal analysis. The chapter's appendix and Add-On 3A provide additional details, focusing in particular on the use of marginal analysis to find best choices, a topic that we discuss at the end of the section.

When economists think about a decision, they focus on its *marginal benefits* and *marginal costs*. Marginal benefits and marginal costs capture the way total benefit and cost *change* as the activity changes just a little bit. Consider again the decision of how much time your mechanic should spend repairing your car. Let H be the number of hours you choose. Marginal benefit and marginal cost measure how much your benefits and costs change due to a small change in repair time—the smallest change that is possible. We'll call the size of this smallest change ΔH. (The Greek symbol Δ, called *delta*, refers to a change in a variable.) In Table 3.1, $\Delta H = 1$, since your mechanic charged for her time in one-hour increments. If instead she were to charge in half-hour increments, then ΔH would equal 0.5. When you are purchasing H hours of repair time, the last ΔH hours you purchase are called the marginal units of repair time. More generally, for any action choice ΔX, the **marginal units** are the last ΔX units, where ΔX is the smallest amount you can add or subtract.

> The **marginal units** of action choice X are the last ΔX units, where ΔX is the smallest amount you can add or subtract.

Marginal Cost

Let's look first at your marginal cost, MC. Marginal cost measures the additional cost you incur because of the last ΔH hours of repair time (the marginal units of repair time). Specifically, suppose that $C(H)$ is the total cost of H hours of repair work. (For example, in Table 3.2, the total cost of three hours of repair work is $C(3) = \$690$.) When you are getting H hours of repair work, the extra cost due to the last ΔH hours is $\Delta C = C(H) - C(H - \Delta H)$, which is the amount it costs to get H hours of repair time less the amount it costs to get only $H - \Delta H$ hours.

> The **marginal cost of an action** at an activity level of X units is equal to the extra cost incurred due to the marginal units, $C(X) - C(X - \Delta X)$, divided by the number of marginal units, ΔX.

This is simple enough. The only added complication is that economists measure marginal cost on a *per unit* basis. That is, MC measures the extra cost due to your last ΔH hours of repair time per hour of extra repair time. To obtain this measure, we divide the extra cost by the number of marginal hours, ΔH.

$$MC = \frac{\Delta C}{\Delta H} = \frac{C(H) - C(H - \Delta H)}{\Delta H} \qquad (1)$$

This expression tells us how much marginal repair time costs *per hour*. More generally, the **marginal cost of an action** at an activity level of X units is equal to the extra cost incurred due to the marginal units, $C(X) - C(X - \Delta X)$, divided by the number of marginal units, ΔX. That is, $MC = [C(X) - C(X - \Delta X)]/\Delta X$.

> *Optional* The **marginal cost of an action** at an activity level of X units is also given by taking the derivative of the cost function $C(X)$, that is
>
> $$MC = C'(X) = \frac{dC(X)}{dX}$$

If measuring the change in cost on a per-unit basis seems confusing, consider a familiar example. Imagine that you're in the supermarket, trying to decide between a 500-gram jar of peanut butter that costs $2.50 and a 1-kilogram jar that costs $4.00. Is the larger jar a good deal? That depends on how much the extra peanut butter you get

Table 3.5
Total Cost and Marginal Cost of Repairing Your Car

Repair Time (Hours)	Total Cost ($)	Marginal Cost (MC) ($/hour)
0	$0	—
1	150	$150
2	380	230
3	690	310
4	1,080	390
5	1,550	470
6	2,100	550

costs per gram. If you choose the larger jar, you're getting an extra 500 grams of peanut butter for an extra $1.50. So the extra peanut butter costs only $3.00 per kilo ($1.50 divided by one half kilo). When we calculate the marginal cost of repair time using formula (1), we're doing the same thing: we measure the additional cost of the marginal units on a per-unit basis.

Table 3.5 shows the total cost and marginal cost of repair work for each possible number of hours. Since you can vary repair work in one-hour increments ($\Delta H = 1$), formula (1) in this case simplifies to $MC = C(H) - C(H - 1)$. So the entries in the marginal cost column are just the change in cost due to the last hour of time purchased (represented graphically by the dashed arrows). For example, your marginal cost when you choose three hours of repair work ($H = 3$) is $C(3) - C(2) = 690 - 380 = \$310$ per hour.

Marginal Benefit

We can find the marginal benefit of repair work in a similar way. Suppose that $B(H)$ is the total benefit of H hours of repair work. Then when you choose H hours of repair work, the extra benefit from the last ΔH hours is $\Delta B = B(H) - B(H - \Delta H)$. Dividing by ΔH expresses this change on a per-hour basis, which gives the marginal benefit

$$MB = \frac{\Delta B}{\Delta H} = \frac{B(H) - B(H - \Delta H)}{\Delta H} \qquad (2)$$

The **marginal benefit of an action** at an activity level of X units is equal to the extra benefit produced by the marginal units, $B(X) - B(X - \Delta X)$, divided by the number of marginal units, ΔX.

More generally, the **marginal benefit of an action** at an activity level of X units is equal to the extra benefit produced by the ΔX marginal units, measured on a per-unit basis. That is, $MB = \Delta B/\Delta X = [B(X) - B(X - \Delta X)]/\Delta X$.

Table 3.6 shows the total and marginal benefits for your car repair decision. The marginal benefit corresponds to formula (2) where $\Delta H = 1$, so $MB = B(H) - B(H - 1)$.

*Optional The **marginal benefit of an action** at an activity level of X units is also given by taking the derivative of the benefit function $B(X)$, that is

$$MB = B'(X) = \frac{\Delta B(X)}{\Delta X}$$

IN-TEXT EXERCISE 3.2 Suppose you can hire your mechanic in quarter-hour increments. For repair work up to two hours, the total benefit (in dollars) is $B(0) = 0$, $B(0.25) = 30$, $B(0.5) = 60$, $B(0.75) = 90$, $B(1) = 120$, $B(1.25) = 140$, $B(1.5) = 160$, $B(1.75) = 180$, $B(2) = 200$. What is the marginal benefit of repair time (measured on a per-hour basis) at each of these possible choices?

Table 3.6

Total Benefit and Marginal Benefit of Repairing Your Car

Repair Time (Hours)	Total Benefit ($)	Marginal Benefit (MB) ($/hour)
0	$0	—
1	615	$615
2	1,150	535
3	1,600	450
4	1,975	375
5	2,270	295
6	2,485	215

Best Choices and Marginal Analysis

By comparing marginal benefits and marginal costs, we can determine whether an increase or a decrease in the level of an activity raises or lowers the net benefit. For an illustration, look at Table 3.7, which lists together the marginal benefits and marginal costs shown in Tables 3.5 and 3.6. Suppose you are wondering whether one hour of repair work is better than zero. According to the table, the marginal benefit of the first hour is $615, while the marginal cost is $150. Since 615 is larger than 150 (as indicated by the > sign in the table), one hour of repair work is better than none—you come out ahead by $465 (that is, $615 − $150). Next, suppose you're thinking about hiring your mechanic for five hours. Is the last hour worthwhile? According to the table, the marginal benefit of the fifth hour is $295, which is less than the marginal cost ($470). So it's better to hire your mechanic for four hours than for five—you lose $175 ($470 − $295) on the fifth hour.

Whenever someone chooses the best level of an activity, a small change in the activity level can't increase the net benefit. If it did, it wouldn't be a best choice! We call this the *No Marginal Improvement Principle*. This principle tells us that, at a best choice, the marginal benefit of the *last* unit must be at least as large as the marginal cost, and the marginal benefit of the *next* unit must be no greater than the marginal cost. The reason is simple.

Table 3.7

Marginal Benefit and Marginal Cost of Repairing Your Car

Repair Time (Hours)	Marginal Benefit (MB) ($/hour)		Marginal Cost (MC) ($/hour)
0	—		—
1	$615	>	$150
2	535	>	230
③ Best choice	450	>	310
4	375	<	390
5	295	<	470
6	215	<	550

If the marginal benefit of the last unit were less than the marginal cost, net benefit would be increased by reducing the activity level by one unit. Similarly, if the marginal benefit of the next unit were greater than the marginal cost, the net benefit would be increased by increasing the activity level by one unit. In either case, the original activity level (before adding or subtracting a unit) wouldn't have been a best choice.

For an illustration, look again at Table 3.7. As you saw in Table 3.3, the best choice is three hours. Notice that the marginal benefit of the third hour exceeds the marginal cost ($450 versus $310), and the marginal benefit of the fourth hour is less than the marginal cost ($375 versus $390).

In a little while, we'll see that the No Marginal Improvement Principle has many useful implications and can even help us identify best choices. Before illustrating those points, though, we'll first show how to extend its logic to situations in which action choices are finely divisible.

Marginal Benefit and Marginal Cost with Finely Divisible Actions

Now let's examine these same concepts in a setting with finely divisible choices. We'll begin with marginal benefit. Figure 3.4 shows again the total benefit curve from Figure 3.2(a). Suppose we pick any point on the curve, such as the point D associated with H hours (see the figure). The total benefit, $B(H)$, is measured on the vertical axis. When hours are finely divisible, so that the smallest amount of time we can add or subtract is very tiny, what is the marginal benefit of a mechanic hired for H hours?

Whatever the size of the smallest possible change in hours, the marginal benefit equals the "rise over run" along the total benefit curve. To illustrate, suppose the smallest

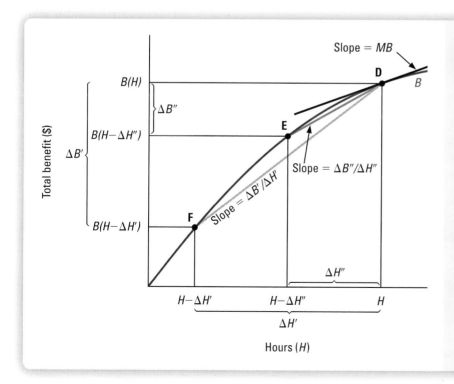

Figure 3.4

Using the Total Benefit Curve to Find the Marginal Benefit. When actions are finely divisible, the marginal benefit at H hours of repair time is equal to the slope of the line drawn tangent to the total benefit curve at point D (shown in this figure as a solid black line). The light and dark gray lines show why this is so. Their slopes are equal to the marginal benefit for two sizes of the marginal units, $\Delta H'$ and $\Delta H''$, that are not tiny. As the size of the marginal unit grows smaller, the slope comes closer and closer to the slope of the solid black line.

possible change is $\Delta H'$. Adding the last $\Delta H'$ hours of repair time involves a movement along the total benefit curve from point F to point D in Figure 3.4. This change increases the total benefit by the amount $\Delta B' = B(H) - B(H - \Delta H')$, shown along the vertical axis in the figure. The marginal benefit, $MB = \Delta B'/\Delta H'$, therefore, equals the vertical rise divided by the horizontal run along the total benefit curve between points F and D; it is the slope of the straight light gray line connecting these two points. Similarly, if the size of the marginal change is instead the smaller amount $\Delta H''$ (see the figure), the marginal benefit would then be $\Delta B''/\Delta H'' = [B(H) - B(H - \Delta H'')]/\Delta H''$, which equals rise over run along the total benefit curve between points D and E. In other words, the marginal benefit is then the slope of the straight dark gray line connecting points D and E.

In Figure 3.4, we have drawn a straight black line through point D, the slope of which equals rise over run—equivalently, marginal benefit—for very tiny changes in hours, starting from point D. (Notice that the straight gray lines would become closer and closer to the straight black line if we considered smaller and smaller changes in hours.) That black line is said to be *tangent* to the total benefit curve at point D. Accordingly, when goods are finely divisible, the marginal benefit at any given point equals the slope of the straight line that is tangent to the curve at that point. A common shorthand expression, which we'll often use, is to say that the slope of the line that is tangent to a curve at a point is "the slope of the curve" at that point. Using this language, we can restate our conclusion in this simple way: *the marginal benefit with H hours of repair time in Figure 3.4 equals the slope of the total benefit curve at point D.*

Intuitively, the slope of the total benefit curve at D captures the rate at which benefits change with small changes in the amount of repair work starting at H hours. If the curve is steep (a large slope), then benefits increase rapidly when the number of hours increases a little, and the marginal benefit is large; if it is flat (a small slope), then benefits increase slowly when the number of hours increases a little, and the marginal benefit is small. This relationship is summarized as follows:

*Optional Using calculus, the slope of the line tangent to a point on a curve can be found by taking the derivative of the curve at that point.

> **The Relationship between Marginal Benefit and the Total Benefit Curve**
> When actions are finely divisible, the marginal benefit when choosing action X is equal to the slope of the total benefit curve at X.

The same principle governs the relationship between marginal cost and the total cost curve.

> **The Relationship between Marginal Cost and the Total Cost Curve**
> When actions are finely divisible, the marginal cost when choosing action X is equal to the slope of the total cost curve at X.

Marginal Benefit and Marginal Cost Curves   By computing the marginal benefit at many different levels of H, we can graph the marginal benefit curve. Figure 3.5(b) shows the marginal benefit curve for the total benefit curve in Figure 3.4, reproduced in Figure 3.5(a). In Figure 3.5(a), we've drawn straight lines tangent to the total benefit curve at three different numbers of hours: $H = 1$, $H = 3$, and $H = 5$. The slope of each line equals the marginal benefit at each of those levels. Figure 3.5(b) plots the marginal

Figure 3.5

The Total and Marginal Benefit Curves When Repair Time Is Finely Divisible. Figure (a) reproduces the total benefit curve in Figure 3.2(a), adding tangents to the total benefit curve at three different numbers of hours ($H = 1$, $H = 3$, $H = 5$). The slope of each tangent equals the marginal benefit at each number of hours. Figure (b) shows the marginal benefit curve: note how the marginal benefit varies with the number of hours. This marginal benefit curve is described by the function $MB(H) = 654 - 80H$.

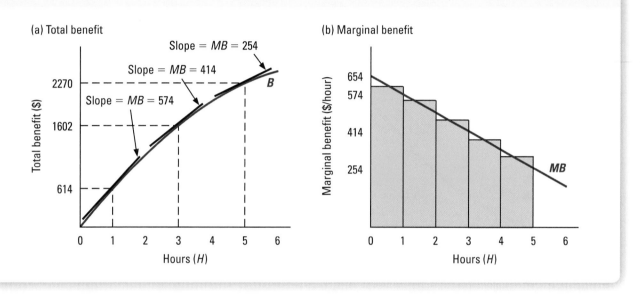

benefit at those levels and others. Note that the marginal benefit curve slopes downward. In other words, marginal benefit shrinks as the amount of repair work increases. This reflects the fact that the tangent lines in Figure 3.5(a) become flatter as we move from left to right along the total benefit curve. The area below the marginal benefit curve up to a specific activity level [for example, the five hours in Figure 3.5(b)], is just equal to total benefits at five hours. To see this we have drawn five rectangles, each the width of one hour on Figure 3.5(b). The bottom of each rectangle is the horizontal axis and the marginal benefit curve passes through top of each rectangle at its midpoint. Hence the area of the first rectangle is equal to the average marginal benefit between zero and one hour, the area of the second rectangle is equal to the average marginal benefit between one and two hours, and so forth. Adding up the average marginal benefits for the five hours equals the total benefit from five hours.

The same idea applies to graphing the marginal cost curve. Figure 3.6(a) reproduces the total cost curve from Figure 3.2(b), with the addition of tangent lines at $H = 1$, $H = 3$, and $H = 5$. The slope of each tangent line tells us the marginal cost at each of those levels. Figure 3.6(b) shows the marginal cost at those levels and others. Note that the marginal cost curve slopes upward. In other words, marginal cost grows larger as the amount of repair work increases. This reflects the fact that the tangent lines in Figure 3.6(a) become steeper as we move from left to right along the total cost curve. As with the marginal benefit curve the area under the marginal cost curve up to five hours is equal to the total cost of five hours of repair work.

We can describe the particular marginal benefit and cost curves shown in Figures 3.5(b) and 3.6(b) by the functions $MB(H) = 654 - 80H$ and $MC(H) = 110 + 80H$,

Figure 3.6

The Total and Marginal Cost Curves When Repair Time Is Finely Divisible. Figure (a) reproduces the total cost curve in Figure 3.2(b), adding tangents to the total cost curve at three different numbers of hours ($H = 1$, $H = 3$, $H = 5$). The slope of each tangent equals the marginal cost at each number of hours. Figure (b) shows the marginal cost curve: note how the marginal cost varies with the number of hours. This marginal cost curve is described by the function $MC(H) = 110 + 80H$.

respectively. How do we know this? Economists usually find formulas for marginal benefits and marginal costs using calculus. The marginal benefit is the derivative of the total benefit function, and the marginal cost is the derivative of the total cost function using calculus (the starred optional boxes in the margins are provided for those students who have taken calculus). In this book we do not assume that you know calculus, so whenever you need a marginal benefit or marginal cost function, we will tell you what it is. (If you do know calculus, you can use these functions to check your own calculations of the marginal benefit and marginal cost.) You need to understand only (a) what marginal benefit and cost mean and (b) that they are equal to the slopes of the total benefit and cost curves.

*Optional Marginal benefits are equal to $MB = dB/dH = B'(H)$ and marginal costs are defined as $MC = dC/dH = C'(H)$.

Best Choices and Marginal Analysis with Finely Divisible Actions

What can we say about the relationship between marginal benefits and marginal costs at best choices when actions are finely divisible? In that case, we have an even simpler version of the No Marginal Improvement Principle:

*Optional The No Marginal Improvement Principle for Finely Divisible Actions is equivalent to the first-order condition for a maximum for an interior value of the activity level. Specifically, when we are choosing H to maximize the function $B(H) - C(H)$, the first-order condition says that $B'(H) = C'(H)$; that is, marginal benefit must equal marginal cost.

> **The No Marginal Improvement Principle (for Finely Divisible Actions)**
> If actions are finely divisible, then marginal benefit equals marginal cost ($MB = MC$) at any best choice at which it is possible to both increase and decrease the level of the activity a little bit.

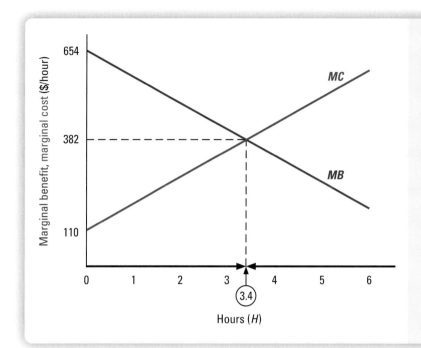

Figure 3.7

Marginal Benefit Equals Marginal Cost at a Best Choice. At the best choice of 3.4 hours, the No Marginal Improvement Principle holds, so $MB = MC$. At any number of hours below 3.4, marginal benefit exceeds marginal cost, so that a small increase in repair time will improve the net benefit (as indicated by the rightward pointing arrow on the horizontal axis). At any number of hours above 3.4, marginal cost exceeds marginal benefit, so that a small decrease in repair time will improve net benefit (as indicated by the leftward pointing arrow on the horizontal axis.)

The logic of this principle is again simple. Suppose that action X^* is the best choice. If it is possible to increase the activity level slightly from X^*, then MB must be no greater than MC at X^*. If it were greater (if $MB > MC$), then a small increase in the activity level would increase the net benefit. Action X^* would not have been a best choice. Likewise, if it is possible to decrease the activity level slightly from X^*, then MB must be no less than MC at X^*. If it were less (if $MB < MC$), then a small decrease in the activity level would increase the net benefit. Again, action X^* would not have been a best choice. Putting these two facts together, if it is possible to both increase and decrease the activity level from some best choice X^*, we must have $MB = MC$ at X^*.[8]

To illustrate, consider again your car repair problem. Recall that the best choice, as shown in Figure 3.2(c), is to hire your mechanic for 3.4 hours. Figure 3.7 combines the marginal benefit and marginal cost curves from Figures 3.5(b) and 3.6(b). Note that marginal benefit equals marginal cost (visually, the two curves intersect) at $H = 3.4$. When H is less than 3.4, marginal benefit is greater than marginal cost, so an increase in H makes you better off (as indicated by the rightward pointing arrow on the horizontal axis). When H is greater than 3.4, marginal benefit is less than marginal cost, so a decrease in H makes you better off (as indicated by the leftward pointing arrow on the horizontal axis).

Figure 3.8 (like Figure 3.2) shows the total benefit and total cost curves for this decision. Since marginal benefit and marginal cost are equal at the best choice of $H = 3.4$, the slopes of the total benefit and total cost curves at that point must be equal. That is, the tangent lines to the two curves at 3.4 hours must be parallel, as shown in the figure. If that were not the case, then by varying the number of hours in one direction or the other we could increase the distance between the total benefit and total cost curves—and thus the net benefit.

---

[8]Note that the No Marginal Improvement Principle applies only to "interior" actions, those between the minimum and maximum activity levels. At a "boundary" the activity level can either be increased or decreased but not both. This special but important case is discussed at length in the appendix.

Figure 3.8

Tangents to the Total Benefit and Total Cost Curves at the Best Choice. At the best choice of $H = 3.4$, the tangents to the total benefit and cost curves have the same slope and are therefore parallel. Thus, marginal benefit equals marginal cost.

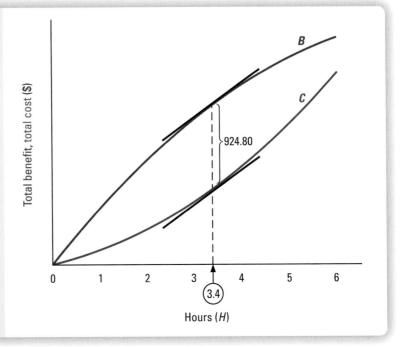

The No Marginal Improvement Principle has numerous important applications in microeconomics. Application 3.2 provides an illustration. You'll see many others throughout this book.

Application 3.2

The Value of a Highway Construction Project

Every day millions of Canadians find themselves stuck in traffic. A study conducted for Transport Canada in 2006 estimated the costs of congestion in nine selected cities as being between $2.3 and $3.7 billion dollars. Montreal and Toronto together account for roughly two thirds of the total congestion costs.[9] Similar costs are experienced by drivers in cities such as Los Angeles, London, Mexico City, and Tokyo.

One way that governments try to alleviate traffic jams is by building new highways. These projects can be costly and some governments have regulated

A Toronto traffic jam

access by charging tolls. Started in 1987, Hwy 407 in Toronto is currently 98 kilometres in length and was built at a cost of more than $2 billion. For many drivers Hwy 407 is an alternative to Hwy 401, which is one of the busiest highways in the world. In 1999 the Ontario government leased the highway to a group of private companies for over $3 billion and the consortium was given control over setting tolls for its use. Today Hwy 407 is one of the most expensive toll roads in North America with a trip along its entire length costing $21.31.[10] Is the cost worth it? To answer

---

[9] "The Cost of Urban Congestion in Canada" study was conducted by a team of consultants comprised of Delcan, iTRANS and ADEC on behalf of Transport Canada in 2006.

[10] http://www.407etr.com/About/custserv_fees.asp, accessed July 12, 2010.

that question, we need to put a dollar value on the time savings from reduced traffic congestion.[11]

If a commuter gains an hour a week because of reduced traffic congestion, what is it worth to him? Does this depend on how he would spend the hour? Would the answer be different depending, for example, on whether he would choose to take an extra hour of leisure or work an extra hour to earn more income?

Fortunately, marginal analysis can help us here. Consider an individual who is allocating his time between two activities, leisure and work, and is free to choose the number of hours he devotes to each (he either has a job with flexible work hours or can choose among jobs with different numbers of hours). The No Marginal Improvement Principle tells us that if he is allocating his time optimally, then his marginal benefit of leisure must equal its marginal cost. The marginal cost of leisure is an opportunity cost—the lost benefit from not being able to spend that hour at work, earning more money. Thus, the No Marginal Improvement Principle tells us that the value of an extra hour spent on leisure must equal the value of an extra hour spent working. In fact, the same logic applies regardless of how many different ways the commuter spends his time: any activity that he can slightly increase or decrease must have a marginal value equal to the value of an extra hour spent working. Thus, the No Marginal Improvement Principle tells us that the value of that extra hour saved in commuting equals the value he would derive by using it to work.

What is that value? If the commuter is not averse to his job, then the value of an extra hour spent working is exactly equal to his hourly wage, W. So the value of the hour saved in commuting is exactly his wage rate. What if he instead finds the marginal hour of work unpleasant? Then that hour will be worth less than W since the benefit from working an extra hour is the wage rate less the displeasure from work.[12] In fact, studies that estimate how individuals value time typically find values equal to about half of their wage rates, indicating that people are averse to work, at least on the margin.

Measured in this way, the value of time lost due to traffic congestion is enormous and explains why drivers might be willing to pay the $0.20 per kilometre that Hwy 407 users are charged. Certainly there is no shortage of drivers that value their time in excess of the toll fees, as more than 360,000 drivers a day use the highway.

Finding Best Choices Using Marginal Analysis

One of the most useful applications of the No Marginal Improvement Principle is to the problem of finding a best choice. When there are just a few possible choices, finding a best choice is a relatively simple matter. We can just compare total benefits and costs directly, as we did in Table 3.3. With more choices, but still a limited number, we could instead do this by creating a spreadsheet. However, when choices are finely divisible, it becomes much more difficult and time consuming to precisely identify best choices in this way. It is then often both quicker and more exact to find the best choice by applying the No Marginal Improvement Principle. Here we show how to do this; the appendix to this chapter and Add-On 3A contain further details.

From the No Marginal Improvement Principle we know that, in searching for a best choice, we can limit our attention to activity levels at which either (a) $MB = MC$, or (b) it is impossible to either increase or decrease the activity level. Often, there are only a few activity levels that satisfy these conditions, and we can find the best choice by comparing the net benefit levels for each of them.

---

[11]Time savings is just one component, although usually the most important, of the benefits that arise from these projects. They can also result in improved safety, reduced air pollution, and reduced fuel use.

[12]Matters are more complicated if the commuter can't adjust the amount of time he spends working. For example, if he must work 40 hours a week, then the marginal benefit from other activities need not equal the value he derives from his last hour of work (that is, the No Marginal Improvement Principle does not apply). In that case, the value of the hour saved in commuting could, in principle, exceed his hourly wage.

As an example, let's return to your car repair problem. Recall that we can describe the marginal benefits and marginal costs shown in Figures 3.5–3.7 by the functions $MB(H) = 654 - 80H$ and $MC(H) = 110 + 80H$. Worked-out problem 3.1 shows how to solve for your best choice using these functions.

WORKED-OUT PROBLEM   3.1

The Problem   Suppose that you can hire a mechanic to work on your car for up to six hours. The total cost of repair work is $C(H) = 110H + 40H^2$ and the total benefit is $B(H) = 654H - 40H^2$, where H is the number of hours. The marginal cost is $MC(H) = 110 + 80H$ and the marginal benefit is $MB(H) = 654 - 80H$. What is your best choice?

The Solution   Any number of repair hours, H, at which $MB = MC$ solves the equation

$$654 - 80H = 110 + 80H$$

The only solution to this equation is $H = 3.4$. So the best choice is either 3.4 hours, 0 hours (since it is then impossible to reduce hours), or 6 hours (since it is then impossible to increase hours). Your net benefit is \$924.80 for $H = 3.4$, \$0 for $H = 0$, and \$384 for $H = 6$ (in Table 3.3 we rounded this \$384 to the nearest \$5). So your best choice is to hire your mechanic for 3.4 hours.

IN-TEXT EXERCISE 3.3   **Suppose that you can hire a mechanic to work on your car for up to six hours. The total cost of repair work is $C(H) = 110H + 24H^2$ and the total benefit is $B(H) = 654H - 40H^2$, where H is the number of hours. The marginal cost is $MC(H) = 110 + 48H$ and the marginal benefit is $MB(H) = 654 - 80H$. What is your best choice?**

3.3 SUNK COSTS AND DECISION MAKING

Sometimes a decision is associated with costs that the decision maker has already incurred or to which she has previously committed. At the time she makes her choice, they are unavoidable regardless of what she does. These are called **sunk costs**. For example, suppose that, in addition to the charges discussed earlier, your mechanic collects a \$500 non-refundable fee when you reserve her time. If you've already paid the \$500 fee, it's a sunk cost. You cannot avoid it even if you subsequently decide not to repair your car. As another example, imagine that you still owe your mechanic \$500 for fixing your transmission three weeks ago. Now you are trying to decide whether to hire her again to work on your car before you sell it. Once again, that \$500 is a sunk cost.

A sunk cost has *no effect on your best choice*, even though it increases the total costs of repairing your car. Figure 3.9 illustrates this point. It shows the same benefit curve as

A **sunk cost** is a cost that the decision maker has already incurred or is committed to pay. It is unavoidable.

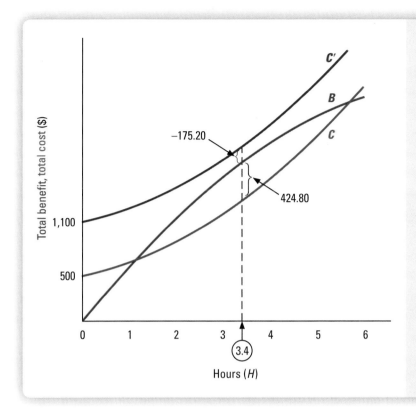

Figure 3.9

Finding a Best Choice with a Sunk Cost. This figure shows a cost-benefit comparison for two possible cost curves with sunk costs. The light red cost curve has a $500 sunk cost, while the dark red cost curve has a $1100 sunk cost. In both cases, the best choice is $H = 3.4$; the level of sunk costs has no effect on the best choice.

in Figure 3.2(a). In addition, the light red total cost curve, labelled C, adds a $500 sunk cost to the cost curve from Figure 3.2(b). (We'll talk about the dark red total cost curve labelled C' soon.) The sunk cost shifts the total cost curve up by $500, reducing the distance between the total benefit and total cost curves by $500 at every number of hours. As the figure shows, the vertical distance between the total benefit curve and the light red total cost curve is still largest at $H = 3.4$. Including the $500 sunk cost, the net benefit is $424.80 ($500 less than before).

This point also follows from thinking on the margin: because you must pay the $500 sunk cost regardless of the number of hours of repair work you choose, it has no effect on *marginal costs*. The marginal benefit and marginal cost curves are exactly the same as they were in Figure 3.7 without the $500 sunk cost, so your best choice doesn't change.

In fact, the same conclusion would hold even if the sunk cost was large enough to make your total cost exceed your total benefit. For example, the dark red cost function labelled C' in Figure 3.9 adds a $1100 sunk cost to the cost function from Figure 3.2(b). With the $1100 sunk cost, the net benefit from choosing 3.4 hours of repair work is −$175.20. Nonetheless, this is the best you can do. Given the non-refundable fee, your net loss is even greater with any other choice.

This observation reflects a general point: *sunk costs never affect a decision maker's best choice.* They are "water under the bridge," as the common saying goes. An implication of this fact is that a decision maker can always make the correct decision by simply ignoring sunk costs—that is, by pretending they are zero.

While sunk costs don't affect a decision maker's best choice, the *sinking* of a cost *can* matter. For example, until you reserve your mechanic's time, you can avoid her non-refundable fee. In that case, if the fee is large enough, it *can* change your best choice. For instance, if her fixed fee is $1100, your best choice if you have not yet made a reservation is to do no repair work. But once you have made a reservation and sunk the $1100, your best choice is to employ her for 3.4 hours. (Before you pay the non-refundable fee, it is known as an *avoidable fixed cost*. For more on avoidable fixed costs, see Add-On 3A.)

Application 3.3

The Chunnel—A Really Sunk Cost

In 1802 Albert Mathieu completed plans for connecting England and France via a tunnel under the English Channel. Work on the tunnel began in the early 1880s, only to be abandoned after 11,500 feet because of British fears of an invasion. The project languished until 1984, when Prime Minister Margaret Thatcher of England and President Francois Mitterrand of France revived it.

The ground breaking for the privately financed 31-mile "Chunnel" occurred in 1987. Construction was expected to last six years and to cost roughly £3 billion (British pounds). The project's sponsors anticipated revenue of approximately £4 billion, and a net profit of £1 billion.[13,14]

Construction of the Chunnel

By 1990, however, prospects did not look so rosy to the Chunnel's investors. Construction was taking longer than anticipated, and costs were escalating. The total estimated cost had risen to £4.5 billion, of which £2.5 billion had already been spent.

Had the project's sponsors foreseen these difficulties in 1987, their best choice would have been not to even start the project. But the £2.5 billion they had already spent by 1990 was a sunk cost, both literally (under the English Channel) and economically. It could not be recovered. Looking forward, investors were clearly better off spending another £2 billion to get the £4 billion in revenue, despite the fact that—including the costs they had already sunk—they would ultimately lose £0.5 billion.

---

[13]These projected revenues and costs were both uncertain and spread out over time. In Chapters 10 and 11, we will explain how to arrive at total benefit and cost figures in such cases.

[14]See Carmen Li and Bob Wearing, "The Financing and Financial Results of Eurotunnel: Retrospect and Prospect," November 2000, Working Paper No. 00/13, University of Essex.

1. **Maximizing benefits less costs (LO1)**

   a. Many economic decisions involve balancing benefits and costs to find a best choice.

   b. A best choice yields the highest net benefit (total benefit less total cost) of all possible alternatives.

2. **Thinking on the margin (LO2, 3, 4)**

   a. Economists often think about a choice in terms of its marginal benefit and marginal cost, which capture the way benefits and costs change as the decision changes.

   b. The No Marginal Improvement Principle says that if an action is a best choice, then a small (marginal) increase or decrease in the activity level can't increase net benefit.

   c. When actions are finely divisible, the No Marginal Improvement Principle tells us that whenever it is possible to both increase and decrease the activity level a little bit starting at a best choice, marginal benefit equals marginal cost at that choice.

   d. The No Marginal Improvement Principle can be used to help identify best choices.

3. **Sunk costs and decision making (LO5)**

   a. The size of a sunk cost has no effect on a decision maker's best choice. It is "water under the bridge." A decision maker can always make the correct choice by ignoring sunk costs.

   b. While sunk costs don't matter for a decision maker's best choice, the act of sinking a cost—which turns an avoidable cost into a sunk cost—*can* matter.

Exercise 3.1: Suppose that the cost of hiring your mechanic (including the cost of parts) is $200 an hour (she charges for her time in one-hour increments). Your benefits and other costs are the same as in Tables 3.1 and 3.2. Construct a table like Table 3.3. What is your best choice? (LO1, 4)

Exercise 3.2: Suppose that the cost of hiring your mechanic (including the cost of parts) is $200 an hour up to four hours and $300 an hour over four hours (she charges for her time in one-hour increments). Your benefits and other costs are the same as in Tables 3.1 and 3.2. Construct a table like Table 3.3. What is your best choice? (LO1, 4)

Exercise 3.3: What are the benefits you expect to derive and the costs you expect to incur from studying for the final exam in this course? (LO1)

Exercise 3.4: Economist Milton Friedman is famous for claiming "There is no such thing as a free lunch." What did he mean? (LO1)

Exercise 3.5: "If the cost of repairing your car goes up you should do less of it." Is this statement correct? If you think the answer is yes, explain why. If you think the answer is no, give an example in which the best choice is higher when costs are higher. (LO1, 2, 3, 4)

Exercise 3.6: Suppose you can hire your mechanic for up to six hours. The total benefit and total cost functions are $B(H) = 654H - 40H^2$ and $C(H) = 110H + 120H^2$. The corresponding formulas for marginal benefit and marginal cost are $MB(H) = 654 - 80H$ and $MC(H) = 110 + 240H$. What is your best choice? (LO4)

Exercise 3.7: Suppose you can hire your mechanic for up to six hours. The total benefit and total cost functions are $B(H) = 420H - 40H^2$ and $C(H) = 100H + 120H^2$. The corresponding formulas for marginal benefit and marginal cost are $MB(H) = 420 - 80H$ and $MC(H) = 100 + 240H$. What is your best choice? (LO4)

Exercise 3.8: Suppose you can hire your mechanic for up to six hours. The total benefit and total cost functions are $B(H) = 400\sqrt{H}$ and $C(H) = 100H$. The corresponding formulas for marginal benefit and marginal cost are $MB = 200/\sqrt{H}$ and $MC(H) = 100$. What is your best choice? (LO4)

Exercise 3.9: What would be the best choice in worked-out problem 3.1 (page 82) after you have made an appointment that committed you to a $1500 non-refundable fee? What would your net benefit be? (LO4, 5)

Exercise 3.10: Once the Chunnel investors (in Application 3.3 on page 84) had incurred expenses of £2.5 billion, at what projected total cost would they have decided to abandon the project? (LO4, 5)

APPENDIX

FINDING A BEST CHOICE USING MARGINAL ANALYSIS

This appendix looks in more detail at how to use marginal analysis to find a best choice when actions are finely divisible.

A TWO-STEP PROCEDURE FOR FINDING A BEST CHOICE

An **interior action**, or **interior choice**, is an action at which it is possible to marginally increase or decrease the activity level. A **boundary action**, or **boundary choice**, is an action at which it is possible to change the activity level in only one direction.

Let's begin by introducing a couple of useful terms. An **interior action**, or **interior choice**, is an action at which it is possible to marginally increase or decrease the activity level. A **boundary action**, or **boundary choice**, is an action at which it is possible to change the activity level in only one direction. (This terminology refers to whether an action is on the inside or the boundary of the set of possible actions.) In your car repair problem, $H = 0$ and $H = 6$ are boundary choices; all repair choices between those two are interior choices.

A simple way to apply the No Marginal Improvement Principle to find a best choice when actions are finely divisible is to use the following two-step procedure, which looks first at interior choices and then at boundary choices:

Two-Step Procedure for Finding a Best Choice when Actions are Finely Divisible

1. Identify any interior actions that satisfy the No Marginal Improvement Principle. If more than one interior action satisfies $MB = MC$, determine which one is best (which produces the highest net benefit).

2. Compare the net benefits at any boundary actions to the net benefit at the best interior action. The best choice is the action with the highest net benefit.

This two-step procedure is exactly the procedure we followed in Section 3.2 in finding your best choice for repairing your car. For step 1, we found that among the repair choices between zero and six hours, $MB = MC$ only at $H = 3.4$. For step 2, we then found that the net benefit at $H = 3.4$ ($924.80) was larger than the net benefit at either $H = 0$ ($0) or $H = 6$ ($384), the two boundary choices. This meant that $H = 3.4$ was your best choice.

In your car repair problem, there was only one interior action at which $MB = MC$. Sometimes, however, there can be more than one. The two-step procedure described above allows for this possibility. To follow step 1 of the two-step procedure in those cases, we simply need to compare the net benefits of any of those choices to see which is best.

TWO SHORTCUTS

Sometimes there are shortcuts to the two-step procedure that can make finding a best choice easier. Here we describe two of them.

Eliminating Boundary Choices

The No Marginal Improvement Principle can be extended to cover boundary choices. Sometimes this provides a way to eliminate some or all boundary choices as possible best choices without actually calculating their net benefits.

To see how to extend the No Marginal Improvement Principle to boundary choices, recall how we found that $MB = MC$ at an interior best choice. First, we said that if it is possible to marginally increase your activity level at X^*, then MB must be no greater than MC at X^* if X^* is a best choice. If not (if $MB > MC$), then a small increase in the activity level would increase your net benefit. Next we said that if it is possible to marginally decrease your activity level at X^*, then MB must be no less than MC at X^* if X^* is a best choice. If not (if $MB < MC$), then a small decrease in the activity level would increase your net benefit. Together, these two facts implied that $MB = MC$ at an interior best choice, since both a marginal increase and a marginal decrease is possible in that case.

At a boundary choice, though, only one direction of change is possible. The above logic can therefore be applied to boundary choices in the following way:

> **The No Marginal Improvement Principle for Boundary Choices (with Finely Divisible Actions)**   If boundary choice X^* is a best choice, then
>
> **1.** If only a marginal increase in the activity level is possible starting from X^*, then $MB \leq MC$ at X^*.
>
> **2.** If only a marginal decrease in the activity level is possible starting from X^*, then $MB \geq MC$ at X^*.

This principle provides another way to decide if a boundary choice could be best in step 2 of the two-step procedure. In particular, instead of comparing the net benefit of each boundary choice to the net benefit at the best interior choice, you can first eliminate from consideration any boundary choices that do not satisfy the No Marginal Improvement Principle for Boundary Choices. Having done so, you need only compare the net benefit of any remaining boundary choices to the net benefit of the best interior choice.

As an example, in your car repair problem neither $H = 0$ nor $H = 6$ satisfy the No Marginal Improvement Principle for Boundary Choices. At $H = 0$, it is possible to marginally increase the amount of repair work, but MB is bigger than MC, while at $H = 6$ it is possible to marginally decrease the amount of repair work, but MB is less than MC [see Figure 3.7 on page 79 or note that $MB(0) = 654 > MC(0) = 110$ and $MB(6) = 174 < MC(6) = 590$]. Thus, we know that neither $H = 0$ nor $H = 6$ is a best choice without ever needing to calculate their net benefits and compare them to the net benefit at $H = 3.4$.

Sometimes applying the No Marginal Improvement Principle for both interior and boundary choices allows us to conclude that the best choice is actually a boundary choice. Worked-out problem 3.2 provides an example.

*Optional This requirement is just the *first-order necessary condition* for a maximum at a boundary point. If we are choosing H to maximize the net benefit function $N(H) = B(H) - C(H)$ and the maximum occurs at a point where H can only be increased, then $B'(H) - C'(H) \leq 0$. If the maximum occurs at a point where H can only be decreased, then $B'(H) - C'(H) \geq 0$.

The Problem   Suppose the marginal benefit and marginal cost curves for your car repair decision are as shown in Figure 3.10(a). What is your best choice?

The Answer   The figure tells us that *MC* exceeds *MB* at every value of *H*. In this case, no value of *H* greater than zero (including *H* = 6) can be a best choice since none satisfies the No Marginal Improvement Principle. *H* = 0 does satisfy the No Marginal Improvement Principle for Boundary Choices, since only marginal increases in hours are possible at this choice. Thus, *H* = 0 is the best choice.

IN-TEXT EXERCISE 3.4   **Suppose the marginal benefit and marginal cost curves for your car repair decision are as shown in Figure 3.10(b). What is your best choice?**

Just like the No Marginal Improvement Principle discussed in Section 3.2 for interior choices, the No Marginal Improvement Principle for Boundary Choices has applications beyond just finding best choices. We'll see an example when we study so-called "corner solutions" to a consumer's choice problem in Chapter 5.

Figure 3.10
Marginal Benefit and Marginal Cost Curves for Worked-Out Problem 3.2 and In-Text Exercise 3.4.

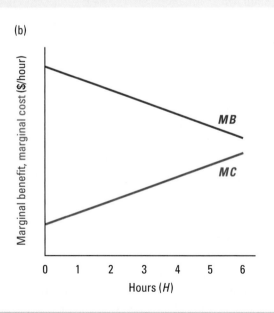

When Using the No Marginal Improvement Principle Is Enough

The two-step procedure uses the No Marginal Improvement Principle, but also involves calculating and comparing the net benefits of interior and boundary choices. We've just seen, though, that sometimes using the No Marginal Improvement Principle alone (for both interior and boundary choices) is enough to identify the best choice. Is there any easy way to know that this is the case when confronting a particular problem? The following shortcut identifies a condition on marginal benefits and marginal costs that guarantees that using only the No Marginal Improvement Principle (for interior and boundary choices) is enough to find the best choice:

> **A Shortcut to the Two-Step Procedure for Finding a Best Choice when Actions Are Finely Divisible** If *MB* grows smaller and *MC* grows larger as the activity level grows larger, then only one action satisfies the No Marginal Improvement Principle and it is the best choice.

This shortcut tells us, for example, that if *MB* grows smaller and *MC* grows larger as the activity level grows larger and you find an interior action that equates *MB* with *MC* in step 1 of the two-step procedure, you can stop; you have found the best choice.

The reason this shortcut works can be seen by looking again at Figures 3.7 (page 79) and 3.10. In each case, *MB* grows smaller and *MC* grows larger as the activity level grows larger. If there is an interior action at which *MB = MC*, as in Figure 3.7, then (1) no other interior action can have *MB = MC*; (2) at $H = 0$, *MB > MC*; and (3) at $H = 6$, *MB < MC*. As a result, no other choice—either interior or boundary—satisfies the No Marginal Improvement Principle. On the other hand, if there is no interior action at which *MB = MC*, as in Figures 3.10(a) and (b), then one and only one of the two boundary choices satisfies the No Marginal Improvement Principle [$H = 0$ in Figure 3.10(a) and $H = 6$ in Figure 3.10(b)]. That choice must be best. The same shortcut works as long as the difference between *MB* and *MC*, *MB − MC*, grows smaller as the activity level grows larger.

If you recognize that *MB* grows smaller and *MC* grows larger as the activity level grows larger, this shortcut can make finding a best choice much easier.

Optional This condition means that the net benefit, $N(H) - B(H) - C(H)$, is a strictly concave function. This follows as $N'(H) = MB - MC = B'(H) - C'(H)$ so $MB - MC$ decreases as the activity level grows larger or smaller when $N''(H) = B''(H) - C''(H) < 0$. Hence the net benefit is a strictly concave function of H. The shortcut amounts to using the *sufficient second order condition*, which says that when the function being maximized is strictly concave, then any choice that satisfies the first-order condition must maximize the net benefit function.

Economic Decision Making

part
II

Consumption Decisions

part
IIA

In the next three chapters, we'll investigate the determinants of decisions involving consumption. We'll develop a theory of consumer behaviour that helps us to understand and predict choices in a wide range of contexts and provides a solid foundation for evaluating the costs and benefits of public policies. In Chapter 4, we'll introduce some basic principles of decision making and explore the concept of consumer preferences. In Chapter 5, we'll investigate the role of prices and income in constraining consumers' available alternatives, and we'll explain how to identify a consumer's most preferred choice given these and other constraints. In Chapter 6, we'll use our theory of consumer behaviour to explore the foundations of demand curve analysis and develop methods of measuring the costs and benefits of public policies.

4

Principles and Preferences

LEARNING OBJECTIVES

After reading this chapter, students should be able to

LO1 Explain the Ranking Principle and the Choice Principle.

LO2 Illustrate consumers' preferences for consumption bundles graphically through indifference curves.

LO3 Understand the properties and functions of indifference curves.

LO4 Determine a consumer's willingness to trade one good for another by examining indifference curves.

LO5 Explain the concept of utility and compare consumption bundles by calculating the numerical values of a given utility function.

I f we know the price of a good, we can use its demand curve to determine the amount purchased. But the price isn't always obvious. Take the case of mobile (wireless) telephones. What's the price of service per minute of conversation? If you own a mobile phone, you know this simple question has no simple answer.

In June 2009 one wireless company, Rogers, offered 55 calling plans in the city of Guelph, each with different prices for different circumstances. In one plan, customers paid a monthly fee of $30.00, received 150 "free" minutes for Canadian local and long distance calls, and paid 35 cents per minute for additional time. In another plan, a monthly fee of $100 bought 800 free Canadian local and long distance minutes, with additional time again charged at 35 cents per minute.

Which price is the relevant one? Free minutes cost nothing—or do they? If a customer incurs a monthly fee of $30.00 and uses exactly 150 "free" minutes, isn't he paying 20 cents per minute? Does the customer using the $100 plan pay 12.5 cents per minute for using exactly 800 "free" minutes? And what about additional minutes? Is 35 cents the average price per minute, or something else entirely? Even if we knew the demand curve for mobile telephone services, which price would we use to determine the amount purchased? The answers to these questions are far from obvious.

Predicting consumers' choices accurately in such situations is important both to businesses and to policymakers. It requires an understanding of consumer behaviour that goes beyond simple demand curves.

A general theory of consumer behaviour is valuable for at least two other reasons. First, economists are often called on to evaluate the costs and benefits of public policies. For example, the government taxes many goods and services and uses the revenues to finance public activities such as police protection, education, and national defence. Weighing costs and benefits, do the expenditures on any given program benefit taxpayers? A general theory of consumer behaviour allows us to determine if these programs make consumers better or worse off, and by how much.

Second, in analyzing markets we often make assumptions about the properties of demand. For example, we usually assume that demand curves slope downward. Is that reasonable? Why or why not? Do demand curves typically have any other properties that might be useful in business or policy applications? A general theory of consumer behaviour can provide answers to these questions.

This is the first of three chapters on consumer behaviour. By the end of Chapter 6, you'll be able to answer each of the questions posed above. In this chapter, we lay the foundations for a theory of consumer behaviour by addressing four topics:

1. *Principles of decision making.* We'll introduce and discuss two basic principles of consumer decision making; both assert that consumers' choices reflect meaningful preferences.

2. *Consumer preferences.* We'll develop useful ways to describe consumers' preferences graphically and identify some tastes that most consumers share.

3. *Substitution between goods.* All economic decisions involve trade-offs between different objectives. We'll show how to determine consumers' willingness to trade one good for another by examining their preferences.

4. *Utility.* We'll introduce a concept called *utility.* Economists use this concept to summarize everything known about consumers' preferences, including their willingness to substitute one good for another.

4.1 PRINCIPLES OF DECISION MAKING

Three friends order dinner at a restaurant. One picks a salad, another chooses a steak, and the third selects pasta. Why do the three make different choices? They don't pick their meals at random; their decisions reflect their likes and dislikes. Economists refer to likes and dislikes as **preferences**.

What do we know about consumer preferences? Clearly, different people like (and dislike) different things. Their reasons for preferring one alternative to another may or may not be practical or tangible. Sometimes, those reasons are personal, emotional, and intangible. For example, many people strongly prefer designer jeans to equally functional jeans with unfashionable labels. Even so, each person's preferences, whatever they are, should provide a coherent basis for comparing possible alternatives. This requirement leads to our first main assumption concerning consumer behaviour.

Preferences tell us about a consumer's likes and dislikes.

The Ranking Principle   A consumer ranks, in order of preference (though possibly with ties), all potentially available alternatives.

The Ranking Principle is a simple but important assumption. It tells us that the consumer has a clear idea of what's good (something with a high rank) and what's bad (something with a low rank). It implies that the consumer is never uncertain or befuddled in making comparisons—at least not after some reflection.[1] While the Ranking Principle may not hold in all circumstances, it's a reasonable starting point for thinking about most economic decisions.

Notice that the Ranking Principle allows for ties. This doesn't mean that the consumer is uncertain or befuddled; it simply means that he likes two (or more) alternatives equally. Economists say that the consumer is **indifferent** between such alternatives.

Our second main assumption concerning consumer behaviour states that consumers follow their preferences in making decisions:

> **The Choice Principle**   Among the available alternatives, the consumer selects the one that he ranks the highest.

Another way to say this is that consumers always try to achieve the highest possible level of well-being.

These two principles are, in a nutshell, the basic building blocks of consumer theory. The rational consumers of economic theory—also known as *homo economicus*—will always follow the Ranking Principle and the Choice Principle. We'll spend the rest of this chapter, as well as Chapters 5 and 6 and portions of several subsequent chapters, exploring the many implications of these principles.

> A consumer is **indifferent** between two alternatives when liking (or disliking) them equally.

Example 4.1

Dinner Selections and the Ranking Principle

Every Tuesday evening, Ethan has dinner at his favourite restaurant. The chef knows how to cook five dishes: hamburgers, tacos, chili, pasta, and pizza. Because he cannot prepare more than three dishes at once, he always limits the menu to three choices, which he varies from day to day. Ethan is familiar with all five dishes, but he has no way of knowing which three will be available on any given day.

On one particular Tuesday, on the way to the restaurant, Ethan's thoughts turn to his potential dinner selection. After sampling each dish in his imagination, he realizes that he is definitely in the mood for tacos. He would be happy with either pasta or a hamburger (both of which seem equally appealing), and could stomach pizza, but he finds the thought of chili unbearable. With this realization, Ethan has ranked all the alternatives that might be available, thereby satisfying the Ranking Principle. Table 4.1 summarizes Ethan's preference ranking on this Tuesday night.

"The little sad faces next to some items mean they don't taste very good."

---

[1]The Ranking Principle is equivalent to two assumptions about comparisons between *pairs* of alternatives. The first, *completeness*, holds that, in comparing any two alternatives X and Y, the consumer either prefers X to Y, prefers Y to X, or is indifferent between them. The second, *transitivity*, holds that, if an individual prefers one alternative, X, to a second alternative, Y, which he prefers to a third alternative, Z, then he must also prefer X to Z. If preferences are complete and transitive, then the consumer can rank the alternatives from best to worst, as required by the Ranking Principle. Likewise, if he can rank all the alternatives from best to worst, he can make complete, transitive comparisons between pairs of alternatives.

Table 4.1

Ethan's Preference Ranking

Choice	Rank
Tacos	1
Hamburger	2 (tie)
Pasta	2 (tie)
Pizza	4
Chili	5

Ethan eventually arrives at the restaurant and inspects the menu. On this particular Tuesday, the menu lists chili, pasta, and pizza. Noticing with disappointment that tacos are unavailable, Ethan orders pasta. Based on his preference ranking, this is the best choice he can make given the available alternatives.

Equipped with a knowledge of Ethan's preference ranking, we can accurately predict the choices he would make, no matter what's on the menu. For example, if the menu lists hamburgers, tacos, and pizza, he will select tacos. If it lists hamburgers, chili, and pizza, he will order a hamburger. If it lists hamburgers, pasta, and pizza, he will choose either pasta or a hamburger. (Since he is indifferent between those two options, we cannot be more specific.)

Application 4.1

Preference Rankings, Home Video Rentals, and Netflix

On the way home from dinner, Ethan decides to spend his evening watching a movie. He drives to the nearest Blockbuster and wanders the aisles, scanning row after row of unfamiliar titles. He scratches his head in bewilderment, confounded by the prospect of choosing among so many unknowns. By reading the video jackets, he gleans some superficial information—actors, director, genre, rating, perhaps a brief plot summary, and some carefully selected snippets from reviews. Based on this information, he tries to pick the movie he would enjoy the most. However, he knows from experience that it's very hard to judge a movie by its jacket. Because he lacks most of the information required to evaluate a movie before he sees it, he is often surprised and disappointed. Ideally, Ethan would like to know how he would rank all the movies in the store *had he already seen them*. Then he would be able to make consistently satisfying choices.

Ethan's familiar dilemma creates an opportunity for profit-seeking firms and entrepreneurs to make money by providing him with useful advice. The most common approach employs reviews and ratings. For example, a variety of published movie guides provide summary information and a simple quantitative evaluation—"three stars" or "two thumbs up"—for each title. However, since different people have different tastes, no single rating system can accurately predict everyone's reactions. As all movie lovers know,

reviews reflect the tastes, preferences, and moods of the *reviewer* rather than those of the consumer.

Netflix.ca, a pioneer in online DVD rental services, which entered the Canadian market in September 2010, solves this problem by offering personalized recommendations. Whenever a subscriber logs into a Netflix account, he or she is invited to rate previously viewed movies, especially recent rentals. Netflix stores this information in an enormous database. A computer program identifies likeminded subscribers based on the similarity of their ratings. For any title that a subscriber has not yet viewed, it consults information supplied by like-minded viewers and predicts the subscriber's rating. Netflix then ranks unwatched movies by these predicted ratings and recommends the most highly ranked selections. In effect, Netflix predicts the subscriber's preference ranking and applies the Choice Principle!

Providing reliable online recommendations is an essential component of the Netflix business model. It is an important aspect of customer service, and it reduces the fees that Netflix pays to movie studios by steering customers toward lesser-known films. Does the approach work? In 2002 Netflix provided more than 18 million personalized recommendations daily. Roughly 70 percent of its rentals were computerized suggestions. Moreover, Netflix viewers enjoyed a much wider range of films than customers of conventional video rental stores.[2] At the typical store,

---

[2]The extent to which Netflix's recommendations account for this pattern is unclear. Netflix may also attract customers with stronger preferences for variety by virtue of its greater selection.

80 percent of rental activity involved just 200 titles. At Netflix, 80 percent of rental activity involved 2000 titles. Web site recommendations steered Netflix users to niche films such as *Memento*, which became the seventh-most-rented movie on Netflix (outpacing marquee offerings such as *Harry Potter* and *Moulin Rouge*), despite grossing only $25 million at the box office.

In September of 2009 the first Netflix prize (www.netflixprize.com) was awarded. The three year long contest with a one-million-dollar prize was designed to improve Netflix's movie recommendation system. Scientists and engineers around the world participated. The winning team called itself BellKor's Pragmatic Chaos. It included two members each from Canada, Austria, and the United States, and one member from Israel. The winners had to improve upon Netflix's in-house recommendation system, Cinematch, by at least 10 percent. The contest prompted the research community to solve a technically challenging problem—one that likely would have cost Netflix much more than the million-dollar prize to solve on its own. Netflix immediately announced a second contest that will provide contestants with demographic data, including previously watched movies but without ratings, to see if the researchers can predict which movies people will like.

4.2 CONSUMER PREFERENCES

Each of the applications we've considered so far has focused on a single decision in isolation—which meal to order, which movie to rent. In practice, however, our decisions tend to be interrelated in two ways. First, the enjoyment of one activity often depends on other activities. For example, many people enjoy jogging and drinking beer, but usually not at the same time. A decision to jog should not be made independently of a decision to drink beer. Second, when an individual spends money to purchase one good, less money is available for other goods. A decision to consume more of one good is therefore also a decision to consume less of another.

To make sound decisions, consumers need to consider these interrelationships. They must keep an eye on the big picture—a master plan for allocating their limited funds to competing needs and desires over some fixed period, such as an hour, a day, a month, a year, or even a lifetime. By following such a plan, the consumer ends up with a collection of goods, known as a **consumption bundle**, for the period in question.[3]

> A **consumption bundle** is the collection of goods that an individual consumes over a given period, such as an hour, a day, a month, a year, or a lifetime.

To illustrate this concept, suppose Ethan cares only for restaurant meals and movie rentals. For a given week, the combination of three restaurant meals and two movie rentals is one possible consumption bundle; the combination of one restaurant meal and eight movie rentals is another. In practice, the consumption bundle for any particular individual includes a very large number of goods.

A consumer's choices should reflect how he feels about various consumption bundles, rather than how he feels about any one good in isolation. Otherwise, he might ignore important interrelationships between decisions. In the rest of this chapter, we'll develop useful ways to describe preferences for alternative bundles, and we'll identify some characteristics of preferences that most consumers share.

How Do People Rank Consumption Bundles?

The Ranking Principle tells us only that consumers can rank consumption bundles. It does not by itself tell us how someone will rank any particular bundle relative to another. Since different consumers have very different tastes, consumer theory allows for a wide variety of rankings.

Despite their differences, consumers do have some things in common. For example, in most contexts, the typical person prefers more to less. Even if people disagree about the

---

[3]Consumption bundles are sometimes called *consumption baskets*, but in this book we'll use the word *bundle*.

relative importance of meals and movies, virtually everyone will agree that three meals and three movies are better than two meals and two movies. We'll state this observation as a third general principle of consumer decision making:[4]

> **The More-Is-Better Principle** When one consumption bundle contains more of every good than a second bundle, a consumer prefers the first bundle.

No doubt you can think of situations in which someone might have too much of a good thing. Consumer theory can accommodate this relatively rare possibility. But for the typical decision, we can reasonably assume that consumers prefer more to less.

The following example illustrates preferences for consumption bundles.

Example 4.2

Preferences for Meals

Madeline eats all of her meals at a restaurant that serves only soup and bread. The restaurant sells soup by the bowl and bread by the loaf. We'll describe her potential consumption bundles by listing the amounts of soup and bread she eats on a given day.

Table 4.2 shows some of her potential choices. The rows indicate the number of loaves of bread and the columns indicate the number of bowls of soup. Obviously, Madeline's options may include eating more than three loaves of bread or more than three bowls of soup on a given day, but we omit these possibilities to keep the table relatively simple. Each cell in the table corresponds to a single consumption bundle. For example, the arrow identifies the cell corresponding to one bowl of soup and two loaves of bread. Altogether, Table 4.2 has 16 different cells, each associated with a different bundle.

Table 4.2

Madeline's Alternatives and Preference Ranking

One bowl of soup, two loaves of bread

Bread (loaves)				
3	11	7	3	1
2	13	8	4	2
1	15	9	6	5
0	16	14	12	10
	0	1	2	3

Soup (bowls)

According to the Ranking Principle, Madeline can rank all the alternatives potentially available to her. Table 4.2 shows her preference ranking. According to this table, Madeline's top choice (ranked 1 among the 16 bundles) is to eat three loaves of bread and three bowls of soup. Her second best choice (ranked 2) is to eat two loaves of bread and three bowls of soup. Notice that Madeline generally prefers soup to bread. For example, she would rather eat three bowls of soup and two loaves of bread (ranked 2) than two bowls of soup and three loaves of bread (ranked 3). However, since she's hungry, she's happy to trade a bowl of soup for several

---

[4]This is also known as the Non-Satiation Principle.

loaves of bread. For example, she prefers two loaves of bread and no soup (ranked 13) to one bowl of soup and no bread (ranked 14). Her least favourite bundle (ranked 16) is to eat nothing.

The preference ranking shown in Table 4.2 satisfies the More-Is-Better Principle. In any single column (such as the one highlighted in yellow), the numbers at the top are smaller than the numbers at the bottom. This means that, given a fixed amount of soup, Madeline prefers more bread. Similarly, in any row, the numbers at the right-hand side are smaller than the numbers at the left-hand side. This means that, given a fixed amount of bread, Madeline prefers more soup.

WORKED-OUT PROBLEM   4.1

The Problem   According to Table 4.2, if Madeline starts with three bowls of soup and no bread, is she willing to trade one bowl of soup for two loaves of bread?

The Solution   She ranks the bundle consisting of three bowls of soup and no bread tenth among the listed alternatives. If she trades one bowl of soup for two loaves of bread, she'll have two bowls of soup and two loaves of bread, which she ranks fourth. According to the Choice Principle, she'll choose the second bundle over the first—that is, she'll make the trade.

IN-TEXT EXERCISE 4.1   **According to Table 4.2, which of the following trades is Madeline willing to make? (a) Starting with one bowl of soup and one loaf of bread, swap one bowl of soup for two loaves of bread. (b) Starting with two bowls of soup and no bread, swap two bowls of soup for three loaves of bread. (c) Starting with three bowls of soup and one loaf of bread, swap two bowls of soup for two loaves of bread.**

Consumer Preferences with Finely Divisible Goods

In Example 4.2, each consumption bundle corresponded to a cell in a table. This approach works well when the number of alternatives is small. When the number of alternatives (and cells) is large, such tables are cumbersome, tedious to construct, and difficult to read.

Suppose, for example, that Madeline's favourite restaurant sells soup by the millilitre and bread by the gram. If we allow for the possibility that she might consume up to 400 millilitres of soup and 500 grams of bread, we have 200,000 (400 × 500) bundles to consider. To depict all of the alternatives, we would need a table with 200,000 cells!

In analyzing decision-making problems involving goods that either are finely divisible or are consumed in large numbers, economists typically assume that consumers can obtain any fraction of a unit, no matter how small. This assumption isn't literally true, but in many situations it's a reasonable approximation. For example, when you prepare your own food, you can vary the amount of soup in a bowl or the size of a loaf of bread.

When goods are available in any fraction of a unit, the number of alternatives is infinite, so we can't show all the consumer's options in a table. Instead, we can represent the alternatives graphically. To illustrate, let's return to Madeline's problem. Here, we'll measure soup in litres and bread in kilograms, recognizing that she can obtain any fraction of either. Figure 4.1 shows the set of potential consumption bundles graphically. Each point on the graph corresponds to a possible consumption bundle. For example, point A corresponds to a consumption bundle consisting of three litres of soup and three kilograms of bread. Note that the layout of Figure 4.1 resembles Table 4.2 in the sense that the amount of soup is measured on the horizontal axis (columns in Table 4.2), while the amount of bread is measured on the vertical axis (rows in Table 4.2). The main difference is that Figure 4.1 shows the bundles as points rather than as cells.

According to the Ranking Principle, Madeline can rank all the alternatives depicted in Figure 4.1. However, if we tried to write a numerical rank on each point (instead of within each cell, as in Example 4.2), the graph would become completely covered with ink. Clearly, we need to find some other way to represent her preference ranking. We do this by drawing objects called *indifference curves*.

Figure 4.1

Identifying Alternatives and Indifference Curves. Starting from bundle A, taking away some soup (moving to bundle C) leaves Madeline no better off. But if we then add enough bread (moving to bundle D), she will be better off than with bundle A. Somewhere on the straight line between C and D, there is a bundle (labelled E) that is exactly as good as A. Similarly, starting from bundle A, adding some soup (moving to bundle F) makes Madeline at least as well off. But if we then take away enough bread (moving to bundle G), she will be worse off than with bundle A. Somewhere on the straight line between F and G, there is a bundle (labelled H) that is exactly as good as A. Bundles E and H lie on the indifference curve running through A.

Consumer Indifference Curves

As you learned in Section 4.1, economists say that an individual is indifferent between two alternatives if he or she likes (or dislikes) them equally. In Example 4.1, Ethan is indifferent between eating a hamburger or pasta for dinner (see Table 4.1). This indifference is something of a coincidence; more likely, he would have at least a slight preference for one of those two options. In contrast, when goods are finely divisible, we can start with any alternative and always find others that the consumer likes equally well. An **indifference curve** shows all these alternatives. When we draw an indifference curve, we declare a "tie" between all the points on the curve, much as we declared a tie between pasta and hamburgers in Table 4.1.

> Starting with any alternative, an **indifference curve** shows all the other alternatives that a consumer likes equally well.

To illustrate the concept of an indifference curve, let's return to Madeline's problem. Consider the consumption bundle labelled A in Figure 4.1. How do we go about identifying other consumption bundles that are neither more nor less attractive than A? Let's start by taking away ΔS litres of soup, leaving Madeline with bundle C (as shown in the figure). According to the More-Is-Better Principle, she likes bundle A at least as well as bundle C.[5] Suppose that, if we give her enough bread, moving her from bundle C to, say, bundle D, we can more than compensate for the lost soup, and make her better off than with A. Since A is at least as good as C and worse than D, there must be a bundle somewhere on the straight line connecting C and D that is exactly as good as A. In the figure, that bundle is E. By definition, E lies on the indifference curve running through A. To reach bundle E from bundle C, we add ΔB kilograms of bread (shown in the figure). So, starting from bundle A, adding ΔB kilograms of bread exactly compensates for the loss of ΔS litres of soup.

We can use this procedure to find other points on the same indifference curve. For example, Madeline likes bundle F at least as well as bundle A because it contains the same amount of bread and an additional $\Delta S'$ litres of soup. Suppose that, if we take away enough bread, moving her from bundle F to, say, bundle G, we can make her worse off than with A. Since A is better than G and no better than F, there must be a bundle somewhere on the straight line connecting F and G—call it H—that is exactly as good as A. By definition, H lies on the indifference curve running through A. To reach bundle H from bundle F, we take away $\Delta B'$ kilograms of bread. So, starting from bundle A, taking away $\Delta B'$ kilograms of bread exactly compensates for $\Delta S'$ extra litres of soup.

Repeating this procedure over and over, we obtain the solid red line in Figure 4.1. Because Madeline is indifferent between bundle A and all other bundles on the red line, such as E and H, the red line is an indifference curve.

Some Properties of Indifference Curves   When the More-Is-Better Principle holds, two bundles can't be equally attractive unless, in swapping one for the other, you get more of one good and give up some of another good (or at least don't get more of the second). If you get more of everything, you're better off, not indifferent. This observation leads to three important conclusions concerning indifference curves.

1. *Indifference curves are thin.* To see why, look at Figure 4.2(a). Since the red curve is thick, we can start at a bundle like A and move to the northeast, reaching a bundle like B, while staying on the curve. Since B contains more soup and more bread than A, the consumer must like B better than A. But this means the thick red curve can't be an indifference curve.

---

[5] If she liked bundle C better than bundle A, she would also like C better than some new bundle containing both a tiny bit more soup and a tiny bit more bread than A. The More-Is-Better Principle rules this out, since bundle C contains less soup and less bread than the new bundle.

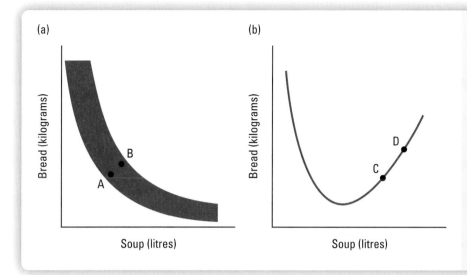

(a)   (b)

Figure 4.2
**Indifference Curves Ruled Out
by the More-Is-Better Principle.**
Figure (a) shows that indifference
curves cannot be thick, since
points A and B cannot lie on the
same indifference curve.
Figure (b) shows that indifference
curves cannot have upward
sloping segments, since points C
and D cannot lie on the same
indifference curve.

2. *Indifference curves do not slope upward.* To see why, look at Figure 4.2(b). Since part
    of the red curve slopes upward, we can start at a bundle like C and move to the
    northeast, reaching a bundle like D, while staying on the curve. Since D contains
    more soup and more bread than C, the consumer must like D better than C. But this
    means the red curve can't be an indifference curve.[6]

3. *The indifference curve that runs through any consumption bundle—call it
    A—separates all the better-than-A bundles from the worse-than-A bundles.* Since
    more is better, the better-than-A bundles lie to the northeast of the indifference curve,
    while the worse-than-A bundles lie to the southwest. In Figure 4.1, we've shaded the
    better than-A bundles light red.

Families of Indifference Curves   In Figure 4.1, we constructed an indifference
curve by finding all the bundles that were neither more nor less attractive to the consumer
than A. As Figure 4.3 shows, we can construct other indifference curves for Madeline
starting from other alternatives, such as C, D, E, and F. This figure illustrates what
is called a **family of indifference curves**.[7] Two indifference curves belong to the same
family if they reflect the preferences of the same individual. Within a family, each
indifference curve corresponds to a different level of well-being.

A **family of indifference
curves** is a collection of
indifference curves that
represents the preferences
of the same individual.

When the More-Is-Better Principle holds, families of indifference curves have two
important properties:

1. *Indifference curves from the same family do not cross.* To see why, look at Figure 4.4,
    which shows two red curves crossing at bundle A. If the dark red curve is an
    indifference curve, then the consumer is indifferent between bundles A and B. Since
    bundle C contains more soup and more bread than bundle B, the consumer prefers C
    to B, so he also prefers C to A. But that means the light red curve *isn't* one of the
    consumer's indifference curves.

---

[6]Later in this section we introduce the concept of a "bad" object or activity which makes the individual worse off. Indifference curves
for a "bad" and a "good" can be upward sloping.

[7]This is sometimes called an *indifference map*, a phrase which emphasizes its similarity to a topographic map. We explain this analogy
in Section 4.4.

Figure 4.3

A Family of Indifference Curves. This figure illustrates five indifference curves belonging to the same family, all of which represent the preferences of the same consumer. The number next to each curve indicates its rank relative to the other curves. The indifference curve that runs through bundle F receives a rank of 1 because it is the best from the consumer's perspective. The indifference curve that runs through bundle C receives a rank of 5 because it is the worst.

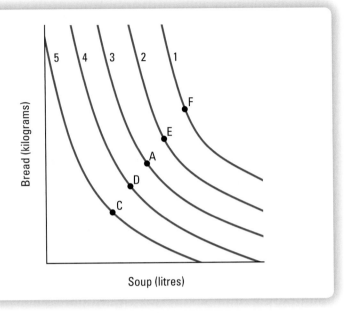

Figure 4.4

Indifference Curves from the Same Family Do Not Cross. If the dark red curve is an indifference curve, then the consumer is indifferent between bundles A and B. Since bundle C contains more soup and more bread than bundle B, the consumer prefers C to B, so he also prefers C to A. But that means the light red curve isn't one of his indifferent curves.

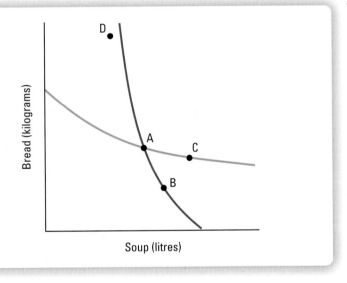

2. *In comparing any two bundles, the consumer prefers the one located on the indifference curve that is furthest from the origin.*[8] This conclusion follows from the fact that, for any bundle A, the better-than-A bundles lie to the northeast of the indifference curve running through A, and the worse-than-A bundles lie to the southwest. For example, Madeline ranks the five indifference curves shown in Figure 4.3 as follows: the curve running through F is first, the curve running through E is second, the curve running through A is third, the curve running through D is fourth, and the curve running through C is last. These ranks appear in the figure.

---

[8]This observation does *not* imply that the consumer always prefers the bundle that is furthest from the origin. In Figure 4.4, for example, bundle D is further from the origin than bundle A, but a consumer with the dark red indifference curve would prefer bundle A to bundle D.

Let's summarize what we've learned about indifference curves:

Properties of Indifference Curves and Families of Indifference Curves

Assuming that the Ranking Principle and the More-Is-Better Principle hold

1. Indifference curves are thin.

2. Indifference curves do not slope upward.

3. The indifference curve that runs through any consumption bundle—call it A—separates all the better-than-A bundles from all the worse-than-A bundles.

4. Indifference curves from the same family never cross.

5. In comparing any two bundles, the consumer prefers the one located on the indifference curve that is furthest from the origin.

Application 4.2

Preferences for Automobile Characteristics

Why does a consumer choose one type of automobile over another? An automobile is a bundle of characteristics and features—style, comfort, power, handling, fuel efficiency, reliability, and so forth. To comprehend the consumer's choice, we must therefore study his preferences for bundles of these characteristics. As with bundles of goods, we can gain an understanding of his preferences by examining indifference curves.

In one study, economist Pinelopi Goldberg examined data on purchases of large passenger cars between 1984 and 1987.[9] Figure 4.5, which is based on her results, shows the preferences of the typical new car buyer for two characteristics, horsepower and fuel economy. Since the

"Nice—but my heart's still set on a helicopter gunship."

© The New Yorker Collection 2003 Lee Lorenz from cartoonbank.com. All Rights Reserved.

curves slope downward, the typical buyer is willing to sacrifice some power and acceleration in return for greater fuel efficiency. For example, consumers are willing to give up roughly 40 horsepower to increase fuel efficiency by 50 percent (compare points A and B).

Understanding consumers' willingness to trade horsepower for fuel efficiency is important for both automobile manufacturers and public policymakers. Automobile manufacturers can use information of this type to determine whether a particular design change will improve a car's appeal to consumers. Policymakers can use it to evaluate the likely success of policies that encourage consumers to purchase fuel-efficient automobiles.

---

[9]Pinelopi Koujianou Goldberg, "Product Differentiation and Oligopoly in International Markets: The Case of the U.S. Automobile Industry," *Econometrica* 63, July 1995, pp. 891–951.

Figure 4.5

Indifference Curves for Horsepower and Fuel Economy. The typical new car buyer's preferences for horsepower and fuel economy correspond to the family of indifference curves shown in this figure. Consumers are willing to give up roughly 40 horsepower to increase fuel efficiency from 4 to 6 kilometres per litre (compare points A and B), but to give up an additional 40 horsepower fuel efficiency would have to double from 6 to 12 kilometres per litre (compare points B and C). To obtain an additional 2 kilometres per litre, the car buyer is only willing to give up 6 horsepower (compare points C and D).

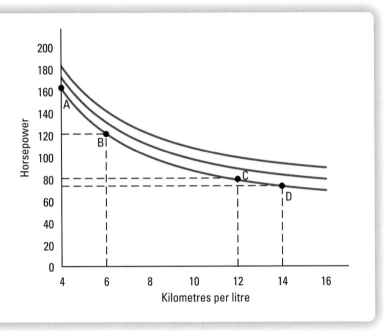

Formulas for Indifference Curves

So far, we've been studying consumer preferences using graphs. Though the graphical approach helps to build understanding and intuition, it has limitations. First, it isn't quantitative: it doesn't allow us to make precise numerical statements about consumer behaviour. Second, graphical illustrations of preferences are always incomplete. A complete family of indifference curves includes curves that run through every single point on the graph. If we tried to draw all of them, the figure would be covered with ink.

To overcome these limitations, economists usually describe consumer preferences using mathematical formulas. As you'll see in Chapter 5, this allows us to treat consumers' decisions as standard mathematical problems.

One way to describe consumer preferences mathematically is to write down the formulas for their indifference curves. For example, the formula for the dark red indifference curve in Figure 4.6 is $B = 10/S$, where B stands for a kilogram of bread and S for a litre of soup. We've graphed this formula by plotting a few points and connecting the dots.[10]

The single formula $B = U/S$ describes an entire family of indifference curves. To obtain a particular indifference curve, we simply plug in a value for the constant U and plot the relationship between B and S. Different values of U will yield different curves.

The figure shows curves for the values $U = 10$, $U = 20$, and $U = 30$. Notice that higher values of U lead to indifference curves that are further from the origin. Therefore, the value of U for the indifference curve that runs through any bundle provides an index of the consumer's well-being, or "utility" (hence the letter U), when consuming that bundle. We will elaborate on that interpretation of U in Section 4.4.

---

[10]You may recall from an algebra course that $B = 10/S$ is the formula for a rectangular hyperbola.

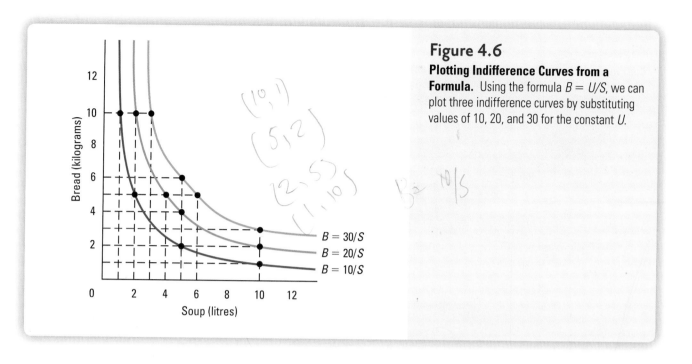

Figure 4.6
Plotting Indifference Curves from a Formula. Using the formula $B = U/S$, we can plot three indifference curves by substituting values of 10, 20, and 30 for the constant U.

IN-TEXT EXERCISE 4.2 **Judy drinks both Coke and Pepsi. Suppose the formula for her indifference curves is $C = U - 1.2P$, where C stands for litres of Coke and P stands for litres of Pepsi consumed over a month. Draw some of Judy's indifference curves. Which does she prefer, a bundle consisting of one litre of Coke and no Pepsi, or a bundle consisting of one litre of Pepsi and no Coke?**

Goods versus Bads

So far, we have focused on decisions involving things that people desire (goods). But people also often make decisions involving objects, conditions, or activities that make them worse off, and that they wish to avoid (**bads**). Think, for example, about studying for your final exam in this course. Everyone likes to get good grades, and most people like to learn, but few people enjoy studying. (There are, of course, exceptions, such as the odd ones who go on to become professors and write textbooks, but we'll leave them out of this discussion.) Most people are willing to make trade-offs between their grades and their study times. As a consequence, we can summarize their preferences by drawing indifference curves.

> A **bad** is an object, condition, or activity that makes a consumer worse off.

Figure 4.7(a) illustrates this trade-off. The vertical axis measures a student's grade on the microeconomics final exam (in percentage points). The horizontal axis measures the number of hours spent studying each evening over some appropriately gruelling period, say a full month before the exam. To construct an indifference curve, we first select a starting point. Let's take the professor's ideal: the student spends six hours per evening studying, learns the material perfectly, and receives a perfect score on the final exam.[11] This ideal is point A in the figure. Oddly, many students feel that academic perfection is not

---

[11]This option, of course, leaves no time to study for other courses, which is reasonable given the importance of microeconomics.

Figure 4.7

Indifference Curves for Studying and Grades. Figure (a) shows an indifference curve for the final exam score, a good, and hours of work per evening, a bad. Figure (b) illustrates the same preferences through an indifference curve for two goods: the final exam score and hours of leisure time per evening.

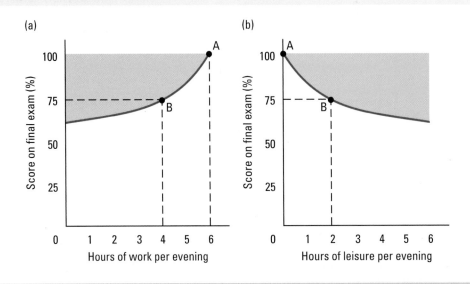

worth the complete absence of a social life. What is the student willing to sacrifice, in terms of exam performance, to get a life? According to the figure, the student is indifferent between point A and point B, which entails studying four hours per night to receive a score of 75 percent. In other words, the student is willing to accept a score that is 25 percentage points lower in return for reducing nightly study time by two hours.

Note that the indifference curve in Figure 4.7(a) slopes upward instead of downward. That is because the More-Is-Better Principle doesn't hold; the student views study time as a bad rather than a good. To compensate him for a lower grade, we have to *reduce* study time. Likewise, since he would like to score higher while studying less, the better-than-A alternatives lie in the red-shaded area to the *northwest* of the indifference curve, instead of to the northeast as in Figure 4.1.

Does this mean that we need separate theories for goods and bads? Fortunately, it doesn't. We can always think of a bad as the absence of a good. In our example, studying is a bad because it crowds out leisure time. So let's think about choosing leisure time instead of study time. That way, the student's decision involves two goods, instead of a good and a bad.

Figure 4.7(b) illustrates this idea. Its horizontal axis measures hours of leisure time per evening instead of hours of studying. Six hours of studying corresponds to no hours of leisure, four hours of studying to two hours of leisure, and so forth. Points A and B represent the same outcomes as in Figure 4.7(a). Note that the indifference curve in Figure 4.7(b) is simply the mirror image of the one in Figure 4.7(a). It slopes downward, and the better-than-A points lie to the northeast. Here, the student's indifference between points A and B reflects a willingness to give up 25 percentage points on the final exam in return for two hours of leisure time per evening.

This example is important because it suggests a way to address one of the central questions in microeconomics: How do people choose the number of hours they work? Most people regard hours of work as a bad, in the sense that they would rather do something more pleasant. We'll attack this question in Chapter 6 by studying the choice of leisure hours (a good) rather than the choice of work hours (a bad).

4.3 SUBSTITUTION BETWEEN GOODS

All economic decisions involve trade-offs. To determine whether a particular choice benefits or harms a consumer, we need to know the rate at which he is willing to make trade-offs. Indifference curves are important in part because they provide us with that information.

Rates of Substitution

In moving from one bundle to another along an indifference curve, we subtract units of one good and compensate the consumer for the loss by adding units of another good. The slope of the indifference curve is important because it tells us how much of the second good is required to compensate the consumer for giving up some of the first good.

Figure 4.8 illustrates this point using Madeline's preferences. Since bundles A and C lie on the same indifference curve, she is equally happy with either. In moving from bundle A to bundle C, the change in soup, ΔS, is -1 litre, and the change in bread, ΔB, is $+2$ kilograms. So starting from bundle A, two additional kilograms of bread exactly compensate Madeline for the loss of a litre of soup. The rate at which she substitutes for soup with bread in moving from bundle A to bundle C is $-\Delta B/\Delta S = 2$ kilograms per litre. The

Figure 4.8
Indifference Curves and Rates of Substitution. In moving from bundle A to bundle C, Madeline loses 1 litre of soup and gains 2 kilograms of bread. So the rate at which she is willing to substitute for soup with bread is 2 kilograms per litre.

expression $\Delta B/\Delta S$ equals rise over run along the indifference curve between bundles A and C; it is also the slope of the straight line connecting bundles A and C.

In Figure 4.8, the movement from bundle A to bundle C involves relatively large changes in the amounts consumed. Economists usually measure rates of substitution in terms of very small changes in quantities, leading to a concept known as the *marginal rate of substitution*.

Let's refer to the goods in question as X and Y. The **marginal rate of substitution for X with Y**, written MRS_{XY}, is the rate at which a consumer must adjust Y to maintain the same level of well-being when X changes by a tiny amount, from a given starting point. The phrase "for X with Y" means that we measure the rate of substitution *compensating for a given change in X with an adjustment to Y*. The change in X can be either positive or negative. If it is positive, we must reduce Y to avoid changing the consumer's level of well-being; if it is negative, we must increase Y (as in Figure 4.8). Mathematically, if ΔX is the tiny change in X and ΔY is the adjustment to Y, then $MRS_{XY} = -\Delta Y/\Delta X$. We multiply $\Delta Y/\Delta X$ by -1 because ΔX and ΔY always have opposite signs. Including the negative sign converts the ratio into a positive number, making it easier to interpret (since a larger positive value then indicates that the adjustment to Y must be larger to compensate for a change in X).

Intuitively, the marginal rate of substitution for X with Y tells us how much Y we need to give a consumer, per unit of X, to compensate for losing a little bit of X. It also tells us how much Y we need to take away from a consumer, per unit of X, to compensate for gaining a little bit of X.

Figure 4.9 illustrates Madeline's marginal rate of substitution for soup with bread, using bundle A as the starting point. Notice that the figure includes a line that lies tangent to her indifference curve at bundle A. (See Section 3.2 for a discussion of tangent lines.) By definition, the slope of the tangent line equals rise over run—that is, $\Delta B/\Delta S$—for very

> The **marginal rate of substitution for X with Y**, written MRS_{XY}, is the rate at which a consumer must adjust Y to maintain the same level of well-being when X changes by a tiny amount, from a given starting point. Mathematically, if ΔX is the tiny change in X and ΔY is the adjustment to Y, then $MRS_{XY} = -\Delta Y/\Delta X$.

Figure 4.9

Indifference Curves and the Marginal Rate of Substitution. The marginal rate of substitution for soup with bread at bundle A is equal to the slope of the line drawn tangent to the indifference curve running through point A times −1. For smaller and smaller changes in the amounts of soup and bread, the slope of the line between A and the new consumption bundle (first D, then E, then F) grows closer and closer to the slope of the tangent line.

small movements along the indifference curve, starting from bundle A. Therefore, the marginal rate of substitution for soup with bread, MRS_{SB}, at bundle A is simply the slope of this tangent line times negative one. We can measure the slope of the tangent line by selecting a second bundle on that line, like C, and computing $\Delta B/\Delta S$ between the bundles A and C.[12] In this case, since $\Delta B = 3$ kilograms and $\Delta S = -2$ litres, we have $\Delta B/\Delta S = -1.5$ kilograms per litre. So Madeline's marginal rate of substitution for soup with bread at bundle A is 1.5 kilograms per litre.[13]

Optional The marginal rate of substitution is the slope of the tangent line to the indifference curve (times negative one). It is the derivative of the curve at a particular bundle times negative one. Hence $MRS_{XY} = -\Delta Y/\Delta X$ and $MRS_{YX} = -\Delta X/\Delta Y$.

The value of 1.5 kilograms per litre signifies that starting at bundle A, Madeline is just willing to give up a small quantity of soup, ΔS litres, in exchange for approximately $\Delta B = 1.5 \times \Delta S$ additional kilograms of bread, or to accept ΔS litres of soup in exchange for giving up approximately $\Delta B = 1.5 \times \Delta S$ kilograms of bread. The quality of this approximation is better for smaller values of ΔS than for larger values. Figure 4.9 illustrates this point. As we consider smaller and smaller changes in the amounts of soup and bread, the slope of the line between A and the new consumption bundle (first D, then E, then F) grows closer and closer to the slope of the tangent line.

Note that MRS_{XY} is *not* the same as MRS_{YX}. For MRS_{XY}, we compensate for a given change in X with an adjustment to Y, and divide this adjustment by the change in X (that is, we compute $-\Delta Y/\Delta X$). For MRS_{YX}, we compensate for a given change in Y with an adjustment to X and divide this adjustment by the change in Y (that is, we compute $-\Delta X/\Delta Y$).[14]

What Determines Rates of Substitution?

Rates of substitution depend on consumers' tastes in predictable and intuitive ways. Figure 4.10 illustrates this point by showing the indifference curves for two consumers. Angie loves soup and likes bread, while Marcus loves bread and likes soup. How do these differences in taste affect their rates of substitution? Starting at bundle A in Figure 4.10, imagine reducing the amount of soup by one litre. Angie needs a large amount of bread, which she likes, to compensate for the lost soup, which she loves. So at A, Angie's marginal rate of substitution for soup with bread is high and her indifference curve, shown in dark red, is relatively steep (it runs through bundle B). In contrast, Marcus needs only a small amount of bread, which he loves, to compensate him for the lost soup, which he likes. So at A, Marcus's marginal rate of substitution for soup with bread is low and his indifference curve, shown in light red, is relatively flat (it runs through C).[15]

Rates of substitution also depend on the consumer's starting point. For example, in Figure 4.11, the slope of the line drawn tangent to Madeline's indifference curve, and therefore her marginal rate of substitution for soup with bread, is different at bundles A, B, and C.

---

[12]The location of this second bundle doesn't matter, as long as it's on the tangent line. Because the tangent line is straight, its slope is constant.

[13]Naturally, the value of MRS_{XY} depends on the scale used to measure X and Y. For example, since there are ten 100 ml units in a litre, substituting for soup with bread at the rate of 1.5 kilograms per litre is equivalent to substituting at the rate of 15 kilograms per litre.

[14]Though MRS_{XY} and MRS_{YX} measure different things, there is a simple relationship between them. Since $\Delta X/\Delta Y = 1/(\Delta Y/\Delta X)$, it follows that $MRS_{XY} = 1/MRS_{YX}$. So, for example, if the marginal rate of substitution for soup with bread is 1.5 kilograms per litre, then the marginal rate of substitution for bread with soup is 0.667 litres per kilogram.

[15]Note that the two indifference curves shown in Figure 4.10 cross. Unlike indifference curves that belong to the *same* consumer, indifference curves belonging to *different* consumers with different tastes always cross.

Figure 4.10

Indifference Curves, Marginal Rates of Substitution, and Consumer Tastes. The slope of an indifference curve depends on the consumer's taste. Angie attaches more importance to soup and less to bread than does Marcus. Her MRS for soup with bread is higher than Marcus's, and her indifference curve is steeper.

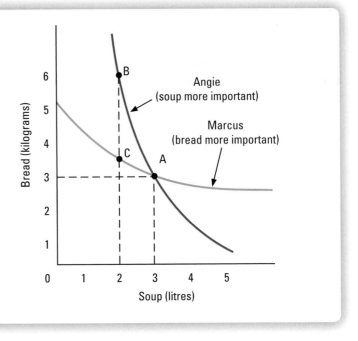

Figure 4.11

The MRS at Different Points on the Same Indifference Curve. The red indifference curve has a declining MRS. Moving in the direction of the blue arrow, bread becomes scarcer and soup becomes more plentiful, so that the MRS for soup with bread falls, and the indifference curve becomes flatter.

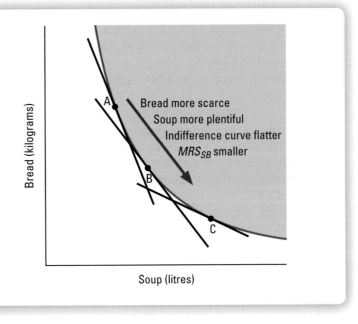

Notice that the indifference curve in Figure 4.11 becomes flatter as we move in the direction of the blue arrow, from the northwest (top left) to the southeast (bottom right). This pattern implies that MRS_{SB} declines as we progress toward bundles offering more soup and less bread (for example, from A to B to C). In other words, when soup is more plentiful and bread more scarce, less bread is needed to compensate for the loss of a litre of soup and more soup is needed to compensate for the loss of a kilogram of bread.

Why should MRS_{SB} decline when moving from northwest to southeast on an indifference curve? One important reason is that people like variety. To illustrate, suppose we start Madeline off with a great deal of bread but little soup (at a bundle like A in Figure 4.11). As a result, she becomes less enthusiastic about bread and craves soup. This means it would take a great deal of bread to compensate her for the loss of a litre of soup—in other words, her MRS_{SB} is high. Now suppose we start her off with a great deal of soup but little bread (at a bundle like C in Figure 4.11). As a result, she becomes less enthusiastic about soup and craves bread. This means it would take only a small amount of bread to compensate her for the loss of a litre of soup—in other words, her MRS_{SB} is low.

The logic of this discussion applies across a wide range of circumstances. If an indifference curve becomes flatter as we move along the curve from the northwest to the southeast (as in Figure 4.11), we will say that it has a **declining MRS**.[16] When an indifference curve has a declining MRS, the amount of one good, Y, required to compensate a consumer for a given change in another good, X, and hence MRS_{XY}, declines as X becomes more plentiful and Y becomes more scarce.

> An indifference curve has a **declining MRS** if it becomes flatter moving along the curve from the northwest to the southeast.

Notice that each of the indifference curves in Figure 4.5, which reflects the typical new car buyer's actual preferences for horsepower and fuel efficiency, has a declining MRS. For example, consumers are willing to give up roughly 40 horsepower to increase fuel efficiency from 4 to 6 kilometres per litre (compare points A and B), but they are willing to give up only 6 horsepower to increase fuel efficiency from 12 to 14 kilometres per litre (compare points C and D).

Formulas for Rates of Substitution

As we've seen, one way to describe consumers' preferences mathematically is to write formulas for their indifference curves. Another way is to write formulas for their marginal rates of substitution (MRS). An MRS formula tells us the rate at which the consumer is willing to exchange one good for another, given the amounts consumed. For many purposes, that is all we need to know about a consumer's preferences.

To illustrate, suppose the rate at which a particular consumer is willing to substitute for soup with bread is given by the formula $MRS_{SB} = B/S$, where B stands for kilograms of bread and S stands for litres of soup. In other words, if the consumer starts out with B kilograms of bread and S litres of soup, tiny changes in the amounts of bread and soup, ΔB and ΔS, will leave the consumer (roughly) on the same indifference curve as long as $\Delta B/\Delta S = -B/S$. When $S = 12$ and $B = 2$, the MRS for soup with bread is 1/6 kilogram per litre. In other words, starting with 12 litres of soup and 2 kilograms of bread, the consumer must receive $(1/6) \times \Delta S$ kilograms of bread to compensate for the loss of ΔS litres of soup (where ΔS is tiny). Likewise, when $S = 5$ and $B = 5$, the MRS for soup with bread is one kilogram per litre. In other words, starting with 5 litres of soup and 5 kilograms of bread, the consumer must receive $\Delta S (=\Delta B)$ kilograms of bread to compensate for the loss of ΔS litres of soup (where again ΔS is tiny).

Checking whether a consumer's indifference curves have declining MRSs using a formula for the MRS is usually easy. For example, when $MRS_{SB} = B/S$, the MRS for soup with bread increases with the amount of bread and decreases with the amount of soup. Every indifference curve must therefore become flatter as we move along the curve from

---

[16]The notion of a declining MRS is associated with a mathematical concept called *convexity*. Notice that, in Figure 4.11, the set of better-than-A alternatives (shaded light red) is shaped like a convex lens that bulges in the direction of the origin. Economists and mathematicians refer to this type of set as *convex*. The indifference curve illustrated in Figure 4.11 is also called a *convex function*, in the sense that the slope of the line drawn tangent to it increases (becomes less negative) as we move from left to right. These characteristics of preferences are both mathematically equivalent to a declining MRS.

the northwest to the southeast, toward bundles with less bread and more soup. Therefore, those indifference curves have declining MRSs.

For every indifference curve formula, there is an MRS formula that describes the same preferences, and vice versa. In fact, the marginal rate of substitution formula examined here, $MRS_{SB} = B/S$, describes the same preferences as the indifference curve formula discussed in Section 4.2, $B = U/S$. How do we know this? In Section 4.4, we'll see why these two particular formulas correspond to the same preferences. Generally, however, the most direct way to obtain an MRS formula from an indifference curve formula involves calculus.[17] In this book we do not assume that you know calculus. So whenever you need an MRS formula, we'll give it to you, although if you know calculus you should determine the MRS formula yourself.

Why Are Rates of Substitution Important?   We'll emphasize throughout this book that the MRS plays a central role in microeconomic theory. To illustrate its importance, let's consider a basic question that lies at the core of microeconomic theory. Suppose two people meet, and each has something the other wants. Will they voluntarily trade with each other? We can assume they will if doing so is *mutually beneficial*—that is, if they can arrange a swap that benefits both parties. Whether or not the trade is mutually beneficial depends in turn on the parties' rates of substitution. A simple example will illustrate this principle.

Example 4.3

The Lunch Box Problem and Mutual Gains from Trade

Kate and Antonio meet in their school cafeteria and examine the contents of their lunch boxes. Tossing their sandwiches aside, they focus on dessert. Kate discovers a bag of Smarties, while Antonio finds a box of Gummies. Each eyes the other's dessert. Will they exchange some Smarties for some Gummies? The answer depends on their marginal rates of substitution.

Suppose Kate's MRS for Gummies with Smarties is eight Smarties per Gummi, while Antonio's is two Smarties per Gummi. To keep things simple, let's assume that these rates of substitution don't depend on the amounts consumed. In that case, swapping one Gummi for, say, five Smarties makes both of them better off. From Kate's MRS, we know that she is willing to part with up to eight Smarties for a Gummi; since she parts with fewer than eight, she's better off. Likewise, from Antonio's MRS, we know that he requires only two Smarties to compensate for the loss of a Gummi; since he receives more than two, he's also better off. In this example, the same conclusion holds for any trade involving Y Gummies and $(Y \times Z)$ Smarties, as long as the number Z is between two and eight. (Why?)

Under some circumstances, mutually beneficial trade cannot occur. Suppose, for example, that Kate's MRS for Gummies with Smarties is two Smarties per Gummi, while Antonio's is three. Then Kate is willing to part with no more than two Smarties for a Gummi, while Antonio requires at least three Smarties to compensate for the loss of a Gummi. Meeting both of their requirements is impossible. If Kate and Antonio were to trade, say, 2.5 Smarties for one Gummi, both would be worse off.

"I'd trade, but peanut butter sticks to my tongue stud."

[17]If $B = U/S$, then $dB/dS = -U/S^2 = = SB/S^2 = -B/S$, so $MRS_{SB} = B/S$.

> **IN-TEXT EXERCISE 4.3**   **Suppose you don't know anything specific about Kate and Antonio's preferences. You do know, however, that they were given a chance to swap eight Smarties for five Gummies, and they both voluntarily agreed to this swap. What can you say about Kate's MRS for Gummies with Smarties? About Antonio's? (As in Example 4.3, assume that these rates of substitution don't depend on the amounts consumed.)**

Special Cases: Perfect Substitutes and Complements

Sometimes consumers use different products to serve essentially the same purpose. When two products' functions are literally identical, so that a consumer is willing to swap one for the other at a fixed rate, we call them **perfect substitutes**. While thinking of products that serve very similar purposes is easy—Coke and Pepsi, Corn Flakes and Special K, Sony PlayStation and Nintendo GameCube—in each case there are some differences. In practice, then, substitutability is a matter of degree. We study the case of *perfect* substitutes because it is one end of the theoretical spectrum.

Sometimes consumers use different products *together* to serve a single purpose. If two goods are valuable only when used together in fixed proportions, we call them **perfect complements**. Again, thinking of examples of products that consumers use together is easy—bicycle tires and frames, left and right shoes, and left and right gloves. However, it is not quite true that these goods are always used in fixed proportions. For example, though most people wear gloves in pairs, some view a single glove as a fashion statement, and others keep unmatched gloves as spares. So in practice, complementarity is also a matter of degree. We study the case of perfect complements because it is the opposite end of the theoretical spectrum.

Graphically, you can identify cases of perfect substitutes and perfect complements by examining families of indifference curves. We'll illustrate this point with a practical application (Application 4.3) and an example.

> Two products are **perfect substitutes** if their functions are identical, so that a consumer is willing to swap one for the other at a fixed rate.

> Two products are **perfect complements** if they are valuable only when used together in fixed proportions.

Application 4.3

Perfect Substitutability Among Pharmaceutical Products

Many examples of near-perfect substitutes can be found in the over-the-counter (OTC) pharmaceutical market, in which products are often differentiated only by dosage. Advil, for example, comes in 200-milligram regular-strength tablets and 400-milligram extra-strength tablets. Obviously, two regular-strength tablets serve exactly the same purpose as one extra-strength tablet. Moreover, as long as a consumer can break a tablet in half, one extra-strength tablet serves exactly the same purpose as two regular-strength tablets. In practice, however, the degree of substitutability may not be perfect;

splitting an extra-strength pill in two may be difficult, and some consumers may incorrectly believe that "extra-strength" implies characteristics other than (or in addition to) a higher dosage. Even so, these products are highly substitutable. For illustrative purposes, we'll assume they are perfectly interchangeable.

As a rule, families of indifference curves for perfectly substitutable products are drawn as parallel straight lines. Figure 4.12 shows the indifference curves for regular-strength and extra-strength Advil tablets. Notice that they have a common slope of $-\frac{1}{2}$. Regardless of the starting point, a consumer must receive one extra-strength tablet to compensate for the loss of two regular-strength tablets. Since the consumer cares only about the total number of milligrams of Advil purchased, the marginal rate of substitution for regular tablets with extra-strength tablets is necessarily fixed at one-half extra-strength per regular strength tablet.

Figure 4.12

Indifference Curves for Perfect Substitutes. The indifference curves for perfect substitutes are straight lines. Because the consumer only cares about the total amount of Advil purchased, two 200-milligram extra-strength tablets are a perfect substitute for one 400-milligram extra-strength tablet.

Example 4.4

Perfect Complementarity between Left and Right Shoes

Figure 4.13 shows a family of indifference curves for left and right shoes, assuming they are perfect complements. For every bundle on the dashed 45-degree line that runs through the origin, the number of left shoes equals the number of right shoes. Consider the point corresponding to five left shoes and five right shoes. What bundles would a consumer find equally attractive? Since extra right shoes are worthless on their own, the consumer would gain nothing from their addition without left shoes and so is therefore indifferent between five left shoes and five right shoes, five left shoes and six right shoes, five left shoes and seven right shoes, and so forth. This conclusion implies that the indifference curve is vertical above the 45-degree line. Similarly, the consumer would gain nothing from the addition of extra left shoes without right shoes and is therefore indifferent between five left shoes and five right shoes, six left shoes and five right shoes, seven left shoes and five right shoes, and so forth. This conclusion implies that the indifference curve is horizontal below the 45-degree line. Combining these observations, we obtain an L-shaped indifference curve, with a "kink" where it intersects the 45-degree line, as shown in the figure.

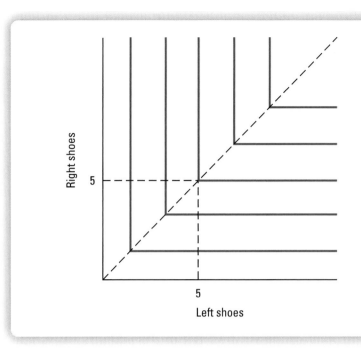

Figure 4.I3

Indifference Curves for Perfect Complements. Indifference curves for perfect complements are L-shaped. Assuming that a left shoe is of no value without a right shoe and vice versa, a consumer's indifference curves for left and right shoes are vertical above the 45-degree line and horizontal below it, with a kink where they meet.

In the real world, product pairs tend to fall somewhere along the spectrum between perfect substitutes and perfect complements. When consumers' indifference curves are reasonably close to straight lines, the degree of substitutability between products is high and the degree of complementarity is low. When consumers' indifference curves bend sharply, the degree of complementarity between products is high, and the degree of substitutability is low.

4.4 UTILITY

To summarize everything that is known about a consumer's preferences, economists use a concept called **utility**. This is simply a numeric value indicating the consumer's relative well-being—higher utility indicates greater satisfaction than lower utility. The word *utility* reminds us that our objective is to capture the use or benefit that someone receives from the goods he consumes. Every time you rate something from, say, one to ten points, or one to five stars, you're using a utility scale.

> **Utility** is a numeric value indicating the consumer's relative well-being. Higher utility indicates greater satisfaction than lower utility.

To describe a consumer's preferences between consumption bundles, we assign a utility value to each bundle; the better the bundle, the higher the value. To determine which of any two bundles is better, we can simply compare their utility values. The consumer prefers the one with the higher value and is indifferent between bundles when their values are identical.

We assign utility values to consumption bundles using mathematical formulas called **utility functions**. For example, the formula $U(S, B) = 2S + 5 (S \times B)$ assigns utility values to consumption bundles based on litres of soup, S, and kilograms of bread, B. For this function, $U(12, 3)$, the utility value associated with 12 litres of soup and 3 kilograms of bread is

> A **utility function** is a mathematical formula that assigns a utility value to each consumption bundle.

$204 = (2 \times 12) + (5 \times 12 \times 3)$. Likewise, $U(9, 4)$, the utility value associated with 9 litres of soup and 4 kilograms of bread is $198 = (2 \times 9) + (5 \times 9 \times 4)$. And $U(17, 2)$, the utility value associated with 17 litres of soup and 2 kilograms of bread, is $204 = (2 \times 17) + (5 \times 17 \times 2)$. In this case, the utilities associated with the first and third bundles are the same, and both are higher than the utility associated with the second bundle. Therefore, the consumer is indifferent between the first and third bundles, and prefers both to the second bundle.

WORKED-OUT PROBLEM   4.2

The Problem   Asha enjoys reading books and watching movies. Her utility function is $U(M, B) = M \times B^2$, where M stands for the number of movies and B stands for the number of books enjoyed during a month. How does Asha rank the following bundles? (1) 4 movies and 5 books, (2) 10 movies and 4 books, (3) 25 movies and 2 books, (4) 40 movies and 1 book, (5) 100 movies and no books.

The Solution   Applying Asha's utility function, we find that (1) $U(4, 5) = 100$, (2) $U(10, 4) = 160$, (3) $U(25, 2) = 100$, (4) $U(40, 1) = 40$, and (5) $U(100, 0) = 0$. Therefore, Asha ranks the bundles listed in the problem, in order of preference, as follows: first, 10 movies and 4 books; next, either 4 movies and 5 books or 25 movies and 2 books (she is indifferent between those two bundles); next, 40 movies and 1 book; and last, 100 movies and no books.

IN-TEXT EXERCISE 4.4   **Bert enjoys both Coke and ginger ale. His preferences correspond to the utility function $U(C, G) = C + 3\sqrt{G}$, where C stands for litres of Coke and G stands for litres of ginger ale consumed in a month. How does Bert rank the following alternatives? (1) 5 litres of Coke and 4 litres of ginger ale, (2) 20 litres of Coke and no ginger ale, (3) 10 litres of ginger ale and no Coke, (4) 8 litres of Coke and 7 litres of ginger ale, (5) 1 litre of Coke and 6 litres of ginger ale.**

From Indifference Curves to Utility Functions and Back

Of course, consumers don't actually have utility functions, they have preferences. A utility function is a formula that an economist develops to summarize consumer preferences. Starting with information about preferences, then, how do we derive an appropriate utility function?

Naturally, a utility function must assign the same value to all the bundles on a single indifference curve. So all we need to do is choose a utility value for each indifference curve, picking higher values for indifference curves that correspond to higher levels of well-being.

When the More-Is-Better Principle holds, we assign higher utility values to indifference curves that are further from the origin. For example, look at Figure 4.14, which shows five indifference curves (labelled I_1 through I_5) for someone who consumes soup and bread. As shown in the figure, we've assigned utility values of 9 to I_1, 12 to I_2, 14 to I_3, 17 to I_4, and 20 to I_5. Between any two bundles, the consumer will always prefer the one with the higher utility value, because it lies on a higher indifference curve. The

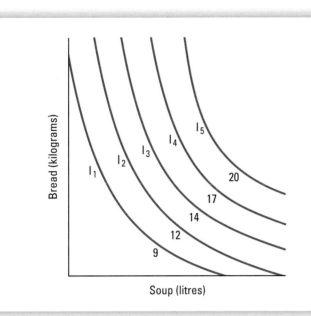

Figure 4.14

Representing Preferences with a Utility Function. To create a utility function, we assign the same value to all points on a single indifference curve, using higher values for indifference curves that correspond to higher levels of well-being. Following the More-Is-Better Principle, we assign higher values to indifference curves that are further from the origin.

consumer will be indifferent between any two bundles with the same utility value, because they lie on the same indifference curve. Thus, the utility function faithfully represents the consumer's preferences.

We can also start with a utility function and construct the associated indifference curves. To find an indifference curve, all we need to do is fix a level of utility and identify all the bundles that will deliver it. To illustrate, take the utility function $U(S, B) = S \times B$. Choose any utility value, say 10. The consumer will be indifferent between all combinations of soup and bread that satisfy the equation $10 = S \times B$. We can rewrite this equation as $B = 10/S$, a formula that describes a single indifference curve. If we select any other utility value, call it U, the consumer will be indifferent between all combinations of soup and bread that satisfy the formula $U = S \times B$, so the formula $B = U/S$ describes the associated indifference curve. In other words, the utility function $U(S, B) = S \times B$ and the indifference curve formula $B = U/S$ summarize the same preferences. We graphed these indifference curves in Figure 4.6 (page 105).

Figure 4.15 illustrates another way to think about the relation between utility functions and indifference curves. It is the same as Figure 4.14, except that we've laid the figure on its side and added a third dimension (the vertical axis) measuring Madeline's utility. For any consumption bundle, like A, Madeline's level of utility corresponds to the height of the hill pictured in the figure. The light red curve shows all the points on the hill that are just as high as the point corresponding to bundle A. The dark red curve directly below it (at "ground level") shows the combinations of soup and bread that are associated with the points on the light red curve. The dark red curve is the indifference curve passing through bundle A.

If you've gone on a camping trip or taken a geography course, you may have seen contour lines on topographic maps. Each contour line shows all the locations that are at a single elevation. Figure 4.14 is essentially a topographic map for the hill shown in Figure 4.15; each indifference curve in Figure 4.14 is a contour line for a particular elevation.

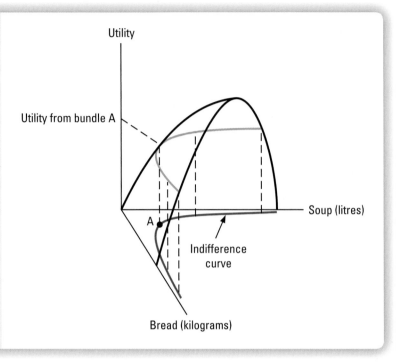

Figure 4.15
Deriving Indifference Curves from a Utility Function. For any consumption bundle, like A, Madeline's utility corresponds to the height of the utility "hill." The indifference curve passing through A consists of all the bundles for which the height of the hill is the same.

Ordinal versus Cardinal Utility

Information about preferences is **ordinal** if it allows us to determine only whether one alternative is better or worse than another. **Cardinal** information tells us something about the *intensity* of those preferences—it answers the question "How much worse?" or "How much better?"

Information about preferences can be either **ordinal** or **cardinal**. Ordinal information allows us to determine only whether one alternative is better or worse than another. Cardinal information tells us something about the *intensity* of those preferences—it answers the question "How much worse?" or "How much better?"

During the nineteenth century and for much of the twentieth century, many prominent scholars, including the influential moral philosopher Jeremy Bentham (1748–1832), thought that utility functions should provide cardinal information about preferences. According to this view, people are "pleasure machines"—they use consumption goods as inputs to produce utility as an output. Bentham and others argued that the aim of public policy should be to maximize the total utility generated through economic activity.

In modern microeconomic theory, utility functions are only intended to summarize ordinal information. If one consumption bundle has a utility value of 10 and a second has a utility value of five, we know the consumer prefers the first to the second, but it doesn't necessarily make him twice as happy. Today, most economists believe that there's no meaningful way to measure human well-being on an absolute scale, so they reject cardinal interpretations of utility.[18] To understand why this is so, think about your own state of mind. You can probably say if you're generally happier today than you were yesterday; that's an ordinal statement. But you can't *measure* the difference in your happiness.

From the modern "ordinalist" perspective, the scale used to measure utility is completely arbitrary. Netflix uses a five-star system for rating movies, but it could just as

---

[18]Though psychologists have developed reasonably reliable measures of human happiness, these measures also convey ordinal information, rather than meaningful cardinal information. In other words, they can tell us whether someone is happier in one situation than another, but they measure the difference in happiness on an arbitrary scale.

easily have used seven happy faces or ten bowls of popcorn. Likewise, when we measure the height of the consumer's utility hill (like the one shown in Figure 4.15), we make up the scale and units of measurement. So, for example, in Figure 4.14, we assigned a utility value of 20 to the indifference curve labelled I_5, but we could have just as well used 21,200, 2,000,000, or any other number greater than the value assigned to I_4.

When we change the scale used to measure utility, the consumer's family of indifference curves, and therefore his preferences, remain unchanged. To illustrate this principle, let's examine the utility function $U(S, B) = 0.5 \times S \times B$, which assigns exactly half as many "utils" (units of utility) to each consumption bundle as the utility function $U(S, B) = S \times B$, considered above. With this new function, the consumer's indifference curve formula is $B = 2U/S$ instead of $B = U/S$. For any given value of U, these two formulas generate different indifference curves. But if we plug any value of U into the formula $B = 2U/S$, and plug a value twice as large into the formula $B = U/S$, we generate the *same* indifference curve. Therefore, the two formulas generate the same family of indifference curves.

Utility Functions and the Marginal Rate of Substitution

Because the marginal rate of substitution tells us the rate at which a consumer is willing to make trade-offs, it's a central concept in microeconomics. In this section, we'll introduce a useful shortcut for deriving an MRS formula, starting from a utility function.

The shortcut involves a new concept, known as **marginal utility**. Marginal utility is defined as the change in the consumer's utility resulting from the addition of a very small amount of some good, divided by the amount added. Mathematically, if ΔX is the tiny change in the amount of a good X and ΔU is the resulting change in the utility value, then the marginal utility of X, written MU_X, is

$$MU_X = \frac{\Delta U}{\Delta X}$$

Usually, the calculation of marginal utility requires calculus. However, as illustrated below, there are many special cases for which simple algebra suffices.

The marginal rate of substitution for any good, X, with any other good, Y, equals the ratio of the marginal utility of X to the marginal utility of Y. In mathematical terms,

$$MRS_{XY} = \frac{MU_X}{MU_Y}$$

Why does this relationship hold? A small change in X, call it ΔX, causes utility to change by approximately $MU_X \Delta X$. Similarly, a small change in Y, call it ΔY, causes utility to change by approximately $MU_Y \Delta Y$. If the combination of these changes leaves us on the same indifference curve, then utility is unaffected, so the changes offset: $MU_X \Delta X = -MU_Y \Delta Y$. Rearranging this formula, we learn that along an indifference curve, $-\Delta Y/\Delta X = MU_X/MU_Y$. Suppose, for example, that an additional unit of X adds 12 utils ($MU_X = 12$) and an additional unit of Y adds 4 utils ($MU_Y = 4$). While utils are meaningless units, a comparison of these numbers nevertheless tells us that the consumer is just willing to exchange one unit of X for three units of Y. Sacrificing one unit of X reduces utility by 12 utils, but gaining three units of Y increases utility by 12 utils, so the exchange does not alter the consumer's well-being. Therefore, the MRS for X with Y is 3. The preceding formula gives the same answer: $MU_X/MU_Y = 3$.

Jeremy Bentham (1748–1832) is regarded as one of the founders of the school of thought known as "utilitarianism." He continues to be a physical presence at University College London, where, at his request, his skeleton is preserved in a wooden cabinet, dressed in his own clothes and adorned with a wax head. According to one unconfirmed legend, the cabinet is solemnly wheeled into each meeting of the College Council, and the minutes record his presence as "Jeremy Bentham—present but not voting."

Marginal utility is the change in the consumer's utility resulting from the addition of a very small amount of some good, divided by the amount added.

*Optional **Marginal utility** can be found using calculus by finding the partial derivative of the utility function. The marginal utility of X is given by $MU_X = \partial U(X,Y)/\partial X$.

To illustrate the use of the shortcut, let's again consider the utility function $U(S, B) = S \times B$.[19] For this function, the marginal utility of soup is B (adding ΔS litres of soup increases the utility value by $B \times \Delta S$ units, so $\Delta U/\Delta S = B$), and the marginal utility of bread is S (adding ΔB kilograms of bread increases the utility value by $S \times \Delta B$ units, so $\Delta U/\Delta B = S$). Therefore, for this utility function, $MRS_{SB} = B/S$ kilograms per litre. As we've explained, the formula $B = U/S$ describes the indifference curves associated with this utility function. Consequently, the formula $MRS_{SB} = B/S$ and the indifference curve formula $B = U/S$ correspond to the same preferences, just as we claimed on page 112.

The concept of marginal utility, though useful, is also the source of much confusion. From our discussion of ordinal and cardinal utility, it should be clear that, by itself, the marginal utility associated with a particular good is completely meaningless. Suppose that Madeline's marginal utility of soup (which we will write as MU_S) is five. You should be asking yourself, five what? Happy faces? Gold stars? Utils? None of these units has any practical meaning.

If marginal utility is not meaningful by itself, how can the ratio of marginal utilities give us the marginal rate of substitution, which is meaningful? The answer is that when we change the units used to measure utility, we don't change the *ratio* of marginal utilities. To illustrate this point, let's change a utility scale by using the utility function $U(S, B) = 2 \times S \times B$, instead of $U(S, B) = S \times B$, as above. For the new utility function, the marginal utility of soup is $2B$ instead of B (adding ΔS litres of soup increases the utility value by $2 \times B \times \Delta S$ units, so $\Delta U/\Delta S = 2B$), and the marginal utility of bread is $2S$ instead of S (adding ΔB kilograms of bread increases the utility value by $2 \times S \times \Delta B$ units, so $\Delta U/\Delta B = 2S$). However, the *ratio* of marginal utilities, and therefore the marginal rate of substitution for soup with bread, remains unchanged: $MRS_{SB} = MU_S/MU_B = B/S$ kilograms per litre.

WORKED-OUT PROBLEM 4.3

The Problem Bobby enjoys reading books and watching movies. His utility function is $U(M, B) = M + 2B$. Find a formula for his indifference curves. What do these curves look like? What is Bobby's marginal utility of movies? Of books? What is his MRS for movies with books? From his perspective, are movies and books perfect substitutes, perfect complements, or something else?

The Solution Fixing any utility value U, Bobby will be indifferent between all combinations of books and movies that satisfy the equation $U = M + 2B$. To find the formula for his indifference curves, we just rearrange this: $B = U/2 - M/2$. So each of his indifference curves is a straight line with a slope of $-\frac{1}{2}$ (just like the ones in Figure 4.12, page 113). From his utility function, we see that $MU_M = 1$ (adding ΔM movies increases the utility value by ΔM units, so $\Delta U/\Delta M = 1$) and $MU_B = 2$ (adding ΔB books increases the utility value by $2 \times \Delta B$ units, so $\Delta U/\Delta B = 2$). His MRS for movies with books is therefore $MU_M/MU_B = \frac{1}{2}$ book per movie—the same as the slope of his indifference curves, times negative one. From his perspective, movies and books are perfect substitutes.

[19]A utility function of the form $U(X, Y) = XY$ is called a Cobb-Douglas utility function. A more general form of the Cobb-Douglas utility function is given by $U(X, Y) = AX^\alpha Y^\beta$ where A, α, and β are positive constants. It is frequently used in the study of consumer choice and exhibits both positive marginal utility for both goods and a diminishing marginal rate of substitution.

IN-TEXT EXERCISE 4.5   Bert's preferences for Coke and ginger ale correspond to the utility function given in in-text exercise 4.4 (page 116). Find a formula for his indifference curves. Pick a level of utility, plot a few points on the corresponding indifference curve, and sketch the curve. From Bert's perspective, are Coke and ginger ale perfect substitutes, perfect complements, or something else? How would your answer change if his preferences corresponded to the utility function $U(C, G) = C + 3\sqrt{G} + 4$? What about $U(C, G) = (C + 3\sqrt{G})^2$? Or $U(C, G) = 2(C + 3\sqrt{M})$?

Application 4.4

Ranking Canadian Universities

Since 1991, *Maclean's* magazine has ranked Canadian universities. These rankings are used by students and parents to make decisions about which university to attend, by universities in their internal decisions and publications, and by politicians who control the funding of universities. In 2009 *Maclean's* ranked 47 universities in three categories classified as Primary undergraduate (21), Comprehensive (11), and Medical Doctoral (15). In ranking the universities *Maclean's* used six broad areas and either 13 or 14 (in the case of Medical Doctoral) indicators. The indicators are all weighted (weights add up to 100 percent) and a score is calculated. The broad areas and their weights (in parentheses) are Student/Classes (20 percent), Faculty (18 percent), Resources (12 percent), Student Support (13 percent), Library (15 percent), and Reputation (22 percent). The formula is, in effect, a utility function, and the scores are utility values. *Maclean's* "utility function" is only one of many possible formulas that could be used to evaluate universities.

Knowing how the different indicators are weighted allows one to determine changes in an indicator that would leave a university's total score unchanged. For example, an increase in the student-to-faculty ratio (which would lower the overall score) could be exactly offset by an increase in the number of books per student in the university's library. Knowing the formula, or utility function, that *Maclean's* is using allows universities to manipulate their final score by making tradeoffs between the various indicators. In practice, the marginal rate of substitution between the various indicators could be calculated.

The *Maclean's* rankings are not without controversy. Not surprisingly, the "utility function" used by *Maclean's* would not be that chosen by most of the universities (except perhaps the school at the top of the rankings). The 16th annual rankings (2007) were boycotted by 26 universities that refused to make public performance indicators available in time to complete the rankings. As a result *Maclean's* changed their formula for ranking schools to use only publically available information. *Maclean's* now lists as additional information some indicators that were used in the past but are not released by some of the schools.

Do the *Maclean's* rankings actually affect the decisions of students, politicians, and the universities themselves? While university decisions and lobbying for funding could be said to have been affected by the rankings, the decision of students to attend university has, for the most part, been unaffected. Qi Kong and Michael Veall of McMaster University wrote a paper in which they found that, except in the case of the Medical-Doctoral category, universities that saw an improvement in their ranking were unable to attract students with higher admission averages. Neither did they find that the enrolment share increased for those universities with high rankings.[20]

---

[20]Qi Kong and Michael R. Veall, "Does the *Maclean's* Ranking Matter?", *Canadian Public Policy* 31, September 2005, pp. 231–242.

1. **Principles of decision making (LO1)**

   a. Consumer preferences tell us about people's likes and dislikes.

   b. Consumer theory assumes that consumers' preferences are coherent, in the sense that they respect the Ranking Principle. It also assumes that their decisions reflect preferences, in the sense that they respect the Choice Principle.

2. **Consumer preferences (LO2, 3)**

   a. Since many consumer decisions are interdependent, decision makers need to compare consumption bundles.

   b. For the typical decision, it's reasonable to assume that consumers prefer more to less. In summarizing the properties of indifference curves below, we make this assumption.

   c. Indifference curves for goods are thin and never slope upward.

   d. The indifference curve that runs through any consumption bundle, call it X, is the boundary that separates all the better-than-X alternatives from all other options. The better-than-X alternatives lie to the northeast of the indifference curve. The worse-than-X alternatives lie to the southwest.

   e. Indifference curves from the same family never cross.

   f. In comparing any two alternatives, the consumer prefers the one located on the indifference curve furthest from the origin.

   g. One way to describe consumers' preferences mathematically is to write formulas for their indifference curves.

   h. For every bad there is an associated good. We can apply consumer theory to bads by thinking about the associated goods.

3. **Substitution between goods (LO4)**

   a. The marginal rate of substitution varies from one consumer to another according to the relative importance the consumer attaches to the goods in question.

   b. As we move along an indifference curve from the northwest to the southeast, the curve usually becomes flatter. Equivalently, the amount of one good, Y, required to compensate a consumer for a fixed change in another good, X—and hence the MRS for X with Y—declines as X becomes more plentiful and Y becomes more scarce. This feature is known as a declining MRS.

   c. A second way to describe consumers' preferences mathematically is to write formulas for their marginal rates of substitution.

   d. Whether or not two individuals can engage in mutually beneficial trade depends on their marginal rates of substitution.

   e. The indifference curves for perfect substitutes are straight lines.

   f. The indifference curves for perfect complements are L-shaped—vertical above a kink point, and horizontal below it.

4. **Utility (LO5)**

   a. Economists use the concept of utility to summarize everything that is known about a consumer's preferences.

   b. We can create a utility function from a family of indifference curves by assigning the same utility value to all bundles on an indifference curve, with higher values assigned to indifference curves that correspond to higher levels of well-being. We can construct indifference curves from a utility function by setting the function equal to a constant.

   c. In modern microeconomic theory, utility functions are only intended to summarize ordinal information.

   d. By itself, the marginal utility of a good does not measure anything meaningful. However, the ratio of the marginal utilities for two goods is equal to the marginal rate of substitution between them.

ADDITIONAL EXERCISES

Exercise 4.1: After reading this chapter, a student complains, "What I like and dislike isn't always the same; it depends on my mood." Is this a problem with consumer preference theory? Why or why not? (LO2)

Exercise 4.2: Suppose there are two types of food, meat and bread. Draw indifference curves for the following consumers. (LO3)

a. Ed likes variety and prefers to eat meat and bread together.

b. Francis dislikes variety; she likes to eat the same thing all the time.

c. Mia is a vegetarian who doesn't care (one way or the other) about meat.

d. Taka, a sumo wrestler, cares only about the number of calories he consumes; he wants to consume as many calories as possible.

e. Larry loves to eat and enjoys variety, but he also wants to lose weight. He therefore thinks that food is a good at low quantities, and a bad at high quantities.

Exercise 4.3: Gary has two children, Kevin and Dora. Each one consumes "yummies" and nothing else. Gary loves both children equally. For example, he is equally happy when Kevin has two yummies and Dora has three, or when Kevin has three yummies and Dora has two. But he is happier when their consumption is more equal. Draw Gary's indifference curves. What would they look like if he loved one child more than the other? (LO2)

Exercise 4.4: As in the previous question, suppose that Gary loves Kevin and Dora equally. What is his marginal rate of substitution between Kevin's yummies and Dora's yummies when each has the same number of yummies? Does it become larger or smaller when Kevin has more yummies than Dora? What about when Dora has more yummies than Kevin? (LO2, 4)

Exercise 4.5: For lunch, Ada prefers to eat soup and bread in fixed proportions. When she eats X litres of soup, she prefers to eat $\sqrt{X}$ kilograms of bread. If she has X litres of soup and more than $\sqrt{X}$ kilograms of bread, she eats all the soup along with $\sqrt{X}$ kilograms of bread, and throws the extra bread away. If she has X litres of soup and fewer than $\sqrt{X}$ kilograms of bread (say Y kilograms), she eats all the bread along with Y^2 litres of soup and throws the extra soup away. Draw Ada's indifference curves between soup and bread. (LO2)

Exercise 4.6: Think of five examples of bads. In each case, what is the associated good? (For example, air pollution is a bad; clean air is the associated good.) (LO2)

Exercise 4.7: Ryan hates both water pollution and air pollution. He thinks that the harm caused when water pollution increases by a fixed amount rises with the total amount of water pollution, and that the harm caused when air pollution increases by a fixed amount rises with the total amount of air pollution. Sketch Ryan's indifference curves for the amount of water pollution and the amount of air pollution. Indicate how he ranks the curves you've drawn. (LO2)

Exercise 4.8: Suppose bundles A and B lie on the same indifference curve. Bundle C lies between bundles A and B, on a straight line that connects them. The consumer's preferences satisfy the Declining MRS Principle. Does the consumer prefer C to A and B, or does he prefer A and B to C? (LO3, 4)

Exercise 4.9: Nora likes to breed rabbits. Clearly, she can't get very far with one rabbit. Thinking about the tradeoffs between rabbits and other goods, would you expect the Declining MRS Principle to hold? Can you think of other situations in which it might be violated? (LO3, 4)

Exercise 4.10: What do you think the indifference curves in Figure 4.5 would look like for the type of person who prefers to purchase a sports car? What about the type of person who prefers to purchase a subcompact? (LO2)

Exercise 4.11: John's MRS for reading books with watching movies is three movies per book regardless of the amounts consumed. Would he rather read two books and watch no movies, or read no books and watch two movies? What is the formula for his family of indifference curves? What do these curves look like? In this example, are movies and books perfect substitutes, perfect complements, or neither? (LO2, 4)

Exercise 4.12: Do the following pairs of products serve as complements or substitutes? In each case, is the degree of complementarity or substitutability high or low? Do your answers depend on the contexts in which the goods are used? (1) Bread and butter. (2) Ball point pens and computers. (3) Facsimile service and mail service. (4) Movies and video games. (5) Gasoline and ethanol. (6) Wireless telephone service and standard (wireline) telephone service. (7) Different CDs recorded by the same rock group. (8) Lettuce and ground beef. (LO2, 4)

Exercise 4.13: Kate has 25 Smarties and Antonio has 10 Gummies. Suppose Kate's MRS for Gummies with Smarties is four regardless of what she consumes, and that Antonio's is three regardless of what he consumes. Kate and Antonio trade until there is no further opportunity for mutual gain. Can you say anything about what they've traded (how many Smarties for how many Gummies)? (LO4)

Exercise 4.14: Latanya likes to talk on the telephone. We can represent her preferences with the utility function $U(B, J) = 18B + 20J$, where B and J are minutes of conversation per month with Bill and Jackie, respectively. If Latanya plans to use the phone for one hour to talk with only one person, with whom would she rather speak? Why? What is the formula for her indifference curves? Plot a few of those curves. (LO5)

Exercise 4.15: Do you think there is a workable way to obtain meaningful *cardinal* information about a consumer's preferences? If so, how might you go about it? If not, why not? (LO2, 5)

Exercise 4.16: In Exercise 4.14, we discussed Latanya's preferences for telephone conversation. According to our assumption, we can represent her preferences with the utility function $U(B, J) = 18B + 20J$, where B and J are minutes of conversation per month with Bill and Jackie, respectively. What is Latanya's implied marginal utility of speaking with Bill? What is her implied marginal utility of speaking with Jackie? What is her MRS for minutes talking to Bill with minutes talking to Jackie? (LO2, 5)

Exercise 4.17: Esteban likes both chocolate ice cream and lemon sorbet. His preferences correspond to the utility function $U(C, S) = C^{1/3}S^{2/3}$, where C stands for scoops of chocolate ice cream and S stands for scoops of lemon sorbet. Write a formula for Esteban's family of indifference curves. Plot some of those curves on a graph. Would Esteban rather have four scoops of chocolate ice cream and two scoops of lemon sorbet or two scoops of chocolate ice cream and four scoops of lemon sorbet? (LO2, 4, 5)

Exercise 4.18: Peter will only eat a hot dog if it is in a bun. His utility function is given by $U(B, H) = \min[B, H]$, where B and H are buns and hot dogs, respectively. The "min" function means to take the minimum of the two terms in brackets. Graph the indifference curves when U takes the values 1, 2, and 3. What is the marginal utility of an extra bun? What is the marginal rate of substitution between hot dogs and buns if there is an extra bun? (LO2, 4, 5)

Exercise 4.19: The marginal utility of chocolate ice cream, given the utility function in Exercise 4.17, is $MU_C = 1/3(S/C)^{2/3}$ while the marginal utility of lemon sorbet is $MU_S = 2/3(C/S)^{1/3}$. Calculate the MRS_{CS} when equal scoops of chocolate ice cream and lemon sorbet are chosen and again if twice as many scoops of chocolate ice cream are chosen. If instead the utility function was given by $U(C, S) = C^{\alpha}S^{(1-\alpha)}$ the marginal utilities would be $MU_C = \alpha(S/C)^{(1-\alpha)}$ and $MU_S = (1 - \alpha)(C/S)^{\alpha}$. Calculate the value for α if the $MRS_{CS} = 3$ and equal amounts of chocolate ice cream and lemon sorbet are chosen. (LO4, 5)

Constraints, Choices, and Demand

LEARNING OBJECTIVES

After reading this chapter, students should be able to

LOI Demonstrate how price and income affect a consumer's budget line.

LO2 Determine a consumer's best choice based on preferences and budget line.

LO3 Understand how to find a consumer's best choice by maximizing a utility function.

LO4 Analyze the effects of changes in prices and income on a consumer's demand.

LO5 Explain how economists determine consumers' preferences based on their choices.

In recent years, the Honda Civic has consistently ranked among the best-selling cars in the United States. Yet if you ask a group of your friends to name their favourite automobiles, few would place the Civic near the top. It lacks the luxury of a Bentley, the engineering of a Mercedes, the sex appeal of a Ferrari, the sophistication of an Aston-Martin, the performance of a Porsche. The Civic is simply a plain-looking car that delivers a safe, comfortable ride with relatively few headaches. Above all, it's affordable: the price is reasonable and the maintenance cost is low. The Ferrari Enzo may turn heads, but having to pay over $1,000,000 to buy one keeps most customers away.

Honda Civic (above) and Ferrari Enzo (below)

When the owner of a $17,190 Honda Civic says the Ferrari Enzo is not affordable, his meaning is obvious. Most people just don't have the necessary cash to buy an Enzo. But when he says he can't afford a $63,100 Mercedes E320, his meaning is probably more subtle. Many Civic owners *could* purchase more expensive cars. They *choose* the Civic because they don't think a flashy car is worth the necessary sacrifices, which could include working overtime, skipping vacations, or living in a smaller home.

Consumer choice is all about constraints and trade-offs. The purpose of this chapter is to describe the constraints consumers face and explain how they resolve trade-offs and make decisions. We'll examine six topics:

1. *Affordable consumption bundles.* Consumers' budget constraints identifiy all the consumption bundles they can afford. We'll see how prices and income determine which consumption bundles are affordable.
2. *Consumer choice.* Faced with a budget constraint, consumers select the best consumption bundles they can afford. We'll explain how to determine the best choice given preferences and budget constraints.
3. *Utility maximization.* Many important economic questions are quantitative, which is why economists use mathematics. We'll see that a consumer's best choice corresponds to the solution to a mathematical problem involving the maximization of utility, a concept that we introduced in Section 4.4, subject to a budget constraint.
4. *Prices and demand.* When the price of a good changes, each consumer's best affordable consumption bundle may change with it. By studying this relationship, we will develop a better understanding of demand curves.
5. *Income and demand.* When a consumer's income changes, the best affordable consumption bundle changes. Studying this relationship will help us understand how and why demand depends on income.
*6. *How economists determine a consumer's preferences.* Economists can't observe consumers' preferences directly. However, they can observe choices. We'll see how economists learn about consumers' preferences from their choices.

5.1 AFFORDABLE CONSUMPTION BUNDLES

When the owner of a Honda Civic says that a Mercedes E320 isn't worth the sacrifice, he means that by buying a Civic, he can afford a better consumption bundle that contains larger amounts of other desirable items. This example underscores the point that in thinking about what's affordable and what isn't, focusing on consumption bundles rather than individual products is important.

Income, Prices, and the Budget Line

A consumer's income consists of the money received during some fixed period of time.

A consumer's **income** consists of the money he receives during some fixed period of time such as an hour, a day, a month, or a year. Throughout this chapter and the next, we'll assume that consumers must spend their income during the period in which they receive it—in other words; they can neither save current income nor borrow against future income. (We'll discuss saving and borrowing in Chapter 10.) Therefore, during any time period, a consumer can afford to purchase a particular consumption bundle if its cost doesn't exceed his income for that period.

$$\text{Cost of consumption bundle} \leq \text{Income} \qquad (1)$$

Economists refer to this inequality as the consumer's **budget constraint**.

A **budget constraint** identifies all of the consumption bundles a consumer can afford over some period of time.

As an illustration, let's assume that the consumer desires only two goods, soup and bread. In market economies, each good is commonly associated with a price at which consumers can buy as much or as little as they like. We'll use P_S for the price per unit of soup and P_B for the price per unit of bread. We can find the total cost of any good by multiplying its price per unit times the number of units purchased. So if a consumption bundle includes S units of soup and B units of bread, the total cost of soup is $P_S S$, the total cost of bread is $P_B B$, and the total cost of the bundle is $P_S S + P_B B$. The consumer's budget constraint tells us that the bundle is affordable if its total cost does not exceed his income, M.

$$P_S S + P_B B \leq M \tag{2}$$

When each good is available at a fixed price per unit, budget constraints take the form shown in formula (2).

Example 5.1

Budgeting for Meals

In Example 4.2 (page 97), we discussed Madeline's preferences for bundles of soup and bread. Let's assume that the prices are $2 per bowl for soup and $2 per loaf for bread, and that Madeline's income is $6 per day. To determine if a bundle is affordable, we apply formula (2). The numbers in Table 5.1 indicate the cost of each bundle. For example, a bundle of three bowls of soup and one loaf of bread costs $8. Madeline can purchase any bundle in Table 5.1 with a cost of $6 or less. All of her affordable bundles are highlighted in green. Madeline must select one of the green cells.

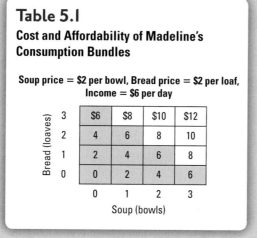

Table 5.1

Cost and Affordability of Madeline's Consumption Bundles

Soup price = $2 per bowl, Bread price = $2 per loaf, Income = $6 per day

Bread (loaves)				
3	$6	$8	$10	$12
2	4	6	8	10
1	2	4	6	8
0	0	2	4	6
	0	1	2	3

Soup (bowls)

IN-TEXT EXERCISE 5.1 **Suppose the price of soup is $4 per bowl, the price of bread is $1 per loaf, and Madeline's income is $6. Identify Madeline's affordable consumption bundles, as in Example 5.1.**

Example 5.1 describes a situation with lumpy goods. Let's now turn our attention to finely divisible goods. As in Chapter 4, we'll measure the amount of soup, S, in litres and the amount of bread, B, in kilograms. The price of soup, P_S, will indicate its cost per litre, and the price of bread, P_B, will indicate its cost per kilogram.

Figure 5.1

The Budget Constraint. When soup costs P_S per litre, bread costs P_B per kilogram, and income is M, the consumer can purchase any bundle on or below a straight line with the horizontal intercept M/P_S, the vertical intercept M/P_B, and a slope of $-P_S/P_B$.

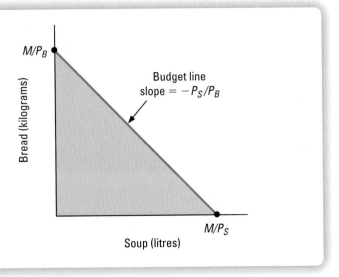

Affordable consumption bundles fall into two categories: those that exhaust the consumer's income and those that do not. A bundle exhausts the consumer's income if $P_S S + P_B B = M$ (that is, cost equals income). After subtracting $P_S S$ from both sides, and then dividing everything through by P_B, we can rewrite that formula as follows.

$$B = \frac{M}{P_B} - \frac{P_S}{P_B} S \qquad (3)$$

A budget line shows all of the consumption bundles that just exhaust a consumer's income.

Formula (3) describes a straight line, known as the consumer's **budget line**. By graphing this line, as in Figure 5.1, we can identify all of the consumption bundles that just exhaust the consumer's income.

According to formula (3), the slope of the budget line equals the ratio of the price of soup to the price of bread, times -1.[1] This price ratio represents the rate at which the consumer can convert litres of soup into kilograms of bread by spending money on bread instead of soup. Suppose, for example, that $P_S = \$10$ per litre and $P_B = \$5$ per kilogram. Since $\$10$ buys either one litre of soup or two kilograms of bread, the consumer can convert litres of soup to kilograms of bread at the rate of two kilograms per litre. In this example, the slope of the budget line, times negative one, is indeed two kilograms per litre. (To check this, divide the price of soup, $\$10$ per litre, by the price of bread, $\$5$ per kilogram.)

The budget line intersects the vertical axis at M/P_B kilograms, and the horizontal axis at M/P_S litres. For example, suppose that $M = \$60$, $P_S = \$10$ per litre, and $P_B = \$5$ per kilogram. If the consumer spends all of his money on bread, he can afford 12 kilograms (because $\$60 \div 5$ per kilogram $= 12$ kilograms). This is the vertical intercept. Likewise, if the consumer spends all of his money on soup, he can afford six litres (because $\$60 \div \$10$ per litre $= 6$ litres). This is the horizontal intercept.

What about consumption bundles that do *not* exhaust the consumer's income? Those satisfy the inequality $P_S S + P_B B < M$, which means they lie in the green-shaded area of

---

[1]Since the slope of a line is rise over run, and since *rise* refers to bread while *run* refers to soup, you might think the slope of the budget line would equal P_B/P_S, rather than P_S/P_B. However, when the price of a good is higher, a smaller change in the amount consumed leads to the same change in expenditure. Therefore, the price of bread is *inversely* related to rise, and the price of soup is *inversely* related to run.

Figure 5.1, to the southwest of the budget line. The budget line is the boundary that separates all the affordable consumption bundles from the unaffordable ones. The green shading in Figure 5.1 plays the same role as it does in Table 5.1: it identifies affordable consumption bundles.

Changes in Income and Prices

Changes in income and prices affect consumption because they move the budget line, altering the set of bundles from which the consumer can choose.

From formula (3), we see that a change in income alters the vertical intercept of the budget line without changing its slope. A reduction in income shifts the budget line inward, shrinking the set of affordable bundles, while an increase in income shifts it outward, expanding the set of affordable bundles. For example, as Figure 5.2 shows, if soup costs $10 per litre and bread costs $5 per kilogram, a reduction in income from $60 to $30 shifts the budget line toward the origin, from the line labelled L_1 to the one labelled L_2.[2] All the consumption bundles between L_1 and L_2 become unaffordable. Likewise, an increase in income from $60 to $90 shifts the budget line away from the origin, from the line labelled L_1 to the one labelled L_3, making all the bundles between L_1 and L_3 affordable. (Why?) The three budget lines are parallel because their slopes all equal the same price ratio, times -1.

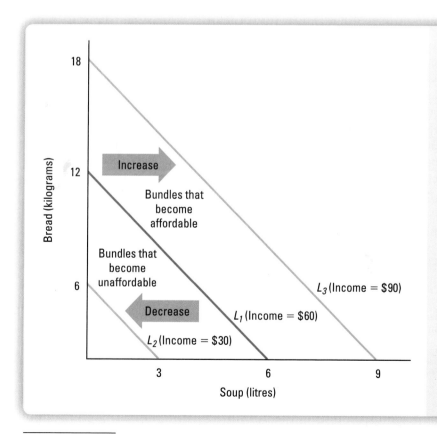

Figure 5.2

Effects of Changes in Income on the Budget Line. Soup costs $10 per litre and bread costs $5 per kilogram. A reduction in income from $60 to $30 shifts the budget line toward the origin, making all the bundles between L_1 and L_2 unaffordable. An increase in income from $60 to $90 shifts the budget line away from the origin, making all the bundles between L_1 and L_3 affordable.

[2]The ratio M/P_S (and hence the horizontal intercept) falls from six litres to three litres, while the ratio M/P_B (and hence the vertical intercept) falls from 12 kilograms to six kilograms.

What if prices and income all change by the same proportion? That scenario would have *no* effect on the budget line, because income changes just enough to compensate for the changing cost of goods. For example, if prices and income all double, the consumer's purchasing power is unchanged.[6]

Let's summarize what we've learned about budget lines:

Properties of Budget Lines

1. The budget line is the boundary that separates the affordable consumption bundles from all other bundles. Choices that do not exhaust the consumer's income lie to the southwest of the budget line.

2. The slope of the budget line equals the price ratio times -1, with the price of the good measured on the horizontal axis appearing in the numerator, and the price of the good measured on the vertical axis appearing in the denominator.

3. The budget line intersects the axis that measures the amount of any particular good, X, at the quantity M/P_X, which is the amount of X the consumer can purchase by spending all income on X.

4. A change in income shifts the budget line—outward for an increase and inward for a decrease—without changing its slope.

5. A change in the price of a good rotates the budget line—outward for a decrease and inward for an increase. The line pivots at the intercept for the good with the unchanged price and changes the slope of the budget line.

6. Multiplying all prices by a single constant has the same effect on the budget line as dividing income by the same constant. Changing prices *and* income by the same proportion has *no* effect on the budget line.

WORKED-OUT PROBLEM   5.1

The Problem   For each of the following cases, graph the consumer's budget line. Compute the horizontal intercept, the vertical intercept, and the slope of the budget line. (a) $P_S = \$15$ per litre, $P_B = \$6$ per kilogram, and $M = \$300$. (b) $P_S = \$5$ per litre, $P_B = \$6$ per kilogram, and $M = \$300$. (c) $P_S = \$15$ per litre, $P_B = \$2$ per kilogram, and $M = \$300$. (d) $P_S = \$10$ per litre, $P_B = \$4$ per kilogram, and $M = \$600$. (e) $P_S = \$30$ per litre, $P_B = \$12$ per kilogram, and $M = \$600$.

The Solution   See Figure 5.4. Notice that the budget constraints in parts (a) and (e) are identical. That's because the prices and income in part (e) are exactly three times as large as in part (a).

---

[6]The horizontal intercept becomes $(2M)/(2P_S)$, which equals M/P_S (since the twos cancel). Likewise, the vertical intercept becomes $(2M)/(2P_B) = M/P_B$, and the slope becomes $-(2P_S)/(2P_B) = -P_S/P_B$. Since the horizontal intercept, vertical intercept, and slope are unchanged, the budget line doesn't move.

Figure 5.4

Budget Lines for Worked-Out Problem 5.1. This figure shows the budget lines for each combination of prices and income listed in parts (a) through (e) of worked-out problem 5.1, along with their horizontal intercepts, vertical intercepts, and slopes.

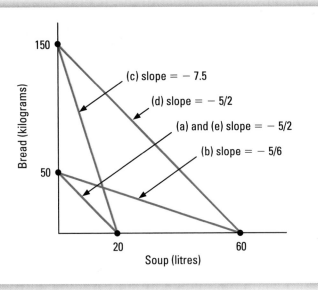

IN-TEXT EXERCISE 5.2   **For each of the following cases, graph the consumer's budget line. Compute the horizontal intercept, the vertical intercept, and the slope of the budget line: (a) P_S = \$20 per litre, P_B = \$5 per kilogram, and M = \$400. (b) P_S = \$40 per litre, P_B = \$5 per kilogram, and M = \$400. (c) P_S = \$20 per litre, P_B = \$10 per kilogram, and M = \$400. (d) P_S = \$20 per litre, P_B = \$5 per kilogram, and M = \$800. (e) P_S = \$40 per litre, P_B = \$10 per kilogram, and M = \$800.**

Other Limits on Consumption

Sometimes, prices and income aren't the only factors that limit consumption. When the demand for a good exceeds the supply at the prevailing price, governments or suppliers may limit the amount that each consumer can purchase. For example, gasoline was widely **rationed** in many countries during World War II and during the oil crisis of 1973.

Figure 5.5 illustrates the effect of rationing on the budget line of a consumer who allocates an income of \$200 between food, which costs \$4 per kilogram, and gasoline, which costs \$1 per litre. Without rationing, the consumer can choose any bundle on or below the straight line that runs between points A and B (part of which is solid and part of which is dashed). With gasoline rationing (80 litres per person), the consumer can no longer purchase any bundle containing more than 80 litres of gasoline. Therefore, the budget line is the solid kinked line through points B, C, and D.

> When the government or a supplier limits the amount that each consumer can purchase, we say that the good is **rationed**.

5.2 CONSUMER CHOICE

According to the Choice Principle (Section 4.1), a consumer selects the highest-ranked alternative among the available options. When the number of potential alternatives is small, finding the best one is easy. We'll illustrate by returning to the problem considered in Examples 4.2 and 5.1.

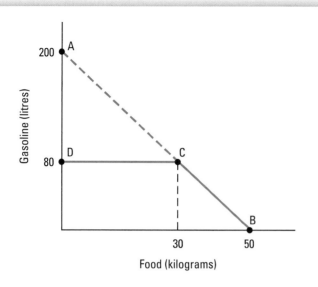

Figure 5.5

A Budget Line with Rationing. A consumer allocates $200 between food, which costs $4 per kilogram, and gasoline, which costs $1 per litre. Without rationing, the consumer can choose any bundle on or below the straight line that runs between points A and B. With gasoline rationing (80 litres per person), the consumer's budget line is the solid kinked line through points B, C, and D.

Example 5.2

Budgeting for Meals, Part 2

As in Example 5.1, let's assume that Madeline's income is $6 per day, soup costs $2 per bowl, and bread costs $2 per loaf. With the preferences shown in Table 4.2 (page 97), what will she choose?

Table 5.2 reproduces Table 4.2, which showed Madeline's preference ranking. As in Table 5.1, we've shaded the affordable bundles green. To determine what her decision will be, we can apply the Choice Principle. Since she ranks the bundle consisting of two bowls of soup and one loaf of bread higher (at number six) than any other green-shaded bundle, this is her best choice.

Since Madeline's cash is limited, the best affordable bundle is not as good as some of the other alternatives listed in Table 5.2 (specifically, those

Table 5.2

Madeline's Best Choice

Soup price = $2 per bowl, Bread price = $2 per loaf,
Income = $6 per day

Bread (loaves)				
3	11	7	3	1
2	13	8	4	2
1	15	9	⑥	5
0	16	14	12	10
	0	1	2	3

Soup (bowls)

ranked one through five). We use red shading to highlight all of the superior bundles. Notice that the red-shaded portion of the graph does not overlap with the green-shaded portion. Why not? Since Madeline prefers each red-shaded bundle to the best affordable bundle, each must cost more than she can afford.

IN-TEXT EXERCISE 5.3   As with in-text exercise 5.1, suppose that a bowl of soup costs $4 instead of $2, while a loaf of bread still costs $2, and Madeline's income is $6. What will she choose?

The No-Overlap Rule

When goods are finely divisible, applying the Choice Principle takes a bit more work. However, the basic idea remains the same as in Example 5.2.

Look at Figure 5.6(a), which reproduces the budget line from Figure 5.1. Of all the bundles on or below that line, which one will the consumer pick? According to the More-Is-Better Principle, he'll pick a bundle on the budget line, rather than one below it. Why? A point below the budget line would leave him with unused cash, which he could spend on something he values. For example, in Figure 5.6(a), he would rather pick bundle B than bundle A, because bundle B contains more of everything than bundle A.

The consumer's choice must also lie on the highest indifference curve that touches the budget line. We can easily recognize such bundles by applying the following simple rule:

The No-Overlap Rule   The area above the indifference curve that runs through the consumer's best affordable bundle does not overlap with the area below the budget line. The area above the indifference curve that runs through any other affordable bundle does overlap with the area below the budget line.

Figure 5.6

Choosing among Affordable Bundles. In figure (a), the consumer would rather pick bundle B than bundle A because bundle B contains more soup and more bread than bundle A. Bundle C is the best choice because there is no overlap between the red-shaded area above the indifference curve that runs through bundle C, and the green-shaded area below the budget line—in other words, between the bundles that are better than C and the ones that are affordable. In figure (b), bundle D is not the best choice because there is overlap between the area above the indifference curve that runs through D and the area under the budget line—in other words, between the bundles that are better than D and the ones that are affordable. For example, the consumer would rather pick bundle E than bundle D.

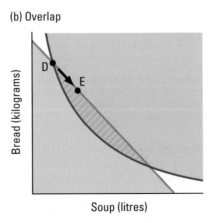

For example, look at Figure 5.6(a). Since the red indifference curve that passes through bundle C does not cross the budget line, the areas above that indifference curve (shaded red) and below the budget line (shaded green) do not overlap. Because none of the better-than-C bundles are affordable, bundle C is the best choice. Notice the similarities between Figure 5.6(a) and Table 5.2. In both cases, the indicated bundle is the best choice because the red and green areas do not overlap (equivalently, no other bundle is both better and affordable).

In contrast, since the red indifference curve that passes through bundle D in Figure 5.6(b) crosses the budget line, the areas above that indifference curve and below the budget line overlap. The overlapping area is striped red and green. Any consumption bundle that lies in the striped area is both affordable (it lies below the budget line) and better than D (it lies above the indifference curve that runs through D). The consumer can therefore do better than D, for example by choosing another bundle, such as E, that lies on the budget line to the southeast of D.

Example 5.3

Purchases of Left and Right Shoes

To illustrate the no-overlap rule, we'll examine a case involving perfect complements, based on Example 4.4 (page 114). Suppose that Maria has a fixed sum of cash to spend on shoes, and that left and right shoes are sold separately. How many of each will she buy? Figure 5.7 shows her indifference curves for left and right shoes (in red), and her budget line (in green). According to the no-overlap rule, bundle A is Maria's best choice. Since bundle A lies on the 45-degree line, Maria buys the same number of left and right shoes. This conclusion doesn't depend on the slope of the budget line. Even if the prices of left and right shoes differ, Maria will still buy the same number of each. For example, if left shoes cost $10 each, right shoes cost $20 each, and Maria can spend $90 on shoes, she will buy three pairs.

Interior Solutions

An affordable bundle is an **interior choice** if, for each good, there are affordable bundles containing a little bit more of that good and affordable bundles containing a little bit less of it.[7] In Figure 5.6(a), bundles A, B, and C are all interior choices; bundle F is not. When the best affordable choice is an interior choice, we call it an **interior solution.** Bundle C in Figure 5.6(a) is an example.

Notice that the consumer's budget line lies tangent to his indifference curve at bundle C. For this reason, we say that bundle C satisfies the **tangency condition**. In fact, interior solutions *always* satisfy the tangency condition.[8] Why? The indifference curve running through any interior choice that does *not* satisfy the tangency condition, like bundle D in

An affordable bundle is an **interior choice** if, for each good, there are affordable bundles containing a little bit more of that good and affordable bundles containing a little bit less of it. When the best affordable choice is an interior choice, we call it an **interior solution**.

A bundle on the budget line satisfies the **tangency condition** if, at that bundle, the budget line lies tangent to the consumer's indifference curve.

---

[7]We previously introduced this term in the appendix to Chapter 3.

[8]This statement assumes that the interior solution is not a bundle at which the consumer's indifference curve is kinked. Because the slope of an indifference curve is not well-defined at kink points, such as bundle A in Figure 5.7, it cannot coincide with the slope of any straight line.

Figure 5.7

The Best Affordable Bundle with Perfect Complements. According to the no-overlap rule, bundle A is Maria's best choice. Since bundle A lies on the 45-degree line, Maria buys the same number of left and right shoes. This conclusion doesn't depend on the slope of the budget line. Even if the prices of left and right shoes differ, Maria will still buy the same number of each.

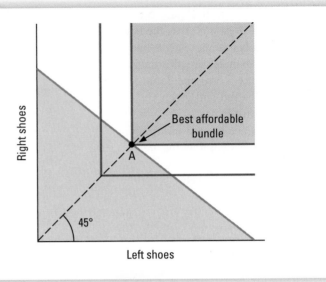

An Implication of the Tangency Condition

Figure 5.6(b), *must* cross the budget line, creating overlap between the areas below the budget line and above the indifference curve. According to the no-overlap rule, such bundles are not best choices.

An Implication of the Tangency Condition   At every interior solution, the marginal rate of substitution between two goods equals their price ratio.[9] To understand why, take another look at Figure 5.6(a). Because the interior solution (bundle C) satisfies the tangency condition, the indifference curve and the budget line share the same slope at that bundle. We know that the slope of the indifference curve is the negative of the marginal rate of substitution for soup with bread, MRS_{SB} (Section 4.3). We also know that the slope of the budget line is the negative of the price ratio, P_S/P_B (Section 5.1). Therefore,

$$MRS_{SB} = \frac{P_S}{P_B} \tag{4}$$

We emphasize that equation (4) holds only at interior solutions. It does not hold at other points on the budget line. Intuitively, the formula says that the rate at which an individual is *willing* to exchange the two goods (the marginal rate of substitution) is equal to the rate at which the consumer is *able* to exchange the two goods in the marketplace (the price ratio).

Equation (4) has many important implications and applications. For instance, it implies that, as long as consumers can buy and sell all goods at marketwide prices, they will reap all the potential gains from trade. Institutions that promote exchange at marketwide prices, therefore, help the economy to get the most out of its resources. Why? In Example 4.3, "The Lunch Box Problem and Mutual Gains from Trade" (page 112), you learned that two people can benefit from trading with each other when their marginal rates of substitution

---

[9]This statement also assumes that the interior solution is not a bundle at which the consumer's indifference curve is kinked.

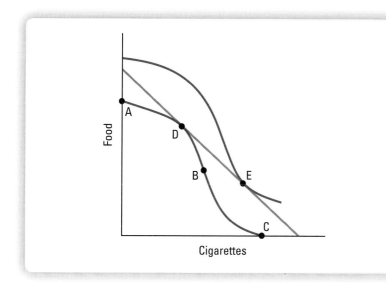

Figure 5.8

A Case in Which Indifference Curves Do Not Have Declining MRSs. Marlene allocates money between cigarettes and food. Because cigarettes are addictive, her indifference curves do not have declining MRSs. She chooses bundle E rather than bundle D, despite the fact that both bundles satisfy the tangency condition.

differ. But if everyone buys and sells goods at market-wide prices, each person will choose a bundle that equates his marginal rate of substitution with the same price ratio. Thus, everyone's marginal rate of substitution will be the *same,* which rules out the possibility of further gains from trade. We'll return to this theme in Part III.

Finding Interior Solutions   Sometimes, economists need to predict consumers' choices. If the consumers' indifference curves have declining MRSs, this task is particularly easy: we simply find an interior choice that satisfies formula (4) (equivalently, the tangency condition). Any such bundle is an interior solution. To understand why, consider any interior bundle that satisfies the tangency condition, like bundle C in Figure 5.6(a). Because the budget line and the indifference curve that runs through bundle C lie tangent to each other, they don't cross at C. Nor can they cross at any other point. With a declining MRS, the indifference curve becomes steeper to the left of point C and flatter to the right. In either direction, it veers away from and remains above the budget line, as shown. Therefore, the areas below the budget line and above the indifference curve that runs through C cannot overlap. According to the no-overlap rule, bundle C is therefore the best choice.

What if the consumer's indifference curves do not have declining MRSs? In those cases, interior choices that satisfy the tangency condition are not necessarily the best affordable choices. Let's examine a case involving cigarette addiction. Suppose that Marlene spends all of her money on food and cigarettes. Figure 5.8 shows her indifference curves. Consider the indifference curve that runs through bundle A. Notice that Marlene's MRS for cigarettes with food *increases* as we move from bundle A to bundle B. Why? As Marlene smokes more cigarettes, she becomes hooked, and her cravings for cigarettes grow more extreme.[10] As a result, the amount of food she is willing to give up

---

[10]One way to interpret addiction is that the marginal utility of a cigarette is increasing initially. If the marginal utility of a cigarette is increasing as more cigarettes are consumed faster than the marginal utility of food is increasing as less food is consumed the MRS for cigarettes with food can increase.

to obtain an additional cigarette grows larger. However, if food becomes sufficiently scarce, she grows extremely hungry and is no longer willing to give up as much food to obtain an additional cigarette. That is why her MRS for cigarettes with food declines as we move from bundle B to bundle C. In Figure 5.8, bundles D and E both satisfy the tangency condition. However, according to the no-overlap rule, bundle E is her best choice; bundle D is not.

WORKED-OUT PROBLEM   5.2

The Problem   Natasha's income is $300 per month. She spends all of it on tickets to concerts and films. A concert ticket costs $15 and a film ticket costs $10. Her marginal rate of substitution for concerts with films, MRS_{CF}, is F/C, where C stands for the number of concert tickets and F stands for the number of films. (Fractions are allowed—for example, if she buys half of a concert ticket, that means she goes to a concert every other month). How many film tickets will she purchase, and how many concert tickets?

The Solution   Notice that MRS_{CF} decreases as C rises and F falls. Therefore, each of Natasha's indifference curves has a declining MRS. To find a best choice, we look for a bundle on her budget line that satisfies the tangency condition.

At Natasha's best choice, her marginal rate of substitution between films and concerts equals the price ratio $MRS_{CF} = P_C/P_F$. Substituting the information contained in the statement of the problem gives us the following: $F/C = 15/10 = 1.5$. In other words, Natasha purchases 1.5 times as many movie tickets as concert tickets.

The formula for Natasha's budget line is $P_CC + P_FF = 300$. Substituting the values of the prices into this formula, we have $15C + 10F = 300$. Using the fact that $F = 1.5C$ gives us $15C + 10(1.5C) = 300$, or $30C = 300$. So $C = 10$, and $F = 15$. Natasha purchases 10 concert tickets and 15 movie tickets.

IN-TEXT EXERCISE 5.4   **In worked-out problem 5.2, how many of each kind of ticket will Natasha choose if her marginal rate of substitution for concerts with films, MRS_{CF}, is $3F/2C$? If it's $\sqrt{F/C}$?**

Boundary Solutions

At a **boundary choice** there are no affordable bundles that contain either a little bit more or a little bit less of some good. When the consumer's best choice is a boundary choice, we call it a **boundary solution**.

In practice, virtually everyone chooses *not* to consume certain goods. Think about your own purchases. There are probably many things that you never consume—possibly octopus, brussels sprouts, or tripe. These types of choices are examples of **boundary choices**.[11] At a boundary choice, there are no affordable bundles that contain either a little bit more or a little bit less of some good. In Figure 5.6(a), bundle F is a boundary choice, because there is no affordable bundle containing a little bit more soup, or a little bit less bread. When the consumer's best choice is a boundary choice, we call it a **boundary solution**.

---

[11]We introduced this language in the appendix to Chapter 3.

Boundary solutions often arise when a good provides a consumer with little value per dollar relative to other alternatives. For example, look at Figure 5.9. Notice that the indifference curves (drawn in red) are quite steep. This means that it takes a great deal of bread to compensate the consumer for losing a litre of soup. According to the no-overlap rule, bundle C is the consumer's best choice on the green budget line. Because it contains no bread, it's also a boundary solution. At any bundle that contains some bread (like bundle A), the indifference curve is steeper than the budget line, so the consumer is better off buying more soup and less bread.

Unlike interior solutions, boundary solutions usually do not satisfy formula (4). For instance, at bundle C in Figure 5.9, the consumer's indifference curve is *steeper* than his budget line. As a result, at bundle C, his MRS for soup with bread is *greater* than the price ratio, P_S/P_B. More generally, if bundle C contains no bread and is a boundary solution, then at that bundle,

"I'll lay it out for you. We're cutting back, and we no longer need a dog."

$$MRS_{SB} \geq \frac{P_S}{P_B} \qquad (5)$$

This inequality, which takes the place of formula (4), is intuitive. Starting at bundle C, the consumer has no bread, so his only option is to buy less soup and more bread. He is *willing* to give up one litre of soup for MRS_{SB} kilograms of bread, but *able* to buy only P_S/P_B kilograms of bread in place of one litre of soup. Since $MRS_{SB} \geq P_S/P_B$, buying more bread and less soup makes him no better off (and indeed makes him worse off if $MRS_{SB} > P_S/P_B$), so he is content to spend all his income on soup.[12] When goods are perfect substitutes, and hence have constant MRS, it is typically the case that the consumer's best choice is a boundary solution.

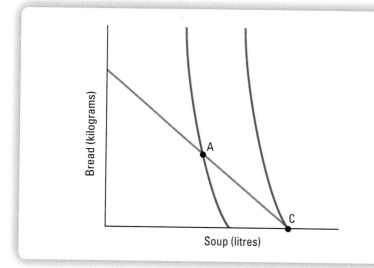

Figure 5.9

A Case in Which the Best Affordable Bundle Is a Boundary Solution. According to the no-overlap rule, bundle C is the consumer's best affordable bundle. The indifference curves through bundles like A are steeper than the budget line, so the consumer is better off purchasing more soup and less bread.

Bread (kilograms)

A

C

Soup (litres)

---

[12]What if the consumer purchases some soup and some bread, but no octopus? Since this choice is a boundary solution, the marginal rates of substitution for soup with octopus, and for bread with octopus, satisfy inequalities like expression (5). However, the marginal rate of substitution for soup with bread still satisfies formula (4). Why? The choices of those goods are interior: there are affordable bundles containing a little more soup and a little less bread, as well as bundles containing a little less soup and a little more bread.

Properties of Best Choices

1. Assuming that more is better, the consumer's best choice lies on the budget line.

2. We can recognize best choices by applying the no-overlap rule.

3. Interior solutions always satisfy the tangency condition. Consequently, if a bundle that includes two goods, X and Y, is an interior solution, then $MRS_{XY} = P_X/P_Y$ at that bundle.

4. When indifference curves have declining MRSs, any interior choice that satisfies the tangency condition is a best affordable choice.

5. Whenever the consumer purchases good X but not good Y, then $MRS_{XY} \geq P_X/P_Y$ at the chosen bundle.

Application 5.1

Tax Credits and Household Expenditures

In 2009 the Canadian federal and provincial governments subsidized various household expenditures using tax credits. A partial list of tax credits offered by the federal government include those for education, children's fitness activities, donations and gifts, and home renovations. In the case of home renovations the tax credit was limited to $1350 (15 percent of the difference between the minimum $1000 expenditure to receive the tax credit and the maximum $10,000 of eligible expenses), and the children's fitness tax credit was capped at $500 per child. For charitable donations and gifts, the tax credit was calculated at 15 percent for the first $200 and 29 percent for donations exceeding $200. Educational tax credits were given for tuition, textbooks, and full- or part-time attendance at an educational institution.

The effect of a tax credit is to change the relative price of goods. Besides tax credits, governments provide additional assistance to households that change the relative prices between goods. Examples include the Food Stamp Program in the United States, school vouchers in Sweden, and subsidized housing in Canada and elsewhere.

Let's examine the effect of tax credits on those expenditures where a tax credit is given. To make the analysis simpler consider all tax-credit-eligible expenditures together. Assume that after-tax income, if no eligible expenditures are made, is $50,000 and that up to $10,000 of eligible expenditures can be made where the tax credit is calculated at 20 percent of the total expenditure. If $10,000 of eligible expenditures is

made, a tax credit of $2000 is given so that after-tax income increases to $52,000. In Figure 5.10 household expenditures on items where no tax credit is given is plotted on the vertical axis while household expenditures on items eligible for a tax credit are plotted on the horizontal axis. The budget constraint in this case has a kink in it since the effective price of expenditures on items receiving a tax credit is only $0.80 up to $10,000. If $10,000 is spent on items receiving a tax credit, $42,000 can be spent on other items. This budget constraint is the green solid line with the kink in it in Figure 5.10.

The tax credit is beneficial for any household that chooses to purchase items where a tax credit is available. What is less obvious is whether a household would be better off with a tax-free payment that is less than or equal to the maximum value of the tax credit, $2000. Suppose that instead of tax credits the government made a $1000 tax-free payment to each household, thereby increasing after-tax income to $51,000. In Figure 5.10 the budget constraint associated with the $1000 payment is the straight green dashed line.

Figure 5.10 includes indifference curves for three consumers, Barney, Bob, and Betty, all of whom face the same resource constraint for each of the two different government programs. Betty's indifference curves are shown in dark red, Barney's indifference curve is dark blue, and Bob's indifference curves are yellow. With the tax credits, Betty chooses bundle A on the solid green budget constraint, while Barney chooses bundle B, and Bob chooses bundle C. Only Bob spends more than $10,000 on the tax credit eligible expenditures. How would these three individuals fare if rather than tax credits a $1000 government payment was made? In this case Betty would choose bundle D, which she could not have purchased under the tax credit program. Betty prefers a payment of $1000 rather than the tax credits. Barney chooses bundle E when the $1000 payment augments his income. Note that he could not have purchased this bundle under the tax rebate program. Does he then prefer the cash payment rather than tax credits? In this example he does not prefer one program over the other as bundle B lies on the same indifference curve as bundle E. Barney is indifferent between the two programs. How about Bob? Bob chooses bundle F if a $1000 cheque rather than tax credits are given by the government. The indifference curve through bundle F lies below the indifference curve that passes through bundle C. Bob prefers tax credits to a $1000 cheque.

What if the cash payment by the government was equal to $2000 (not shown)? In this case the reader should be able to verify that Betty's preferences remain the same as with the $1000 cheque. However, Barney would prefer the larger payment of $2000 as he could purchase a bundle of goods strictly preferred to bundle B. Finally, Bob would be no better off with the $2000 cash payment as he would prefer to spend more than the $10,000 on goods and services formerly covered by the tax credits.

Why does the Canadian government provide tax credits for schooling, children's fitness, home renovations, and donations, rather than cash payments? The objective of the various government programs is to promote expenditures on goods and services that the government believes will benefit households, children, charitable groups, particular firms, or society itself. For example, advocates of the child fitness tax credit believe that a dollar spent subsidizing children's sports activities benefits households more than an equivalent amount of money given back to the household. Since all individuals in our example are no worse off with a $2000 cheque from the government than with the tax credits one might question this viewpoint. However, some may argue that society also benefits from particular purchases of goods and services, or that a child's interest with regard to schooling and health might not be properly accounted for by the family member(s) controlling household expenditures.

Figure 5.10

The Effect of the Tax Credits and Cash Payments on Purchases. Barney, Betty, and Bob each receive $50,000 in after-tax income. The federal government of Canada gives a 20-percent tax credit for up to $10,000 in expenditures on a variety of goods and services. Alternatively the government can make a tax-free $1000 payment to each individual. With the tax credit, Barney, Betty, and Bob each choose a bundle on the kinked budget line. With an additional $1000 in after-tax income they each choose a bundle on the straight dashed budget line. Changing from tax credits to a cash payment moves Barney's best choice from bundle B to bundle E, Betty's best choice from bundle A to D, and Bob's best choice from bundle C to F. Betty is better off when changing from tax credits to a $1000 tax payment while Bob is worse off. Barney is indifferent between the two programs.

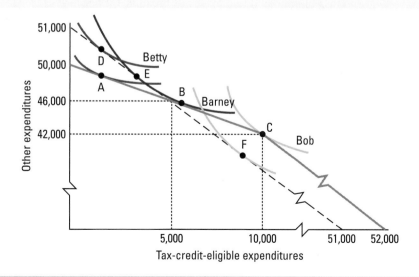

5.3 UTILITY MAXIMIZATION

Many important economic questions are quantitative, which is why economists use mathematics. The notion of utility, introduced in Section 4.4, is valuable because it allows us to analyze consumers' choices using precise mathematics, rather than graphs.

Remember that a utility function assigns a utility value to each consumption bundle. The consumer prefers bundles with higher utility values to bundles with lower utility values. Making the best choice is therefore the same as finding the affordable consumption bundle with the highest utility value. Mathematically, the best bundle maximizes the consumer's utility function while respecting his budget constraint. For example, if he spends his income on soup and bread, we write his problem as follows.

$$\text{Maximize } U(S, B) \text{ subject to } P_S S + P_B B \leq M$$

*Optional The utility maximization problem with a budget constraint can be solve using calculus. The interested student should read Add-On 5A.

where $U(S, B)$ is the utility value assigned to a bundle containing S litres of soup and B kilograms of bread, P_S is the price of a litre of soup, P_B is the price of a kilogram of bread, and M is income.

As we illustrate in worked-out problem 5.3, finding the utility-maximizing choice is easy when the number of alternatives is small.

WORKED-OUT PROBLEM   5.3

The Problem   As in Examples 5.1 and 5.2, assume that Madeline's income is $6 per day, soup costs $2 per bowl, and bread costs $2 per loaf. Suppose that her preferences correspond to the utility function $U(S, B) = 2S + B + SB$, where S stands for bowls of soup and B stands for loaves of bread. What will Madeline choose? What if her income is $4 per day instead of $6 per day?

The Solution   Each cell in Table 5.3(a) represents a possible choice. In contrast to Table 5.2, the number in each cell is the utility value for that particular bundle, not Madeline's preference ranking. For example, the utility index associated with three bowls of soup and two loaves of bread is 14, because $(2 \times 3) + 2 + (3 \times 2) = 14$. Since prices and income are the same as in Example 5.2, the affordable bundles (the green-shaded cells) are the same as those shown in Table 5.2. The green-shaded cell with the highest utility index, seven, corresponds to a consumption bundle with two bowls of soup and one loaf of bread. That is Madeline's best choice.

If Madeline can spend only $4, fewer choices are available to her [see Table 5.3(b)]. Two of the available choices share the highest utility index. One offers two bowls of soup and no bread, the other offers one bowl of soup and one loaf of bread. These are Madeline's best choices, and she is indifferent between them.

IN-TEXT EXERCISE 5.5   **Suppose Madeline's preferences correspond to the utility function $U = SB$. Assume that her income is $8 per day, soup costs $2 per bowl, and bread costs $2 per loaf. What will she choose? What if bread costs $4 per loaf instead of $2 per loaf? How would your answers change if her preferences corresponded to the utility function $U = 4SB$? To $U = (SB)^2$? What do these comparisons tell you about utility functions?**

Table 5.3

Maximizing Madeline's Utility

Soup price = $2 per bowl, Bread price = $2 per loaf, Utility = 2S + B + SB

(a) Income = $6 per day

Bread (loaves)				
3	3	8	13	18
2	2	6	10	14
1	1	4	⑦	10
0	0	2	4	6
	0	1	2	3

Soup (bowls)

(b) Income = $4 per day

Bread (loaves)				
3	3	8	13	18
2	2	6	10	14
1	1	④	7	10
0	0	2	④	6
	0	1	2	3

Soup (bowls)

Maximizing Utility with Finely Divisible Goods

In cases with finely divisible goods, we can solve utility maximization problems and thereby identify consumers' best choices using standard mathematical tools, including calculus. That is why the utility maximization framework is so useful. In this book, we do not assume you know calculus. However, even without calculus, we can still explain the basic principles of utility maximization.

Let's think about decisions involving soup and bread. We know that the consumer's best choice lies on his budget line. To find the bundle on the budget line that delivers the highest level of utility, we'll start at the bundle he obtains by spending all of his income on soup [bundle F in Figure 5.6(a)] and move along the budget line by shifting resources from soup to bread.

In terms of utility, every dollar of income shifted from soup to bread creates both a benefit and a cost. The benefit is the increase in utility resulting from the increase in the amount of bread consumed. The cost is the decrease in utility resulting from the reduction in the amount of soup consumed. In Section 3.2, we learned that the marginal benefit must equal the marginal cost at any interior choice that maximizes the net benefit. What does that principle imply in this context?

Let's start with the marginal benefit of shifting resources from soup to bread. If the consumer spends one more dollar on bread, he will have $1/P_B$ additional kilograms. For example, if bread costs $5 per kilogram, then an extra dollar buys 1/2 kilogram. If he adds one kilogram of bread, his utility will increase by approximately MU_B, the marginal utility of bread. (We discussed the concept of marginal utility in Section 4.4.) To determine the gain in utility resulting from the additional dollar's worth of bread, we multiply the number of kilograms added, $1/P_B$, by the increase in utility per kilogram added, MU_B, which gives us MU_B/P_B. This is the marginal benefit of shifting resources to bread.

Now consider the marginal cost of shifting resources from soup to bread. If the consumer spends a dollar less on soup, he will buy $1/P_S$ fewer litres. The loss of one litre causes his utility to fall by approximately MU_S, the marginal utility of soup. So his utility falls by MU_S/P_S with the loss of $1/P_S$ litres. This is the marginal cost of shifting resources to bread.

Setting marginal benefit equal to marginal cost, we have

$$\frac{MU_B}{P_B} = \frac{MU_S}{P_S} \tag{6}$$

This formula holds at any interior solution. It tells us that the alternative uses of the consumer's resources are equally valuable on the margin.[13]

What about boundary solutions? If the utility maximizing bundle contains no bread, then the marginal benefit of shifting resources from soup to bread must not exceed the marginal cost (see the appendix to Chapter 3). Therefore,

$$\frac{MU_S}{P_S} \geq \frac{MU_B}{P_B} \tag{7}$$

This formula tells us that, at the boundary solution, the consumer gains at least as much by spending money on soup rather than bread on the margin.

WORKED-OUT PROBLEM   5.4

The Problem   As in worked-out problem 5.2, Natasha's income is $300 per month. She spends all of it on tickets to concerts and films. A concert ticket costs $15 and a film ticket costs $10. Her preferences correspond to the utility function $U(C,F) = C \times F$, where C stands for the number of concerts and F stands for the number of films. For that utility function, the marginal benefit of concert tickets is F (the number of film tickets), and the marginal benefit of film tickets is C (the number of concert tickets). To understand why, refer back to Section 4.4, where we discussed a similar utility function for soup and bread. As before, fractions are allowed. How many film tickets will she purchase, and how many concert tickets?

The Solution   The same logic that led us to formula (6) tells us that $MU_C/P_C = MU_F/P_F$ at an interior optimum. Substituting $MU_C = F$, $MU_F = C$, $P_C = 15$, and $P_F = 10$ into the preceding formula, we discover that $F/15 = C/10$, which implies that $F/C = 1.5$. Reasoning exactly as in the last paragraph of the solution to worked-out problem 5.2, we conclude that $C = 10$, and $F = 15$.

IN-TEXT EXERCISE 5.6   **In worked-out problem 5.4, how many of each kind of ticket will Natasha choose if concert tickets cost $30 each and film tickets cost $15 each?**

Utility Maximization and Best Affordable Bundles

Utility maximization isn't different from the theory of consumer choice described in Section 5.2. It's simply another way to describe the same theory. A consumer's best affordable bundle is also his utility maximizing bundle and vice versa.

---

[13]This equally can be generalized to any number of goods or services consumed in positive quantities by an individual.

To underscore this point, we'll show that formula (6), which holds for interior choices that maximize utility, is just another way of writing formula (4), the tangency condition for best affordable choices. Let's start by rearranging formula (6) as follows.

$$\frac{P_S}{P_B} = \frac{MU_S}{MU_B}$$

Now recall from Section 4.4 that

$$\frac{MU_S}{MU_B} = MRS_{SB}$$

If we substitute the last formula into the previous one, we obtain formula (4).

Similarly, expression (7), which holds for boundary solutions, is just another way of writing expression (5). To show this, we rearrange expression (7) as follows.

$$\frac{MU_S}{MU_B} \geq \frac{P_S}{P_B}$$

Combining this expression with the previous formula produces expression (5).

5.4 PRICES AND DEMAND

In the last few sections, we developed a theory that explains how consumers allocate their limited resources over available goods. If we know the price of each good together with the consumer's income and preferences, the theory tells us what the consumer will purchase. If a price changes, the theory tells us how the consumer's purchases will change. Put another way, the theory allows us to study the properties of demand curves (which we introduced in Chapter 2).

The Price-Consumption Curve

Oscar spends his income, $100 per week, on soup and bread. Bread costs $5 per kilogram. If his preferences correspond to the red indifference curves shown in Figure 5.11, how will his best choice vary with the price of soup?

If soup costs $10 per litre, the green line labelled L_1 in Figure 5.11 will be Oscar's budget line, and he will choose bundle A. If soup costs $20 per litre, the green line labelled L_2 will be his budget line, and he will choose bundle B. If soup costs $5 per litre, the green line labelled L_3 will be his budget line, and he will choose bundle C. Table 5.4 lists his chosen bundle for each of these three soup prices.

If we plotted Oscar's best choices for many other prices in Figure 5.11, the chosen bundles would trace out a curve, drawn as the blue line running through bundles A, B, and C. This is known as the **price-consumption curve**. It shows how the best affordable consumption bundle changes as the price of a good changes, holding everything else fixed (including the consumer's income and preferences, as well as all other prices).

> The **price-consumption curve** shows how the best affordable consumption bundle changes as the price of a good changes, holding everything else fixed (including the consumer's income and preferences, as well as all other prices).

Individual Demand Curves

An **individual demand curve** describes the relationship between the price of a good and the amount a particular consumer purchases, holding everything else fixed (including the

> An **individual demand curve** describes the relationship between the price of a good and the amount a particular consumer purchases, holding everything else fix[ed] (including the consumer'[s] income and preference[s] as well as all other pr[ices]).

Figure 5.11

Effects of a Change in the Price of Soup on Soup and Bread Consumption. The price of bread is $5 per kilogram and Oscar's income is $100. When the price of soup is $10 per litre, the budget line is L_1 and Oscar chooses bundle A. When the price of soup is $20 per litre, the budget line is L_2 and he chooses bundle B. When the price of soup is $5 per litre, the budget line is L_3 and he chooses bundle C.

consumer's income and preferences, as well as all other prices). In the process of finding a consumer's price-consumption curve, we learn everything we need to plot his demand curve.

For an illustration, look at Figure 5.12. The horizontal axis measures litres of soup and the vertical axis measures the price of soup. We've used this graph to plot the data on prices and soup consumption from Table 5.4. The figure shows that Oscar purchases 3.5 litres of soup when the price of soup is $20 per litre (point E), 6 litres when the price is $10 per litre (point F), and 11 litres when the price is $5 per litre (point G). If we plotted Oscar's choices for many other soup prices, the chosen bundles would trace out the blue curve running through E, F, and G. This is an individual demand curve for soup. For every soup price, it shows the amount of soup consumed.

Table 5.4

Best Choices of Soup and Bread at Selected Soup Prices

Assumes the price of bread is $5.00 per kilogram and Oscar's income is $100. Based on Figure 5.11.

Price of Soup (per litre)	Best Choice (from Fig. 5.11)	Soup (litres)	Bread (kilograms)
$ 5.00	C	11	9
10.00	A	6	8
20.00	B	3.5	6

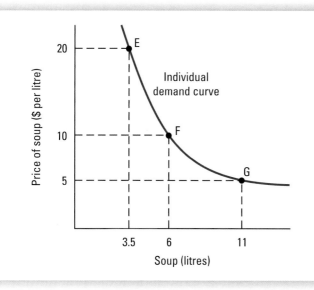

Figure 5.12
An Individual Demand Curve for Soup.
According to Table 5.4, Oscar purchases 3.5 litres of soup when soup costs $20 per litre (point E), 6 litres when the price is $10 per litre (point F), and 11 litres when the price is $5 per litre (point G). These points lie on Oscar's demand curve for soup, shown here in blue.

Movements along an individual demand curve—for example, from point E to point F in Figure 5.12—show the sensitivity of the amount purchased to the good's price. The price elasticity of demand, which we discussed in Section 2.4, measures this sensitivity; it indicates the percentage change in demand resulting from a one percent change in price. When the price elasticity of demand is large in magnitude, a slight increase in price leads to a substantial reduction in the amount purchased, and the demand curve is relatively flat. When this elasticity is small in magnitude, a large increase in price leads to a slight reduction in the amount purchased, and the demand curve is relatively steep. For additional details, review Section 2.4.

IN-TEXT EXERCISE 5.7   **In Figure 5.12 the individual demand curve for soup was determined from the price consumption curve in Figure 5.11. Suppose that soup and bread are perfect substitutes and preferences can be described by the utility function $U = S + (2/5)B$. Find the demand curve for soup for the same prices and income as in Table 5.4 as well as when soup costs $12.50.**

Application 5.2

Individual Demand Curves for Groceries

What do individual demand curves actually look like? One study carefully tracked the grocery purchases of 80 British consumers for 16 weeks.[14] Each consumer made multiple shopping trips during that time period. The prices of various products fluctuated from one shopping trip to another, producing variation in the amounts purchased. If

---

[14]Jorge Oliveira-Castro, Gordon Foxall, and Teresa Schrezenmaier, "Consumer Brand Choice: Individual and Group Analysis of Demand Elasticity," *Journal of the Experimental Analysis of Behavior* 85, March 2006, pp. 147–166.

we assume that the consumers' demand curves were stable over the 16-week study period, we can plot those curves using the data on prices and the amounts purchased.[15]

Figure 5.13 shows the individual demand curves for five of the 80 consumers and three product categories (biscuits, cheese, and breakfast cereal). Instead of plotting the data points, we have graphed the constant elasticity curves that best fit these points. (For a discussion of how economists estimate demand curves, see the appendix to Chapter 2.) We've used colors to indicate which demand curve belongs to which consumer. For example, the yellow demand curves in Figures 5.13(a), (b), and (c) all belong to the same consumer.

Notice that all of the individual demand curves in Figure 5.13 are downward sloping; these consumers buy less as prices rise. The sensitivity of purchases to prices varies across consumers and across goods. Among these five consumers, the price elasticity of the demand for biscuits ranges from −0.30 (the dark red curve) to −1.02 (the blue curve); the price elasticity of demand for cheese ranges from −0.47 (the yellow curve) to −2.11 (the green curve); and the price elasticity of demand for breakfast cereal ranges from −0.17 (the blue curve) to −0.78 (the green curve, which is almost indistinguishable from the dark red curve). The average demand elasticities for all 80 consumers in the study are −0.54 for biscuits, −1.01 for cheese, and −0.55 for breakfast cereal.

Figure 5.13

Individual Demand Curves for Three Product Categories. This figure shows the individual demand curves for five actual consumers and three product categories (biscuits, cheese, and breakfast cereal). The curves are based on prices and the amounts purchased during shopping trips over a 16-week period. Each consumer is associated with the same color in figures (a), (b), and (c).

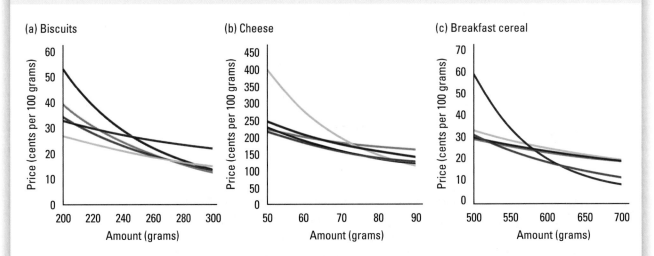

Source: Jorge Oliveira-Castro, Gordon Foxall, and Teresa Schrezenmaier, "Consumer Brand Choice: Individual and Group Analysis of Demand Elasticity," *Journal of the Experimental Analysis of Behavior* 85, March 2006, pp. 147–166.

[15]Plots of prices against the amounts purchased will not correspond to demand curves if these curves were not stable during the 16-week study period, and if sellers changed their prices in response to changes in demand. We discussed this type of problem in the appendix to Chapter 2. In such cases, economists estimate demand curves using more sophisticated statistical techniques.

WORKED-OUT PROBLEM   5.5

The Problem   As in worked-out problem 5.2, Natasha's marginal rate of substitution for concerts with films, MRS_{CF}, is F/C, where C stands for the number of concert tickets and F stands for the number of films. Natasha's income is $100 per month, and concert tickets cost $5 each. Draw her price-consumption curve (allowing the price of film tickets, P_F, to vary) and her demand curve for film tickets. What is her elasticity of demand for film tickets? What fraction of her income does she spend on film tickets, and how does that fraction depend on the price of film tickets?

The Solution   Since Natasha's best choice must satisfy the tangency condition, it equates her marginal rate of substitution, F/C, with the price ratio, P_C/P_F, so $F/C = P_C/P_F$. Rearranging this formula, we learn that the tangency condition requires the following relationship between film tickets and concert tickets.

$$F = (P_C/P_F)C$$

Since Natasha's best choice also lies on her budget line, it also satisfies $M = P_C C + P_F F$. To find a bundle that satisfies both the tangency condition formula and the budget line formula, we substitute for F in the budget constraint using the tangency condition formula.

$$M = P_C C + P_F(P_C/P_F)C = 2P_C C$$

So $C = M/(2P_C)$. Plugging this into the tangency condition formula gives us $F = M/(2P_F)$. With $M = 100$ and $P_C = 5$, we have $C = 10$ and $F = 50/P_F$. So, for example, when $P_F = 5$, Natasha buys 10 concert tickets and 10 film tickets; when $P_F = 10$, she buys 10 concert tickets and 5 film tickets. We show her price-consumption curve in Figure 5.14(a) and her demand curve for film tickets in Figure 5.14(b). Notice in Figure 5.14(a) that the number of concert tickets does not vary with the price of film tickets. That property is a consequence of Natasha's particular preferences.

   Notice that we can rewrite the formula $F = M/(2P_F)$ as $F = (M/2)P_F^{-1}$. From our discussion of demand elasticity in Section 2.4, we recognize this as a constant elasticity demand curve, where the demand elasticity is -1. Multiplying both sides of the demand function by P_F, we see that $FP_F = M/2$, which means that Natasha always spends exactly half her income on film tickets, regardless of the price of film tickets.

IN-TEXT EXERCISE 5.8   **For Alejandro, concert tickets and film tickets are perfect complements—he does not enjoy additional concerts when he has attended more concerts than films, or additional films when he has attended more films than concerts. Alejandro's preferences can be mathematically described by the utility function $U = \min[C,F]$. Here utility is the minimum number of films or concerts attended so that the number of films or concerts attended are always the same. (Why is this?) Assume he can spend $200 on tickets, and that film tickets cost $8 per ticket. Draw his price-consumption curve (allowing the price of concert tickets to vary) and his demand curve for concert tickets. Given that Alejandro attends the same number of concerts as films, show that the demands for concerts and films are identical and equal to $C = F = M/(P_C + P_F)$. How many concerts and films does Alejandro attend if concert tickets are $12?**

Figure 5.14

Effects of a Change in the Price of Film Tickets on Natasha's Purchases of Film and Concert Tickets. The solution to worked-out problem 5.5 implies that with an income of $100 per month, Natasha spends $50 to buy 10 concert tickets, regardless of the price of film tickets. The price-consumption curve, shown in figure (a), is therefore a flat line. She spends the remaining $50 on film tickets, so her film ticket purchases fall as the price of a film ticket rises, as shown in figure (b).

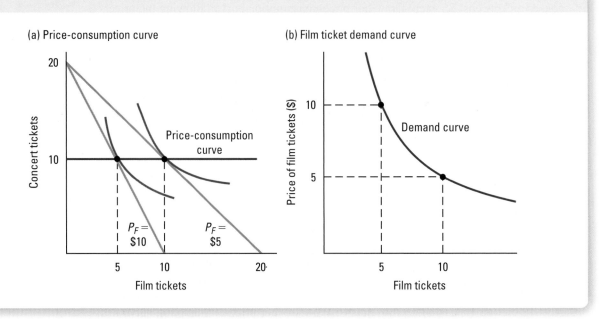

Optional The marginal utility of concerts and films can be found using calculus by partially differentiating the utility function. The marginal utility of a concert is given by $MU_C = \partial U/\partial C$ and the marginal utility of a film is $MU_F = \partial U/\partial F$.

IN-TEXT EXERCISE 5.9   **Suppose that Natasha's preferences are described by the utility function $U = C^{1/3}F^{2/3}$. The marginal utility of concerts and films are given by $MU_C = (1/3)(F/C)^{2/3}$ and $MU_F = (2/3)(C/F)^{1/3}$ respectively. Equate the marginal rate of substitution to the price ratio and use the equation for the budget constraint to find the demand for concerts and films as in worked-out problem 5.4. How many concerts and films are demanded if income is $M = 300$, $P_C = 5$, and $P_F = 10$?**

Price Changes and Shifts in Demand

In Section 2.1, we saw that a change in the price of one good can shift the demand curve for a second good. For an illustration of this effect, look back at Table 5.4. To construct this table, we fixed the price of bread at $5 per kilogram and varied the price of soup. According to the table, when soup costs $5 per litre, Oscar buys nine kilograms of bread; this means that his demand curve for bread, labelled D_1 in Figure 5.15, passes through point H. Likewise, when soup costs $10 per litre, he buys eight kilograms of bread, so his demand curve for bread, labelled D_2 in Figure 5.15, passes through point J. Finally, when soup costs $20 per litre, he buys six kilograms of bread, so his demand curve for bread, labelled D_3 in Figure 5.15, passes through point K. We can trace out the rest of each

Figure 5.15

Demand for Bread and the Price of Soup. Bread costs $5 per kilogram and Oscar's income is $100. According to Table 5.4, Oscar purchases 9 kilograms of bread when the price of soup is $5 per litre (point H), 8 kilograms of bread when the price of soup is $10 per litre (point J), and 6 kilograms of bread when the price of soup is $20 per litre (point K). Each of these points lies on a different demand curve for bread—point H lies on D_1, point J lies on D_2, and point K lies on D_3. In this example, bread and soup are complements: an increase in the price of soup shifts the demand curve for bread to the left.

demand curve by finding his best choice at other bread prices, holding income and the price of soup fixed.

Figure 5.15 shows how changes in the price of soup shift Oscar's demand curve for bread. An *increase* in the price of soup from $10 to $20 per litre shifts the demand curve for bread to the left, and the consumption of bread *falls* at any fixed bread price. A *reduction* in the price of soup from $10 to $5 per litre shifts the demand curve for bread to the right; the consumption of bread *rises* at any fixed bread price.

In Section 2.1, we observed that some pairs of goods are complements. When the price of a complement increases, a consumer buys less of the good in question. Since the consumption of complementary goods tends to move together, the price-consumption curve is upward sloping, as in Figure 5.11. For Oscar, soup and bread are complements.

We also observed in Section 2.1 that some pairs of goods are substitutes. When the price of a substitute increases, the consumer buys more of the good in question. Since the consumption of substitutable goods tends to move in opposite directions, the price-consumption curve is downward sloping.

For an illustration, look at Figure 5.16. Daphne purchases butter and margarine. Her preferences correspond to the red indifference curves. Margarine costs 25 cents per 100 grams and she can spend $10 total over the course of a month. When butter costs $1.00 per 100 grams, her budget line is L_1, and she chooses bundle A. When butter costs 50 cents per 100 grams, her budget line is L_2, and she chooses bundle B. When butter costs 25 cents per 100 grams, her budget line is L_3, and she chooses bundle C. Notice that an increase in the price of butter leads Daphne to purchase more margarine. This means that her margarine demand curve (not shown) shifts to the right. A reduction in the price of butter leads her to purchase less margarine, which shifts her margarine demand curve to the left. For Daphne, butter and margarine are substitutes.

Products tend to be complements when consumers use them together. Think of DVD players and DVDs, bathing suits and sunscreen, or flashlights and batteries. Products tend to be substitutes when consumers use them interchangeably for similar purposes. Think of Corn Flakes and Cheerios, Coke and Pepsi, or voice mail and answering machines. For a practical illustration of substitution between goods, read Add-On 5B.

Figure 5.16

Effects of a Change in the Price of Butter on the Consumption of Butter and Margarine. The price of margarine is $0.25 per 100 grams, and Daphne can spend $10 on butter and margarine. When the price of butter is $1.00 per 100 grams, her budget line is L_1 and she chooses bundle A. When the price of butter is $0.50 per 100 grams, her budget line is L_2 and she chooses bundle B. When the price of butter is $0.25 per 100 grams, her budget line is L_3 and she chooses bundle C. The blue line is her price-consumption curve.

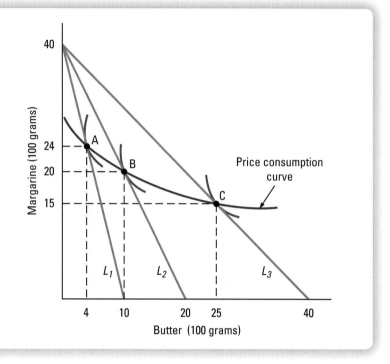

Unfortunately, it isn't always possible to tell whether goods are complements or substitutes by thinking about whether they are used together or interchangeably. For example, since people use gasoline and automobiles together, these products may seem to be complements. But the truth is not so simple. An increase in the price of gasoline encourages people to buy fuel-efficient cars rather than gas-guzzling sport utility vehicles (SUVs). That means gasoline is a complement to SUVs but may be a substitute for fuel-efficient cars, even though fuel-efficient cars use gas.

5.5 INCOME AND DEMAND

The next time you're in the checkout line at a grocery store, pay attention to the items in other shoppers' carts. If you look closely, you'll see patterns. A well-groomed woman dangles a Lexus key chain while the checker rings up premium cuts of filet mignon and an expensive bottle of balsamic vinegar. An elderly man purchasing basic supplies eyes the register nervously while sorting through his coupons. What do we learn from these observations? Though prices and preferences influence consumers' decisions, they don't explain everything. Income is clearly an important consideration. Were the Lexus driver to lose her high-paying job, she might forgo filet mignon and start clipping coupons. Were the elderly man to win the lottery, he might regularly indulge in premium steaks.

An **income effect** is the change in the consumption of a good that results from a change in income.

Economists refer to a change in the consumption of a good that results from a change in income as an **income effect**. For a better understanding of income effects, we turn once more to the theory of consumer behaviour.

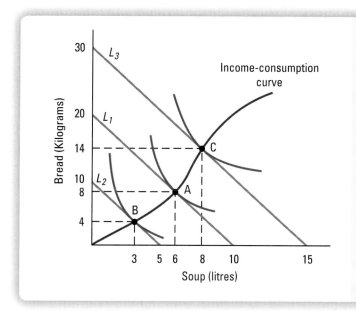

Figure 5.17

Effect of a Change in Income on Soup and Bread Consumption. Soup costs $10 per litre and bread costs $5 per kilogram. When Oscar's income is $100, his budget line is L_1 and he chooses bundle A. When his income is $50, his budget line is L_2 and he chooses bundle B. When his income is $150, his budget line is L_3 and he chooses bundle C.

The Income-Consumption Curve

Let's return to our discussion of Oscar's soup and bread purchases. We'll assume that soup costs $10 per litre and bread costs $5 per kilogram, and that Oscar's preferences correspond to the red indifference curves in Figure 5.17. How does his choice vary as we change his income? If his income is $100, his budget line is L_1, and he chooses bundle A (just as in Figure 5.11). If his income is $50, his budget line is L_2, and he chooses bundle B. If his income is $150, his budget line is L_3, and he chooses bundle C. Table 5.5 summarizes these choices.

If we plotted Oscar's choices for many other income levels in Figure 5.17, the chosen bundles would trace out a curve, shown as the blue line running through bundles A, B, and C. This is known as the **income-consumption curve**. It shows how the best affordable consumption bundle changes as income changes, holding everything else fixed (including prices and the consumer's preferences).

> The **income-consumption curve** shows how the best affordable consumption bundle changes as income changes, holding everything else fixed (including prices and the consumer's preferences).

Normal versus Inferior Goods

Economists say that a good is **normal** if an increase in income raises the amount that is consumed. In Figure 5.17, soup and bread are both normal goods. Why? As Oscar's income rises from $5 to $10 to $15, the best choice shifts from bundle B to bundle A to bundle C. The consumption of soup rises with income, as does the consumption of bread—see Table 5.5.

> If the demand for a product increases when income grows larger, the product is called a **normal good**. If it instead decreases, it is called an **inferior good**.

This term reflects the fact that a good is **inferior** if an increase in income *reduces* the amount that is consumed. This term rejects the fact that the consumption of many goods declines as income rises because people shift toward higher-quality products that fill similar needs. For example, posters are popular among university students who typically have limited funds with which to decorate their rooms and apartments. As incomes

Table 5.5

Best Choices of Soup and Bread with Selected Income Levels

Assumes soup costs $10 per litre and bread costs $5 per kilogram. Based on Figure 5.17.

Income	Best Choice (from Fig. 5.17)	Soup (litres)	Bread (kilograms)
$ 50	B	3	4
		Normal ↓	Normal ↓
100	A	6	8
		Normal ↓	Normal ↓
150	C	8	14

rise, most people graduate from posters to prints and reproductions, and finally to original artwork. Few, if any, posters graced the walls of those who appeared on *Lifestyles of the Rich and Famous*.

For a graphical illustration, look at Figure 5.18. The red indifference curves correspond to the preferences of a consumer, Erin, whose diet consists exclusively of beef and potatoes, and who has no other expenses. Erin prefers the taste of meat to potatoes, but her first priority is to avoid hunger. With meat priced at $3 per kilogram compared to $0.50 per kilogram for potatoes, a dollar spent on meat is much less filling than a dollar spent on potatoes.

When Erin can spend $18 per month, her budget line is L_1 and bundle A is her best choice. Since she can't afford filling meals, she buys 30 kilograms of potatoes and only one kilogram of beef. When her income increases to $36, her budget line is L_2 and her best choice is bundle B. Though she spends much of the extra cash on potatoes, purchasing

Figure 5.18

Effects of a Change in Income on Potato and Beef Consumption. Beef costs $3 per kilogram and potatoes cost $0.50 per kilogram. When Erin can spend $18 in total, her budget line is L_1 and she chooses bundle A. When she can spend $36 in total, her budget line is L_2 and she chooses bundle B. When she can spend $54 in total, her budget line is L_3 and she chooses bundle C.

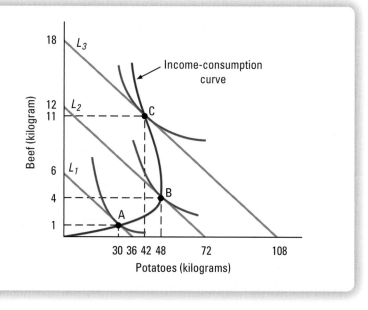

Table 5.6

Best Choices of Potatoes and Beef with Selected Income Levels

Assumes beef costs $3 per kg and potatoes cost $0.50 per kg. Based on Figure 5.18.

Income	Best Choice	Potatoes (kg)	Beef (kg)
$18	A	30	1
		Normal ↓	Normal ↓
36	B	48	4
		Inferior ↓	Normal ↓
54	C	42	11

48 kilograms, she also buys more beef (four kilograms), because her meals are now reasonably filling. When her income increases beyond $36, she tries to make her meals as tasty as possible while making sure that they remain filling. With $54, her budget line is L_3. While she *could* purchase even more potatoes, she wouldn't benefit much from them—they aren't tasty, and she's already full. Instead, she chooses bundle C. Her beef consumption rises to 11 kilograms, but her potato consumption *falls* to 42 kilograms. Table 5.6 summarizes these choices. Here, beef is a normal good at all levels of income, but potatoes change from normal to inferior as income rises.

In Section 2.4, we studied the income elasticity of demand for a good, which measures the sensitivity of purchases to changes in income. The income elasticity of demand is positive for normal goods because consumption rises with income, and negative for inferior goods because consumption falls with income. For example, according to one study of British households, the income elasticity of demand is 0.20 for butter and −0.37 for margarine.[16] As income rises, these households shift their purchases from margarine, an inferior good, to butter, a normal good.

It's easy to tell whether goods are normal or inferior by examining the income-consumption curve. Figure 5.19 illustrates this point. When the consumer's budget line is L_1, he selects point A. Budget line L_2 corresponds to a higher level of income.

- If the income-consumption curve slopes upward, the best choice on L_2 lies to the northeast of A (for example, the dark blue curve labelled ICC_1 runs through bundle B). That means potatoes and beef are both normal goods.

- If the income-consumption curve bends back toward the vertical axis, the best choice on L_2 lies to the northwest of A (for example, the medium blue curve labelled ICC_2 runs through bundle C). That means potatoes are inferior and beef is normal.

- If the income-consumption curve bends downward toward the horizontal axis, the best choice on L_2 lies to the southeast of A (for example, the light blue curve labelled ICC_3 runs through bundle D). That means potatoes are normal and beef is inferior.

To understand the characteristics of consumer preferences that make a particular good normal or inferior, read Add-On 5C.

---

[16]Department of Environment, Food, and Rural Affairs, *National Food Survey: 2000*, U.K.

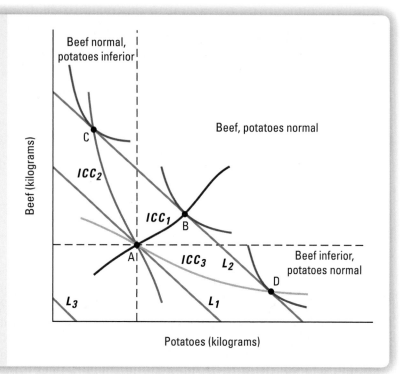

Figure 5.19

Classifying the Effects of a Change in Income on Potato and Beef Consumption. Initially, the consumer's budget line is L_1 and he chooses bundle A. An increase in income shifts his budget line outward to L_2. If he selects a bundle to the northeast of A, such as B, both potatoes and beef are normal goods. If he selects a bundle to the northwest of A, such as C, potatoes are inferior and beef is normal. If he selects a bundle to the southeast of A, such as D, potatoes are normal and beef is inferior.

Can all goods be inferior starting from any particular income level? No. At least one good must be normal. Look again at Figure 5.19. When the consumer moves from bundle A on the budget line L_1 to a bundle on the new budget line, L_2, the consumption of *something* must rise. If he purchased less of *everything*, the new bundle would have to lie to the southwest of A, which means it would not lie on the new budget line.

Can a good be inferior at all levels of income? No—every good must be normal over some income range. Figure 5.19 again provides the reason. Suppose the consumer's income falls sharply, leaving him on budget line L_3. We know that his best choice must lie somewhere on this new budget line. But *all* the bundles on this line lie to the southwest of A, which means they contain both fewer potatoes and less beef. In general, if income declines sufficiently, the consumption of *every* good must fall.

Let's summarize what we've learned about normal and inferior goods:

Properties of Normal and Inferior Goods

1. The income elasticity of demand is positive for normal goods and negative for inferior goods.

2. We can tell whether goods are normal or inferior by examining the slope of the income-consumption curve.

3. At least one good must be normal starting from any particular income level.

4. No good can be inferior at all levels of income.

Knowing whether products are normal or inferior is often important in business settings. Companies that sell inferior goods typically target their marketing efforts at lower-income households. But as Application 5.3 illustrates, they can also do quite well during economic downturns and recessions, when household incomes fall.

Application 5.3

Two Buck Chuck

After 10 years of steady growth, U.S. economic activity reached a peak in March 2001 and then slid into a recession. As jobs disappeared and household incomes slipped, many consumers were forced to curtail unnecessary spending. Sales of luxury products, such as high-end wines, were particularly hard hit.

Enter Franzia, best known as the producer of low-end "wine-in-a-box." The company's strategy was to capitalize on the recession-driven shift to lower-quality products with an inexpensive but acceptable alternative to mid-range wines. This strategy required careful attention to both packaging and product development.

Reasoning that any acceptable alternative would have to have the look and feel of better products, Franzia's product development team chose expensive-looking wine bottles (rather than boxes or jugs), synthetic corks, and upscale foil capsules. Instead of brewing generic white and red offerings, they made varietals, including a Chardonnay, a Sauvignon Blanc, a Cabernet Sauvignon, and a Merlot. In each case, they created a relatively dry wine to distance the new products from cheap alternatives, which tend to be sweet. Finally, they devised a sophisticated-looking label bearing the name Charles Shaw. There is in fact no Charles Shaw winery, nor even a vintner named Charles Shaw, but the name conveys more refinement than "Franzia."

Franzia introduced the Charles Shaw line in California, selling it for $1.99 a bottle exclusively through Trader Joe's, a well-known discount retailer. Despite a predictably cool

reception from skeptical wine experts, who found the quality of the wine little better than other low-end alternatives, "Two Buck Chuck" was an immediate hit with consumers. Stores had trouble keeping the wine in stock. Soon it was outselling famous budget brands, such as Gallo and Mondavi. Franzia expanded distribution into other states, with similar results. By early 2003, Charles Shaw was a national phenomenon, and Franzia was shipping an estimated one million cases a month.

While many factors contributed to the success of Two Buck Chuck, timing was critical. Franzia capitalized on the economic downturn by providing a cleverly designed inferior good (in the sense that economists use the term) just as declining incomes drove consumers away from higher-quality alternatives.

Figure 5.20

Engel Curves for Soup and Potatoes. Figure (a) shows Oscar's Engel curve for soup, based on the information in Table 5.5. Soup is a normal good at all levels of income. Figure (b) shows Erin's Engel curve for potatoes, based on the information in Table 5.6. Potatoes are normal when income is less than $36 and inferior when income is greater than $36.

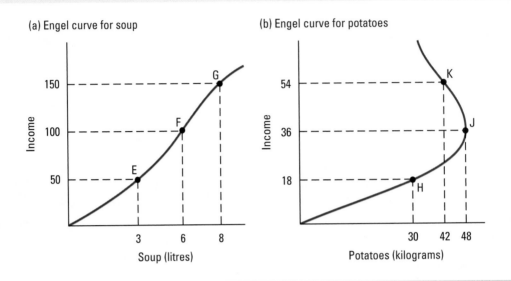

Engel Curves

The Engel curve for a good describes the relationship between income and the amount consumed, holding everything else fixed (including prices and the consumer's preferences).

The **Engel curve** for a good describes the relationship between income and the amount consumed, holding everything else fixed (including prices and the consumer's preferences). To graph an Engel curve, we measure income on the vertical axis and the amount consumed on the horizontal axis. For a normal good, an increase in income raises consumption, so the Engel curve slopes upward. For an inferior good, an increase in income reduces consumption, so the Engel curve slopes downward.

Figure 5.20(a) uses the data in Table 5.5 to plot three points (E, F, and G) on Oscar's Engel curve for soup (fixing the price of soup at $10 per litre and the price of bread at $5 per kilogram). If we plotted Oscar's choices for many other income levels, we would trace out his Engel curve for soup, shown as the blue line that runs through points E, F, and G. In this example, soup is a normal good, so the Engel curve slopes upward.

Figure 5.20(b) uses the data in Table 5.6 to plot three points (H, J, and K) on Erin's Engel curve for potatoes (fixing the price of potatoes at $0.50 per kilogram and the price of beef at $3 per kilogram). If we plotted Erin's choices for many other income levels, we would trace out her Engel curve for potatoes, shown as the blue line that runs through points H, J, and K. In this example, potatoes are a normal good when income is less than $36, so the lower part of the Engel curve slopes upward. However, since potatoes are an inferior good when income exceeds $36, the upper part of the Engel curve bends backward toward the vertical axis.

WORKED-OUT PROBLEM   5.6

The Problem   Keiko spends all her money on airtime for her wireless phone and gasoline for her car. We'll use the symbols W to stand for the number of minutes she spends talking on her wireless phone and G to stand for the number of litres of gasoline she uses during a week. Her marginal rate of substitution for gasoline with wireless minutes, in minutes per litre, is given by the formula $MRS_{GW} = 10/\sqrt{G}$. The price of gasoline, P_G, is $1 per litre and the price of wireless minutes, P_W, is $0.50 per minute. Draw Keiko's income-consumption curve and her Engel curves for gasoline and wireless minutes.

The Solution   As long as Keiko's best choice includes positive amounts of gasoline and wireless minutes, it equates her marginal rate of substitution, $10/\sqrt{G}$ minutes per litre, with the price ratio, $P_G/P_W = 1/0.5 = 2$ minutes per litre. From the resulting formula, $10/\sqrt{G} = 2$, we see that $G = 25$ litres. Since the price of gasoline is $1 per litre, 25 litres cost $25. For the moment, we'll suppose that Keiko's income, M, exceeds $25. If so, she spends $\$(M - 25)$ on wireless minutes. Since a wireless minute costs $0.50, she buys $W = 2(M - 25)$ minutes. In other words, she spends the first $25 of her budget on gasoline and the rest on airtime. In Figures 5.21(a), (b), and (c), choices with income above $25 account for the blue portions of the income-consumption curve and the Engel curves for gasoline and wireless minutes. Notice that as long as Keiko's income exceeds $25, her consumption of gasoline does not depend on her income. Gasoline is neither a normal nor an inferior good—for this good in this income range, there are no income effects.

What if Keiko's income is less than $25? In that case, she spends her entire income on gasoline. Why? Since she purchases fewer than 25 litres of gasoline, her marginal rate of substitution, $10/\sqrt{G}$ minutes per litre, is greater than 2, which means it is also greater than the price ratio. At a bundle like X in Figure 5.21(a), her indifference curve is steeper than the budget line, and the indifference curve has a diminishing MRS, so that bundle is a boundary solution. Choices with income below $25 correspond to the yellow portions of the income-consumption curve and the Engel curves for gasoline and wireless minutes shown in Figures 5.21(a), (b), and (c).

IN-TEXT EXERCISE 5.10   **Alejandro's preferences for concert tickets and film tickets are the same as those described in in-text exercise 5.8 (page 149). Film tickets cost $8 each and concert tickets cost $5 each. Draw his income-consumption curve and his Engel curves for film and concert tickets. Are these two goods normal or inferior?**

Changes in Income and Shifts in the Demand Curve

We've seen that a demand curve describes the relationship between the price of a good and the amount purchased, holding everything else fixed, including income. If income changes, the demand curve shifts. When the good in question is normal, an increase in income raises consumption at each price, so the demand curve shifts to the right. A decline

Figure 5.21

Keiko's Income-Consumption Curve and Engel Curves. The solution to worked-out problem 5.6 implies that Keiko spends the first $25 of her income on gasoline and the rest on wireless minutes. This choice produces the income-consumption curve shown in figure (a) and the Engel curves shown in figures (b) and (c).

in income reduces consumption at each price, so the demand curve shifts to the left. When a good is inferior, these effects are reversed.

To illustrate, let's revisit Oscar's consumption of soup, a normal good (see Figure 5.17 on page 153, and Table 5.5 on page 154). Suppose that bread costs $5 per kilogram. With an income of $100, Oscar's demand curve for soup, labelled D_{10} in Figure 5.22, passes through point F. Oscar purchases six litres at a price of $10 per litre. (This demand

Figure 5.22

Changes in Income Shift the Demand for Soup. According to Table 5.5, which assumes that soup costs $10 per litre and bread costs $5 per kilogram, Oscar purchases six litres of soup when his income is $100, so his demand curve for soup, D_{10}, passes through point F. He purchases three litres of soup when his income is $50, so his demand curve for soup, D_5, passes through point H. Finally, he purchases eight litres of soup when his income is $150, so his demand curve for soup, D_{15}, passes through point J. Because soup is a normal good, an increase in Oscar's income shifts the demand curve to the right; a decrease in income shifts it to the left.

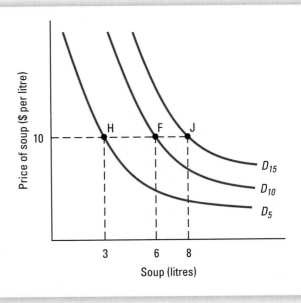

curve is the same one pictured in Figure 5.12 on page 147.) With an income of $50, Oscar purchases three litres of soup at a price of $10 per litre, so his demand curve for soup, labelled D_5, passes through point H. A *reduction* in income from $100 to $50 therefore shifts his demand curve to the left. With an income of $150, Oscar purchases eight litres of soup at a price of $10 per litre, so his demand curve for soup, labelled D_{15}, passes through point J. An *increase* in income from $100 to $150 therefore shifts his demand curve to the right.

To see an example of how a change in income shifts the demand curve for a good that is inferior over some income range, work through the following exercise.

IN-TEXT EXERCISE 5.11   **Using the information in Table 5.6 on page 155, for each level of income plot a point on Erin's demand curve for potatoes and sketch the curve through this point (like Figure 5.22). Does an increase in her income shift her demand curve for potatoes to the left or the right? Does the answer depend on her initial income?**

Application 5.4 illustrates how economists use information about consumer sensitivity to changes in both prices and income to predict choices.

Application 5.4

Forecasting Electricity Demand with Tiered Rates

In Canada, provincial governments have the authority to regulate the price of electricity. In some cases, the regulated price of extra electricity increases in a series of steps as the consumer's usage rises. This arrangement is known as a *tiered* rate structure. For example, the Ontario Energy Board in May 2009 charged consumers 5.7 cents per kilowatt hour (kWh) for the first 1000 kWh and 6.6 cents per kWh for usage over 1000 kWh. Another way to price electricity is to charge different amounts at different times of day. This arrangement is know as *peak load* pricing. Currently in Ontario utilities are installing "smart" meters in residences that allow a record of electricity use by time of day. For those consumers with smart meters electricity rates are 4.2 cents per kWh during "off-peak" periods, 7.6 cents per kWh during "mid-peak" periods, and 9.1 cents per kWh during "on-peak" periods. (To learn about consumer choice with other types of volume-sensitive pricing, read Add-On 5D.) The main purpose of tiered rates is to encourage conservation through higher prices, while keeping electricity affordable for the basic needs of low-income households, such as cooking, heating, and refrigeration.

To evaluate a possible change in a tiered rate structure, power companies and regulators need to know how electricity usage will change. Fortunately, forecasting changes in usage patterns requires little more than reliable measures of price and income elasticities.

To keep our analysis simple, let's assume that a consumer, Sean, spends his income on two goods, electricity and food. We'll assume that food costs $1 per kilogram, and that Sean's income is $200. Figure 5.23 shows the affordable consumption bundles associated with two alternative tiered rate structures for electricity. The horizontal axis measures kilowatt hours (kWh) of electricity and the vertical axis measures kilograms of food.

Under the first rate structure, electricity costs 10 cents per kWh up to 500 kWh and 20 cents per kWh for each additional kWh. As shown in Figure 5.23, Sean's budget line is kinked; it consists of the solid portions of the lines labelled L_1 and L_2. As long as Sean uses less than 500 kWh, he can choose a bundle on the solid portion of L_1. The slope of that line equals −0.1 kilogram per kWh ($0.10 per kWh ÷ $1 per kilogram). If he uses more than 500 kWh, electricity becomes more costly, so his budget line becomes steeper; he can choose a bundle on the solid portion of L_2, the slope of which is −0.2 kilogram per kWh ($0.20 per kWh ÷ $1 per kilogram). Assuming that Sean's preferences correspond to the red indifference curves, his best choice is bundle A.

Under the second rate structure, electricity again costs 10 cents per kWh up to 500 kWh, but only 15 cents for each additional kWh. Sean's budget line consists of the solid segments of the lines labelled L_1 and L_3 (the slope of which is -0.15). His best choice is bundle B.

Let's suppose that the first rate structure is currently in place. Power companies and regulators are studying the consequences of switching to the second rate structure, which means reducing the charge for consumption over 500 kWh from 20 cents to 15 cents per kWh. How might they forecast the resulting change in electricity use?

Notice that Sean would also pick bundle A from the budget line L_2 (the whole thing, not just the solid part). Similarly, he would pick bundle B from the budget line L_3 (again, the whole thing, not just the solid part). So the change in the rate structure has the same effect on his choice as switching from budget line L_2 to budget line L_3.

We can separate the change from budget line L_2 to L_3 into two parts. The first is a reduction in the price of electricity from 20 cents to 15 cents per kWh, which rotates the budget constraint from L_2 to L_4. The second is a reduction in income sufficient to produce a parallel shift of the budget constraint from L_4 to L_3. Knowing the price elasticity of demand, we can forecast the effect of the first part. Knowing the income elasticity of demand, we can forecast the effect of the

second part. Putting the two parts together, we can forecast the total impact on electricity usage.

One such study was conducted in the United States. In the spring of 2001, the California Public Utilities Commission substantially increased electricity rates for customers with moderate to high usage. Economists Peter Reiss and Matthew White forecasted the effects of the rate change by analyzing data on electricity consumption for 1307 California households in 1993 and 1997.[17] A central objective of their study was to determine the effects of the change in rate structure on households with different income levels. Did the new rate structure impact primarily wealthy households, or did it also affect the poor? To what extent did it encourage conservation, and by whom? Taking into account the differences in income and price elasticities across consumers with different incomes, Reiss and White forecasted substantial reductions in electricity use (11 percent for high-income households and 9.7 percent for low-income households), as well as substantial increases in average expenditures (28.3 percent for high-income households and 21.6 percent for low-income households). According to these predictions, the burden of the policy fell disproportionately on high-income households (as intended), but the burden on low-income households was still considerable.

Figure 5.23

Effect of a Change in Tiered Rates on Demand for Electricity. Initially, higher rates apply to electricity usage above 500 kWh, and the budget constraint is the solid portions of L_1 and L_2. Sean chooses bundle A. Facing the budget line L_2, he would make the same choice. If the rate for usage over 500 kWh is reduced, the budget constraint becomes the solid portions of L_1 and L_3. Sean chooses bundle B. Facing the budget line L_3, he would make the same choice. The effect of the change in rates is therefore the same as the effect of a shift in the budget line from L_2 to L_4 (a standard price change) plus a shift from L_4 to L_3 (a standard income change). Thus it is possible to forecast the effect of a rate change on electricity consumption using price and income elasticities.

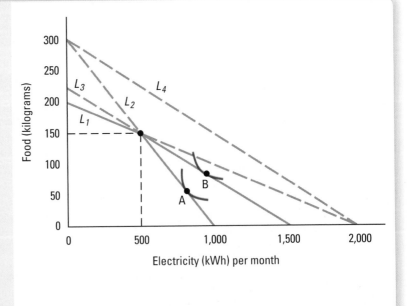

[17]Peter C. Reiss and Matthew W. White, "Household Electricity Demand, Revisited," *Review of Economic Studies* 72, July 2005, pp. 853–83.

*5.6 HOW ECONOMISTS DETERMINE A CONSUMER'S PREFERENCES

Our theory of consumer behaviour is potentially valuable in a wide range of applications. For example, an economist can use it to advise a government official on the likely effects of a policy proposal, or to forecast the success of a new pricing strategy for a business. To exploit the full power of the theory, however, we need to know a great deal about consumer preferences. How do we obtain this information?

There are two different ways to learn about consumer preferences. First, we can ask about them directly. Marketing organizations often use surveys and questionnaires to acquire information about consumer preferences. This approach has a number of limitations, however. Perhaps most important, questions about preferences are generally hypothetical. Subjects are asked to imagine two or more alternatives and say which they would prefer, but they do not actually make choices. Few people take such hypothetical questions as seriously as they would actual choices. Many also have difficulty forecasting their own behaviour, even when they think seriously about it. For example, some people tend to answer questions about hypothetical choices by saying what they think they should do rather than what they actually would do. The answers to hypothetical questions also become less reliable when the comparisons become more complex.

The second approach is to infer a consumer's preferences from his actual choices. In other words, instead of reasoning from preferences to choices as we've done so far in this chapter, we reason backwards from choices to preferences. This method is known as the **revealed preference approach**. Most economists favour this approach because it relies on information about actual behaviour rather than hypothetical choices.

> The **revealed preference approach** is a method of gathering information about consumers' preferences by observing their actual choices.

The Principle of Revealed Preference

To understand intuitively how the revealed preference approach works, look at Figure 5.24. Imagine that the consumer chooses bundle A on the green budget line. By itself, this information doesn't pin down the shape of the indifference curve that runs through bundle A, but it does provide us with some useful clues.

First, we can rule out the possibility that the indifference curve running through bundle A crosses into the yellow-shaded area below the budget line. Since bundle A is the best choice on the budget line, this conclusion follows directly from the no-overlap rule. Economists say that bundle A is **revealed preferred** to each of the bundles in the yellow-shaded area. The consumer could have chosen any of the bundles in this area, but instead chose bundle A.

> One consumption bundle is **revealed preferred** to another if the consumer chooses it when both are available.

Second, we can rule out the possibility that the indifference curve running through bundle A crosses into the blue-shaded area. Once again, the reason is simple: the bundles in this area contain more soup and more bread than bundle A, and we've assumed that more is better.

From the last two paragraphs, we know that the indifference curve running through bundle A must lie entirely in the two unshaded areas of Figure 5.24 (or along their boundaries). To say more, we must observe the consumer's choices in other settings.

As shown in Figure 5.25(a), we can learn much from the choices the consumer makes when bundle A is not available. We've changed the blue and yellow shading in Figure 5.24

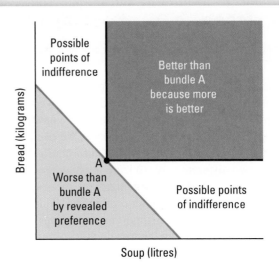

Figure 5.24

Finding the Consumer's Indifference Curve by Process of Elimination: Getting Started. The consumer chooses bundle A on the green budget line. Bundle A is revealed preferred to all the other bundles he could have purchased, which lie in the yellow-shaded area below the budget line. Since bundle A satisfies the no-overlap condition, the indifference curve that runs through bundle A cannot pass through the yellow-shaded area. Neither can it pass through the blue-shaded area, because more is better.

to gray, indicating that we have ruled out those areas. Suppose that when faced with the green budget line in Figure 5.25(a), the consumer chooses bundle B. This choice reveals that he prefers bundle B to all the bundles below the green budget line. Many of those bundles lie in the gray-shaded triangle, but some of them lie in the yellow-shaded triangle—for example, bundle C. The consumer's choices reveal that he prefers bundle A to bundle B, and that he prefers bundle B to bundle C. According to the Ranking Principle, he must therefore prefer bundle A to bundle C. This implies that the indifference curve running through bundle A does not pass through the yellow-shaded triangle.

As shown in Figure 5.25(b), we can also learn much from the choices the consumer makes when bundle A is available. We've changed the yellow shading in Figure 5.25(a) to gray, indicating that we have ruled this area out, along with the other gray-shaded areas. Suppose that when faced with the green budget line in Figure 5.25(b), the consumer chooses bundle D. Since bundle A is available, this choice reveals that the consumer prefers bundle D to bundle A.

We can rule out the possibility that the indifference curve running through bundle A passes through the blue-shaded rectangle to the northeast of bundle D. According to the More-Is-Better Principle, the consumer prefers any bundle in this area to bundle D. According to the Ranking Principle, he must therefore prefer it to bundle A.

As long as we assume that the indifference curve running through bundle A has a declining MRS, we can also rule out the possibility that it crosses into the blue-shaded triangle to the northwest of bundle D. Why? Since the consumer prefers bundle D to bundle A, the indifference curve cannot pass through or above bundle D. To enter the blue-shaded triangle while moving from left to right, it must be flatter than the line connecting bundles A and D. To exit the triangle and pass below bundle D, it must then become steeper than the line connecting bundles A and D. With a declining MRS, that can't happen—moving from left to right, the indifference curve must become flatter, not steeper.

As we observe more consumer choices, we can continue to narrow down the possibilities. With enough observations, we can locate points on the indifference curve with a high degree of precision.

Figure 5.25

Finding the Consumer's Indifference Curve by Process of Elimination: New Choices. In figure (a), bundle A is revealed preferred to bundle B and bundle B is revealed preferred to all the bundles in the yellow-shaded area (like bundle C), so the consumer must prefer bundle A to the bundles in the yellow-shaded area. In figure (b), bundle D is revealed preferred to bundle A, so all bundles that are preferred to bundle D must be preferred to bundle A as well. Since more is better, all of the bundles in the blue-shaded rectangle are preferred to bundle D and, therefore, to bundle A. If the indifference curve has a declining MRS, all of the bundles in the blue-shaded triangle are also preferred to bundle A.

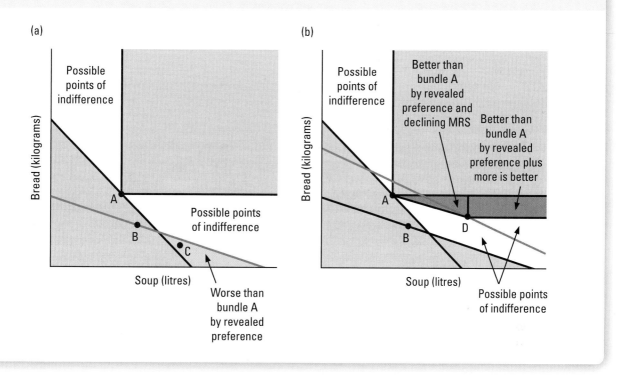

The Use of Statistical Tools

In practice, economists have few opportunities to observe large numbers of choices made by a single individual. Instead, they usually combine data on the choices of many individuals. Doing so can be tricky, since different people have different preferences. However, by using the principle of revealed preference in combination with some statistical tools, we can learn a great deal about consumers' preferences while allowing for the differences among them.

For example, in Application 4.2 (page 103), how did we know that the indifference curves shown in Figure 4.5 correspond to the actual preferences of the typical new car buyer? We derived those curves from the published results of an elaborate statistical study of new car purchases, conducted by economist Pinelopi Goldberg.[18] The data for the study were obtained from interviews of roughly 32,000 households conducted between 1983

[18]Pinelopi Koujianou Goldberg, "Product Differentiation and Oligopoly in International Markets: The Case of the U.S. Automobile Industry," *Econometrica* 63, July 1995, pp. 891–951.

and 1987. Those interviews were part of the Consumer Expenditure Survey (CES), which collects extensive data on consumer spending patterns, including detailed information on automobile purchases.

Though the process Goldberg used to determine consumer preferences is complex, it isn't mysterious. Rather, it's based on the concept of revealed preference. When a household with particular characteristics buys a particular automobile, it reveals that it prefers that alternative to all others. Each new choice reveals a bit more information. An economist usually discovers the nature of consumer preferences through statistical methods that weave together data on many choices by many individuals.

CHAPTER SUMMARY

1. **Affordable consumption bundles (LO1)**

   a. A budget line consists of all the consumption bundles that just exhaust the consumer's income. It is the boundary that separates all the affordable consumption bundles from all other bundles. Affordable choices that do not exhaust the consumer's income lie to the southwest of the budget line.

   b. The slope of the budget line equals the price ratio times -1, with the price of the good measured on the horizontal axis appearing in the numerator, and the price of the good measured on the vertical axis appearing in the denominator.

   c. The budget line intersects the axis that measures the amount of any particular good, X, at the quantity M/P_X, which is the amount of X the consumer can purchase by spending all income on X.

   d. A change in income shifts the budget line—outward for an increase and inward for a decrease—without changing its slope.

   e. A change in the price of a good rotates the budget line—outward for a decrease and inward for an increase. The line pivots at the intercept for the good with the unchanged price.

   f. Multiplying all prices by a single constant has the same effect on the budget line as dividing income by the same constant. Changing prices *and* income by the same proportion has *no* effect on the budget line.

2. **Consumer choice (LO2)**

   a. Assuming that more is better, the consumer's best choice lies on the budget line.

   b. We can recognize best choices by applying the no-overlap rule.

   c. Interior solutions always satisfy the tangency condition. Consequently, if a bundle that includes two goods, X and Y, is an interior solution, then $MRS_{XY} = P_X/P_Y$ at that bundle.

   d. When indifference curves have declining MRSs, any interior choice that satisfies the tangency condition is a best affordable choice.

   e. Whenever the consumer purchases good X but not good Y, then $MRS_{XY} \geq P_X/P_Y$ at the chosen bundle.

3. **Utility maximization (LO3)**

   a. If a utility function represents a consumer's preference, then the affordable bundle that maximizes the utility function is the consumer's best choice.

   b. At the best choice, a small amount of additional income generates the same increase in the consumer's utility value when spent on any good whose quantity is positive. That is, at the best choice, the ratio of marginal utility to price is the same for all goods. The increase in utility is at least as large as when the additional income is spent on any good whose quantity is zero.

4. **Prices and demand (LO4)**

   a. The price-consumption curve provides all the information necessary to draw an individual demand curve.

   b. When the price of one good changes, the demand curve for another good may shift. The demand curve shifts to the left when the price of a complement rises and to the right when it decreases. When the price of a substitute changes, these effects are reversed.

5. **Income and demand (LO4)**

   a. We can determine how the consumption of a good varies with income, and whether it is normal or inferior, by examining the income-consumption curve.

b. At least one good must be normal starting from any particular income level.

c. No good can be inferior at all levels of income.

d. The income elasticity of demand is positive for normal goods and negative for inferior goods.

e. When a good is normal, the Engel curve slopes upward; when a good is inferior, it slopes downward.

f. An individual demand curve for a good shifts when income changes. When the good is normal, an increase in income shifts the demand curve to the right, and a decline in income shifts the demand curve to the left. When a good is inferior, these patterns are reversed.

*6 How economists determine a consumer's preferences (LO5)

a. If we can observe a sufficient number of consumer choices with sufficient variation in prices and income, we can trace the shape of a consumer's indifference curve. These choices reveal the consumer's preferences.

b. In practice, economists have few opportunities to observe a single consumer make a large number of choices. Instead, they usually combine data on the choices of many individuals, using statistical procedures to allow for differences in individual preferences.

ADDITIONAL EXERCISES

Exercise 5.1: The price of bread is $5 per kilogram, and the price of butter is $10 per kilogram. Channing spends all of her income, buying six kilograms of bread, two kilograms of butter, and nothing else. What is her income? Draw her budget constraint and identify her chosen consumption bundle. (LO1, 2)

Exercise 5.2: The price of bread is $7.50 per kilogram, and the price of butter is $10 per kilogram. Rupert's income is $120, with which he buys 12 kilograms of bread. How much butter does he buy, assuming that he consumes nothing else? Draw his budget constraint and identify his chosen consumption bundle. (LO1, 2)

Exercise 5.3: The price of bread is $6 per kilogram and Aaron's income is $180. He buys 15 kilograms of bread, 10 kilograms of butter, and nothing else. What is the price of butter? Draw Aaron's budget constraint and identify his chosen consumption bundle. (LO1, 2)

Exercise 5.4: As in exercise 4.3, Gary has two children, Kevin and Dora, who consume "yummies" and nothing else. He loves them equally and is happiest when their consumption is equal. Suppose that Kevin starts out with two yummies and Dora with eight yummies, and that Gary can redistribute their yummies. Draw a "budget line" that shows his available choices and indicate his best choice by adding indifference curves. How would your answer differ if Kevin started out with six yummies and Dora with four? (LO1, 2)

Exercise 5.5: Oscar starts out with budget line L_1, consuming bundle A in Figure 5.17 (page 153). What point will he choose if the prices of soup and bread double? If they fall by 50 percent? If his income doubles along with prices? (LO4)

Exercise 5.6: Alan can spend $10 a week on snacks. He likes ice cream, which costs $1 per scoop, and popcorn, which costs 40 cents per bag. Draw Alan's budget constraint and indifference curves (assuming that each of his indifference

curves has a declining MRS) and show his best choice. Now imagine that his older sister Alice hates ice cream but always steals half his popcorn. How does this problem change Alan's budget constraint? On the indifference curves you've drawn, show his new best choice. (LO1, 2)

Exercise 5.7: Assuming that indifference curves have declining MRSs, could a consumer like the one depicted in Figure 5.6(a) (page 134) have more than one best choice on the budget line? To answer this question, pick two points on the budget line and try drawing two indifference curves, one through each point, and both tangent to the budget line. (LO2)

Exercise 5.8: Olivia has received a $15 gift certificate that is redeemable only for roasted peanuts. Bags of roasted peanuts come in two sizes, regular and jumbo. A regular bag contains 30 peanuts and a jumbo bag contains 50. If a regular bag costs 50 cents and a jumbo bag costs 75 cents, how many of each will Olivia purchase? What if the jumbo bag costs $1? In each case, draw a budget line that shows her available choices, and indicate her best choice by adding indifference curves. Assume that Olivia cares only about the number of peanuts, and not about the size of the bag. (LO2)

Exercise 5.9: Natasha's marginal rate of substitution for concerts with films, MRS_{CF}, is F/C, where C stands for the number of concerts and F stands for the number of films. Natasha's income is $100 per month. Suppose she buys twice as many film tickets as concert tickets. If the price of a film ticket is $4, what is the price of a concert ticket? (LO3)

Exercise 5.10: Suppose Table 4.2 (page 97) describes Madeline's preference ranking. As in Examples 5.1 and 5.2 (pages 127 and 133), assume that her income is $6 per day and bread costs $2 per loaf. We know from Example 5.2 that when soup costs $2 per bowl, she eats two bowls of soup and one loaf of bread. From in-text exercise 5.3 (page 134), you should know how much soup and bread she consumes when soup costs $4 per bowl. What will she consume if soup costs $6 per bowl? Each of these choices corresponds to a point on her demand curve for soup. Plot them. (LO2, 4)

Exercise 5.11: Given income of $400 and concert and movie ticket prices of $25 and $10 respectively, Elena is considering whether to attend 10 concerts and 15 movies. If Elena's MRS_{CF} is equal to F/C would she maximize utility with this choice? If not, how many movies and concerts should she attend? (LO3)

Exercise 5.12: As in worked-out problems 5.2 and 5.5 (pages 138 and 149), imagine that Natasha spends all of her monthly income on tickets to concerts and films. Suppose the formula for her marginal rate of substitution is $MRS_{CF} = (3 + F)/(2C)$. (Remember that fractions of tickets are allowed; if she buys half a concert ticket it means she watches a concert every other month.) Suppose Natasha's income is $300 per month. Concert tickets cost $5 each. Draw her price-consumption curve (allowing the price of film tickets to vary), and draw her demand curve for film tickets. (LO3)

Exercise 5.13: Using the information in Table 5.5 (page 154), plot the Engel curve for bread. Using the information in Table 5.6 (page 155), plot the Engel curve for beef. Do these curves slope upward or downward? Why? (LO4)

Exercise 5.14: As in exercise 4.5, Ada prefers to eat soup and bread in fixed proportions. When she eats X litres of soup, she prefers to eat $\sqrt{X}$ kilograms of bread. If she has X litres of soup and more than $\sqrt{X}$ kilograms of bread, she eats all the soup along with $\sqrt{X}$ kilograms of bread, and throws the extra bread away. If she has X litres of soup and fewer than $\sqrt{X}$ kilograms of bread (say Y kilograms), she eats all the bread along with Y^2 kilograms of soup and throws the extra soup away. Assume she spends all her income on soup and bread. Plot her income-consumption curve, her Engel curve for soup, and her Engel curve for bread. (LO3, 4)

****Exercise 5.15:** Ashley spends all her income on gasoline and food. At first she earns $100, buys 25 litres of gasoline at $2 per litre, and purchases 10 kilograms of food at $5 per kilogram. Her income later rises to $200, but the price of gasoline increases to $5 per litre, and the price of food rises to $7 per kilogram. Is she better or worse off? Why? Draw Ashley's budget constraint before and after the change in income, and identify her best choice before the change. (LO4)

****Exercise 5.16:** Make the same assumptions as in exercise 5.14, except that the price of food rises to $8 instead of $7. Can you say whether Ashley is better or worse off? What if she purchases 11 kilograms of food after the change in prices and income? What if she purchases 15 kilograms of food after the change? In each case, draw Ashley's budget constraint before and after the change and identify her best choices. (LO4)

From Demand to Welfare

LEARNING OBJECTIVES

After reading this chapter, students should be able to

LO1 Distinguish between the two main effects of a price change and understand why demand curves generally slope downward.

LO2 Explain how to use demand curves to measure changes in consumer welfare.

LO3 Explain the purpose of a cost-of-living index and define the Laspeyres index.

LO4 Use cost-of-living indexes to measure changes in consumer welfare and explain why those measures may be biased.

LO5 Understand the trade-off between consumption and leisure and explain how the wage rate affects labour supply.

LO6 Understand the difference between compensated and uncompensated demand curves and their relationship to consumer welfare.

In 1943, T. J. Watson, Sr., the founder, president, and later chairman of IBM, famously speculated that "there is a world market for maybe five computers." With the benefit of 20/20 hindsight, we know that his forecast was low by a factor of at least several hundred million. But Watson didn't lack vision or imagination—he simply failed to anticipate how inexpensive computers would become. Today, a $1000 computer that weighs very little and slips into a briefcase performs computations more than a million times as fast as ENIAC, the world's first all-purpose electronic digital computer, built in 1946 at an inflation-adjusted cost of nearly $5 million.

As a result of the dramatic reduction in the price of computing power, consumers are presumably better off today than 10, 20, or 30 years ago—but by how much? We know what we *pay* for our computers, but what are they *worth* to us? In dollar terms, what has the digital revolution contributed to our well-being?

Policymakers have a keen interest in the answers to questions like these. For example, when they use citizens' tax dollars to support the development of new technologies (as they did with digital computing), they are betting that the net social benefits will exceed the costs. Similarly, businesses can sometimes profit from better knowledge of the value that consumers derive from a product or service (see, for example, the discussion of price discrimination in Chapter 18).

In this chapter, we'll continue our exploration of consumer decision making by examining five topics:

1. *The effects of a price change.* Price changes affect purchases in two ways. First, consumers shift their purchases toward those goods that have become relatively less expensive. Second, when prices rise, consumer purchasing power falls, because a dollar doesn't go as far as it once did. We'll see that this distinction helps us understand why demand curves usually slope downward.

2. *Changes in consumer welfare using demand curves.* When economists evaluate changes in a consumer's well-being (also known as *consumer welfare*), they use money as a yardstick. We'll examine a common measure of a change in welfare, and we'll explain how to determine its size using demand curves.

3. *Changes in consumer welfare using cost-of-living indexes.* Sometimes, economists are unable to estimate either preferences or demand curves reliably (for example, because there isn't enough data). We'll see that it is still possible to say something about changes in consumer welfare using cost-of-living indexes.

4. *Labour supply and the demand for leisure.* Labour supply is the flip side of the demand for leisure. By dissecting the effects of a change in the wage rate, we'll see why an ordinary consumer's labour supply curve can slope either upward or downward.

*5. *Another type of demand curve.* By dissecting the effects of price changes, we can construct a new type of demand curve—one that holds a consumer's welfare fixed, rather than his income. We'll explain how economists use these demand curves to compute changes in consumer welfare more accurately.

6.1 DISSECTING THE EFFECTS OF A PRICE CHANGE

When the price of a good increases, two things happen:

1. That good becomes more expensive relative to all other goods. Consumers tend to shift their purchases away from the more expensive good and toward other goods.

2. Consumers' purchasing power declines. A dollar doesn't buy as much as it once did. Because consumers can no longer afford the consumption bundles they would have chosen if the price hadn't risen, they are effectively poorer and must adjust their purchases accordingly.

In this section, we'll explain how to divide the effect of a price change into these two components. Why should we bother? Isn't it enough to know the overall effect of a price change? As we'll see, economists have learned quite a bit about consumer demand and welfare from dissecting price changes in this way.

Compensated Price Changes

As the price of a good changes, the consumer's well-being varies. To illustrate this point, let's assume once again that Oscar (whom we introduced in Section 5.4) spends all his income on soup and bread. Oscar can spend $100 per week, and bread costs $5 per kilogram.

Figure 6.1

The Compensated Price Effects of an Increase and a Decrease in the Price of Soup. Initially, Oscar faces budget line L_1 and chooses bundle A. In figure (a), an increase in the price of soup rotates the budget line to L_2, and Oscar chooses bundle B. For a compensated increase in the price of soup, his budget line would shift to L_3, and he would pick bundle C. In figure (b), a reduction in the price of soup rotates the budget line to L_4, and Oscar chooses bundle D. For a compensated decrease in the price of soup, his budget line would shift to L_5, and he would pick bundle E.

When soup costs $5 per litre, Oscar's budget constraint is the line labelled L_1 in Figure 6.1, and he chooses bundle A. When the price of soup rises to $10 per litre, Oscar's purchasing power declines. As shown in Figure 6.1(a), his budget line rotates to L_2 and he chooses bundle B. Notice that bundle B lies on a lower indifference curve than bundle A. The price increase makes him worse off because it reduces his purchasing power.

How much money would we need to give Oscar to compensate him for the higher price of soup? Suppose we give him an extra $50, bringing his income to $150 per day. That level of compensation would allow him to buy any bundle on or below the black budget line (labelled L_3) in Figure 6.1(a). According to the figure, he would choose bundle C. Notice that bundles A and C are on the same indifference curve. Oscar is therefore indifferent between paying $5 per litre for soup with an income of $100, and paying $10 per litre for soup with an income of $150. The extra $50 exactly compensates him for the $5 increase in the price of soup. The yellow arrow shows the effect of that compensation on his budget line.

The shift from the budget line labelled L_1 to the one labelled L_2 in Figure 6.1(a) illustrates an **uncompensated price change**—it consists of a price change with no change in income. We studied uncompensated price changes in Chapter 5. Usually, we use the phrase *price change* by itself to mean an uncompensated change. The shift from the budget constraint labelled L_1 to the one labelled L_3 in Figure 6.1(a) illustrates a **compensated price change**—it consists of a price change and an income change which, together, leave the consumer's well-being unaffected.

An **uncompensated price change** consists of a price change with no change in income. A **compensated price change** consists of a price change and an income change which, together, leave the consumer's well-being unaffected.

Figure 6.1(b) illustrates the effect of a *reduction* in the price of soup from $5 to $2.50. The uncompensated price change rotates Oscar's budget line from L_1 to L_4, and his choice shifts from bundle A to bundle D. He is *better off* as a result. To compensate for the price change, we would need to take away income. As indicated by the yellow arrow, taking away $37.50 shifts his budget line from L_4 to L_5. With L_5, he chooses bundle E, which lies on the same indifference curve as bundle A. He is therefore indifferent between paying $5 per litre for soup with an income of $100, and paying $2.50 per litre for soup with an income of $62.50. In this case, the shift from the budget line labelled L_1 to the one labelled L_5 reflects the compensated price change.

Substitution and Income Effects

By definition, a compensated price change consists of an uncompensated price change plus compensation. Therefore, the effect of a compensated price change on consumption is the same as the effect of an uncompensated price change, plus the effect of compensation.

Effect of a compensated price change =

Effect of an uncompensated price change + Effect of providing compensation

For example, in Figure 6.1(a), the effect of the uncompensated price change is to shift consumption from bundle A to bundle B, and the effect of the compensation is to shift consumption from bundle B to bundle C. Together, these changes shift consumption from bundle A to bundle C, just like a compensated price change.

We can gain a better understanding of uncompensated price changes by rearranging the preceding formula. Let's add to both sides of the last formula the effect on consumption of *removing* the compensation. Since the effect of removing the compensation exactly offsets the effect of providing it, we obtain the following formula.

Effect of an uncompensated price change =

Effect of a compensated price change + Effect of removing compensation   **(1)**

For example, in Figure 6.1(a), the effect of the compensated price change is to shift consumption from bundle A to bundle C, and the effect of removing the compensation is to shift consumption from bundle C to bundle B. Together, these changes shift consumption from bundle A to bundle B, just like an uncompensated price change.

Equation (1) tells us that we can break up the effect of an uncompensated price change into two pieces. The first piece—the effect on consumption of a compensated price change—is known as the **substitution effect of a price change**. The name of this effect reminds us that a change in relative prices causes the consumer to substitute one good for another. The substitution effect always involves a movement along an indifference curve to a point where the slope of the indifference curve is the same as the slope of the new budget line. In Figure 6.2, which illustrates the same price changes as Figure 6.1, we indicate the substitution effects with gray arrows. In Figure 6.2(a), the substitution effect of an increase in the soup price from $5 to $10 per litre shifts Oscar's choice from bundle A on L_1 to bundle C on L_3. In Figure 6.2(b), the substitution effect of a reduction in the soup price from $5 to $2.50 per litre shifts his choice from bundle A on L_1 to bundle E on L_5.

The second piece—the effect on consumption of removing the compensation—is known as the **income effect of a price change**. The name of this effect reminds us that a price change affects the consumer's purchasing power. The income effect always involves

The effect on consumption of a compensated price change is known as the **substitution effect of a price change.**

The effect on consumption of removing the compensation after creating a compensated price change is known as the **income effect of a price change.**

Figure 6.2

Dissection of the Effects of an Increase and a Decrease in the Price of a Normal Good. In figure (a), an increase in the soup price rotates the budget line from L_1 to L_2. The uncompensated price effect consists of a substitution effect (the movement from bundle A to bundle C) and an income effect (the movement from bundle C to bundle B). In figure (b), a reduction in the soup price rotates the budget line from L_1 to L_4. The uncompensated price effect consists of a substitution effect (the movement from bundle A to bundle E) and an income effect (the movement from bundle E to bundle D). We indicate uncompensated price effects with blue arrows, substitution effects with gray arrows, and income effects with yellow arrows.

a parallel shift in the budget constraint, toward the origin for a price increase (since the consumer's purchasing power declines) and away from the origin for a price reduction (since his purchasing power rises).[1] In Figure 6.2, we indicate the income effects with yellow arrows. In Figure 6.2(a), the income effect of an increase in the soup price from $5 to $10 per litre shifts the consumer's choice from bundle C on L_3 to bundle B on L_2. In Figure 6.2(b), the income effect of a reduction in the soup price from $5 to $2.50 per litre shifts the choice from bundle E on L_5 to bundle D on L_4.

Using these definitions, we can rewrite equation (1) as follows.

$$\text{Effect of an uncompensated price change} =$$
$$\text{Substitution effect of the price change} + \text{Income effect of the price change} \quad \textbf{(2)}$$

In Figure 6.2, we indicate the effects of the uncompensated price changes with blue arrows. Equation (2) tells us that, together, the gray and yellow arrows start and end at the same bundles as the blue arrows.

---

[1] A price increase requires positive compensation, so removing the compensation reduces income and shifts the budget line inward. A price reduction requires negative compensation, so removing the compensation increases income and shifts the budget line outward.

In short, an uncompensated price change involves both a change in relative prices (which rotates the budget line) and a change in purchasing power (which causes a parallel shift of the budget line). The substitution effect isolates the influence of the change in relative prices, while the income effect isolates the influence of the change in purchasing power.

WORKED-OUT PROBLEM   6.1

The Problem   As in worked-out problem 5.5 (page 149), Natasha's marginal rate of substitution for concerts with films, MRS_{CF}, is F/C, where C stands for the number of concert tickets and F stands for the number of film tickets. For this problem, you will also need the formula for her indifference curves: $F = U/C$. Natasha can spend $100 and concert tickets cost $5 per ticket. Suppose the price of film tickets falls from $5 to $1.25 per ticket. What is the uncompensated effect on her purchases of film and concert tickets? What is the compensated effect? How much compensation is involved? Break up the effect of the uncompensated price change into the substitution and income effects.

The Solution   From the answer to worked-out problem 5.5, we know that Natasha will choose $F = M/(2P_F)$ and $C = M/(2P_C)$, where M is her income, P_F is the price of a film ticket, and P_C is the price of a concert ticket. So, with $M = \$100$, $P_F = \$5$, and $P_C = \$5$, she chooses $(C, F) = (10, 10)$. If P_F falls to $1.25, she chooses $(C, F) = (10, 40)$. This uncompensated price reduction raises her film ticket purchases from 10 to 40 and leaves her concert ticket purchases unchanged.

Now let's solve for her choice when the price change is compensated. Since Natasha's best choice must satisfy the tangency condition, it equates her marginal rate of substitution, F/C, with the price ratio, P_C/P_F, so $F/C = P_C/P_F$. With $M = \$100$, $P_C = \$5$, and $P_F = \$1.25$, the tangency condition therefore requires the following relationship between film tickets and concert tickets.

$$F = 4C$$

Natasha's best choice with a compensated price change also lies on the indifference curve that runs through the bundle $(C, F) = (10, 10)$. Since the formula for her indifference curves is $F = U/C$, the value of U for the indifference curve that runs through the bundle $(C, F) = (10, 10)$ must be 100, which means the formula for this indifference curve is

$$F = 100/C$$

A bundle can satisfy both the tangency condition formula and the indifference curve formula at the same time only if $4C = 100/C$. This requires $C^2 = 25$, or $C = 5$. Using either the tangency condition formula or the indifference curve formula, we then see that $F = 20$. So the compensated price effect shifts Natasha from the bundle $(C, F) = (10, 10)$ to the bundle $(C, F) = (5, 20)$.

At the new prices, Natasha requires only $50 to buy the bundle $(C, F) = (5, 20)$. Since her income is $100, we would take $50 away from Natasha to compensate for the price cut.

The substitution effect is the same as the effect of the compensated price change. The income effect is the residual: it shifts Natasha from the bundle $(C, F) = (5, 20)$ to the bundle $(C, F) = (10, 40)$.

IN-TEXT EXERCISE 6.1   **As in worked-out problem 5.6 (page 144), Keiko's marginal rate of substitution for gasoline with wireless minutes, MRS_{GW}, is $10/\sqrt{G}$, where G stands for litres of gasoline. For this problem, you will also need the formula for her indifference curves: $W = U - 20\sqrt{G}$, where W stands for the number of wireless minutes. Keiko can spend \$40 and wireless minutes cost \$0.50 per minute. Suppose the price of gasoline rises from \$1 to \$2.50 per litre. What is the effect on her purchases of gasoline and wireless minutes? Break up this effect into the substitution and income effects. How much compensation does the substitution effect involve?**

IN-TEXT EXERCISE 6.2   **If goods are perfect complements show that the substitution effect is equal to zero and the income effect is always opposite the sign of the price change. If goods are perfect substitutes provide an example where the substitution and income effects are both non-zero. Additional Exercise 6.2 at the end of the chapter explores the case in which the substitution and income effects may separately or together equal zero.**

The Direction of Substitution and Income Effects

A compensated *increase* in the price of a good always causes the consumer to buy *less* of that good—he substitutes *away* from the good as it becomes more expensive. Conversely, a compensated *reduction* in the price of a good always causes the consumer to buy *more* of that good—he substitutes *toward* the good as it becomes less expensive. The substitution effect is therefore negative for a price increase and positive for a price reduction.

Figure 6.3 illustrates this point. In drawing Figure 6.3(a), we have assumed that the consumer's indifference curve has a declining MRS. With the budget line labelled L_1, the consumer chooses bundle A. After a compensated increase in the price of soup, he faces a steeper budget line (labelled L_2) and chooses another bundle, B, on the indifference curve that runs through A. Since the indifference curve is tangent to a steeper budget line at B than at A, and since it has a declining MRS, B must lie to the northwest of A (as shown), which means it contains less soup.

Figure 6.3(b) makes the same point without assuming that the consumer's indifference curve has a declining MRS. Let's assume that the consumer starts out with the budget line labelled L_1. After a compensated increase in the price of soup, his budget line is L_2. These two lines cross at the bundle labelled X. Because the price change is compensated, the consumer must be indifferent between her best choice on L_1 and his best choice on L_2. Therefore, his best choice on L_1 can't lie below L_2, and his best choice on L_2 can't lie below L_1. This observation implies that his best choice on L_1 must lie to the right of bundle X, like bundle A, and his best choice on L_2 must lie to the left of bundle X, like bundle B. Since the compensated increase in the price of soup moves the consumer from the right of X to the left of X, it reduces his soup consumption.

What about income effects? The direction of an income effect depends on whether the good in question is normal or inferior. An increase in the price of a good reduces the consumer's purchasing power, which causes him to buy less if the good is normal and more if it is inferior. Conversely, a reduction in the price of a good increases the consumer's purchasing power, which causes him to buy more if the good is normal and less if it is inferior. If the good is normal, the income effect is therefore negative for a price increase and positive for a price reduction. If the good is inferior, the income effect is positive for a price increase and negative for a price reduction.

Figure 6.3

The Direction of the Substitution Effect. Figure (a) shows that, with a declining MRS, the point of tangency between an indifference curve and a relatively steep budget line (reflecting a high price of soup) must be to the left of the point of tangency between the same indifference curve and a relatively flat budget line (reflecting a low price of soup). This implies that the substitution effect of an increase in the price of soup reduces soup consumption. Figure (b) makes the same point without assuming a declining MRS. If the consumer is indifferent between his best choice on the budget line L_1 (which reflects a low price of soup) and his best choice on the budget line L_2 (which reflects a high price of soup), then his best point on L_2 must lie to the left of X, and his best choice on L_1 must lie to the right of X.

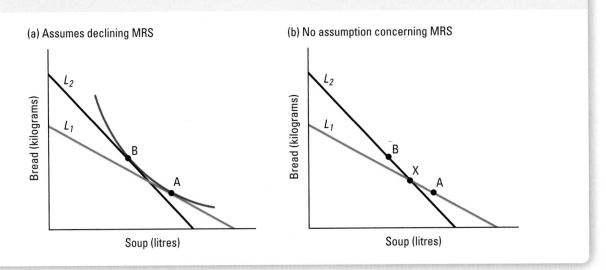

For a normal good, the income effect therefore works in the same direction as the substitution effect. Both are negative for a price increase, and both are positive for a price reduction. For a graphical illustration, look again at Figure 6.2. In this figure, soup is a normal good: a shift from L_2 to L_3 in Figure 6.2(a) increases soup consumption, as does a shift from L_5 to L_4 in Figure 6.2(b). In Figure 6.2(a), the substitution and income effects both reduce soup consumption; in Figure 6.2(b), they both increase soup consumption.

For an inferior good, the substitution and income effects work in *opposite* directions. For a price increase, the income effect increases consumption and the substitution effect reduces it. For a price reduction, the directions are reversed.

Figure 6.4 illustrates the opposing substitution and income effects for an inferior good. We'll assume that Erin, whom we introduced in Section 5.5, divides her income between potatoes and beef, and that potatoes are inferior. To start, potatoes cost $1 per kilogram, beef costs $6 per kilogram, and Erin's income is $72 per month. The budget line is L_1 and Erin picks bundle A. If the price of potatoes falls to 50 cents per kilogram, the budget line rotates to L_2 and Erin picks bundle B.

Let's break up this change into a substitution effect and an income effect. Bundle C is the point of tangency between the indifference curve that runs through bundle A and a line with the same slope as the new budget constraint. The substitution effect corresponds to the movement from bundle A to bundle C, and the income effect corresponds to the movement from bundle C to bundle B.

Figure 6.4

Dissection of the Effect of a Reduction in the Price of an Inferior Good. Initially, Erin faces budget line L_1 and chooses bundle A. A reduction in the price of potatoes rotates her budget line to L_2, and she chooses bundle B. This uncompensated price effect, which shifts her choice from bundle A to bundle B (the blue arrow), consists of a substitution effect, which shifts her choice from bundle A to bundle C (the gray arrow), and an income effect, which shifts her choice from bundle C to bundle B (the yellow arrow).

The substitution effect in Figure 6.4 involves an increase in the number of potatoes. In other words, when potatoes become less expensive, the consumer substitutes toward potatoes. In this respect, potatoes and soup are similar. However, the income effect in Figure 6.4 involves a *reduction* in the number of potatoes. Why? To compensate for the price reduction, we have to take away income. When we eliminate this compensation, income rises, shifting the budget line from L_3 to L_2. Since potatoes are inferior, Erin buys fewer potatoes.

Let's summarize our conclusions:

The Direction of Income and Substitution Effects

1. The substitution effect is negative for a price increase and positive for a price reduction.

2. If a good is normal, the income effect reinforces the substitution effect. It is negative for a price increase and positive for a price reduction.

3. If a good is inferior, the income effect opposes the substitution effect. It is positive for a price increase and negative for a price reduction.

Why Do Demand Curves Usually Slope Downward?

In Chapter 2, we observed that demand curves usually slope downward. This principle, known as the **Law of Demand**, has very few exceptions (see Application 6.1 below). By dissecting the effects of a price change, we can learn why most but not all goods obey this law.

The **Law of Demand** states that demand curves usually slope downward.

The substitution effect of a price change is *always* consistent with the Law of Demand. An increase in the price of a good causes the consumer to substitute away from it, reducing demand, and a reduction in the price of a good causes the consumer to substitute toward it, raising demand. If a good violates the Law of Demand, the explanation must therefore involve income effects.

For a normal good, we've seen that the income effect reinforces the substitution effect. As a result, normal goods *always* obey the Law of Demand.

But what about inferior goods? In the previous section, we saw that the income effect for an inferior good *opposes* the substitution effect. Theoretically, if the income effect is large, the substitution effect is small, and the good is inferior, the amount purchased could increase when the price rises, violating the Law of Demand.

Figure 6.5 illustrates this possibility. The figure is identical to Figure 6.4, except that this consumer, Robert, chooses bundle D (instead of bundle B) when the budget line is L_2. The increase in income associated with the outward shift in the budget line from L_3 to L_2 reduces potato consumption by a larger amount than in Figure 6.4 (from 65 to 36 kilograms). In other words, potatoes are more inferior in Figure 6.5 than they are in Figure 6.4. In fact, the magnitude of the income effect is larger than the magnitude of the substitution effect, so that the drop in price reduces the consumption of potatoes (from 48 to 36 kilograms). As a result, in this example, the demand curve for potatoes slopes upward.

> A product is called a **Giffen good** if the amount purchased increases as the price rises.

A product is called a **Giffen good** if the amount purchased increases as the price rises. In practice, Giffen goods are extremely hard to find, for two reasons. First, most goods are normal. Second, if spending on a good accounts for a small fraction of a consumer's budget (as it does for most goods), even a large increase in the good's price doesn't have much of an impact on the consumer's overall purchasing power, so the income effect is small. (See the appendix to this chapter for a more detailed explanation of this point).

Even so, there may be exceptions to the Law of Demand. Application 6.1 discusses two possible cases of Giffen goods.

Figure 6.5

Dissection of the Effect of a Reduction in the Price of a Giffen Good. Initially, Robert faces budget line L_1 and chooses bundle A. A reduction in the price of potatoes rotates his budget line to L_2, and he chooses bundle D. The uncompensated price effect, which shifts Robert's choice from bundle A to bundle D (the blue arrow), consists of a substitution effect, which shifts his choice from bundle A to bundle C (the gray arrow), and an income effect, which shifts his choice from bundle C to bundle D (the yellow arrow).

Application 6.1

Irish Potatoes and Japanese Shochu

The potato was introduced in Ireland at the beginning of the seventeenth century. It caught on rapidly, in large part because it yielded more food per acre than native crops. The resulting abundance of food permitted the Irish population to swell from three million in the late 1500s to roughly eight million by 1840. In the process, Ireland became increasingly dependent on potato production. Of those eight million inhabitants, roughly three million subsisted almost entirely on potatoes.

In 1845, a fungus spread through the Irish potato fields, causing a blight that destroyed most of the crop. The blight struck again in 1846 and 1848. Food became so scarce that the price of potatoes skyrocketed. By the end of the Great Potato Famine, nearly a million Irish people had died of starvation and disease, and another million had emigrated to escape those consequences.

From the London Illustrated News, January 30, 1847

Reflecting on his experiences in Ireland as a boy, Sir Robert Giffen later wrote that some Irish families increased their consumption of potatoes during the famine. For families whose diet consisted mainly but not exclusively of potatoes, the price increase took a substantial bite out of their purchasing power. Finding themselves poorer and needing to maintain an adequate caloric intake, they gave up the more expensive foods that had supplemented their diets and turned increasingly to potatoes, their only staple food. Thus the term *Giffen goods*.

Or so the story goes. Some economists have disputed the accuracy of Giffen's recollections, arguing that this alleged violation of the Law of Demand is little more than legend. Surely potato consumption could not have increased

for the *average* Irish family, since potatoes were in short supply. Unfortunately, the facts are obscured by the veil of history, so that the truth will never be known with certainty.

More recently, some economists have claimed that shochu, a Japanese alcoholic beverage, may violate the Law of Demand. Like sake, shochu is distilled from rice. In Japan, it is considered the lowest-quality form of rice-based alcoholic beverage, behind second-grade sake, first-grade sake, and special-grade sake. Shochu is consumed disproportionately by lower-income households, whereas special-grade sake is consumed disproportionately by the wealthy.

The consumption of shochu falls sharply with increased income, so it is plainly an inferior good. But is it a Giffen good? As the price of shochu rises, those with lower incomes may feel compelled to give up the better grades of sake so they can afford to maintain their alcohol intake. Such behaviour is particularly plausible for those who drink to satisfy an alcohol addiction.

In one study, economists Shmuel Baruch and Yakar Kannai examined prices and consumption of shochu and the three grades of sake from January 1987 through March 1989.[2] They used statistical techniques to assess the effect of price on the quantity consumed, accounting for the fact that demand also affects price, as we saw in the appendix to Chapter 2. The estimated price elasticity of demand for special-grade sake was −6.11. In contrast, the estimated price elasticity of demand for shochu was +8.81. According to these results, the demand curve for special-grade sake slopes downward, but the demand curve for shochu slopes *upward*, violating the Law of Demand!

---

[2]Shmuel Baruch and Yakar Kannai, "Inferior Goods, Giffen Goods, and Shochu," in Debreu, Neufeind, and Trockel, eds., *Economic Essays, A Festschrift for Werner Hilden-brand*, 2001, pp. 1–9.

6.2 MEASURING CHANGES IN CONSUMER WELFARE USING DEMAND CURVES

Many important questions in microeconomics concern the welfare effects of changes in the prices and quantities of consumer goods. We began this chapter with an example: How much have consumers benefited from the dramatic drop in the price of computing power over the last few decades? In this section, we'll explain how to measure changes in consumer welfare.

Compensating Variation

When a consumer's economic circumstances change, how can we evaluate his gains and losses in monetary terms? One common measure is called the **compensating variation**. This is the amount of money that exactly compensates the consumer for the change.[3] It is the most he is willing to pay to experience something beneficial, or the least he is willing to receive to experience something harmful. It's an appealing concept because it expresses benefits and costs in a way that is concrete and easy to interpret. If the compensating variation for a road improvement project is −$100, then the consumer is better off with the project as long as his contribution is less than $100. If the compensating variation for a gasoline tax is $50, then he's better off with the tax as long as he receives a rebate for more than $50.

A simple example will illustrate the usefulness of this concept. Let's suppose that Carol and Rachel potentially benefit from a $100 project. Can they split the costs in a way that makes both better off? They can if their compensating variations (times −1) sum to more than $100; otherwise they can't. For example, if Carol's compensating variation is −$80 and Rachel's is −$30, and if we collect $75 from Carol and $25 from Rachel, both are better off because each gives up less than she is willing to pay. Alternatively, if Carol's compensating variation is −$60 and Rachel's is −$30, we can't collect $100 from them without making at least one worse off. If Carol is rich and Rachel is poor, we might be tempted to collect, say, $90 from Carol and $10 from Rachel, leaving Carol worse off and Rachel better off than without the project. However, because Carol's net loss is then $30 while Rachel's net gain is only $20, this is an inefficient way to help Rachel at Carol's expense: both of them would be happier if we skipped the project and simply transferred $25 from Carol to Rachel.

We've actually used the concept of compensating variation earlier in this chapter without naming it. The amount of compensation associated with the income effect of a price change is the compensating variation for the price change: if the consumer receives that amount of compensation following the price change, he will be neither better off nor worse off. For an example, look again at Figure 6.1(a) (page 171). Because $50 fully compensates Oscar for an increase in the price of soup from $5 to $10 per litre, the compensating variation for this price increase is $50. Similarly, the compensating variation for the price reduction illustrated in Figure 6.1(b) is −$37.50, and the compensating variation for the price reduction in worked-out problem 6.1 is −$50.

---

[3]Sometimes economists also evaluate changes using a concept called the *equivalent variation*. This is the amount of money that produces an equivalent effect on the consumer's well-being; that is, the amount he is just willing to accept *in place of* (rather than in addition to) the change. The equivalent variation for a change from one situation, *A*, to another situation, *B*, is the same as the compensating variation for the opposite change—that is, from situation *B* to situation *A*.

WORKED-OUT PROBLEM   6.2

The Problem   As in in-text exercise 6.1, Keiko's marginal rate of substitution for gasoline with wireless minutes, MRS_{GW}, is $10/\sqrt{G}$, where G stands for litres of gasoline. The formula for her indifference curves is $W = U - 20\sqrt{G}$, where W stands for the number of wireless minutes. Keiko's income is $125, gasoline costs $1 per litre, and wireless calls cost $0.50 per minute. How much would we have to pay Keiko to compensate her for the loss of her phone (assuming she can't buy a new one)?

The Solution   From our answer to worked-out problem 5.6 (page 159), we know that Keiko buys 25 litres of gasoline and uses 200 minutes of wireless service. For the indifference curve that runs through this bundle, $U = 300$ (since $200 = 300 - 20\sqrt{25}$. But if Keiko is without her cell phone, $W = 0$. To place her on the same indifference curve as before, we must therefore pick the value of G for which $0 = 300 - 20\sqrt{G}$. But that means $G = 225$. To buy 225 litres of gasoline, Keiko needs $225 dollars—an amount that exceeds her budget by $100. So we have to pay Keiko $100 to compensate her fully for the loss of her phone. This is her compensating variation.

IN-TEXT EXERCISE 6.3   **Suppose that Keiko's phone malfunctions and will operate for only 100 minutes each week. Otherwise, everything is the same as in worked-out problem 6.2. What is Keiko's compensating variation for the malfunction?**

If we know a consumer's preferences, we can compute the compensating variation for a price change (as in Figure 6.1, and worked-out problems 6.1 and 6.2). However, the task of determining a consumer's preferences can be challenging—recall our discussion of revealed preference in Section 5.6. Fortunately, we can calculate compensating variations directly from demand curves. The rest of this section shows how to do this.

Consumer Surplus

When measuring a consumer's well-being, economists often rely on a concept known as **consumer surplus**. This term refers to the net benefit a consumer receives from participating in the market for some good. Equivalently, it is the amount of money that would fully compensate the consumer (in other words, the compensating variation) for losing access to the market.

> **Consumer surplus** is the net benefit a consumer receives from participating in the market for some good.

To compute the consumer surplus for some particular good, we need to start by measuring the gross benefit of consuming that good. The consumer's demand curve provides us with that information: at any given quantity, its height indicates the consumer's willingness to pay for the marginal unit. This willingness to pay is a measure of the consumer's gross benefit from that unit.

For an illustration, consider the demand curve for computers in Figure 6.6(a). It looks like a staircase instead of a straight line because there's isn't much point in buying a fraction of a computer. For one computer, the height of the demand curve is $4000. This

Figure 6.6

Measuring Consumer Surplus Using Standard Demand Curves. The height of the demand curve indicates the consumer's willingness to pay for an additional unit. In figure (a), the price of a computer is $1500 and the consumer buys three computers. For each computer, the net benefit (the area of the green bar) is the difference between the total benefit (the combined areas of the red and green bars) and the price (the area of the red bar). Adding up the areas of the green bars gives us the consumer surplus (total net benefit). figure (b) shows that when a good is finely divisible (like gasoline), consumer surplus is the area under the demand curve and above the horizontal line drawn at the market price.

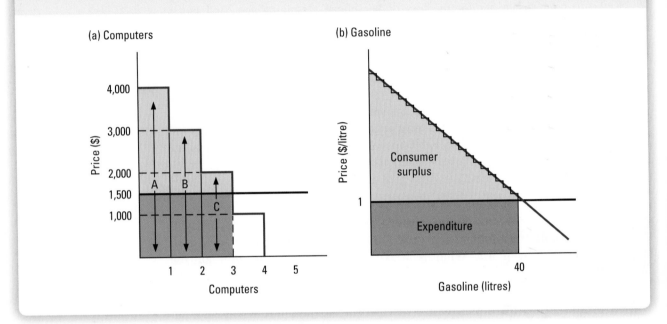

means that the consumer will buy a computer at a price of $4000 (or any lower price), but will not buy a computer at any higher price. Therefore, his willingness to pay for the first computer is exactly $4000: since he would buy it at a price of $4000, his willingness to pay must be at least that high, and it can't be any higher, or he would demand a computer at a higher price. Similarly, for two computers, the height of the demand curve is $3000. Since he would buy both the first and the second computer at a price of $3000, his willingness to pay for the second must be at least that high, and it can't be any higher, or he would demand two computers at a higher price. Likewise, according to the figure, his willingness to pay for a third computer is $2000.

The consumer's net benefit is the difference between his gross benefit and the amount he pays. Let's say computers sell for $1500 each. According to Figure 6.6(a), the consumer will buy three computers. He is willing to pay $4000 for the first, so he enjoys a net benefit of $2500 when he buys it ($4000 minus $1500). Similarly, his net benefit from the second computer is $1500 ($3000 minus $1500), and his net benefit from the third computer is $500 ($2000 minus $1500). Therefore, his consumer surplus—the total net benefit he receives from participating in the computer market—is $4500 ($2500 plus $1500 plus $500).

Graphically, consumer surplus corresponds to the area below the demand curve and above a horizontal line drawn at the good's price. In Figure 6.6(a), we have shaded that area green. Why does that area represent consumer surplus? The consumer's gross benefit from the first computer equals the height of the bar labelled A ($4000). The red portion of the bar represents the cost of acquiring this computer ($1500), so his net benefit equals the green portion of the bar ($2500). His gross benefit from the second computer equals the height of the bar labelled B ($3000), and his net benefit equals the green portion of that bar ($1500); his gross benefit from the third computer equals the height of the bar labelled C ($2000), and his net benefit equals the green portion of that bar ($500). Therefore, the green-shaded area in the figure represents the consumer's total net benefit, or consumer surplus.

The same principle applies to finely divisible goods. Figure 6.6(b) illustrates this point using gasoline as an example. The weekly demand curve for gasoline is the downward-sloping blue line. At a price of $1 per litre, the household purchases 20 litres over the course of a week. As we explain next, consumer surplus once again equals the green-shaded area below the demand curve and above the horizontal line drawn at the price (here, $1 per litre).

The total gross benefit of 20 litres of gasoline corresponds to the sum of the green- and red-shaded areas under the demand curve. Why? Imagine for the moment that gasoline is sold only in whole litres, not in fractions of a litre. In that case, the demand curve would be shaped like the staircase superimposed on the demand curve. As with computers, the height of each step measures the consumer's willingness to pay for the marginal unit. The area directly beneath the highest step measures the benefit from the first litre, the area directly beneath the second highest step measures the benefit from the second litre, and so forth. We can determine the total benefit by adding up these amounts. The result is fairly close to the sum of the green- and red-shaded areas under the demand curve.

Instead of assuming that gasoline is sold only in litres, we could have chosen a smaller unit— decilitres (100 millilitres), millilitres, or even drops. As the unit grows smaller, so does each step on the demand curve, so that the staircase becomes harder and harder to distinguish from the blue line. Likewise, the total area under all the steps becomes almost indistinguishable from the total area under the demand curve.

The total expenditure on gasoline corresponds to the area of the red-shaded rectangle. The rectangle's height equals the price ($1 per litre) and its width equals the quantity (20 litres). Its area—the height times the width—is therefore the same as the price times the quantity, which produces a total cost, or expenditure, of $20. Since the green- and red- shaded areas represent the total gross benefit, while the red-shaded area represents the total cost, the green-shaded area is the net benefit, or consumer surplus.

The method of computing consumer surplus described above is actually an approximation rather than an exact measure of the compensating variation associated with the loss of access to a market. As we explain in Section 6.5, the quality of the approximation is quite good when the income effects of price changes are small. Consequently, this method is sufficiently accurate for most purposes.

Figure 6.7

Measuring a Change in Consumer Surplus Using a Demand Curve. When the price of gasoline is $1 per litre, the consumer surplus corresponds to the green- and yellow-shaded areas. When the price of gasoline rises to $2 per litre, the consumer surplus corresponds to the green-shaded area. The yellow-shaded area is the reduction in consumer surplus that results from the price increase.

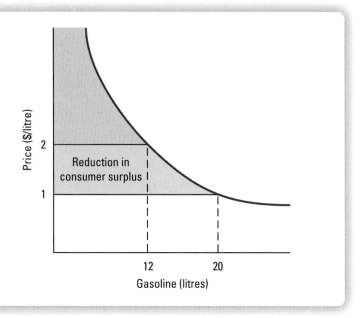

Using Consumer Surplus to Measure Changes in Welfare

Some public policies literally create or destroy markets. Application 6.2 is an example. In these cases, the concept of consumer surplus is clearly applicable: it tells us how much economic value is created or destroyed. Other public policies alter the prices and amounts of traded goods without affecting a market's existence. For example, gasoline taxes may increase the price of gasoline, but they don't eliminate the gasoline market. In these cases, the concept of consumer surplus is still useful because it allows us to measure the *change* in the net economic benefit that results from the policy. This change in net benefit is simply another way to describe the compensating variation for the policy. For example, if a policy reduces the net benefit that a consumer receives as a participant in a market from $100 to $80, we must provide him with $20 to compensate him fully for the policy's effects.

Figure 6.7 illustrates this point using gasoline as an example. The downward-sloping blue curve represents a consumer's demand curve for gasoline. At $1 per litre, the consumer buys 20 litres, and his consumer surplus corresponds to the green-shaded area plus the yellow-shaded area. Now imagine the government imposes a large gasoline tax, increasing the price to $2 per litre. In that case, the consumer buys 12 litres, and his consumer surplus corresponds to the green-shaded area. The price increase has made the gasoline market less valuable to this consumer. The yellow-shaded area represents his loss; it is also the compensating variation associated with the price change. To determine whether the tax is worthwhile, we can add up the losses for all consumers and compare the total loss to the potential benefits, such as reduced air pollution and revenue for public projects (see Chapter 20).

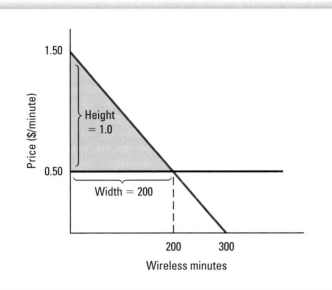

Figure 6.8

Abigail's Consumer Surplus for Wireless Service. The blue line is Abigail's demand curve for wireless telephone service. Her consumer surplus is the green-shaded area below the demand curve and above the horizontal line drawn at the wireless service price, $0.50 per minute.

WORKED-OUT PROBLEM 6.3

The Problem The formula for Abigail's monthly demand curve for minutes of wireless telephone service is $W = 300 - 200P_W$, where W stands for the number of minutes and P_W is the price per minute of service. Suppose that $P_W = \$0.50$ per minute. Using the approach described in this section, calculate Abigail's consumer surplus.

The Solution We have graphed Abigail's demand curve in Figure 6.8. Her consumer surplus is the area of the green triangle. The height of the triangle is 1 and the width is 200, so the area is $1/2 \times (200 \times 1) = 100$. Therefore, Abigail's consumer surplus is $100.

IN-TEXT EXERCISE 6.4 **Suppose P_W increases from \$0.50 per minute to \$1 per minute. Calculate the change in Abigail's consumer surplus.**

Application 6.2

The Introduction of New Telecommunication Services

How much do consumers benefit from the introduction of new goods and services? While many new products are relatively inconsequential, others transform the way we live in a relatively short period of time. Think about handheld wireless telephones. As recently as the early 1980s, they were found only in science fiction novels. Yet in 2006, roughly 60 percent of Canadians owned these devices; in many other countries, including the United States, the percentage was significantly higher. According to one estimate, there were more than 2 billion wireless phones in operation worldwide.

It's relatively easy to figure out how much consumers spend on a new product, and it's safe to assume that their benefits exceed their spending. However, the amount of their spending tells us nothing about the good's *net* benefit to them. If we want to know consumers' net gains, the concept to use is consumer surplus.

In one study, economist Jerry Hausman measured the total consumer surplus generated by the introduction of cellular telephones (the first widespread handheld wireless technology).[4] Using data on cellular prices and subscribership in the 30 largest metropolitan areas of the United States from 1989 through 1993, Hausman estimated the demand curve for cellular telephone service. He then computed the total consumer surplus from cellular phones by measuring the area between the demand curve and a horizontal line drawn at the market price. On the basis of his calculations, he concluded that in 1994, cellular telephone

© The New Yorker Collection 1993 Bernard Schoenbaum from cartoonbank.com. All Rights Reserved.

service generated just under $50 billion of consumer surplus or almost U.S.$200 per U.S. resident.

Aside from being impressively large, Hausman's estimate of consumer surplus has important implications for public policy. Historically, the telecommunications industry has been heavily regulated. Hausman argued that cellular telephone technology was sufficiently advanced for commercial deployment in the early 1970s— roughly 10 years before its roll-out in the United States. He attributed the 10-year delay to a series of decisions by the Federal Communications Commission (FCC), which oversees the telecommunications industry. In all likelihood, the service would have been more costly and of lower quality in 1975 than it was in 1985. Even so, the delay deprived consumers of the surplus they would have enjoyed had cellular service been available earlier—a loss of more than U.S.$100 billion, according to Hausman's estimates.

6.3 MEASURING CHANGES IN CONSUMER WELFARE USING COST-OF-LIVING INDEXES

In this section, we describe an alternative method for measuring changes in consumer well-being, one that requires no information concerning preferences or demand elasticities. Why would we want such a measure? First, it's simple and easy to compute. Second, economists are sometimes unable to estimate either preferences or demand elasticities reliably (for example, because there isn't enough data). This prevents them from measuring changes in consumer well-being using the methods described in Section 6.2. Third, different consumers have different preferences. It's useful to have a measure of the change in well-being—even an approximate one—that applies broadly to a wide range of consumers. The alternative method involves a concept known as a *cost-of-living index*.

What Is a Cost-of-Living Index?

A **cost-of-living index** measures the relative cost of achieving a fixed standard of living in different situations.

A **cost-of-living index** measures the relative cost of achieving a fixed standard of living in different situations. These indexes are commonly used to measure changes in the cost of living over time. However, they can also be used to measure changes in consumer well-being after the implementation of public policies that alter prices and income.

---

[4]Jerry A. Hausman, "Valuing the Effect of Regulation on New Services in Telecommunications," *Brookings Papers on Economic Activity, Microeconomics*, 1997, pp. 1–38.

The typical cost-of-living index has a base value of 1.0 during some specific period. If the value of the index is, say, 1.2 at some later time, then the cost of living has risen by 20 percent. The level of the index in the base period is unimportant. All that matters is the percentage change in the index. To indicate that the cost of living has risen by 20 percent, we could also set the value of the index at 2.0 for the base period and at 2.4 for the later period.

Economists often use price indexes to convert **nominal income** into **real income**. Nominal income is the amount of money that someone actually receives in a particular period. If, for example, your employer pays you $3000 per month, that is your nominal income. Real income is the amount of money received in a particular period adjusted for changes in purchasing power that alter the cost of living over time. To compute real income, we divide nominal income by the cost-of-living index.

> **Nominal income** is the amount of money actually received in a particular period.

> **Real income** is the amount of money received in a particular period adjusted for changes in purchasing power that alter the cost of living over time.

$$\text{Real income} = \frac{\text{Nominal income}}{\text{Value of cost-of-living index}}$$

For example, suppose the index is 1.0 in the base period and 1.1 at some later time, indicating that the cost of living has risen by 10 percent. If the consumer's nominal income rose from $24,000 to $33,000 over the same period, then real income increased from $24,000 to only $30,000 (since $30,000 = $33,000/1.1).

Ideally, a cost-of-living index should allow us to quickly evaluate changes in consumer well-being following changes in prices and income. If real income has risen, then nominal income has grown more rapidly than the cost of living, and the consumer should be better off. If real income has fallen, then nominal income has grown more slowly than the cost of living, and the consumer should be worse off. If real income has not changed, then nominal income has kept pace with the cost of living, and the consumer should be equally well off. Moreover, the change in real income should measure the change in the consumer's well-being.

If all prices always changed by the same proportion, constructing a perfect cost-of-living index would be easy; we would simply use the percentage change in prices. So, if prices increased by 20 percent, we would conclude that the cost of living rose by 20 percent. To determine if the consumer was better or worse off, we would compare that increase to the change in income. If income also increased by 20 percent, then the budget line would be unchanged, and the consumer's well-being would be unaffected, regardless of her preferences. If the consumer's income increased by more than 20 percent, she would be better off because the budget constraint would shift outward; if her income increased by less than 20 percent, she would be worse off because the budget constraint would shift inward—in each case, without rotating.

In actuality, constructing a good cost-of-living index is challenging, because different prices usually change by different proportions. Frequently some prices rise and others fall. As we will see, designing an index that always performs well in practice, let alone one that is perfect, is quite difficult to do.

A Perfect Cost-of-Living Index

If we knew a great deal about a consumer's preferences, then theoretically we could construct a perfect cost-of-living index. Suppose we calculate the compensating variation associated with a change in prices and then divide it by the consumer's initial income. The result (multiplied by 100) would be the *percentage* change in income required to compensate the consumer fully for the price change. The consumer is better off if his income rises by more than this percentage and worse off if it rises by less than this percentage. That is exactly how a perfect cost-of-living index should work.

To illustrate, look back at Figure 6.1(a) (page 188). When the price of soup rises from $5 to $10 per litre, Oscar's cost of living rises by 50 percent. Why? At the initial price of $5 per litre, and with his initial income of $100, he chooses bundle A from the budget line labelled L_1. At the new price of $10 per litre, and with an income of $150 (including $50 in compensation), he chooses bundle C from the budget line labelled L_3. Since bundles A and C lie on the same indifference curve, the increase in income from $100 to $150 fully compensates him for the rise in price. Notice that the compensating variation for the price change ($50) is 50 percent of Oscar's initial income. If his actual income increases by exactly 50 percent, he chooses point C and his well-being is unchanged. If his income increases by less than 50 percent, he ends up on a lower indifference curve, and his well-being falls. If his income increases by more than 50 percent, he ends up on a higher indifference curve and his well-being rises.

In practice, perfect measures of changes in the cost of living are typically unavailable for two reasons. First, the calculation just illustrated requires detailed and accurate information about consumer preferences. As we've said, that information is often unavailable. Second, preferences vary across the population. The perfect price index for one individual can badly mismeasure the change in cost of living for another individual.

Fixed-Weight Price Indexes

How, then, do we compute cost-of-living indexes in practice? Let's say we want to determine the change in the cost of living in Edmonton between January 2006 and January 2007. The usual approach is to select some consumption bundle and determine its cost in both months using the prices at which the goods were actually available. The percentage change in the cost of the bundle is taken to be the change in the cost of living. So if we choose January 2006 as the base period, and the cost of the fixed bundle rises by five percent over the course of 2006, the value of the cost-of-living index is 1.0 in January 2006 and 1.05 in January 2007. This type of index is known as a **fixed-weight price index**. Fixed-weight indexes are relatively easy to calculate because they require no information about consumer preferences.

Of course, the use of a fixed-weight index raises an important question: Which fixed consumption bundle should we use? The choices are almost limitless. Using a bundle that represents the mix of goods that consumers actually purchase certainly makes sense. Even that seemingly innocuous guideline is problematic, however, because the bundles consumers purchase change as prices change.

One common approach is to use a fixed-weight price index based on the consumption bundle actually purchased during the base period. This is known as a **Laspeyres price index**.[5] By comparing the value of a Laspeyres index for different periods, we can determine if the cost of the base-period consumption bundle has risen or fallen, and by how much. For example, if the base year for a Laspeyres price index is 2003, and the value of the index is 1.2 in 2005 and 1.5 in 2007, then the cost of the bundle consumed in 2003 rose by 20 percent between 2003 and 2005, by 50 percent between 2003 and 2007, and by 25 percent between 2005 and 2007 (since $1.2 \times 1.25 = 1.5$).

A **fixed-weight price index** measures the percentage change in the cost of a fixed consumption bundle.

A **Laspeyres price index** is a fixed-weight index that is based on the consumption bundle actually purchased in the base period. It tells us whether the cost of the base-period consumption bundle has risen or fallen, and by how much.

---

[5]Another common choice is a fixed-weight price index based on the consumption bundle actually purchased in the *current* period. This is known as a Paasche price index. The value of a Paasche index tells us if the cost of the current consumption bundle has risen or fallen since the base period, and by how much. For example, if the base year for a Paasche price index is 2004, and the value of the index is 1.15 in 2007, then the cost of the bundle consumed in 2007 rose by 15 percent between 2004 and 2007.

To illustrate the application of a Laspeyres index, let's return to the problem of computing the change in Oscar's cost of living when the price of soup rises from $5 to $10 per litre. In the base period, soup costs $5 per cup and bread costs $5 per kilogram. According to Figure 6.1(a), Oscar's best choice is bundle A, which contains 13 litres of soup and 7 kilograms of bread. We'll construct the index based on this fixed bundle. Initially, the cost of this bundle is $100. When the price of soup rises to $10 per litre, the cost of this bundle rises by 65 percent, to $165.00 (13 cups of soup at $10 per cup plus 7 kilograms of bread at $5 per kilogram). The Laspeyres index is therefore 1.0 in the base period and 1.65 after the price change.

Does the Laspeyres index accurately reflect the true change in the cost of living? The answer is no. For this example, we know from our discussion of the perfect price index that Oscar's income must rise by exactly 50 percent to maintain his level of well-being. The Laspeyres index exaggerates the required increase in income by a substantial amount. If Oscar's income were to increase to $150 along with the price change, his true standard of living would be unaffected. But according to the Laspeyres index, his real income would be $150/165 = $90.90, a decline of roughly 9 percent compared with the base period!

It is no accident that the Laspeyres index exaggerates the change in the cost of living for this example. A change in the perfect cost-of-living index tells us how much more income is needed to achieve the consumer's original level of well-being. But a change in the Laspeyres index tells us how much more income is needed to achieve the consumer's original level of well-being *by purchasing the consumer's original consumption bundle.* Since the italicized restriction rules out cheaper ways to achieve the original level of well-being, the Laspeyres index overstates the amount of income actually required. When prices are rising, the Laspeyres index exaggerates the increase in the cost of living, an error known as the **substitution bias**. It does so by failing to capture the consumer's tendency to moderate the impact of a price increase by substituting away from goods that have become more expensive.

Figure 6.9 illustrates the substitution bias. We've drawn two budget lines, one for the base period and one for the current period. On each budget line, we've indicated the consumer's best choice. Notice that the consumer has just enough income in the current period to buy the base-period consumption bundle—no more and no less. Therefore, according to the Laspeyres price index, his real income is the same in the base period and

> The **substitution bias** of a Laspeyres price index involves a failure to capture the consumer's tendency to moderate the impact of a price increase by substituting away from goods that have become more expensive. As a result, the index overstates increases in the cost of living.

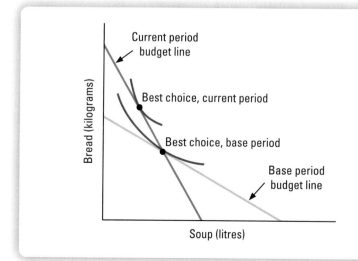

Best choice, current period

Best choice, base period

Current period budget line

Base period budget line

Bread (kilograms)

Soup (litres)

Figure 6.9

A Laspeyres Price Index Overstates Increases in the Cost of Living.

If prices have changed between the base period and the current period, and if real income has remained constant according to the index, then the consumer can afford his best choice from the base period. His best choice in the current period is even better. He is therefore better off, even though his real income is supposedly the same.

the current period. Yet this conclusion is misleading: the consumer is actually *better off* in the current period than in the base period, which means that the Laspeyres index has overstated the increase in the cost of living. How do we know that the consumer is better off in the current period? Because the indifference curve that runs through the base-period best choice is tangent to the base-period budget line, it must cross the current-period budget line, as shown. The best choice in the current period must therefore lie on a higher indifference curve than the base-period best choice.

As Application 6.3 illustrates, such problems are extremely important in practice.

Application 6.3

Bias in the Consumer Price Index

Inflation refers to the change in the cost of living over time. Though measuring the rate of inflation may sound like a tedious bean-counting exercise, it's in fact a controversial subject that stirs impassioned debate and sometimes even public outcry.

Under current law, Canada Pension Plan benefits rise automatically with increases in the cost of living, as measured by Statistics Canada's consumer price index (CPI). So do the levels of personal income that define the boundaries between different federal tax brackets. As a result, the federal government could both dramatically reduce retirement benefits and raise taxes simply by reducing the *measured* rate of inflation by fractions of a percentage point! Similarly, private-sector contracts between individuals and companies often include cost-of-living adjustments that are tied to price indexes such as the CPI. Because of these laws and contractual arrangements, literally billions of dollars hang in the balance when government statisticians compute the official cost-of-living indexes. No wonder at least one prominent economist received death threats after proposing to change the CPI.

There are several reasons to suspect the CPI exaggerates increases in the true cost of living. First, it's a Laspeyres price index, so it suffers from substitution bias. Second, when Statistics Canada rotates new retail outlets into the sample used to collect data on prices, it attributes all the differences in price between the new outlets and the old ones to the quality of goods sold. Yet the fact that the new outlets have taken business from the old ones strongly suggests that their lower prices reflect better deals, not lower quality. Third, the CPI understates reductions in the

cost of living that result from improvements in the quality of goods purchased. Take personal computers, for example. Each year, these machines become faster and smaller, more reliable and user-friendly. New capabilities and features are constantly being added. Manufacturers come and go; models are retired and new ones introduced. A PC that costs $1000 today is vastly superior to one that cost the same amount five years ago. Though government agencies computing inflation try to adjust for this disparity, one study suggests that it understates the annual decline in quality-adjusted computer prices by four percentage points.[6]

"We project, sir, in '86, a real economic growth of four and five-tenths per cent after adjustment for inflation and ideology."

---

[6]Anna Aizcorbe, Carol Corrado, and Mark Doms, "Constructing Price and Quantity Indexes for High Technology Goods," mimeo, Federal Reserve Board, 2000.

These issues received a great deal of attention at the Bank of Canada and among academic economists. Timothy Beatty and Erling Larson in 2005 concluded that between 1978 and 2000 the CPI overestimated inflation between 1.33 percent and 1.86 percent depending on the type of household considered.[7] This conclusion implied that automatic increases in Canada Pension Plan benefits had for many years substantially outstripped true increases in the cost of living, adding significantly to the government's budgetary woes.

In recent years, the Statistics Canada has made many improvements in the CPI. Even so, significant bias remains. A 2005 study by James Rossiter at the Bank of Canada estimates that in recent years the CPI overstates inflation by roughly 0.6 percent. Rossiter attributes 0.15 percent of the bias to commodity substitution, 0.08 percent to new outlets, 0.15 percent to mismeasured quality improvements, and 0.20 percent to new goods bias.[8]

6.4 LABOUR SUPPLY AND THE DEMAND FOR LEISURE

So far, we've focused on decisions involving the goods consumers buy. But what about the things they *sell*? For example, most adults earn all or part of their incomes by selling their time and effort to employers. This is known as **labour supply**.

> **Labour supply** refers to the sale of a consumer's time and effort to an employer.

Understanding consumer supply—particularly labour supply—is every bit as important as understanding consumer demand. Fortunately, we don't need a separate theory for supply. We mentioned the reason for this in our discussion of goods and bads (Chapter 4, page 105). Let's assume that people regard hours of work as a bad, in the sense that they would rather do something more pleasant.[9] For every bad, there is a corresponding good, defined by the absence of the bad. For labour, the corresponding good is leisure. The price of this good is the wage rate. For example, if a consumer earns $10 per hour, then every hour of leisure costs him $10. To understand the supply of labour, we study the demand for leisure.

Let's consider an example. Javier is taking a year off between high school and college. He doesn't want to work, but he needs money. His wealthy uncle generously gives him an allowance of $210 per week ($30 per day) for living expenses, no strings attached. (Lucky Javier!) The owner of the local 24-hour convenience store has offered him a job that pays $6 per hour and has told Javier that he can work as much or as little as he likes. What should he do?

Javier needs to spend nine hours per day sleeping, eating, and otherwise taking care of himself. This leaves him with 15 hours per day for work and leisure. Figure 6.10 shows his alternatives. For simplicity, we'll assume that he spends all of his money on food, which costs $15 per kilogram. The horizontal axis measures hours of leisure, and the vertical axis measures kilograms of food. If Javier chooses not to work, he'll enjoy 15 hours of leisure per day and consume two kilograms of food. In the figure, this is bundle A. For each hour of leisure he gives up, he'll earn $6, which will allow him to buy another two-fifths of a kilogram of food. The slope of his budget line, shown in green, is therefore two-fifths of a kilogram per hour. For example, if Javier works 15 hours per day, he'll earn $90. Along with his $30-per-day allowance, this income will allow him to buy 8 kilograms of food (bundle B in the figure).

---

[7]Timothy K.M. Beatty and Erling Roed Larsen, "Using Engel curves to estimate bias in the Canadian CPI as a cost of living index." *Canadian Journal of Economics*, May 2005, pp. 482–499.

[8]James Rossiter, "Measurement Bias in the Canadian Consumer Price Index," *Bank of Canada Working Paper* 2005–39.

[9]Many people derive great satisfaction from their work, or see hard work as virtuous. Consumer theory can also accommodate these possibilities, but we ignore them here for the sake of simplicity.

Figure 6.10

A Labour-Leisure Choice. Javier can work for up to 15 hours per day at $6 per hour. He also receives an allowance of $30 per day from a wealthy uncle. He uses his income to buy food, which costs $15 per kilogram. With the dark red indifference curves, he chooses 8 hours of leisure per day, which means he works for 7 hours. With the light red indifference curves, he chooses 15 hours of leisure per day, which means he doesn't work.

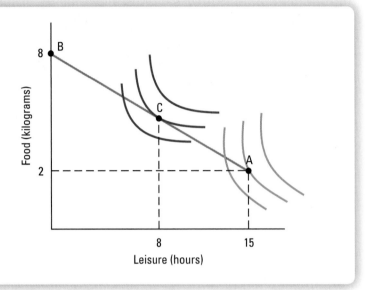

The figure shows two families of indifference curves. Compared with the dark red curves, the light red curves attach more importance to leisure and less to food. (Can you explain why?) With the dark red indifference curves, Javier chooses 8 hours of leisure per day, which means he works for 7 hours. With the light red indifference curves, Javier chooses 15 hours of leisure per day, which means he doesn't work.

In the rest of this section, we study how a change in Javier's wage rate affects his labour supply.

The Effect of Wages on Hours of Work

How does a change in Javier's hourly wage affect his budget line? If he chooses not to work, he'll have $30 to spend on food regardless of his wage. As a result, his budget line always passes through bundle A in Figure 6.10. A change in Javier's wage rotates his budget line, pivoting it around bundle A. With a wage of $4 per hour, he would face the flatter green budget line in Figure 6.11(a). With a wage of $8 per hour, he would face the steeper green budget line. An increase in his hourly wage makes his budget line steeper because it improves the terms at which he can convert his time into food.

Figure 6.11(a) also reproduces the family of dark red indifference curves from Figure 6.10. The points of tangency between the indifference curves and the budget lines form a price-consumption path. Notice that Javier consumes nine hours of leisure with a wage rate of either $4 or $8 (bundles D and E) compared with eight hours of leisure with a wage rate of $6.

We've plotted Javier's leisure demand curve in Figure 6.11(b). Points C, D, and E correspond to the bundles with the same labels in Figure 6.11(a). For low wages, this demand curve slopes downward, but for high wages, it slopes upward—as Javier's wage increases beyond $5 per hour, he demands more leisure.

In Section 6.1, we learned that the demand curve for the typical good can slope upward only if the good is inferior, and if the income effect of a price change is sufficiently large. We also pointed out that these conditions are rarely satisfied, which is why Giffen goods are hard to find. In contrast, the demand curve for leisure will slope upward if leisure is a normal good, and if the income effect of a wage change is sufficiently large.

Figure 6.11

A Leisure Demand Curve and a Labour Supply Curve. Figure (a) shows Javier's choices for three different wage rates: $4, $6, and $8 per hour. Figure (b) uses the information from figure (a) to plot Javier's demand curve for leisure. Since Javier's hours of labour equal his total available hours minus his hours of leisure, his labour supply curve is the mirror image of his leisure demand curve. Javier's labour supply curve is backward-bending.

Since these conditions are plausible, some consumers may well have upward-sloping leisure demand curves.[10] What accounts for this difference between leisure and typical goods, like soup and potatoes?

For most goods, consumers initially own less than they consume; they buy the difference from producers. In contrast, Javier initially owns more time than he consumes; he sells the difference to his employer. This distinction reverses the direction of the income effect. When the price of soup rises, the typical consumer is *worse* off as a buyer. Assuming soup is a normal good, he therefore demands less soup as a consequence of the income effect. In contrast, when the price of Javier's time rises, he is *better* off as a seller. Therefore, if leisure is a normal good, he demands *more* leisure as a consequence of the income effect. If this effect is sufficiently large, it will more than offset the substitution effect, which involves a shift toward less leisure.

Figure 6.12 illustrates the opposing substitution and income effects for an increase in Javier's wage rate from $6 to $8, assuming that leisure is a normal good. Bundle F is the point of tangency between the indifference curve that runs through bundle C and a line with the same slope as the new budget constraint. The substitution effect corresponds to the movement from bundle C to bundle F. Since leisure becomes more expensive, Javier substitutes away from it, consuming seven hours instead of eight. The income effect

[10]If a consumer's income is derived mostly from employment, then the amount of money required to compensate him fully for a substantial change in his wage rate will be large, in which case the associated income effects may also be large.

Figure 6.12

Dissection of the Effect of an Increase in a Wage Rate. An uncompensated increase in Javier's wage rotates his budget line upward from L_1 to L_2, and his choice shifts from bundle C to bundle E (the blue arrow). The movement from bundle C to bundle F is the substitution effect (the gray arrow), and the movement from bundle F to bundle E is the income effect (the yellow arrow). Since Javier consumes less time than he owns, the income and substitution effects work in opposite directions, even though leisure is a normal good. For Javier, the income effect is larger in magnitude than the substitution effect, so an increase in his wage increases his hours of leisure and reduces his hours of labour.

corresponds to the movement from bundle F to bundle E. Since an increase in Javier's wage raises his purchasing power, and since leisure is a normal good, Javier consumes more of it (nine hours instead of seven). Overall, his leisure time rises.

Using the fact that Javier's hours of labour and leisure must add up to 15, we've also plotted Javier's labour supply curve in Figure 6.11(b). For example, with a wage of $6, Javier takes eight hours of leisure (point C) and spends seven hours working (point C').

In this example, Javier's labour supply curve is *backward bending*—when the wage is above $5, an increase in the wage *increases* the amount of leisure he demands, and *reduces* the amount of labour he supplies. There is good evidence that some people actually behave this way. For many prime-age men, labour supply usually does not change much, and may even decline, as the wage rate rises. Our analysis of labour supply decisions attributes this pattern to income effects: since people own more time than they consume, an increase in the wage rate raises their purchasing power and thereby increases their consumption of normal goods like leisure.

The Effect of Wages on Labour Force Participation

If labour supply curves can bend backward, can a cut in the wage rate cause someone who otherwise would not work to enter the labour market? Can an increase in the wage rate drive someone who otherwise would work out of the labour market?

The answer to both of these questions is no. An increase in the wage rate must increase labour force participation, and a decrease must reduce it. To understand why, look at Figure 6.13. Here we have reproduced Javier's three budget lines from Figure 6.11(a), along with the family of light red indifference curves from Figure 6.10. In the figure, an increase in Javier's wage rate from $6 to $8 per hour lures him into the labour market and leads him to choose bundle *G*. However, if the wage rate falls from $6 to $4 per hour, his set of affordable bundles shrinks. Since bundle A is his best choice in the larger set of affordable alternatives (with a wage of $6 per hour), it must also be his best choice in the smaller set (with a wage of $4 per hour). Therefore, he will definitely remain out of the

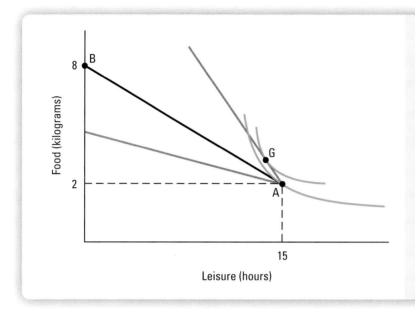

Figure 6.13
The Effect of the Wage Rate on Labour Force Participation. With the black budget line, Javier chooses not to work. An increase in his wage rotates the budget line upward and leads him to enter the labour force—he chooses bundle G. A reduction in his wage rotates the budget line downward and cannot lead him to enter the labour force.

labour market. (To check your understanding of this point, use a graph to show why an increase in the wage rate can't drive a worker out of the labour market.)

We can make the same point by dissecting the effects of a wage change. When Javier chooses not to work, the amount of time he owns is the same as the amount of time he consumes. Since he neither sells nor buys his time, a change in the price of his time makes him neither better off nor worse off. That means there's no income effect—only a substitution effect. Since a compensated reduction in the price of leisure cannot produce substitution away from leisure, Javier remains out of the labour force when his wage rate falls.

Application 6.4

Women in the Labour Force

It wasn't until World Wars I and II that Canadian women started working outside the home in significant numbers. As late as 1953, the labour force participation rate among women stood at only 23 percent. The last quarter of the 20th century witnessed much more dramatic changes in female labour force participation. By 1976, 44.2 percent of women were in the labour force. This figure climbed steadily to 54.5 percent in 1986, 56.3 percent in 1996, and 61.1 percent in 2006. Labour force participation rates for adult men declined somewhat during the same period.

What caused this dramatic change among women? Our analysis of labour supply decisions points to two types of explanations: changing opportunities, including better wages and a wider range of potential careers, and changing preferences.

Let's start with wages. According to Statistics Canada, in 1976, the typical adult female full-time employee earned only 59.4 percent as much as the typical adult male employee. In 2007, this figure stood at 71.4 percent. In light of the discussion that preceded this application, this sharp increase in wages may well account for a significant fraction of the increase in female labour force participation over this period.[11]

---

[11]The information in this application is taken from Statistics Canada's "Women in Canada Fifth Edition: A Gender-based Statistical Report", March 2006.

Now let's turn to career opportunities. Women were once largely confined to traditional "female" occupations, like teaching, nursing, and clerical work. This is no longer the case. Their ability to pursue a wider range of potential careers has two effects. First, it contributes to higher wages. Second, it potentially increases the enjoyment (or at least reduces the displeasure) that women derive from their chosen occupations. This reduces the relative attractiveness of leisure (as well as of unpaid work in the home), flattening the indifference curves in Figure 6.13, and thereby increasing the odds that a woman will choose to join the labour force.

Why did the opportunities for women improve so dramatically? The main causes include changing social norms and customs, measures to discourage discrimination

based on gender, and greater educational attainment. Of course, the rising level of educational attainment among women is also a consequence of their expanding opportunities. For example, the number of women pursuing law degrees has grown in part because their career prospects in the field of law have improved.

As a result of changing social norms and customs, women's preferences for paid employment, housework, and leisure have also changed. Today, working women no longer face the social stigma they once did. Many women now grow up with expectations for professional success and measure themselves against these expectations. Those considerations also flatten the indifference curves in Figure 6.13, contributing further to the rise in female labour force participation.

6.5 ANOTHER TYPE OF DEMAND CURVE

A standard demand curve shows the effect of an uncompensated change in a good's price on the amount consumed. For example, according to the blue demand curve for beef in Figure 6.14(a), an uncompensated increase in the price of beef from \$4 to \$6 per kilogram reduces beef consumption from 20 to 10 kilograms; an uncompensated price cut from \$4 to \$2 per kilogram increases consumption from 20 to 30 kilograms. For this reason, a standard demand curve is sometimes called an **uncompensated demand curve**. It describes the relationship between the price of a good and the amount consumed holding the consumer's income fixed and allowing her well-being to vary. Uncompensated demand curves are also known as **Marshallian demand curves**, in recognition of Alfred Marshall, the nineteenth-century British economist who originated supply-and-demand analysis, as well as the concept of consumer surplus. When people use the phrase *demand curve*, they generally mean an uncompensated (standard) curve.

As explained in Section 6.1, we can break up the effect of any uncompensated price change into a substitution effect and an income effect. Fixing a starting price, we can show these effects in the same graph as a standard demand curve. To illustrate, let's assume that the price of beef starts out at \$4 per kilogram, placing the consumer at point A on the blue demand curve in Figure 6.14(a). Assume that the substitution effect of a price increase from \$4 to \$6 per kilogram reduces beef consumption from 20 to 15 kilograms, while the income effect reduces it from 15 to 10 kilograms. Then the substitution effect moves the consumer from point A to point B, and the income effect moves him from point B to point C. Similarly, assume that the substitution effect of a price cut from \$4 to \$2 per kilogram increases consumption from 20 to 25 kilograms, while the income effect raises it from 25 to 30 kilograms. Then the substitution effect corresponds to the movement from point A to point D, and the income effect corresponds to the movement from point D to point E.

Now consider the yellow curve that runs through the points A, B, and D. This curve shows *only* the substitution effect of a price change—in other words, the effect of a

An **uncompensated demand curve**, or **Marshallian demand curve**, shows the effect of an uncompensated change in a good's price on the amount consumed. In other words, it describes the relationship between the price and the amount consumed holding the consumer's income fixed and allowing well-being to vary.

Figure 6.14

Compensated and Uncompensated Demand Curves. In figure (a), the blue line is the uncompensated demand curve for beef. The yellow line shows the effects of a compensated change in the price of beef starting from $4 per kilogram; the horizontal distance between the yellow and blue lines is the income effect of the price change. In figure (b), the blue line is the uncompensated demand curve for potatoes. The yellow line shows the effects of a compensated change in the price of potatoes starting from $0.40 per kilogram; the horizontal distance between the yellow and blue lines is the income effect of the price change. The uncompensated demand curve is flatter than the compensated demand curve in figure (a) and steeper in figure (b) because we have assumed that beef is normal and potatoes are inferior.

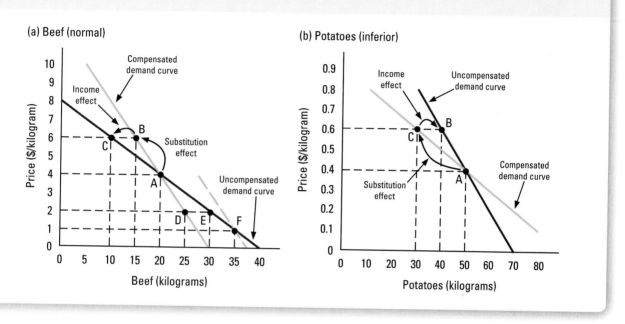

compensated price change—from $4 per kilogram to any other price. This is called a **compensated demand curve**. It describes the relationship between the price of a good and the amount consumed, holding the consumer's well-being fixed and allowing his income to vary. Compensated demand curves are also known as **Hicksian demand curves**, in recognition of Nobel laureate John R. Hicks.

Unlike uncompensated demand curves, compensated demand curves *always* slope downward. Why? As we explained in Section 6.1, substitution effects always reduce the consumption of a good when its price rises, and increase its consumption when its price falls. A compensated demand curve shows these effects.

As we explained in Section 5.5, the level of a consumer's income determines the location of her uncompensated demand curve. Similarly, the level of his well-being determines the location of his compensated demand curve. To illustrate, let's suppose that the price of beef starts out at $1 per kilogram instead of $4 per kilogram. With the same level of income, the consumer is better off. According to the blue uncompensated demand curve in Figure 6.14(a), he buys 35 kilograms of beef (point F). The dashed yellow curve that runs through point F shows the effect of a compensated price change from $1 per kilogram to any other price. Like the solid yellow curve that runs through point A, it is a compensated demand curve—one that corresponds to a higher level of well-being.

> A **compensated demand curve**, or **Hicksian demand curve**, shows the effect of a compensated change in a good's price on the amount consumed. In other words, it describes the relationship between the price and the amount consumed holding the consumer's well-being fixed and allowing income to vary.

Sir John R. Hicks (1904–1989) won
the 1972 Nobel Prize in Economics.

The Relationship between the Two Types of Demand Curves

For a normal good, the income and substitution effects work in the same direction, as in Figure 6.14(a).[12] A price change therefore produces a larger change in uncompensated demand than in compensated demand. As a result, wherever a compensated demand curve intersects an uncompensated demand curve, the uncompensated demand curve is necessarily flatter, as shown.

For an inferior good, the income and substitution effects work in opposite directions. As a result, wherever a compensated demand curve intersects an uncompensated demand curve, the uncompensated demand curve is either steeper or upward sloping.

Figure 6.14(b) illustrates the case of an inferior good. The blue line is the uncompensated demand curve for potatoes, which we assume are inferior. An uncompensated price increase from \$0.40 to \$0.60 per kilogram reduces consumption from 50 to 40 kilograms, moving the consumer from point A to point B. According to the figure, the substitution effect of this price change reduces potato consumption from 50 to 30 kilograms, while the income effect increases it from 30 to 40 kilograms. Since the substitution and income effects work in opposite directions, the uncompensated demand curve (which runs through points A and B) is steeper than the compensated demand curve (which runs through points A and C).

What if a good is neither normal nor inferior? In that case, the compensated and uncompensated effects of a price change are the same. Therefore, the compensated and uncompensated demand curves coincide with each other.

For a more detailed and technical discussion of the relationship between compensated and uncompensated demand curves, read the appendix to this chapter.

Application 6.5

Discount Warehouse Clubs and Two-Part Tariffs

Millions of Canadians do the bulk of their shopping at discount warehouse clubs. The typical club charges an annual membership fee and sells a variety of products at discounted prices. Perhaps the most familiar warehouse club is Costco which charges an annual membership fee of \$55. Costco is the largest Canadian warehouse club with 77 stores and over 7 million members. Its annual revenue is approximately \$10 billion.

Let's think about how a discount club might set prices and a membership fee. To keep the analysis simple, let's divide all the products into two categories, groceries and other goods. Figure 6.15(a) illustrates the consumer's potential choices. The horizontal axis shows the quantity of groceries and the vertical axis, the quantity of other goods purchased. If the consumer chooses not to join the discount club, he purchases groceries and other goods at regular prices. His budget line is the steepest green line, L_1, and he chooses bundle A.

The discount club sells groceries at a discounted price in return for a membership fee. The discount rotates his budget constraint, making it flatter, while the membership fee shifts it toward the origin. In the figure, the parallel budget lines labelled L_2 and L_3 correspond to the same grocery discount; L_2 involves no membership fee, while L_3 involves a positive fee.

Fixing the grocery discount, how high can the club set its membership fee? For simplicity, let's assume that other goods cost \$1 per unit. As we've drawn the figure, the club can set the fee as high as F_1, but no higher. With this fee, the consumer is willing to join the club. As a member, his budget line is L_2 and he chooses bundle B, which he likes exactly as well as bundle A. With any higher fee, his best choice would be worse than bundle A, and he would not join.

Now suppose the club offers an even larger discount on regular grocery prices. Membership becomes more attractive, so that the club can charge a higher membership fee. As before, it can increase the fee to the point where the consumer is just willing to join. In Figure 6.15(b), the club increases the fee, F_2, to the point where the resulting budget constraint, L_4 (which is flatter than L_3 due to the larger grocery discount), is again tangent to the indifference curve. After joining the club the consumer selects bundle C.

To make sound business decisions, managers of the warehouse club need to understand the relationship between their pricing strategy and sales. In Figure 6.15(b), we see that as the club changes the discounted price, it should alter the membership fee to keep the consumer on the same indifference curve. The amount the consumer would purchase at each possible discounted price is given by his compensated demand curve for groceries.

Pricing is, of course, more complicated than this in practice. Because different consumers have different preferences, setting a single fee that makes them all just willing to join is impossible. Nevertheless, steeper discounts always permit clubs to charge a higher membership fee, at least partly to compensate for the resulting price differential. We will discuss these types of pricing strategies at greater length in Chapter 18.

Figure 6.15

Discount Clubs and Compensated Demand. As shown in figure (a), if the consumer decides not to become a member of the discount club, his budget constraint is L_1 and he chooses bundle A. The figure also shows the largest membership fee, F_1, for which the customer will join the club to obtain a fixed grocery discount. Figure (b) shows that the club can increase the membership fee to F_2 when it increases its grocery discount.

(a) Low membership fee and grocery discount

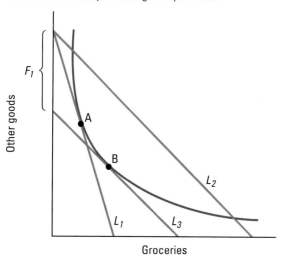

(b) High membership fee and grocery discount

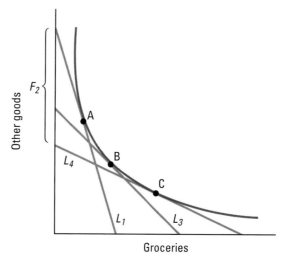

WORKED-OUT PROBLEM   6.4

The Problem   Using the information in Figure 6.1 (page 171), plot three points on the uncompensated soup demand curve (assuming that the consumer's income is $100 and that the price of bread is $5 per kilogram). Also plot three points on a compensated soup demand curve. Sketch the curves.

The Solution   The consumer purchases five litres of soup when the price is $10 per cup [bundle B in Figure 6.1(a)], 13 litres when the price is $4 per litre [bundle A in Figures 6.1(a) and (b)], and 22 litres when the price is $2.50 per litre [bundle D in Figure 6.1(b)]. We have plotted these points in Figure 6.16(a) using the same labels. The uncompensated demand curve is shown in blue.

We will plot the compensated demand curve that runs through point A in Figure 6.16(a). A compensated price change from $5 to $10 per cup leads the consumer to buy 8 cups of soup [bundle C in Figure 6.1(a)]. A compensated price change from $5 to $2.50 leads the consumer to buy 18 cups of soup [bundle E in Figure 6.1(b)]. We have plotted these points in Figure 6.16(a) using the same labels. The compensated demand curve is shown in yellow.

Figure 6.16
Compensated and Uncompensated Demand Curves for Worked-Out Problems 6.4 and 6.5. In figure (a), we've plotted an uncompensated demand curve (blue) and a compensated demand curve (yellow) for soup, using the information in Figure 6.1, as required for worked-out problem 6.4. In figure (b), we've plotted an uncompensated demand curve (blue) and a compensated demand curve (yellow) for film tickets, using the formulas obtained in the solution to worked-out problem 6.5.

IN-TEXT EXERCISE 6.5   **Using the information in Figure 6.4 (page 177), plot two points on the uncompensated potato demand curve (assuming that the consumer's income is $72 and that the price of beef is $6 per kilogram). Also plot two points on a compensated potato demand curve. Sketch the curves.**

WORKED-OUT PROBLEM   6.5

The Problem   As in worked-out problem 6.1 (page 174), Natasha's marginal rate of substitution for concerts with films, MRS_{CF}, is F/C, where C stands for the number of concert tickets and F stands for the number of film tickets. The formula for her indifference curves is $F = U/C$. Her income is $100 per month. As we discovered in the solution to worked-out problem 5.5 (page 149), when concert and film prices are both $5 per ticket, she buys 10 of each. Find the compensated demand curve for films that passes through this point and graph it. How does it compare to her uncompensated demand curve?

The Solution   First we'll solve for Natasha's compensated demand curve. With a compensated change in the price of film tickets, her best choice must satisfy the tangency condition and lie on the indifference curve through the bundle $(C, F) = (10, 10)$. As in the solution to worked-out problem 6.1, the formula for the tangency condition is $F/C = P_C/P_F$. With $P_C = 5$, we can rewrite this formula as follows.

$$C = FP_F/5$$

As in worked-out problem 6.1, the formula for the indifference curve that runs through the bundle $(C, F) = (10, 10)$ is $F = 100/C$, which we will rewrite as

$$C = 100/F$$

A bundle can satisfy both the tangency condition formula and the indifference curve formula at the same time only if $FP_F/5 = 100/F$. This requires $F^2 = 500/P_F$, or $F = \sqrt{500/P_F}$. This expression represents the number of tickets Natasha will buy following a compensated change in the price of film tickets from $5 to any other price P_F. In other words, it is the formula for her compensated demand curve.

Our answer to worked-out problem 5.5 provided a formula for Natasha's uncompensated demand curve: $F = M/(2P_F)$. With $M = \$100$, the formula becomes $F = 50/P_F$.

We've graphed Natasha's compensated and uncompensated demand curves in Figure 6.16(b), plotting the amounts purchased for three film ticket prices: $P_F = \$1.25$, 5, and 20. Notice that the compensated demand curve is steeper than the uncompensated demand curve. In this example, film tickets are normal goods.

IN-TEXT EXERCISE 6.6   **As in in-text exercise 6.1, Keiko's marginal rate of substitution for gasoline with wireless minutes, MRS_{GW}, is $10/\sqrt{G}$, where G stands for litres of gasoline. The formula for her indifference curves is $W = U - 20\sqrt{G}$, where W stands for the number of wireless minutes. Keiko's income is $125 and gasoline costs $1 per litre. How many wireless minutes will Keiko purchase if the**

> price is $0.50 per minute? Find the compensated demand curve for wireless
> service that passes through this point and graph it. How does it compare to her
> uncompensated demand curve? Will her compensated and uncompensated
> demand curves for gasoline differ? (Hint: You should be able to answer this last
> question without solving for the curves. Apply what you learned about Keiko's
> income effects for gasoline in worked-out problem 5.6, page 159.)

Exact Consumer Surplus

As we've mentioned, the method of computing consumer surplus described in Section 6.2 is actually an approximation rather than an exact measure of the compensating variation associated with the loss of access to a market. To understand the problem, look again at Figure 6.6(a). According to our calculation, the household receives $4500 in consumer surplus from the computer market. If we abolished the computer market and compensated this household by paying it $4500, its income would be $4500 higher. As we noted in Section 5.5, a change in income shifts the demand curve. If computers are normal goods, the demand curve would shift outward, expanding the green-shaded area and increasing our measure of the household's consumer surplus beyond $4500. In other words, when the household receives $4500 as compensation for the ability to buy computers, the value of that ability grows beyond $4500.

To overcome this problem, we compute consumer surplus following the same procedure as in Section 6.2 (recall Figure 6.6), except we use a compensated demand curve instead of an uncompensated demand curve. For an illustration, look at Figure 6.17(a), which reproduces the blue uncompensated computer demand curve from Figure 6.6(a). As before, computers sell for $1500 each, and the consumer buys three. We've added a yellow curve, which shows the effects of compensated price changes starting from a price of $1500. This is a compensated demand curve. (Where the compensated and uncompensated demand curves overlap, we use a dashed line that alternates blue and yellow segments.)

How much would we have to compensate the consumer for the loss of access to the computer market? To answer this question, let's imagine taking the computers away from him one by one, and calculate the required compensation for each. Let's start with the third computer. From either demand curve, we know that it's worth $2000 to the consumer. He buys it for $1500, so his net benefit is $500. If we pay him $500, he should be willing to give it up. In the figure, that payment equals the area of the green-shaded rectangle labelled C.

How much must we pay the consumer to compensate him for the loss of the second computer? According to the uncompensated (blue) demand curve, the net economic benefit of that computer is $1500; according to the compensated (yellow) demand curve, it's $2000. Which number is correct? To compensate the consumer for the loss of the second computer, we need to know its worth to him *after compensating him for the loss of the third computer*. The height of the compensated demand curve indicates the consumer's willingness to pay for the second computer after receiving this compensation, while the height of the uncompensated demand curve does not. Therefore, we must use the compensated demand curve. In this example, after receiving compensation for the third computer, the consumer is just willing to give up the second computer for a payment of $2000 (the area of the green-shaded rectangle labelled B).

Through almost identical reasoning, we learn that, after receiving compensation for the second and third computers, the consumer should be willing to give up the first computer for a payment of $3500 (the area of the green-shaded rectangle labelled A). To compensate him for the loss of all of his computers, we therefore have to pay him $6000.

Figure 6.17

Measuring Exact Consumer Surplus and Compensating Variations Using Compensated Demand Curves. In figure (a), the payments required to compensate the consumer for the loss of the third, second, and first computers in succession equal the areas of the green-shaded rectangles labelled C (for the third computer), B (for the second computer), and A (for the first computer). The consumer surplus for computers is therefore equal to the total green-shaded area. In figure (b), the compensating variation for an increase in the price of gasoline from $1 to $2 per litre equals the green-shaded area (which compensates for reduced consumption) plus the red-shaded area (which compensates for the higher price paid on litres purchased at $2 per litre).

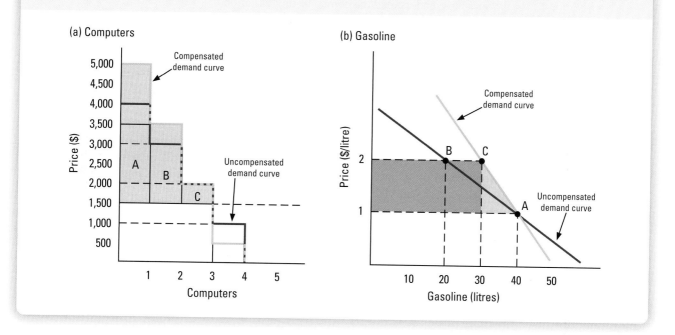

(a) Computers

(b) Gasoline

Notice that this compensating variation equals the area between the compensated demand curve and a horizontal line drawn at the market price.

Exact Changes in Consumer Surplus

In Section 6.3, we explained how to use an uncompensated demand curve not only to measure consumer surplus, but also to determine the change in welfare that results from a change in price (recall Figure 6.7). We now know that this procedure is actually an approximation. To compute the change in consumer surplus exactly rather than approximately, we follow the same procedure as in Section 6.3, except that we use a compensated demand curve instead of an uncompensated demand curve.

Suppose, for example, that a proposed gasoline tax will increase the price of gas from $2 to $4 per litre. What is the economic cost to any given consumer? Look at Figure 6.17(b). The blue line is the consumer's uncompensated demand curve. At $1 per litre, he would buy 40 litres (point A); at $2 per litre, he would buy only 20 litres (point B). The yellow line is a compensated demand curve; it shows the effect of compensated prices changes starting from a price of $1 per litre.

To compute the compensating variation for the price increase, we start at point A, which the consumer chooses without the tax. Then we take away gasoline little by little, compensating him as we go. As shown in the figure, the compensated increase in the price of gasoline from $1 to $2 reduces the consumer's gasoline purchases to 30 litres (point C).

The required rate of compensation for the last unit of gasoline always equals the height of the compensated demand curve, minus the original price, $1. So the total payment required to compensate the consumer for the reduction in gasoline consumption from 40 to 30 litres equals the area of the green-shaded triangle. The consumer also loses $1 on each of the 30 litres he continues to purchase. To compensate him for this loss, we have to pay him an additional $30, the area of the red rectangle. The compensating variation therefore equals the area of the green triangle plus the area of the red rectangle. Had we used the uncompensated demand curve rather than the compensated demand curve, we would have understated the compensating variation.

Approximate versus Exact Consumer Surplus   Suppose for the moment that computers are neither normal nor inferior—in other words, that there are no income effects. In that case, the compensated and uncompensated demand curves for computers are identical, and we can compute exact consumer surplus using either one. Intuitively, with no income effects, compensating the consumer for the loss of a computer doesn't change her willingness to pay for the remaining computers.

When income effects are small, the uncompensated demand curve lies close to the compensated demand curve. If we compute consumer surplus using the uncompensated demand curve, we won't measure consumer surplus with complete accuracy, but we won't be far off. Consequently, the procedure for measuring consumer surplus described in Section 6.2 will yield a good approximation. This makes intuitive sense. Suppose, for example, that a consumer receives $50 in consumer surplus annually from the butter market, and that his income is $50,000. If he were to receive a $50 payment, his income would be $50,050, and his uncompensated demand curve for butter would barely move. Adjusting for this movement would make little difference.

Sometimes, however, the approach described in Section 6.2 does not closely approximate consumer surplus. Suppose, for example, that a consumer receives $30,000 in consumer surplus annually from leisure. If he were to receive a $30,000 payment, his uncompensated demand curve for leisure may shift dramatically. To compute his consumer surplus accurately, we must therefore use his compensated leisure demand curve.

WORKED-OUT PROBLEM 6.6

The Problem   Repeat worked-out problem 6.2 (page 181), but compute Keiko's compensating variation using a compensated demand curve. Is the answer the same as in worked-out problem 6.2?

The Solution   To compute the compensating variation, we use the compensated demand curve for wireless minutes that describes the effects of compensated changes in the price of minutes starting from the market price ($0.50 per minute). If you solved in-text exercise 6.5 (page 201) correctly, you know that the formula for this compensated demand curve is $W = 300 - 200P_W$. Notice that this is the same as Abigail's uncompensated demand curve for wireless minutes in worked-out problem 6.3 (page 185). Figure 6.8 is therefore also a graph of one of Keiko's compensated demand curves. The compensating variation for the loss of her wireless phone is the area of the green triangle. We already determined that the area of this triangle is $100. Therefore, Keiko's compensating variation is $100. Notice that we obtained exactly the same answer in worked-out problem 6.2.

IN-TEXT EXERCISE 6.7 **Suppose the price of wireless service rises from $0.50 per minute to $1 per minute. What is Keiko's compensating variation? Show the lost consumer surplus on a graph.**

CHAPTER SUMMARY

1. **Dissecting the effects of a price change (LO1)**
   a. The effect of an uncompensated change in the price of a good equals the effect of a compensated change in the price of the good (the substitution effect), plus the effect of removing the compensation (the income effect).
   b. The substitution effect is negative for a price increase and positive for a price reduction. If a good is normal, the income effect is negative for a price increase and positive for a price reduction. If a good is inferior, the income effect is positive for a price increase and negative for a price reduction.
   c. For a normal good, the income effect reinforces the substitution effect, so the demand curve slopes downward.
   d. For an inferior good, the income effect and the substitution effect work in opposite directions.
   e. If a good is sufficiently inferior, and if it accounts for a sufficiently large fraction of the consumer's spending, its demand curve may slope upward.

2. **Measuring changes in consumer welfare using demand curves (LO2)**
   a. Economists often evaluate the gains or losses that consumers experience when economic circumstances change by computing compensating variations.
   b. Consumer surplus is the compensating variation associated with the loss of access to a market.
   c. The height of a good's demand curve indicates the consumer's willingness to pay for another unit of the good.
   d. One common method of calculating the consumer surplus derived from a good is to determine the area below the good's demand curve and above a horizontal line drawn at the good's price.
   e. The compensating variation for a price change equals the resulting change in consumer surplus. Therefore, economists use the change in consumer surplus as a measure of the change in the consumer's well-being.

3. **Measuring changes in consumer welfare using cost-of-living indexes (LO3, 4)**
   a. A cost-of-living index allows us to approximate changes in a consumer's well-being caused by changes in

prices without knowing preferences or demand elasticities.
   b. With a perfect cost-of-living index, the consumer would be better off when real income rises according to the index, and worse off when real income falls according to the index.
   c. In theory, it's possible to construct a perfect price index by computing compensating variations. In practice, doing so requires knowledge of consumer preferences, which vary across the population.
   d. Most price indexes indicate the change in the cost of a fixed bundle of goods.
   e. Laspeyres price indexes suffer from substitution bias because they fail to capture the consumer's tendency to moderate the impact of a price increase by substituting away from goods that have become more expensive. As a result, they tend to overstate increases in the cost of living.
   f. Inflation is the change in the cost of living over time. A common official measure of inflation is based on the Consumer Price Index (CPI), which is a Laspeyres index. Recent estimates suggest that the CPI significantly exaggerates the rate at which the cost of living increases.

4. **Labour supply and the demand for leisure (LO5)**
   a. To understand the supply of labour, we study the demand for leisure, treating the wage rate as the price of leisure.
   b. The substitution effect of an increase in the wage rate decreases leisure demand and increases labour supply.
   c. Since consumers are sellers of their time rather than buyers, income effects are reversed. When leisure is a normal good, the income effect and the substitution effect work in opposite directions. As a result, labour supply curves may bend backwards. There is evidence that, for many prime-age men, labour supply usually does not change much and may even decline as the wage rate rises.
   d. An increase in the wage rate should increase labour force participation. This principle helps to explain the dramatic increase in female labour force participation during the second half of the last century.

*5. Another type of demand curve (LO6)

   a. Compensated demand curves always slope downward.

   b. Different compensated demand curves correspond to different levels of the consumer's well-being.

   c. For a normal good, wherever a compensated demand curve intersects an uncompensated demand curve, the uncompensated demand curve is necessarily flatter. For an inferior good, wherever a compensated demand curve intersects an uncompensated demand curve, the uncompensated demand curve is either steeper or upward sloping. If a good is neither normal nor inferior, the compensated and uncompensated demand curves coincide with each other.

   d. To compute consumer surplus exactly, we must use compensated demand curves. If we calculate consumer surplus using uncompensated demand curves, we obtain an approximation of consumer surplus. This approximation will be good if income effects are small.

ADDITIONAL EXERCISES

Exercise 6.1: Nuts and bolts are perfect complements; a nut is valuable only when paired with a bolt, and vice versa. Ted spends all his money on nuts and bolts. On a graph, illustrate the effect of a compensated change in the price of nuts. Does this change alter the consumption of nuts or bolts? What does your answer tell you about the size of substitution effects resulting from changes in the price of nuts? (LO1)

Exercise 6.2: Regular- and extra-strength pain killers are perfect substitutes; one extra-strength tablet is equivalent to two regular-strength tablets. In each of the following cases, show graphically the effect of a compensated increase in the price of regular-strength tablets. Does this change alter the consumption of regular- or extra-strength tablets? What do your answers tell you about the size of the substitution effects resulting from increases in the price of regular-strength tablets? (LO1)

   a. The price of an extra-strength tablet is more than twice the final price of a regular-strength tablet.

   b. The price of an extra-strength tablet is more than twice the initial price of a regular-strength tablet, but less than twice the final price.

   c. The price of an extra-strength tablet is less than twice the initial price of a regular-strength tablet.

Exercise 6.3: Figure 6.4 (page 174) shows the income and substitution effects associated with a reduction in the price of an inferior good. Draw a similar graph showing the income and substitution effects associated with an increase in the price of an inferior good. (LO1)

Exercise 6.4: Figure 6.5 (page 175) shows the income and substitution effects associated with a reduction in the price of a Giffen good. Draw a similar graph showing the income and substitution effects associated with an increase in the price of a Giffen good. (LO1)

Exercise 6.5: Can every good be a Giffen good? Why or why not? (LO1)

Exercise 6.6: Think about your own preferences. What is your compensating variation for each of the following changes in your plans or expectations? (LO2)

   a. Listening to your economics professor perform a one-hour poetry reading.

   b. Meeting your favourite musician.

   c. Adding a week to the length of your spring break.

   d. Majoring in economics if you plan to major in something else; majoring in something else if you plan to major in economics.

Exercise 6.7: Sam currently earns $30,000 a year. The government is considering a policy that would increase Sam's income by 12 percent, but raise all prices by 8 percent. What is Sam's compensating variation for the proposed policy? Can you compute it without knowing his preferences? Why or why not? (LO2)

Exercise 6.8: Suppose policymakers are considering two potential projects that are mutually exclusive. Should they always pick the one for which the compensating variation is the largest negative number (in other words, the one for which the individual is willing to pay the most)? Why, or why not? If not, is there a way to compare the benefits of these projects using the concept of compensating variation? (Hint: Think about the compensating variation of reversing each policy.) (LO2)

Exercise 6.9: The formula for Albert's demand curve for music downloads is $M = 150 - 60P_M$, where M is the number of downloads and P_M is the price of a download. Suppose the price of a music download falls from $2 to $1. Using the method described in Section 6.2, calculate the change in Albert's consumer surplus. (LO2)

Exercise 6.10: Beatriz enjoys writing and uses a large amount of paper. Currently, paper costs $2 for 100 sheets. The formula for her demand curve is $S = 525 - 50P_S$, where P_S is the price of 100 sheets and S is the number of sheets purchased. Her provincial government has proposed taxing paper at the rate of

$0.50 for each 100 sheets. Assume that this policy would increase the price of paper to $2.50 (including tax). (LO2)

a. Draw Beatriz' demand curve. Using the method described in Section 6.2, compute the change in her consumer surplus for the proposed tax increase.

b. How much revenue will the government raise by taxing Beatriz? How does that revenue compare to her economic losses? Does the new tax raise enough revenue for the government to compensate her for her loss?

Exercise 6.11: Arnold spends all his money on sunscreen and lemonade. In June he bought five 50 ml tubes of sunscreen at $1 per tube and twenty litres of lemonade at $1.30 per litre. In July he bought seven tubes of sunscreen at $1.10 per tube and eighteen litres of lemonade at $1.70 per litre. In August he bought three tubes of sunscreen at $1.40 per tube and 23 litres of lemonade at $1.80 per litre. (LO3)

a. Create a Laspeyres price index using June as the base period (that is, use Arnold's consumption bundle for June to create the fixed weights). How did his cost of living change according to this measure?

b. Repeat part (a) initially using July as the base period and then using August as the base period.

c. Do the Laspeyres price indexes you obtained in parts (a) and (b) imply the same percentage increases in Arnold's cost of living over time? If not, by how much do they differ?

Exercise 6.12: Is it possible for the true cost of living to rise for one consumer and fall for another in response to the same change in prices? If so, explain why, and give an example using graphs. If not, explain why not. (LO4)

Exercise 6.13: Sheryl spends all of her leisure time and all of her money on sailing. She doesn't value leisure time if she can't sail, and she can only sail if she has leisure time. Sailboat rentals cost $10 per hour, and Sheryl earns W per hour. She has to decide how to allocate 15 hours per day between work and leisure. How many hours will she work if she earns $20 per hour? Find a formula for her labour supply curve. Is it upward or downward sloping? Why? (LO5)

*__Exercise 6.14:__ For Alejandro, concert tickets and film tickets are perfect complements—he does not enjoy additional concerts when he has attended more concerts than films, or additional films when he has attended more films than concerts (as in in-text exercise 5.8, page 149). Initially, he can spend $200, film tickets cost $8 per ticket, and concert tickets cost $12 per ticket. Solve for a compensated demand curve for film tickets, showing the effects of compensated price changes starting from the initial film ticket price of $8 per ticket. How does this curve compare to his uncompensated demand curve for film tickets, found in the solution to in-text exercise 5.8? (LO6)

*__Exercise 6.15:__ How would you measure consumer surplus if the demand curve is upward sloping? Warning: this is a trick question. (LO6)

APPENDIX

THE SLUTSKY EQUATION

The relationship between compensated and uncompensated demand is summarized by an important formula known as the **Slutsky equation**. This equation is a precise statement of the principle, stated earlier as formulas (1) and (2), that the effect of an uncompensated price change equals the effect of a compensated price change (the substitution effect) plus the effect of removing the compensation (the income effect).

$$\left(\frac{\Delta Q}{\Delta P}\right)^{Uncomp} = \left(\frac{\Delta Q}{\Delta P}\right)^{Comp} - Q \times \left(\frac{\Delta Q}{\Delta M}\right) \tag{3}$$

Optional The **Slutsky equation** can be expressed using calculus as

$$\left(\frac{\partial Q}{\partial P}\right)^{Uncomp}$$

$$= \left(\frac{\partial Q}{\partial P}\right)^{Comp} - Q \times \left(\frac{\partial Q}{\partial M}\right)$$

Given the demand function for the good (see worked out problem 5.5) the substitution effect,

$$\left(\frac{\partial Q}{\partial P}\right)^{Comp}, \text{ and income effect,}$$

$$\left(-Q\frac{\partial Q}{\partial M}\right) \text{can be calculated,}$$

where Q is the uncompensated demand as a function of income and prices.

The symbol $(\Delta Q/\Delta P)^{Uncomp}$ stands for the uncompensated price effect. It is the change (per dollar) in the amount purchased resulting from a small uncompensated price change. The symbol $(\Delta Q/\Delta P)^{Comp}$ stands for the change (per dollar) in the amount purchased resulting from a small compensated price change. That term is the substitution effect. Finally, $(\Delta Q/\Delta M)$ stands for the change (per dollar) in the amount purchased resulting from a small change in income. That term, multiplied by $-Q$, is the income effect.

Why do we need to multiply $\Delta Q/\Delta M$ by $-Q$? The income effect equals $\Delta Q/\Delta M$—the change in the amount purchased per dollar of income—times the change in purchasing power resulting from the price increase. As it turns out, the change in purchasing power is $-Q$. Why? Suppose a consumer purchases Q kilograms of beef at a price of $\$P$ per kilogram, spending $\$PQ$. If the price increases by $\$1$ per kilogram, the same amount of beef costs $\$(P + 1)Q$, so he needs an additional $\$Q$ to purchase it. If his income hasn't changed and he attempts to buy the same bundle as before, he finds himself $\$Q$ short. So roughly speaking, he has lost $\$Q$ worth of purchasing power.

We can also write the Slutsky equation in terms of elasticities.[13]

$$E^d_{Uncomp} = E^d_{Comp} - S \times E^d_M \tag{4}$$

In this equation, E^d_{Uncomp} stands for the elasticity of demand along the uncompensated demand curve (previously written simply as E^d in Chapter 2). E^d_{Comp} stands for the elasticity of demand along the compensated demand curve. S is the good's budget share (that is, the fraction of income spent on it), and E^d_M is the good's income elasticity.

---

[13]To get from equation (3) to equation (4), multiply both sides of (3) by P/Q. The term to the left of the equals sign becomes $(P/Q)(\Delta Q/\Delta P)^{Uncomp}$. You should recognize this expression as the price elasticity of demand for the uncompensated demand curve. The first term to the right of the equals sign becomes $(P/Q)(\Delta Q/(P)^{Comp}$, the price elasticity of demand for the compensated demand curve. Finally, the second term to the right of the equals sign becomes $-(P/Q) \times Q \times (\Delta Q/\Delta M)$, which is equivalent to $-(PQ/M) \times (M/Q)(\Delta Q/\Delta M)$. The first part of that expression, PQ/M, is the good's budget share. You should recognize the second part, $(M/Q) \times (\Delta Q/\Delta M)$, as the income elasticity of demand. Substituting these definitions into equation (3) gives us equation (4).

Using the Slutsky Equation to Determine Consumers' Preferences

Since a consumer's well-being is not observable, we can't measure the compensated elasticity of demand for a good directly. However, using the Slutsky equation, we can determine it indirectly. Since prices, income, and purchases are observable, we can measure the good's uncompensated elasticity of demand, its income elasticity, and its budget share. We can then compute the compensated price elasticity of demand simply by rearranging the Slutsky equation:

$$E^d_{Comp} = E^d_{Uncomp} + S \times E^d_M$$

With this equation, we can easily reconstruct the compensated demand curve for a good by observing a consumer's response to changes in prices and income. This allows us to measure consumer surplus exactly, rather than approximately, using the approach described earlier in Section 5.6. Since compensated price changes keep the consumer on the same indifference curve, we can, if necessary, also use the Slutsky equation to reconstruct the shape of the indifference curves.

Are Income Effects Important?

The Slutsky equation also tells us that the income effect is relatively unimportant when either a good's budget share (S) or its income elasticity (E^d_M) is small. This observation is useful because, with small income effects, the discrepancies between the compensated and uncompensated demand curves are minor. In that case, we can compute consumer surplus using standard (uncompensated) demand curves without introducing much error.

For the vast majority of products, the budget share is very small, simply because people buy so many different things. As a result, income effects are usually tiny. This observation may help to explain why there are so few exceptions to the Law of Demand.

Let's take cheese as an example. According to recent estimates for the United Kingdom, the uncompensated price elasticity of cheese is 0.350 and its income elasticity is 0.23. The budget share is 0.0046, which means that an individual with an annual income of £30,000 spends about £138 per year on cheese. Multiplying the budget share by the income elasticity and rounding off the answer gives us 0.001. From equation (5), we see that the compensated price elasticity must be 0.349, practically the same as the uncompensated price elasticity.

This makes sense. Suppose that Nigel earns £30,000 annually and spends £138 per year on cheese. If the price of cheese increases by 20 percent, he needs an additional £27.60 to make the same purchases. If his income hasn't changed and he attempts to buy the same consumption bundle as before, he finds himself £27.60 short. So, roughly speaking, his purchasing power has fallen by £27.60. Nigel will spread this tiny reduction in purchasing power over everything he purchases. Its impact on his cheese consumption will be almost negligible compared to the direct impact of the price increase via the substitution effect.

Though income effects are typically small, there are exceptions. Generally, the exceptions involve goods with large budget shares. For example, the income effects of a change in the price of potatoes were undoubtedly important for many nineteenth-century Irish households, who spent much of their incomes on potatoes. Similarly, the income effects of a change in the price of housing may be large for many contemporary consumers. For such goods, compensated and uncompensated demand curves may diverge significantly, and measures of consumer well-being that are derived from standard (uncompensated) demand curves, as described in Section 6.2, may be highly inaccurate.

IN-TEXT EXERCISE 6.8 **Rico spends three percent of his income on CDs. His uncompensated (standard) price elasticity of demand for CDs is 1.5, and his income elasticity of demand is two. What is Rico's compensated price elasticity of demand?**

Production Decisions

In Part IIA, we studied how consumers decide which products to purchase. In the next three chapters we'll see where the supply of those products comes from. In a free market economy, most goods are produced by *firms*—privately owned companies whose owners keep the profits generated by the sale of their products. The people who run firms decide what to produce and how to produce it. Our discussion of firms' choices is broken into three parts. First, in Chapter 7, we'll discuss production technology—that is, what firms are able to produce. Then, in Chapter 8, we'll see how a firm can produce its products at the lowest possible cost. Finally, in Chapter 9, we'll study how a firm that wants to maximize its profit chooses how much of its product to sell and its price.

7 Technology and Production

LEARNING OBJECTIVES

After reading this chapter, students should be able to

LO1 Explain how to identify a firm's efficient production methods.

LO2 Calculate average product and marginal product and explain how they measure a firm's productivity.

LO3 Discuss input substitution in production with two variable inputs.

LO4 Understand the concept of returns to scale and its causes.

LO5 Discuss the sources of productivity differences across firms and over time.

In January 1907 Henry Ford was preparing to introduce the Model T, the car that would change automobile history. At that time, the automobile was an exciting new product that many entrepreneurs were trying to develop and sell. Yet few individuals could afford to buy one. Cars were assembled by small numbers of workers using custom-fitted parts; the high cost of production made them a product only for the wealthy.

Ford dreamed of changing that with the Model T but faced a number of crucial questions. How should he produce the Model T? Was the production method his competitors used the right choice? Could he employ machines or use labour more effectively to lower the cost of production and expand sales? Ford's novel answers to these questions revolutionized the automobile industry, making him a rich man. Ford Motor Company of Canada was founded in 1904. In 1913 Canadian production of the Model T was only 1500 vehicles and by 1917 production had increased to 50,000 vehicles. In a free market economy, most goods are produced by *firms*—privately owned companies whose owners keep the profits generated by the sale of their products. In this chapter, we'll begin our discussion of firms' production decisions by examining what firms are able to produce and how they can produce it.[1]

We'll cover five topics:

1. *Production technologies.* Firms can use many different methods to make their products. A firm's owner or manager should focus on the ones that are efficient, in the sense that they get the most output possible from the firm's available inputs. We'll see how to describe a firm's efficient production methods.

2. *Production with one variable input.* In the short-run, a firm may not be able to adjust its use of many of its inputs. We'll discuss the simplest case of short-run production, in which the firm has a single input whose use it can vary. We'll discuss two key measures of a firm's productivity: average product and marginal product.

3. *Production with two variable inputs.* In most cases, firms use many inputs to produce a product and, in the long-run, have the ability to substitute the use of one input for another. We'll study input substitution in the simplest case, in which the firm can choose how much to use of two inputs.

4. *Returns to scale.* As a firm produces more output, it may become more or less effective at transforming inputs into outputs. We'll discuss this concept, known as returns to scale, and the factors leading to it. The degree of returns to scale in the technology for producing a product can have important consequences for market structure and public policy.

5. *Productivity differences and technological change.* Firms within an industry can differ in their technologies and a single firm's technology can change over time. We'll discuss what it means for one firm to be more productive than another, or for a given firm to become more or less productive over time. We'll also discuss the sources of these productivity differences and changes.

7.1 PRODUCTION TECHNOLOGIES

Firms try to produce products or services that they can sell profitably. Whether they produce physical products, such as a Dell computer, or services, such as McKinsey's management consulting advice, economists refer to those products or services as **outputs**. Economists refer to the materials, labour, land, and equipment firms use to produce those outputs as **inputs**. For example, Dell uses various materials (memory chips, hard drives, shipping boxes), capital equipment (conveyor belts, testing equipment, trucks), labour (computer assemblers, advertising executives, truck drivers), and land (for its factories) to produce direct-to-home-or-office personal computers.

> **Outputs** are the physical products or services a firm produces. **Inputs** are the materials, labour, land, or equipment that firms use to produce their outputs.

While most firms produce multiple outputs (Dell, for example, produces a range of desktop and laptop computers, televisions, and other products), in this chapter we'll focus on the simpler case in which a firm produces a single output. The basic lessons you'll learn, however, apply as well to the multiple-output case.

---

[1]Although most of our discussion will focus on profit-maximizing firms, it also applies to other types of organizations that produce goods. For example, our study of production technologies in this chapter is relevant for *any* producer, including nonprofit organizations and government agencies.

A firm's **production technology** summarizes all of its possible methods for producing its output.

A production method is **efficient** if there is no other way for the firm to produce a larger amount of output using the same amounts of inputs.

The first thing a firm's owner or manager needs to know is *how* she can produce the products she wants to sell. This involves understanding the firm's production technology. A firm's **production technology** summarizes all of its possible methods for producing its output. Different methods can use the same amounts of inputs but produce different amounts of output.

Economists say that a production method is **efficient** if there is no other way for the firm to produce a larger amount of output using the same amounts of inputs. Owners and managers of firms should try to produce outputs efficiently. In practice, identifying efficient production methods is often a difficult task; good managers devote a great deal of time and effort to it.

Let's look at an example.

Example 7.1

Building Garden Benches

Noah and Naomi want to start a company in their 100-square-metre garage to assemble garden benches from pre-cut bench "kits" that customers provide. Naomi will take charge of the production process; Noah will keep track of the firm's revenues and costs. They will also need to hire some workers to assemble the benches.

Assembling a bench involves three basic steps. The trickiest step is assembling the back section; assembling the frame (including the seat) and attaching the back section to the frame are easier.

A single worker can assemble 33 benches a week by herself. This possibility is labelled production method A in Table 7.1, which describes the number of assembly workers (the input) used and the number of garden benches (the output) produced. (Their garage space is also an input, but we'll assume for now that it cannot be varied.)

What can two workers produce? That depends on how they divide up their tasks. There are several possibilities. They could work by themselves, producing 66 benches a week—twice what a single worker could produce. This method is labelled production method B in Table 7.1. However, there are two other attractive possibilities. First, the workers could help each other in assembling the back sections. Because having a second set of hands makes the assembly of the back section much easier, their output increases to 70 benches a week. This method is labelled production method C in the table. Second, besides helping each other produce back

Table 7.1

Inputs and Output for Various Methods of Producing Garden Benches

Production Method	Number of Assembly Workers	Garden Benches Produced per Week	Efficient?
A	1	33	Yes
B	2	66	No
C	2	70	No
D	2	74	Yes
E	4	125	No
F	4	132	Yes

sections, the workers could specialize in the other tasks—one of the workers could assemble the frames, while the other could attach the back sections to the frames. Because the workers would then not need to keep changing what they were doing, they would be able to produce more—in this case, 74 benches per week. (See Application 7.1 to learn more about the specialization of labour.) This method is labelled method D. Other methods of using two workers not listed in the table produce less output than methods B, C, and D.

For Noah and Naomi, methods A and D are efficient. Method A is efficient because it is the only way to produce benches with one assembly worker. Method D is efficient because it yields the largest output of all possible production methods using two assembly workers.

Noah and Naomi could hire still more workers. With four workers, for example, there would be numerous ways to produce the benches. One possibility would be to form two teams, each of which operates like the two workers in production method D. Unfortunately for Noah and Naomi, however, their garage is fairly small, so that the two teams of workers would sometimes get in each other's way. As a result, this production method would produce only 125 benches per week, less than double the output from method D, the efficient method with two assembly workers. This method is labelled method E in the table. The efficient method with four workers uses three teams: two workers who work together assembling only back sections, one worker who assembles only frames, and one worker who attaches back sections to the frames. This approach—labelled method F—produces 132 benches a week. Though it is better than two teams, the workers still sometimes get in each other's way, so they fail to produce double the output of method D.

IN-TEXT EXERCISE 7.1 **Suppose that Noah and Naomi decide instead to produce garden chairs. There are two different methods for producing garden chairs with two assembly workers: A and B. There are three methods with three assembly workers: methods C, D, and E. The weekly output of each method is: 24 from A, 36 from B, 30 from C, 44 from D, and 24 from E. Which of these production methods are efficient?**

Application 7.1

The Specialization of Labour from Adam Smith to Simba

The specialization of labour is one of the most important methods for increasing workers' productivity. The Scottish economist and philosopher Adam Smith, in his famous book *The Wealth of Nations* (1776), first discussed its effects, describing the operations of a pin factory:

> To take an example, therefore, from a very trifling manufacture; but one in which the division of labour has been very often taken notice of, the trade of the pin-maker . . . it is divided into a number of

Adam Smith (1723–1790)

> branches . . . One man draws out the wire, another straights it, a third cuts it, a fourth points it, a fifth grinds it at the top for receiving, the head; to make the head requires two or three distinct operations; to put it on is a peculiar business, to whiten the pins is another; it is even a trade by itself to put them into the paper; and the important business of making a pin is, in this manner, divided into about eighteen distinct operations . . . I have seen a small manufactory of this kind where ten men only were

employed, and where some of them consequently performed two or three distinct operations . . . [T]hose ten persons . . . could make among them upwards of forty-eight thousand pins in a day. Each person, therefore, making a tenth part of forty-eight thousand pins, might be considered as making four thousand eight hundred pins in a day. But if they had all wrought separately . . . they certainly could not each of them had made twenty . . .

One hundred thirty years later, Henry Ford put exactly the same principle to work in organizing the production of the Model T. His efforts at achieving an efficient production method culminated in 1913 with the introduction of the moving assembly line on which each worker performed a single specialized operation. As Ford put it, "The man who places a part does not fasten it. The man who puts in a bolt does not put on the nut; the man who puts on the nut does not tighten it." This arrangement greatly increased workers' productivity, because they could become more proficient at their specialized tasks and did not waste time switching between tasks. As a result, the time required to assemble an automobile chassis fell from over 12 hours to 93 minutes, and the price of the Model T fell from $850 when it was introduced to $440 in 1915. These advances made cars affordable to a broad range of households, greatly expanding Ford's sales.

The specialization of labour is no less important today. A look at the credits for Disney's classic animated film *The Lion King* reveals that the artists who worked on the film had highly specialized jobs. Many worked only on a single character, such as Simba; others worked only on scene backgrounds. Specializing in this way not only ensures continuity in the artistic representations, it also saves the artists from having to switch between numerous tasks, making them more efficient. For the same reason, new houses are built by teams of specialized workers— carpenters, plumbers, and electricians— and large law firms contain lawyers who work in well-defined specialties, such as corporate law, tax law, and litigation.

Moving assembly line at Ford Motor Company's Michigan plant

The Production Possibilities Set and the Efficient Production Frontier

A firm's **production possibilities set** contains all combinations of inputs and outputs that are possible given the firm's technology.

A firm's **efficient production frontier** contains the combinations of inputs and outputs that a firm can achieve using efficient production methods.

A firm's **production possibilities set** contains all the input and output combinations that are possible given the firm's technology. In Example 7.1, Noah and Naomi's production possibilities set includes the input-output combinations for methods A–F, plus those for any other possible production methods. Figure 7.1 shows Noah and Naomi's weekly bench output and the number of assembly workers for methods A–F. The horizontal axis measures the number of assembly workers they employ, while the vertical axis measures the number of garden benches produced per week. Each labelled point represents the inputs used and the output produced for one production method. Figure 7.1 also shows the output levels for the two best production methods involving three assembly workers, which are labelled methods G and H. Method G produces 111 garden benches per week, while method H produces 99 benches per week. The eight points shown in the figure are part of Noah and Naomi's production possibilities set.

In Figure 7.1, the efficient production method for each number of assembly workers corresponds to the highest point on the vertical line at a given input level. For example, method D is the highest point on the dashed vertical line at two assembly workers in the figure. A firm's **efficient production frontier** contains the input-output combinations from all of its

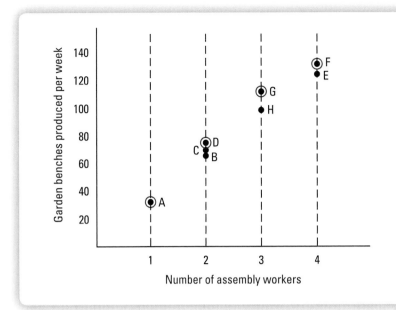

Figure 7.1

The Production Possibilities Set and Efficient Production Frontier for Producing Garden Benches. The labelled points are the input-output combinations for production methods A–H. These points are part of Noah and Naomi's production possibilities set. The points circled in blue are the input-output combinations for the efficient production methods A, D, F, and G. They are each part of Noah and Naomi's efficient production frontier.

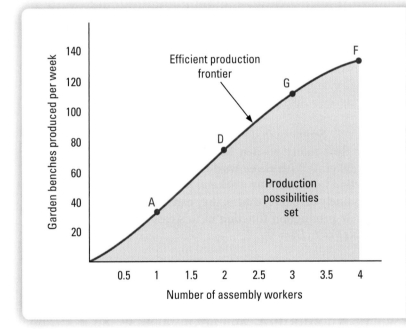

Figure 7.2

The Production Possibility Set and Efficient Production Frontier for Garden Benches When Workers Can Be Hired for Part of a Week. When workers can be hired for part of a week, so that their inputs are finely divisible, Noah and Naomi's production possibility set will look like the shaded region in the figure. Their efficient production frontier is the upper (northwest) boundary of these points, represented by the blue curve in the figure. The input-output combinations for methods A, D, G, and F are shown as blue dots lying along this curve.

efficient production methods. Noah and Naomi's efficient production frontier in Figure 7.1 consists of the points in blue circles, representing the efficient methods A, D, G, and F.

If Noah and Naomi can hire workers for any part of a week, their labour input becomes finely divisible. For example, Noah and Naomi might hire three workers for 40 hours a week and one worker for 16 hours a week, in which case they have hired 3.4 workers. Figure 7.2 shows Noah and Naomi's production possibility set when they can hire workers for any part of a week and their output is also finely divisible.[2] Their many possible

---

[2]The number of garden benches is finely divisible if, for example, part of a bench can be carried over for completion the next week.

input-output combinations appear as the shaded production possibility set in the figure. Their efficient production frontier is the upper (northwest) boundary of this production possibilities set, which is drawn in blue. Methods A, D, G, and F are just four of the many points on this blue curve.

Production Functions

A **production function** is a function of the form *Output* = *F(Inputs)*, giving the amount of output a firm can produce from given amounts of inputs using efficient production methods.

We can describe the efficient production frontier mathematically by means of a **production function**. This is a function of the form *Output* = *F(Inputs)* that describes the amount of output that a firm can produce from given amounts of inputs using efficient production methods.

For example, the production function of a firm whose only input is labour might be $Q = F(L) = 10L$, where Q is the amount of output the firm produces and L is the amount of labour the firm hires. By substituting different amounts of labour for L, we see that the firm can produce 10 units of output if it hires one worker ($L = 1$), 20 units of output if it hires two workers ($L = 2$), and 30 units of output if it hires three workers ($L = 3$).

In Figure 7.2, Noah and Noami's efficient production frontier is described (for up to four workers) by the production function

$$Q = F(L) = -2L^3 + 10L^2 + 25L$$

For example, substituting different values for L we see that output is 33 benches with one worker, 74 benches with two, 111 benches with three, and 132 benches with four. If we graph these combinations of inputs and outputs we get points A, D, G, and F in Figure 7.2. (Noah and Naomi may have discovered that this production function describes the relationship between their labour input and their garden bench output for efficient production methods by using statistical regression techniques, like those we mentioned in the appendix of Chapter 2.[3])

> **IN-TEXT EXERCISE 7.2**   **Suppose that Noah and Naomi's production function is $Q = F(L) = 25L$. How many garden benches can they produce with one worker? With two workers? With three workers? With four workers? Graph their production function for up to four workers. Suppose now that the number of workers they hire is finely divisible (that is, they can hire workers for a fraction of a week). Graph their production function in this case. What if instead their production function is $Q = F(L) = \sqrt{L}$?**

Notice that Noah and Naomi's production function, drawn in Figure 7.2, slopes upward. The amount of output never falls when the amount of labour increases. The same is true of the production functions you examined in in-text exercise 7.2. Why is this so? Remember that a production function gives the output produced for *efficient* production methods. Suppose that with eight workers, a firm can produce 15 units of output. With nine workers, the firm certainly can produce *at least* that much: one worker could just be told to read magazines at home (and thereby not get in any other's way)! And there may be some way to organize the nine workers that produces even more output. Thus, the most efficient production method with nine workers has to produce at least as much output as

---

[3]In the appendix of Chapter 2 we discussed how to learn about the relationship between the amount of a good that consumers demand (the dependent variable) and its price and other factors (the explanatory variables). Here, instead, the dependent variable would be the amount of output Noah and Naomi produce, while the explanatory variables would be the amount of labour they use, as well as its square and cube.

the most efficient method with eight workers. (Of course, if the best way to use nine work-ers is to have one sit at home, the firm will never actually want to hire a ninth worker.) More generally, as long as a firm can freely dispose of any extra inputs it may have, such as by sending a worker home, its production function cannot slope downward.

When a firm uses more than one input, the basic concept of a production function is the same as for the case with a single input, but the amount of output produced depends on the firm's use of all of these inputs. In the rest of the chapter, for example, we'll often consider a firm that uses two inputs, labour (L) and capital equipment (K). Its production function takes the form $Q = F(L, K)$. For instance, the firm's production function might be $Q = F(L, K) = 10\sqrt{L}\sqrt{K}$. In this case, if the firm hires 10 workers and employs 10 units of capital, it can produce 100 units of output (since $10\sqrt{10}\sqrt{10} = 100$.).

Production in the Short Run and the Long Run

Most firms use many inputs to produce their output. Some of these may be freely varied at any time. Others may take quite a while to be changed. When considering production over any given time period, an input is **fixed** if it cannot be adjusted and is **variable** if it can be. For example, in Example 7.1, Noah and Naomi's garage space was a fixed input, while their number of assembly workers was a variable input.

Economists often distinguish between production in the short run and the long run. The **short run** is a period of time over which one or more inputs is fixed. The **long run** is a period of time over which all inputs are variable. For example, in the long run, Noah and Naomi will be able to change their garage space. They could build an addition onto their garage or rent a new, larger garage down the street. Using efficient production methods, they might then have the production possibilities shown in Table 7.2. The table shows the number of benches they produce each week for each number of assembly workers and amount of garage space, using efficient production methods. Each row in the table corres-ponds to the number of assembly workers they hire, while each column corresponds to the amount of garage space they use. For example, Noah and Naomi can produce 140 garden benches a week by hiring three assembly workers and using 150 square metres of garage space. Noah and Naomi's short-run production possibilities in Example 7.1 correspond to the second column in this table, where their garage space is fixed at 100 square metres.

What constitutes the long run depends on the production process being considered. For example, it may take an automobile manufacturer several years to build a new produc-tion facility, while Noah and Naomi may need only a month or two to rent and move into

> A **variable input** can be adjusted over the time period being considered, while a **fixed input** cannot.
>
> The **short run** is a period of time over which one or more inputs is fixed. The **long run** is a period of time over which all inputs are variable.

Table 7.2

Weekly Output of Garden Benches for Various Combinations of Labour and Garage Space (Using Efficient Production Methods)

Number of Assembly Workers	Amount of Garage Space (Square Metres)				
	50	100	150	200	250
1	20	33	45	55	60
2	42	74	105	130	140
3	70	111	140	167	189
4	88	132	170	205	220

a new garage. And for a few production processes, there may literally be no short run. For example, a management consultant's only input may be the amount of time she spends talking to her clients and thinking, which she may be able to vary at will.

In reality, of course, the flexibility of input choices is a matter of degree. A given input may become flexible in a gradual way over time. Also, different inputs may become flexible at different rates over time. Nonetheless, as we'll see in Chapter 8, the short-run versus long-run distinction is useful and has important implications about the ways in which firms adjust to changes in their markets.

As Table 7.2 suggests, a firm's short-run and long-run production functions are closely related. In Sections 7.2 and 7.3, for example, we'll focus for simplicity on the case of a firm that uses only two inputs, labour and capital, one of which—capital—is fixed in the short run. The firm's long-run production function is $F(L, K)$. Its production function in the short run, when its capital is fixed at $\overline{K}$, is $F(L, \overline{K})$. Often, for simplicity, we'll write the firm's short-run production function given a level of capital simply as $F(L)$, as we did earlier in this section.

> **IN-TEXT EXERCISE 7.3** **Suppose that a firm uses both labour (L) and capital (K) as inputs and has the long-run production function $Q = F(L, K) = 10\sqrt{L}\ \sqrt{K}$. If its capital is fixed at $K = 10$ in the short run, what is its short-run production function? How much does it produce in the short run (using efficient production methods) if it hires one worker? Two workers? Three?**

7.2 PRODUCTION WITH ONE VARIABLE INPUT

In this section, we look in more detail at production technology for the case in which a firm uses a single variable input. As we discussed in Section 7.1, we can think of this situation as describing the production possibilities of a firm whose other inputs are fixed in the short run.[4] For example, in Example 7.1, Noah and Naomi used garage space and assembly workers to produce garden benches. While they could add assembly workers, they couldn't enlarge their garage—at least, not in the time frame we considered. For convenience, throughout this section we'll refer to the firm's single variable input as *labour*, which we will assume is perfectly homogeneous (different workers are equally productive).

Average and Marginal Products

For a firm that uses labour as an input, two useful measures of its workers' productivity are the average and marginal products of labour. The **average product of labour**, denoted AP_L, is the amount of output that is produced per worker. We calculate it using the formula

The **average product of labour,** denoted AP_L, equals the amount of output divided by the number of workers employed.

$$AP_L = \frac{Q}{L} = \frac{F(L)}{L}$$

Noah and Naomi's AP_L for up to four workers, when their garage space is fixed at 100 square metres, is shown in the last column of Table 7.3, which describes the production technology for garden benches. For each number of workers, AP_L equals the second

---

[4]It also describes the long-run production possibilities of those firms that only have one input (such as the management consultant mentioned in Section 7.1).

column (output) divided by the first column (labour input). In general, the average product of labour will depend on the number of workers. For Noah and Naomi's production process, AP_L first rises (from 33 with one worker to 37 with two workers) and then falls (beyond three workers). It rises when we add a second worker because the workers can help each other in assembling back sections and can specialize in the other tasks. It falls when the number of workers increases beyond three because of crowding in the garage.

The **marginal product of labour**, denoted MP_L, measures how much extra output is produced when the firm changes the amount of labour it uses by a little bit. This measure of productivity will be very useful when we ask whether a firm should change the amount of labour it uses. (In worked-out problem 7.1, for example, we'll consider how a firm should assign workers between two production plants.)

When we say a *little bit*, we mean the smallest amount of labour a firm can add or subtract. We'll call this ΔL. If only full-time workers are available, then $\Delta L = 1$. If half-time workers are available, then $\Delta L = \frac{1}{2}$. If the firm can hire temporary workers by the day, and we measure labour in worker weeks, then $\Delta L = 0.2$ (since there are five work days in a week).

When L workers are employed, we call the last ΔL units of labour hired the **marginal units of labour**. The marginal product of labour measures how much extra output we get by hiring these marginal units of labour, per unit of labour added. (The idea is the same as the marginal benefit concept that we discussed in Chapter 3.) Starting with L units of labour, the change in output due to the marginal units is $\Delta Q = F(L) - F(L - \Delta L)$. Dividing by the amount of labour added, ΔL, gives us the marginal product of labour

$$MP_L = \frac{\Delta Q}{\Delta L} = \frac{F(L) - F(L - \Delta L)}{\Delta L}$$

By dividing the change in output by ΔL, we make the marginal product of labour measure the output change on a per-unit basis. We do this because it turns our measure of output change into something we can interpret. For example, if you are told that the marginal units of labour increased Noah and Naomi's output by three benches, you wouldn't know anything about the marginal workers' productivity. But if you are told that the marginal units of labour added 1.5 benches per worker, that tells you those marginal workers' productivity.

For Noah and Naomi's production function, the marginal product of labour is shown in the third column of Table 7.3. Since Noah and Naomi must hire workers by the week,

> The **marginal product of labour** with L workers, denoted MP_L, equals the extra output produced due to the ΔL marginal units of labour, per unit of labour added.

> The **marginal units of labour** are the last ΔL units hired, where ΔL is the smallest amount of labour an employer can add or subtract.

Table 7.3

Output, Marginal Product of Labour, and Average Product of Labour for Producing Garden Benches, Given Various Amounts of Labour Input

Number of Assembly Workers	Garden Benches Produced per Week	MP_L	AP_L
0	0	—	—
1	33	33	33
2	74	41	37
3	111	37	37
4	132	21	33

$\Delta L = 1$ and the marginal product of labour is simply equal to $MP_L = F(L) - F(L - \Delta L)$. For example, their MP_L with two workers is equal to the extra output that results from their second worker, which is $F(2) - F(1) = 74 - 33 = 41$. In the table, dashed arrows show graphically the output levels whose difference is equal to MP_L.

Noah and Naomi's MP_L first increases (from $L = 1$ to $L = 2$) and then declines as the number of workers rises above two. The marginal product of labour eventually decreases because workers begin to crowd each other in the garage. We expect a similar effect to occur in most short-run production processes. The expectation that an input's marginal product will eventually decline as its use increases, holding all other inputs (such as garage space) fixed, is known as the **Law of Diminishing Marginal Returns**.

The **Law of Diminishing Marginal Returns** states the general tendency for the marginal product of an input to eventually decline as its use is increased, holding all other inputs fixed.

The Relationship between Average and Marginal Product

The average and marginal products of an input are closely related. By comparing the marginal product to the average product, we can tell whether the average product rises or falls as more input is added. The marginal product tells us how much output the marginal worker adds. If he is more productive than average, he brings the average up. If he is less productive than average, he drives the average down.

Table 7.3 illustrates this point. With two workers, the marginal product of labour (41) is *greater than* the average product (37), and the average product *rises* when the marginal (second) worker is added (from 33 to 37). In contrast, with four workers, the marginal product (21) is *less than* the average product (33), and the average product *falls* (from 37 to 33) when the marginal worker is added. With three workers, the marginal and average products are the same (37), and the average product does not change when the marginal (third) worker is added.

You've seen the same principle at work in other contexts. Think about your grade average. If your grade average last semester (your marginal product) was higher than your overall grade average, then last semester's grades pulled your grade average up. If your grades were lower, then they pulled your grade average down. If they were the same, then they left your grade average unchanged.

We can summarize this relationship as follows:

> **The Relationship between a Firm's Average and Marginal Product Curves**
> When the marginal product of an input is (larger than/smaller than/the same as) the average product, the marginal units of the input (raise/lower/do not affect) the average product.

Average and Marginal Product Curves with Finely Divisible Inputs

When labour is finely divisible, we can graph the average and marginal products as curves to show how they vary with the amount of labour hired. Let's start with the average product of labour. The curve shown in Figure 7.3(a) represents a typical short-run production function. Pick any point on the curve and draw a straight line connecting it to the origin. The slope of this line equals the output at this point (*rise*) divided by the amount of labour used to produce this output (*run*). By definition, that's the average product. The figure illustrates the calculation of the average product at three different levels of labour: 10, 20, and

Figure 7.3

A Production Function (a) and Its Average Product Curve (b). Figure (a) shows a typical short-run production function. If we pick any point on the curve and draw a straight line connecting it to the origin, the slope of the line equals the average product of labour. The graph shows the average product at three different input levels ($L = 10$, $L = 20$, $L = 30$). Figure (b) shows how the average product of labour varies with the amount of labour.

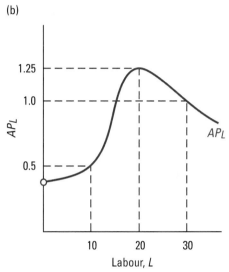

30 workers. For example, with 20 workers, the average product is $25/20 = 1.25$. Figure 7.3(b) shows how the average product varies with the amount of labour. As in Table 7.3, the average product of labour for this production function first rises and then falls as labour increases. Note that an average product cannot be calculated when $L = 0$ (since there are then no workers); this is indicated in the figure by the little blue circle at $L = 0$.

Now let's think about the marginal product of labour. When labour inputs are finely divisible, the smallest amount of labour a firm can add or subtract is very tiny. In this case, with L units of labour, the marginal product of labour equals the slope of the dark red line tangent to the production function at point A in Figure 7.4. Why? The logic parallels our discussion of marginal benefit with finely divisible actions in Section 3.2, but we'll repeat it here for completeness.

Whatever the size of the smallest possible change in labour, the marginal product of labour equals rise over run along the production function. Suppose the smallest possible change is $\Delta L'$. Adding the last $\Delta L'$ units of labour involves a movement along the production function from point B to point A in Figure 7.4. This change increases output by the amount $\Delta Q' = F(L) - F(L - \Delta L')$, shown along the vertical axis in the figure. The marginal product of labour, $MP_L = \Delta Q'/\Delta L'$, therefore equals rise over run along the production function between points B and A; it is the slope of the straight light red line connecting these two points. Similarly, if the size of the marginal change is instead the smaller amount $\Delta L''$ (see the figure), the marginal product of labour would then be $\Delta Q''/\Delta L'' = [F(L) - F(L - \Delta L'')]/\Delta L''$, which equals rise over run along the production

Figure 7.4

The Marginal Product of Labour When Labour Is Finely Divisible. When labour input is finely divisible, the marginal product of labour with L units of labour equals the slope of the dark red line tangent to the production function at point A, also known simply as the *slope of the production function at point A*. The light and medium red lines connecting points A and B and points A and C, respectively, show why this is so. Their slopes equal the marginal product of labour for two different numbers of marginal units of labour, $\Delta L'$ and $\Delta L''$, that are not tiny. As labour becomes finely divisible, so that the number of marginal units grows small, their slopes get closer and closer to the slope of the dark red line.

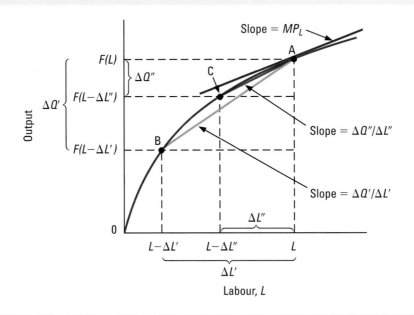

*Optional The **marginal product of labour** is the derivative of the production function at a specific level of the labour input, L, such as point A in Figure 7.4. Hence $MP_L = dF(L)/dL = F'(L)$.

function between points C and A. In other words, the marginal product of labour is then the slope of the straight medium red line connecting points C and A.

In Figure 7.4, the slope of the straight dark red line through point A equals rise over run—equivalently, the marginal product of labour—for very tiny changes in labour input, starting from point A. (Notice that the straight light and medium red lines would become closer and closer to the straight dark red line if we considered smaller and smaller changes in hours.) That dark red line is said to be tangent to the production function at point A.[5] Accordingly, when labour is finely divisible, the marginal product of labour at any given amount of labour equals the slope of the straight line that is tangent to the production function at that level of labour input. A common shorthand expression, which we'll often use, says that the slope of the line tangent to a curve at a point is "the slope of the curve" at that point. Using this language, we can restate our conclusion in this simple way: the marginal product of labour with L units of labour input in Figure 7.4 equals the slope of the production function at point A.

We can now graph the marginal product of labour curve for the production function in Figure 7.3(a), which is reproduced in Figure 7.5(a). There, we've drawn straight lines tangent to the production function at three different levels of labour. The slope of each

---

[5]In mathematics, a line is said to be tangent to a curve at a point if its slope equals the rise over the run for very small changes along the curve starting at the point.

Figure 7.5

A Production Function (a) and Its Marginal Product Curve (b). Figure (a) shows the same production function as in Figure 7.3(a). Here we have drawn straight lines tangent to the production function at three levels of labour input ($L = 10$, $L = 20$, $L = 30$). Their slopes equal the marginal product of labour at those levels of labour. Figure (b) shows how the marginal product of labour varies with the amount of labour.

(a)

(b)

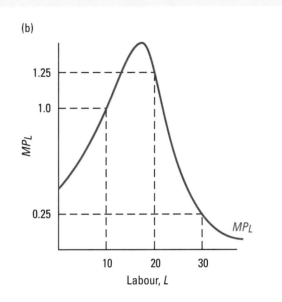

line tells us the corresponding marginal product of labour. We've plotted the value of the marginal product for these levels of labour and others in Figure 7.5(b). Just as for Noah and Naomi's production function, the marginal product of labour curve in Figure 7.5(b) satisfies the Law of Diminishing Marginal Returns. Notice that in Figure 7.5(a), the tangent line at $L = 20$ goes through the origin, which means that the marginal and average products are equal at that point.

Figure 7.6 shows the average and marginal product of labour curves together. Notice that the average product curve slopes upward when it's below the marginal product curve and downward when it's above the marginal product curve. It is flat where it crosses the marginal product curve. This reflects the same principle we saw at work before, applied now to the case in which inputs are finely divisible.[6,7] Total output can be related to both average and marginal product curves. Total output for any labour input is the area below the marginal product curve up to that labour input. This must be the case as total output at

---

[6]Observe also that the AP_L and MP_L curves approach each other as the number of workers gets close to zero. The reason can be seen by looking again at Figures 7.3(a) and 7.5(a), where straight lines whose slopes are equal to and would have almost the same AP_L and MP_L slope near $L = 0$. Intuitively, when there are very few workers, the productivity of all workers is very close to the productivity of the marginal workers.

[7]If you have had calculus, you can see this point by noting that the derivative of the average product function $\dfrac{F(L)}{L}$ equals $\left(\dfrac{1}{L}\right)\left[F'(L) - \dfrac{F(L)}{L}\right]$. Thus, the average product is increasing at L if and only if the marginal product at L, $F'(L)$, is greater than the average product at L, $\dfrac{F(L)}{L}$.

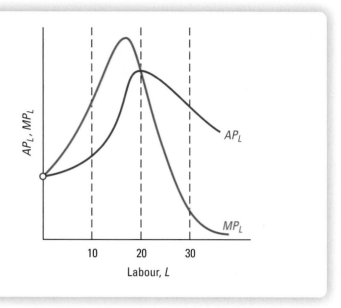

Figure 7.6

The Average and Marginal Product Curves. The figure shows together the average and marginal product curves from Figures 7.3(b) and 7.5(b). The average product slopes upward when it is below the marginal product curve and downward when it is above the marginal product curve. It is neither rising nor falling where the two curves cross.

*Optional The area under a nonlinear curve, such as the marginal product curve in Figure 7.6 for 10 units of labour, can be found using calculus by calculating the integral of the marginal product function over the interval 0 to 10.

a particular level of the labour input, for example ten workers, is just the sum of the marginal products of labour at each input level from one to ten workers. Recalling the discussion of Figure 3.5(b) imagine ten vertical bars, which are not shown on the graph, each one worker in width. The bottom of each bar is the horizontal axis and the top of each bar is centered on the marginal product curve. When added together the ten bars "cover" the area below the marginal product curve.[8] Alternatively, total output can be found by multiplying the value of the average product of labour at a specific labour input by the labour input itself.

> **The Relationship between a Firm's Average and Marginal Product Curves**
> When labour inputs are finely divisible, the average product of labour curve is (rising/falling/neither rising nor falling) at L if the marginal product is (above/below/equal to) the average product.

IN-TEXT EXERCISE 7.4   **Consider again the production function $Q = F(L) = 25L$. Suppose that labour is finely divisible. Draw graphs like those in Figures 7.3, 7.5, and 7.6: one pair of graphs to derive the average product curve, one pair of graphs to derive the marginal product curve, and one graph showing both curves. How does the last graph reflect the relationship between a firm's average and marginal product?**

Using the Marginal Product of Labour to Make Production Decisions

The average and marginal products of labour are useful in practical applications. Here we'll discuss an example; others appear later in this book.

[8]In Chapter 3 the marginal benefit curve was linear so that it was easy to construct rectangles so their summed areas were equal to total benefits. In the case of nonlinear curves, such as the marginal product curves of Figure 7.5 or Figure 7.6, the sum of the areas of the rectangles provides only an approximation of total output. In this instance, determining the area below a nonlinear marginal product curve would require calculus.

Figure 7.7

The Optimal Assignment of Workers between Two Plants with Decreasing Marginal Products of Labour. Figures (a) and (b) show the production functions for the two plants. Figure (c) shows the marginal products of labour for the two plants as functions of the amount of labour assigned to plant 1, L_1 (measured from left to right along the lower horizontal axis) and the amount of labour used in plant 2, L_2 (measured from right to left along the upper horizontal axis). At L_1' the marginal product is greater at plant 1 than at plant 2, and so we can increase output by shifting some labour from plant 2 to plant 1. At L_1'' the marginal product is greater at plant 2 than at plant 1, and so we can increase output by shifting some labour from plant 1 to plant 2. The best assignment of workers is the point at which the two marginal product curves cross, resulting in L_1^* workers being assigned to plant 1, and $100 - L_1^*$ workers being assigned to plant 2.

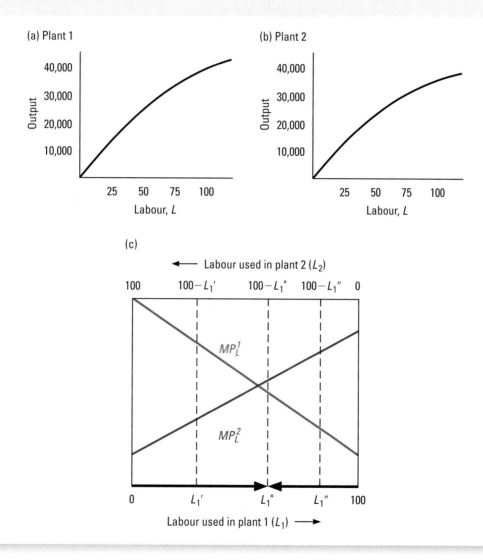

Consider a firm that has 100 workers and two production plants, whose production functions are shown in Figures 7.7(a) and (b). In each plant, the marginal product of labour declines as the amount of labour increases. How should the firm allocate its workers between the plants to maximize the amount it produces? When labour is finely divisible, we can use marginal product of labour curves to answer this question.

Figure 7.7(c) shows the plants' marginal products as a function of the amount of labour used in plant 1, which is measured along the lower horizontal axis. The marginal product of labour curve for plant 1, labelled MP_L^1, is drawn in red; it falls as the amount of labour used in plant 1 increases.

Drawing the marginal product of labour curve for plant 2, labelled MP_L^2, as a function of how much labour is used in plant 1 is a little trickier. If L_1 units of labour are used in plant 1, then $100 - L_1$ units of labour are used in plant 2. In Figure 7.7(c) we can therefore track the amount of labour used in plant 2 by measuring it *backward* (from right to left) along the upper horizontal axis. For example, all the way to the left of the graph, where the lower horizontal axis indicates that zero units of labour are assigned to plant 1, the upper horizontal axis indicates that 100 units are assigned to plant 2. The opposite is true all the way to the right of the graph. Once we have measured the number of workers assigned to plant 2 in this way, we can draw the marginal product curve for plant 2 in blue. Note that because the marginal product in plant 2 falls when the amount of labour used there increases, the curve rises as we move from left to right in the graph. That is, MP_L^2 increases with the amount of labour used in plant 1.

Now let's figure out how many workers to assign to plant 1. This number, L_1^*, is the point at which the two marginal product curves cross. Why? If we were to assign fewer than L_1^* workers to plant 1—such as the amount L_1' in the figure—then the marginal product of labour would be greater in plant 1 than in plant 2 and it would be better to move some units of labour from plant 2 to plant 1. The gain in output is MP_L^1 at plant 1, and the loss is MP_L^2 at plant 2, so there is a net gain of $MP_L^1 - MP_L^2 > 0$ (this is shown by in the rightward-pointing arrow on the horizontal axis). Likewise, if we were to assign more than L_1^* workers to plant 1—such as the amount L_1'' in the figure—then the marginal product of labour would be greater in plant 2 than in plant 1, and it would be better to move some units of labour from plant 1 to plant 2 (this is shown by the leftward-pointing arrow on the horizontal axis). Remembering that output is the area below the marginal product curve, the best assignment of labour between the two plants maximizes output when the area below the two marginal product curves is at its greatest.

This conclusion reflects a general principle: If labour is finely divisible and workers are best assigned to both plants, the marginal product of labour at each plant must be *equal*. Otherwise, we could do better by changing the assignment of labour a little bit, shifting labour to the plant with the higher marginal product.

The problem of allocating labour between two plants is an example of maximizing benefits less costs, which we studied in Chapter 3. When we assign more workers to plant 1, the benefit is that plant 1 produces more output, so the marginal benefit is $MB = MP_L^1$. The cost of assigning more workers to plant 1 is an opportunity cost: plant 2 produces less. So the marginal cost is $MC = MP_L^2$. Thus, assigning inputs to equalize marginal products across the two plants is just an example of equating marginal benefit and marginal cost.[9]

Worked-out problem 7.1 shows how to determine the best assignment of workers across plants using algebra.

---

[9]In some cases, there is no assignment of workers at which the marginal products of the two plants are equal. If so, it's best to assign all the workers to just one plant, the one with the higher marginal product, and close the other plant. In other cases, the marginal product of labour may not be decreasing in the amount of labour used in a plant, and there could be more than one assignment of workers at which the marginal products of the plants are equal. To find the best assignment in such cases you can apply the approach discussed in the appendix of Chapter 3.

WORKED-OUT PROBLEM 7.1

The Problem John, April, and Tristan own JATjuice, a firm that produces freshly squeezed orange juice. Oranges are their only variable input. They have two production facilities. Suppose the marginal product of oranges in plant 1 is $MP_O^1 = 1000 - O_1$, where O_1 is the number of crates of oranges allocated to plant 1. The marginal product of oranges in plant 2 is $MP_O^2 = 1200 - O_2$, where O_2 is the number of crates of oranges assigned to plant 2. Suppose that John, April, and Tristan have a total of 600 crates of oranges. What is the best assignment of oranges to the two plants?

The Solution Start by writing the marginal product in plant 2 as a function of the number of crates of oranges assigned to plant 1, O_1.

$$MP_O^2 = 1200 - (600 - O_1) = 600 + O_1$$

Now find the level of O_1 that equates the marginal product of oranges in the two plants. We can do so with algebra by setting $MP_O^1 = MP_O^2$ and solving

$$1000 - O_1 = 600 + O_1 \Rightarrow O_1^* = 200$$

John, April, and Tristan should assign 200 crates to plant 1 and the rest (400) to plant 2.

IN-TEXT EXERCISE 7.5 **Suppose that John, April, and Tristan have a total of 700 crates of oranges and that the marginal product of oranges in plant 1 is $MP_O^1 = 1000 - O_1$ and in plant 2 is $MP_O^2 = 1200 - 2O_2$. What is the best assignment of oranges between the two plants?**

7.3 PRODUCTION WITH TWO VARIABLE INPUTS

Few production processes use only a single variable input. Indeed, most require many. Economists often divide inputs into four categories: labour, capital, materials, and land. Capital inputs are long-lived assets, such as the physical plant, operating machinery, and vehicles that are used in the production process. Materials are inputs that are fully used up in the production process. Labour includes all human services. And land is, well…land.

As we've discussed in Section 7.1, in the long run all of a firm's inputs are variable. In this section, we'll study the problem faced by a firm that uses two (variable) inputs in the long run.[10] For simplicity, in most of our discussion we will call these two inputs labour (L) and capital (K). We'll assume that each of these inputs is homogeneous—that is, all capital is equally productive as is all labour. (If this were not true, we would need to treat each type of labour or capital as a distinct input, so we would have more than two variable inputs.) In this case, the firm's production function is written $Q = F(L, K)$.

When a firm has more than one variable input, it can usually produce a given amount of output with many different combinations of inputs. Ford's assembly line, for example, not only specialized workers' tasks, it also substituted capital for labour. The assembly

---

[10] Obviously inputs such as land and materials are crucial to the production of agricultural and manufactured goods. If raw materials are used in a constant proportion to output we can suppress their inclusion in a mathematical representation of the production function. Production using only labour and capital is most closely associated with the production of services.

line provided a mechanized way to move the car between workers' stations, which meant that fewer workers were needed to produce any given amount of output. The following example illustrates input substitution in more detail.

Example 7.2

Building Garden Benches, Part 2

Table 7.4 shows how much Noah and Naomi can produce in the long run when they use different combinations of assembly workers and garage space. For up to four workers, the information in the table is exactly the same as in Table 7.2 on page 219, but to make things look more like the graphs we'll soon draw, we've presented it in a slightly different way. Now the rows correspond to the amount of garage space, while the columns—labelled on the bottom of the table—correspond to the numbers of workers. (We did something similar when studying consumption in Chapters 4 and 5.) We've also added information on their output if they have five or six workers. Each entry tells us the most output that can be produced from a particular combination of labour and garage space.

As more of either input is added, Noah and Naomi's production increases if they hold the other input fixed. This means that, if they want to keep their output unchanged, they can lower the amount they use of the other input. For example, the table shows that there are three different input combinations that produce 140 garden benches a week (these are circled). The larger the amount of garage space in one of these input combinations, the smaller the required number of assembly workers.

Table 7.4

Three Input Combinations that Produce 140 Garden Benches per Week (Using Efficient Production Methods)

Amount of garage space (square metres)						
250	60	(140)	189	220	241	255
200	55	130	167	205	220	230
150	45	105	(140)	170	182	188
100	33	74	111	132	(140)	145
50	20	42	70	88	95	100
	1	2	3	4	5	6
			Number of assembly workers			

As in the case of a single variable input, a production function with more than one variable input cannot produce less output when the amount of any input is increased, as long as the firm can freely dispose of any extra inputs. In fact, for most production processes, increasing *all* inputs leads to a *strictly greater* amount of output. In what follows, we will therefore assume the following:

The Productive Inputs Principle   Increasing the amounts of all inputs strictly increases the amount of output the firm can produce (using efficient production methods).

Isoquants

Suppose a firm wants to produce a certain amount of output using capital and labour. What is the best way to do this? Should it use a lot of capital and not much labour, or a lot of labour and not much capital? We will provide a complete answer to this question in Chapter 8. The first step, though, is to identify the possible choices. That is, what combinations of inputs can produce the desired amount of output?

An **isoquant** identifies all of the input combinations that efficiently produce a given level of output. For example, Noah and Naomi can use the circled combinations of labour and garage space in Table 7.4 to produce 140 garden benches per week. We have plotted these input combinations in blue in Figure 7.8. The horizontal axis measures the number of assembly workers; the vertical axis measures the amount of garage space. The three blue points in Figure 7.8 are therefore part of Noah and Naomi's isoquant for 140 units of output. If Noah and Naomi's inputs are finely divisible, there will probably be many input combinations that efficiently produce 140 garden benches a week. If so, their isoquant for producing 140 garden benches a week might look like the solid black curve in Figure 7.8.

There is a close parallel between isoquants and consumer indifference curves. An isoquant identifies the input combinations that efficiently produce a given output level; an indifference curve identifies the different consumption good combinations that produce a given level of well-being. Recall that we can think of indifference curves as being like topographic contour lines. Similarly, we can think of isoquants as contour lines for the "hill" created by the production function.[11] Figure 7.9 shows a contour line for a hypothetical production function with two inputs, labour and capital. The amount of output at any given input combination is measured by the height of the function. The light blue curve shows all of the points on the production function that result in 100 units of output. The dark blue curve directly below (at ground level) shows the combinations of labour and capital that are associated with the points on the light blue curve. This dark blue curve is the isoquant for 100 units of output.

> An **isoquant** identifies all the input combinations that efficiently produce a given amount of output.

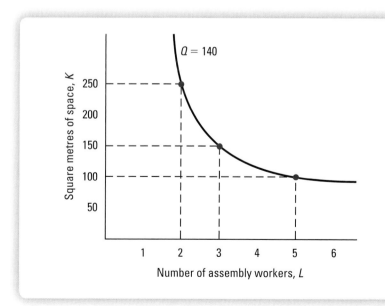

Figure 7.8

The Isoquant for Producing 140 Garden Benches per Week. The blue points graph the combinations of labour and garage space from Table 7.4 that produce 140 garden benches per week. These input combinations are part of Noah and Naomi's isoquant for 140 units of output. If labour and garage space are finely divisible, there will be many input combinations that produce 140 garden benches per week. In this case, the isoquant for 140 units of output might look like the black curve in the figure.

---

[11]One difference from consumer theory, however, is that here the height of the hill has real meaning. That is, outputs levels are *cardinal*, unlike utility levels, which are only ordinal (see Chapter 4).

Figure 7.9

A Two-Input Production Function and One of Its Isoquants. Isoquants are the contour lines for the "hill" created by the production function. In the figure, the light blue curve shows all the points on the production function that yield 100 units of output. The dark blue curve directly below it (at "ground level") is the isoquant for 100 units of output; it shows the input combinations that produce that level of output.

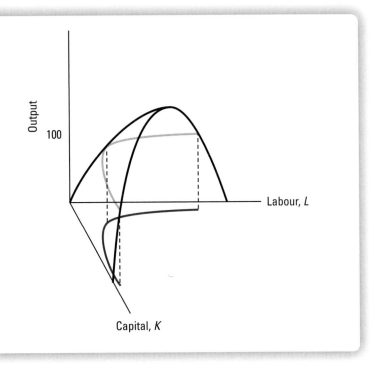

A firm's **family of isoquants** consists of the isoquants corresponding to all of its possible output levels.

A firm's **family of isoquants** consists of the isoquants corresponding to all of its possible output levels. Let's discuss some of the properties of isoquants and families of isoquants.

The Productive Inputs Principle implies that isoquants and families of isoquants have several properties:

1. *Isoquants are thin.* To see why, consider Figure 7.10(a). If an isoquant was thick, then there would be two input combinations on the same isoquant, such as A and B, with one having more of every input than the other. This can't happen according to the Productive Inputs Principle.

2. *Isoquants do not slope upward.* The isoquant in Figure 7.8 slopes downward, from northwest to southeast. Thus, if we compare two points on this isoquant and one uses more assembly workers, then the other uses less garage space. Figure 7.10(b) shows why isoquants can't slope upward. There would then be two different input combinations on the isoquant, such as A and B, with one having more of every input than the other. The Productive Inputs Principle implies that this can't happen.

3. *An isoquant is the boundary between input combinations that produce more and less than a given amount of output.* The input combinations that produce more than Q lie above and to the right of the isoquant for output level Q. Those that produce less lie below and to the left of that isoquant.

4. *Isoquants for the same technology do not cross.* Suppose two isoquants for different production levels crossed, as in Figure 7.10(c). Then there would be two points A and B, one of which (A) has more of all inputs than the other, but produces less output, which can't happen according to the Productive Inputs Principle.

5. *Higher-level isoquants lie farther from the origin.* Since using more of all inputs lead to more output, isoquants for higher output levels lie farther from the origin, as Figure 7.10(d) shows.

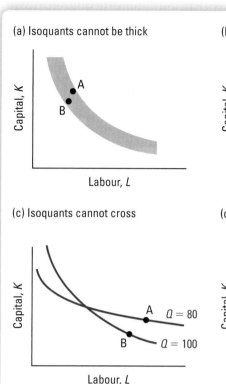

(a) Isoquants cannot be thick

(c) Isoquants cannot cross

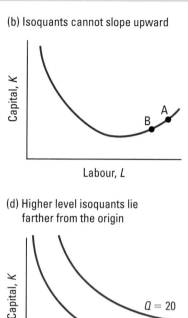

(b) Isoquants cannot slope upward

(d) Higher level isoquants lie
     farther from the origin

Figure 7.10

Some Properties of Isoquants and Families of Isoquants. Figure (a) shows that isoquants are thin. If an isoquant was thick, as in figure (a), there would be two points like A and B that produce the same output using efficient production methods, even though one uses more of all inputs than the other. That is inconsistent with the Productive Inputs Principle. Figures (b) and (c) show that an upward-sloping isoquant or isoquants that cross are also inconsistent with the Productive Inputs Principle. Figure (d) shows that isoquants for higher output levels lie farther from the origin.

In sum:

Five Properties of Isoquants and Families of Isoquants

1. Isoquants are thin.
2. Isoquants do not slope upward.
3. An isoquant is the boundary between input combinations that produce more and less than a given amount of output.
4. Isoquants from the same technology do not cross.
5. Higher-level isoquants lie farther from the origin.

Application 7.2

A Pressing Need for Labour and Capital

Henry Snider's cider mill first started operation around 1850 and was originally located in North York, Ontario. In 1959 it was moved to the Black Creek Pioneer Village where it now sits among other historic buildings. The mill could produce about 2000 litres of cider a day using a hand operated screw press.

Making apple cider today is a relatively simple process. Ground-up apples are squeezed, or pressed, and the juice is bottled. It takes approximately one kilogram of apples to make one litre of cider. Three types of machines can be used in the pressing process. They differ in cost, in daily capacity, and in the amount of labour they require.

After the screw press, the oldest type of machine is the rack-and-cloth vertical press. The rack is a lasagna-like structure with cloth layers, between which workers carefully spread mashed apples. The rack is then rolled over a hydraulic press (like the one that raises your car when a mechanic works on it), which squeezes the juice from the apples. The juice filters through the cloth into a collection tank. Workers then roll the rack back, clean out the mashed apples, and begin the process again. The two other types of machine, the belt press and the rack-and-bag horizontal press, are more modern and use less labour than the rack-and-cloth vertical press.

A single rack-and-cloth vertical press can make 20,000 litres of cider in an eight-hour day using two and a half workers. (Workers can be hired part-time or assigned to other tasks when they are not needed to run the machine.) A single belt press can make 26,000 litres a day using one and a half workers. A single rack-and-bag horizontal press can make 32,000 litres a day using just one worker.

Let's look at a cider mill's isoquant for producing 40,000 litres a day. Table 7.5 lists the labour and capital requirements for three possible ways of producing 40,000 litres a day.[12] The first method (A) uses two rack-and-cloth vertical presses up to their capacity. Let's measure capital according to its cost. The cheapest machine is the rack-and-cloth vertical press. We'll count one of those machines as one unit of capital. The belt press costs four times as much as the rack-and-cloth vertical press, so we'll count it as four units of capital. And the rack-and-bag horizontal press costs 10 times as much, so we'll count it as 10 units of capital. As the table shows, method A uses 40 hours of labour and two units of capital each day (five workers over an eight-hour day equals 40 hours of labour).

The second method (B) uses one belt press up to its full 26,000 litre capacity and one rack-and-cloth vertical press for the remaining 14,000 litres.[13] This method involves five units of

A rack-and-cloth vertical press

capital and requires a total of 26 hours of labour, 12 hours for the belt press and 14 hours for the rack-and-cloth vertical press. (The rack-and-cloth vertical press will run for $(14{,}000/20{,}000) \times 8 = 5.6$ hours a day, so its total labour use is $5.6 \times 2.5 = 14$ hours.)

The third method (C) uses one rack-and-bag horizontal press up to its full 32,000 litre capacity and one rack-and-cloth vertical press for the remaining 2000 units. It uses 11 units of capital and requires 16 hours of labour, 8 hours for the rack-and-bag horizontal press, and 8 hours for the vertical rack-and-cloth press. (In this case the rack-and-bag vertical press runs for 3.2 hours each day, so its total labour use equals $3.2 \times 2.5 = 8$ hours.)[14]

Figure 7.11 shows the three labour and capital combinations. Together the three points form the cider mill's isoquant for producing 40,000 litres of cider a day. If the cider mill could (unrealistically, perhaps) rent its capital for part of a day, it could use the combinations of labour and capital on the dashed lines that connect the three points in the figure. For example, the cider mill could produce 40,000 litres a day by using method A in the morning and method B in the afternoon, which would correspond to using 3.5 units of capital and 33 hours of labour each day. If many different types of machines were available instead of just three, the cider mill's isoquant would instead include many points like A, B, and C, and would look more like a smoothly rounded curve.

Table 7.5

Three Production Methods for Producing 40,000 Litres/Day of Apple Cider

| | Types of Presses | | | | |
Method	Rack-and-Cloth Vertical Press	Belt Press	Rack-and-Bag Horizontal Press	Hours of Labour/Day	Units of Capital
A	2	0	0	40	2
B	1	1	0	26	5
C	1	0	1	16	11

---

[12]We will ignore the number of apples used since it is the same (40,000 kilograms) for all machines. Energy costs for the three machines are also roughly equal.

[13]There are other methods that use one belt press and one rack-and-cloth vertical press, with each type of machine producing different amounts of cider than in method B. But method B uses the least labour of all of those possibilities.

[14]Again, method C uses the least labour of any method that uses one rack-and-bag horizontal press and one rack-and-cloth vertical press.

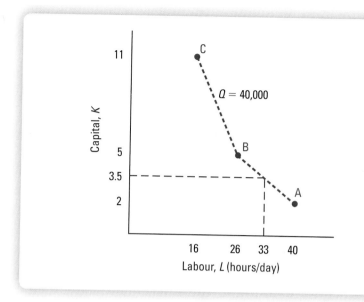

Figure 7.11

A Cider Mill's Isoquant for 40,000 Litres of Cider per Day. The three labelled points show the input combinations for methods A, B, and C in Table 7.5. These three points form the cider mill's isoquant for 40,000 litres/day. If the cider mill could rent its capital for part of a day, it could also use the input combinations on the dashed lines by employing different methods during different parts of the day.

Average and Marginal Products with More than One Input

When a firm's production technology uses more than one input, we can define the marginal and average products of any particular input just as we did in Section 7.2. As there, we do so holding the levels of other inputs fixed. We then speak of the average and marginal products of labour (still denoted AP_L and MP_L) given 150 square metres of space, or of the average and marginal product of capital (denoted AP_K and MP_K) given five workers. The average and marginal products of labour in Table 7.3, for example, are the levels of those measures given 100 square metres of garage space.

The Law of Diminishing Marginal Returns tells us to expect that holding other inputs fixed, the marginal product of an input will eventually decline as more of that input is used. What happens to the marginal product of an input as more of other inputs are added? Often, it increases. For example, with more space, each of Noah and Naomi's workers may be more productive. But sometimes the marginal product decreases—for example, when the inputs are close substitutes. To take an extreme example, imagine that in Section 7.2 we had decided to measure labour inputs as "workers named Bob," "workers named Jim," and so on, and that these workers are equally productive. If the marginal product of labour decreases as more workers are added, then the marginal product of workers named Bob will fall when we add more workers named Jim.

IN-TEXT EXERCISE 7.6 How does Noah and Naomi's marginal product of labour with three workers change in Table 7.4 on page 224 as the amount of garage space increases from 100 to 150 square metres (assuming workers must be hired by the week, so that $\Delta L = 1$)? To 200? What is Noah and Naomi's marginal product of capital with 150 square metres of garage space and four workers if garage space can be changed in increments no smaller than 50 square metres (so that $\Delta K = 50$)?

Substitution between Inputs

An important factor for a manager in choosing her firm's best mix of inputs is the rate at which one input can be substituted for another. This information is captured in the shape of the firm's isoquants. Figure 7.12 shows a firm's isoquant for producing 100 units of output from labour and capital, measured in hours of labour and machine time per week. Suppose the firm starts with 250 hours of labour and 1000 hours of capital, labelled as point A in the figure. How much capital must the firm add to make up for a reduction of 50 hours of labour per week? From the isoquant we see that when it moves from 250 to 200 hours of labour the firm must add 50 hours of machine time to continue producing 100 units of output. The new input combination is point B.

For this change, the rate of substitution for labour with capital is measured by the ratio $-\frac{\Delta K}{\Delta L}$, which tells us how many machine hours of capital we must add per hour of labour that we eliminate. Because isoquants slope down, the ratio $\frac{\Delta K}{\Delta L}$ without the minus sign is a negative number. Including the minus sign in front of the ratio converts our measure of the rate of substitution into a positive number, making it easier to interpret (since a bigger positive number then indicates that more capital is required to compensate for a fixed reduction in labour).

Figure 7.12

Substitution between Labour and Capital Along an Isoquant and the Marginal Rate of Technical Substitution (MRTS). If we start at input combination A and reduce labour by 50 hours, moving to point B, we must add 50 hours of machine time to keep output unchanged. The rate of substitution for labour with capital for this change equals 1, which is the slope of the line connecting points A and B, times −1. If we instead reduce labour by 20 hours, moving to point C, we must add 10 hours of machine time to keep output constant. The rate of substitution for this change, 1/2, equals the slope of the line connecting points A and C, times −1. If we consider smaller and smaller changes, the rate of substitution comes to equal −1 times the slope of the dark red line that is tangent to the isoquant at point A, also known as the *slope of the isoquant at point A*. This slope, times −1, is the marginal rate of technical substitution for labour with capital at input combination A.

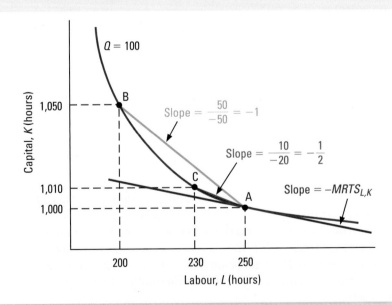

When we move from point A to point B in Figure 7.12, the change in labour is $\Delta L = -50$, and the required compensating change in capital is $\Delta K = 50$. The rate of substitution for labour with capital for this change is therefore $-\frac{\Delta K}{\Delta L} = \frac{50}{-50} = 1$, which equals the slope of the light red line connecting points A and B, times -1 (its rise is $\Delta K = 50$ and its run is $\Delta L = -50$).

Suppose instead that we reduce labour by only 20 hours, from 250 to 230. To keep output unchanged, we must move from point A to point C in Figure 7.12. For this change, the rate of substitution between labour and capital is $-\frac{\Delta K}{\Delta L} = -\frac{10}{-20} = \frac{1}{2}$, which equals the slope of the medium red line connecting points A and C, times -1.

From Figure 7.12 we can see that if we consider smaller and smaller changes in labour, the slope of the lines connecting the original and new input combinations will come closer and closer to the slope of the dark red line tangent to the isoquant at point A, often called simply the "slope of the isoquant" at point A. Thus, for *very small* (*marginal*) changes, the rate of substitution for labour with capital at a given input combination—which we call the **marginal rate of technical substitution (MRTS) for labour with capital**, written as $MRTS_{LK}$—equals the slope of the isoquant at that point, times -1.[15] (Recall seeing a similar point when we discussed the marginal rate of substitution in Chapter 4.)

This measure is closely related to that of a consumer's marginal rate of substitution, introduced in Chapter 4. The MRS is the rate at which a consumer can substitute one good for another without changing well-being; the MRTS is the rate at which a firm can substitute one input for another without changing output.

> **The marginal rate of technical substitution (MRTS) for input *X* with input *Y*,** written as $MRTS_{XY}$, is the rate $\left(-\frac{\Delta Y}{\Delta X}\right)$ at which a firm must replace units of *X* with units of *Y* to keep output unchanged starting at a given input combination, when the changes involved are tiny. It equals the slope of the firm's isoquant at this input combination, times -1.

The MRTS and Marginal Products

How does $MRTS_{LK}$ relate to the productivity of labour and capital? Recall that the marginal product of an input captures how much additional output we can get for each additional unit of input when we increase the input a little bit. Imagine that we change slightly the amount of labour by ΔL and the amount of capital by ΔK. Multiplying the marginal product of labour, MP_L, by the amount of labour added or removed, ΔL, gives us the change in output due to the adjustment in labour, $MP_L \times \Delta L$. Likewise, multiplying the marginal product of capital, MP_K, by the amount of capital added or removed, ΔK, gives us the change in output due to the adjustment in capital, $MP_K \times \Delta K$. If we choose ΔK and ΔL to keep output unchanged (that is, stay on the same isoquant), these two effects must sum to zero. Using symbols,

$$(MP_L \times \Delta L) + (MP_K \times \Delta K) = 0$$

Rearranging this expression gives us $-\Delta K/\Delta L = MP_L/MP_K$. Therefore,

$$MRTS_{LK} = \frac{MP_L}{MP_K}$$

*Optional Equivalently the $MRTS_{LK}$ can be found by totally differentiating the production function and solving for $-dK/dL$.

This formula tells us that $MRTS_{LK}$ at a given input combination equals the ratio formed when we divide the marginal product of labour by the marginal product of capital. The more productive labour is relative to capital, the more capital we must add to make up for any given reduction in labour, so the larger the marginal rate of substitution.

---

[15]Note that the marginal rate of technical substitution for labour with capital, $MRTS_{LK}$, is *not* the same as the marginal rate of *technical* substitution for capital with labour, $MRTS_{KL}$. The former measures how much capital we must add to keep output unchanged per unit of labour that is taken away; the latter measures how much labour we must add to keep output unchanged per unit of capital that is taken away. In fact, one is the reciprocal of the other: $MRTS_{LK} = 1/MRTS_{KL}$.

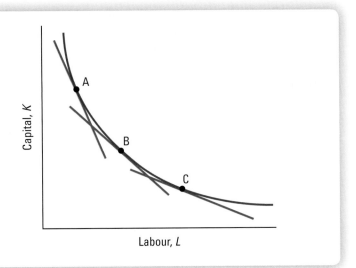

Figure 7.13
A Declining Marginal Rate of Technical Substitution. This figure shows the $MRTS_{LK}$ at three different points on an isoquant, with tangent lines drawn at each of those points. The $MRTS_{LK}$ falls as we move to the south-east along the isoquant, increasing labour and decreasing capital, so that the isoquant has a declining marginal rate of technical substitution. If all of the firm's isoquants have this feature, then we say that the firm's technology has a declining marginal rate of technical substitution.

An isoquant for a production process using two inputs, X and Y, has a **declining marginal rate of technical substitution** if $MRTS_{XY}$ declines as we move along the isoquant, increasing input X and decreasing input Y.

Figure 7.13 shows the $MRTS_{LK}$ at three points (A, B, and C) on an isoquant. The $MRTS_{LK}$ declines as we increase L and decrease K (moving to the southeast) so that the isoquant has a **declining marginal rate of technical substitution**. We will often assume that all of a firm's isoquants have this property when we study cost minimization in Chapter 8 (we'll then say that the firm's *technology* has a declining MRTS). It will hold whenever (a) an increase in the amount of one of the inputs raises the marginal product of the other, and (b) an increase in the amount of one of the inputs lowers the marginal product of that input. Why? MP_L falls as we move to the southeast both because L is bigger [by (b)] and because K is smaller [by (a)]. Using similar reasoning, we can see that MP_K rises. Together, these changes in marginal products cause $MRTS_{LK}$ to fall.[16]

Input Substitution for Three Special Production Technologies

Technologies differ in how much the MRTS changes as a firm alters the inputs it uses to produce a given amount of output. At one extreme, two inputs may be perfectly substitutable for one another. At another extreme, a firm may have to use two inputs in fixed proportions, so that no substitution is possible. Let's look at these two extreme cases in more detail, as well as at an intermediate case known as the Cobb-Douglas production function.

Two products are **perfect substitutes** if their functions are identical, so that a consumer is willing to swap one for the other at a fixed rate.

I. Perfect Substitutes   Two inputs are **perfect substitutes** if their functions are identical, so that a firm is able to exchange one for another at a fixed rate. For example, suppose there are two types of workers, those with a university education and those without. We'll use the symbol U for the amount of university-educated labour and H for the amount of high-school educated labour. For some jobs (like janitor), the amount of education is unimportant, so the two types of worker are perfectly substitutable. In this case, as Figure 7.14(a) shows, each isoquant is a straight line with a slope of -1, so that $MRTS_{HU} = 1$ for all combinations of H and U. For inputs to be perfect substitutes, they need not be

---

[16]While (a) and (b) ensure that the firm's technology has a declining marginal rate of technical substitution, this property can still hold if either (a) or (b) is not satisfied.

Figure 7.14

Isoquants for Inputs That Are Perfect Substitutes. In figure (a), a high-school-educated worker and a university-educated worker are equally productive. In figure (b), a university-educated worker is twice as productive as a high-school-educated worker. In both cases, the $MRTS_{HC}$ is always the same, regardless of the amounts of inputs the firm uses. The two inputs are therefore perfect substitutes.

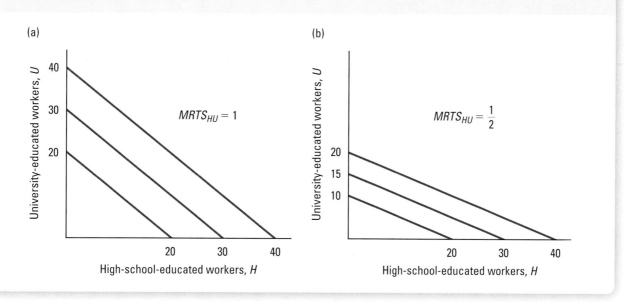

equally productive. If, for example, university-educated workers are exactly twice as productive as high-school-educated workers, then a university-educated worker is perfectly substitutable for *two* high school educated workers. In that case, isoquants are still straight lines, as shown in Figure 7.14(b), but $MRTS_{HU} = 1/2$ for all combinations of inputs.

2. Perfect Complements (Fixed Proportions)   In some cases, a firm must combine inputs in **fixed proportions**. Those inputs are then **perfect complements**. For example, consider a manufacturer of salt whose production process involves a chemical reaction between sodium and chlorine. The reaction uses 1.54 grams of chlorine per gram of sodium. If any extra sodium or extra chlorine is used, the extra amount is left over at the end of the reaction. Figure 7.15 shows a family of isoquants for making salt. The combinations of sodium and chlorine that are in the required ratio lie on the dashed line drawn through the origin. The isoquants are L-shaped, with their kinks lying along the dashed line. Why?

Suppose the firm starts at the point labelled A and gets one extra gram of chlorine but no sodium, moving to point B. The extra chlorine is of no help in making more salt since there is no extra sodium to go with it. Similarly, if the firm has extra sodium without any extra chlorine, moving to point C, it also can't make any more salt. Since these points and any others that involve an increase in just one of the inputs produce the same amount of output, the isoquant is L-shaped, with a kink at point A.

3. The Cobb-Douglas Production Function   Many analyses in economics assume firms have a particular type of production function first introduced by mathematician

> Two inputs are used in **fixed proportions** when they must be combined in a fixed ratio. They are then known as perfect complements.
>
> Two products are **perfect complements** if they are valuable only when used together in fixed proportions.

Figure 7.15

Isoquants for Inputs That Must Be Used in Fixed Proportions. The dashed line from the origin represents the input combinations in which sodium and chlorine are combined in a 1:1.54 ratio. Starting at point A in the figure, adding only more chlorine (moving to point B) or only more sodium (moving to point C) does not yield more salt. All such points lie on the same isoquant, which is L-shaped, with a kink at the 1:1.54 ratio line.

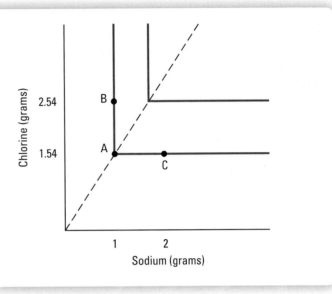

Charles Cobb and economist (and U.S. Senator) Paul Douglas. The **Cobb-Douglas production function** is

$$Q = F(L, K) = AL^\alpha K^\beta$$

where A, α, and β are parameters that take specific values for a given firm. For example, if $A = 10$ and $\alpha = \beta = 0.5$ then we get the production function $Q = F(L, K) = 10\sqrt{L}\ \sqrt{K}$ that we introduced in Section 7.2. The variable A captures the firm's general productivity level. For example, if A doubles, the firm produces twice as much for every combination of inputs. The parameters α and β affect the *relative* productivities of labour and capital. In particular, for this production function, the marginal product of labour is

$$MP_L = \alpha AL^{\alpha-1}K^\beta$$

and the marginal product of capital is

$$MP_K = \beta AL^\alpha K^{\beta-1}$$

Optional The **marginal product of labour** and **capital** are the partial derivatives of the production function evaluated at a specific level of labour and capital. Hence $MP_L = \partial F(L,K)/\partial L$ and $MP_K = \partial F(L,K)/\partial K$

Therefore, the marginal rate of technical substitution between capital and labour is

$$MRTS_{LK} = \left(\frac{\alpha}{\beta}\right)\left(\frac{K}{L}\right) \qquad \textbf{(1)}$$

The $MRTS_{LK}$ depends on the parameters α and β, which capture the relative productivities of labour and capital, but does not depend upon A, the firm's general productivity level. Increases in α increase labour's productivity and raise $MRTS_{LK}$, since more capital is required to compensate for any loss of labour. In contrast, increases in β increase capital's productivity and lower $MRTS_{LK}$. The $MRTS_{LK}$ also depends on the ratio of capital to labour—the lower the ratio of capital to labour, the smaller is $MRTS_{LK}$. Isoquants for Cobb-Douglas production functions therefore have a declining marginal rate of technical substitution.

Figure 7.16

Isoquants for Two Cobb-Douglas Production Functions. Figure (a) shows the isoquants for a Cobb-Douglas production function with A = 10 and $\alpha = \beta = 1/2$. In figure (b), A = 10, $\alpha = 3/2$, and $\beta = 1/2$. The dashed line from the origin represents input combinations with equal amounts of labour and capital. The red tangent lines show that at these input combinations, the $MRTS_{LK}$ in figure (b) is larger than the one in figure (a).

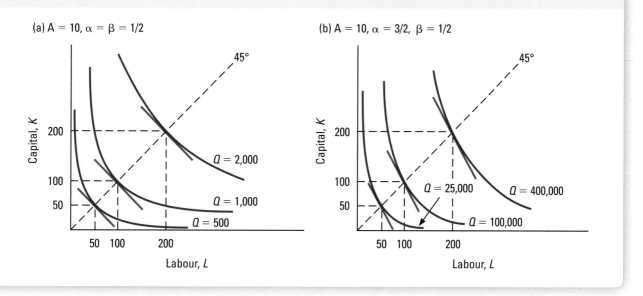

(a) A = 10, $\alpha = \beta = 1/2$ (b) A = 10, $\alpha = 3/2$, $\beta = 1/2$

Figure 7.16 shows families of isoquants for two Cobb-Douglas production functions. In Figure 7.16(a), A = 10 and $\alpha = \beta = 1/2$; in Figure 7.16(b), A = 10, $\alpha = 3/2$, and $\beta = 1/2$. In each of the figures the 45-degree line drawn from the origin shows points along which the amounts of labour and capital are equal. The lines drawn tangent to the isoquants where they cross the 45-degree line show that the $MRTS_{LK}$ for production function (b) is larger than the one for production function (a) at those input combinations.

7.4 RETURNS TO SCALE

Some markets are served by many small firms: think of shoe repair stores, flower shops, and convenience stores. Other markets are dominated by a few very large firms: think of airplane manufacturing, pharmaceuticals, express package delivery. Why is this so? In Chapter 19 we'll see that part of the explanation involves technological differences. When large producers in a market can produce at lower cost than small ones, small producers will have a hard time surviving.

Economists determine whether larger firms produce more effectively by examining returns to scale. To do so, they ask: What would happen if the firm increased the amounts of all its inputs by the same proportion? There are three possibilities:

1. The firm has **constant returns to scale**: a proportional change in the use of all inputs produces the same proportional change in output. For example, for a firm using only capital and labour, doubling the amount of both inputs doubles its output.

A firm has **constant returns to scale** if a proportional change in all inputs produces the same proportional change in output.

A firm has **increasing returns to scale** if a proportional change in all inputs produces a more than proportional change in output.

A firm has **decreasing returns to scale** if a proportional change in all inputs produces a less than proportional change in output.

2. The firm has **increasing returns to scale**: a proportional change in the use of all inputs produces a more than proportional change in output. For example, for a firm using only capital and labour, doubling the amount of both inputs more than doubles its output.

3. The firm has **decreasing returns to scale**: a proportional change in the use of all inputs produces a less than proportional change in output. For example, for a firm using only capital and labour, doubling the amount of both inputs less than doubles its output.

Suppose a firm uses two inputs, labour and capital, to produce its output. Figure 7.17(a) shows a case of constant returns to scale. If the firm initially is using 50 hours of labour and 25 hours of capital to produce 100 units of output, doubling its labour and capital to 100 and 50, respectively, doubles its output to 200. Doubling labour and capital again to 200 and 100, doubles output again to 400. Figure 7.17(b) shows a case of increasing returns to scale: each doubling of labour and capital now more than doubles output, increasing it by 150 percent. Figure 7.17(c) shows decreasing returns to scale: each doubling of labour and capital increases output by only 50 percent.

To see examples of production functions that have constant, increasing, and decreasing returns to scale, let's take another look at the Cobb-Douglas production function, $Q = F(L, K) = AL^\alpha K^\beta$, introduced in Section 7.3. For this production function, returns to scale are constant whenever $\alpha + \beta = 1$. How do we know this? With $2L$ units of labour and $2K$ units of capital, output is

$$F(2L, 2K) = A(2L)^\alpha(2K)^\beta = 2^{\alpha+\beta}(AL^\alpha K^\beta) = 2^{\alpha+\beta} F(L, K)$$

Thus, output exactly doubles if $\alpha + \beta = 1$ (since then $2^{\alpha+\beta} = 2$). By similar reasoning, when $\alpha + \beta < 1$, the Cobb-Douglas production function has decreasing returns to scale, and when $\alpha + \beta > 1$, it has increasing returns to scale.

So far we've talked as if a technology has either constant, increasing, or decreasing returns to scale. But, in reality, a technology's returns to scale may vary, having increasing returns to scale in some ranges of output and decreasing returns to scale in others.

Figure 7.17

Constant, Increasing, and Decreasing Returns to Scale with Two Inputs. Figure (a) shows a case of constant returns to scale in which doubling of labour and capital exactly doubles output. In figure (b), each doubling of labour and capital more than doubles output, a case of increasing returns to scale. In figure (c), each doubling of labour and capital raises output by only 50 percent, a case of decreasing returns to scale.

(a) Constant returns to scale

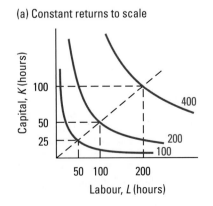

(b) Increasing returns to scale

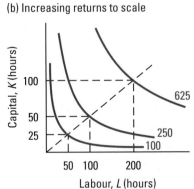

(c) Decreasing returns to scale

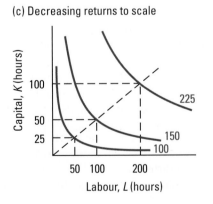

WORKED-OUT PROBLEM   7.2

The Problem   Robert runs a cleaning company that uses labour, L, and capital, K, as inputs. If he hires L workers on a given day and uses K units of capital, he can clean $F(L, K) = \sqrt{L + K}$ houses. Does his technology have increasing, decreasing, or constant returns to scale?

The Solution   If Robert doubles the inputs he uses from L workers and K units of capital to $2L$ workers and $2K$ units of capital his output will be

$$F(2L, 2K) = \sqrt{2L + 2K} = \sqrt{2(L + K)} = \sqrt{2}\,\sqrt{L + K} = \sqrt{2}\,F(L, K)$$

Since $\sqrt{2}$ is less than 2, output less than doubles when he doubles his inputs, and thus production exhibits decreasing returns to scale.

IN-TEXT EXERCISE 7.7   **Suppose that Robert's production function is instead $F(L, K) = (L + K)^2$. Does his production function have constant, increasing, or decreasing returns to scale?**

IN-TEXT EXERCISE 7.8   **Show that the Cobb-Douglas production function $Q = F(L, K) = AL^\alpha K^\beta$ where α and β both lie between 1/2 and 1 exhibits increasing returns to scale and both labour and capital exhibit diminishing marginal productivity. Recall that the marginal product of labour is given by the expression $MP_L = \alpha AL^{\alpha-1}K^\beta$ and that given by the marginal product of capital is $MP_K = \beta AL^\alpha K^{\beta-1}$.**

Application 7.3

Returns-to-Scale in Express Package Delivery

It's 4 p.m. and your graduate school applications are due at 10 a.m. the next morning. Like many other applicants, you'll probably call an express package delivery service, such as Canada Post, Purolator (owned by Canada Post), Federal Express (FedEx), or United Parcel Service (UPS). They will send a truck to pick up your application, take it to a nearby airport, fly it to a sorting facility somewhere in the middle of the country, transport it to the city where the school is located, load it onto another truck, and deliver it to the school's admissions office—all by 10 a.m. the next morning. Guaranteed.

The Canadian parcel delivery sector is highly competitive even though only a few firms dominate the market. Why are there so few choices for express package delivery?

The answer to the question is that there are significant increasing returns to scale in express package delivery. Think about local pickup and delivery. When the number of packages doubles, fewer than double the number of trucks and drivers can do the job. The reason is that delivery routes can become more specialized. For example, a single truck would need to make deliveries all over town. With two trucks, the company will not need to send both trucks all over town. Instead, it might assign one truck to deliver to the northern half of town, and the other to deliver to the southern half. The amount of time spent driving from one delivery stop to another falls, and the number of packages that can be delivered by a truck in one day rises. This effect continues as the number of packages increases. If it gets large enough, each fully loaded truck may be able to make just one stop, delivering to a single business or apartment building.

The presence of increasing returns to scale makes it difficult for new express package delivery companies to enter the market. Their per-unit delivery costs would initially be much higher than those of Canada Post, Purolator, FedEx, or UPS, which have much larger scales of operation.

Reasons for Increasing and Decreasing Returns to Scale

The factors that produce increasing returns to scale are varied. One is the specialization of inputs as scale increases. We have seen in Example 7.1 how the specialization of labour can cause the average product of labour to rise with the number of workers. This effect can lead to increasing returns to scale. Application 7.3 shows how specialization of trucks' delivery routes produces increasing returns in express package delivery. In other cases, physical laws generate increasing returns. For example, doubling the floor space of a building does not double its construction cost.[17] Similar effects arise with oil tanker ships. A tanker that can carry 200,000 deadweight tonnes of oil costs only a little more than three times as much to build as a tanker that carries 20,000 deadweight tonnes.

The factors that produce *decreasing* returns to scale are somewhat harder to understand. Think about a manufacturer that currently uses L units of labour and K units of capital. Suppose the firm doubles both inputs. Certainly, *one* option is to simply replicate current operations, opening a new factory exactly like the current one and hiring the same number of workers to staff it. This approach should double output, achieving constant returns to scale. Possibly the firm can do even better by using its inputs in some other way to achieve increasing returns to scale (perhaps by expanding its current factory). However, as long as replication is possible, it can't do worse than doubling its output. So we should never see decreasing returns to scale.

In practice, though, we *do* see firms that appear to have decreasing returns to scale. Why? One possibility is that there is some fixed input that isn't being considered. For example, when Noah and Naomi double their assembly workers and garage space, they do not double Noah and Naomi themselves. Their limited managerial capacity is a fixed input. Decreasing returns may set in because they manage a larger firm less effectively. Of course, if Noah and Naomi could hire another equally qualified pair of managers, then doubling all three inputs—assembly workers, garage space, and managerial attention—should in principle increase output by a factor of two or more.

Replicating a firm's managerial team, however, may run into some problems. Suppose, for example, that Noah and Naomi decide to bring in another pair of managers to run a second identical plant. If those managers are given complete autonomy, Noah and Naomi may worry that they will misuse the company's resources, not work hard enough, or make less than ideal decisions. Someone has to oversee them. Noah and Naomi are likely to find themselves reviewing and intervening in the managers' decisions. This need for oversight leads to increased bureaucratic costs, which may prevent the firm from doubling its output when it opens the second plant.

Implications of Returns to Scale

We've already mentioned that returns to scale can have important consequences for a market's structure, a topic we'll return to later in the book. It can also create conflicts in public policy. With increasing returns to scale, production is most efficient if there is a single producer. Without the discipline of competition, however, a single producer may not operate as we would like. For example, as we will see in Chapter 17, it may set its

---

[17]To see why, observe that if the area of a building is M metres squared, the building's perimeter is $4\sqrt{M}$ metres in length. So when the area of the building doubles, the amount of material required to build the walls less than doubles. (In contrast, the amount of material required to build a flat roof approximately doubles.)

price too high. In some cases, policymakers have resolved this tension by regulating a single producer (for example, local telephone companies), or by having the government take over production (for example, Canada Post). We'll discuss this subject further in Chapter 17.

7.5 PRODUCTIVITY DIFFERENCES AND TECHNOLOGICAL CHANGE

Firms producing a given good often differ in their abilities to turn inputs into output (we'll discuss an example in Application 7.4). Likewise, a given firm's technology may change over time, making it more or less effective at turning inputs into output, a process known as **technological change**.

When economists say that one firm has **higher productivity** than another, or that a firm has become **more productive**, they mean that it can produce more from the same amounts of inputs. An improvement in productivity shifts a firm's efficient production frontier upward. This corresponds to an increase in the level of its production function at each possible combination of inputs.

For example, suppose Noah and Naomi have recently discovered how to produce garden benches more effectively, changing their production function given 100 square metres of garage space to $Q = F(L) = -2L^3 + 10L^2 + 30L$ from $Q = F(L) = -2L^3 + 10L^2 + 25L$. Their new short-run production function gives a larger level of output than their old one for every positive amount of labour they might use. For example, with four workers they can now produce 152 garden benches a week instead of 132. In Figure 7.18 we show their original efficient production frontier in blue and their new one in red. For each amount of labour used, the red technology produces more output than the blue one.

> **Technological change** occurs when a firm's ability to turn inputs into output changes over time.
>
> A firm is **more productive** or has **higher productivity** when it can produce more output using the same amounts of inputs. Equivalently, its production function shifts upward at each combination of inputs.

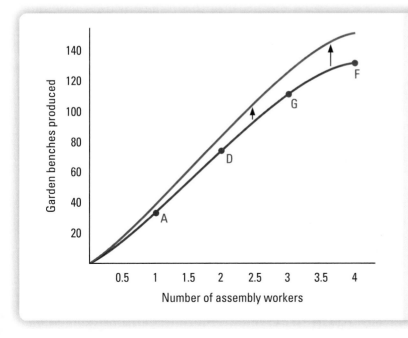

Figure 7.18
A Productivity Improvement. The red technology is more productive than the blue one because it results in more output at every positive level of input.

"Things were done very differently on the farm when I was your age, Kenny."

Productivity Differences and Technological Change with Two Inputs

With more than one input, a difference in productivity between two firms or a change in the productivity of a given firm over time may be either general or specifically linked to the use of one input. As an illustration, consider again the case of a Cobb-Douglas technology, $Q = F(L, K) = AL^\alpha K^\beta$. If the variable A increases, say from 10 to 15, this will increase the amount the firm produces by the same proportion (in this case, 50 percent) for every combination of inputs. As a result, if two different input combinations produced equal amounts before the change, they will also produce equal amounts after the change. This means that the firm's isoquants do not change in appearance, there is just a larger output level associated with each isoquant. For example, if A changes from 10 to 15 in Figure 7.16(a) on page 241, the isoquants would be labelled 750, 1500, and 3000 instead of 500, 1000, and 2000. The firm's marginal rate of technical substitution at each input combination would not change.[18] More generally, a productivity improvement that keeps the MRTS unchanged at every input combination is called a **factor-neutral technical change**.

A **factor-neutral technical change** has no effect on the MRTS at any input combination. It simply changes the output level associated with each of a firm's isoquants.

In contrast, technological differences or changes sometimes involve changes in the relative productivities of different inputs. For example, the technology depicted in Figure 7.16(b) is more productive than the one in Figure 7.16(a) because it has a larger value of α. Because labour is more productive with the technology in Figure 7.16(b), starting at any given input combination, it takes more capital to substitute for any given reduction in labour than with the technology in Figure 7.16(a).

Application 7.4

A Concrete Example of Productivity Differences

Ready-mix concrete is used in a wide range of construction projects including highways, sidewalks, swimming pools, and new home foundations. The product itself varies little across different firms and is made using a common method. You might expect that no firm would have a significant productivity advantage over others. But that is not the case.

Economist Chad Syverson used statistical methods to estimate plant-level production functions for ready-mix concrete firms using data on output, labour, and capital. He found large differences in productivity across plants within local markets.[19] According to his estimates, a plant at the 75th percentile of the efficiency distribution (the 25th most efficient plant out of every 100) can produce approximately 37 percent more output from the same inputs than a plant at the 25th percentile (the 75th most efficient plant out of every 100).

What accounts for such large differences in measured productivity across firms in the same market that use the same basic technology? Part of the explanation is that there is undoubtedly variation in the quality of firms' inputs that is not captured well in the data. For example, the productivity of firms' capital (machines, trucks, etc.) is likely to differ

---

[18]You can also see this by recalling that equation (1) for the MRTS of a Cobb-Douglas production function (page 240) does not depend on A.

[19]Chad Syverson, "Market Structure and Productivity: A Concrete Example," *Journal of Political Economy* 112, December 2004, pp. 1181–1222.

depending on how well the firms have maintained it. Workers may also differ in their abilities, experience, and training. If so, then part of the explanation does not involve true differences in productivity, which are about producing different levels of output with the *same* inputs. But an equally important part of the story is likely to be that owners and managers of these firms differ in their knowledge of how to efficiently organize production and motivate workers. Such knowledge differences lead to true productivity differences across seemingly similar firms.

Productivity Comparisons

In asking if one firm is more productive than another, or if a given firm has become more productive, it is important to distinguish differences between and changes in firms' production functions from differences and changes caused by movements along a given production function. Sometimes, for example, one sees comparisons of different firms' labour productivity, measured by their average product of labour. One reason for a firm's average product of labour to be higher than another's is that the first firm is truly more productive in the sense just discussed. Another, however, is that it has chosen a different input mix for producing its output or is producing a different amount of output. Since the average product of an input can vary with both the input mix and the output level, the firm with the higher average product of labour is not necessarily more productive.

Reasons for Productivity Differences

Why might the productivity of two firms, or a given firm at two points of time, differ? First, firms may be subject to different regulations or market circumstances. These differences can involve labour laws, union contracts, and restrictions on hours of operation, among others. For example, airlines' labour contracts differ in the work rules that govern employees, such as the maximum number of hours a pilot can be on duty in one day. Such differences in work rules result in different productivity levels.

In addition, firms may have different levels of technical and organizational knowledge. One firm may have discovered a better production method than its rivals, or its managers may have figured out a better way of training, motivating, or organizing its workforce. This may come about through research and development, such as Henry Ford's efforts to develop assembly line production, or from the learning that results from the accumulation of production experience, a process known as "learning-by-doing" (see Application 7.5).

Productivity improvements by individual firms are key factors leading to economy-wide productivity growth. These gains arise from investments in research and development (R&D), as well as learning by doing. R&D and the intellectual property (knowledge) that it generates are playing an increasingly important role in the economy. Industries in which research and development are critical to a firm's success—the so-called new economy—are now among the Canadian economy's most important industries. Statistics Canada reported that in 2003 the average percentage of revenue spent by all firms on research and development was 2.1 percent. Small firms (1–99 employees) spent the greatest percentage of revenue, 12.6 percent, on R&D. In the midst of the worldwide recession in 2009 a survey of 500 small businesses found that 28 percent of firms planned to spend between 1 and 5 percent of revenue on R&D, 10 percent planned to spend between 6 and 10 percent and 13 percent planned to spend more than 10 percent.[20]

Policies that stimulate firms to make those investments play an important role in fostering continued economic growth. Intellectual property protection, such as patent rights, helps ensure that a firm that makes a discovery will not see it immediately copied by rivals. By doing so, this protection can provide an incentive for firms to innovate. At the same time, by granting sole use of an innovation to the innovator, these policies can create the kinds of monopoly losses that we'll study in Chapter 17. The optimal policy for encouraging innovation must therefore balance these concerns.

Application 7.5

Learning-by-Doing in Producing the Lockheed Tristar L-1011

In cases where firms make complex products, productivity can increase dramatically with experience. Producing a commercial airliner, for example, is an involved process. Once a design is set and a production facility is built, workers engage in the complex process of assembling the aircraft. Workers engaged in this process often become substantially more efficient as they gain experience with the tasks required for a given aircraft model.

Using data on Lockheed's production of the L-1011 airplane from 1970–1984, economist C. Lanier Benkard found that Lockheed's productivity changed as the company gained experience producing the airplane.[21] According to his estimates, over the first 112 planes Lockheed produced, workers became roughly 42 percent more productive with each doubling of cumulative output (so that Lockheed would need roughly 30 percent fewer worker-hours to complete assembly of a plane). Benkard also showed that those gains were partially lost when production was temporarily scaled back (probably

The Lockheed TriStar L-1011

because this led to worker turnover) and when the plane's design changed. Firms involved in such production processes can therefore gain significant cost advantages by trying to insure stability in their product designs and production levels.

[20]See Statistics Canada, *Industrial Research and Development—2005 Intentions*, Cat. No. 88-202-XIB, January 2006, and American Express Canadian Small Business Monitor July 2009.

[21]C. Lanier Benkard, "Learning and Forgetting: The Dynamics of Aircraft Production," *American Economic Review* 90, September 2000, pp. 1034–1054.

CHAPTER SUMMARY

1. **Production technologies (LO1)**

   a. A firm's production possibilities set contains all of the input-output combinations that are possible given the firm's technology.

   b. A production method is efficient if there is no way to produce larger amounts of outputs using the same amounts of inputs. A firm's efficient production frontier contains all of the input-output combinations that can be achieved using efficient production methods. It can be described using a production function, a function of the form *Output = F(Inputs)*.

2. **Production with one variable input and one output (LO2)**

   a. The average product of labour is equal to the amount of output divided by the number of workers employed, $Q/L = F(L)/L$.

   b. The marginal product of labour is equal to the extra output produced by adding the marginal units of labour ΔL—the smallest amount of labour the firm can add or subtract—divided by the number of units added, $[F(L) - F(L - \Delta L)]/\Delta L$.

   c. When the marginal product of labour is (bigger than/less than/equal to) the average product of labour, the average product is (increased by/decreased by/unchanged by) an increase in labour.

   d. A multiplant firm can use the marginal product of labour to assign workers to its plants to maximize the amount it produces from any given amount of labour. If at each plant the marginal product of labour falls when more workers are assigned to the plant, then the best assignment of workers equalizes the plants' marginal products.

3. **Production with two variable inputs and one output (LO3)**

   a. An isoquant contains all of the input combinations that produce a given amount of output.

   b. Isoquants are thin and do not slope upward. They separate input combinations that produce larger and smaller amounts of output than the combinations on the

isoquant. Isoquants from the same technology do not cross and higher level isoquants lie farther from the origin.

   c. The marginal rate of technical substitution for input X with input Y ($MRTS_{XY}$) is the rate $(-\Delta Y/\Delta X)$ at which the firm must add units of Y to keep output unchanged when the amount of input X is reduced by a small amount. It is equal to the marginal product of X divided by the marginal product of Y, $MRTS_{XY} = MP_X/MP_Y$.

   d. A technology using inputs X and Y has a diminishing marginal rate of technical substitution if $MRTS_{XY}$ declines as we move along an isoquant increasing input X and decreasing input Y.

   e. Technologies differ in how much the MRTS changes as we move along an isoquant. At one extreme, inputs may be perfect substitutes, at another extreme, perfect complements. An intermediate case is the Cobb-Douglas production function $Q = F(L, K) = AL^\alpha K^\beta$, whose MRTS changes gradually as we move along an isoquant.

4. **Returns to scale (LO4)**

   a. Economists determine whether large or small firms produce more effectively by examining returns to scale.

   b. A firm has (constant/increasing/decreasing) returns to scale if a proportional change in all inputs leads to (the same/a greater than/a less than) proportional change in output.

   c. Increasing returns to scale arise because of the specialization of inputs as well as certain physical laws. The reasons we observe decreasing returns to scale are more elusive. They include the presence of implicitly fixed inputs, and bureaucratic costs.

5. **Productivity differences and technological change (LO5)**

   a. A firm is more productive, or has higher productivity, when it can produce more output using the same amount of inputs. Higher productivity corresponds to an upward shift in a firm's efficient production frontier, an increase in its production at every input combination.

   b. Intellectual property protection (patents) helps provide incentives for firms to innovate, although at the cost of creating monopoly power.

ADDITIONAL EXERCISES

Exercise 7.1: The law firm of Dewey, Cheetham, and Howe files claims against unscrupulous car repair shops that take advantage of consumers who know nothing about cars. A lawyer who takes a 20-minute break after every two hours of work can process one claim with six hours of work. If the lawyer takes a 20-minute break after every four hours of work she can process one claim with eight hours of work. If she takes a 20-minute break after every hour of work, she is a claim superwoman and can process one claim with just five hours of work. What is the efficient method of production for Dewey, Cheetham, and Howe? Graph its production possibilities set. What is its production function? (LO1)

Exercise 7.2: Pete and Mary run a firm that packs coffee beans. The number of kilograms of coffee they pack depends on the number of workers they hire. They are able to hire workers for a fraction of a day. The number of kilograms of coffee they pack in a day is given by the production function $Q = F(L) = 10L$, where L is the number of hours of labour they hire. Graph their production function. (LO1)

Exercise 7.3: Suppose that in Table 7.3 (page 221) the number of garden benches produced by 0, 1, 2, 3, and 4 workers is instead 0, 35, 70, 99, and 112. Calculate the marginal and average products of labour that would have resulted. Check that the relation between these average and marginal products satisfies the properties that we discussed in Section 7.2. (LO2)

Exercise 7.4: Emily draws cartoons that she sells to her classmates. Her average product of labour is five cartoons per hour if she works for one hour, four per hour if she works for two hours, three per hour if she works for three hours, and two-and-a-half per hour if she works for four hours. What is her marginal product of labour at one, two, three, and four hours of work? (LO2)

Exercise 7.5: "The marginal product of labour can never be negative." Is this statement correct? What does it assume? (LO2)

Exercise 7.6: Suppose that a firm uses both labour (L) and capital (K) as inputs and has the long-run production function $Q = F(L, K) = L \times \sqrt{L + K}$. If its capital is fixed at $K = 10$ in the short run, what is its short-run production function? How much does it produce in the short run (using efficient production methods) if it hires one worker? Two workers? Three? (LO1)

Exercise 7.7: Suppose that a firm's production function is $Q = F(L) = L^3 - 200L^2 + 10{,}000L$. Its marginal product of labour is $MP_L = 3L^2 - 400L + 10{,}000$. At what amount of labour input are the firm's average and marginal product of labour equal? Confirm that the average and marginal product curves satisfy the relationship discussed in the text. (LO2)

Exercise 7.8: Suppose that John, April, and Tristan have two production plants for producing orange juice. They have a total of 850 crates of oranges and the marginal product of oranges in plant 1 is $MP_O^1 = 1000 - O_1$ and in plant 2 is $MP_O^2 = 1200 - 2O_2$. What is the best assignment of oranges between the two plants? (LO2)

Exercise 7.9: Is the following statement true or false? "If a firm has two plants for producing output using only labour and plant B is more productive than plant A, a manager who wants to get the most output from a fixed amount of labour should always assign more labour to plant B." If you think this is true, say why. If you think it is false, give an example to prove your point. (LO2)

Exercise 7.10: You have an economics test in two weeks. It will cover both micro and macroeconomics. Each part will be worth 50 points. You have a total of 100 hours that you can spend studying for this exam. For the first 25 hours you spend studying microeconomics, you will get one point more for each hour of studying. After that, you will get one point more for each three hours you spend studying, up to the maximum possible of

50 points. Macroeconomics is different. For your first 15 hours of studying you will get one point for each 45 minutes you spend studying. After that, you will get one point for each 1.5 hours you spend up to the maximum of 50 points. How should you allocate your studying time to get the best grade? Why? (LO2)

Exercise 7.11: Beta Inc. has two production plants that use finely divisible labour to produce its output. The marginal product of labour at plant 1 is $MP_L^1 = 100/L_1$, and the marginal product of labour at plant 2 is $MP_L^2 = 100/L_2$. Beta Inc. wants to find the best assignment of 90 workers between the two plants. What is it? (LO2)

Exercise 7.12: A supermarket is considering adding self-scan checkout machines. Currently the supermarket checks out 200 customers an hour using 10 checkout clerks. Customers differ in their abilities to use these machines. Market research suggests that 20 percent of the store's customers can check themselves out using these machines in three minutes (on average), 30 percent can check themselves out in five minutes, and 50 percent will refuse to use the new machines. One employee can monitor up to four self-scan machines. If there are fewer than four machines, this employee can use her extra time in other productive ways. Draw an isoquant for checking out 200 customers an hour where the variable inputs are checkout clerks and self-scan checkout machines. (LO3)

Exercise 7.13: You run a firm that has two plants in the same city. The two plants use the same two inputs to produce your output. A consulting firm just told you that the MRTS is different across your plants. Are you assigning your inputs correctly? (*Hint:* Look back at Example 4.3's discussion of gains from trade on page 112.) (LO3)

Exercise 7.14: Jason has a boat-building firm. It uses labour L, capital K, and materials M, to build its boats. Its production function is $Q = F(L, K, M) = AL^\alpha K^\beta M^\gamma$. For what values of α, β, and γ does Jason's technology have constant returns to scale? Increasing returns to scale? Decreasing returns to scale? (LO4)

Exercise 7.15: Suppose that because of a technological breakthrough a firm that uses labour and capital to produce its output is able to double its production for any given amounts of inputs. What happens to the firm's MRTS at any given input combination? (LO5)

Exercise 7.16: Suppose that because of a technological breakthrough a firm that uses a single input to produce its output is able to double its production for any given amount of the input. What happens to the firm's average product of labour? What about its marginal product of labour? (LO2, 5)

Exercise 7.17: You are the manager of a new firm that can choose between two technologies for producing output using only labour. Technology A can produce two units of output for each hour of labour input. Technology B can produce three units of output for each hour of labour input up to 100 hours, and β units of output for each hour of labour above 100 hours. For what values of β is technology B more productive than technology A? (LO5)

Cost

Michael Dell began selling personal computers out of his dorm room as an undergraduate student in university. In 1984, with $1000 in start-up funds, he founded the Dell Computer Corporation.

Dell saw great inefficiencies in the operations of giant rivals like IBM and Compaq. In response, he pioneered direct-to-consumer marketing of computers. Cutting out intermediaries such as wholesalers and retailers, he pushed his company to produce PCs at the lowest possible cost. This strategy required some gutsy and insightful decisions, which we'll examine later in the chapter.

Today, success in the PC market requires high-quality manufacturing at costs that are at or below those of competitors. Because Dell understood this point early on, his company profited handsomely. In 2004 Dell Computer Corporation's sales totalled $49.2 billion, and Michael Dell's personal net worth was more than $14 billion.

In Chapter 7, we studied technology and production. Once managers understand how they can produce their products, like Dell they need to figure out how to do so in the most economical way. In this chapter we'll study this problem by covering nine topics:

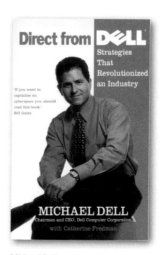

Michael Dell

1. *Types of cost.* Some costs vary with the amount produced, while others do not. In addition, some costs may be avoided by shutting down production, while others are unavoidable. We'll discuss these distinctions and introduce the notion of a firm's cost function.

2. *What do economic costs include?* Sometimes the costs a firm incurs aren't immediately obvious. A firm's true costs include not only its out-of-pocket expenditures, but also the costs it incurs by forgoing opportunities to use resources in other ways.

3. *Short-run cost—one variable input.* In the simplest case, a firm uses only a single variable input to produce its output in the short run. We'll show how to determine a firm's cost function from its production function in this case.

4. *Long-run cost—cost minimization with two variable inputs.* In most cases, firms use many inputs to produce their products. In the long run, a firm can produce a given level of output using many technologically efficient methods, each involving different inputs and costs. We'll show how to find the method that results in the lowest possible cost and derive the firm's cost function, focusing on the simplest case in which the firm uses just two inputs.

5. *Average and marginal costs.* Just as average and marginal products are useful measures of a firm's productivity (see Chapter 7), average and marginal costs are useful measures of a firm's costs. We'll define these notions and discuss their relationships with one another.

6. *Effects of input price changes.* Changes in a firm's input prices generally lead to changes in its least-cost input combination. We'll study the directions of those effects.

7. *Short-run versus long-run costs.* We'll discuss the relationship between a firm's long-run and short-run costs.

8. *Economies and diseconomies of scale.* In Chapter 7 we discussed the notions of increasing and decreasing returns to scale. Here we'll examine the cost implications of returns to scale. This leads to the notions of economies and diseconomies of scale.

*9. *Multiproduct firms and economies of scope.* Most firms produce many products. One reason involves the presence of economies of scope, which arise when the cost of producing products together is lower than the cost of producing them separately. Sometimes diseconomies of scope discourage firms from producing multiple products. We'll define these concepts and discuss the reasons for their existence.

8.1 TYPES OF COST

A firm's **total cost** of producing a given level of output is the expenditure required to produce that output in the most economical way.

A firm's **total cost** of producing a particular level of output is the expenditure required to produce that output in the most economical way. We'll see in Chapter 9 (and later, again, in Chapters 14, 17, and 19) that to make good pricing and output decisions, managers need to know the total cost of producing different levels of output.

To illustrate, suppose the manager of an oil refinery is trying to decide how much gasoline to produce and sell at the going market price of $1 per litre. She can sell either 1.5 or 1.2 million litres of high-octane gasoline this month. To determine which is best (a decision that we'll study in Chapter 9), one thing she definitely needs to know is how much it costs to produce these two different amounts of gasoline.

How can she determine this? To produce 1.5 million litres a month, the manager can use various combinations of crude oil, additives, and refining equipment. (In the terms of Chapter 7, these different input combinations correspond to her isoquant for 1.5 million litres.) Gasoline additives, such as MTBE (methyl tertiary butyl ether), are costly. An alternative is to use catalytic reforming equipment, which requires expenditures on machinery. It also reduces yields, which means it requires more crude oil. Which method is cheaper, and what is its cost? And how does the answer change if the refinery produces only 1.2 million litres?

In this chapter, we'll show how to answer these questions. Specifically, taking the amount the firm wishes to produce as given (this choice will be the subject of Chapters 9, 14, 17, and 19), we'll ask how the firm can most economically produce that level of output, and we'll determine its total cost of doing so. As in Chapter 7, for simplicity, we will mostly focus on the case of a firm that produces a single product. (An exception is Section 8.9.)

First, though, we need to introduce a few concepts.

We can break total cost into two types of costs. **Variable costs** are the costs of inputs that vary with the firm's output level. These costs typically include inputs like labour and materials. **Fixed costs** are the costs of inputs whose use does not vary as the firm's level of output changes, with the possible exception that the firm might not incur the cost if it decides to produce nothing.

For example, a Toronto taxicab owner needs to purchase a licence regardless of how many hours he or someone else drives the taxi. That is a fixed cost. In contrast, the gasoline he needs to run his cab is a variable cost.

A fixed cost is **avoidable** if the firm doesn't incur the cost (or can recoup it) if it produces no output. For example, if the owner of the taxi cab can sell the licence and recoup his initial expenditure, then the licence cost is an avoidable fixed cost. A cost that is incurred even if the firm decides not to operate is **sunk**. If Toronto were to prohibit the resale of taxi licences, then the taxicab owner's expenditure on the licence, once incurred, would be a sunk cost.[1] Whether a fixed cost is avoidable or sunk can have important implications for decision making. (We've discussed this point in Section 3.3 and Add-On 3A.) Which it is (avoidable or sunk) can depend on the time frame we are considering. For example, if the taxi commission instead sells annual nontransferable taxi licences, then the cost is sunk within the time frame of a year but avoidable over longer periods.

How do these distinctions (variable versus fixed costs, and avoidable versus sunk costs) relate to the concepts of variable and fixed inputs discussed in Chapter 7? The cost of an input that is fixed in the sense introduced in Chapter 7 is a sunk fixed cost; it does not vary with the firm's output level and can't be avoided. On the other hand, although the terminology is a little confusing, the cost of an input that is variable in the sense introduced in Chapter 7 can be an avoidable fixed cost. Consider, for example, the case of annual nontransferable taxi licences. In the long run a taxi owner can decide to buy one or not; it is a variable input into his production process. But it is an (avoidable) fixed cost because its use is lumpy. To operate at all the owner needs a licence, but he needs just one regardless of the number of hours he drives his cab.

The total cost of producing different levels of output is summarized in the firm's **cost function**, a function of the form *Total cost = C(Output)*. The firm's **variable cost function** gives the firm's variable cost at each possible combination of outputs. It is a function of the form *Variable cost = VC(Output)*. Since total cost equals fixed cost (*FC*) plus variable cost, we can write the firm's cost function as *C(Output) = FC + VC(Output)*.

Variable costs are the costs of inputs that vary with the firm's output level.

Fixed costs are the costs of inputs whose use does not vary as the firm's level of output changes, with the possible exception that the cost might not be incurred if the firm decides to produce nothing.

A fixed cost is **avoidable** if it is not incurred when the firm decides to produce no output. It is **sunk** if it is incurred even when the firm decides not to operate.

A firm's **cost function** describes the total cost of producing each possible level of output. It is a function of the form *Total cost = C (Output)*.

A firm's **variable cost function** describes the variable cost of producing each possible level of output. It is a function of the form *Variable cost = VC (Output)*.

---

[1]The city of Toronto actually issues several types of taxi licences or permits. "Standard" taxi licences can be leased, and permit a second driver. "Ambassador" permits restrict taxis to one driver and the permit cannot be transferred. The Standard permits can be viewed as an avoidable fixed cost while the Ambassador permits are an unavoidable fixed cost for the term of the permit. Not surprisingly the Ambassador permits are sold for much less than the market price of a Standard transferable licence.

Let's look at an example.

Example 8.1

The Cost of Producing Garden Benches

In Example 7.1 (page 214) we determined Noah and Naomi's efficient production methods for assembling garden benches with up to four workers. Recall that Noah and Naomi produce their garden benches in a 100-square-metre garage. Let's suppose they've rented the garage for $1000 per week, a cost they cannot avoid in the short run. The weekly wage of an assembly worker is $500. Table 8.1 shows the fixed, variable, and total costs of producing 33, 74, and 132 benches per week using the efficient production methods A, D, and F from Table 7.1 (page 214), which employ one, two, and four workers, respectively. Noah and Naomi's fixed cost is simply the cost of renting the garage. Their variable cost is the cost of hiring the assembly workers. Their total cost is the sum of the fixed and variable costs. The table also shows the total, fixed, and variable costs of producing no output. Since the rental cost of the garage is sunk, producing nothing costs Noah and Naomi $1000.

Table 8.1
Fixed, Variable, and Total Costs of Producing Garden Benches

Number of Garden Benches Produced per Week	Fixed Cost (per Week)	Variable Cost (per Week)	Total Cost (per Week)
0	$1,000	$ 0	$1,000
33	1,000	500	1,500
74	1,000	1,000	2,000
132	1,000	2,000	3,000

Application 8.1

Taking Flight: Variable and Fixed Costs at WestJet

WestJet first took to the air on February 29, 1996 serving five western Canadian cities with just three aircraft. WestJet was founded by a team of Calgary entrepreneurs, Clive Beddoe, Mark Hill, Tim Morgan, and Donald Bell. As the company's first CEO, Clive Beddoe's vision was to follow the successful model of Southwest Airlines by keeping operating costs as low as possible and to align the interests of employees with that of the company. Today WestJet has one of Canada's most admired corporate cultures and its employees, described by the company as "fun, friendly, and caring," all receive profit sharing cheques and overwhelmingly (83 percent) participate in its employee share purchase plan. By early 2009 WestJet had captured 37 percent of the domestic market while serving 30 Canadian destinations, making it one of the most successful new airline launches ever.

While Beddoe and the other company founders had a vision of what would make their new airline special, they also needed a keen understanding of the airline's costs. As a veteran pilot and businessman, Beddoe knew all too well that a firm's ability to keep costs low can make the difference between success and bankruptcy court.

Let's examine WestJet's costs. WestJet produces air travel services—literally, leather seats flying through the air from one place to another, along with accompanying services like luggage transfer and satellite TV. When WestJet's managers think about the cost of providing air travel service, they face both variable and fixed costs. One important variable cost is labour. Managers can adjust the number and hours of the airline's flight attendants, ground crew, and ticket counter staff, depending on how many flights they plan to offer. Unlike managers at their primary competition, Air Canada, they have more flexibility to adjust the number and hours of the airline's pilots, who are not unionized. Another important variable cost is jet fuel, which varies directly with the number of flights that managers schedule.

WestJet also needs counter and gate space at airports. The airline signs long term leases for gate space at airports such as Lester B. Pearson which is the most slot-constrained airport in Canada. This cost is fixed: it cannot be adjusted if WestJet alters the number of flights. Moreover, given the long term commitment (and assuming they cannot sublease it to another airline), it is a sunk cost: WestJet must pay for gate space even if it ceases to operate at Pearson.

WestJet also pays a variety of airport fees that depend on the number of flights or the number of passengers flown. At Calgary International Airport, WestJet's western hub, airlines are subject to landing fees, apron fees, passenger loading bridge fees, and a general terminal fee, all of which are based on the type of aircraft. The airport improvement fee, common use terminal equipment system fee, and pre-clearance fee are assessed on each passenger. These are considered to be variable costs as they can be avoided if WestJet chooses to cancel a flight. At airports that are not slot-constrained WestJet can rent gate and counter space by the month or even the day. These costs are fixed over the duration of the rental period but after that they are avoidable. If managers decide not to serve these airports, they can simply stop renting the gates and counter space.

Another cost that is (mostly) fixed is the compensation paid to the airline's administrative staff. Regardless of the number of flights, WestJet needs a CEO and managers to head its finance, operations, and human resource departments. Since its contracts with all administrative personnel are short term, however, these are avoidable fixed costs.

What about the costs of the planes WestJet flies? These costs are a bit more complicated. In 2009 WestJet owned two-thirds of its planes and leased the remaining one-third. Since we won't discuss the cost of owned durable goods until Section 8.2, let's focus on the leased planes. Whether those costs are fixed or variable depends on whether managers can alter the number of planes should they decide to alter the number of flights. Certainly, they can increase the number of leased planes whenever they want to. But what if they want to decrease that number? If the leases have opt-out clauses, can be renegotiated, or can be transferred to other airlines, then WestJet's plane costs are variable costs. If not, they are fixed and sunk for the term of the lease.

8.2 WHAT DO ECONOMIC COSTS INCLUDE?

When you think of a firm's costs, its out-of-pocket expenditures on labour, materials, and rental of land and capital come readily to mind. But some of its costs are harder to identify. These do not involve out-of-pocket payments to others, but rather are hidden costs associated with lost opportunities to use resources to earn profits in other ways. Another tricky issue concerns the costs associated with capital equipment that the firm has previously purchased. In this section, we'll explain how to think properly about both of these kinds of costs.

Opportunity Costs

To produce their garden benches, Noah and Naomi hired workers and rented garage space. Were those their only costs? Not if they were spending their own time running their company. While the time they devoted to the business would not show up in their firm's accounts, it is still an economic cost of production because Noah and Naomi could have been earning money doing something else. By spending their time running their firm, they are each giving up the opportunity to earn a salary elsewhere. This forgone opportunity is an example of an opportunity cost. In general, an **opportunity cost** is the cost associated with forgoing the opportunity to employ a resource in its best alternative use (see also Section 3.1).

An **opportunity cost** is the cost associated with forgoing the opportunity to employ a resource in its best alternative use.

"And to think if I hadn't been home having dinner I might have missed this wonderful investment opportunity."

To give another example, suppose a firm has stored some materials. What is the true economic cost it incurs when it uses those materials in production? Since the firm incurs no out-of-pocket expenses in using these inputs, should it behave as if they are free? Alternatively, should the firm use some standard accounting rule for determining the cost of the inputs, based on their original purchase price?

If a well-functioning market exists for these inputs, the correct answer is that the cost of using a stored input equals the price the firm could sell it for. That is the firm's opportunity cost. By using the inputs, the firm forgoes the opportunity to sell them.

When managers make decisions, then, they must consider not only the costs that show up in the firm's accounting statements, but also its unstated opportunity costs, which are part of its true economic costs of production.

Application 8.2

The Cost of a Beer

John Molson opened the doors of North America's oldest brewery in 1786. Adolph Coors, Sr. opened the doors of his brewery in Colorado in 1873. In 2005 the two companies merged and Molson Coors Brewing Company became the fifth largest brewer in the world.

Both brewers initially followed a production strategy known as *vertical integration* where production, marketing, and distribution are all controlled by the company. John Molson brought barley seeds over from England and gave them to Montreal farmers who agreed to grow them as a source of malt for the brewery. He also started a steamship company to move goods between Montreal and Toronto. Today Molson continues to be vertically integrated in that it controls 49 percent of Brewer's Retail in Ontario and 50 percent of Brewers Distributing in western Canada. Over the years, Coors has supplied its own cans, coal, machinery, and trucking service. The company also owns the springs from which its "Rocky Mountain Spring Water" flows.[2] Why did John Molson and Adolph Coors follow this strategy?

One often-cited reason for vertical integration is the desire to protect a firm's competitive position against cost increases due to input price fluctuations. Does this reasoning make sense? If the barley Molson grew was available for purchase elsewhere, the opportunity cost of using the company's supplies is exactly the market price. After all, instead of using a tonne of barley, managers could have sold it at the market price. This logic tells us that if the input in question is available in the marketplace, pursuing integration to protect Molson Coors' competitive position against cost increases doesn't make sense.

A company may have other legitimate motives for integration. For example, if Molson Coors needs a special kind of barley tailored specifically to its own needs, procuring it through market transactions may sometimes be difficult. To ensure the availability of a key ingredient, managers may decide to produce their own as John Molson did. Another possibility is that a firm's managers or owners may be risk-averse and want to stabilize the firm's cash flow. (We'll discuss risk aversion in Chapter 11.) Investments whose payoffs rise when the firm's profit falls can do this. Molson Coors' vertical integration is an example of such investments, since when input price increases cause Molson Coors' true economic cost of beer production to rise, and beer profit therefore to fall, the payoff from production of the input rises (even if it is sold to other firms).

---

[2]To read more about Coors' vertical integration see "Adolph Coors in the Brewing Industry," Harvard Business School Case No. 9-388-014.

The User Cost of Capital

Most firms own much of the capital they use in production. Once the firm has paid for that capital, it may incur little or no additional out-of-pocket cost. But what is the true economic cost associated with using that capital? Thinking about opportunity costs provides the answer. If a well-functioning rental market for capital exists, then the cost of using the capital is equal to the market rental price. This is the amount of money the firm forgoes by using its own capital instead of renting it to another firm. For example, if a firm owns a five-year-old truck, the cost of using the truck for a year is simply the market rental price for a five-year-old truck.[3]

This cost typically differs from the costs shown in a firm's financial accounts. Sometimes long-lived assets are *expensed*, meaning that the firm records the full amount of the purchase in the year it occurs and nothing in later years. More often, a firm *amortizes* the purchase cost of a long-lived asset, recording part of the price as an expense in each year of the asset's lifetime using a standard depreciation schedule. Neither of these methods reveals the true cost of using the asset, however, which is the market rental price.

8.3 SHORT-RUN COST: ONE VARIABLE INPUT

In Chapter 7 we distinguished between production in the short run, where some inputs are fixed, and the long run, where all inputs are variable. We then studied production in a simple case in which a firm used two inputs in the long run, one of which is fixed in the short run. For Noah and Naomi's garden bench company, for example, the amount of garage space was fixed in the short run, but variable in the long run, while the number of assembly workers was variable in both the long and the short run. In this section and the next we'll investigate such a firm's short-run and long-run costs. Here we'll focus on the short run.

Determining a firm's short-run cost function with only one variable input is simple. Once we have identified the efficient method for producing a given level of output, we know immediately how much of the variable input the firm must use. The firm's variable cost is equal to the cost of that amount of input; its total cost is the variable cost plus any fixed costs.

To illustrate, let's return to Noah and Naomi's garden bench company.

Example 8.2

The Cost of Producing Garden Benches, Part 2

To derive Noah and Naomi's variable cost curve, we'll start with their production function. Figure 8.1(a) shows the production function for using up to four assembly workers when workers can be hired for part of the week and output is finely divisible, reproduced from Figure 7.2 (page 217). We've also written the cost of the labour hired (at $500 per week) in dark red on the horizontal axis. This is Noah and Naomi's variable cost. Figure 8.1(b) shows Noah and Naomi's variable cost curve. Note that we've flipped the production function in

---

[3]Sometimes there is no well-functioning rental market for a capital good. What's the cost of using the truck then? We'll return to this question in Chapter 10.

Figure 8.1(a) by switching the two axes, recording the number of garden benches produced on the horizontal axis and the variable (labour) cost on the vertical axis. The variable costs of points A, D, and F correspond to the amounts listed in the third column of Table 8.1.

Figure 8.2 shows this variable cost curve in dark red (labelled VC), along with Noah and Naomi's fixed and total cost curves in green and medium red, respectively (labelled FC and C). The fixed cost curve is a straight line at $1000.[4] The total cost curve is the vertical sum of the fixed and variable cost curves. For example, the height of the total cost curve at $Q = 33$ is $1500, which equals the height of the fixed cost curve ($1000) plus the height of the variable cost curve ($500) at that output level.

Example 8.2 showed how to determine a firm's short-run costs graphically. We can also find a firm's short-run cost function using algebra. To do so, we'll use the firm's production function to find the amount of input needed to produce a given amount of output. For example, suppose a firm's short-run production function is $Q = F(L) = 2L$. This formula means that each worker produces two units of output. Solving for the quantity of labour L needed for any quantity of output Q tells us that $L = Q/2$. In other words, the firm

Figure 8.1

Deriving Noah and Naomi's Variable Cost Curve from Their Production Function. Figure (a) shows Noah and Naomi's production function from Figure 7.2, in which the only variable input is the number of assembly workers. Here we've added the cost of hiring various numbers of workers in dark red on the horizontal axis. Figure (b) shows Noah and Naomi's variable cost curve. We've flipped the production function in figure (a) putting variable (labour) cost on the vertical axis and the number of benches produced on the horizontal axis.

(a) Production function

(b) Variable cost curve

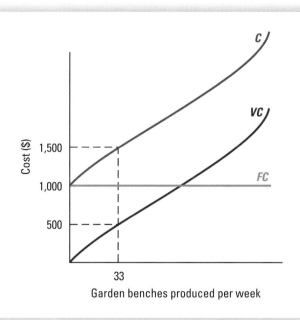

Figure 8.2
Noah and Naomi's Fixed, Variable, and Total Cost Curves. The dark red curve is Noah and Naomi's variable cost function, from Figure 8.1(b). The green curve is their fixed cost curve, which is $1000 at every output level. The medium red curve is Noah and Naomi's total cost curve, which equals the vertical sum of their fixed and variable cost curves.

needs $Q/2$ units of labour to produce Q units of output. The firm's variable cost function for producing Q units of output is simply this labour requirement times the wage rate W. For example, if the wage rate is $15 per hour, the variable cost function is $VC(Q) = (15/2)Q$. If the firm has sunk fixed costs associated with its fixed inputs of $100 per week, then its cost function is $C(Q) = 100 + (15/2)Q$.

WORKED-OUT PROBLEM   8.1

The Problem   Noah and Naomi have decided to start a firm to produce garden tables. Their short-run weekly production function is $Q = F(L) = \sqrt{L}$, where L is the amount of labour they hire, in hours. The wage rate is $12 an hour. Noah and Naomi have committed to a long-term lease of their production facility, which costs them $250 per week. This is a sunk cost. What is their short-run weekly cost function for producing garden tables? Graph it.

The Solution   The relationship between Noah and Naomi's labour input and their garden table output is described by the formula $Q = \sqrt{L}$. Squaring both sides of this formula, we can solve for the number of hours of labour needed to produce Q tables per week: $L = Q^2$. Multiplying by the wage rate, we get the variable cost function $VC(Q) = 12Q^2$. The short-run cost function is therefore $C(Q) = 250 + 12Q^2$, shown in Figure 8.3.

IN-TEXT EXERCISE 8.1   Suppose Noah and Naomi's short-run weekly production function is $Q = F(L) = 2\sqrt{L}$ and the wage rate is $12 an hour. Suppose also that the sunk cost (for their fixed garage-space input) is $500 per week. What is their short-run weekly cost function? Graph this cost function.

Figure 8.3
Cost Function in Worked-Out Problem
8.1. The figure graphs Noah and Naomi's short-run cost function; their fixed cost, a long-term lease, is sunk.

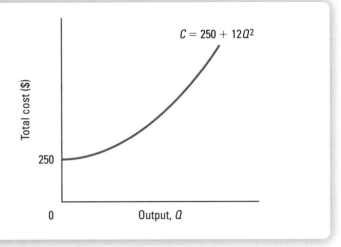

$$C = 250 + 12Q^2$$

Total cost ($)

250

0   Output, Q

Application 8.3

Variable Costs for an Electric Utility

Usually we don't think much about where our electricity comes from or what it costs. That changes rapidly, however, when costs rise suddenly or continued service is threatened. In August 2003, for example, a massive blackout left 50 million people in major Canadian and U.S. cities without power. In Toronto subways and streetcars came to a halt and the country's largest airport was closed. The U.S.-Canada Power System Outage Task Force traced the blackout's cause to an Eastlake, Ohio generating plant's inability to manage a system failure when overgrown trees came in contact with power lines.

Electricity can be produced using a variety of technologies and inputs, including coal, natural gas, wind, water, and nuclear reactions. Different firms use different mixes of these inputs. Some have invested only in technologies that use natural gas. In the short run, when the capital of these technologically specialized firms is fixed, natural gas is their only significant variable input.

One such international firm is Calpine, which generates approximately 30,000 megawatts of electricity per hour across the United States, Mexico, and the United Kingdom—enough to meet the needs of more than 22 million households. In Texas, Calpine operates only gas-fired generating units. These units differ in efficiency. Most but not all of

Calpine's generating capacity in Texas comes from modern combined-cycle units which are more efficient at turning gas into electricity than are older units.

What is Calpine's daily variable cost function in Texas? For any amount of electricity it produces in Texas, Calpine's efficient production method is simple. First, use the most efficient generating unit until it hits capacity, then use the second most

Calpine's Freestone Energy Center in Fairfield, Texas

efficient unit, and so on until the desired output level is reached. Calpine's variable cost function is the cost of the natural gas used in this efficient production method. Each of Calpine's 10 generating units has a different level of efficiency, resulting in 10 different cost levels. Table 8.2 shows these costs per megawatt hour on August 6, 2002, along with Calpine's capacity at each cost level. Most of its units have similar costs, ranging from about $23 to $26 per megawatt hour. The least efficient unit, however, has a cost of about $36 per megawatt hour.

Figure 8.4 shows Calpine's variable cost curve. Notice that this curve is a series of ten line segments. The slope of each line segment is equal to the cost per megawatt hour of the corresponding generating unit in Table 8.2. If you lay a ruler along these segments, you'll see that they grow progressively steeper (if only slightly so), reflecting the fact that Calpine uses its most efficient generating units first. This is most pronounced for the last two steps, which are shown at a larger scale in the magnified box.

Table 8.2

Calpine's Costs for Various Generating Units in Texas (August 6, 2002)

Cost per Megawatt Hour	Capacity (Megawatt Hours)
$22.893	982
23.336	545
23.516	455
23.886	381
24.117	1,151
24.258	150
24.448	262
24.497	302
26.176	524
36.047	115

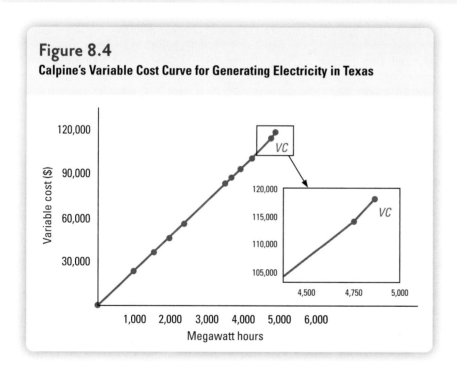

Figure 8.4
Calpine's Variable Cost Curve for Generating Electricity in Texas

8.4 LONG-RUN COST: COST MINIMIZATION WITH TWO VARIABLE INPUTS

Let's turn now to the long run, in which all of the firm's inputs are variable. As we saw in Section 7.3, in this case a firm will usually have many efficient ways to produce a given amount of output, each with a different input combination. Which of these is cheapest?

For simplicity, we'll suppose as we did in Section 7.3 that the firm has only two variable inputs, labour (L) and capital (K). We'll also assume through most of our discussion that the firm's output and inputs are finely divisible. We'll return to this point at the end of the section to discuss the case of a lumpy input, which gives rise to an avoidable fixed cost.

Before we start, we should note that, in reality, most firms have many inputs that are variable in the short run. The lessons of this section apply as well to such a firm's problem of minimizing its short-run cost of production.

Let's start with an example.

Example 8.3

The Cost of Producing Garden Benches, Part 3

Suppose Noah and Naomi can vary both the amount of garage space they rent and the number of assembly workers they hire per week. Both these inputs and their output are finely divisible. As in Example 8.1, an assembly worker earns $500 per week. Garage space rents for $10 per square metre per week. (In Example 8.1, a 100-square-metre garage rented for $1000.) These are Noah and Naomi's only inputs.

Figure 8.5 reproduces Figure 7.8 (page 231). Each point on the isoquant represents the labour and capital required to produce 140 garden benches per week efficiently. While all those input combinations are associated with efficient production methods, their costs are not all equal. One efficient method (labelled A in the figure) uses two workers and a 250-square-metre garage at a cost of $3500 per week. Another one (B) uses five workers and a 100-square-metre garage, also at a cost of $3500 per week. Yet another efficient method (D) uses three workers and a 150-square-metre garage at a cost of $3000 per week. Methods A and B are equally costly and more costly than D. Are there any less expensive input combinations than these three on the isoquant? Which is the least expensive one, and what is its cost? We'll see how to answer these questions next.

Figure 8.5

Isoquant for Producing 140 Garden Benches per Week. This isoquant shows the combinations of assembly workers and garage space that Noah and Naomi can use to produce 140 garden benches a week given efficient production methods. Different points on the isoquant involve different costs. For example, since a worker earns $500 per week and garage space rents for $10 per square metre per week, the costs of input combinations A and B are both $3500 per week, while the cost of input combination D is $3000 per week.

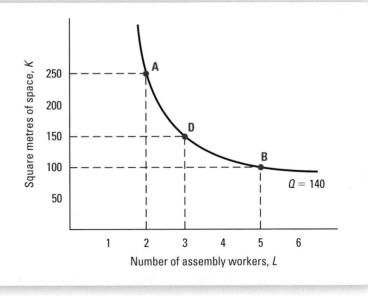

Isocost Lines

Let's begin by finding the least-costly method of production graphically. To do so, we start by identifying all possible input combinations with the same cost. Together they form an **isocost line**. Figure 8.6(a) shows Noah and Naomi's isocost line for a total expenditure of $3500 per week when, on a weekly basis, workers earn $500 and garage space rents for $10 per square metre. Input combinations A and B in Example 8.3 lie on this line. But so do other points, like input combination E with three workers and a 200-square-metre garage.

> An **isocost line** contains all the input combinations with the same cost.

In general, if W is the cost of a unit of labour and R is the cost of a unit of capital, the isocost line for total cost C satisfies the formula

$$WL + RK = C$$

Rearranging this formula, we can solve for the level of capital K that is associated with each level of labour L on this line

$$K = \left(\frac{C}{R}\right) - \left(\frac{W}{R}\right)L$$

For example, the isocost line in Figure 8.6(a) can be represented as

$$K = \left(\frac{3500}{10}\right) - \left(\frac{500}{10}\right)L = 350 - 50L$$

The slope of an isocost line is equal to $-(W/R)$, the negative of the ratio of input prices.

Figure 8.6

Isocost Lines for Producing Garden Benches. Figure (a) shows Noah and Naomi's isocost line for a total cost of $3500 per week. This line contains all the input combinations whose total cost is $3500. It includes the input combinations A and B, as well as many others such as E. Figure (b) shows several isocost lines (corresponding to total costs of $2500, $3500, and $4500) in Noah and Naomi's family of isocost lines. These lines lie parallel to one another, with slope equal to $-\left(\frac{W}{R}\right) = -\left(\frac{500}{10}\right) = -50$. Lines that lie farther from the origin correspond to higher levels of total cost.

(a) Isocost line

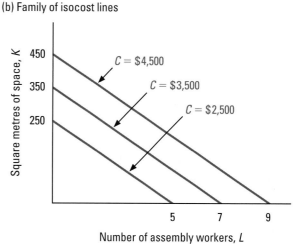

(b) Family of isocost lines

There is a close relationship between firms' isocost lines and consumers' budget lines, discussed in Section 5.1. In each case, the line shows the bundles (of inputs or goods) that have the same cost, and its slope is the negative of the price ratio. Like a consumer's budget line, an isocost line separates the points that cost less than C, all of which lie below the isocost line, from the points that cost more than C, all of which lie above it.

Each level of cost C has its own isocost line. If we were to draw an isocost line for every cost level C, we would have a **family of isocost lines**. All members of a family of isocost lines are parallel, because all have a slope that is equal to the negative of the same price ratio, $-(W/R)$. Isocost lines associated with a lower total cost lie closer to the origin. Figure 8.6(b), for example, shows three of Noah and Naomi's isocost lines, corresponding to the cost levels $2500, $3500, and $4500.

> A **family of isocost lines** contains, for given input prices, the isocost lines for all of the possible cost levels of the firm.

Least-Cost Production

How do we find the least-cost input combination for a given level of output? We do so by finding the lowest isocost line that touches the isoquant for producing that level of output. Let's look at an example. Figure 8.7 shows again Noah and Naomi's isoquant for 140 garden benches a week. It also shows two isocost lines, one of them for a total cost of $3500. Note that this line intersects the isoquant at two points, point A (with two workers and 250 square metres of garage space) and point B (with five workers and 100 square metres of garage space). Neither of these points is the least-cost input combination, because this isn't the lowest isocost line that touches the isoquant. The least-cost input combination is point D, which uses three workers and 150 square metres of garage space. It lies on the dark red isocost line representing the cost level $C = $3000. No lower isocost line touches the 140-bench isoquant.

We can easily recognize a least-cost input combination for producing Q units by applying the following simple rule:

> **The No-Overlap Rule**   The area below the isocost line that contains the firm's least-cost input combination for producing Q units does not overlap with the area above the Q-unit isoquant.

In Figure 8.7, for example, the area below the isocost line that contains input combination A overlaps with the area above the 140-bench isoquant; A is therefore not the least-cost input combination. In contrast, the area below the isocost line that contains input combination D does not overlap with the area above the 140-bench isoquant; D is a least-cost input combination.

Figure 8.7 looks a lot like the figures we saw when we studied consumer choice in Chapter 5, and the no-overlap rule for least-cost production is a lot like the no-overlap rule for consumer choice. This is no accident. There, the consumer was trying to reach the highest possible indifference curve while remaining on the budget line. Here, the firm is trying to reach the lowest possible isocost line while remaining on the isoquant. In each case, a decision maker is trying to spend money in an economically efficient way—in one case to maximize well-being given a fixed budget, in the other to minimize cost given a fixed production level.

Example 8.4 illustrates a particularly easy application of the no-overlap rule: the case in which production involves fixed proportions.

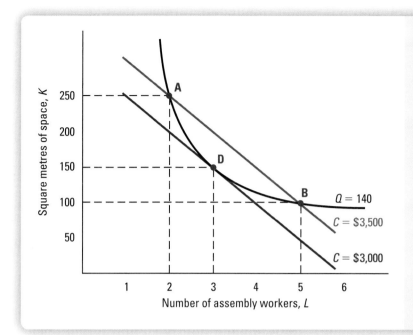

Figure 8.7

Noah and Naomi's Least-Cost Method for Producing 140 Garden Benches per Week. The least-cost method for producing 140 garden benches per week is the point on the 140-unit isoquant that lies on the lowest isocost line. In this figure, the lowest isocost line, shown in dark red, represents a cost of $3000 per week. The least-cost input combination is point D, representing the input combination with three workers and 150 square metres of space.

Example 8.4

The Least-Cost Input Combination for Salt

Recall the technology for producing salt, described in Section 7.3 on page 229. Figure 8.8 shows an isoquant for producing 254 grams of salt, which requires 154 grams of chlorine and 100 grams of sodium. Also shown in red are several isocost lines corresponding to some given prices of chlorine and sodium. The least-cost input combination is point A, which is the only point on the isoquant that satisfies the no-overlap rule. To minimize production costs requires purchasing inputs in exactly the required ratio. Any other choice on the isoquant would involve purchasing more of some input than is necessary.

Interior Solutions

Let's look at cost minimization in a little more detail. An input combination is an **interior choice** if it uses at least a little bit of every input. When the least-cost input combination is an interior choice, we call it an **interior solution**. We'll consider this first.

Input combination D in Figure 8.7 is an interior solution. Notice that Noah and Naomi's 140-bench isoquant has the same slope at input combination D as does their $3000-isocost line through this point. That is, at input combination D, the isocost line is tangent to the isoquant.[5] For this reason, we say that input combination D satisfies the **tangency condition**. In fact, interior solutions *always* satisfy the tangency condition: if the isocost line were *not* tangent to the isoquant, as at point A, then the isocost line would cross the isoquant, creating an overlap between the area under the isocost line and the area above

An input combination is an **interior choice** if it uses at least a little bit of every input. When the least-cost input combination is an interior choice, we call it an **interior solution**.

An input combination satisfies the **tangency condition** if, at that input combination, the isocost line is tangent to the isoquant.

---

[5]Recall that a line is tangent to a curve at a point if the line and the curve have the same slope at that point.

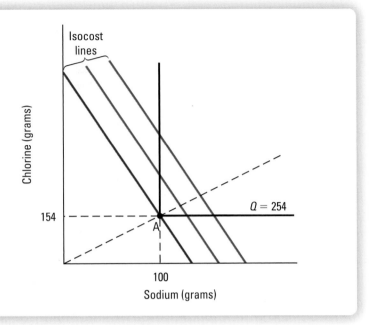

Figure 8.8
The Least-Cost Method of Making Salt. This figure shows the isoquant for making 254 grams of salt, a fixed-proportion production process that requires sodium and chlorine be combined in a 1:1.54 ratio. The least-cost production method lies at point A where the dark red isocost line touches the isoquant; it represents 100 grams of sodium and 154 grams of chlorine.

the isoquant. According to the no-overlap rule, such input combinations don't minimize the cost of production.

Notice again the parallel with our study of consumer choice in Chapter 5. At an interior solution to a consumer's choice problem, the consumer's budget line is tangent to her indifference curve; here, at an interior solution to a firm's cost minimization problem, the firm's isocost line is tangent to its isoquant.

An Implication of the Tangency Condition   The tangency condition can be restated in terms of a relationship between the ratio of the firm's marginal products and the ratio of its input prices. To derive this relationship, recall from Section 7.3 that the slope of the firm's isoquant is equal to the firm's marginal rate of technical substitution for labour with capital ($MRTS_{LK}$) times -1. In turn, the $MRTS_{LK}$ is equal to the ratio of the firm's marginal product of labour to its marginal product of capital.

$$MRTS_{LK} = \frac{MP_L}{MP_K}$$

The slope of the firm's isocost lines, on the other hand, equals $-(W/R)$. The tangency condition is therefore equivalent to the statement that the ratio of marginal products equals the ratio of input prices.

$$\frac{MP_L}{MP_K} = \frac{W}{R} \qquad\qquad \textbf{(1)}$$

Formula (1) has many important implications and applications. For example, in worked out problem 8.2, we'll see that it can provide an easy way to identify a firm's least-cost input combination.

The formula can be interpreted as another example of the general principle that marginal benefit should equal marginal cost at a best choice (see Section 3.2). As we move from northwest to southeast along an isoquant, the amount of labour used increases. The manager's choice can therefore be thought of as a decision of how much labour to use.

The marginal cost of using one more unit of labour is W; the marginal benefit equals the resulting reduction in expenditures on capital. This saving equals the resulting reduction in capital—which equals $MRTS_{LK}$—times the cost of capital R. When the firm's best choice is interior, this marginal benefit must equal the marginal cost, so that

$$R \times MRTS_{LK} = W$$

Since $MRTS_{LK}$ equals the ratio of the inputs' marginal products, this implies that

$$R\left(\frac{MP_L}{MP_K}\right) = W$$

Dividing both sides of this expression by R gives us formula (1). We can also write formula (1) as

$$\frac{MP_L}{W} = \frac{MP_K}{R} \qquad (2)$$

The left-hand side of formula (2) can be interpreted as the increase in output for each extra dollar the firm spends on labour. To see why, observe that the firm can hire $(1/W)$ additional units of labour by spending one dollar more on labour. Multiplying this extra amount of labour by MP_L gives the amount of extra output the extra labour produces. For similar reasons, the right-hand side can be interpreted as the increase in output for each extra dollar the firm spends on capital.

Formula (2) nicely captures the idea of least-cost production: if the firm is using a least-cost input combination, then the marginal product of a dollar spent on labour must equal the marginal product of a dollar spent on capital. If that were not the case, the firm could produce more by shifting a dollar of its expenditure from the input with a lower marginal product per dollar to the one with a higher marginal product per dollar. It could then reduce both inputs, producing the original output at lower cost.[6]

Boundary Solutions

A firm's least-cost input combination may not be an interior solution, however. Some inputs may not be used at all. This will happen when a particular input is not very productive compared to its cost.

When the least-cost input combination excludes some inputs it is called a **boundary solution**. In Section 7.3, for example, we saw that for some jobs (like janitors), university- and high-school-educated workers, denoted U and H, are perfect substitutes. The isoquant for producing 100 units of output is then a straight line with the slope -1, as shown in black in Figure 8.9. The wage rate, however, is higher for university-educated workers. This discrepancy implies that the firm's isocost lines, shown in red in Figure 8.9, are everywhere flatter than its isoquant (their slope is $-(W_H/W_U)$, the ratio of the wage rates, which is closer to zero than -1). As a result, the firm's least-cost input combination, point A, involves hiring only high-school–educated workers (that is the only point on the isoquant at which the no-overlap rule holds). Notice, though, that the tangency condition does not hold at point A. Rather, $(MP_H/MP_U) > (W_H/W_U)$ at this point—that is, the marginal rate of technical substitution for labour with capital exceeds the input price ratio. More generally, for the least-cost input combination to include no university-educated

[6]As this logic suggests, if the firm has more than two inputs, the tangency condition must hold for any two inputs that the firm uses in positive amounts. To see this, observe that holding all other inputs fixed, the firm must be choosing those two inputs in a way that minimizes the firm's cost.

Figure 8.9

A Boundary Solution when High School and University Graduates are Perfect Substitutes. This figure shows a case in which high school (H) and university (U) graduates are equally productive, and therefore perfect substitutes. Since the wage rate of university graduates is higher, the least-cost method of production involves hiring only high school graduates. At the firm's least-cost input combination, point A, $(MP_H/MP_U) > (W_H/W_U)$.

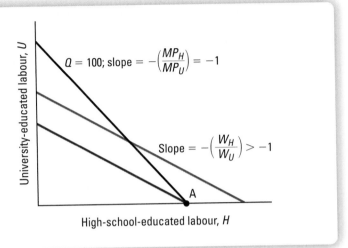

labour, it must be that $(MP_H/W_H) \geq (MP_U/W_U)$—a dollar spent on the marginal high-school-educated worker must produce at least as much output as a dollar spent on the marginal university-educated worker, or else the firm would do better producing its output with at least some university-educated workers. It follows that $(MP_H/MP_U) \geq (W_H/W_U)$.[7]

By similar reasoning, if a firm's least-cost input combination uses only university–educated workers, then it must be that $(MP_H/MP_U) \leq (W_H/W_U)$ at that point.

Application 8.4

Input Substitution at Dell Computer Corporation

In 1984 Michael Dell noticed that computer manufacturers produced their products long before consumers bought them. A personal computer manufacturer such as IBM or Compaq would order large inventories of parts, use them to produce many computers, and ship the computers to retailers, where they would sit on the shelf until purchased. The process would start many months before a computer was actually sold to a consumer.

Dell organized his production process in a very different way. Rather than build his computers before consumers made their purchases, he built them only after an order was placed. He also implemented a production method known as *just-in-time manufacturing*, in which a firm purchases inputs only as they are needed, rather than keeping large inventories of parts.

Delaying the assembly of computers and purchase of parts can lower production costs significantly. The price of

computer parts falls quickly over time, sometimes 10 percent in just a couple of months. By producing only after an order is in hand and buying parts just before assembly, Dell delays its purchases, buying at lower prices. This strategy also allows Dell to keep its money in the bank longer where it earns interest (the loss of interest is an important opportunity cost in manufacturing).[8]

Implementing this production system, however, required an investment in capital. Consumers would be happy only if Dell could assemble their computers quickly and reliably. To do so, Dell needed to invest in manufacturing equipment that would speed production and in information technology that would ensure the availability of parts in the right place at the right time. So Dell's manufacturing strategy relied on input substitution: it substituted manufacturing equipment and information technology for inventories of parts and finished goods.

---

[7]The inequality reflects the same properties of boundary choices that we encountered in our discussion of marginal benefit, marginal cost, and the No Marginal Improvement Principle in the appendix of Chapter 3. Here, at point A the number of high-school-educated workers cannot be increased any further along the isoquant. So the marginal benefit of a high-school-educated worker, $W_U \times (MP_H/MP_U)$, must not be less than the marginal cost, W_H, which is equivalent to saying that $(MP_H/MP_U) \geq (W_H/W_U)$.

[8]See Chapter 10 for a discussion of interest and the time value of money.

Finding the Least-Cost Input Combination

How can we find a firm's least-cost input combination? The tangency condition leads to a useful method for doing so. In parallel to our study of consumer choice, matters are particularly easy when the firm's isoquant for the desired level of output has a declining MRTS. In that case, if we find an interior input combination at which formula (1) (and, hence, the tangency condition) holds, that input combination must also satisfy the no-overlap rule and so must be the least-cost input combination. You can see why in Figure 8.7 (page 265): since the tangency condition holds at point D and the isoquant has a declining MRTS, the isoquant becomes steeper to the left of point D and flatter to the right. In either direction, it veers away from and remains above the isocost line, as shown. So input combination D must satisfy the no-overlap rule and therefore be the least-cost input combination.

Worked-out problem 8.2 illustrates how to use this method to find a least-cost input combination with algebra.

WORKED-OUT PROBLEM 8.2

The Problem Hannah and Sam run Moretown Makeovers, a home painting business. The number of square metres they can paint in a week is described by the Cobb-Douglas production function $Q = F(L, K) = 10L^{0.5}K^{0.5}$ (see Section 7.3), where L is the number of workers and K is units of capital. The wage rate is $1000 per week, and a unit of capital costs $250 per week. What is their least-cost input combination for painting 100 square metres a week? What is their total cost?

The Solution In Section 7.3 we saw that the $MRTS_{LK}$ for the Cobb-Douglas production function $Q = F(L, K) = 10L^{\alpha}K^{\beta}$ is

$$MRTS_{LK} = \left(\frac{\alpha}{\beta}\right)\left(\frac{K}{L}\right)$$

which has a declining MRTS. Let's look for an interior input combination at which formula (1) holds. To locate this point, we need to set $MRTS_{LK}$ equal to the input price ratio.

$$\left(\frac{\alpha}{\beta}\right)\left(\frac{K}{L}\right) = \left(\frac{W}{R}\right) \tag{3}$$

Substituting the values $\alpha = 0.5$, $\beta = 0.5$, $W = 1000$, and $R = 250$ tells us that

$$\left(\frac{K}{L}\right) = 4$$

That is, the tangency condition holds at the point on the 100-square-metre isoquant at which the capital-labour ratio equals 4 (meaning that the number of units of capital is four times the number of workers). When Hannah and Sam use L units of labour and $4L$ units of capital, output is

$$F(L, 4L) = 10L^{0.5}(4L)^{0.5} = 10L^{0.5}2L^{0.5} = 20L$$

So to paint 100 square metres a week requires $L = 5$. Their least-cost input combination therefore uses five workers and, since $K = 4L$, twenty units of capital. Their total cost is $10,000 per week [$= (5 \times 1000) + (20 \times 250)$].

IN-TEXT EXERCISE 8.2 **Suppose instead that Hannah and Sam need to paint 200 square metres a week. Their production function and input prices are the same as in worked-out problem 8.2. What is their least-cost input combination? What is their total cost?**

When the firm's isoquant for the desired level of output does not have a declining MRTS, we can still use the tangency condition to find the least-cost input combination, but matters are a little more complicated. We can now use a procedure like the one developed in Section 3.2 (see also the two-step procedure in the appendix of Chapter 3). We first identify interior input combinations that satisfy the tangency condition, if any. We then compare the costs of those input combinations to the costs of any input combinations on the isoquant that use none of some inputs (possible boundary solutions).

The Firm's Cost Function

Recall that the firm's cost function summarizes how total cost varies with the firm's output level, for fixed input prices. To determine the firm's cost function, we therefore need to find its least-cost input combination for every output level.

A firm's **output expansion path** shows the least-cost input combinations at all possible levels of output for fixed input prices.

Figure 8.10 shows a firm's least-cost input combinations at 100, 200, and 300 units of output, for fixed input prices. They are points D, E, and F, respectively. If we were to compare many different output levels, the least-cost points would form a curve, like the one shown in blue. That curve is called the firm's **output expansion path**.

Figure 8.10

A Firm's Output Expansion Path and Total Cost Curve. Given fixed input prices, a firm's output expansion path, shown in figure (a), contains the least-cost input combinations at all possible levels of output. The firm's total cost curve, shown in figure (b), shows how its total cost changes with its output level, given fixed input prices. Each point on the firm's total cost curve corresponds to the cost level associated with a point on its output expansion path.

(a) Output expansion path

(b) Total cost curve

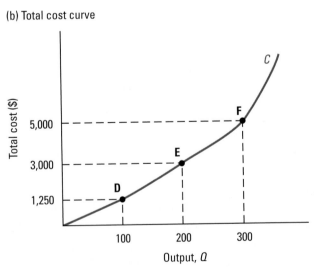

Sometimes the output expansion path is a straight line. In that case, the capital-labour ratio does not change as the firm produces more. For example, if you look back at worked-out problem 8.2, you'll see that the capital-labour ratio at the least-cost input combination does not depend on the level of output for a Cobb-Douglas production function. Sometimes, though, the output expansion path bends. In Figure 8.10(a), for example, the firm's capital-labour ratio shrinks as its output increases.

We're now ready to determine the firm's cost function given fixed input prices and to graph the firm's total cost curve. Figure 8.10(b) graphs the total cost of 100, 200, and 300 units of output by plotting the cost of input combinations D, E, and F in Figure 8.10(a). Those costs—\$1250, \$3000, and \$5000—give us three points on the firm's cost function: $C(100) = 1{,}250$, $C(200) = 3000$, and $C(300) = 5000$. We can find other points on the total cost curve in a similar way.

WORKED-OUT PROBLEM   8.3

The Problem   Consider again Hannah and Sam's painting business in worked-out problem 8.2 (page 269). What is their cost function?

The Solution   The solution to worked-out problem 8.2 tells us that to paint Q square metres Hannah and Sam need the amount of labour L that solves the formula

$$Q = 20L$$

and they need four times that amount of capital. So they need $(Q/20)$ workers and $(4Q/20)$ units of capital. Their cost of producing Q units is therefore

$$C(Q) = 1000(Q/20) + 250(4Q/20) = 100Q$$

IN-TEXT EXERCISE 8.3   **Suppose that a unit of capital instead costs Hannah and Sam \$1000 per week. (Their production function is the same as in worked-out problems 8.2 and 8.3.) What is their cost function?**

Lumpy Inputs and Avoidable Fixed Costs   Firms can vary all of their inputs in the long run, but sometimes some of those inputs are lumpy. Either the input isn't finely divisible, so that at least some minimum amount must be used, or the production process is such that producing any output requires a minimum amount of the input. As an example, think of a hospital that wants to perform CT scans. The lowest capacity scanner might be able to scan five patients a day. Even if the hospital is in a small town and needs to scan only one patient a day, it still must buy or rent this scanner.[9]

Lumpy inputs give firms avoidable fixed costs in the long run (see Section 8.1). Figure 8.11 illustrates this situation. There, capital costs \$1000 per unit. Figure 8.11(a) shows the isoquants for a firm that must use at least one unit of capital to produce any output. The yellow-shaded area represents the input combinations that produce no output because

---

[9]Because of the time involved in moving a scanner, the hospital can't rent it for just part of a day.

Figure 8.11

A Firm's Output Expansion Path and Total Cost Curve with a Lumpy Input. Figure (a) shows the output expansion path for a firm that must use at least one unit of capital to produce any output, but never finds it worthwhile to use more than one unit. Its capital cost is therefore an avoidable fixed cost of $1000, which gives rise to the total cost function shown in figure (b). Total cost is zero when no output is produced, but jumps up to approximately $1000 as soon as the firm's output is positive. This jump is indicated by the little circle at $Q = 0$.

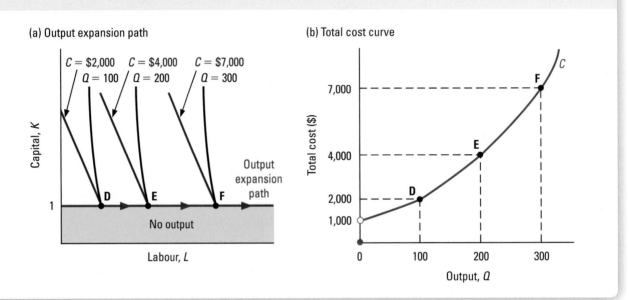

(a) Output expansion path

(b) Total cost curve

they do not include at least one unit of capital. But having more than one unit of capital isn't very useful: the firm's $MRTS_{LK}$ is very large when K is at least one.[10] The firm therefore minimizes its costs of producing any given level of output by using exactly one unit of capital. Its output expansion path is shown in blue.

Figure 8.11(b) shows the firm's total cost function. Cost is zero when no output is produced. But to produce any positive output, the firm must acquire one unit of capital at a cost of $1000. That $1000 is therefore an avoidable fixed cost: the firm incurs it regardless of how much it produces as long as production is positive, but can avoid it by shutting down and producing nothing. It causes the cost function to jump up as soon as output is positive, which is indicated by the little circle in Figure 8.11(b) at $Q = 0$.

---

[10]In an extreme case, in which having more than one unit of capital isn't useful at all—such as the Toronto taxicab owner who needs one, and only one licence to operate his taxi—the firm's isoquants would be perfectly vertical for K greater than one.

WORKED-OUT PROBLEM   8.4

The Problem Noah and Naomi have decided to start a firm to produce garden tables. If Noah and Naomi have at least 50 square metres of garage space their weekly production is $Q = F(L) = \sqrt{L}$, where L is the amount of labour they hire, in hours. Additional garage space beyond 50 square metres does not increase their production. The wage rate is $12 an hour, and a 50-square-metre garage rents for $250 per week. What is their long-run weekly cost function for producing garden tables? Graph it.

The Solution The relationship between Noah and Naomi's labour input and their garden table output is the same as in worked-out problem 8.1 (page 259). So their cost function is

$$C(Q) = \begin{cases} 0 & \text{if } Q = 0 \\ 250 + 12Q^2 & \text{if } Q > 0 \end{cases}$$

which is shown in Figure 8.12. In the figure, costs for $Q = 0$ are represented by the solid dot at the origin. The total cost curve jumps upward as soon as Noah and Naomi begin to produce a positive amount of output, since they must then incur the garage rental cost of $250.

IN-TEXT EXERCISE 8.4 **Noah and Naomi have decided to start a firm to produce garden tables. If Noah and Naomi have at least 50 square metres of garage space their weekly production is $Q = F(L) = 2\sqrt{L}$, where L is the amount of labour they hire, in hours. Additional garage space beyond 50 square metres does not increase their production. The wage rate is $12 an hour, and a 50-square-metre garage rents for $500 per week. What is their long-run weekly cost function for producing garden tables? Graph it.**

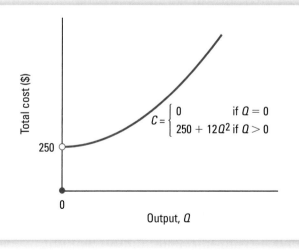

$$C = \begin{cases} 0 & \text{if } Q = 0 \\ 250 + 12Q^2 & \text{if } Q > 0 \end{cases}$$

Figure 8.12

Total Cost Curve in Worked-Out Problem 8.4. The figure shows the total cost curve in worked-out problem 8.4. Noah and Naomi's garage rental is an avoidable fixed cost.

Application 8.5

Variable Costs for An(other) Electric Utility

The same methods we have just studied can be used to find the least-cost input combination for a firm that has a fixed level of capital and two variable inputs in the short run. In Application 8.3, it was easy to derive Calpine's short-run variable cost function for generating electricity in Texas because Calpine used only one type of fuel, natural gas. Unlike Calpine, West Texas Utilities (WTU), another generator of electric power, uses both coal and natural gas. WTU can generate up to 658 megawatts of electricity per hour in its coal-fired plants, and up to 420 megawatts per hour in its gas-fired plants. Typically, coal plants are much cheaper to run than gas plants. WTU's coal plant requires 10.58 million BTUs (British thermal units) of coal for each megawatt hour produced. On August 6, 2002 coal cost $1.40 per million BTUs, so a megawatt hour produced with coal cost $14.81. In contrast, WTU's gas-fired plants require 10.21 million BTUs of natural gas for each megawatt hour produced. On August 6, 2002 natural gas cost $2.86 per million BTUs, so a megawatt hour produced with gas cost $29.20.

Since each megawatt hour produced with coal costs less than each megawatt hour produced with gas, WTU will use only its coal-fired plants until they reach capacity, and then use its gas-fired plants until their capacity is also reached. Figure 8.13(a), which measures the amount of coal and natural gas used per hour in millions of BTUs, shows WTU's output expansion path as the two blue line segments.

The figure also shows some of WTU's isoquants up to its capacity of 1078 megawatt hours. WTU can choose any input combination that does not exceed its coal and gas-fired generating capacities. When run at full capacity, its coal generating plant uses 658 × 10.58 × 6962 million BTUs of coal and its gas plants use 420 × 10.21 = 4288 million BTUs of natural gas. So WTU's feasible input choices are shown as the green-shaded area in the figure.

WTU's isoquants are shown in black and are less steeply sloped than are its isocost lines, which are shown in dark red. Why? The isoquants' slopes are −(10.21/10.58) ≈ −0.96 (the marginal product of coal is 1/10.58 megawatt hours per million BTUs, since 10.58 million BTUs of coal are needed to generate one megawatt hour of electricity, while the marginal product of gas is 1/10.21 megawatt hours per million BTUs). WTU's isocost lines have slope −(1.40/2.86) ≈ −0.49, the ratio of the price of coal to the price of gas, times −1. Observe that only points on the lower and right-hand borders of the green-shaded region satisfy the no-overlap rule.

Figure 8.13(b) shows WTU's variable cost curve up to its capacity. (WTU's fixed costs are not included in the figure.) It consists of two line segments. The slope of the first segment is $14.81, the cost per megawatt hour of its coal-fired plant. The slope of the second is $29.20, the cost per megawatt hour of its gas-fired plant.

8.5 AVERAGE AND MARGINAL COSTS

In Sections 8.3 and 8.4 we saw how to derive a firm's cost function, $C(Q)$. Just as the average and marginal product, discussed in Chapter 7, are useful measures of a firm's productivity, average and marginal cost are useful measures of a firm's costs.

A firm's **average cost,** AC, is its cost per unit of output produced. We calculate it by dividing the firm's total cost, C, by the number of units the firm produces, Q.

A firm's **average cost**, $AC = C/Q$, is its cost per unit of output produced.

$$AC = \frac{C}{Q}$$

A firm's marginal cost, MC, captures how much extra cost is incurred when the firm changes the amount of output it produces a little bit. We've discussed marginal cost already in Section 3.2; let's review that discussion briefly. (The basic ideas are also the same as in our discussion of marginal product in Section 7.2.) As in Section 3.2, when we

Figure 8.13

WTU's Output Expansion Path and Variable Cost Curve. WTU's least-cost production method is to use its coal-fired generating plants until their capacity has been reached, then add its gas-fired generating units. This strategy results in the output expansion path shown in blue in figure (a). WTU's variable cost curve can be determined from the cost levels along its output expansion path. The curve, shown in figure (b), consists of two line segments. The slope of the first segment is $14.81, the cost per megawatt hour at its coal-fired plants; the slope of the second is $29.20, the cost per megawatt hour at its gas-fired plants.

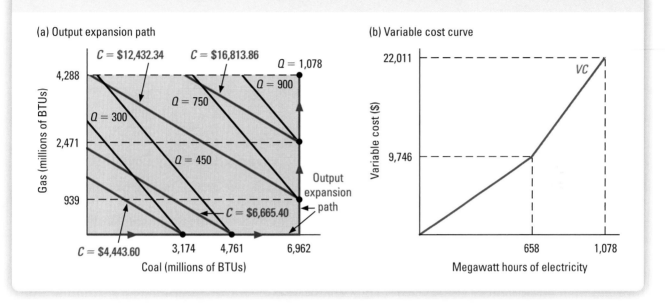

say a "little bit," we mean the smallest amount of output the firm can add or subtract. We'll call this amount ΔQ. When the firm produces Q units, we say that the last ΔQ units are the **marginal units of output.** If the firm can produce its output only in one-litre batches and output is measured in millilitres, then $\Delta Q = 1000$ (since there are 1000 millilitres in a litre). If the firm can produce output in one-quart batches, then $\Delta Q = 32$; in one-ounce batches, then $\Delta Q = 1$. In some cases, there may be virtually no limit to how finely a firm's output level can be adjusted.

> The **marginal units of output** are the last ΔQ units, where ΔQ is the smallest amount of output the firm can add or subtract.

The firm's **marginal cost** measures how much extra cost the firm incurs to produce the marginal units of output, per unit of output added. When the firm produces Q units of output, the change in cost due to the marginal units is $\Delta C = C(Q) - C(Q - \Delta Q)$. Dividing by the amount of output added, ΔQ (to express this change on a per unit basis) gives us the marginal cost:

> A firm's **marginal cost**, MC, measures how much extra cost the firm incurs to produce the marginal units of output, per unit of output added.

$$MC = \frac{\Delta C}{\Delta Q} = \frac{C(Q) - C(Q - \Delta Q)}{\Delta Q}$$

Table 8.3 illustrates the costs for a firm that can produce output in one-tonne increments, so that $\Delta Q = 1$. The first column shows the level of output per day in tonnes. The second column shows the total cost per day at each output level. The third and fourth columns show the firm's marginal and average costs per tonne at each output level. The dashed arrows show the change in cost that corresponds to marginal cost. Note that as output increases, marginal cost first falls and then rises. Average cost follows the same pattern.

> *Optional* **Marginal cost**, MC, can be found using calculus by differentiating the total cost function with respect to output.
>
> $MC = dC(Q)/dQ = C'(Q)$

Table 8.3

Cost, Average Cost, and Marginal Cost for a Hypothetical Firm

Output, Q (tonnes per day)	Total Cost, C ($ per day)		Marginal Cost, MC ($ per tonne)	Average Cost, AC ($ per tonne)
0	$0		—	—
1	1,000		$1,000	$1,000
2	1,800		800	900
3	2,100		300	700
4	2,500		400	625
5	3,000		500	600
6	3,600		600	600
7	4,300		700	614
8	5,600		1,300	700

Average and Marginal Cost Curves with Finely Divisible Output

When output is finely divisible, we can graph average and marginal cost as curves to show how they vary with the firm's output.

Let's start with the average cost. Figure 8.14(a) shows the cost function for another new venture of Noah and Naomi's, producing garden hoses. The horizontal axis shows the firm's output of garden hoses, measured in metres; the vertical axis shows the total cost of production per week. If we pick any point on the cost curve and draw a straight line connecting it to the origin, the slope of that line will equal the cost (the rise) divided

Figure 8.14

Average Cost. Figure (a) shows that at any output level, average cost equals the slope of a line running from the origin to the point on the firm's total cost curve that corresponds to that output level. Figure (b) shows the firm's average cost at each output level.

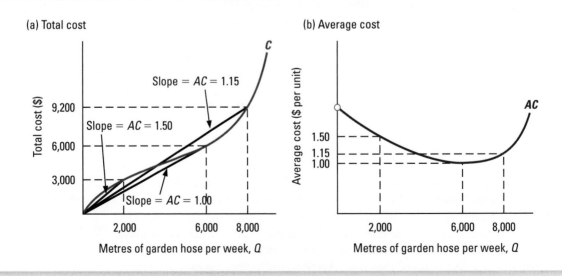

by the amount of output produced (the run). By definition, that's the average cost. The figure illustrates the calculation of the average cost at three different levels of output: 2000, 6000, and 8000 metres of hose per week. For example, when output is 2000 metres, the average cost is $1.50 per metre. Figure 8.14(b) shows the average cost curve. As in Table 8.3, average cost first falls and then rises as output increases. (Average cost is only defined for positive output levels; this is indicated by the little circle at $Q = 0$.)

Note that the average cost of production is lowest when the firm produces 6000 metres per week. This level of output is known as the firm's **efficient scale of production**. Its name does *not* mean that the firm should always try to produce at this level of output. Rather, it tells us that if we want to produce a large amount of output at the lowest possible cost, we should try to divide it up among a number of firms, each of which produces at the efficient scale of production. For example, the cheapest way to produce 180,000 metres a week would be to have 30 firms produce 6000 metres each. This observation will play an important role in Chapter 14, when we study long-run competitive equilibrium.

> A firm's **efficient scale of production** is the output level at which its average cost is lowest.

Now let's think about marginal cost. When output is finely divisible, the smallest amount of output that a firm can add or subtract, ΔQ, is very tiny. In this case, when a firm produces Q units of output, its marginal cost is equal to the slope of its cost function at output level Q. (The logic is the same as in our discussions of marginal product in Section 7.2, and of marginal benefit and marginal cost in Section 3.2.)

We can now graph Noah and Naomi's marginal cost curve for producing garden hoses. Figure 8.15(a) shows lines drawn tangent to the total cost curve at the same three levels of output as in Figure 8.14: 2000, 6000, and 8000 metres per week. The slope of each line tells us the corresponding marginal cost. For example, the marginal cost at $Q = 2000$ is $1.15 per unit. We've plotted the marginal cost at these levels of output and

Figure 8.15

Marginal Cost. Figure (a) shows that at any output level, the firm's marginal cost equals the slope of the total cost curve at that output level. Figure (b) shows the firm's marginal cost at each output level.

(a) Total cost

(b) Marginal cost

others in Figure 8.15(b), which shows the firm's marginal cost curve. Notice that the tangent line at $Q = 6000$ runs through the origin, indicating that the marginal and average costs are equal at that output level.

Figure 8.16 shows Noah and Naomi's average and marginal cost curves together. Notice that the average cost curve slopes downward where it lies above the marginal cost curve and upward where it lies below the marginal cost curve. Where the average and marginal cost curves cross, the average cost curve is neither rising nor falling. This reflects the same relationship between average and marginal variables we've seen before.

This relationship between average and marginal cost means that the marginal cost curve always crosses the average cost curve at its lowest point, the efficient scale of production, since the average cost curve is neither rising nor falling at that output level (see Figure 8.16). Moreover, this crossing must be from below. Why? At output levels a little below the efficient scale of production, average cost must be declining, which means that marginal cost must be below average cost. At output levels a little above the efficient scale of production, average cost must be rising, which means that marginal cost is above average cost.

> **The Relationship between the Average and Marginal Cost Curves**   When output is finely divisible, the average cost curve is upward sloping at Q if marginal cost is above average cost. It is downward sloping if marginal cost is below average cost, and neither rising nor falling if marginal cost equals average cost. Moreover, the marginal cost curve always crosses the average cost curve from below at the efficient scale of production.

In Chapters 9, 14, 17, and 19 marginal and average costs will play central roles in our discussions of profit-maximizing sales quantities or prices. Worked-out problem 8.5 shows another way that the concept of marginal cost is useful.

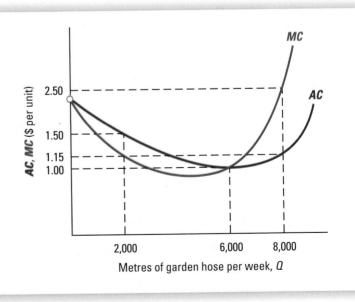

Figure 8.16

The Relationship between Average and Marginal Cost. This figure shows the average and marginal cost curves from Figures 8.14(b) and 8.15(b). At output levels at which marginal cost is less than average cost, the average cost curve is downward sloping; it is upward sloping at output levels at which marginal cost exceeds average cost. The marginal cost curve crosses the average cost curve from below at the efficient scale of production ($Q = 6000$). At that point, average cost is at its lowest level, and the average cost curve is neither rising nor falling.

WORKED-OUT PROBLEM   8.5

The Problem   Suppose Noah and Naomi have just acquired a second garden bench production plant. As with their first plant, they can adjust both the production area and the number of workers in this second facility. Suppose production costs are $C_1 = 3(Q_1)^2$ at plant 1 and $C_2 = 2(Q_2)^2$ at plant 2, where Q_1 and Q_2 are the number of benches produced at each plant per week. The corresponding marginal costs at the two plants are $MC_1 = 6Q_1$ and $MC_2 = 4Q_2$. If Noah and Naomi plan to produce 100 garden benches per week and want to do it as economically as possible, how many benches should they produce at each plant?

The Solution   The basic principle behind the solution to this problem is the same as in worked-out problem 7.1 (page 229). With a least-cost plan that assigns a positive amount of output to each plant, *marginal cost must be the same at both plants.* If that were not true, the total cost could be lowered by reassigning a little bit of output from the plant with the higher marginal cost to the plant with the lower marginal cost.

Noah and Naomi need to divide production between the two plants so that their marginal costs are equal. Doing so means choosing Q_1 and Q_2 so that $MC_1 = MC_2$. Since total output equals 100, we know that $Q_2 = 100 - Q_1$, so we can express the marginal cost in plant 2 as a function of the amount of output produced in plant 1: $MC_2 = 4(100 - Q_1)$. We can then find the output assignment that equates marginal costs in the two plants by solving the formula $MC_1 = MC_2$, which is equivalent to

$$6Q_1 = 4(100 - Q_1)$$

The solution is $Q_1 = 40$. Noah and Naomi should produce 40 garden benches a week in their first facility and 60 garden benches a week in their second facility. Their total production costs will then be

$$C = 3(40)^2 + 2(60)^2 = \$12,000$$

IN-TEXT EXERCISE 8.5   **Repeat worked-out problem 8.5, but assume instead that the total cost and marginal cost at plant 1 are $C_1 = 6(Q_1)^2$ and $MC_1 = 12\,Q_1$, respectively.**

Marginal Cost, Marginal Products, and Input Prices

Intuitively, a firm's costs should be lower the more productive it is and the lower are the input prices it faces. This observation suggests that there should be a relationship between a firm's marginal cost and its marginal products and input prices. To derive this relationship, consider a firm that is producing 100 units of output. If it wants to increase its output by one unit, one possibility is that it can use only more labour. This requires $(1/MP_L)$ additional units of labour and costs $W \times (1/MP_L) = W/MP_L$. Alternatively, it could use only capital, which would cost $R \times (1/MP_K) = R/MP_K$. But equation (2) tells us that these two amounts are equal. So the firm's marginal cost equals each input's price divided by its marginal product at the firm's least-cost input combination; that is

$$MC = \frac{R}{MP_K} = \frac{W}{MP_L}$$

Marginal Costs and Variable Cost

Marginal cost measures the extra cost of each additional unit the firm produces. A firm's variable cost is therefore equal to the sum of the marginal costs of the individual units it produces. To see this point, look at Figure 8.17(a), which shows the marginal cost curve for a firm that is producing 50 units. If the firm's output were lumpy so that it could produce only in batches of 10 units each, the extra cost from producing each batch of 10 units would be the series of red-shaded steps. The firm's variable cost would equal the sum of these steps; that is, the total red-shaded area. When the firm's output is finely divisible, these steps become very small, and variable cost comes to equal the area under the marginal cost curve, as Figure 8.17(b) shows. This relationship also means that the change in variable cost between any two output levels is equal to the area under the marginal cost curve between those output levels.

More Average and Marginal Costs

We can also apply the notions of average and marginal cost to a firm's variable and fixed costs. A firm's average variable cost, AVC, is

$$AVC = \frac{VC}{Q}$$

while its average fixed cost, AFC, is

$$AFC = \frac{FC}{Q}$$

Figure 8.17

Variable Cost Equals the Area Under the Marginal Cost Curve. Figure (a) shows that when output is lumpy and can be produced only in 10-unit batches, variable cost for a firm producing 50 units equals the sum of the red-shaded rectangles, representing the marginal costs of the five 10-unit batches the firm produces. Figure (b) shows that when output is finely divisible, variable cost equals the area under the marginal cost curve up to 50 units.

(a) Lumpy output

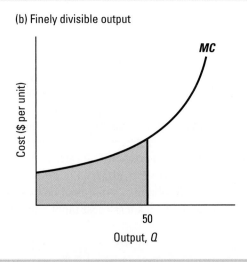

(b) Finely divisible output

Since total cost is equal to the sum of variable and fixed costs, average cost is equal to the sum of the average variable and average fixed costs.

$$AC = \frac{C}{Q} = \frac{VC + FC}{Q} = \frac{VC}{Q} + \frac{FC}{Q} = AVC + AFC$$

Figure 8.18 shows a hypothetical firm's average variable cost curve (in black), average fixed cost curve (in green), and average cost curve (in red). Since a firm's fixed cost, FC, is a fixed number, its AFC curve is always downward sloping (as the output level increases, we are dividing the same fixed cost among more and more units). At each level of output the AC curve is the vertical sum of the AVC and AFC curves. Thus, the average cost curve lies above both the average variable and average fixed cost curves at every output level.

Notice that the efficient scale of production, Q^e (the output level at which average cost is lowest), exceeds the output level where AVC is lowest, labelled Q^e_{VC}. In fact, the output level that minimizes AC can *never* be below Q^e_{VC}. Why not? First, since both AVC and AFC are lower at Q^e_{VC} than at any lower quantity, this must also be true of AC (which is the sum of AVC and AFC). Next, observe that the AVC curve is neither rising nor falling right at Q^e_{VC} (see Figure 8.18), while the AFC curve is downward sloping. Since the AC curve is the sum of those two curves, it must slope downward at Q^e_{VC}, which implies that there are larger outputs than Q^e_{VC} that have a lower average cost.

Now let's think about marginal costs. Because fixed cost is a fixed number, marginal units of output always add zero fixed cost. So *all* the costs of producing marginal units are variable costs. That means there is no difference between marginal cost and marginal variable cost. Figure 8.19 illustrates this point. The figure shows a firm's total cost and variable cost curves. Since total cost at each output level is just the variable cost curve shifted up by the constant fixed cost, the slopes of the two curves are the same at each output level and equal MC. The figure demonstrates this fact at two output levels, Q' and Q''.

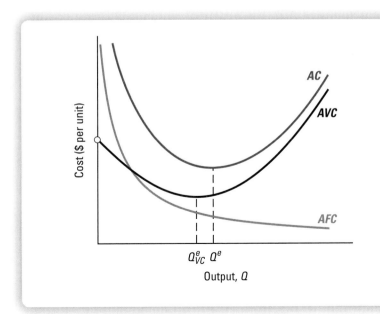

Figure 8.18

Average Fixed Cost, Average Variable Cost, and Average Cost. At each output level, the average cost (AC) curve is the sum of the average fixed cost (AFC) and average variable cost (AVC). Thus, at every output level the AC curve lies above the AFC and AVC curves. The average fixed cost curve is downward sloping at all output levels. The output level at which AC is lowest, the efficient scale Q^e, is never below Q^e_{VC}, the output level at which AVC is lowest.

Finally, what about the relationship between average variable cost and marginal cost? The usual relationship between average and marginal variables applies. Average variable cost increases, decreases, or remains constant where it is less than, more than, or equal to marginal cost (this follows from the fact that MC equals marginal variable cost). Figure 8.20 shows this relationship.

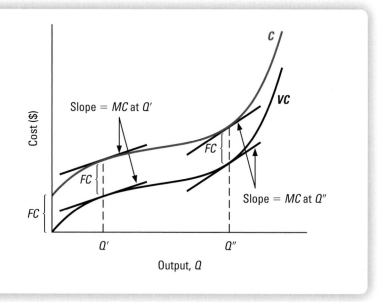

Figure 8.19

Marginal Variable Cost Equals Marginal Cost. At every output level the slopes of the variable cost and total cost curves are the same, since the total cost curve is simply the variable cost curve shifted up by the constant amount of fixed cost.

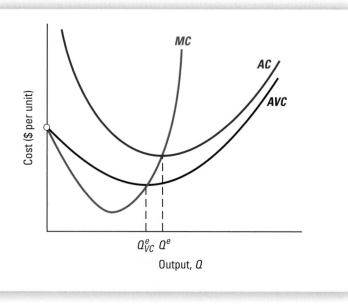

Figure 8.20

Relationship between Average Cost, Average Variable Cost, and Marginal Cost. The marginal cost curve crosses both the average and average variable cost curves from below at their minimums. It lies below each of these curves where they are downward sloping and is above them where they are upward sloping.

8.6 EFFECTS OF INPUT PRICE CHANGES

Changes in a firm's input prices generally lead to changes in its least-cost production method. Intuitively, if an input becomes more expensive, we would expect the firm to use less of it, substituting toward the use of other inputs in its place. To illustrate, let's look again at worked-out problem 8.2 (page 269). There we solved for Hannah and Sam's least-cost input combination for painting 100 square metres per week with a wage rate of $1000 per week and capital cost of $250 per unit. That least-cost input combination, labelled point A in Figure 8.21, was five workers and twenty units of capital.

What if the cost of capital were instead $1000 per week? If you've solved in-text exercise 8.3 (page 271), you've seen that the new least-cost input combination, shown as point B in Figure 8.21, is ten workers and ten units of capital (if you haven't, check this now). So when the price of capital increases, the least-cost production method uses less capital and more labour.

Can we draw any general conclusions about the effects of input price changes on the least-cost input combination? The answer is *yes*. After an increase in the price of an input, a firm *never* uses more of that input in its least-cost input combination, and usually employs less. Likewise, after a decrease in the price of an input, a firm *never* uses less of that input in its least-cost input combination, and usually employs more.

Figure 8.22 demonstrates this point for an input price increase. The dark red isocost line labelled R reflects the initial prices of labour and capital, W and R. Suppose that the least-cost input combination at those input prices is point A. (The figure deliberately omits the firm's isoquant.) Now suppose the price of capital increases to $R' > R$, resulting in a flatter isocost line. The new isocost line that contains point A is shown in light red. Where will the new least-cost input combination lie? The answer is that it must be somewhere in the green-shaded region, like point B. Why? Since the new least-cost input combination was not cheaper than A at the old prices, it must lie on or above the original isocost line through A. On the other hand, since it is no more expensive than A at the new

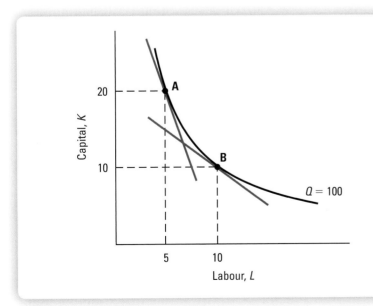

Figure 8.21

The Effect of an Input Price Change on the Least-Cost Production Method for a Cobb-Douglas Production Function. Point A is the least-cost input combination when workers earn $1000 per week and a unit of capital costs $250 per week. When a unit of capital instead costs $1000 per week, the least-cost input combination is point B, where the firm uses less capital and more labour.

Figure 8.22

Effects of an Input Price Change. In the figure, the least-cost combination when capital costs R per unit is A. When the price of capital rises to R', the new least-cost input combination must lie in the green-shaded region, such as point B. This means that it uses no more capital than does input combination A.

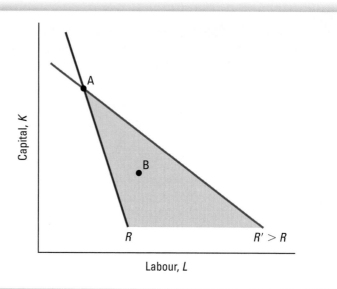

prices it must lie on or below the new isocost line through A. Since *all* of the points in the green-shaded region require no more capital than input combination A, so must the new least-cost input combination.

The same argument works for *any* change in *any* input price (check this for an input price decrease on your own). The only caveat is that sometimes (as illustrated in Application 8.6) the firm's input choice does not change when an input price changes.

In sum:

> **Responses to a Change in an Input Price**   When the price of an input decreases, a firm's least-cost production method never uses less of that input, and usually employs more. Likewise, when the price of an input increases, a firm's least-cost production method never uses more of that input, and usually employs less.

Application 8.6

Least-Cost Production at a Cider Mill

In Application 7.2 (page 233) we derived a traditional cider mill's isoquant for producing 40,000 litres of apple cider per day. Recall that a cider mill can use three different machines to produce its cider: a traditional rack-and-cloth vertical press, a belt press, and a rack-and-bag horizontal press. If

the cider mill manager anticipates producing 40,000 litres per day, what is his least-cost production method? How does it depend on the wage rate?

To answer this question, we need to know the cider mill's input costs. Suppose a unit of capital costs $10 per day, while workers earn $8.50 an hour. Figure 8.23 shows the cider mill's isoquant for producing 40,000 litres of cider per day along with three isocost lines, corresponding to three different prices of capital, R. The isocost line labelled R = $10 has a slope of −(8.5/10). As the figure shows, the least-cost input combination when R = $10 is point C, which uses one rack-and-bag horizontal press, one rack-and-cloth vertical press, and 16 hours of labour (see Table 7.5 on page 234). The total cost of production is [(11)($10) + (16)($8.50)] = $246 per day.

Since the mill's isoquant is kinked, its least-cost input combination will remain the same over a range of input prices. For example, an increase in the price of a unit of capital to $12 will flatten the cider mill's isocost lines but leave its least-cost input combination unchanged, as shown in the figure by the isocost line labelled R = $12. However, as is also shown in the figure, if the price of a unit of capital rises to $25 per day (R = $25), then the mill's least-cost input combination would be B, which uses less capital and more labour.

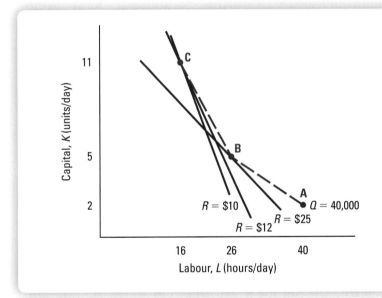

Figure 8.23

A Cider Mill's Least-Cost Method of Producing 40,000 Litres of Cider per Day. This figure shows a cider mill's isoquant for producing 40,000 litres of cider per day, reproduced from Figure 7.11. When the price of capital is $10 per unit per day and the wage rate is $8.50 per hour, the mill's least-cost input combination is point C. It is the same if the price of capital increases to $12 per unit per day, but switches to point B if the price of capital increases to $25 per unit per day.

8.7 SHORT-RUN VERSUS LONG-RUN COSTS

What is the relationship between a firm's short-run and long-run costs? To answer this question, Figure 8.24 shows three of Noah and Naomi's isoquants for producing garden benches: $Q = 120$, $Q = 140$, and $Q = 160$ benches per week. Imagine that the wage rate is $500 per week and garage space rents for $10 per square metre. In the long run, Noah and Naomi can vary both these inputs. At each of the three output levels, they will choose the least-cost input combination, which occurs at the tangency of the isoquant with an isocost line. In the figure, these least-cost input combinations are labelled A, B, and D, respectively.

Now suppose Noah and Naomi are producing 140 garden benches per week (point B) when the demand for garden benches suddenly increases, raising the amount of output they want to produce to 160 benches a week. Suppose, too, that over the short run, they can't vary their garage space which is fixed at 150 square metres. How will they produce

Figure 8.24

Input Responses over the Long and Short Run. Noah and Naomi are producing 140 garden benches per week at input combination B. If they decide to increase their output to 160 benches per week they will shift to input combination F over the short run, when they cannot adjust their garage space. In the long run, when they can adjust their garage space, they will shift to input combination D. Thus, their cost is lower in the long run. Likewise, if they decide to decrease their output to 120 garden benches a week, they will shift to input combination E in the short run, and to input combination A in the long run. Again, their cost is lower in the long run.

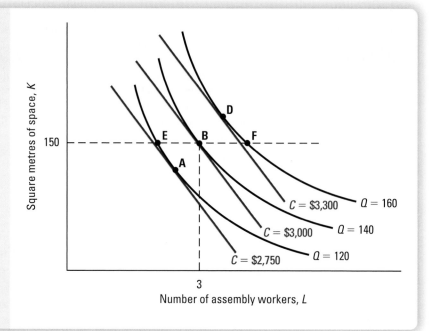

the extra output? The only way to do it is to increase the number of workers. The required input combination is point F, which has the same amount of garage space as point B, but a greater number of workers. Notice that the cost of production at point F is greater than at point D, the least-cost input combination at $Q = 160$.

Similarly, if Noah and Naomi unexpectedly needed to reduce their output to 120 benches per week, they would use the input combination labelled E. Again, point E involves a greater cost than point A, the least-cost input combination at $Q = 120$.

Figure 8.25(a) shows the resulting long-run and short-run total cost curves, labelled C_{LR} and C_{SR}^{140}. At 140 garden benches per week the two curves coincide, since Noah and Naomi choose point B in either case. But at all other output levels, the short-run cost curve lies above the long-run cost curve because the extra flexibility Noah and Naomi have over the long run allows them to produce at a lower cost.

Figure 8.25(b) shows the long-run and short-run average cost curves, labelled AC_{LR} and AC_{SR}^{140}. Since short-run cost is greater than long-run cost at all positive output levels other than 140, the same is true of short-run and long-run average cost.

Figure 8.26 shows Noah and Naomi's short-run average cost curves starting at various output levels. For example, AC_{SR}^{40} is their short-run average cost curve when they start off using the least-cost input combination for producing 40 garden benches per week. AC_{SR}^{100} corresponds to initially producing 100 garden benches per week. The figure shows that their long-run average cost curve is the *lower envelope* of their various short-run average cost curves. (This lower envelope is the highest curve that lies below all of the short-run curves.) At each output level Q, the long-run average cost curve just touches the short-run average cost curve AC_{SR}^{Q}, and it lies below that short-run average cost curve everywhere else.

What about short-run and long-run marginal cost? Look back at Figure 8.25(a). The slopes of the short-run and long-run cost functions are equal at $Q = 140$; thus, short-run marginal cost equals long-run marginal cost at that output level. Just above $Q = 140$, short-run cost rises more quickly than long-run cost, so short-run marginal cost is greater than

Figure 8.25

Long-Run and Short-Run Costs. Figure (a) shows Noah and Naomi's long-run and short-run cost curves, labelled as C_{LR} and C_{SR}^{140}, respectively, when they are initially producing 140 garden benches per week. The two curves coincide at $Q = 140$; elsewhere, the long-run cost curve lies below the short-run cost curve for the reasons shown in Figure 8.24. Figure (b) shows the long- and short-run average cost curves. Again, they coincide at $Q = 140$; elsewhere, the long-run average cost curve lies below the short-run average cost curve.

(a) Long- and short-run cost

(b) Long- and short-run average cost

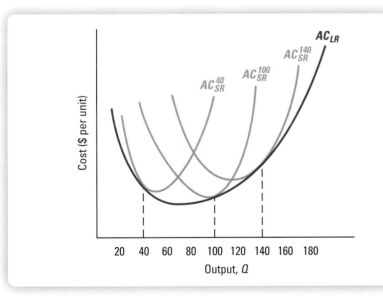

Figure 8.26

Long-Run and Short-Run Average Cost Curves. The long-run average cost curve AC_{LR} is the lower envelope of the various short-run average cost curves. Each short-run average cost curve AC_{SR}^{Q} touches the long-run average cost curve at output level Q, and lies above it everywhere else.

long-run marginal cost. Just below $Q = 140$, short-run cost rises more slowly than long-run cost, so short-run marginal cost is lower than long-run marginal cost. Thus, if Noah and Naomi are producing 140 garden benches per week at point B, their short-run and long-run marginal cost curves have the relationship shown in Figure 8.27. In Chapter 9, we'll see that this relationship has an important implication: competitive firms will respond more to changes in output prices over the long run than they will over the short run.

Figure 8.27

Long-Run and Short-Run Marginal Cost. This figure shows Noah and Naomi's long-run and short-run marginal cost curves when they are initially producing 140 garden benches per week. The short-run marginal cost curve is steeper than the long-run marginal cost curve, and the two curves cross at $Q = 140$.

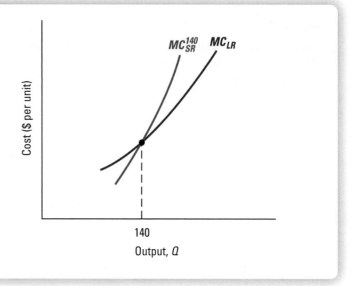

WORKED-OUT PROBLEM   8.6

The Problem   Consider again Hannah and Sam's painting business in worked-out problems 8.2 and 8.3 (pages 269 and 271). Suppose that they are initially painting 100 square metres per week. What are their short-run and long-run cost functions?

The Solution   The solution to worked-out problem 8.2 tells us that they initially use 20 units of capital. So, if their capital is fixed at 20 units, to paint Q square metres Hannah and Sam need the amount of labour L that solves the formula

$$10\sqrt{L}\,\sqrt{20} = Q$$

which means that $L = (Q^2/2000)$. So, their short-run cost function is

$$C_{SR}^{100}(Q) = (250)(20) + (1000)\left(\frac{Q^2}{2000}\right)$$

or equivalently,

$$C_{SR}^{100}(Q) = 5000 + \left(\frac{Q^2}{2}\right)$$

In contrast, the solution to worked-out problem 8.3 tells us that Hannah and Sam's long-run cost function is

$$C_{LR}(Q) = 100Q$$

Observe, though, that their short-run and long-run costs are equal when $Q = 100$ (since $C_{SR}^{100}(100) = C_{LR}(100) = 10{,}000$), just as our discussion indicated they should be.

IN-TEXT EXERCISE 8.6   **Suppose that a unit of capital instead costs Hannah and Sam $1000 per week. (Their production function is the same as in worked-out problems 8.2 and 8.3.) They are initially painting 100 square metres per week. What are their short-run and long-run cost functions?**

8.8 ECONOMIES AND DISECONOMIES OF SCALE

In Section 7.4 we introduced the concept of returns to scale. We learned that a firm has constant, increasing, or decreasing returns to scale depending on whether an increase in its inputs increases its output proportionately, more than proportionately, or less than proportionately. In this section we'll look at the cost implications of returns to scale.

A firm experiences **economies of scale** when its average cost falls as it produces more. This occurs when cost rises less, proportionately, than the increase in output. For example, suppose a firm increases its output from Q to $2Q$. If costs less than double, then $C(2Q) < 2C(Q)$; dividing both sides by $2Q$ tells us that $C(2Q)/2Q < C(Q)/Q$, so average cost is lower at $2Q$ than at Q. When the production technology for a good creates economies of scale, small producers will have a hard time surviving, because their average cost will be higher than that of larger competitors.

> A firm experiences **economies of scale** when its average cost falls as it produces more.

A firm experiences **diseconomies of scale** when its average cost rises as it produces more. Diseconomies occur when cost rises more, proportionately, than the increase in output.

> A firm experiences **diseconomies of scale** when its average cost rises as it produces more.

What is the relationship between returns to scale and economies of scale? When a firm's input prices do not vary with the amount it produces, it experiences economies of scale if its technology has increasing returns to scale, and experiences diseconomies of scale if its technology has decreasing returns to scale.

Figure 8.28 illustrates why. Let's first consider the firm with increasing returns to scale in Figure 8.28(a). Suppose the firm begins by producing 100 units of output per month using input combination A. If the firm decides to double its output to 200 units by increasing its use of all inputs in the same proportion, it must use input combination C. Because the firm has increasing returns to scale, C will use less than double the amount of inputs used in A, so it will be less than twice as costly (the input combination that uses double the inputs in A is labelled 2A in the figure). Since the least-cost bundle for producing 200 units, bundle B, is less costly than bundle C, it must also cost less than twice as much as bundle A. This means that the firm's average cost of producing 200 units is less than its average cost of producing 100 units; it has economies of scale.

Now consider the firm with decreasing returns to scale in Figure 8.28(b). Suppose the firm starts by producing 200 units a month using input combination B. If it decides to cut its production in half to 100 units by reducing its use of all inputs in the same proportion, it must use input combination D. Because the firm has decreasing returns to scale, D will use *less* than half of the amount of inputs as B, so it will be less than half as costly (the input combination that uses half the inputs in B is labelled B/2 in the figure). Since the least cost bundle for producing 100 units, bundle A, is less costly than D, it must also be less than half as costly as B. This means that the firm's average cost for

Figure 8.28

Returns to Scale and Economies of Scale. The figures illustrate that increasing returns to scale implies economies of scale and that decreasing returns to scale implies diseconomies of scale. In figure (a) with increasing returns to scale, input combination C costs less than twice as much as A. So B, which costs less than C, must also cost less than twice as much as A. In figure (b) with decreasing returns to scale, input combination D costs less than half as much as B. So A, which costs less than D, must also cost less than half as much as B.

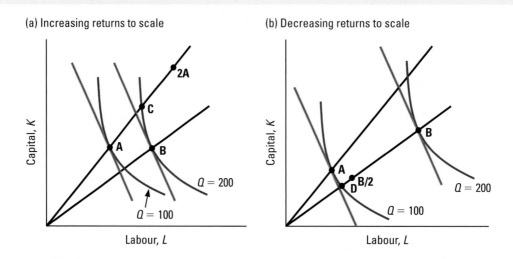

producing 100 units is less than the average cost of producing 200 units; it has diseconomies of scale.[11]

We have discussed situations in which a firm's cost function has either economies of scale, diseconomies of scale, or a constant average cost. However, a firm's cost function may have economies of scale over a particular range of output, and diseconomies of scale over another range of output. The cost function shown in Figure 8.14 (page 276) is one example.

*8.9 MULTIPRODUCT FIRMS AND ECONOMIES OF SCOPE

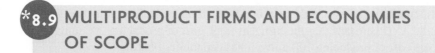

In most of this chapter we have focused, for simplicity, on firms that produce a single product. Yet few firms actually do so. Hewlett Packard produces notebook computers, printers, and printer cartridges; Microsoft produces Windows®, Office®, and computer

---

[11]Sometimes a firm's input prices vary with the amount it produces. For example, the firm may get a quantity discount or face a quantity penalty (see Add-On 5D), so that its input price changes when it uses more or less of the input. In that case, there is a factor in addition to the firm's technology that contributes to economies or diseconomies of scale. For example, a firm facing a quantity discount for its inputs could have economies of scale even though it has decreasing returns to scale. Similarly, a firm that faces a quantity penalty for its inputs could have diseconomies of scale even though it has increasing returns to scale.

games. Even the corner gas station sells multiple grades of gasoline—"regular," "super," and "premium."

Fortunately, the basic concepts we've studied apply equally well to firms that produce many products. Suppose you're the manager of a firm that sells two products, whose output levels are Q_1 and Q_2. To make sound decisions, you need to determine your firm's cost function, which takes the form $C(Q_1, Q_2)$. This function tells you the total cost of producing each possible bundle of outputs. To derive it, you need to find the least-cost production method for each possible output bundle (Q_1, Q_2). Just as with a single product, there is an isoquant that gives the combinations of inputs that will allow you to produce this bundle of outputs using efficient production methods. Least-cost production involves finding the least costly point on that isoquant.

Why do firms produce multiple products? Just as economies of scale determine whether small or large firms are more effective competitors in a single-product market, the nature of technology and input costs help to determine whether single-product or multi-product firms are more effective competitors. **Economies of scope** occur when a single firm can produce two or more products more cheaply than two separate firms. For example, a single firm can produce the output bundle (Q_1, Q_2) more cheaply than two separate firms if

> **Economies of scope** occur when a single firm can produce two or more products more cheaply than two separate firms.

$$C(Q_1, Q_2) < C(Q_1, 0) + C(0, Q_2)$$

Diseconomies of scope occur when producing two products in the same firm is more expensive than producing them separately, in different firms, so that $C(Q_1, Q_2) > C(Q_1, 0) + C(0, Q_2)$.

> **Diseconomies of scope** occur when producing two products in a single firm is more expensive than producing them separately, in different firms.

Economies of scope arise for many of the same reasons as increasing returns to scale (see Section 7.4). If Noah and Naomi produce both garden benches and garden chairs, for example, workers may be able to specialize even further (perhaps by assembling similar portions of both products). Likewise, delivery routes may become more efficient when a truck delivers more than one product, perhaps by delivering multiple products to the same address. Sometimes physical processes create opportunities for joint production. Many manufacturing firms now sell electricity generated from the heat produced as a by-product of their production processes.

Another reason for economies of scope, at least over some range of production, is the more intensive utilization of lumpy, indivisible inputs. The top executives of a firm that produces only one product may find they have the time and ability to manage the production of a second, related product. A similar effect comes from the transfer of knowledge. For example, Xerox invested a great deal in learning how to design paper-feeding mechanisms for copy machines. That same knowledge can be used for printers.

As in our discussion of returns to scale in Section 7.4, it's harder to see why a firm might have diseconomies of scope. Couldn't the firm always set up a separate facility to produce each product, thereby producing just as cheaply as separate firms? Not necessarily. Indeed, in the 1990s, many firms decided that some of their divisions would be more efficient if they were run as separate firms; they sold off those divisions to other firms or to division managers. One of the motives behind these sales was to overcome the kinds of bureaucratic costs we discussed as a reason for decreasing returns to scale. When a firm has many divisions, the CEO can't run all of them; she relies on other managers. But the CEO often maintains some oversight of those managers, sometimes intervening in their decisions or controlling their access to capital. This lack of autonomy can make such divisions less efficient than separate firms.

Application 8.7

Purolator Goes International

Purolator Courier Ltd. began in 1960 as Trans Canadian Couriers serving Ontario and Quebec with just two employees. Today Purolator is Canada's largest overnight delivery company and moves more packages than its two main competitors, UPS and FedEx, combined. Purolator is dominant in the business-to-business and business-to-consumer markets within Canada; the only market it does not dominate is the consumer-to-consumer market. That market is the domain of Canada Post which just happens to own a 90-percent stake in Purolator.

Although dominant in the Canadian market, Purolator has not been able to capture the express delivery market between Canada and the rest of the world. Over the past 10 years that has changed as Purolator formed strategic international alliances to build upon its industry-leading domestic delivery infrastructure. In 1998 Purolator formed a strategic alliance with DHL Worldwide Express and entered the international market. Purolator also started Purolator Freight, Purolator USA, Purolator International, and Purolator Global Supply Chain Services to better compete in the worldwide delivery market to and from Canada. Coupled with the company's investments in transport hubs throughout Canada to serve the domestic market, Purolator's international business has been the fastest growing part of the company. In 2008 Purolator Freight saw revenue increase by 50 percent and Purolator USA had a 25 percent increase in business revenue.

Why would Purolator, a company that until 10 years ago only served the Canadian domestic market, be a good competitor for UPS and FedEx in the international delivery market? Might it have lower costs than a separate domestic shipping company? That is, might Purolator profit from economies of scope between domestic and international delivery?

Given Purolator's industry leading domestic infra-structure, Purolator might benefit from economies of scope by using the same trucks, hubs, and delivery routes for picking up and delivering packages coming into and leaving the country it uses for its domestic deliveries. It might also use the many existing Purolator offices to accept packages for both the domestic and international markets. Purolator also had a lot of accumulated experience in the efficient organization of transportation systems, which is applicable to both domestic and international shipping. Finally, within Canada Purolator has an excellent brand name and reputation, and outside Canada its partner DHL has similar visibility. By leveraging its existing reputation for high quality service in express package delivery, Purolator may have avoided some of the costs of developing brand recognition.

Although our focus is on costs, demand factors may also have made Purolator a natural entrant into the cross-border shipping industry. If existing Purolator customers valued the opportunity to use just one shipper for all of their shipping needs, Purolator could offer more value to those customers than a company that offers only domestic service.

CHAPTER SUMMARY

1. **Types of cost (LO1)**
   a. A firm's total cost of producing a given level of output is the expenditure required to produce that output in the most economical way.
   b. Costs can be either variable or fixed. Variable cost is the cost of inputs that vary as the firm's output changes. Fixed cost is the cost of inputs that do not vary as the firm's output changes.

   c. Fixed costs can be either avoidable or sunk. A firm will not incur an avoidable fixed cost if it decides to produce no output, but it cannot avoid a cost that is sunk.

2. **What do economic costs include? (LO1)**
   a. A firm's true economic costs of production include not only its out-of-pocket expenditures, but also the opportunity costs it incurs when it forgoes opportunities to use resources in their best alternative use.

b. When a firm owns some of the long-lived capital used in production, the true economic cost of its use is an opportunity cost. This cost equals the amount the firm could have received by renting the capital to someone else.

3. **Short-run cost—one variable input (LO1)**

a. In the short run, if a firm has just one variable input, we can find the firm's short-run variable cost curve by "flipping" the production function, plotting output on the horizontal axis and variable cost (the input price times the input level) on the vertical axis.

b. The short-run variable cost function can be determined mathematically by using the production function to solve for the amount of variable input needed at each level of output and multiplying by the input's price. The firm's total cost is equal to this variable cost plus its fixed cost.

4. **Long-run cost—cost minimization with two variable inputs (LO2)**

a. When a firm has more than one variable input, the least-cost production method for producing Q units is the point on the Q-unit isoquant that lies on the lowest possible isocost line, which is equivalent to satisfying the no-overlap rule.

b. If the least-cost production method is an interior solution, it must satisfy the tangency condition: the MRTS—the ratio of marginal products—equals the input price ratio.

c. If the least-cost input combination is a boundary solution, then the relationship between the MRTS and the input price ratio may instead satisfy an inequality condition.

d. If the firm's isoquants have a declining MRTS, then any interior input combination that satisfies the tangency condition (so that the ratio of marginal products equals the input price ratio) is a least-cost input combination.

e. The firm's output expansion path contains the least-cost input combinations at various levels of output at given input prices. The firm's cost function gives the cost of the input combinations along the firm's output expansion path.

5. **Average and marginal costs (LO3)**

a. Average cost is total cost divided by the number of units produced: $AC = C/Q$.

b. Marginal cost is the extra cost associated with the ΔQ marginal units of output, measured on a per-unit basis: $MC = [C(Q) - C(Q - \Delta Q)]/\Delta Q$.

c. When output is finely divisible, marginal cost at Q units of output equals the slope of the line drawn tangent to the cost curve at Q, while average cost equals the slope of the line from this point on the cost curve to the origin.

d. A firm's average cost curve is downward sloping where marginal cost is less than average cost, upward sloping where marginal cost is greater than average cost, and neither rising nor falling where marginal cost equals average cost. The marginal cost curve crosses the average cost curve from below at the efficient scale of production. The same is true of the relationship between marginal cost and average variable cost.

6. **Effects of input price changes (LO4)**

When the price of an input increases (decreases), the least-cost production method uses less (more) of that input, or remains unchanged.

7. **Short-run versus long-run costs (LO5)**

a. If a firm cannot adjust one of its inputs in the short run but can do so over the long run, its costs when its output level changes will be higher in the short run than in the long run.

b. The long-run average cost curve is the lower envelope of the firm's short-run average cost curves.

c. Starting at any initial output level, the firm's short-run marginal cost curve is steeper than its long-run marginal cost curve. It crosses the long-run marginal cost curve at the initial output level.

8. **Economies and diseconomies of scale (LO6)**

a. A firm enjoys economies of scale if its average cost decreases as the quantity produced increases. It suffers diseconomies of scale if its average cost increases as the quantity produced increases.

b. A firm whose technology has increasing returns to scale will enjoy economies of scale when input prices are unaffected by the firm's output level, while a firm with decreasing returns to scale will have diseconomies of scale.

*9. **Multiproduct firms and economies of scope (LO7)**

a. Most firms produce many products. One reason they do so is to take advantage of economies of scope, which arise when the cost of producing products together is lower than the cost of producing them in separate firms.

b. When firms experience diseconomies of scope, it is cheaper to produce different products in separate firms.

ADDITIONAL EXERCISES

Exercise 8.1: Economist Milton Friedman is famous for remarking that "There is no such thing as a free lunch." Interpret this comment in light of the discussion in Section 8.2. (LO1)

Exercise 8.2: Many resort hotels remain open in the off season, even though they appear to be losing money. Why would they do so? (LO1)

Exercise 8.3: Suppose Noah and Naomi's short-run weekly production function for garden benches is $F(L) = (3/2)L$, where L represents the number of hours of labour employed. The wage rate is $15 an hour. What is their short-run cost function? (LO1)

Exercise 8.4: Suppose Noah and Naomi's short-run weekly production function for garden benches is $F(L) = \min\{0, L - 2\}$, where L represents the number of hours of labour employed. The wage rate is $15 an hour. What is their short-run cost function? (LO1)

Exercise 8.5: "A production method must be efficient to be a least-cost method of producing Q units of output, but an efficient method need not be a least-cost method." True or false? Why? (LO1, 2)

Exercise 8.6: Johnson Tools produces hammers. It has signed a labour contract that guarantees workers a minimum of 30 hours per week of work. The contract also doubles the regular $20 per hour wage for overtime (more than 30 hours per week). Johnson's production technology uses only one variable input, labour. The company can produce two hammers per hour of employed labour. What is its variable cost function? Graph its variable cost curve. (LO1)

Exercise 8.7: Suppose university graduates earn $25 an hour and high school graduates earn $15 an hour. Suppose too that the marginal product of university graduates at Johnson Tools is five hammers per hour, while the marginal product of high school graduates is four hammers per hour (regardless of the number of each type of worker employed). What is the least-cost production method for producing 100 hammers in an eight-hour day? What if the marginal product of high school graduates were instead two hammers per hour? What is the critical difference in productivity (in percentage terms) at which the type of worker hired changes? (LO2)

Exercise 8.8: Suppose that the production function for Hannah and Sam's home painting business is $Q = F(L, K) = 10L^{0.2}K^{0.3}$. If the wage rate is $1500 per week and the cost of renting a unit of capital is $1000 per week, what is the least-cost input combination for painting 100 square metres each week? What is the total cost? (LO2)

Exercise 8.9: Suppose that XYZ Corporation's total wages are twice the company's total expenditure on capital. XYZ has a Cobb-Douglas production function that has constant returns to scale. What can you deduce about parameters α and β of this production function? (LO2)

Exercise 8.10: Suppose that in worked-out problem 8.5 (page 279) Noah and Naomi wanted to produce 200 garden

benches per week. What would be the best assignment of output to their two plants? (LO3)

Exercise 8.11: Suppose that in worked-out problem 8.5 (page 279), the cost function at plant 2 was $C_2 = 650Q_2 + 2(Q_2)^2$, and marginal cost at that plant was $MC_2 = 650 + 4Q_2$. What would be the best assignment of output between the two plants? (LO3)

Exercise 8.12: Noah and Naomi want to produce 100 garden benches per week in two production plants. The cost functions at the two plants are $C_1 = 600Q_1 - 3(Q_1)^2$ and $C_2 = 650Q_2 - 2(Q_2)^2$, and the corresponding marginal costs are $MC_1 = 600 - 6Q_1$ and $MC_2 = 650 - 4Q_2$. What is the best assignment of output between the two plants? (LO3)

Exercise 8.13: Consider again worked-out problem 8.2 (page 269). Let a unit of capital cost $1000 a week rather than $250, as illustrated in Figure 8.21. If desired output increased to 300, what would be the least-cost input combination? (LO4)

Exercise 8.14: Consider again worked-out problem 8.6 (page 288) but assume that a unit of capital costs $1000 per week and that Hannah and Sam are initially painting 200 square metres per week. What are their short-run and long-run cost functions? (LO5)

Exercise 8.15: Suppose that Hannah and Sam have the Cobb-Douglas production function $Q = F(L, K) = 10L^{0.25}K^{0.25}$. Both a worker and a unit of capital cost $1000 per week. If Hannah and Sam begin by painting 100 square metres per week, and if their capital is fixed in the short run but variable in the long run, what are their long-run and short-run cost functions? What are their long-run and short-run average cost functions for positive output levels? (LO5)

Exercise 8.16: Does a firm with the cost function $C(Q) = Q^2$ experience economies of scale, diseconomies of scale, or neither? (LO6)

Exercise 8.17: Provide a situation in which a firm exhibiting constant returns to scale can experience diseconomies of scale. (LO6)

Exercise 8.18: In Figure 8.26 the long run average cost curve reaches its minimum point at a unique level of output. Could the long run average cost curve have a horizontal section over a range of output levels? Explain. (LO5)

*Exercise 8.19 Many airlines operate a hub-and-spoke system in which passengers headed for different destinations fly into the hub on the same plane, then switch planes to reach their final destinations. How does this system reflect the presence of economies of scope? (LO7)

Profit Maximization

LEARNING OBJECTIVES

After reading this chapter, students should be able to

LOI Describe the relationship between a firm's profit-maximizing sales quantity and the firm's marginal revenue and marginal cost.

LO2 Demonstrate how price-taking firms should determine their profit-maximizing sales quantities.

LO3 Determine a price-taking firm's supply function.

LO4 Explain why price-taking firms usually respond to price changes more over the long run than they do over the short run.

LO5 Define producer surplus and describe its measurement.

LO6 Understand how supply decisions are made when the firm produces more than one good.

On June 29, 2007 Apple's iPhone first went on sale in the United States; it was introduced in Canada a little over a year later on July 11, 2008. In the first full quarter after its introduction, 1.1 million iPhones were sold worldwide. By the end of the fourth quarter of 2009 Apple had sold 26.4 million units worldwide and captured approximately 11 percent of the worldwide smartphone market. The smartphone market is dominated by only a few firms with Nokia and Research in Motion holding the number one and two positions respectively, just ahead of Apple in third place.

Accompanying the dramatic rise in market share in the smartphone market has been an equally remarkable fall in the iPhone's price. When the iPhone was first introduced in 2007 the price was $599 in the United States. Just two years later the price of the 8GB iPhone 3G had fallen to $99 in both Canada and the United States.

The pricing of the iPhone has not been without controversy. Within two months of the introduction of the iPhone the price of the 8GB model was reduced to $399 from $599. The public outcry that resulted from those buying the iPhone at the higher

Apple iPhone

price led Steve Jobs, the CEO of Apple, to take the unusual step of apologizing to those who purchased the phone at the higher price and offering them a $100 store credit. (In Application 9.2 we'll see what impact Apple's pricing strategy might have had on profits.). When Rogers, the exclusive provider of the iPhone in Canada, first revealed the pricing of its voice and data plans the outrage was sufficient to cause Rogers to offer its $100 data plan for $30 to those locking in for three years.

While it is not surprising that the falling price of the iPhone would be accompanied by an increase in market share, one might wonder whether the pricing strategy maximized Apple's profits on its iPhone sales. Certainly Apple's profits have never been higher. In the second quarter of 2009 Apple reported quarterly profits of $1.61 billion on revenues of $10.17 billion.

A firm that understands its technology and knows how to produce its output in the most economical way possible—the topics of Chapters 7 and 8—has taken the first steps toward maximizing its profit. But other decisions the firm faces also influence its profitability. In this chapter we'll discuss the most central of these decisions: how a firm chooses a product's price or sales quantity.

Here we'll introduce some general concepts and then focus on the special case of a firm that takes the price at which it can sell its product as given, as in the competitive markets we'll study in detail in Chapters 14 and 15 (and already discussed in Chapter 2). We'll consider cases in which firms are not price takers in Chapters 17–19 when we study monopoly and oligopoly.

In this chapter, we'll cover six topics:

1. *Profit-maximizing quantities and prices.* We'll explain that a manager who wants to maximize profit, the difference between revenue and cost, can equivalently think of her choice as one of finding the best price or of finding the best sales quantity.

2. *Marginal revenue, marginal cost, and profit maximization.* In Chapter 3, we learned how to use the concepts of marginal benefit and marginal cost to find a best choice. Here we'll apply those lessons to the problem of finding the price or sales quantity that maximizes the firm's profit.

3. *Supply decisions by price-taking firms.* In Chapters 14–16 we'll continue our study of competitive markets in which firms take the market price for their product as given. Here we'll apply lessons learned to show how price-taking firms should determine their profit-maximizing sales quantities.

4. *Short-run versus long-run supply by price-taking firms.* In Section 8.7 we discussed ways that a firm's cost function may differ over the short and long run. Those differences can affect the firm's short-run and long-run responses to a change in the price at which they can sell their output. We'll see why firms typically respond more over the long run than they do in the short run.

5. *Producer surplus.* We'll discuss a measure of a firm's profit that focuses on its avoidable costs and that can be measured in a very convenient way using demand and supply curves. We'll use this measure frequently in later chapters when discussing the effects of public policies.

*6. *Supply by multiproduct price-taking firms.* Most firms produce and sell more than one product. We'll discuss how a price-taking firm that sells more than one product can determine its profit-maximizing sales quantities. We'll also see how a change in the price of one product affects how much the firm sells of its other products.

9.1 PROFIT-MAXIMIZING QUANTITIES AND PRICES

A firm's **profit**, which we'll write as the Greek letter Π (pronounced "pie"), equals its revenue R less its cost C: that is, $\Pi = R - C$. The firm's profit maximization problem is to find the quantity or price that results in the largest possible profit.[1]

> A firm's **profit**, Π, is equal to its revenue R less its cost C: that is, $\Pi = R - C$.

Do firms really try to maximize their profits? Certainly there are some cases in which they don't. A family-owned business might employ a family member even if she is not the best candidate for the job. And as newspaper headlines show, sometimes a firm's managers seek to enrich themselves at the expense of the firm's shareholders. Nevertheless, the typical family business makes most of its decisions with an eye toward maximizing the family's income. Similarly, in large corporations, a number of mechanisms help to ensure that managers act primarily in the interest of shareholders. Those mechanisms include managerial incentives, corporate oversight, and the threat that an underperforming firm will be acquired and its managers replaced. Moreover, in very competitive industries, a firm that does not maximize profit will simply fail to survive. Despite the exceptions, economists have found the assumption that firms maximize their profit both useful and reasonably accurate.

Choosing Price versus Choosing Quantity

Before they attempt to sell a product, managers need to think about how many units they can sell and at what price.[2] This information is captured in the demand function and demand curve for the firm's product. As we saw in Chapter 2, a product's demand function states how many units buyers will demand at each price. It takes the form *Quantity demanded* = *D*(*Price*). Here we are implicitly holding fixed all of the factors other than price that might affect demand for the product—consumer tastes, consumer income, the prices of substitutes, et cetera.

Figure 9.1 shows a typical demand curve, with the price P measured on the vertical axis and the quantity demanded, Q, measured on the horizontal axis. It shows how many units the firm will sell at each price. The lower the price, the more units it sells. Notice, however, that the manager could equally well think in terms of how many units she wants to sell. In that case, reading the demand curve in reverse tells her the price she needs to charge, $P(Q)$, to sell quantity Q (see Figure 9.1). This relationship is known as the product's **inverse demand function**, a function of the form *Price* = *P* (*Quantity demanded*).

> The **inverse demand function** for a firm's product describes how much the firm must charge to sell any given quantity of its product. It takes the form *Price* = *P*(*Quantity demanded*).

---

[1] In this chapter we'll focus on pricing and output decisions. For decisions that have long-run effects, such as advertising or research and development, the firm will want to make a choice that maximizes its profit over time. We'll explain how to measure long-run profit in Chapter 10.

[2] In most of this chapter, we'll focus for simplicity on firms that sell a single product. In Section 9.6, we'll extend the analysis to a firm that sells many products.

Figure 9.1

The Demand Curve for a Firm's Product. The demand for the firm's product at any price P is given by the firm's demand curve, shown here. Alternatively, we can use the demand curve to determine the price, $P(Q)$, the firm must charge to sell a given quantity Q.

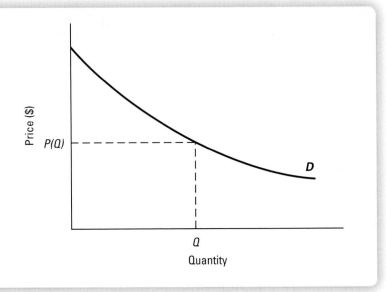

WORKED-OUT PROBLEM   9.1

The Problem   The weekly demand for Noah and Naomi's garden benches is described by the demand function $Q^d = D(P) = 200 - P$. What price must Noah and Naomi charge if they want to sell 50 garden benches per week? What is Noah and Naomi's inverse demand function?

The Solution   We want to determine the price at which $Q^d = 50$. That is, we want to solve for P such that

$$200 - P = 50$$

The solution is $P = 150$. More generally, we can find the inverse demand function $P(Q)$ by solving the formula

$$200 - P = Q$$

for P, which gives us

$$P(Q) = 200 - Q$$

IN-TEXT EXERCISE 9.1   Suppose the weekly demand for Noah and Naomi's garden benches is $Q^d = D(P) = 450 - 2P$. What price must they charge if they want to sell 100 benches per week? If they want to sell 150 benches per week? What is Noah and Naomi's inverse demand function?

Maximizing Profit

Let's think about the firm's choice in terms of the quantity it sells. Recall that the firm's profit, Π, is equal to its revenue R less its total costs C; that is, $\Pi = R - C$. (In what follows, where it creates no confusion, we will just refer to the firm's total costs as its costs.)

Consider first the firm's revenue. If the firm wants to sell Q units, it must charge price $P(Q)$. Its revenue R when it sells Q units is therefore

$$R = P(Q) \times Q$$

To earn the greatest possible profit, the firm should choose the sales quantity that maximizes revenue less cost, where both revenue and cost depend on how much the firm decides to sell.

$$\Pi = R(Q) - C(Q)$$

$$= [P(Q) \times Q] - C(Q)$$

This problem is another example of finding a best choice by balancing benefits and costs, a topic we studied in Chapter 3. The *benefit* of selling quantity Q is the firm's revenue $R(Q) = P(Q) \times Q$. The *cost* of selling quantity Q is the firm's cost of production $C(Q)$.

Example 9.1

The Profit-Maximizing Price of Garden Benches

Suppose Noah and Naomi can produce up to 100 garden benches per week in batches of 10. Of all their possible production quantities (0, 10, 20, et cetera), which will yield the highest profit? What price should they charge?

To start, we need to know the weekly demand function for Noah and Naomi's garden benches. Let's suppose that it is $Q^d = D(P) = 200 - P$. Worked-out problem 9.1 shows that their inverse demand function is $P(Q) = 200 - Q$. That is, to sell Q garden benches per week, Noah and Naomi need to set their price equal to $200 - Q$.

The second thing we need to know is Noah and Naomi's weekly cost function for producing garden benches. Let's suppose that it is $C(Q) = Q^2$.

Table 9.1 contains the information we need to find Noah and Naomi's best choice. The first column lists their possible sales quantities. The second column records the price Noah

Table 9.1
Profits from Garden Bench Sales

	Sales Quantity	Price (per Unit)	Revenue	Cost	Profit
	0	$200	$0	$0	$0
	10	190	1,900	100	1,800
	20	180	3,600	400	3,200
	30	170	5,100	900	4,200
	40	160	6,400	1,600	4,800
Best choice ⟶	(50)	150	7,500	2,500	(5,000)
	60	140	8,400	3,600	4,800
	70	130	9,100	4,900	4,200
	80	120	9,600	6,400	3,200
	90	110	9,900	8,100	1,800
	100	100	10,000	10,000	0

and Naomi must charge to sell each possible quantity Q of garden benches. The third column shows the revenue R from each choice, which is the product of columns 1 and 2. The fourth column gives the cost C of each choice. Finally, the fifth column shows the profit from each choice, equal to the revenue (column 3) minus the cost (column 4). Noah and Naomi's profit-maximizing choice is to sell 50 garden benches per week at a price of $150, which gives them a profit of $5000 per week.

Figure 9.2(a) shows this solution graphically. The revenue at each possible quantity is plotted in blue and the cost in red. The best choice is 50 benches per week, at which point the vertical distance between the blue revenue points and the red cost points is greatest.

When output is finely divisible, we can find a firm's profit-maximizing sales quantity by graphing its revenue and cost curves. Let's now suppose that Noah and Naomi's garden bench output is finely divisible. Figure 9.2(b) shows Noah and Naomi's revenue and cost curves. The profit-maximizing quantity, $Q = 50$, is located where the vertical distance between the revenue and cost curves is greatest; their profit is $5000 per week.

Figure 9.2

The Profit-Maximizing Sales Quantity of Garden Benches. Noah and Naomi's profit is maximized when they sell 50 garden benches per week, the quantity at which the vertical distance between their revenue (in blue) and their cost (in red) is greatest. At this sales quantity, their profit is $5000 per week. Figure (a) shows the case where benches must be produced in batches of 10. Figure (b) shows the case where their output is finely divisible.

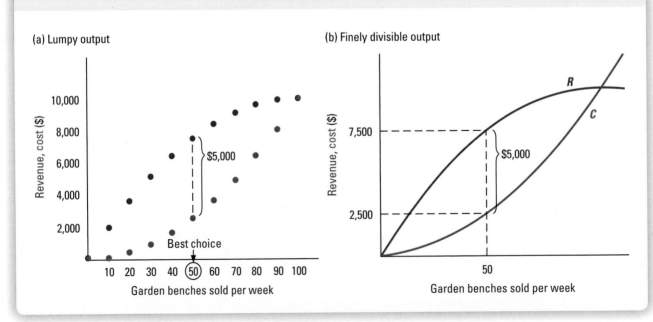

Application 9.1

A Textbook-Pricing Example

Setting the right price for a textbook can have an important effect on the profits it generates. But who sets the price, the authors or the publisher, and does the answer to this question affect the price you pay?

Typically, the publisher of a book sets the price, not the author or authors (that is, not us!). This fact can have an important effect on the book's price. An author's income from a book's sales is usually a fixed percentage of the revenue. For example, an author might receive 15 percent of revenue so that her profit is $(0.15)R$. In contrast, the publisher's profit from a book's sales is the remaining revenue less the book's production costs, all of which are borne by the publisher. So if the author gets $(0.15)R$, the publisher's profit is $(0.85)R - C$.

This difference in earnings means that the publisher and the author will prefer different prices. Figure 9.3 illustrates the difference. An author, who bears none of the production costs,

"I don't have a title yet, or even a subject. All I have is the price: twenty-three ninety-five in hardcover."

wants to set a price (or, equivalently, a sales quantity) that maximizes the revenue R. Thus, the author's best sales quantity is Q_A, the quantity at which the dark blue revenue curve is highest. The publisher's revenue curve, $(0.85)R$, is shown in light blue, and the publisher's cost curve in red. The publisher's profit-maximizing sales quantity, Q_P, is the quantity at which the distance between those two curves is greatest.[3]

Note that Q_P, the publisher's profit-maximizing quantity, is less than Q_A, the author's profit-maximizing quantity. Thus, the author wants to set a lower price than the publisher (to sell the higher quantity). Intuitively, the author finds selling additional books a more attractive proposition than the publisher does, because the author doesn't bear the cost of producing those extra books.[4] In fact, it is common for authors to urge their publishers to set a lower price.

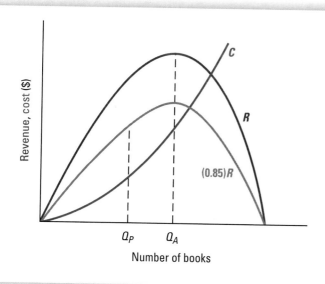

Figure 9.3

The Profit-Maximizing Sales Quantity for a Textbook's Author versus the Textbook's Publisher. If a textbook author receives 15 percent of revenue, $(0.15)R$, her profit is maximized when Q_A books are sold. The textbook's publisher receives the remainder of revenue and pays all costs, earning the profit $(0.85)R - C$. The publisher's profit is therefore maximized at Q_P books, which is less than Q_A. Thus, the publisher wants to charge a higher price for the book than does the author.

---

[3]Figure 9.3 is similar to Figures 3.2(c) and Figure 3.8 in Chapter 3, where the best choice was found by finding the activity level that maximized the vertical distance between the total benefit and total cost curves. The total revenue from textbook sales is the total benefit to the publisher, and profits are the net benefits.

[4]Authors also prefer a lower price because they usually care about how many people read their books. The publisher, in contrast, cares mainly about profit.

9.2 MARGINAL REVENUE, MARGINAL COST, AND PROFIT MAXIMIZATION

In Section 3.2, we saw how marginal benefit must equal marginal cost at a decision maker's best choice whenever small increases and decreases in her action are possible. We can apply the same ideas to the firm's profit maximization problem.

Marginal Revenue

Here the benefit is revenue, so the firm's marginal benefit is its marginal revenue, denoted MR. The firm's **marginal revenue** captures the additional revenue it gets from the marginal units it sells (the smallest possible increment ΔQ in sales quantity), measured on a per unit basis. So if the firm is selling Q units of its product, its marginal revenue is

A firm's **marginal revenue** at Q units equals the extra revenue produced by the ΔQ marginal units sold, measured on a per unit basis.

$$MR = \frac{\Delta R}{\Delta Q} = \frac{R(Q) - R(Q - \Delta Q)}{\Delta Q}$$

Table 9.2 shows the quantity, price, revenue, and marginal revenue for Noah and Naomi's business, whose revenues and costs were shown in Table 9.1. Arrows indicate the change in revenue captured with each change in quantity (note that here $\Delta Q = 10$).

Notice in Table 9.2 that Noah and Naomi's marginal revenue is equal to the price at $Q = 10$ but is less than the price at all sales quantities above 10. Why? Think about how much revenue their last ΔQ units contribute. The increase in their sales quantity from $Q - \Delta Q$ to Q changes their revenue in two ways. The first is obvious: they sell ΔQ additional units, each at a price of $P(Q)$. We'll call this the *output expansion effect*. The second is more subtle: the increase in their sales quantity requires that they lower their price from $P(Q - \Delta Q)$ to $P(Q)$, which reduces the revenue they earn from the $Q - \Delta Q$ units that are *not* marginal, known as **inframarginal units**. This is the *price reduction effect*.

*Optional **Marginal revenue**, MR, can be found using calculus by differentiating the revenue function with respect to output.

$$MR = \frac{dR}{dQ} = \frac{dP(Q)Q}{dQ} = P(Q) + \frac{dP(Q)}{dQ}Q$$

The **inframarginal units** are the units the firm sells other than the ΔQ marginal units.

Table 9.2
Revenue and Marginal Revenue from Garden Bench Sales

Sales Quantity	Price (per Unit)	Revenue	Marginal Revenue (per Unit)
0	$200	$0	—
10	190	1,900	$190
20	180	3,600	170
30	170	5,100	150
40	160	6,400	130
50	150	7,500	110
60	140	8,400	90
70	130	9,100	70
80	120	9,600	50
90	110	9,900	30
100	100	10,000	10

Figure 9.4

The Relationship between Marginal Revenue and Price. When the firm expands its sales from $Q - \Delta Q$ to Q, it earns $P(Q) \times \Delta Q$ in revenue on the extra units it sells, equal to the green-shaded rectangle in both figures. Were that the only change in its revenue, as in figure (a), its marginal revenue—the extra revenue earned per marginal unit sold—would exactly equal the price. However, when the demand curve is downward-sloping, the firm also suffers a loss in revenue on the $Q - \Delta Q$ inframarginal units because it must lower its price by the amount $P(Q - \Delta Q) - P(Q)$ to sell the extra units. This revenue loss equals the yellow-shaded rectangle in figure (b). The firm's marginal revenue in that case is less than the price $P(Q)$.

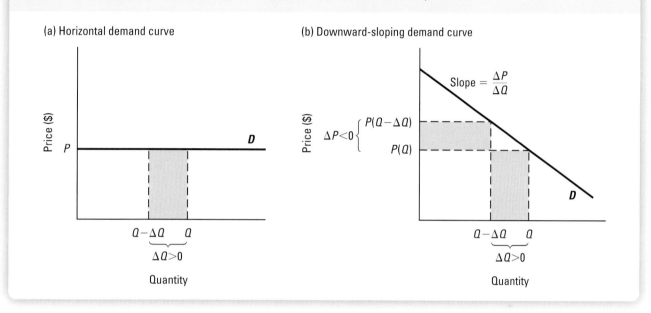

(a) Horizontal demand curve   (b) Downward-sloping demand curve

To explore these two effects further, consider first the case in which the firm's demand curve is horizontal at price P, illustrated in Figure 9.4(a). In that case, the firm can sell as much as it wants at the price P, but nothing at any higher price. Such a firm is called a **price taker**. (A firm in a perfectly competitive market is a price taker since it can sell as much as it wants at the market price, but nothing at any higher price. Examples of price takers include the producers of agricultural products such as wheat, corn, and soybeans.) In this case, only the output expansion effect is present, because increasing the firm's sales quantity does not require a reduction in price. The firm's extra revenue is the area of the green-shaded rectangle in the figure (with a height of P and a width of ΔQ) equal to $P \times \Delta Q$. So, dividing that revenue change by ΔQ, marginal revenue is exactly P per unit.

> A firm is a **price taker** when it can sell as much as it wants at some given price P, but nothing at any higher price.

Figure 9.4(b) shows a case in which demand is downward sloping. The extra ΔQ sales at price $P(Q)$ contribute additional revenue of $P(Q) \times \Delta Q$, equal to the area of the green-shaded rectangle in the figure. That's the output expansion effect. To sell the ΔQ marginal units, Noah and Naomi must reduce their price from $P(Q - \Delta Q)$ to $P(Q)$. They lose the difference, $P \Delta Q - (Q) - P(Q)$, on each inframarginal unit. Notice that this price difference equals the height of the yellow rectangle in Figure 9.4(b). Since there are $Q - \Delta Q$ inframarginal units (the width of the yellow rectangle), Noah and Naomi's revenue falls by $[P(Q - \Delta Q) - P(Q)](Q - \Delta Q)$, the area of the yellow rectangle. This is the price reduction effect. The overall change in revenue equals the green-shaded area less the yellow-shaded area, which together is less than $P(Q) \times \Delta Q$. Dividing by ΔQ, marginal revenue is less than $P(Q)$.

Figure 9.5

Marginal Revenue and Demand Curves. Figure (a) shows that the marginal revenue curve coincides with the demand curve when the demand curve is horizontal. With a downward-sloping demand curve, as in figure (b), the marginal revenue curve lies below the demand curve at all positive sales quantities, and coincides with it at a quantity of zero.

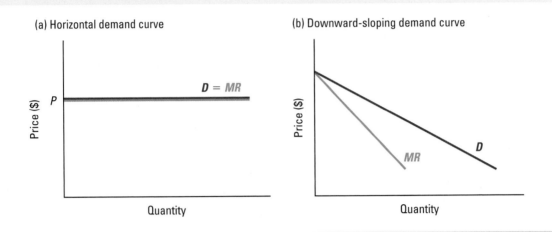

(a) Horizontal demand curve

$D = MR$

Price ($)

P

Quantity

(b) Downward-sloping demand curve

Price ($)

MR

D

Quantity

Notice also that when sales are very small, the second effect—the revenue loss on the inframarginal units—will be small. Indeed, when the firm sells its first ΔQ units, there are no inframarginal units, so marginal revenue equals the price.

Figure 9.5 shows the relationship between marginal revenue and price when output is finely divisible. The same principles hold (the logic above did not depend on whether output is finely divisible). Figure 9.5(a) shows the case of a firm that is a price taker—its demand curve is horizontal. In that case, the marginal revenue and demand curves coincide since MR equals the price P. Figure 9.5(b) shows the case of a downward-sloping demand curve. In that case, marginal revenue equals the price when sales (and, hence, inframarginal units) are zero, and is less than the price at every positive sales quantity.

Application 9.2

Apple iPhone Profits

On September 5, 2007 executives at Apple made a bold move, announcing a reduction in the price of the 8GB iPhone of $200. The price drop outraged those who had purchased the iPhone for $599 in the weeks after its introduction on June 29. The announcement sent shock waves through the smartphone industry. The reaction in the stock market was swift and punishing: Apple's stock price opened at $144.97 the day of the announcement and closed at $136.76, erasing billions in shareholder value.

Was the price reduction a good idea for Apple? That depends on two things: (1) how much iPhone sales would increase after the price reduction, and (2) how much it would cost Apple to produce the extra phones. Let's denote iPhone sales before the price reduction as Q_B, and sales afterward as Q_A. The price reduction would raise profit if

$$(399)Q_A - C(Q_A) > (599)Q_B - C(Q_B)$$

Put another way, overall profit would increase if the profit earned on the extra sales exceeded the revenue lost on existing sales.

$$(399)(Q_A - Q_B) - [C(Q_A) - C(Q_B)] > (200)Q_B$$

Without access to Apple's proprietary information, we cannot know the cost of the extra units. Lets assume that the costs of producing an 8GB iPhone in 2007 was $300.[5] If the extra iPhones Apple sold as a result of the price reduction each cost $300 to produce, so that $C(Q_A) - C(Q_B) = 300[Q_A - Q_B]$, then the price reduction would be a good idea if

$$(99)(Q_A - Q_B) > (200)Q_B$$

Dividing by Q_B and rearranging terms, this expression tells us that the price reduction would raise profit if

$$\frac{Q_A - Q_B}{Q_B} > \frac{200}{99} \approx 2$$

That is, if we are using the correct cost for the extra units, then the $200 price reduction would increase profit if iPhone sales increased by a factor of 2 or more.

Sales of iPhones did increase after the price reduction as did Apple's market share. In the days following the price reduction sales increase from 9000 to 27,000 units per day (a factor of 3). For the entire third quarter of 2007 iPhone sales were 1.12 million worldwide and in the fourth quarter of 2007 sales reached 2.32 million. In the fourth quarter of 2008 iPhone sales peaked at 6.89 million units.[6] The market share of the iPhone increased from approximately 21 percent in the third quarter of 2007, when the price reduction took place, to 30 percent in the fourth quarter of 2008.[7]

The Profit-Maximizing Sales Quantity

In Section 3.2 (and the appendix to Chapter 3), we saw that a best choice must satisfy the No Marginal Improvement Principle, which says that no marginal increase or decrease in the choice can produce an increase in net benefit. That is, when actions are finely divisible, marginal benefit (*MB*) equals marginal cost (*MC*) at an interior best choice (one at which the action can be slightly increased and slightly decreased). If $MB > MC$, then it would be better to increase the action a little bit because the extra benefit would be larger than the extra cost. If, instead, $MB < MC$, then it would be better to slightly decrease the action because the cost savings would be larger than the lost benefits.

This fact helped us to devise a convenient method for finding a best choice. This method had two steps:

Step 1: Identify any interior actions at which $MB = MC$. If more than one interior action satisfies $MB = MC$, determine which produces the highest net benefit.

Step 2: Compare the net benefits at any boundary actions to the net benefit at the best interior action. The best choice is the action with the highest net benefit.

---

[5]The pricing decision for Apple is more complicated than our simple analysis, as Apple sells its iPhone through mobile phone vendors such as Rogers in Canada and AT&T in the United States. Vendors subsidize the handsets by paying Apple an unknown amount for the iPhones and then selling the iPhone to customers who pay a monthly fee for use. The estimated iPhone cost includes all variable production costs, taxes, and retail mark-ups.

[6]We are omitting some other factors as well. First, Apple introduced other iPhone models, and introduced the iPhone in other countries, and presumably production costs continued to fall. We have also assumed that, without the price reduction, iPhone sales would have remained consistent in the third quarter of 2007.

[7]Another complication in trying to discover the impact on profit of the price reduction is that Apple releases sales figures on a quarterly basis and the price reduction happened with most of the last month of the quarter remaining.

We can apply the same principles here to the firm's profit maximization problem by comparing marginal revenue and marginal cost. For the firm's profit maximization problem, any positive sales quantity is interior. So, if the firm's profit-maximizing sales quantity is positive, marginal revenue equals marginal cost at that quantity. For the second step, the only possible boundary choice involves selling nothing (shutting down). The two-step procedure becomes:

Finding the Profit-Maximizing Sales Quantity Using Marginal Revenue and Marginal Cost

Step 1: Quantity rule. Identify any positive sales quantities at which $MR = MC$. If more than one positive sales quantity satisfies $MR = MC$, determine which one is best (which produces the highest profit).

Step 2: Shut-down rule. Check whether the most profitable positive sales quantity from step 1 results in greater profit than shutting down. If it does, that is the profit-maximizing choice. If not, then selling nothing is the best option. If they are the same, then either choice maximizes profit.

Optional If you have taken calculus the profit maximizing sales quantity rule is equivalent to the following: If an interior sales quantity Q satisfies both

$$\frac{d\Pi}{dQ} = \Pi'(Q) = \frac{dR(Q)}{dQ} - \frac{dC(Q)}{dQ} = 0,$$

and $\frac{d^2\Pi}{dQ^2} = \Pi''(Q) < 0$ then Q is the profit maximizing sales quantity. Note that the first condition when rearranged yields $\frac{dR(Q)}{dQ} = \frac{dC(Q)}{dQ}$

or $MR = MC$.

In the remainder of this chapter, we'll use this procedure to study profit maximization by firms that are price takers. In Chapters 17–19 we'll use it again to look at the behaviour of firms that face downward-sloping demand curves.

9.3 SUPPLY DECISIONS BY PRICE-TAKING FIRMS

The rest of this chapter is devoted to the supply decisions of firms that are price takers. Recall that these are firms that can sell as much as they want at some price P, but nothing at any higher price. A firm that is a price taker faces a perfectly horizontal demand curve for its product as in Figures 9.4(a) and 9.5(a). Firms in perfectly competitive markets, which we examined briefly in Chapter 2 and will study further in Chapters 14–16, are price takers.

The methods we'll discuss in this section apply for any cost function the firm may have. As a result, they apply whether we are considering the short run or the long run. In Section 9.4, we'll examine their implications for differences in a firm's behaviour in the short run and long run.

The Profit-Maximizing Sales Quantity of a Price-Taking Firm

In Section 9.2 we saw that profit maximization means selling the quantity at which marginal revenue equals marginal cost if that quantity yields a larger profit than shutting down, and selling nothing otherwise. Here, we'll apply this general principle to the case of a price-taking firm.

When a firm is a price taker, changes in its sales quantity have no effect on the price P it can charge. In Section 9.2, we saw that this implies that a price-taking firm's marginal revenue (MR) equals the price of its output. As a result, the firm's price must equal its marginal cost at its profit-maximizing sales quantity (also called its profit-maximizing output level): that is, since $MR = MC$ at a firm's profit-maximizing quantity, and since

$MR = P$ for a price-taking firm, we must have $P = MC$. Moreover, the two-step procedure for finding the firm's profit-maximizing sales quantity that we discussed in Section 9.2 can be adapted as follows:

Finding the Profit-Maximizing Sales Quantity (or Output Level) for a Price-Taking Firm

Step 1: Quantity rule. Identify any positive sales quantities at which $P = MC$. If more than one positive sales quantity satisfies $P = MC$, determine which one is best (which produces the highest profit).

Step 2: Shut-down rule. Determine if the most profitable positive sales quantity from step 1 results in greater profit than shutting down. If it does, that is the profit-maximizing choice. If it does not, then selling nothing is the best option. If they are the same, then either choice maximizes profit.

If a firm has no sunk fixed costs, then the profit from shutting down is zero. The shut-down rule then amounts to determining if profit is non-negative at the best positive sales quantity ($PQ - C \geq 0$) or, equivalently, if the price is at least as large as the firm's average cost ($P \geq AC$).

Figure 9.6 illustrates this procedure. The firm in Figure 9.6(a) faces a perfectly horizontal demand curve for its product at price P. Applying the quantity rule, the best positive

Figure 9.6

The Profit-Maximizing Sales Level for a Price-Taking Firm. Figure (a) illustrates the quantity rule: The most profitable positive sales quantity is the quantity Q^* at which price equals marginal cost. Figure (b) illustrates the shut-down rule: Since the profit at sales quantity Q^* is positive (the green-shaded area), selling quantity Q^* is better than shutting down. Note that the price is greater than average cost at quantity Q^*.

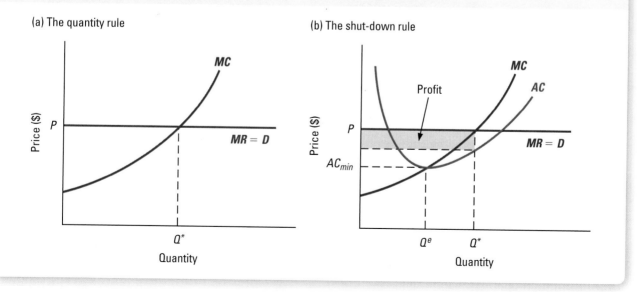

sales quantity is Q^*, the quantity at which marginal cost equals the price P. Figure 9.6(b) adds the firm's average cost curve to illustrate the shut-down rule. Since the firm's average cost curve is below the price P at Q^*, the firm's profit from selling Q^* units is positive and equals the area of the green-shaded rectangle, which is $(P - AC)Q^*$. (Notice that $(P - AC)Q^* = [P - (C/Q^*)]Q^* = PQ^* - C$, which is the firm's profit.) The firm is better off selling Q^* units than it would be if it shut down.

In fact, for a price-taking firm without sunk fixed costs, the shut-down rule takes a particularly simple form. Let's use AC_{min} to stand for the firm's average cost at its efficient scale Q^e—the lowest point on its average cost curve [see Figure 9.6(b)]. If the price P exceeds AC_{min}, then the firm could make a positive profit by selling Q^e units. Its profit at its best sales quantity is therefore surely positive. On the other hand, if P is less than AC_{min} then AC is greater than the price at every possible sales quantity. The firm can't make a positive profit in that case. So an equivalent way to state the shut-down rule for a price-taking firm without sunk fixed costs is:

> **The Shut-Down Rule without Sunk Fixed Costs**   If P exceeds AC_{min}, the best positive sales quantity maximizes profit. If P is less than AC_{min}, shutting down maximizes profit. If P equals AC_{min}, then both the best positive sales quantity and shutting down yield zero profit, which is the best the firm can do.

What if the firm does have sunk fixed costs, so that its profit, should it shut down, is negative (equal to those sunk costs)? Since, as we discussed in Section 3.3, the level of sunk fixed costs doesn't affect a decision maker's best choice (sunk fixed costs are "water under the bridge") we can just ignore them in calculating costs and proceed exactly as above. This amounts to comparing the price P not to average cost in making the shut-down decision but to average cost excluding any fixed sunk costs—that is, to *average avoidable cost*.[8]

Worked-out problem 9.2 shows how to solve for a price-taking firm's profit-maximizing sales quantity using algebra.

WORKED-OUT PROBLEM   9.2

The Problem   Dan loves pizza. His firm, Dan's Pizza Company, makes frozen pizzas. The market price of a pizza is $10, and Dan is a price taker. His daily cost of making pizzas is $C(Q) = 5Q + (Q^2/80)$, and his marginal cost is $MC = 5 + (Q/40)$. How many pizzas should Dan sell each day? What if he also has an avoidable fixed cost of $845 per day? What if the $845 fixed cost were sunk rather than avoidable?

The Solution   Applying the quantity rule, Dan's best positive sales quantity solves the formula $P = MC$, or

$$10 = 5 + \frac{Q}{40}$$

---

[8]Avoidable cost equals variable cost plus avoidable fixed cost. Average avoidable cost is this amount divided by the quantity Q. There is also another way to determine if comparing the price to average avoidable cost is the right comparison. The firm wants to operate provided that its profit is no less than its profit if it shuts down: Profit $\geq -$ (Sunk Cost). Since profit equals $(PQ -$ Avoidable Cost $-$ Sunk Cost), adding sunk costs to both sides of the inequality tells us that this is equivalent to saying that the firm wants to operate if $PQ -$ Avoidable Cost ≥ 0. This is equivalent to saying that $P \geq$ Average Avoidable Cost.

The solution is $Q = 200$. Now let's consider the shut-down rule. We can verify that the profit from producing 200 pizzas per day is positive in several ways: (a) by directly calculating that the profit is $\Pi = (10 \times 200) - (5 \times 200) - (200^2/80) = \$500$; (b) by observing that average cost when $Q = 200$ [\$7.50 per pizza, since $AC(Q) = 5 + (Q/80)$] is less than the price (\$10); or (c) by observing that the price (\$10) is greater than AC_{min} (\$5). (To find AC_{min}, note that Dan's average cost $AC(Q) = 5 + (Q/80)$ increases as his output increases so it is lowest (approaching \$5) when his output is very close to zero.)

If Dan also has an avoidable fixed cost of \$845 per day, his profit at $Q = 200$ would be $-\$345$, and the shut-down rule would tell us that he should stop selling frozen pizzas altogether. [Alternatively, we could see that the price (\$10) is now less than the average cost at 200 pizzas, which is \$11.73, rounded to the nearest penny. Note that once avoidable fixed costs are accounted for, average costs are given by $AC(Q) = (845/Q) + 5 + (Q/80)$].

If the fixed cost of \$845 were sunk, his profit at $Q = 200$ would still be $-\$345$. However, a $-\$345$ profit would be greater than his profit of $-\$845$ if he stopped selling pizzas altogether. By selling pizzas he is able to cover all of his avoidable variable costs of production and all but \$345 of his sunk fixed costs. In Section 9.4 the distinction between average costs and average avoidable costs when there are sunk fixed costs is discussed further.

IN-TEXT EXERCISE 9.2   **Suppose the price of a pizza rises to \$15. What is Dan's profit-maximizing sales quantity? What if he also has an avoidable fixed cost of \$750?**

The Supply Function of a Price-Taking Firm

The **supply function** of a price-taking firm tells us how much the firm wants to sell at each possible price P. It is a function of the form *Quantity Supplied = S(Price)*. To find a firm's supply function, we can apply the quantity and shut-down rules. At each price above the lowest level of (avoidable) average cost, AC_{min}, the firm's profit-maximizing quantity is positive and equates price with marginal cost. At each price below the lowest level of average cost, AC_{min}, the firm supplies nothing. When the price exactly equals AC_{min}, the firm is indifferent between producing nothing and producing at its efficient scale Q^e, the quantity at which its average cost is lowest, if that is different from zero.

Figure 9.7 shows two examples of a price-taking firm's supply curve. In Figure 9.7(a), average cost increases as the firm's output rises, so AC is smallest at $Q = 0$ and marginal cost is everywhere above average cost. In Figure 9.7(b), average cost first falls and then rises, so the firm's efficient scale Q^e is positive. In both cases, when the price exceeds AC_{min}, the firm's supply curve (shown in green) coincides with its marginal cost curve. For example, at the price P' (shown in both figures), the firm supplies the quantity $S(P')$. At prices below AC_{min}, the firm supplies nothing. (Whenever the part of a firm's supply curve that coincides with its marginal cost curve hits the vertical axis, as in Figure 9.7(a), we won't draw the portion of the supply curve below that point. Supply is zero for all lower prices. However, whenever a firm's supply jumps upward when the price reaches AC_{min}, as in Figure 9.7(b), we will draw the portion of the supply curve that lies along the vertical axis, indicating zero supply, to avoid any confusion.) Notice also that in Figure 9.7(b), the firm is willing to supply either zero or Q^e when the price equals AC_{min}.

> The **supply function** of a price-taking firm tells us how much the firm wants to sell at each possible price P. It is a function of the form *Quantity Supplied = S(Price)*.

Figure 9.7

The Supply Curve of a Price-Taking Firm. Figures (a) and (b) show the supply curve of a price-taking firm when the firm's efficient scale of production Q^e—the quantity at which average cost is smallest—is zero in figure (a), and positive in figure (b). In each case, the supply curve coincides with the firm's marginal cost curve at prices above the lowest level of average cost, AC_{min}, and involves zero supply at prices below the minimum average cost.

(a) Average cost is lowest at zero quantity

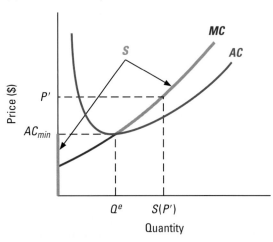

(b) Efficient scale is positive

Worked-out problem 9.3 shows how to find a firm's supply function using algebra.

The Problem   Recall Dan's Pizza Company from worked-out problem 9.2 on page 308. What is Dan's supply function if he has no avoidable fixed cost? What if his avoidable fixed cost is $845 per day?

The Solution   Using the same logic as in the solution to worked-out problem 9.2, the best positive sales quantity Q when the price is P sets price equal to marginal cost, so that

$$P = 5 + \frac{Q}{40}$$

Solving this expression for Q, we find that

$$Q = 40P - 200$$

Recall that when Dan has no avoidable fixed cost, $AC_{min} = \$5$. So using the shutdown rule, Dan's supply function is

$$S(P) = \begin{cases} 40P - 200 \text{ if } P \geq 5 \\ 0 \text{ if } P \leq 5 \end{cases}$$

Figure 9.8(a) shows this supply curve.

When we add an avoidable fixed cost of $845 per day, the implications of the quantity rule do not change (the avoidable fixed cost changes neither marginal revenue nor marginal cost). However, the desirability of staying in business does change, so we need to determine the new level of AC_{min}. Let's first find the new efficient scale of production by determining the output level at which marginal cost equals average cost. It is the quantity Q^e at which

$$MC = 5 + \frac{Q^e}{40} = \frac{845}{Q^e} + 5 + \frac{Q^e}{80} = AC$$

Solving, we find that $Q^e = 260$. Substituting this quantity into the expression for average cost tells us that

$$AC_{min} = \frac{845}{260} + 5 + \frac{260}{80} = \$11.50$$

So Dan's supply function is now

$$S(P) = \begin{cases} 40P - 200 \text{ if } P \geq 11.50 \\ 0 \text{ if } P \leq 11.50 \end{cases}$$

Figure 9.8(b) shows this supply curve.

IN-TEXT EXERCISE 9.3   **Consider again Dan's Pizza Company from worked-out problem 9.2 on page 308. What is Dan's supply function if he has a daily variable cost of $VC = Q^2/2$, a marginal cost of $MC = Q$, and an avoidable fixed cost of $50 per day?**

Figure 9.8

Dan's Supply Curves. Figure (a) shows Dan's supply curve when he has no avoidable fixed cost. Figure (b) shows Dan's supply curve with an avoidable fixed cost of $845 per day.

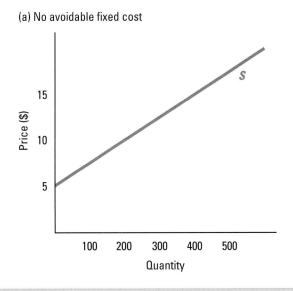

(a) No avoidable fixed cost

(b) Avoidable fixed cost of $845 per day

The Law of Supply

You may have noticed that in all the supply functions we've derived, a competitive firm's sales quantity either increases or remains unchanged when the market price rises. That is not an accident. The **Law of Supply** says that is the way things always work. Indeed, unlike the Law of Demand for consumers (which, as we saw in Chapter 6, need not hold if the good is inferior and income effects are sufficiently large) the Law of Supply always holds for price-taking firms.

To see why, look at Figure 9.9. There we've drawn a price-taking firm's revenue curve at the initial price $\overline{P}$, $R(Q) = \overline{P} - Q$, in dark blue. It's a straight line with a slope of $\overline{P}$ that runs through the origin. The firm's cost function is shown in red. We've deliberately drawn it with a fixed cost (total cost jumps from \$0 to a positive number when the firm produces a very small amount) and an odd shape to emphasize that the Law of Supply holds for *any* cost function. The profit-maximizing sales quantity at price $\overline{P}$ is Q^*, where the vertical distance between the revenue and cost curves is greatest (and the slopes of the revenue and cost curves are equal since $MR = MC$).

Now suppose the price rises to $\hat{P}$, shifting the firm's revenue curve to $R(Q) = \hat{P}Q$, the light blue line running through the origin. The firm's revenue rises at each sales level. The size of the increase is given by the length of the arrows pointing from the old revenue curve to the new one. Notice that the arrows become longer as we move from left to right, so that the increase in revenue at Q^* is greater than the increase in revenue at any quantity below Q^*. Since, before the price increase, selling Q^* units was more profitable than selling any smaller number of units, it must still be better after the price increase. This analysis implies that a competitive firm's profit-maximizing sales quantity *cannot decrease* when the market price increases. (In fact, it will usually increase. For example, in Figure 9.9, the new quantity that maximizes the distance between the revenue and cost curves lies to the right of Q^*.)

Figure 9.9

The Law of Supply. This figure shows why the Law of Supply, which says that a price-taking firm never decreases its supply when the market price rises, holds. Quantity Q^* maximizes the distance between the firm's revenue and cost curves at price $\overline{P}$. When the market price rises to $\hat{P}$, revenue rises more at quantity Q^* than at any smaller quantity. As a result, since quantity Q^* was better than any smaller quantity before the price increase, it must still be better than any smaller quantity after the price increase. This analysis implies that the firm's most profitable sales quantity after a price increase cannot be lower than Q^*.

Changes in Input Prices and Shifts in the Supply Function

How does a change in an input price affect a firm's supply function? Imagine that a wheat farmer faces an increase in the price of water, raising his cost by $5 for each bushel he produces. Figure 9.10(a) shows his marginal and average cost curves before the change, labelled MC_B and AC_B. His supply curve before the change, labelled S_B, is shown in green. Figure 9.10(b) shows the average and marginal cost curves after the change, labelled MC_A and AC_A. Both curves have shifted up by exactly $5 at every quantity. The new supply curve, S_A, has also shifted up by $5. In essence, if the farmer receives exactly $5 more per bushel, he is willing to supply the same amount of wheat as before.

Figure 9.11 shows how the farmer's supply curve changes with an increase in avoidable fixed cost. Figure 9.11(a) shows the farmer's marginal and average cost curves and the supply function before the change, labelled MC_B, AC_B, and S_B. Figure 9.11(b) shows these same curves after the change, labelled MC_A, AC_A, and S_A. AC_{min} has risen from $5 to $10. Notice that the average cost curve shifts upward, but the marginal cost curve is unaffected. As a result, the farmer sells exactly the same quantity as before, provided he doesn't shut down. Now, however, he requires a higher price—at least $10 instead of $5—to stay in business.

Determining the change in a firm's supply function using algebra is just a matter of finding its supply function twice, once for before the change and once after. In essence, this is what we did in worked-out problem 9.2 (page 308), where we found Dan's supply function both with and without an avoidable fixed cost of $845.

Changes in a firm's input prices change not only the firm's profit-maximizing sales quantity, but also its input (or factor) demands. In Add-On 9A we discuss the direction of those effects.

Figure 9.10

A Change in a Wheat Farmer's Supply Curve. Figure (a) shows a wheat farmer's initial costs and supply curve. Figure (b) shows the change in the farmer's supply curve when his cost rises by $5 per bushel, shifting the supply curve upward by $5 at every quantity.

Figure 9.11

Another Change in a Wheat Farmer's Supply Curve. The farmer's initial situation, shown in figure (a), is the same as in Figure 9.10(a). This time, the farmer experiences an increase in avoidable fixed cost. Figure (b) shows the shift in average cost and the resulting supply curve. Note that the marginal cost curve does not change, so the farmer's supply is unchanged if he doesn't shut down.

(a) Initial situation

(b) After increase in avoidable fixed cost

Application 9.3

Canadian Softwood Exports and the Canada–U.S. Softwood Lumber Agreement of 1996–2001

Softwood lumber is one of Canada's largest exports to the United States, with over 21.5 billion board feet (worth $8.5 billion) shipped in 2005 alone. It is also one of the biggest headaches in Canada–U.S. relations. While the North American Free Trade Agreement (NAFTA) eliminated most trade restrictions between the two countries, softwood lumber is a notable exception. For years, a dispute has raged over the product. In the United States, the main proponents of limited Canadian imports are U.S. lumber producers, who have often successfully lobbied the U.S. government for protection.

Under a bilateral agreement that was in effect from 1996 to 2001, lumber producers in the provinces of Alberta, British Columbia, Ontario, and Quebec faced penalties for exceeding certain limits on exports. Producers could export up to a "fee-free limit" without penalty. Above the limit, they had to pay a penalty of $50 per 1000 board feet up to another limit

(the "low-fee limit"), and above that a penalty of $100 per 1000 board feet. (In 1995, the average softwood lumber price was $337 per 1000 board feet, or $143 per cubic metre, so the penalties were substantial.)

Figure 9.12 shows the effect of the penalties on the supply curve of a typical Canadian softwood lumber producer. Figure 9.12(a) shows the producer's average and marginal costs before the agreement, labelled AC and MC. Without the agreement, the supply curve coincides with the MC curve at prices above AC_{min}, and with the vertical axis (zero supply) at prices below AC_{min}.

Figure 9.12(a) also shows the average and marginal cost curves with the agreement, labelled AC_A and MC_A. The fee-free limit is Q_0; the low-fee limit is Q_1. At all quantities between Q_0 and Q_1 the Canadian producer must pay a penalty of $50 per 1000 board feet, which shifts the marginal cost curve up by $50. At all quantities above Q_1 the Canadian producer must pay a penalty of $100 per 1000 board feet, which shifts the marginal cost curve up by another $50. As a result, the curve MC_A jumps up by $50 at Q_0 and Q_1 (the jumps at those quantities are indicated by dashed vertical lines).

Average cost is also higher at each output level over Q_0 because of the agreement. However, at each such output level, the difference between the two average cost curves is smaller than the change in marginal cost because in calculating average cost the penalties are averaged over all units, including those for which there is no penalty.

Figure 9.12(b) shows the firm's supply curve after the agreement in green. As usual, it coincides with the MC_A curve at prices above AC_{min}, and with the vertical axis (zero supply) at prices below AC_{min}. The only tricky parts are the vertical segments of the supply curve at Q_0 and Q_1. Suppose the price is between $\underline{P}_0$ and $\overline{P}$. In that case, the firm's (horizontal) marginal revenue curve passes through the jump in the marginal cost curve at Q_0. There is therefore no positive quantity at which P equals MC. Nonetheless, Q_0 is the firm's most profitable choice. To see why, observe that at quantities below Q_0, the price exceeds marginal cost, so it pays to increase output. At all quantities above Q_0, the price is less than marginal cost, so it pays to reduce output.[9] So the supply curve in Figure 9.12(b) shows that for all such prices the firm will export exactly Q_0 thousand board feet of lumber. Similarly, at all prices between $\underline{P}_1$ and $\overline{P}_1$, the firm will export exactly Q_1 thousand board feet of lumber.

Figure 9.12

The Effect of the U.S.-Canada Softwood Lumber Agreement on the Supply Curve of a Canadian Lumber Producer.
Figure (a) shows the effect of the agreement on the Canadian lumber producer's marginal and average costs. The original marginal and average cost curves, in light red, are labelled MC and AC; the new marginal and average cost curves are labelled MC_A and AC_A. At export quantities between the fee-free limit Q_0 and the low-fee limit Q_1, the penalty shifts the producer's marginal cost curve up by $50. Above Q_1, the marginal cost curve shifts up by $100. The firm's supply curve with the agreement, shown in figure (b), coincides with its new marginal cost curve at all prices above AC_{min}, and also includes the vertical segments where the MC_A curve jumps upward at Q_0 and Q_1.

(a) Marginal and average costs

Canadian exports (thousands of board feet)

(b) Supply curve

Canadian exports (thousands of board feet)

---

[9]The two-step procedure in the text assumes that the firm's MC curve has no jumps. When the marginal cost curve has jumps, as here, the No Marginal Improvement Principle (see Section 3.2) requires us to determine in step 1 of the two-step procedure if a small increase or decrease in output would raise profit at the output levels at which marginal cost jumps. An increase doesn't raise profit if $P \geq MC$ at slightly higher outputs; a decrease doesn't raise profit if $P \geq MC$ at slightly lower outputs. For example, at prices between $\underline{P}_0$ and $\overline{P}_0$, quantity Q_0 is the only output level that satisfies the test in this amended step 1.

SHORT-RUN VERSUS LONG-RUN SUPPLY BY PRICE-TAKING FIRMS

In Section 8.7 we saw that a firm's marginal and average costs may differ in the long and short run because, in the short run, some inputs are fixed rather than variable. Those differences affect the way the firm responds over time to a change in the price it faces for its product.

Figure 9.13 shows how a price-taking firm responds when the price at which it can sell its product rises suddenly from $\overline{P}$ to $\hat{P}$ and remains at that new level. Figure 9.13(a) shows the firm's short-run and long-run marginal cost curves, labelled MC_{SR} and MC_{LR} respectively. These curves reflect the relationship between short-run and long-run marginal cost discussed in Section 8.7: the curves cross at the initial price $\overline{P}$, and the short-run marginal cost curve is steeper than the long-run curve. These curves can be used to apply the quantity rule. In the short run, the firm's best positive quantity is Q_{SR}^*, but in the long run it is the larger amount Q_{LR}^*.

Figure 9.13(b) adds average cost curves to the picture to consider the shut-down rule. The figure shows three average cost curves. AC_{LR} is the firm's long-run average cost curve. The long-run marginal cost curve crosses the AC_{LR} curve at its lowest point. AC_{SR} is the firm's short-run average cost curve, including the sunk cost of its fixed inputs. It

Figure 9.13

Long-Run and Short-Run Supply Responses to a Price Increase. The figure shows the long-run and short-run increases in the quantity supplied for a price-taking firm in response to a price increase from $\overline{P}$ to $\hat{P}$. Figure (a) considers the quantity rule. It shows the firm's short-run and long-run marginal cost curves. They cross at Q^*, with the short-run curve steeper than the long-run curve, for the reasons discussed in Section 8.7. In the short run, the firm's best positive output level is Q_{SR}^*, while in the long run it is Q_{LR}^*. Figure (b) considers the shut-down rule. The firm prefers to operate in both the short run and the long run.

reflects the relation to the firm's long-run average cost curve we discussed in Section 8.7: it touches the long-run average cost curve at the firm's initial output level Q^*, and lies above it everywhere else. Finally, the curve Avoidable AC_{SR} is the firm's short-run avoidable average cost curve. It includes only the firm's avoidable costs, and so lies below the curve AC_{SR}. There is not a similar distinction between the long-run average cost curve and the long- run avoidable average cost curve as all costs are avoidable in the long-run—that is, there are no sunk fixed costs. The short-run marginal cost curve crosses both of these short-run average cost curves at their lowest points. Since the new price $\hat{P}$ is above the avoidable short-run average cost at Q_{SR}^* and the long-run average cost at Q_{LR}^*, the firm will choose to operate in both the short run and the long run.

Combining the quantity rule and shut-down rule, we see that the firm will increase its output to Q_{SR}^* in the short run, and increase it further to Q_{LR}^* in the long run.[10]

IN-TEXT EXERCISE 9.4   **Suppose that the price at which a price-taking firm can sell its product decreases. Use a figure like Figure 9.13 to show how the firm's profit-maximizing sales quantity adjusts in the short run and the long run. Is the firm more likely to shut down in the short run or the long run?**

Application 9.4

Short-Run and Long-Run Supply Responses by Crude Oil Producers

Jed Clampett, the lead character on the 1960s TV sitcom *The Beverly Hillbillies*, strikes it rich one day when he misses his target while hunting. Up from the ground bubbled crude—"oil that is, black gold, Texas tea." Clampett sold his land to the OK Oil Company and moved to Beverly Hills. The rest is TV history.

Making money in the oil business isn't always so easy. Oil companies need to spend considerable resources to find oil and then extract it. In 2008, Canada, the United States, and Mexico produced 17.7 percent of the world's oil. Because individual producers supply only a tiny fraction of that amount, many economists would regard them as price takers.

The price that a producer receives for a barrel of oil has fluctuated dramatically over the last 30 years, due to changes in both oil regulations and the world oil market. Figure 9.14 shows the nominal and real prices per barrel (in U.S. dollars) that crude oil producers received from 1970 to 2002. The "real" prices are adjusted for inflation, and are stated in year 2000 dollars (see Section 6.3). Two price changes are particularly noticeable. First, the price increased more than 150 percent between 1978 and 1981, due to the combined effects of the Iran-Iraq war, which reduced world oil supplies and raised oil prices, and the deregulation of domestic crude oil prices. (The Arab oil embargo of 1973 led to a much smaller price increase, 60 percent.) Second, from 1985–1986, crude oil prices plunged, falling about 50 percent, when OPEC (the Organization of Petroleum Exporting Countries), the cartel that had helped to elevate oil prices since the 1973 embargo, lost its ability to control its members' production.

The responses of oil producers to these dramatic price changes illustrate the difference between long-run and short-run supply by price-taking firms. For example, there has been a tremendous investment in the Athabasca oil sands of Alberta since the real price of oil bottomed out in the late nineties. As a result Canadian production increased from 2.63 million barrels a day in 1999 to 3.35 million barrels a

---

[10]The situation shown in Figure 9.13 is the typical one, in which a competitive firm's long-run response to a price change exceeds its short-run response. Sometimes, however, the reverse happens. Such cases can arise when a firm's short-run marginal costs are interrelated across time. For example, if a firm's workforce is more rested and productive because the firm produced less in the preceding month, the firm's marginal cost of production will be lower in the current month. To be specific, imagine that the price of the firm's product suddenly increases on January 1. The price increase will lead the firm to increase its output from its December level. That increase in January's output, however, will increase February's marginal cost and lead the firm to sell less in February than in January.

day in 2008. While data on individual producers' output is not publicly available, we can examine fairly detailed production data at the state level in the United States.[11] Figure 9.15 shows the number of active oil wells (in red) and annual production (in blue) in the state of New Mexico from 1970 to 2002. (The number of wells is measured on the left vertical axis; the number of barrels produced on the right vertical axis.) The period of sharp price changes, 1978–1988, is highlighted in green with dashed vertical lines distinguishing three periods: 1978–1981, when real prices rose sharply; 1981–1985, when real prices fell gradually; and 1985–1988, after the sharp price decline in 1985–1986.

Over 32 years, New Mexico's oil production declined almost every year. A notable exception to this trend occurred in 1981–1985, when production increased almost 15 percent at the same time that crude oil prices were falling. How could supply rise while the price fell? The explanation lies in the large increase in the number of active wells during and prior to this time period, stimulated by the price increases of 1978–1981. The response to the price increases, which led firms to increase the amount of two critical inputs, oil wells and drilling machinery, took some time. Companies needed to identify new oil locations and drill new wells. By 1985 the number of active wells had increased almost 30 percent over its 1978 level. As the new wells became active, they led New

The Beverly Hillbillies

Mexico producers to supply more oil than before, even after prices dropped.[12]

In 1985–1986 real crude oil prices dropped back to 1975 levels. Over the next two years the number of active wells declined as producers shut down older more costly wells and drilled few new ones. As a result, production fell during those years.

Figure 9.14

Nominal and Real Prices (U.S. Dollars) Received by Crude Oil Producers, 1970–2002. The figure shows the average nominal and real prices received by crude oil producers each year from 1970 to 2002. Real prices are shown in year 2000 dollars. Oil prices increased more than 150 percent from 1978 to 1981 and fell dramatically from 1985 to 1986.

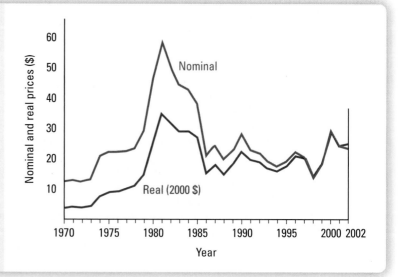

---

[11]This information can be found at www.eia.doe.gov.

[12]The fact that supply increased as prices fell does *not* contradict the Law of Supply (see Section 9.3), because here an oil refinery's short-run cost function changes over time as more oil wells become active. The fact that the number of active wells continued to increase for a while after prices started falling (see Figure 9.15) probably reflects the fact that producers had already sunk much of the costs of their development.

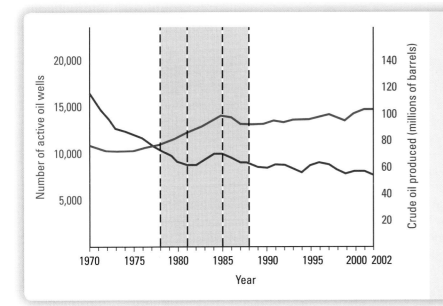

Figure 9.15

The Number of Active Oil Wells and Crude Oil Production in New Mexico, 1970–2002. This figure shows the number of active oil wells (in red) and total crude oil production (in blue) in New Mexico from 1970 to 2002. The number of oil wells and production increased for several years following the 1979–1981 price increase, and continued to increase even after prices started to decline, reflecting the time needed to find suitable sites and drill new oil wells. After the 1985–1986 price decline, the number of active oil wells and total production fell.

WORKED-OUT PROBLEM   9.4

The Problem   Suppose that Hannah and Sam's short-run and long-run cost functions are $C_{SR}(Q) = 5000 + (Q^2/2)$ and $C_{LR}(Q) = 100Q$. (These are the short-run and long-run cost functions derived in worked-out problem 8.6 on page 288.) Given these cost functions, their short-run marginal cost is $MC_{SR} = Q$ and their long-run marginal cost is $MC_{LR} = 100$. What are their short-run and long-run supply functions?

The Solution   Let's consider their long-run supply function first. If the price is above 100, there is no quantity at which $P = MC$: we have $P > MC$ at every output level. Since they make a positive profit on every unit they sell, they will want to sell an infinite amount. If the price is below 100, they want to sell nothing, and if the price is exactly 100 they are willing to supply any amount, since they earn zero regardless of how much they sell.

   Now consider the short run. Applying the quantity rule, the sales quantity at which $P = MC$ solves the formula $P = Q$. So the most profitable positive sales quantity given price P is $Q = P$. Since, at this quantity, Hannah and Sam's revenue is P^2 and their avoidable costs are $P^2/2$, they will produce in the short run as long as the price is positive. Thus, their short-run supply function is $S_{SR}(P) = P$.

IN-TEXT EXERCISE 9.5   **Suppose that Hannah and Sam's short-run and long-run cost functions are $C_{SR}(Q) = 10,000 + Q^2$ and $C_{LR}(Q) = 200Q$. (These are the short-run and long-run cost functions in the situation you were asked to study in in-text exercise 8.6 on page 288.) Given these cost functions, their short-run marginal cost is $MC_{SR} = 2Q$, and their long-run marginal cost is $MC_{LR} = 200$. What are their short-run and long-run supply functions?**

9.5 PRODUCER SURPLUS

A firm's **producer surplus** equals its revenue less its avoidable costs.

We've seen that profit is the excess of revenue over total cost. At times it will be convenient to work with a related concept, called producer surplus. **Producer surplus** equals the firm's revenue less its avoidable cost, which includes both its variable cost and its avoidable fixed cost, but does not include its sunk fixed costs. So

$$\text{Profit} = \text{Producer surplus} - \text{Sunk cost}$$

Since sunk costs are incurred no matter what, they can generally be ignored in making economic decisions (see Section 3.3). So it is often the case that we can focus on producer surplus rather than profit. For example, another way of stating the shut-down rule is to say that the firm will shut down if its producer surplus from producing its most profitable positive quantity would be negative. Likewise, in later chapters we'll investigate the welfare implications of various government policies. When we consider how firms are affected by these policies, it often suffices to focus on their effects on firms' producer surpluses because such policies often don't have any effects on sunk costs. In that case, the change in a firm's profit is the same as the change in its producer surplus.

One advantage of focusing on producer surplus when we consider policy changes is that we can conveniently measure it using supply curves.

Figure 9.16 shows that producer surplus for a firm selling Q units equals the area between a horizontal line drawn at the level of the firm's price P and the firm's supply curve. Why? Consider Figure 9.16(a), which shows a case in which the firm has no avoidable fixed costs and its supply curve has no jumps. Recall from Section 8.5 that the firm's variable cost equals the area under its marginal cost curve up to Q units. This is the

Figure 9.16

Producer Surplus. Producer surplus, which equals revenue [area ABCD in figure (a); area ABHF in figure (b)] less avoidable cost (the red-shaded region), is the yellow-shaded area in each figure.

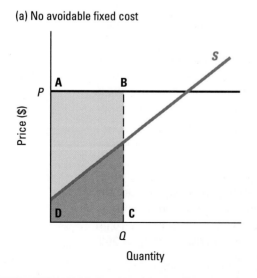

(a) No avoidable fixed cost

(b) With an avoidable fixed cost

red-shaded area in Figure 9.16(a). The firm's revenue, on the other hand, equals its price P times the amount it produces. Its revenue therefore equals the area of rectangle ABCD. If we subtract the red-shaded variable cost area from that revenue rectangle we are left with the yellow-shaded area, which is the firm's producer surplus.

Now consider a case with an avoidable fixed cost, shown in Figure 9.16(b).[13] With an avoidable fixed cost, the firm's supply curve jumps from 0 to Q^e when the price equals AC_{min}. Nonetheless, just as in Figure 9.16(a), the firm's producer surplus equals the yellow-shaded area between the horizontal line drawn at the level of the firm's price P and the firm's supply curve (here we fill in the horizontal jump in the supply curve to define that area). Why? Recall that the firm's profit from producing quantity Q^e when the price equals AC_{min} exactly equals its profit from producing zero. This means that the firm's added cost from producing quantity Q^e rather than 0 must exactly equal its revenue from selling Q^e units at a price of AC_{min}, which is the area of rectangle DEFG. To determine the avoidable costs of producing Q units, we then need to add to this amount the cost of increasing output from Q^e to Q. That additional cost equals the area under the supply curve between Q^e and Q, which is area CDGH. Thus, the firm's avoidable cost of producing quantity Q is equal to the red-shaded area. Its producer surplus, equal to its revenue at price P (rectangle ABHF) less its avoidable costs (the red-shaded area), therefore equals the yellow-shaded area.

There is a second way to measure the firm's producer surplus when it has an avoidable fixed cost. In this approach we use the firm's marginal cost curve rather than its supply curve: determine the firm's revenue less its variable cost by measuring the area between a horizontal line drawn at the level of its price P and its marginal cost curve (just as in Figure 9.16(a), where there were no avoidable fixed costs so the marginal cost and supply curves coincided). Then, subtract its avoidable fixed cost to get its producer surplus.

SUPPLY BY MULTIPRODUCT PRICE-TAKING FIRMS

Most firms produce more than one product. As we discussed in Section 8.9, the firm's cost function then depends on its output of all of its products. For example, a firm that produces two outputs, Q_1 and Q_2, will have a cost function of the form $C(Q_1, Q_2)$. In these cases, the marginal cost of producing one product often depends on the production levels of other products. For example, oil refineries produce many different products, including high-octane gasoline, low-octane gasoline, and heating oil. If a refinery increases the production of one product, the marginal cost of producing the others can change.

Sometimes the marginal cost of a product increases when the firm produces more of another good, sometimes it decreases. For example, if Noah and Naomi produce both garden benches and garden chairs, the more garden chairs they produce the more crowded their production facility becomes, increasing their marginal cost of producing benches. On the other hand, if they are producing a lot of benches, they may decide to invest in equipment that lowers the marginal cost of producing chairs as well.

To find the profit-maximizing sales quantities and prices for two products, we need to extend the quantity and shut-down rules. The new quantity rule says to find the most profitable pair of positive sales quantities at which price equals marginal cost for *both* products. The new shut-down rule compares the profit from those quantities to three

---

[13]The avoidable fixed cost is not explicitly shown in figure 9.16(b). Region EDGF is comprised of both variable costs and the avoidable fixed cost.

alternatives: (1) shutting down the first product while continuing to sell the second, (2) shutting down the second product while continuing to sell the first, and (3) shutting down both products. Worked-out problem 9.5 shows how this procedure works.

WORKED-OUT PROBLEM   9.5

The Problem   Noah and Naomi produce both garden benches and garden chairs. They are price takers. Their cost function for garden benches is $C_B(Q_B, Q_C) = 50Q_B + Q^2B - Q_BQ_C$ and their marginal cost is $MC_B = 50 + 2Q_B - Q_C$, where Q_B and Q_C are their output levels of benches and chairs respectively. Their cost function for garden chairs is $C_C(Q_B, Q_C) = 25Q_C + Q^2{}_C - Q_CQ_B$, and their marginal cost is $MC_C = 25 + 2Q_C - Q_B$. The price of a garden bench, P_B, is \$140; the price of a garden chair, P_C, is \$55. What are Noah and Naomi's profit-maximizing sales quantities?

The Solution   Applying the quantity rule, we find the sales quantities for both benches and chairs at which price equals marginal cost, which means finding Q_B and Q_C such that

$$140 = 50 + 2Q_B - Q_C$$

and

$$55 = 25 + 2Q_C - Q_B$$

Doing so gives us two equations for the two unknowns Q_B and Q_C. Solving, we find that the best positive quantities are $Q_B = 70$ and $Q_C = 50$. (You can solve these by using the first equation to determine that $Q_C = 2Q_B - 90$, and then substitute this expression for Q_C into the second equation and solve it for Q_B. This yields $Q_B = 70$. Since $Q_C = 2Q_B - 90$, this implies that $Q_C = 50$.) Noah and Naomi's profit is \$7400.

Applying the shutdown rule, we compare this profit not just to the profit Noah and Naomi earn if they shut down completely (zero) but to their profit if they stop producing one of the two products. If they stop producing garden chairs, so that $Q_C = 0$, their cost function for benches becomes $C_B(Q_B) = 50Q_B + Q^2{}_B$ (because $Q_C = 0$) and their marginal cost is $MC_B = 50 + 2Q_B$. The best sales quantity of benches is then $Q_B = 45$, which yields a profit of \$2025 (you should check this). That is less than Noah and Naomi will make by producing both products.

If instead Noah and Naomi stop producing garden benches, so that $Q_B = 0$, their cost function for chairs becomes $C_C(Q_C) = 25Q_C + Q^2{}_C$, and their marginal cost is $MC_C = 25 + 2Q_C$. The best sales quantity for garden chairs is then $Q_C = 15$, which yields a profit of \$225 (you should also check this). Again, this is less than they would make by producing both products, so Noah and Naomi's profit-maximizing sales quantities are $Q_B = 70$ and $Q_C = 50$.

IN-TEXT EXERCISE 9.6   **In worked-out problem 9.5, how would Noah and Naomi's profit-maximizing sales quantities change if the price of garden benches were \$110?**

For a multiproduct firm that is a price taker, a change in the price of one product can affect the profit-maximizing sales quantities of other products. The direction of the effect depends on how the production of one product affects the marginal cost of another. Suppose the marginal cost of a product decreases when the firm sells more of a second product. If the price of the second product increases, the firm will increase sales of that product (in accord with the Law of Supply, which remains true for multiproduct firms). Since this change also decreases the marginal cost of the first product, it will *increase* sales of that product. The solution to in-text exercise 9.6, compared with the solution of worked-out problem 9.4, illustrates this case. If, instead, the marginal cost of one product increases with increased sales of another, then an increase in the price of the second product will reduce the sales of the first (see end-of-chapter exercise 9.15).

CHAPTER SUMMARY

1. **Profit-maximizing quantities and prices (LO1)**
   a. The relationship between a firm's price and sales quantity is described by the demand curve for its product.
   b. A firm's manager can think in terms of finding either the profit-maximizing price or the profit-maximizing sales quantity.

2. **Marginal revenue, marginal cost, and profit maximization (LO1)**
   a. Marginal revenue measures the extra revenue produced by the ΔQ marginal units sold, measured on a per-unit basis: $MR = \Delta R/\Delta Q = [R(Q) - R(Q - \Delta Q)]/\Delta Q$.
   b. When a firm's demand curve is downward sloping, its marginal revenue at any positive sales quantity is less than its price, because selling the marginal units reduces the amount the firm receives on inframarginal sales. A price-taking firm, however, need not lower its price to sell more, so its marginal revenue always equals the price.
   c. When a firm's profit-maximizing sales quantity is positive, its marginal revenue equals its marginal cost at that quantity.
   d. We can follow a two-step procedure to find the firm's profit-maximizing sales quantity. In the first step, the quantity rule, identify the best positive sales quantity at which $MR = MC$. In the second step, the shut-down rule, check whether the profit from that sales quantity is at least as large as the profit from shutting down.
   e. If the firm has no sunk costs, or if these are ignored in calculating its cost, the shut-down rule is equivalent to checking whether the profit from the best positive sales quantity is non-negative ($PQ - C(Q) \geq 0$) or,

equivalently, if the firm's price is at least as large as its average cost ($P \geq AC$).

3. **Supply decisions by price-taking firms (LO3)**
   a. A price-taking firm can use the two-step procedure to find its best sales quantity. Doing so involves identifying sales quantities at which marginal cost equals the price in applying the quantity rule.
   b. The Law of Supply tells us that a competitive firm's supply never decreases when the market price increases.
   c. When a firm's marginal cost curve is upward sloping, its supply curve coincides with its marginal cost curve at prices above AC_{min}; it coincides with the vertical axis (representing zero supply) at prices below AC_{min}.

4. **Short-run versus long-run supply by price-taking firms (LO4)**
   The fact that a firm's short-run marginal cost curve is steeper than its long-run marginal cost curve means that a competitive firm responds more to a price change in the long run than it does in the short run.

5. **Producer surplus (LO5)**
   a. A firm's producer surplus equals its revenue less its avoidable costs. Therefore, the firm's profit equals its producer surplus less its sunk costs.
   b. A firm's producer surplus equals the area between a horizontal line drawn at the level of its price P and its supply curve.

*6. **Supply by multiproduct price-taking firms (LO6)**
   When a firm's marginal cost of production for one product changes with the quantity of a second product it produces, an increase in the price of the second product can change the firm's supply of the first product.

Exercise 9.1: If the demand function for Noah and Naomi's garden benches is $Q^d = D(P) = 1000/\sqrt{P}$, what is their inverse demand function? (LO1)

Exercise 9.2: Consider the preferred prices of the author and the publisher of an electronic book, whose marginal cost of production is close to zero. Would the two disagree about the price to be charged for the book? (LO1)

Exercise 9.3: Reconsider the textbook pricing issue in Application 9.1 (page 301). Show why the publisher wants a higher price using MR and MC. (LO1)

Exercise 9.4: How does the price preferred by an author who gets a 25 percent royalty compare to that preferred by an author who gets a 15 percent royalty? (LO1)

Exercise 9.5: Consider again Apple Computer's decision in Application 9.2 (page 304). How much would iPhone sales have had to increase in response to a price reduction to $499 for that price reduction to increase profit? (LO1)

Exercise 9.6: A price-taking firm's variable cost function is $VC = Q^3$, where Q is its output per week. It has a sunk fixed cost of $3000 per week. Its marginal cost is $MC = 3Q^2$. What is its profit-maximizing output when the price is $P = \$243$? What if the fixed cost is avoidable? (LO2)

Exercise 9.7: In exercise 9.6, what is the firm's supply function when the $3000 fixed cost is sunk? When it is avoidable? (LO3)

Exercise 9.8: Suppose Dan's cost of making pizzas is $C(Q) = 4Q + (Q^2/40)$, and his marginal cost is $MC = 4 + (Q/20)$. Dan is a price taker. What is Dan's supply function? What if Dan has an avoidable fixed cost of $10? (LO3)

Exercise 9.9: Consider again exercise 9.8. If Dan's cost increases by $2 per pizza, so that his cost function becomes $C(Q) = 6Q + (Q^2/40)$ and his marginal cost becomes $MC = 6 + (Q/20)$, how will his supply function change? (LO3)

Exercise 9.10: Consider again exercise 9.8. If Dan's avoidable fixed cost increases from $10 to $22.50, how will his supply function change? (LO3)

Exercise 9.11: Suppose that it costs a firm $2 to produce each unit of its output. What is its supply function? Graph it. (LO3)

Exercise 9.12: In exercise 8.14 (page 294) you derived Hannah and Sam's long-run and short-run cost function when they have the Cobb-Douglas production function $Q = F(L, K) = 10L^{0.5}K^{0.5}$, both a worker and a unit of capital cost $1000 per week, and they initially painted 200 square metres per week. Their capital is fixed in the short run but variable in the long run. What are their long-run and short-run supply functions? Graph them. (LO4)

Exercise 9.13: In exercise 8.15 (page 294) you derived Hannah and Sam's long-run and short-run cost function when they have the Cobb-Douglas production function $Q = F(L, K) = 10L^{0.25}K^{0.25}$, both a worker and a unit of capital cost $1000 per week, and they initially painted 100 square metres a week. Their capital is fixed in the short run but variable in the long run. What are their long-run and short-run supply functions? Graph them. (LO4)

Exercise 9.14: Argue that another way to represent a firm's producer surplus is as the area between its marginal revenue curve and its supply curve. Use this fact to show why $MR = MC$ at any positive profit-maximizing sales quantity. (LO5)

*Exercise 9.15: Noah and Naomi produce both garden benches and garden chairs; they are price takers in both markets. The cost function for garden benches is $C_B(Q_B, Q_C) = 50Q_B + Q^2_B + Q_BQ_C$, and the marginal cost is $MC_B = 50 + 2Q_B + QC$. The cost function for garden chairs is $C_C(Q_B, Q_C) = 25Q_C + Q^2_C + Q_CQ_B$, and the marginal cost is $MC_C = 25 + 2Q_C + Q_B$. The price of a garden bench, P_B, is $120; the price of a garden chair, P_C, is $75. What are Noah and Naomi's profit-maximizing sales quantities of benches and chairs? What happens if the price of benches increases to $135? (LO6)

Additional Topics
Concerning Decisions

The next four chapters extend and enrich the theory of decision making developed in Chapters 4 through 9. In Chapter 10 we'll examine decisions involving time, such as saving and investment. In Chapter 11 we'll turn to decisions involving uncertainty, such as gambling, insurance, and risk management. As we'll see, it's possible to understand decisions involving time and uncertainty by applying the tools that we've already developed. In Chapter 12 we'll develop new tools for thinking about decisions involving strategy. Finally, in Chapter 13, we'll survey a field known as behavioural economics, which attempts to modify, supplement, and enrich economic theories of decision making by incorporating insights from psychology.

10

Choices Involving Time

LEARNING OBJECTIVES

After reading this chapter, students should be able to

LOI Explain how consumers and firms move cash from one point in time to another by borrowing and lending.

LO2 Calculate the present discounted value of a claim on future resources.

LO3 Understand consumers' decisions regarding saving and borrowing.

LO4 Analyze the profitability of investment projects with future cash flows.

LO5 Explain how saving, borrowing, and investment depend on the interest rate.

Interior (above) and exterior (below) of Volkswagen's Phaeton production plant in Dresden, Germany

In the 1990s, Volkswagen executives set their sights on the market for luxury automobiles. They conceived both a new car—the Phaeton—and a state-of-the-art production facility in Dresden, Germany. Eager to impress well-heeled customers, they located the new plant along the banks of the historic Elbe River, on more than 20 acres of manicured parkland. With walls of glass—roughly 290,000 square feet in all—and floors of polished Canadian maple, it was easily mistaken for an art gallery. In fact, after the Dresden Opera House flooded, 17 performances of the opera *Carmen* were held in the factory's sumptuous visitors' centre.

Like Rome, the Phaeton plant wasn't built in a day. The first Phaeton didn't hit the streets of Europe until

2002. Volkswagen sank more than $200 million into the project years before the plant began generating revenue.

Designing, producing, and selling products, be they Volkswagen Phaetons or garden benches, *always* requires time. Companies often invest substantial sums of money long before they receive any revenue, particularly when, as in the case of the Phaeton, new designs and production facilities are needed. How should companies evaluate investments when production isn't instantaneous? How do they obtain the necessary cash to cover their up-front expenses? Why are lenders and investors willing to part with their cash, forgoing consumption goods today in exchange for some future benefit?

In this chapter, we provide some answers to these and other questions concerning economic decisions involving time. We organize our discussion around three topics:

1. *Transactions involving time.* By lending and borrowing, people can move resources from one point in time to another. As we'll see, these financial transactions allow consumers and firms to make sure cash is available when it's needed.

2. *Saving and borrowing.* Consumers don't usually earn money at the same time they want to spend it. After retirement, for example, their needs remain basically the same even though their incomes plummet. We'll examine how people can provide for their needs later in life by saving when they're young.

3. *Investment.* Before producing anything, a company must usually invest in a plant and equipment. We'll explain how to distinguish between investments that are profitable and those that aren't. The same principles apply to other types of investment, such as the decision to go to university.

10.1 TRANSACTIONS INVOLVING TIME

Consumers and firms often need to move cash from one point in time to another. Various types of financial transactions help them to do so. For example, by temporarily lending someone money or depositing it in a bank account, they can move their resources from the present to the future. Alternatively, by borrowing money, they can move resources from the future to the present. To understand economic decisions involving time, we must begin with a careful examination of these transactions and the trade-offs they imply.

To keep the analysis reasonably concrete, we'll focus primarily on the use of bank accounts. As we explain below, a bank account is simply a loan from a depositor to a bank. Keep in mind, however, that similar principles apply whether we are borrowing or lending, and no matter which particular financial vehicle we're using.

Interest Rates and Compound Interest

When one person (or firm) lends money to another, the amount borrowed is known as the lender's **principal**. The borrower is usually obliged to repay the principal at some particular point (or points) in time, along with compensation for the privilege of holding and using the lender's money. This compensation is known as **interest**.

It's useful to think about bank accounts in the same terms. That is, the bank is the borrower, the depositor is the lender, and the amount deposited is the principal. Many

Principal is the amount borrowed when one person (or firm) lends money to another.

Interest is the amount of money a borrower is obliged to pay a lender, over and above the principal.

bank accounts pay interest; that is one reason bank accounts are better than stuffing money in a mattress. Some accounts allow the depositor to withdraw money at will, which means the bank must repay the loan on demand. Others require the funds to remain on deposit for a fixed period.

The **interest rate** is the amount of interest paid on a loan during a particular time period (usually a year), stated as a percentage of the principal. So if a bank account pays an interest rate of 3 percent per year, a $100 deposit generates $3 in interest over the course of a year.

For some loans, the interest obligation is simply added to the loan balance and remains unpaid until the principal comes due. At any point in time, the lender earns interest on the total loan balance, which includes all of the interest earned prior to that point. Since the amount of interest earned during any fixed interval rises proportionately with the growing loan balance, the balance grows faster as time passes. This process is known as **compounding**.

To illustrate, let's suppose you deposit $100 into an account that pays 10 percent interest per year.[1] Rather than withdrawing the interest, you allow it to accumulate within the account.

- Since your balance at the start of the first year is $100, you receive $10 in interest over the course of the first year (10 percent of $100), finishing with $110.
- Since your balance at the start of the second year is $110, you receive $11 in interest over the course of the second year (10 percent of $110), finishing with $121.
- Since your balance at the start of the third year is $121, you receive $12.10 in interest over the course of the third year (10 percent of $121), finishing with $133.10.

In Figure 10.1, the blue line shows the growth of your account balance over time, and the red line shows the growth of the interest payments you receive. Since the amount of interest received increases each year, your balance grows faster as time passes. This accelerating growth is a consequence of compound interest.

We can describe the effects of compound interest on your account balance with a simple formula. Let's use the symbol R to stand for the rate of interest, expressed as a decimal rather than a percentage. For example, at an interest rate of 10 percent, $R = 0.10$. If your balance is B dollars at the start of the year, you receive BR dollars in interest over the course of the year, finishing with a balance of $(B + BR) = B(1 + R)$ dollars. Let's say your initial deposit is D dollars.

- Since your balance at the start of the first year is D dollars, you finish the first year with $D(1 + R)$ dollars.
- Since your balance at the start of the second year is $D(1 + R)$ dollars, you finish the second year with $D(1 + R)^2$ dollars.
- Since your balance at the start of the third year is $D(1 + R)^2$ dollars, you finish the third year with $D(1 + R)^3$ dollars.

---

[1]To keep things simple, we will assume throughout this chapter that interest *compounds annually.* That is, the interest earned during a year is included in the account balance used to calculate additional interest only in *subsequent* years. Interest compounds monthly if it is included in the account balance used to calculate additional interest only in subsequent months; it compounds daily if it is included in the account balance used to calculate additional interest only on subsequent days, and so forth.

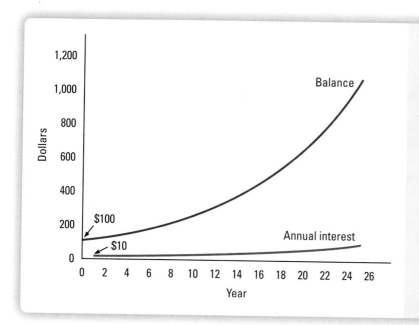

Figure 10.1
The Effects of Compound Interest. $100 deposited in a bank account at 10 percent interest for 25 years grows faster over time, as the blue line shows. The amount of interest paid during each year grows in proportion to the total balance, as the red line shows.

By repeating this calculation, we discover that at the end of T years, your account balance, B_T, is

$$B_T = D(1 + R)^T \qquad (1)$$

Table 10.1 shows how account balances grow over time at a range of interest rates. In each case, we start with an initial deposit of $100. From the numbers in the table, we can see that higher interest rates magnify the importance of compounding. For example, at an interest rate of 5 percent, the account earns $332.19 in interest over 30 years (the final balance of $432.19 minus the initial deposit of $100). In contrast, at an interest rate of 10 percent, it earns $1644.94 in interest over the same period. So doubling the interest rate from 5 percent to 10 percent produces a nearly five-fold increase in total interest earned over 30 years!

Table 10.1

Growth in Account Balances at Various Interest Rates
(Note: initial deposit of $100)

Years	Interest rate				
	1%	3%	5%	10%	15%
1	101.00	103.00	105.00	110.00	115.00
5	105.10	115.93	127.63	161.05	201.14
10	110.46	134.39	162.89	259.37	404.56
15	116.10	155.80	207.89	417.72	813.71
20	122.02	180.61	265.33	672.75	1636.65
30	134.78	242.73	432.19	1744.94	6621.18

Present Value and the Price of a Future Dollar

At first, depositing money in a bank account may seem a very different kind of transaction than, say, buying apples at a grocery store. But in fact, these two transactions have much in common.

Suppose a grocery store sells apples for 30 cents each. The price tells customers the rate at which they can trade money for apples. For example, a customer can trade $3.60 for a dozen apples.

Now think about a bank that accepts deposits, returning customers' cash one year later with interest. The bank is like the grocery store, except that instead of apples, it's selling a product called *future cash.* Like a price, the interest rate tells customers the rate at which they can trade cash-in-hand for the bank's product (future cash). At an interest rate of 10 percent, a customer can trade $3.60 of cash-in-hand for $3.96 of cash delivered a year from now.

Let's explore the similarity between interest rates and prices a bit further. What is the price today of $1 delivered a year from now? In other words, how much must you "pay" a bank today (by depositing money in an account) to "purchase" (withdraw) $1 a year from now? Let's say the interest rate is 25 percent. In that case, the answer is 80 cents. Why? If you put 80 cents in the bank today, you'll earn 20 cents in interest over the course of the next year (25 percent of 80 cents), leaving you with exactly $1 at the end of the year.

Given any interest rate $R,$ we can find today's price for $1 delivered in a year. If you deposit D dollars today, we know you'll have $D(1 + R)$ dollars at the end of the year. If you want to have exactly one dollar at the end of the year, you need to choose your deposit, D dollars, so that $D(1 + R) = 1.$ Solving for $D,$ we see that $D = 1/(1 + R).$ So the price that you must pay today to receive $1 delivered one year from now is $1/(1 + R)$ dollars.

Present discounted value (or PDV) of a claim on future resources is the monetary value of that claim today.

The **present discounted value (PDV)** of a claim on future resources is the monetary value of that claim today.[2] The expression $1/(1 + R)$ is the present discounted value of $1 received a year in the future. We use the word *value* because $1/(1 + R)$ is the price of a future dollar, and price is one measure of economic value. We use the word *present* because we're measuring *today's* price for the future dollar. And we use the word *discounted* because at a positive interest rate, $1 received in the future sells for less than a dollar today. In other words, *present discounted value* means *today's lower price*—it tells us how much we must pay today for a claim on future resources.

Given a choice between receiving $1 a year from now, or the PDV of that dollar immediately, you should be indifferent. Why? Even after you pick one of those alternatives, you can always swap it for the other. Say the interest rate is 25 percent, so that the PDV is 80 cents. Suppose you choose one dollar a year from now. You could still swap this for 80 cents today—just borrow 80 cents, and after a year, use the dollar to pay off your loan, with interest. Suppose you choose 80 cents today. You can still swap it for $1 in a year—just put the 80 cents in a bank account and let the interest accumulate.

Figure 10.2 shows the PDV of $1 received a year from now at various rates of interest. Notice that as the interest rate rises, PDV declines—that is, future dollars become less expensive. This makes sense—at a higher interest rate, you don't need to deposit as much to reach the $1 target. So, rounding to the nearest penny, when the interest rate is 3 percent, the PDV of $1 a year from now is 97 cents; when the interest rate is 10 percent, the PDV is 91 cents; when the interest rate is 15 percent, the PDV is 87 cents.

[2]This concept is also known more simply as *present value.*

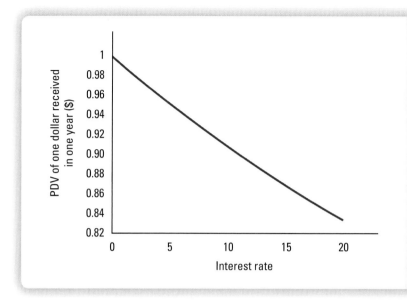

Figure 10.2

The PDV of $1 Received in One Year. The blue line shows the PDV of $1 received in one year—in other words, the price that you must pay today to receive $1 one year from today—at various interest rates.

By making deposits in bank accounts, people can trade cash today for cash at any point in the future. Suppose you want to have exactly one dollar available in T years. How much can you "buy" it for today? From formula (1), we know that if you deposit D dollars today, you'll have $D(1 + R)^T$ dollars after T years. To end up with exactly $1, you need to choose D so that $D(1 + R)^T = 1$. Solving for D, we see that $D = 1/(1 + R)^T$. In other words, the price that you must pay today to receive one future dollar delivered T years from now is $\$1/(1 + R)^T$. Since present discounted value is the equivalent of today's lower price, we have

$$\text{PDV of } \$1 \text{ delivered in } T \text{ years} = \$1/(1 + R)^T \qquad (2)$$

Table 10.2 shows how the PDV of a dollar delivered in T years changes with T and with the interest rate. Note that the PDV is smaller when the number of years is larger, and when the interest rate is higher. This makes sense; in both cases, any initial deposit accumulates to a larger balance, so you don't need to deposit as much to reach the $1 target.

Table 10.2

The PDV of $1 Received at Various Points in the Future, at Various Interest Rates

(Note: The amounts listed in this table are in cents)

Years	Interest rate				
	1%	3%	5%	10%	15%
1	99.01	97.09	95.24	90.91	86.96
5	95.15	86.26	78.35	62.09	49.72
10	90.53	74.41	61.39	38.55	24.72
15	86.13	64.19	48.10	23.94	12.29
20	81.95	55.37	37.69	14.86	6.11
30	74.19	41.20	23.14	5.73	1.51

At an interest rate of 5 percent, for example, $1 delivered next year costs 95.24 cents today, while $1 delivered in 30 years costs only 23.14 cents today. Likewise, at an interest rate of 1 percent, you can "buy" $1 delivered 30 years from now for 74.19 cents today. But if the interest rate is 15 percent, the same dollar costs only 1.51 cents!

> **IN-TEXT EXERCISE 10.1   Calculate the PDV of: (a) $1 delivered 7 years from now if the interest rate is 5 percent; (b) $1 delivered 12 years from now if the interest rate is 7 percent; (c) $1 delivered 100 years from now if the interest rate is 2 percent.**

Once we know the price today of future dollars, we can determine the PDV of any amount of money at any point in the future. To illustrate, let's compute the PDV of $100 delivered in 30 years, assuming the interest rate is 5 percent. If we were talking about 100 apples, we would take the price per apple (say 30 cents) and multiply it by 100 to find the total cost (30 cents × 100 = $30). The same principle applies here. According to Table 10.2, each dollar delivered 30 years from now costs 23.14 cents. Today, you can buy 100 future dollars for 100 × 23.14 cents = $23.14.[3] The PDV of $100 delivered in 30 years is therefore $23.14.

In thinking about decisions involving time, it's useful to have a general formula for PDV. Formula (2) tells us that a dollar delivered T years from now costs $1/(1 + R)^T$ dollars today. So a claim on F dollars in T years (the future value) costs $F/(1 + R)^T$ dollars today.[4] In other words,

$$\text{PDV} = \frac{\text{Future value (\$}F)}{(1 + R)^T} \tag{3}$$

So far we've focused on the PDV of money *received* in the future. The same principles apply to an obligation to *pay* money in the future. That is, formula (3) works even when F is a negative number. For example, at an interest rate of 25 percent, there is no difference between owing someone a dollar a year from now and owing 80 cents today. If you owe $1 a year from now, you can pay the debt off today with 80 cents—just deposit 80 cents in a bank account, let it sit for a year, and then use the principal and interest to meet your obligation. Likewise, if you owe 80 cents today, you can pay the obligation off with $1 a year from now—just borrow 80 cents to pay the obligation today, and then use $1 to pay off the new loan plus interest in a year.

Valuing Streams of Future Payments or Receipts

Many economic decisions require us to evaluate streams of future payments or receipts, rather than a single payment or receipt at a fixed point in the future. Let's say you need to buy a washing machine. Sears sells it for $600. Home Depot charges $625 for the same machine but doesn't require you to make any payments for a year. Future Shop charges $640, but offers an installment plan: you pay $200 up front, then $110 per year for the next four years. The interest rate is 5 percent. In this hypothetical example, which store offers the best deal?

---

[3]To do so, you would deposit $23.10 in a bank account paying five percent interest, and allow the balance to accumulate for 30 years, at which point you would have exactly $100.

[4]To purchase this claim, you would deposit $F/(1 + R)^T$ dollars in a bank account that pays interest at the rate R, and allow the balance to accumulate for T years, at which point you would have exactly $(1 + R)^T \times F/(1 + R)^T = F$ dollars.

Table 10.3

The True Cost of a Washing Machine Purchased on an Installment Plan

(Note: assumes an interest rate of 5 percent)

	Now	One Year	Two Years	Three Years	Four Years	Total
Number of dollars needed	200.00	110.00	110.00	110.00	110.00	**640.00**
Price of a dollar, from today's perspective	1.00	0.952	0.907	0.864	0.823	
Cost in today's dollars	200.00	104.76	99.77	95.02	90.50	**590.05**

To compare these choices, we have to figure out what each washing machine costs in today's dollars. For Sears, the answer is obvious: $600. What about Home Depot? From Table 10.2, we know that a dollar delivered one year from now costs 95.2 cents today. Since we need $625 delivered one year from now, the total cost is $625 × $0.952 = $595.24. In other words, if you deposit $595.24 in a bank account paying 5 percent interest today, you'll have just enough to make the $625 payment in one year. Home Depot's deal is better than Sears's, even though its price appears to be higher!

Future Shop's deal involves a stream of payments; Table 10.3 computes the cost in today's dollars. The $200 payment up front obviously costs $200. The four installment payments cost $104.76, $99.77, $95.02, and $90.50 respectively in today's dollars (in each case, we multiply the number of future dollars required, 110, by the cost of buying one future dollar today).[5] In total, Future Shop's washer costs $200 + $104.76 + $99.77 + $95.02 + $90.50 = $590.05 today. The washing machine is therefore cheaper at Future Shop than at either Sears or Home Depot, even though Future Shop appears to charge the highest price!

In this example, we've computed the PDV of a particular stream of payments. We can do the same for any stream of payments or receipts occurring over any period of time, and for any interest rate. Suppose you are obliged to pay someone F_0 dollars today, F_1 dollars one year from now, F_2 dollars two years from now, and so forth, with the final payment, F_T dollars, due T years from now. How much do you owe in today's dollars? The answer is

$$\text{PDV of Stream} = F_0 + \frac{F_1}{1 + R} + \frac{F_2}{(1 + R)^2} + \ldots + \frac{F_T}{(1 + R)^T} \qquad (4)$$

We can also use formula (4) to calculate the PDV of a stream of future receipts rather than payments, or a stream that includes both payments and receipts.

To understand formula (4), consider an analogy. Suppose apples cost 25 cents each and oranges cost 20 cents each. You are obliged to give someone four apples and six oranges. To determine the total cost of this obligation, you multiply the prices times the quantities ($0.25 × 4 = $1.00 for apples and $0.20 × 6 = $1.20 for oranges), and then add ($1.00 + $1.20 = $2.20). Formula (4) involves the same type of calculation. To meet your entire obligation immediately, you need to come up with F_0 dollars today, which cost a dollar each, plus F_1 dollars delivered one year from now, which cost $1/(1 + R)$ each today, plus

---

[5]If you put $104.76 in the bank today, you'll have just enough to make the first installment payment in one year; if you add $99.77 today, you'll have just enough to make the second payment in two years, and so forth.

F_2 dollars delivered two years from now, which cost $\$1/(1 + R)^2$ each today, and so forth. The formula simply tells us to multiply prices by quantities and then add up the results.

Some transactions involve streams of payments or receipts that don't change over time. For example, to repay a typical car loan, the borrower has to make the same payment month after month for several years. When the payment stream is constant, there's an easier way to calculate the PDV. Let's say you are obliged to pay someone F dollars annually, starting one year from today, with the final payment to be made in T years. How much do you owe in today's dollars? The answer is[6]

$$\text{PDV of constant stream} = \frac{F}{R}\left(1 - \frac{1}{(1 + R)^T}\right) \qquad (5)$$

As we'll see, formula (5) is often useful.

Here's an easy way to understand why formula (5) holds. Suppose you put F/R dollars in a bank account. During the first year, you'll earn F dollars of interest, which you can use to make your first payment, leaving you with F/R dollars in your account at the start of the second year. Likewise, during the second year, you'll earn F dollars of interest, which you can use to make your second payment, leaving you with F/R dollars in your account at the start of the third year. If you continue in this way, you'll make all of your required payments over the course of T years, and you'll have F/R dollars left in your account. Since you have something left over, your original deposit was larger than it had to be to cover your obligations. How much larger? Since the PDV of your ending balance is $(F/R)/(1 + R)^T$ dollars, you deposited $(F/R)/(1 + R)^T$ dollars too much. You could have covered all of the required payments with an initial deposit of $F/R - (F/R)/(1 + R)^T = F/R(1 - 1/(1 + R)^T)$ dollars. According to formula (5), this is indeed the PDV of your payments.

If you're obliged to make the same payment periodically for a very long time, the PDV of your future payments is approximately F/R dollars. Why? When T is a very large number, the last term in formula (5), $1/(1 + R)^T$, is close to zero. (For example, remember that, with an interest rate of 15 percent, the PDV of $\$1$ received 30 years from now is 1.5 cents.) As a result, formula (5) delivers a value very close to F/R dollars.

Application 10.1

Interest Rates and Bond Prices

Depositing money in a bank account is just one way to swap current dollars for future dollars. Another is to buy a *bond*, a legally binding promise to make specific future payments. In other words, a bond is an I.O.U. Corporations and governments create (or issue) bonds to borrow money from the public. They sell them on the open market at whatever prices investors are willing to pay and must then make the promised payments to the bonds' owners. The purchaser of a bond is usually free to sell it to another investor. When the bond changes hands, the new owner is entitled to the remaining payments.

In Canada, the value of all outstanding bonds exceeded $\$2.5$ trillion in 2008. That figure includes more than $\$1.8$ trillion of federal, provincial, and municipal government securities, and roughly $\$760$ billion of corporate debt.[7]

---

[6]Here's one way to derive formula (5). Let's use X to stand for the PDV of the promised payments. That is, $X = F/(1 + R) + F/(1 + R)^2 + F/(1 + R)^3 + \ldots + F/(1 + R)^T$. Multiplying both sides of this formula by $(1 + R)$ yields $(1 + R)X = F + F/(1 + R) + F/(1 + R)^2 + \ldots + F/1 + R)^{T-1}$. Subtracting the first formula from the second, we obtain $RX = F - F/(1 + R)^T$, which we can rewrite as $RX = F[1 - 1/(1 + R)^T]$. Dividing both sides by R produces formula (5).

[7]Information taken from Table 53 of Statistics Canada National Balance Sheet Accounts, First Quarter 2009.

Some people buy bonds as long-term investments. Others try to make money by anticipating changes in bond prices, buying right before prices rise, and selling right before they fall. The high-stakes business of bond trading requires a thorough knowledge of the economic factors that influence bond prices.

Listen to a few financial reports, and you'll quickly learn that bond prices rise when interest rates fall and fall when interest rates rise. For example, in Figure 10.3, we've plotted the price of a particular type of bond—a six-month Canadian treasury bill—against the prime interest rate (that is, the interest rate that banks charge their most creditworthy customers). The figure includes a data point for each month between January 1999 and June 2009. These data clearly show that the bond price and the interest rate move in opposite directions.

What accounts for this pattern? Unlike a bank account, a bond contract usually describes future payments in dollar amounts rather than as rates of interest. When the interest rate rises, the present discounted value of the promised future payments declines. Since the promised payments are worth less in current dollars, the bond's price falls.

Many bonds provide a regular, constant payment known as the *coupon*, for a fixed period, known as the *maturity*. Usually, the issuer promises to make a larger payment, known as the *face value*, with the final coupon payment. For example, a bond might pay $100 per year for 30 years, with a $1000 payment at maturity. Using the symbols C for the coupon, M for the maturity, V for the face value, and R for the rate of interest, we can write a formula for the PDV of the promised future payments.

$$\text{PDV of promised bond payment} = \frac{C}{1+R} + \frac{C}{(1+R)^2} + \cdots + \frac{C+V}{(1+R)^M}$$

Equivalently, we can use formula (5) to compute the PDV of the constant coupon payments, and then add the PDV of the face value payment.

$$\text{PDV of promised bond payment} = \frac{C}{R}\left(1 - \frac{1}{(1+R)^M}\right) + \frac{V}{(1+R)^M} \quad (6)$$

(Since this expression is the amount people are willing to pay for the bond, it is also the price at which the bond will trade.)

Using these formulas, we can calculate the PDV of the promised payments for any bond at any interest rate. As an example, let's examine six-month Canadian treasury bills. These are zero coupon bonds, sold at a discount to their face value at maturity. The minimum investment pays $5000 when the treasury bill matures. In other words, $C = 0$, $V = 5000$, and $M = \frac{1}{2}$ (since six months is half of a year). By plugging these values into formula (6), we learn that the PDV of a six-month treasury bill is $5000/(1 + R)^{1/2}$ dollars. Clearly, as the interest rate rises, the PDV must fall. For instance, the PDV falls from $4880 to $4767 as the interest rises from 5 percent to 10 percent.[8]

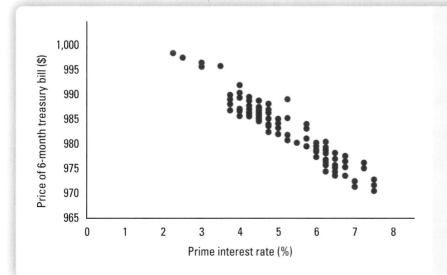

Figure 10.3
The Price of a Bond versus the Prime Interest Rate. In this figure, we've plotted the price of a particular type of bond—a six-month Canadian treasury bill—against the prime interest rate (that is, the interest rate that banks charge their most creditworthy customers) using monthly data from January 1999 and June 2009. The bond price and the interest rate move in opposite directions.

[8]The treasury bill prices shown in Figure 10.3 are slightly higher than those PDVs. That's because the prime rate isn't quite the right interest rate to use when valuing Canadian government securities. Since the Department of Finance is more reliable than even the most creditworthy bank customer, it pays interest at a rate below the prime rate.

WORKED-OUT PROBLEM   10.1

The Problem   Calculate the PDV of promised payments for a 30-year bond with a $100 coupon and a face value of $1000 at interest rates of 5 percent, 10 percent, and 15 percent. Assume that the coupon payments are made at the end of each year.[9]

The Solution   For this bond, we have $C = 100$, $M = 30$, and $V = 1000$. According to formula (6), the PDV of the promised payments is therefore

$$\frac{100}{R}\left(1 - \frac{1}{(1 + R)^{30}}\right) + \frac{1000}{(1 + R)^{30}}$$

By plugging in different interest rates, we find that the PDV is $1768.62 at 5 percent, $1000 at 10 percent, and $671.70 at 15 percent.

IN-TEXT EXERCISE 10.2   Calculate the PDV of promised payments for a 15-year bond with a $4000 coupon and a face value of $50,000 at interest rates of 5 percent, 10 percent, and 15 percent. What if the interest rate is 0 percent?

Why Do Interest Rates Differ?

So far, we've assumed that there is a single rate of interest, but in fact, there are many. For consumers, interest rates on bank deposits differ across banks and account types. For example, a guaranteed investment certificate (or GIC)—which places restrictions on deposits and withdrawals for a fixed period—typically pays a higher interest rate than a money market chequing account.

Consumers also pay interest when they borrow money, and different types of loans carry different interest rates. The interest rates for credit card balances, for example, are typically much higher than home mortgage rates. The maturity of a loan also has a significant effect on the interest rate. In 2009, rates were lower for 5-year mortgages than for 10-year mortgages.

Why do interest rates differ? Risk plays an important role. Sometimes individuals, corporations, and even governments **default**—that is, they fail to pay back the money they've borrowed. To compensate for this risk, lenders demand higher interest payments. The interest rates on credit cards are high in part because a sizable fraction of cardholders are somewhat unreliable. In contrast, the Department of Finance can borrow at a low interest rate because almost everyone expects the Canadian government to honour its obligations.[10] (We'll discuss risk at greater length in Chapter 11.)

Interest rates also depend on some specific features of the agreement between a borrower and a lender. For example, banks must pay higher rates on GICs than on money market chequing accounts to compensate their customers for the loss of financial

Default is the failure to pay back borrowed money.

---

[9]Many bonds promise payments at other intervals, such as semiannually.

[10]Even if a government never defaults, it can still choose to pay less in real terms by adopting policies that lead to higher rates of inflation, a concept that we discussed in Section 6.3. In that case, we say that the government has *monetized* a portion of its debt.

flexibility. The timing of repayment is also important. Lenders charge different rates for short-term loans than for long-term loans. These advanced topics aren't covered in this book, but you'll learn more about them if you go on to study finance or money and banking.

In computing the present value of some future payment, it's important to use an interest rate for an obligation that has similar characteristics. When the future payment involves little or no risk (as we assume throughout this section), we can use the rate paid by an extremely reliable borrower, like the Canadian government. When the future payment is risky, we need to use the rate paid by a less reliable borrower. Likewise, in valuing dollars delivered, say, 30 years in the future, it's appropriate to use a long-term interest rate. A short-term rate is useful in valuing a dollar delivered within, say, three months.

Real versus Nominal Interest

Whenever we lend or borrow money, it's important to remember that future dollars may not carry the same purchasing power as current dollars. (Recall our discussion of inflation in Section 6.3.) If the interest rate is 10 percent, we can trade $10 today for $11 next year. From that perspective, we appear to come out ahead. But if Donald spends all of his money on beef, and if the price of beef is expected to increase by 10 percent over the next year from $5 to $5.50, then trading $10 today for $11 next year amounts to trading two kilograms of beef this year for two kilograms of beef next year. Donald may come out ahead in terms of dollars, but not in terms of beef.

For this reason, economists distinguish between **nominal interest** and **real interest**, a distinction that parallels the one between nominal income and real (inflation-adjusted) income, discussed in Section 6.3. Nominal interest is the compensation received by the lender over and above the principal, measured in nominal dollars (that is, without adjusting for inflation). Real interest is the compensation received by the lender over and above the principal, measured in real dollars (that is, adjusted for inflation). When a bank or a lender quotes an interest rate, it's usually a nominal rate.

To calculate the annual real interest rate earned on money deposited in a bank account, R^{real}, we express the change in the real account balance over a year as a fraction of the real dollars deposited.

$$R^{real} = \frac{\text{Real dollars next year } - \text{ Real dollars deposited}}{\text{Real dollars deposited}}$$

Let's suppose the deposit is one real dollar. Over one year, that deposit will grow to $1 + R^{nominal}$ dollars, where $R^{nominal}$ is the nominal interest rate. However, due to inflation, those $1 + R^{nominal}$ dollars will be worth only $(1 + R^{nominal})/(1 + INFL)$ real dollars, where $INFL$ is the rate of inflation (see Section 6.3). When we substitute this expression into the previous formula, and remember that the original deposit is one real dollar, we discover that

$$R^{real} = \frac{((1 + R^{nominal})/(1 + INFL)) - 1}{1} = \frac{R^{nominal} - INFL}{1 + INFL} \qquad (7)$$

Using formula (7), we can calculate the real interest rate from the nominal interest rate and the inflation rate. For example, in Donald's case, the nominal interest rate and

> **Nominal interest** is the compensation received by the lender over and above the principal, measured in nominal dollars (that is, without adjusting for inflation).
>
> **Real interest** is the compensation received by the lender over and above the principal, measured in real dollars (that is, adjusted for inflation).

the inflation rate (the expected change in the price of beef) are both 10 percent, so the real rate of interest is 0 percent (because $(0.10 - 0.10)/(1 + 0.10) = 0$). This rate reflects the fact that Donald can trade a kilogram of beef today for a kilogram of beef next year, no more and no less.

If the rate of inflation is low, dividing by $1 + INFL$ in formula (7) doesn't make much of a difference. As a result, the real interest rate is roughly equal to the difference between the nominal interest rate and the inflation rate.

$$R^{real} \approx R^{nominal} - INFL \qquad\qquad (8)$$

For example, if the nominal interest rate is 5 percent and the inflation rate is 3 percent, formula (7) implies that the real interest rate is 1.942 percent ($R^{real} = 0.02/1.03 = 0.01942$). Formula (8) tells us that it's approximately 2 percent, which is off by only six one-hundredths of a percentage point. However, formula (8) is sometimes less reliable. If the nominal interest rate were 30 percent and the inflation rate were 25 percent, formula (7) tells us that the real interest rate would be 4 percent. Formula (8) yields an answer of approximately 5 percent, a full percentage point off.

In the last section, we didn't say explicitly whether we were dealing with real interest rates or nominal interest rates. Does it matter? The answer is no, as long as we're consistent. That is, we can calculate the PDV of a *nominal* future cash flow using a *nominal* interest rate, or we can calculate the PDV of a *real* future cash flow using a *real* interest rate. Either way, we'll get the same answer.[11]

WORKED-OUT PROBLEM   **10.2**

The Problem   If the real interest rate is 5 percent and the inflation rate is 3 percent, what is the nominal interest rate?

The Solution   Rearranging formula (7), we see that $R^{nominal} = INFL + R^{real}(1 + INFL)$. When we substitute $R^{real} = 0.05$ and $INFL = 0.03$, we find that $R^{nominal} = 0.0815$. So the nominal interest rate is 8.15 percent.

IN-TEXT EXERCISE 10.3   **Suppose the nominal interest rate is 4 percent and the inflation rate is 1 percent. What is the real interest rate? What if the nominal interest rate is 5 percent and the inflation rate is 2 percent? In general, if the nominal interest rate and the inflation rate both rise by one percentage point, does the real interest rate change? What about the approximate value of the real interest rate given by formula (8)?**

---

[11]Suppose you expect to receive $1 one year from now. Using the nominal cash flow and the nominal interest rate, the PDV is $1/(1 + R^{nominal})$. Using the real cash flow and the real interest rate, the PDV is $(1/(1 + INFL))/(1 + R^{real})$. By adding one to both sides of formula (7), we learn that $1 + R^{real} = (1 + R^{nominal})/(1 + INFL)$. Substituting this formula into the previous expression, we discover that $(1/(1 + INFL))/(1 + R^{real}) = 1/(1 + R^{nominal})$, so the two PDVs are the same.

Application 10.2

Now that You've Won the Lottery …

In March of 2009 Calgarians beat the odds by winning three of the four available $1 million prizes in the Western Canada Lottery Corporation's (WCLC) Millionaire Life contest for which 13 million tickets were purchased across Canada. The grand prize winner, also from Alberta, was given the choice of receiving $1 million a year for the next 25 years, totalling $25 million, or a one time $17 million pay out. Why the difference?

Some lotteries pay out people's winnings in annual installments, over a period of 20 years or more. The size of the advertised jackpot refers to the total nominal amount paid and not to the PDV of those earnings. For example, a $10 million prize might yield annual nominal payments of $500,000 per year for 20 years. The lottery corporation spread the payments out over time precisely so they can advertise a larger prize without actually giving up more money.

The WCLC allows the grand prize winner in the Millionaire Life contest to claim the prize in the form of an immediate lump-sum payment. However, the amount paid out in that form is less than the total advertised jackpot.

Would the grand prize winner be foolish to give up $8 million for the sake of gaining instant access to the prize?

Not necessarily. Since the $25 million was a claim on future nominal dollars, it was worth considerably less than $25 million in March 2009. The question is whether it was worth more or less than $17 million.[12]

To answer this question, it's helpful to understand how lottery jackpots are determined. For every drawing, the WCLC allocates some fixed amount of money to a grand prize. That amount is what a winner receives upon choosing the lump-sum option. It differs from the advertised jackpot, which is the sum of winnings paid out in 25 annual installments. The size of the advertised jackpot is chosen so that the PDV of those installments, using the prevailing nominal interest rates, exactly equals the amount of money allocated to the prize. If a winner chooses to receive the prize in installments, the WCLC contracts with a third party to pay out the $1 million annually and pays the third party the $17 million.

As long as the lump sum equals the PDV of the nominal installment payments, it is neither a good deal nor a bad one. It simply reflects the jackpot's current value. The implicit interest rate used in the Millionaire Life contest turns out to be 3.2 percent.

10.2 SAVING AND BORROWING

To keep matters as simple as possible while introducing the basic principles of consumer decision making, we assumed throughout Chapters 5 and 6 that consumers could neither save current income nor borrow against future income. This assumption is obviously unrealistic. In this section, we'll see how the theory of consumer choice accounts for saving and borrowing.

The Timing of Consumption

You might think that adding saving and borrowing to the mix would significantly complicate our analysis of consumer choice. If so, you're in for a pleasant surprise! You've already learned all the basic concepts required to understand saving and borrowing. For

---

[12]In part, the answer to this question depends on the income tax treatment of lottery winnings. Here, we'll keep the analysis simple by ignoring taxes, which only are payable if the annuity option is selected. If you ever win the lottery, we recommend consulting a reliable financial planner before deciding whether to take your prize as a lump sum or a series of installments!

the most part, all you need to do is apply what you learned in Chapters 4 through 6, using some of the tools developed in the last section.

Before we proceed, let's first address a basic question: When are two consumable items different goods and when are they the same good? In some cases, the answer is obvious. For example, a litre of water and a litre of gasoline are plainly different goods. Why? They serve different purposes and meet different needs. You drink the water and put the gasoline in your car's gas tank. Disastrous consequences follow if you drink the gasoline and put water in your gas tank.

Now think about two separate litres of water, litre A and litre B, with identical chemical compositions. Are they examples of the same good? If you're like most people, you're probably tempted to say yes (unless you sense, correctly, that this is a trick question). The two litres appear to serve the same purposes and meet the same needs. Both are equally well suited for drinking, watering plants, and washing hands.

Or are they? What if litre A is available today and litre B is available a year from now? In that case, they no longer meet the same needs. If I'm thirsty today, I can satisfy my need for water only by drinking from litre A, but not by drinking from litre B. This means we should think of them as *different* goods. In contrast, if litre A and litre B are both available at the same moment in time, at the same place, and under the same conditions, then they do indeed serve the same needs and are examples of the same good.

To study consumption decisions involving time, then, we simply think of a good's time of availability as a physical characteristic, just like size, color, or function. We treat identical physical objects (or services) as distinct goods if they are available at different points in time. Otherwise, we proceed as we did in Chapters 4 through 6.

Preferences for the Timing of Consumption   In Section 4.2, we began by describing the consumer's preferences for consumption bundles. Remember that a consumption bundle lists the amount of each good consumed. Since we must distinguish among goods according to the time at which they are available, our list must itemize separately goods consumed now and goods consumed at particular points in the future. For real consumers, the list will be quite long.

To keep the analysis relatively simple, we'll examine a case in which the consumer, whom we'll call Brian, cares only about two goods, food this year and food next year (both measured in kilograms). Figure 10.4(a) shows Brian's set of potential consumption bundles graphically. Each point on the graph corresponds to a different bundle. For example, point A represents the consumption bundle consisting of 300 kilograms of food this year and 300 kilograms of food next year. At all points lying on the 45-degree line through the origin, like point A, Brian eats the same amount of food this year and next. For all points above the 45-degree line, like point B, Brian eats less food this year than next. And at all points below the 45-degree line, like point C, Brian eats more food this year than next.

We've illustrated Brian's preferences for these bundles by drawing the red indifference curves in Figure 10.4(a). Note that they have the same general shape as the indifference curves in Sections 4.2 and 4.3, for essentially the same reasons. Since we can compensate Brian for a reduction in food this year by providing him with more food next year (and vice versa), the curves slope downward. And since having extra food is relatively more important when food is scarce, each indifference curve has a declining marginal rate of substitution.

Figure 10.4(b) shows a family of indifference curves (in blue) for a second consumer, Ryan. At any particular point, like point E in both figures, Ryan's indifference curve is

Figure 10.4

Consumer Preferences for the Timing of Consumption. Each point on these graphs corresponds to a consumption bundle consisting of food this year and food next year. At points on the 45-degree line, like point A in figure (a), consumption is the same in both years. At points above the 45-degree line, like point B in figure (a), consumption is lower this year than next. At points below the 45-degree line, like point C in figure (a), consumption is higher this year than next. At any particular point, like point E in both figures, Ryan's indifference curve [in figure (b)] is steeper than Brian's [in figure (a)], which means that Ryan's marginal rate of substitution for food this year with food next year is larger. The greater steepness of Ryan's indifference curves therefore indicates greater impatience.

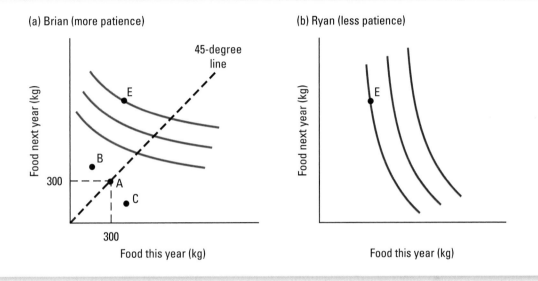

steeper than Brian's, which means that Ryan's marginal rate of substitution for food this year with food next year is larger. To compensate for the loss of a kilogram of food this year, Ryan would require a larger increase in food next year than Brian. The greater steepness of Ryan's indifference curves therefore indicates greater impatience.

Affordable Consumption Bundles   As in Section 5.1, the next step is to identify affordable consumption bundles. Let's start with an example. Suppose that Brian expects to earn $380 this year and $220 next year. The interest rate is 10 percent and the price of food is $1 per kilogram both this year and next. Which bundles can Brian afford?

Clearly, Brian can afford the bundle A in Figure 10.5(a), which contains 380 kilograms of food this year and 220 kilograms of food next year. To purchase this bundle, he simply spends his income when he receives it.

Brian can also purchase any bundle on the green line that runs through bundle A in Figure 10.5(a). For bundles on this line to the left of point A, income exceeds spending this year, and spending exceeds income next year. Brian can obtain these bundles by saving. For example, if he puts $180 in a bank account this year (leaving him with $200 to spend on food), he'll be able to spend $418 next year (his income, $220, plus the amount he saved, $180, plus interest on his saving, $18). This possibility corresponds to bundle B in Figure 10.5(a). For bundles on the green line to the right of point A, spending exceeds

Figure 10.5

Affordable Alternatives with Saving and Borrowing. Brian earns $380 this year and $220 next year. If he spends his money when he receives it, he consumes the bundle labelled A in both figures. Figure (a) shows that he can reach point B by saving $180 this year, which will give him an extra $198 next year. Figure (b) shows that he can reach point C by borrowing $100 this year and repaying $110 next year.

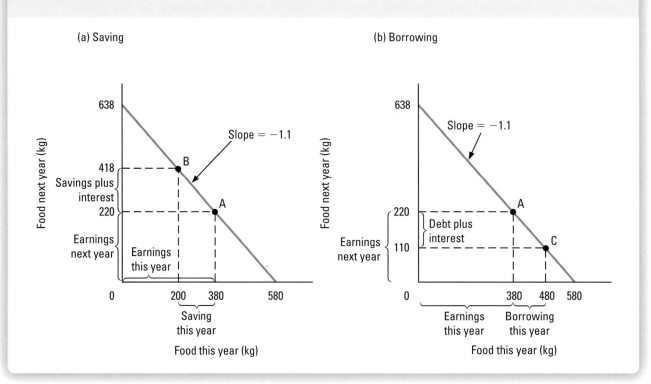

income this year, and income exceeds spending next year. Brian can obtain these bundles by borrowing. For example, if he borrows $100 this year and spends $480 on food, he'll be able to spend $110 next year (his income, $220, minus the amount he borrowed, $100, minus interest on his debt, $10). This possibility corresponds to bundle C in Figure 10.5(b).

Notice that the slope of the green line is −1.1. If Brian reduces his consumption this year by one kilogram, he can either increase his saving by $1, in which case he will earn 10 cents more interest, or reduce his borrowing by $1, in which case he will pay 10 cents less interest. In either case, he will have an extra $1.10 next year, which buys 1.1 kilograms of food.

More generally, a consumption bundle is affordable if, through borrowing and lending, the consumer can make all the required payments as they come due. That is possible as long as the PDV of the consumption stream doesn't exceed the PDV of the income stream. When the More-Is-Better Principle holds, the best choice leaves no income unspent, so

$$\text{PDV of consumption stream} = \text{PDV of income stream} \tag{9}$$

Let's apply this formula to Brian's problem. We'll use P_0 to stand for the price per kilogram of food this year, P_1 for the price per kilogram of food next year, and R for the interest rate. Formula (9) implies that

$$\text{Food this year (kg)} \times P_0 + \text{Food next year (kg)} \times \left(\frac{P_1}{1+R}\right)$$
$$= \text{Income this year} + \frac{\text{Income next year}}{1+R} \qquad (10)$$

Using the same numerical values as above ($P_0 = P_1 = 1$, $R = 0.10$, income this year is \$380, and income next year is \$220), formula (10) simplifies as

$$\text{Food this year (kg)} + \text{Food next year (kg)} \times \left(\frac{1}{1.1}\right) = 580$$

The consumption bundles that satisfy this formula lie on the green line in Figures 10.5(a) and (b). (Check this!)

The expression $P_1/(1+R)$, which appears in formula (10), is the PDV of the price-per-kilogram of food next year. We can also interpret $P_1/(1+R)$ as the price of food next year *from today's perspective*. Why? The price of a good is the amount of money you need to give up in exchange for it. If you give up $P_1/(1+R)$ dollars today by putting it in the bank, you'll have just enough money to buy a kilogram of food a year from now (P_1 dollars).

With this interpretation of $P_1/(1+R)$ in mind, we see that formula (10) describes a budget line, just like the ones introduced in Section 5.1. In the first line of this formula, we multiply the amount of food purchased in each year times its price from today's perspective, then we add these numbers up to find total spending. The second line tells us that total spending equals total income—again valued from today's perspective.

In Section 5.1, we saw that the slope of a budget line equals the ratio of the goods' prices, times 1. In the context of Brian's problem, the price of food this year is P_0 and the price of food next year (from today's perspective) is $P_1/(1+R)$. We therefore have the following formula for the slope of the budget line:

$$\text{Slope of budget line} = -\frac{P_0}{P_1/(1+R)} = -(1+R)\left(\frac{P_0}{P_1}\right) \qquad (11)$$

In our numerical example, we assumed that food costs \$1 per kilogram in each year ($P_0 = P_1 = 1$), and that the interest rate is 10 percent ($R = 0.10$). Therefore, formula (11) tells us that the slope of Brian's budget line is $-(1+0.10)(1/1) = -1.1$, just as we determined above.

Consumption Choices   To determine Brian's best choice, we apply the no-overlap rule (which we introduced in Section 5.2). When Brian's preferences correspond to the family of red indifference curves in Figure 10.4(a), he chooses point B in Figure 10.6(a). Since point B is to the left of point A, we know he saves something this year so he can consume more food next year.

Figure 10.6(b) examines Ryan's best choice assuming that his preferences correspond to the blue family of indifference curves in Figure 10.4(b). Since the blue indifference curves are steeper than the red curves, the blue curve that runs through point B crosses the budget line, as shown. Ryan can do better than point B by moving along the

Figure 10.6

Best Choices with Saving and Borrowing. Based on his earnings, Brian starts out at point A in figure (a). His best choice with the red indifference curves is point B. Since point B is to the left of point A, he saves. With the blue indifference curves in figure (b), which reflect greater impatience, Ryan's best choice is point C. Since point C is to the right of point A, he borrows.

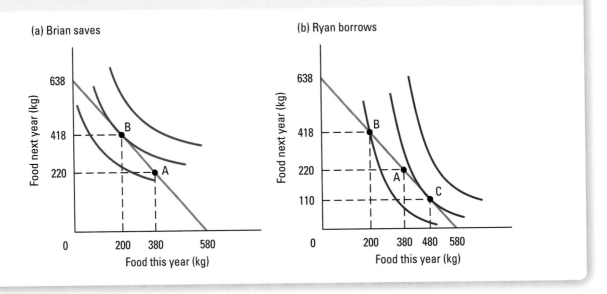

(a) Brian saves   (b) Ryan borrows

budget line to the southeast. His best choice is point C. Since point C is to the right of point A, we know that Ryan borrows money this year so he can consume more food than his current income would allow. There is nothing wrong with that—compared with Brian, he simply prefers to consume more this year and less next year.

Saving, Borrowing, and the Interest Rate

When the interest rate rises, saving becomes more rewarding and borrowing becomes more costly. It's natural to think that people would respond to a rise in the interest rate by saving more and borrowing less. However, the truth is not quite so straightforward. Suppose, for example, that your objective is to accumulate $30,000 over the next five years so you can buy a nice car. If the interest rate rises, you'll earn more interest on each dollar saved, which means you won't need to save as much to reach your target. Therefore, you might decide to save *less*.

To understand how saving and borrowing respond to changes in the interest rate, we first need to study how those changes affect consumers' budget constraints. Let's assume that point A in Figure 10.7(a) is the bundle Brian can afford if he spends all of his income when he receives it. Let's also assume that he can purchase any bundle on the line labelled L_1 at the prevailing interest rate. An increase in the interest rate rotates his budget line to L_2, pivoting it around point A. Why? He can still spend all of his income when he receives it, so bundle A remains affordable. However, according to formula (11), the budget line becomes steeper. Intuitively, an increase in the interest

Figure 10.7

The Effect of a Change in the Interest Rate on Saving. In figure (a), Brian initially chooses point B. When the interest rate rises, he picks point D. Figure (b) breaks this change up into a substitution effect (the movement from B to E) and an income effect (the movement from E to D). Assuming food this year is a normal good, these effects work in opposite directions. Brian's consumption of food this year can therefore rise or fall. This means that, in response to an increase in the interest rate, his saving can rise or fall.

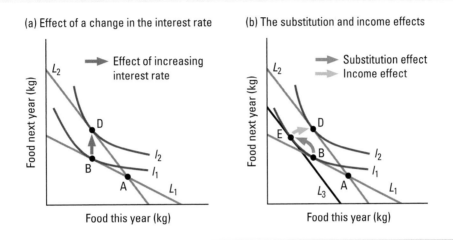

(a) Effect of a change in the interest rate   (b) The substitution and income effects

rate reduces the amount of money Brian must set aside today to purchase a kilogram of food next year. This allows him to exchange food this year for food next year at a more favourable rate.

How is Brian's saving affected by this change in the interest rate? To answer this question, we examine the resulting change in food consumption this year. If food consumption this year rises, Brian must save less if he is a saver, or borrow more if he is a borrower. If food consumption this year falls, Brian must either save more if he is a saver, or borrow less if he is a borrower.

In Figure 10.7(a), we reproduce Brian's indifference curves (shown in red) from Figure 10.4(a). At the lower interest rate he faces the budget line labelled L_1 and chooses point B, which involves saving. If the interest rate rises, changing his budget line to L_2, his best choice shifts to point D.

Will Brian's food consumption this year rise or fall? In Figure 10.7(a), it declines slightly; more generally, the answer is unclear. Why? In Section 6.1 we learned that a change in the price of a good creates both a substitution effect and an income effect. We illustrate these effects in Figure 10.7(b). The substitution effect involves a movement along indifference curve I_1 from point B to point E (budget line L_3 runs parallel to L_2 and is tangent to I_1 at point E). Since point E lies to the left of B, consumption this year falls and saving rises. Intuitively, Brian substitutes away from food this year because food next year has become comparatively less expensive. What about the income effect? Since Brian is a saver, the higher interest rate *increases* his purchasing power. The income effect therefore involves an *outward* shift of the budget line, from L_3 to L_2, which moves him

Figure 10.8

The Effect of a Change in the Interest Rate on Borrowing. In figure (a) Ryan chooses point C. When the interest rate rises, he picks point F. Figure (b) breaks this change up into a substitution effect (the movement from C to G) and an income effect (the movement from G to F). Assuming food this year is a normal good, these effects work in the same direction, and food this year necessarily falls. This means that, in response to an increase in the interest rate, borrowing necessarily falls.

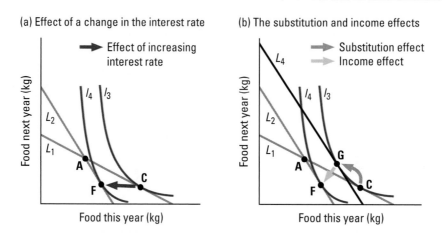

(a) Effect of a change in the interest rate

(b) The substitution and income effects

from point E to point D. As long as food this year is a normal good, Brian will consume more of it as a result of the income effect, and save less. So just as in our analysis of labour supply decisions (Section 6.4), the income and substitution effects work in opposite directions. Brian's food consumption this year, and therefore his saving, can either rise or fall, depending on which effect is larger.

How does an increase in the interest rate affect borrowing? In Figure 10.8(a), we reproduce Ryan's indifference curves (shown in blue) from Figure 10.4(b). At the lower interest rate, he faces the budget line labelled L_1 and chooses point C, which involves borrowing. The change in the interest rate shifts his budget line to L_2 and his best choice to point F. Because point F lies to the left of point C, Ryan's borrowing falls. Ryan's response involves an income effect and a substitution effect, which we illustrate in Figure 10.8(b). Like Brian in Figure 10.7(b), Ryan consumes less food this year as a result of the substitution effect, which moves him along indifference curve I_3 from point C to point G (budget line L_4 is parallel to L_2 and tangent to I_3 at point G). In this case, Ryan is a borrower, so the higher interest rate *reduces* his purchasing power. The income effect therefore involves an *inward* shift of the budget line, from L_4 to L_2, which moves Ryan from point G to point F. As long as food this year is a normal good, Ryan will consume less of it as a result of the income effect. So the income and substitution effects push food consumption this year in the *same* direction. Therefore, borrowing will definitely fall.

In sum, if we assume that consumption at each point in time is a normal good, then among savers, an increase in the interest rate can either raise or lower saving, but among borrowers, an increase in the interest rate definitely reduces borrowing.

WORKED-OUT PROBLEM   10.3

The Problem   Angela cares only about food this year and food next year. Let's use F_0 to stand for food this year (in kilograms) and F_1 to stand for food next year (also in kilograms). Assume that Angela's marginal rate of substitution between food this year and food next year is F_1/F_0. Suppose she earns \$100 this year and nothing next year. Food costs \$1 per kilogram in both years and the interest rate is 10 percent. How much does she consume this year and how much does she save? Write a formula for her saving as a function of the interest rate, R. Does she save more, less, or the same amount when the interest rate rises?

The Solution   First, let's identify bundles that satisfy the tangency condition. The slope of Angela's indifference curve is $-F_1/F_0$ (her marginal rate of substitution for food this year with food next year, times -1), and the slope of her budget line is $-(1 + R)$. At her best choice, her indifference curve and her budget line must have the same slope, which requires $F_1/F_0 = 1 + R$, or equivalently $F_1 = F_0(1 + R)$. This tangency condition formula tells us that Angela eats $1 + R$ times as much food next year as this year.

The formula for Angela's budget line is $F_0 + F_1/(1 + R) = 100$. To find a bundle satisfying both the tangency condition formula and the budget line formula, we substitute for F_1 in the budget line formula using the tangency condition formula. This substitution yields the formula $F_0 + F_0(1 + R)/(1 + R) = 100$, which simplifies to $2F_0 = 100$, or $F_0 = 50$. So, this year Angela spends \$50 and saves \$50; next year she spends $\$50(1 + R)$. Because the interest rate is 10 percent, she consumes 50 kilograms of food this year and 55 kilograms next year.

The formula for saving, S, is simply $S = 50$. Angela's saving doesn't depend on the interest rate.

IN-TEXT EXERCISE 10.4   **Assume that Angela earns nothing this year and \$100 next year. To consume food this year, she must borrow. Repeat worked-out problem 10.3. This time, write a formula for her borrowing as a function of the interest rate. According to your formula, does she borrow more or less as the interest rate rises? Why does the interest rate affect borrowing in this exercise, even though it didn't affect saving in worked-out problem 10.3?**

Saving and Consumption over the Life Cycle

In practice, decisions involving saving are a good deal more complicated than Brian's simple problem. Among other things, if we expect to live for many years, we have to provide resources not merely for next year, but for the year after that, and the year after that.

In the 1950s and 1960s, economists Franco Modigliani (who later received the Nobel Prize), Richard Brumberg, and Albert Ando developed a theory of consumption and saving known as the Life Cycle Hypothesis, which describes the choices of consumers who live for a long time. Today, their theory is widely applied and is one of the most important tools economists use.

Figure 10.9

The Life Cycle Hypothesis. As figure (a) shows, earnings usually rise with experience, level off in middle age, and then decline a bit before disappearing after retirement. Assuming that the consumer prefers a stable living standard, he'll choose a consumption path that doesn't vary with age, like C_1, C_2, or C_3 Of these choices, C_2 is the best feasible alternative: C_1 isn't feasible, and C_3 doesn't exhaust the consumer's lifetime resources. C_2 is also better than the wavy green consumption path, because it avoids ups and downs. Figure (b) shows how the consumer's saving and wealth change with age when he follows consumption path C_2. After retirement, he will spend down his wealth to maintain his living standard.

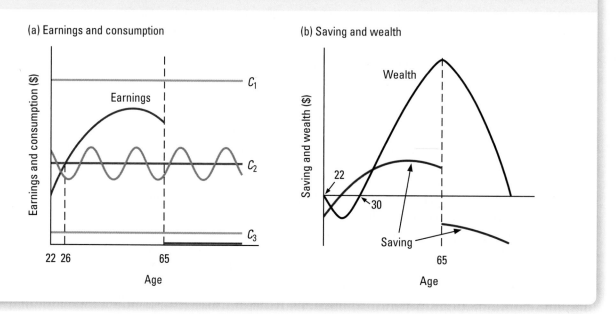

(a) Earnings and consumption

(b) Saving and wealth

The Life Cycle Hypothesis applies the same logic we used to solve Brian's problem, but it adds two assumptions. The first, concerning earnings, holds that the typical person's adult life has two main stages. In the first stage, he or she is gainfully employed. Earnings rise with experience, level off in middle age, and then may decline a bit. In the second stage, the person is retired and earns nothing.[13]

The second assumption, concerning preferences, is that people like stability. That is, they prefer a constant or slowly changing lifestyle to a feast-or-famine roller-coaster ride. Of course, in comparing two stable alternatives, they favour the one that offers the higher living standard.

To see where these assumptions lead, look at Figure 10.9(a), which presents a more realistic version of Brian's problem. The blue curve shows his earnings rising steadily through middle age, falling a bit as retirement nears, and dropping to zero after retirement—a fairly typical pattern. The light and dark red lines show three possible consumption levels. In each of these cases, Brian's living standard is completely stable—consumption doesn't

---

[13]The theory also allows for the possibility that people may partially retire or receive pension income after retirement. In either case, their cash income from employment falls after retirement, but not necessarily to zero. Economists have explored many other variations of the basic theory, including situations in which people are uncertain about how long they'll live and in which they invest in risky assets.

change at all with his age. Naturally, the line labelled C_1 is the best of the three, and the line labelled C_3 is the worst.

To determine whether any particular consumption path is feasible, we need to make sure its PDV doesn't exceed the PDV of Brian's earnings. The light red consumption path C_1 isn't feasible because it lies above the blue earnings line at every age; Brian doesn't earn enough money over his lifetime to pay for it. The light red consumption path C_3 is feasible but not particularly desirable, since it doesn't even begin to exhaust his earnings. Somewhere between these two possibilities lies a line like C_2 (shown in dark red) for which the PDV of consumption equals the PDV of Brian's earnings. Paying for this consumption stream will just exhaust Brian's lifetime earnings. This is the best available choice—better, for example, than living hand-to-mouth, spending income as it is earned, because it avoids an enormous drop in living standard at retirement. It is also better than following the wavy green curve, because it avoids ups and downs.[14]

Figure 10.9(b) shows how Brian's saving and his wealth (that is, his accumulated savings minus his accumulated debt) changes as he ages. When Brian follows consumption path C_2, he spends more than he earns from ages 22 through 26. To make up the vertical gap between the red and blue curves in Figure 10.9(a), he has to borrow.[15] That means his saving is negative, as shown by the brown line in Figure 10.9(b). Since he accumulates debt, his wealth also becomes negative, as shown by the black line. Fortunately, Brian's earnings rise with experience. After age 26, his income is sufficient to pay for his consumption. The vertical gap between the blue and red curves represents extra funds, which he uses to pay the interest on his debt. If anything is left over after interest payments, he repays part of the balance on his debt. At that point, his saving becomes positive and his wealth—though still negative—begins to rise.

According to Figure 10.9(b), Brian pays off all of his debts by age 30. Then he begins to accumulate positive wealth. As time passes, his saving increases, reflecting both the growing difference between his earnings and his spending, and the rising interest on his wealth. At retirement, however, his earnings disappear. To maintain the same living standard, he has to pay his living expenses out of his interest income and his wealth. His wealth therefore declines steadily, which means his saving is negative, as in his youth. With less wealth, he earns less interest income, and is forced to pay more expenses out of his wealth. This is why the brown curve (saving) declines after retirement, and why the black curve (wealth) declines at an increasing rate. If Brian times this drawdown perfectly, he will die with just enough money left to cover his funeral expenses.[16]

The Life Cycle Hypothesis has many important implications. For example, it helps us to understand and predict how changes in the age structure of a country's population will affect its overall rate of saving. Saving tends to be low in developing countries which have high concentrations of young people. Overall saving is also projected to decline in many developed countries because a significant proportion of their population is shifting steadily toward retirement age.

---

[14]Though we've drawn flat consumption lines, most people seem to prefer a gradually rising living standard. The Life Cycle Hypothesis easily accommodates this preference.

[15]In addition to the difference between his planned consumption and his earnings, Brian also needs to borrow enough money to pay the interest on his outstanding debt. In practice, many young people have difficulty finding lenders from whom to borrow at reasonable terms, due mostly to informational problems (see Chapter 21). Some versions of the Life Cycle Hypothesis include these types of restrictions.

[16]In practice, people don't know how long they'll live, and many wish to leave bequests. In versions of the Life Cycle Hypothesis that allow for these possibilities, people die with some positive wealth.

Application 10.3

Stimulating Saving for Retirement

Many economists and policymakers think Canadians save too little for retirement. Some attribute this tendency, at least in part, to the income tax system, which reduces the economic rewards of saving by, for example, taxing interest income. To illustrate, suppose the interest rate is 5 percent, and individuals must pay the government 20 percent of each additional dollar earned. If a taxpayer puts away $1 today, he'll have only $1.04 a year from now instead of $1.05; the extra penny will go to the government. In other words, the after-tax interest rate is only 4 percent.

To stimulate saving, the Canadian government offers taxpayers the opportunity to open a Registered Retirement Savings Plan (RRSP). Funds in an RRSP account earn interest tax-free until withdrawal, and under some circumstances, contributions are tax-deductible. (Of interest to students is a provision that allows the tax credit from RRSP contributions to be used in the future when earnings are greater.) As a result, the after-tax return on RRSP savings is significantly higher than it is on normal saving.

The effect of an RRSP on household saving is the subject of considerable disagreement and debate, however. Opponents of the policy emphasize two concerns. First, as we've seen in this chapter, there is no reason to think saving *necessarily* rises with the interest rate. An increase in the interest rate creates both a substitution effect, which reduces current consumption, and an income effect, which can increase consumption. Overall, saving could remain constant or even decline. Historically, higher-than-normal rates of saving have not coincided with higher-than-normal real interest rates.

The second concern emphasized by RRSP opponents is that RRSP contributions are limited by law. Someone who wants to save more than the limit receives no tax relief on the last dollar saved, and therefore has no incentive to save more.

Figure 10.10 illustrates this second concern. The consumer allocates his resources between consumption before retirement and consumption after retirement. He starts out at point A, with positive earnings before retirement and nothing after retirement. Given his after-tax rate of return, he can choose any point on the line labelled L_1.

Now suppose the government allows him to save up to some fixed amount in a RRSP, and taxes interest on RRSP savings at a lower rate. In that case, the consumer can choose any point on the kinked line labelled L_2. As he starts

"*Remember, son, it's never too early to start saving for retirement.*"

to save, he is able to trade consumption before retirement for consumption after retirement at a more attractive rate. That is why L_2 is steeper than L_1 between points A and B. However, once the consumer reaches the contribution limit, he goes back to earning the original interest rate on each additional dollar saved. That is why L_2 is parallel L_1 to the left of point B.

How does the RRSP affect saving? The consumer with the blue indifference curves chooses point C without an RRSP and point D with an RRSP, in each case saving *less* than the contribution limit. Since the shift from point C to point D involves both an income effect and a substitution effect, his saving can either rise or fall. In contrast, the consumer with the red indifference curves picks point E without an RRSP and point F with an RRSP, in each case saving *more* than the contribution limit. The shift from point E to point F involves an income effect but no substitution effect. Ordinarily, therefore, point F involves more consumption and *less* saving before retirement.

Proponents of RRSPs respond that many people save less than the contribution limit, and that few replace contributed funds by borrowing. They also contend that opponents ignore various indirect effects of RRSPs. For example, the program may focus the public's attention on retirement, and it may induce financial institutions to advertise and market retirement savings products aggressively.

Unfortunately, the available evidence on the effects of RRSPs is mixed. Some studies have found that each dollar contributed to an RRSP account adds one dollar to total saving; others have concluded that RRSP contributions are offset by a combination of reduced saving in other forms. While early research argued that RRSP contributions could explain the divergence between saving rates in Canada and the United States during the 1970s, John Burbidge, Deborah Fretz, and Michael Veall of McMaster University argue that those same contributions are not well correlated with Canadian saving rates.[17]

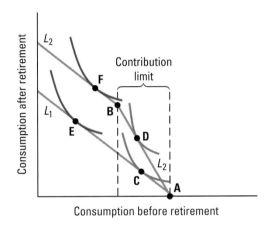

Figure 10.10

The Effect of RRSPs on Saving. Without an RRSP, the consumer's budget line is L_1. With an RRSP, his budget line L_2 is kinked at point B where his saving reaches the contribution limit. For someone who is saving less than the contribution limit (the blue indifference curves), an RRSP creates both an income and a substitution effect, so that saving can either rise or fall. For someone who is saving more than the contribution limit (the red indifference curves), an RRSP creates only an income effect, so that saving falls.

10.3 INVESTMENT

Time is almost always an important consideration in decisions involving production. Why? Production usually requires capital, and most types of capital—factories, office buildings, machines, tools, and so forth—are reasonably durable. Machines can last for years, factories often remain productive for decades, and buildings are sometimes used for centuries. In addition, some capital inputs take time to assemble. While companies can purchase many common tools and machines without delay, complex factories (like Volkswagen's Phaeton plant) often require many years of planning and construction.

When a company acquires capital, it incurs up-front costs with the expectation of generating future profits. This type of transaction is known as **investment**.[18] A firm's

Investment refers to up-front costs incurred with the expectation of generating future profits.

---

[17]See J. B. Burbidge, D. Fretz, and M. R. Veall (1998) "Canadian and American Saving Rates and the Role of RRSPs," *Canadian Public Policy*, 26(2), pp. 259–263 and C. Carroll and L. H. Summers (1987) "Why Have Private Savings Rates in the United States and Canada Diverged?", *Journal of Monetary Economics*, 20(2), pp. 249–279.

[18]Economists sometimes distinguish between *physical* investment, such as equipment and the construction of a plant, and *financial* investment, such as the purchase of a bond or shares of a company's stock. Financial investment is closely related to saving; however, the two concepts are not identical. To illustrate the difference, suppose someone borrows $1000 to purchase $1000 worth of a company's stock. Together, these transactions involve financial investment, but no saving (since current consumption is unaffected).

economic performance is tied closely to the types and levels of investment it makes. Thus, knowing how to distinguish between a good investment and a bad one is an essential management skill.

Let's examine a simple hypothetical investment opportunity for a company called Snow Stuff, Inc., which specializes in winter recreation products. After studying trends in demand, one of the company's managers has proposed launching a line of snowboards. None of Snow Stuff's existing facilities are suited for manufacturing snowboards, so the new product would require a new factory. Careful research indicates that Snow Stuff could construct a factory with a capacity of 1200 snowboards per year at a cost of $300,000 the first year and an additional $100,000 the second year. The factory would have limited production capacity during the second year (only 200 units), but would be fully operational at the start of the third year.

Table 10.4 shows the required investments, along with the related sales, revenue, and cost forecasts. As the market grows, sales are expected to rise steadily from 200 units in the second year to 1200 in the sixth year. Until the sixth year, demand will be too low to run the plant at capacity. Snow Stuff expects to sell the boards to retail outlets for $400 each. Rent on the land will run $50,000 per year (listed as a fixed cost). All other costs (labour, materials, et cetera) are variable; they total $275 per board. At the end of 10 years the factory will be obsolete, and Snow Stuff expects to sell its old equipment for $50,000 (listed in the table as scrap value). It does not plan to replace the factory.

In the next few sections, we'll consider whether this investment is a good idea.

Measuring the Profitability of Investments: Net Present Value

In Section 9.1 we learned that a well-functioning firm seeks to maximize its profits, defined as the difference between its total revenue and total cost. To evaluate Snow Stuff's

Table 10.4
Data for Snow Stuff's Proposed Factory

Calendar Year (Project Year)	Investment	Units	Revenue	Variable Fixed Cost	Cost	Scrap Value
2011 (1)	300,000	0	0	50,000	0	0
2012 (2)	100,000	200	80,000	50,000	55,000	0
2013 (3)	0	400	160,000	50,000	110,000	0
2014 (4)	0	800	320,000	50,000	220,000	0
2015 (5)	0	1,000	400,000	50,000	275,000	0
2016 (6)	0	1,200	480,000	50,000	330,000	0
2017 (7)	0	1,200	480,000	50,000	330,000	0
2018 (8)	0	1,200	480,000	50,000	330,000	0
2019 (9)	0	1,200	480,000	50,000	330,000	0
2020 (10)	0	1,200	480,000	50,000	330,000	0
2021 (11)	0	0	0	0	0	50,000

investment, we apply the same principle with a new twist: in computing profit, we need to remember that a dollar in the future is worth less than a dollar today.

Before grappling with Snow Stuff's relatively complex problem, let's start with a much simpler example. Jennifer has an opportunity to buy a case of fine Pinot Noir from an Okanagan Valley winery for $500. She doesn't like wine, so she is thinking about this transaction as an investment. The wine is freshly bottled and not yet drinkable, but experts expect it to become exceptional in five years, at which point the case will be worth $1000.

Is this purchase a profitable investment? Revenue consists of $1000 received in five years. In terms of PDV, that revenue is worth $1000/(1 + R)^5$ today. The cost is $500 today. From today's perspective, profit is therefore $1000/(1 + R)^5 - $500. So, if the interest rate is 10 percent, Jennifer clears a profit of $1000/(1 + 0.1)^5 - $500 = $121.

More generally, to assess the profitability of any investment project, we compute the difference between the PDV of the revenue stream and the PDV of the cost stream. This difference is known as the project's **net present value** (abbreviated NPV). An investment project is profitable when its NPV is positive, and unprofitable when its NPV is negative. This important principle is known as the **NPV criterion**.

The definition of NPV suggests a two-step procedure for determining an investment's profitability. First, we separately discount the project's revenue and cost streams. Second, we find the project's NPV by netting the PDV of the cost stream against the PDV of the revenue stream. In practice, investors often use a different procedure. First, they compute the project's net cash flows. A **net cash flow (NCF)** is the difference between revenue and cost during any single year of the project's life. We'll use NCF_T to stand for the net cash flow received (or paid) in T years. Second, they determine the project's NPV by computing the PDV of its net cash flows.

$$NPV = NCF_0 + \frac{NCF_1}{1 + R} + \frac{NCF_2}{(1 + R)^2} + \ldots + \frac{NCF_T}{(1 + R)^T}$$

> The **net present value (NPV)** of an investment project is the difference between the PDV of the revenue stream and the PDV of the cost stream.
>
> The **NPV criterion** states that an investment project is profitable when its NPV is positive, and unprofitable when its NPV is negative.
>
> A **net cash flow (NCF)** is the difference between revenue and cost during a single year of a project's life.

These two procedures involve the same calculations, performed in a different order. Since the order doesn't matter, they always produce the same answer.

Let's compute the NPV of Snow Stuff's proposed investment in a snowboard factory. First we add up costs and revenues listed in Table 10.4 to obtain a net cash flow for each year. Table 10.5 shows the results. The last column of the table lists the PDV of each year's net cash flow, assuming an interest rate of five percent. Adding up these numbers, we discover that the project's NPV is $22,730. Since this figure is positive, the project is profitable.

That is not the way an accountant thinks about profit. To an accountant, *profit* refers to net gain within some fixed period, such as a year. To an economist, it refers to the economic gain from the entire project. Since this difference can cause confusion, it is important to remember that we are concerned with economic profits, not accounting profits.

Net Present Value as Instant Cash
Here's another way to see that NPV is the correct measure of a project's profit. In Section 10.1, we learned that the present discounted value of a stream of future payments represents the amount of money you would have to set aside immediately to cover all of the payments as they come due. A similar principle applies to investments. Suppose a project has a stream of net cash flows with an NPV of X dollars. By saving and borrowing, an investor can rearrange the timing of the project's cash flows so that he receives X dollars instantly if X is positive or pays X dollars instantly

Table 10.5
PDV of Snow Stuff's Proposed Factory
(Calculations assume an interest rate of 5 percent)

Calendar Year (Project Year)	Net Cash Flow	PDV of $1	PDV of NCF
2011 (1)	−350,000	1.000	−350,000
2012 (2)	−125,000	0.952	−119,048
2013 (3)	0	0.907	0
2014 (4)	50,000	0.864	43,192
2015 (5)	75,000	0.823	61,703
2016 (6)	100,000	0.784	78,353
2017 (7)	100,000	0.746	74,622
2018 (8)	100,000	0.711	71,068
2019 (9)	100,000	0.677	67,684
2020 (10)	100,000	0.645	64,461
2021 (11)	50,000	0.614	30,696
Total	200,000		22,730

if X is negative, and neither receives nor pays anything in the future. The project is therefore just as good as X dollars of instant cash.

To illustrate, let's return to Jennifer's investment decision. If she wanted to, Jennifer could borrow $621 today (at 10 percent interest), use $500 to buy the wine, and keep the remaining $121 (the project's NPV) as instant cash profit. After five years, she would owe exactly $1000 ($621 $\times$ 1.1^5), which she could pay off with the proceeds from selling the wine. In other words, after taking her $121 in the form of an instant cash profit, she would receive zero net cash flow from the project every year after that.

Net Present Value and the Opportunity Cost of Funds
In Sections 3.1 and 8.2, we learned that our actions often have *opportunity costs,* consisting of the benefits we sacrifice by forgoing other attractive alternatives. Every investment project excludes at least one reasonably attractive alternative—lending the required cash at the prevailing interest rate (for example by putting it in the bank or buying a bond). Positive NPV means that the project is better than that alternative, negative NPV means that it's worse. By computing NPV, we're simply netting out the opportunity cost of the interest we would have earned had we lent the money at the prevailing interest rate. Economists sometimes call this cost the **time value of money**, or the **opportunity cost of funds**.

The **time value of money** (also called the **opportunity cost of funds**) is the opportunity cost associated with the economic benefit an investor could receive by lending money at the prevailing interest rate.

To illustrate, let's return to Jennifer's problem. If, instead of buying the wine for $500, she chose to deposit the same sum in a bank account that earns 10 percent interest, she would have $805 in five years. The wine is a good investment because it beats the bank account: in five years, it gives her $1000, which is $195 more than she receives from the bank account. What is the extra $195 worth today? At a 10 percent interest the PDV of $195 received in five years is $121, the investment's NPV.

The Internal Rate of Return

Every project's NPV depends on the interest rate. Usually, there's an interest rate at which the NPV is exactly zero. This is known as the project's **internal rate of return (IRR)**. For example, the IRR of Jennifer's wine investment is roughly 14.9 percent. We can confirm this by checking that the NPV of her investment is approximately zero at an interest rate of 14.9 percent: $1000/(1 + 0.149)^5 - 500 \approx 0$.

A project's **internal rate of return** (or **IRR**) is the rate of interest at which its NPV is exactly zero.

Why is it useful to know a project's IRR? Suppose that a project's cash inflows (negative values of NCF) occur before its cash outflows (positive values of NCF). In that case, we can determine whether the investment is profitable simply by comparing its IRR to the interest rate. The project is profitable when the rate of interest is less than its IRR, and unprofitable when the rate of interest is greater than its IRR.[19] For example, the NPV of Jennifer's project is positive when the interest rate is less than 14.9 percent, and negative when it's greater than 14.9 percent. (Check this by calculating the project's NPV at other interest rates.) In effect, the investor should decide whether to put cash into a project or into a bank account based on which of the two investments yields the higher rate of return.

For a two-period investment (one with all cash flows concentrated in periods 0 and 1), the IRR is easy to calculate. The investment's NPV is $NCF_0 + NCF_1/(1 + R)$. Setting this expression equal to zero and solving for R, we discover that $R = -(NCF_1 + NCF_0)/NCF_0$.[20] For example, if a project requires an investment of $1000 in period 0 ($NCF_0 = -1000$) and returns of $1200 in period 1 ($NCF_1 = 1200$), its IRR is 0.2, or 20 percent.

For investments lasting more than two periods, the IRR is more difficult to calculate. For example, the NPV of a three-period investment is $NCF_0 + NCF_1/(1 + R) + NCF_2/(1 + R)^2$. As in the two-period case, we can set this expression equal to zero and solve for R. But to find the solution, we need to use the quadratic formula. For longer term investments, we usually solve for IRRs numerically, using spreadsheets or other computer programs.

Here's an example. Figure 10.11 shows the NPV of Snow Stuff's proposed factory at interest rates ranging from zero to 10 percent. At zero percent, the NPV is $200,000. At 10 percent, it's −$96,652. Between those two extremes, NPV declines as the interest rate rises. At 5 percent (the rate assumed in Snow Stuff's NPV calculations), it's $22,730. At roughly 5.8 percent, NPV passes from positive to negative. The IRR for Snow Stuff's project is therefore 5.8 percent. As the figure shows, the project is profitable when the interest rate is below 5.8 percent, and unprofitable when it's above 5.8 percent.

Investment and the Interest Rate

The interest rate plays a key role in determining the amount of investment undertaken by a single company, or by a group of companies (for example, all the companies located in a country). When interest rates rise, most potential projects become less profitable. Some become unprofitable, which causes the total amount of investment to fall. Falling interest rates have the opposite effect.

---

[19]Sometimes, an investment project requires net cash outflows (negative values of NCF) *after* generating net cash inflows (positive values of NCF). For example, a factory with a service life of 30 years may require not only substantial up-front investment, but a costly refurbishment after 15 years of profitable operation. In such cases, NPV may *increase* with the interest rate over some ranges, and may even equal zero at several different interest rates (that is, the project may have several IRRs). In some cases, a project may be unprofitable—that is, it may have negative NPV—even when its IRR exceeds the interest rate. For a numerical illustration, see exercise 10.14 at the end of the chapter.

[20]Similarly, we determined the IRR for Jennifer's wine investment by writing down the formula for its NPV as a function of the interest rate: NPV = $1000/(1 + R)^5 - 500$. By setting this expression equal to zero and solving for R, we discovered that $R = 2^{1/5} - 1 = 0.149$, or 14.9 percent (rounding to the nearest tenth of a percentage point).

Figure 10.11

The NPV of Snow Stuff's Proposed Factory. The blue line shows the NPV of Snow Stuff's proposed factory as a function of the interest rate. The line crosses the horizontal axis at a rate of 5.8 percent, which means that the factory has an IRR of 5.8 percent. The factory's NPV is positive if the interest is less than 5.8 percent, and negative if the interest rate is greater than 5.8 percent.

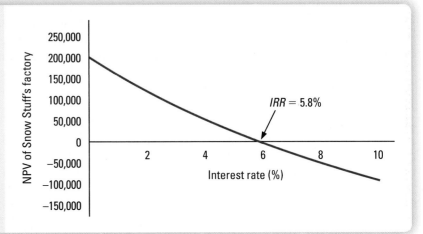

Here are two different ways to understand why an increase in the interest rate usually makes investment projects less attractive:

1. At a higher interest rate, future dollars are worth less than current dollars. Since the typical investment project incurs a disproportionate fraction of its cost early in its life and generates a disproportionate fraction of its revenue later in its life, a higher interest rate reduces the value of its revenue relative to its cost.

2. At a higher interest rate, putting money in the bank becomes more attractive (and borrowing becomes less attractive). Thus, the opportunity cost of funds is greater. Net of the opportunity cost, profit is lower.

Projects with different IRRs are profitable at different ranges of the interest rate. As the interest rate rises, it exceeds the IRRs of more and more projects, and the overall level of investment falls. When the interest rate is 4 percent, for example, Snow Stuff's factory and Jennifer's wine investment are both profitable. If the interest rate rises to 12 percent, it's still lower than Jennifer's IRR, but higher than Snow Stuff's. So Jennifer's project is still profitable, but Snow Stuff's isn't. If the interest rate climbs to 18 percent, it exceeds the IRRs of both projects, so neither is profitable.

Application 10.4

Bond Yields

When someone buys a bond, he gives up the bond's price in exchange for future income. The IRR for this financial investment is known as the bond's *yield to maturity* (often abbreviated as either *yield*, or *YTM*). If a bank account paid interest at a rate equal to the bond's yield, a depositor could reproduce the bond's promised payments, given an initial deposit equal to the bond's price.

Consider a bond with a face value of *V* dollars and a coupon of *C* dollars that matures in *M* years. If the bond sells for *P* dollars, its yield to maturity is the interest rate *R* that satisfies the formula

$$\frac{C}{R}\left(1 - \frac{1}{(1 + R)^M}\right) + \frac{V}{(1 + R)^M} = P \qquad (12)$$

Why? We learned earlier that the expression to the left of the equal sign in formula (12) is the PDV of the bond's future payments (look again at formula (6) on page 335). When we subtract the bond's price from the PDV of its future payments, we obtain the investment's NPV. The interest rate that results in an NPV of zero (in other words, the IRR) must therefore also result in equality between the bond's price and the PDV of its future payments, which is what formula (12) requires.

To illustrate, suppose that a 10-year bond with a $100 coupon and a $1000 face value sells for $749 dollars. At an interest rate of 15 percent, the PDV of the bond's promised payments is exactly $749 (to check this, plug those numbers into the expression to the left of the equals sign in formula (12). That means the bond's yield to maturity is 15 percent. The larger the promised payments and the lower the bond's price, the greater the yield. For example, if the same bond sells for $581, its yield to maturity is 20 percent. (Check this!)

Investors evaluate bonds in part by examining their yields. If a bond's yield is too low, investors won't be willing to buy it. Supply will exceed demand, causing the bond's price to fall. At a lower price, the bond will have a higher yield, making it more attractive to investors. The bond's price continues to fall until its yield is high enough to compensate investors for the opportunity cost of their funds.

Table 10.6 provides information on the prices and yields of Canadian government bonds of various maturities on July 22, 2009. The information in this table appears much as

it would online in the financial press. The first column lists the type of bond, based on the time remaining until maturity. The bond's coupon, expressed as a percentage of face value, appears in the second column, and its date of maturity in the third column. The fourth column tells us the price at which the bond traded, expressed as a percentage of its face value. The final column lists the yield to maturity. So, for example, a 5-year bond with a 4.50 percent coupon maturing on June 1, 2015, sold for 109.19 percent of its face value, implying a yield to maturity of 2.79 percent.

Table 10.6

Prices and Yields on Canadian Government Bonds of Various Maturities

(Coupon and price are expressed as a percentage of face value.)

Type	Coupon	Date of Maturity	Price	Yield to Maturity
2-year	6.00	6/1/2011	108.75%	1.22%
3-year	5.25	6/1/2012	109.45%	1.83%
5-year	4.50	6/1/2015	109.19%	2.79%
10-year	3.79	6/1/2019	102.48%	3.45%
20-year	5.75	6/1/2029	121.98%	4.12%

Choosing between Mutually Exclusive Projects

The mere fact that a project is profitable doesn't necessarily mean that a firm should invest in it. Sometimes profitable projects are mutually exclusive. For example, a firm might have to choose between several locations for a new factory. As in Chapter 9, the best choice among mutually exclusive alternatives is the one that yields the greatest profit. For investment projects, that means the one with the highest NPV.[21]

Let's revisit Snow Stuff's investment problem. Imagine that another manager suggests a different location for Snow Stuff's new factory—Sudbury instead of Edmonton—on the grounds that labour costs are lower in Sudbury. After careful analysis, the company concludes that the NPV of the Sudbury project is $28,200. Since that amount exceeds the NPV of the Edmonton project, $22,730, Snow Stuff should build the factory in Sudbury.

Other Criteria for Choosing between Mutually Exclusive Projects

Companies sometimes compare mutually exclusive projects using criteria other than NPV. This can lead to poor decision making. There is no guarantee that any other criteria will correctly identify the most profitable project.

For example, it's usually inappropriate to choose between two mutually exclusive projects by selecting the one with the higher IRR. Comparing IRRs, Jennifer's wine investment

---

[21]This statement assumes that projects involving facilities with different operational lifetimes are evaluated over the same time horizon. For example, to compare a project involving a facility with a 30-year lifetime to one involving a facility that would require replacement after 15 years, we would include the cash flows from the replacement facility.

looks better than Snow Stuff's factory. Yet if an investor were forced to choose between the two, the correct choice, based on a comparison of their NPVs, would hinge on the interest rate. At an interest rate between 5.8 and 14.9 percent, Jennifer's investment is clearly the better one because it's profitable and the factory isn't. But if the interest rate is 3 percent, the factory provides an NPV of $85,140, while the wine provides an NPV of only $363.

The **payback period** is the amount of time before a project's total inflows match its total outflows.

Another commonly used criterion is the **payback period**, the amount of time required before a project's total inflows match its total outflows. For example, in the case of Snow Stuff's investment, $475,000 flows out of the firm before any money flows back in (see Table 10.5, page 354). Total inflows reach $425,000 in year eight and $525,000 in year nine, so the payback period is roughly 8½ years. Companies sometimes look for projects with short payback periods; some even establish fixed payback requirements (for example, payback within five years).

The payback period provides sound investment guidance only when it happens to coincide with the maximization of NPV. Often it doesn't. For example, which would you prefer, a $1000 investment that returns $1001 in one year and nothing thereafter, or a $1000 investment that returns $300 per year for the next 50 years? Unless the interest rate is near 30 percent, the second investment has a much higher NPV than the first. But judged by the payback period, the first investment looks far better—it breaks even after a single year, compared with more than three years for the second investment.

One possible justification for looking at payback periods is that investors are less certain about net cash flows that occur further into the future. In that case, insisting on a quick payback is one way to express an aversion to uncertainty. As we'll see in the next chapter, however, there are better ways to handle uncertainty. Another possible justification is that a company with limited credit might need to generate cash quickly to pay for other investment projects. While it's useful to take these kinds of concerns into account, the payback period is at best only a rough rule of thumb.

Investing Now or Later   Every investment project excludes at least one other alternative: waiting. A company shouldn't start a project immediately just because its NPV is positive, even if it doesn't preclude other projects. Why not? Unless the company expects the opportunity to evaporate, it may achieve an even greater NPV by starting at a later date.

To illustrate, suppose Snow Stuff has the option of waiting a year before starting work on its factory. As Table 10.7 shows, investment, production, and cash flows during the project's first and second years will not change. In the project's third year, the company will produce 800 snowboards instead of 400, because the year will be 2014 instead of 2013, and the demand for snowboards will be higher. For the same reason, the company will produce 1000 snowboards instead of 800 in the project's fourth year, and 1200 instead of 1000 in its fifth year. Thereafter, the factory will operate at capacity, whether or not the project is delayed.

To compare Snow Stuff's two alternatives—starting the factory immediately and starting it after one year—we must discount net cash flows for both alternatives to the *same point in time.*[22] Discounting net cash flows to the beginning of 2011, we find that the NPV of the delayed project is $104,995. Since this amount is far greater than $22,730, the NPV of the project if it begins immediately, the company is better off waiting a year. The reason is simple: if Snow Stuff waits for demand to grow, it won't waste as much money maintaining idle production capacity.

---

[22]If we discounted the cash flows for each alternative to the project's start date—2011 for the first alternative and 2012 for the second—the two figures would not be comparable; they would refer to dollars at different points in time.

Table 10.7

The Value of Delaying Construction of Snow Stuff's Factory

(Calculations assume an interest rate of 5 percent.)

Calendar Year (Project Year)	Investment	Units	Revenue	Fixed Cost	Variable Cost	Scrap Value	Net Cash Flow	PDV of $1	PDV of NCF
2011	0	0	0	0	0	0	0	1.000	0
2012 (1)	300,000	0	0	50,000	0	0	350,000	0.952	333,333
2013 (2)	100,000	200	80,000	50,000	55,000	0	125,000	0.907	113,379
2014 (3)	0	800	320,000	50,000	220,000	0	50,000	0.864	43,192
2015 (4)	0	1,000	400,000	50,000	275,000	0	75,000	0.823	61,703
2016 (5)	0	1,200	480,000	50,000	330,000	0	100,000	0.784	78,353
2017 (6)	0	1,200	480,000	50,000	330,000	0	100,000	0.746	74,622
2018 (7)	0	1,200	480,000	50,000	330,000	0	100,000	0.711	71,068
2019 (8)	0	1,200	480,000	50,000	330,000	0	100,000	0.677	67,684
2020 (9)	0	1,200	480,000	50,000	330,000	0	100,000	0.645	64,461
2021 (10)	0	1,200	480,000	50,000	330,000	0	100,000	0.614	61,391
2022 (11)	0	0	0	0	0	50,000	50,000	0.585	29,234
Total							200,000		104,995

WORKED-OUT PROBLEM   10.4

The Problem   Managers at Investments R Us, Inc., must choose between three mutually exclusive projects, A, B, and C. They can also decide to skip all three projects. Each project requires an investment in the first year and produces a positive net cash flow for the next four years. The top half of Table 10.8 shows the net cash flows, by year, for each project. Assuming that the interest rate is five percent, what is the NPV of the cash flows from each project? Which one should the company choose? Does the best project have the highest total net cash flow? The shortest payback period? The highest internal rate of return?

The Solution   The lower half of Table 10.8 shows the PDV of the annual net cash flows for each project, and then sums them to obtain the NPV of each project. The NPV of project A is $4004, the NPV of project B is $4685, and the NPV of project C is $4595. The company should choose project B.

Project B also has the highest total nominal net cash flow ($8750 compared to $8000 for project C and $6750 for project A). However, it has the longest payback period (total net cash flow doesn't become positive until year 5, compared to year 4 for the other two projects).

To compute the internal rate of return for each project, we find the interest rate at which the project's NPV is zero. One way to do this is to create a spreadsheet that computes the NPV for different interest rates, and search systematically for the IRR.[23] Take project A as an example. To start, we would compute the NPV at whole interest

---

[23]With some spreadsheet programs, the user can set up the NPV calculation and then instruct the program to search automatically for an interest rate that produces an NPV of zero.

Table 10.8

Data for Worked-Out-Problem 10.4

Net Cash Flows and NPVs for Three Mutually Exclusive Investments
(Calculations assume an interest rate of 5 percent.)

Year	1	2	3	4	5	Total
Net Cash Flow for:						
Project A	−21,250	10,000	8,000	6,000	4,000	6,750
Project B	−23,250	5,000	7,000	9,000	11,000	8,750
Project C	−22,000	7,500	7,500	7,500	7,500	8,000
PDV of $1	1.000	0.952	0.907	0.864	0.823	
PDV of Net Cash Flow for:						
Project A	−21,250	9,524	7,256	5,183	3,291	4,004
Project B	−23,250	4,762	6,349	7,775	9,050	4,685
Project C	−22,000	7,143	6,803	6,479	6,170	4,595

rates (1 percent, 2 percent, etc.). We'd discover that the NPV is positive at an interest rate of 14 percent but negative at an interest rate of 15 percent. This means that the IRR is between 14 and 15 percent. Next we'd compute the NPV at interest rates of 14.1 percent, 14.2 percent, and so forth, up to 14.9 percent. We'd learn that the IRR is between 14.2 percent (at which the NPV is positive) and 14.3 percent (at which it is negative). Finally, we'd compute the NPV at interest rates of 14.21 percent, 14.22 percent, and so forth, up to 14.29 percent. We'd find that the NPV is approximately zero at an interest rate of 14.26 percent. While we could pin the IRR down even more precisely, that is close enough.

Table 10.9 lists the IRRs for projects A, B, and C, and verifies that the project's NPV is zero in each case. Project B, the best alternative at an interest rate of 5 percent, has the lowest IRR of the three projects, 12.34 percent, while project A has the highest, 14.26 percent. Therefore, using the IRRs to decide between those projects would lead to the wrong decision.

 IN-TEXT EXERCISE 10.5   **Compute the NPVs for the projects described in worked-out problem 10.4 at the following interest rates: 8 percent, 12 percent, and 16 percent.**

Investing in Human Capital

Not all investments involve buildings, machines, inventories, and other forms of physical capital. Sometimes companies invest in knowledge through research and development. Sometimes they invest in reputation through advertising and public relations. The same investment principles apply to any situation in which the costs and benefits of a project occur at different points in time.

Education (including occupational training) is also an investment. A student incurs up-front costs in the hope of acquiring durable, marketable skills that will generate higher

Table 10.9

Data for Worked-Out Problem 10.4

Internal Rates of Return for Three Mutually Exclusive Investments

(Note: numbers may not add up exactly due to rounding.)

Year	1	2	3	4	5	Total
Project A with interest rate of 14.26%						
NCF	−21,250	10,000	8,000	6,000	4,000	6,750
PDV of $1	1.000	0.875	0.766	0.670	0.587	
PDV of NCF	−21,250	8,752	6,128	4,023	2,347	0
Project B with interest rate of 12.34%						
NCF	−23,250	5,000	7,000	9,000	11,000	8,750
PDV of $1	1.000	0.890	0.792	0.705	0.628	
PDV of NCF	−23,250	4,451	5,546	6,348	6,906	0
Project C with interest rate of 13.67%						
NCF	−22,000	7,500	7,500	7,500	7,500	8,000
PDV of $1	1.000	0.880	0.774	0.681	0.599	
PDV of NCF	−22,000	6,598	5,804	5,106	4,492	0

income. Indeed, economists often refer to these skills as **human capital**. But education isn't always worthwhile (remember Application 3.1 from Chapter 3, page 70). Standard investment principles allow us to determine if education makes sense from a purely financial perspective in a particular instance.[24]

Human capital consists of marketable skills acquired through investments in education and training.

To illustrate, let's examine a typical educational decision in detail. Thomas took a job after graduating from university at age 22. He's turning 26 next year and is thinking about going to business school full time for two years to improve his earnings potential. If he receives a business degree, Thomas expects to earn an extra $15,000 per year through his retirement at age 65. Unfortunately, business school is expensive. He'll have to come up with $20,000 per year to cover tuition, plus an additional $2000 for books and supplies.

To evaluate this option, we need to compute the NPV of the financial costs and benefits. Have we listed all the relevant costs? Not yet. To attend business school full time, Thomas would have to give up his current job, which pays $45,000 per year. This sacrifice is an important opportunity cost. In fact, it's significantly larger than the costs of tuition, books, and supplies combined. If Thomas ignores this cost, he's likely to make a faulty decision.

Table 10.10 calculates the NPV of attending business school, assuming an interest rate of eight percent. As the table shows, Thomas gives up a total of $67,000 per year while he's in school in return for an extra $15,000 per year after he finishes. Simply adding up the costs and benefits yields a net gain of $436,000. But because that figure makes no adjustment for the fact that the costs are incurred up front while the benefits are delayed, it exaggerates the true gains. The last column of the table lists the PDV of the net cash flow in each year. For simplicity, we've assumed that all payments are made and all income is received at the beginning of each year. (We've used formula (5) to compute the

[24]Nonfinancial concerns may also influence decisions concerning education and training. Completing a degree confers greater social status, and is also a direct source of satisfaction to many people, some of whom also find education more pleasant than work.

Table 10.10
The PDV of Attending Business School
(Hypothetical data, 8 percent interest rate)

Age	Tuition	Books and Supplies	Increase in Earnings	Opportunity Cost	Total Net Change	PDV
26	20,000	2,000	0	45,000	−67,000	−67,000
27	20,000	2,000	0	45,000	−67,000	−62,037
28–65	0	0	15,000/yr	0	15,000/yr	164,290
Total					436,000	35,253

PDV at age 27 of the increase in earnings between ages 28 and 65, then we've discounted the result back to age 26.) Adding up these discounted cash flows, we find that the NPV is $35,253. Though this is far less than $436,000, the investment is still justified.

Economists often summarize the financial returns to education by calculating an internal rate of return. For Thomas, the IRR of attending business school is 10.4 percent. As long as the interest rate is less than 10.4 percent, an MBA would be a good deal for him.

Application 10.5

The Economic Value of Education

In 1958, an economist named Jacob Mincer pioneered a method for measuring the effects of schooling on wages, while simultaneously estimating the rate of return earned on investments in human capital. Mincer's method has been refined and extended over 50 years through a long sequence of scholarly papers. At its core, the refined method involves a comparison of the wages earned by people with different levels of education and experience.

Two recent studies on the returns to post-secondary education, one by economist Torben Drewes of Trent University and the other by Jorgen Hansen of Concordia University, were conducted at the request of Human Resources and Skills Development Canada (HRSDC).[25] The two studies used data from the National Graduates Survey in the years 1990, 1995, and 2000. Both studies calculated internal rates of return to post-secondary education using methods similar to those described above. The study by Torben Drewes found that the return on two years of college

"They may be your grades, but they're the return on my investment."

---

[25]See Torben Drewes (2006) "Returns to College Education: Evidence from the 1990, 1995, and 2000 National Graduates Surveys," HRSDC SP-654-09-06E, and Jorgen Hansen (2006) "Returns to University Level Education: Variations Within Disciplines, Occupations, and Employment Sectors," HRSCD SP-662-09-06E.

was 11.8 percent for males and 11.4 percent for females. A four-year university education had similar rates of return, 11.4 percent for males and 12.8 percent for females, despite the fact that earnings with a university degree are approximately 25 percent greater higher for men and 35 percent higher for women than those with a two-year college degree. The reason that rates of return to university are lower in the case of men is that the additional earnings in the future are not enough to offset the additional cost of forgone earnings for several years.

The study by Jorgen Hansen found a similar relationship between rates of return for college and university educations for men and women and also reported internal rates of return by major field of study. In 2001 the five majors with the highest internal rates of return for females were Math/Computers/Physical Science (14 percent), Health (14 percent), Business/Commerce (14 percent), Engineering (13 percent), and Social Science (10 percent). For males, the five majors with the highest rates of return were Engineering (16 percent), Math/Computers/Physical Science (13 percent), Business/Commerce (13 percent), Health (10 percent), and Social Science (10 percent). The major with the lowest return was Fine Arts where the internal rate of return was 4 percent for females and 7 percent for males.

One difficulty with this approach, however, is that it fails to recognize the strong correlation between education and ability. More talented people tend both to stay in school longer and to earn higher incomes. Unfortunately, it isn't clear whether their greater earnings reflect their schooling or their talent.

To address this problem, economists have searched for characteristics that influence the amount of schooling received, but are unrelated to talent. An American study by economists Joshua Angrist and Alan Krueger notes that people born earlier in the calendar year tend to receive slightly less schooling than people born later in the calendar year.[26] One possible explanation for this pattern involves compulsory schooling laws: those who are born earlier in the year tend to be older for their grade levels and are therefore eligible to drop out of school at lower grade levels. Those who are born later in the year also earn more, on average, than those born earlier in the year, which suggests that forcing students to remain in school does raise their earnings. Other studies have attempted to infer the effects of schooling on earnings from differences in educational attainment that are attributable to factors such as the distance from an individual's home to the nearest two-year or four-year college, the disruption of schooling due to war, changes in compulsory schooling laws, and changes in rules governing eligibility for educational subsidies.

CHAPTER SUMMARY

1. **Transactions involving time (LO1, 2)**

   a. Consumers and firms often need to move cash from one point in time to another. They do so by borrowing and lending.

   b. For any interest-bearing account or loan, compounding of interest causes the account or loan balance to grow faster as time passes.

   c. The PDV of a claim on future resources represents the price at which someone could buy or sell that claim today.

   d. The longer the delay until payment and the higher the interest rate, the smaller the PDV of $1.

   e. To find the PDV of a stream of payments, we take the PDV of each payment and then total them.

   f. Interest rates differ because of variations in default risk, lender flexibility, and the timing of payments. When computing the PDV of some future payment, it's important to select an interest rate for an obligation with similar characteristics.

   g. The real interest rate is approximately equal to the nominal interest rate minus the rate of inflation. This approximation works well when interest and inflation rates are low. When a bank or lender quotes an interest rate, it's usually a nominal rate.

2. **Saving and borrowing (LO3)**

   a. Saving reflects decisions about the timing of consumption. To analyze saving, we can apply the theory

---

[26]Joshua D. Angrist and Alan B. Krueger, "Does Compulsory School Attendance Affect Schooling and Earnings?" *Quarterly Journal of Economics* 106, November 1991, pp. 979–1014.

developed in Chapters 4 through 6, treating a good's "time of availability" as a physical characteristic. We use indifference curves to represent a consumer's preferences for consumption at different points in time, and a budget line to represent the available opportunities. In constructing the budget line, we use the price of each good from today's perspective—that is, the PDV of the future price.

b. Sufficiently patient consumers save and sufficiently impatient consumers borrow. Among savers, an increase in the interest rate can either raise or lower saving, because the income and substitution effects work in opposite directions. In contrast, among borrowers, an increase in the interest rate typically reduces borrowing, because the income and substitution effects usually work in the same direction.

c. The Life Cycle Hypothesis relies on two additional assumptions: (1) that earnings tend to rise with experience, level off in middle age, and fall sharply at retirement, and (2) that people like stability. The theory implies that people smooth consumption over their lifetimes, borrowing when they are young, saving during middle age, and spending down their wealth in retirement. The theory helps us to understand why saving rates differ from one country to another.

3. **Investment (LO4, 5)**

   a. NPV is a measure of profitability—it is the difference between the value of a project's outputs and the value of its inputs, from today's perspective. An investment project is profitable when its NPV is positive and unprofitable when its NPV is negative.

   b. By saving and borrowing, an investor can rearrange the timing of the project's cash flows so that he receives

its NPV instantly if the NPV is positive, or pays its NPV instantly if the NPV is negative, and neither receives nor pays anything in the future. The project's NPV therefore tells us what it is worth in terms of instant cash.

   c. When we compute the NPV of a project, we are netting out the opportunity cost of funds.

   d. When faced with a choice between two or more mutually exclusive projects with positive NPVs, a company should choose the one with the highest NPV.

   e. Every investment project excludes waiting as an alternative. Even when a project's NPV is positive, waiting may be better than starting the project immediately.

   f. When interest rates rise, most potential projects become less profitable, and the general level of investment falls. Falling interest rates have the opposite effects.

   g. As long as cash inflows occur before cash outflows, a project is profitable when the rate of interest is less than its internal rate of return (IRR), and unprofitable when the rate of interest is greater than its IRR. It is, however, not usually appropriate to choose between mutually exclusive projects based on their IRRs.

   h. The payback period is the amount of time required before a project's total inflows match its total outflows. In general, the payback period is not a reliable criterion for evaluating investment projects.

   i. Human capital consists of marketable skills acquired through investments in education and training. Standard investment principles allow us to determine whether, in a particular instance, acquiring an education makes sense from a purely financial perspective.

ADDITIONAL EXERCISES

Exercise 10.1: In each of the following cases, calculate the balance in a bank account after the specified number of years, given the specified initial deposit and rate of interest. (LO1)

a. $300 deposited at 8 percent interest for 15 years

b. $4200 deposited at 3 percent interest for 40 years

c. $525 deposited at 6 percent interest for 5 years

Exercise 10.2: During the 1984 presidential election campaign in the United States, Democratic hopeful Walter Mondale criticized the Reagan administration's economic record by arguing that high real interest rates were choking off investment and consumer spending. Vice President George H. W. Bush famously responded that interest rates had fallen dramatically from a peak of 21 percent at the end of the Carter administration, and that "the real interest rate is what you pay when you go down and try to buy a TV set or buy a car." Evaluate the logic of Mr. Bush's argument. (LO5)

Exercise 10.3: In each of the following cases, calculate the PDV of the specified amount under the specified circumstances. (LO2)

a. $6300 received in eight years, at an interest rate of 4 percent

b. $115,000 received in two years, at an interest rate of 18 percent

c. $45,000 received in 100 years, at an interest rate of 1 percent

Exercise 10.4: Calculate the PDV of the following bonds. (LO2)

a. A 5-year bond with an annual coupon payment of $200, and a principle payment at maturity of $5000, at an interest rate of 4 percent.

b. A 15-year bond with an annual coupon payment of $50, and a principle payment at maturity of $600, at an interest rate of 10 percent.

Exercise 10.5: Consider a bond with a face value of $1000 and a coupon of $100. Suppose the interest rate is 10 percent. Does the PDV of the promised payments depend on the bond's maturity? Why or why not? (Hint: Think about putting $1000 in a bank account that pays 10 percent interest. If you withdraw $100 at the end of each year, what do you always have left?) (LO2)

Exercise 10.6: Repeat worked-out problem 10.3 (page 347), but assume that Angela earns $70 this year and $30 next year. (LO3)

Exercise 10.7: Repeat worked-out problem 10.3 (page 347), but assume that, in Angela's view, one kilogram of food this year is the perfect complement to one kilogram of food next year. In other words, assume that her indifference curves are L-shaped, and that the corner of the L in each curve lies on the 45-degree line. How would you interpret her preferences? (LO3)

Exercise 10.8: People like to have a stable living standard from one year to the next. Yet studies show that the level of consumption drops suddenly, predictably, and significantly at retirement [contrary to Figure 10.9(a)]. Why? Can you think of an explanation that is consistent with the approach to saving taken in Section 10.2? (LO3)

Exercise 10.9: The net cash flows from an investment project are −$15,000 in the first year, −$11,000 in the second year, $5000 in the third year, $1800 in the fourth year, $7000 in the fifth year, $6400 in the sixth year, $4300 in the seventh year, and $6200 in the eighth year. Compute the NPV of this project at the following interest rates: 2 percent, 5 percent, and 8 percent. (LO4)

Exercise 10.10: For each of the following investments, compute the IRR. (LO4)

a. The net cash flows are −$12,000 in the first year and +$15,000 in the second year. (Use the formula for two-period investments given in the text.)

b. The net cash flows are −$10,000 in the first year, +$5000 in the second year, and +$6000 in the third year. (Use the quadratic formula.)

c. The net cash flows are the same as in exercise 10.9. (Use either the search method illustrated in worked-out problem 10.4 on page 359, or the automatic search feature of a spreadsheet program.)

Exercise 10.11: The net cash flows from an investment are −X dollars in the first year, +Y dollars in year T, and zero in all other years. Write a formula for the NPV. Set the NPV equal to zero, and solve for the IRR in terms of X and Y. (LO4)

Exercise 10.12: Calculate the yield to maturity for each of the following bonds. (LO5)

a. A 20-year bond with a coupon of $100, principle payment at maturity of $2000, and a current price of $2000.

b. A 5-year bond with a coupon of $500, principle payment at maturity of $10,000, and a current price of $8000.

Exercise 10.13: Two mutually exclusive projects, A and B, require the same up-front investment in the first year. Project A generates positive net cash flows in years two through five and nothing after that. Project B generates nothing in years two through five, positive net cash flows in years six through ten, and nothing after that. At an interest rate of 10 percent, project A is a better investment than project B. Explain intuitively why project A must be better than project B at higher interest rates as well. (LO5)

Exercise 10.14: A project that requires an investment of $6000 in the first year generates a positive net cash flow of $15,000 in the fourth year. It leaves the investor with an obligation to pay $10,000 in the eighth year, and yields no net cash flow in any other year. (LO5)

a. Find the NPV of this investment at the following interest rates: 0 percent, 5 percent, 10 percent, 15 percent, and 20 percent.

b. This investment has two different IRRs. Find them, using the method illustrated in worked-out problem 10.4 (page 359).

c. At what interest rates is this project profitable? (Create a graph similar to Figure 10.11 on page 356.) Is it always profitable when one of the IRRs exceeds the interest rate? What if both of the IRRs exceed the interest rate?

d. Why does this example produce two IRRs? How does it differ from the examples presented in this chapter? (Hint: Using a spreadsheet, graph the NPV against the interest rate. How does this graph change when you reduce the value of the payment in the eighth year from $10,000 to some smaller number? What happens to the IRRs?)

Exercise 10.15: A project requires a cash investment in the first year and generates a positive net cash flow in all future years. Knowing only that Janet is more patient than Michael, would you say she is more likely to undertake the project than Michael? Justify your answer. (LO5)

Exercise 10.16: Make your best guess about the various financial costs and benefits of attending your current educational institution (assuming that you complete your degree). Think about your likely earnings with and without the degree, the cost of tuition and books, and any other factors you consider relevant. Based on your estimates, compute the PDV and the IRR of your investment in human capital. (LO4, 5)

11

Choices Involving Risk

LEARNING OBJECTIVES

After reading this chapter, students should be able to

LO1 Define and measure economic risk.

LO2 Illustrate an individual's risk preferences graphically.

LO3 Explain why people purchase insurance policies.

LO4 Analyze why people take certain risks and avoid others.

LO5 Identify and explain several strategies for managing risk.

Early in 1996, two graduate students at California's Stanford University, Larry Page and Sergey Brin, began developing a new technology for retrieving information from huge databases. With no business experience to speak of, they tried but failed to convince investors of their technology's commercial potential. Reluctantly, they set up operations in Page's dorm room, where they cobbled together a patchwork data centre made of surplus computer memory acquired at bargain prices. Over the next two years, they managed to raise just under $1 million from interested investors, which they used to launch a company. By September 1998, Google Inc. was officially open for business. Six years later, on August 19, 2004, the company held an initial public offering (IPO) in which for the first time members of the general public were allowed to buy shares. Page and Brin both collected more than $40 million in cash, retaining shares valued at more than $3.2 billion each! They (and their investors) had taken a big chance—one that had paid off beyond their wildest expectations.

During the dot-com mania of the late 1990s, thousands of bright young entrepreneurs with clever ideas launched risky new ventures. Unlike Page and Brin, most came up empty handed. A grocery delivery service called Webvan went belly-up in 2001 with accumulated

Google, Inc. founders Larry Page and Sergey Brin

losses of $830 million. Clothing outlet Boo.com blew through $225 million of investors' money, only to be acquired for well under $1 million by Fashionmall.com. Web sites like "The Museum of E-Failure" were created just to keep track of the duds. Some of them, like "Dot-Com Flop Tracker," flopped themselves. For an investor, the trick was to distinguish the Googles from the Webvans. Many of those who guessed right became wealthy; many guessed wrong and lost their shirts. Still others watched from the sidelines, unwilling to gamble their hard-earned savings on such risky prospects.

© The New Yorker Collection 2001 Mick Stevens from cartoonbank.com. All Rights Reserved.

Though most people aren't dot-com entrepreneurs, everyone takes risks. Obviously, buying a lottery ticket is a risky proposition, as are going to university (since jobs aren't guaranteed), lending money to a friend (since default is possible), and driving a car (since accidents do happen). Risk is the rule, not the exception.

In this chapter, we'll examine four topics related to risky economic decisions.

1. *What is risk?* Common sense tells us when a decision involves risk. Economics and statistics show us how to gauge the amount of risk with some precision.

2. *Risk preferences.* In Chapter 4, we learned how to describe an individual's consumption preferences. Here, we'll apply the same concepts to situations in which the outcome is uncertain.

3. *Insurance.* Much of life is unavoidably risky. People address a wide range of financial risks by purchasing insurance policies. We'll see why insurance makes them better off.

4. *Other methods of managing risk.* Most people avoid some risks but voluntarily accept others. For example, they reduce risk by purchasing insurance, but then introduce new risks by investing in the stock market. We'll see why doing so makes sense. We'll also study the steps people take to moderate the risks they accept.

11.1 WHAT IS RISK?

Risk exists whenever the consequences of a decision are uncertain. In this section, we'll explain how economists analyze risks and gauge their magnitude.

Possibilities

The consequences of any risky decision depend on events outside the decision maker's control. Usually, events can unfold in many different ways. Economists and statisticians refer to each possible unfolding of events as a **state of nature**, or *state* for short.

To illustrate, suppose that Jeff is trying to decide whether to buy tickets to a Saskatchewan Roughriders football game in Regina. His enjoyment of the game will depend on two uncertain events that are beyond his control: whether it rains and whether his team wins. He will be happiest if it doesn't rain and his team wins. That is one possible state of nature.

To analyze a risky decision, economists begin by describing every possible state of nature. In Jeff's case, events can unfold in four different ways: it rains and his team wins, it rains and his team loses, it doesn't rain and his team wins, or it doesn't rain and his team loses. Each item on this list is a state of nature.

A **state of nature** is one possible way in which events relevant to a risky decision can unfold.

Once someone makes a choice, he experiences one and only one state of nature. For example, Jeff will experience one of the four states listed in the last paragraph, because we haven't left out any possibilities. He can't experience more than one state, however, because we've described each one in a way that rules out the others.

Probability

Some states of nature are more likely than others. For example, in Jeff's hometown of Regina (where it rains an average of nine days a month during football season), states of nature involving rain occur about one third of the time.

Probability is a measure of the likelihood that a specific state of nature will occur.

Probability is a measure of the likelihood that a specific state of nature will occur. It's usually written either as a number between zero and one or as a percentage. A probability of zero (or zero percent) means that a state is impossible; a probability of one (or 100 percent) means that it's certain. A probability of, say, three-quarters (or 75 percent) means that the odds of the state in question occurring are three out of four.

By adding the probabilities of two states of nature, we obtain the probability that one of those two states will occur. For example, let's suppose the odds are 1 in 10 (10 percent) that it will rain and Jeff's team will win, and 2 in 10 (20 percent) that it will rain and Jeff's team will lose. Then the odds of it raining (with Jeff's team either winning or losing) must be 3 in 10 (30% = 10% + 20%). The probabilities of *all* states of nature always add up to 1 (or 100 percent), because it's certain that *something* will happen.

An objective probability is a measure of the likelihood that a specific state of nature will occur based on the frequency with which it has occurred in the past, under comparable conditions.

Sometimes we can measure the probability of a state of nature by determining the frequency with which it has occurred in the past, under comparable conditions. Such measures are known as **objective probabilities**. For example, if we flip a coin thousands of times, we'll find that it comes up heads and tails with roughly equal frequency. Thus, we conclude that the probability of each outcome is the same—in each case, one-half (or 50 percent). Likewise, Jeff might estimate the probability of each state of nature based on the historical frequency of rain and his team's won-lost record.

A subjective probability is a measure of the likelihood that an event will occur based on subjective judgment.

Sometimes we can measure the probability of a state of nature, at least in part, by exercising our own judgment. While this type of assessment, known as **subjective probability**, may be informed by facts, it may also reflect "instinct" or a "gut feeling." Naturally, different people may come to very different subjective judgments. For example, if the Senators play the Canucks for the Stanley Cup, their fans may have radically different views concerning the likely outcome, even if their views are based on the same information (see Application 11.2 on page 381).

Uncertain Payoffs

Risky choices often have financial consequences, also known as *payoffs*. Payoffs can be either positive (gains) or negative (losses). To evaluate a choice, we need to know the **probability distribution** of the payoffs—that is, the likelihood of each possible payoff occurring. Like other consequences, payoffs depend on unfolding events, in other words, on the state of nature. As long as we know the probability of each possible state of nature, we can determine the probability of each possible payoff.

The probability distribution of a set of payoffs tells us the likelihood that each possible payoff will occur.

Here's an example. The managers of New Stuff Inc. are thinking about building a factory to make a new product called a thingamajig. A competitor has already started producing a similar product and has filed for patent protection. If approved, the patent would prevent New Stuff from making thingamajigs. In addition, the market for thingamajigs is untested. Eventually, demand will turn out to be either high or low. If it's low, New Stuff will have to shut its factory down, whether or not the competitor's patent is approved.

In this example, there are four possible states of nature: the competitor's patent is approved and demand is low, the competitor's patent is approved and demand is high, the competitor's patent is not approved and demand is low, or the competitor's patent is not approved and demand is high. Based on both objective evidence and subjective judgment, New Stuff's managers arrive at the probabilities shown in the second column of Table 11.1.

Unsure of their best course of action, the managers have drawn up two sets of plans, one for a large factory and the other for a small one. If the competitor's patent is not approved and demand is high, New Stuff expects to make $8.5 million from the large factory and $4.5 million from the small one, net of investment costs. With all other states of nature, they expect to lose their investment ($1.5 million for the large factory and $0.5 million for the small one). All of these figures refer to net present values, defined in Section 10.3. New Stuff's payoffs are shown in the third and fourth columns of Table 11.1.

Table 11.2 shows the probability distributions of the payoffs from the two factories. (For the moment, ignore the last column in the table, as well as the rows labelled *expected*

Table 11.1
States of Nature, Probabilities, and Payoffs for New Stuff's Thingamajig

State of Nature	Probability	Payoff (NPV, $ million) Large Factory	Small Factory
Patent approved, low demand	30%	−1.5	−0.5
Patent approved, high demand	20	−1.5	−0.5
Patent not approved, low demand	30	−1.5	−0.5
Patent not approved, high demand	20	+8.5	+4.5

Table 11.2
Expected Value of New Stuff's Profits on the Thingamajig

Large Factory

	Payoff ($)	Probability	Probability × Payoff
	8,500,000	20%	1,700,000
	−1,500,000	80%	−1,200,000
Expected payoff			**500,000**

Small Factory

	Payoff ($)	Probability	Probability × Payoff
	4,500,000	20%	900,000
	−500,000	80%	−400,000
Expected payoff			**500,000**

payoff.) With the large factory, New Stuff receives a payoff of $8.5 million with 20 percent probability, which is the probability that the competitor's patent is not approved and demand is high, and a payoff of −$1.5 million with 80 percent probability, which is the total probability of all other states of nature. Similarly, with the small factory, New Stuff receives a payoff of $4.5 million with 20 percent probability and a payoff of −$0.5 million with 80 percent probability (as shown in the lower half of Table 11.2).

Histograms can help us to visualize probability distributions. The one in Figure 11.1(a) summarizes the possible consequences of New Stuff's large factory. The horizontal axis measures the payoff, and the vertical axis measures probability. The taller of the two red bars tells us that New Stuff loses $1.5 million (the horizontal coordinate) with 80 percent probability (the vertical coordinate). The shorter bar tells us that the company gains $8.5 million (the horizontal coordinate) with 20 percent probability (the vertical coordinate). The histogram in Figure 11.1(b) summarizes the smaller factory's possible consequences. The two blue bars tell us that New Stuff loses $0.5 million with 80 percent probability and gains $4.5 million with 20 percent probability.

To evaluate a choice with risky financial prospects, we usually begin with two simple questions. First, what do we expect to gain or lose, on average? Second, do we expect the actual gain or loss to be close to that average or far from it? We'll tackle these two questions in turn.

Figure 11.1

Possible Consequences of New Stuff's Investment in the Thingamajig. New Stuff's large factory [figure (a)] results in a loss of $1.5 million with 80 percent probability and a gain of $8.5 million with 20 percent probability. The small factory [figure (b)] results in a loss of $0.5 million with 80 percent probability and a gain of $4.5 million with 80 percent probability.

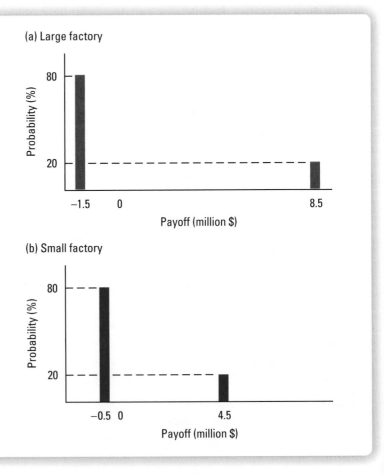

Expected Payoff

To determine the average gain or loss from a risky financial choice, we can calculate its **expected payoff**. The expected payoff is a weighted average of all the possible payoffs, using the probability of each payoff as its weight.

> The **expected payoff** of a risky financial choice is a weighted average of all the possible payoffs, using the probability of each payoff as its weight.

To illustrate, suppose Ilya and Napoleon bet $5 on the flip of a coin. If the outcome is heads (H), Napoleon pays Ilya $5; if tails (T), Ilya pays Napoleon $5. We compute Ilya's expected payoff as follows.

$$\text{Ilya's expected payoff} =$$
$$(\text{Probability of H}) \times (\text{Ilya's payoff if H}) + (\text{Probability of T}) \times (\text{Ilya's payoff if T})$$
$$= (\tfrac{1}{2}) \times (5) + (\tfrac{1}{2}) \times (-5) = 0$$

Using the same logic, we see that Napoleon's expected payoff is also zero.

More generally, suppose the payoff from a risky choice can take on one of N different values, $P_1, P_2, \ldots, P_N$, and that it turns out to be P_n with the probability π_n (the Greek letter *pi*). We can calculate the expected payoff, abbreviated *EP*, using the following formula:

$$EP = \pi_1 \times P_1 + \pi_2 \times P_2 + \ldots + \pi_N \times P_N \qquad (1)$$

The final column of Table 11.2 applies this formula to New Stuff's proposed factories. As indicated, the two factories have exactly the same expected payoff, $500,000.

Notice that in these examples, the actual payoff *never* equals the expected payoff. In general, the expected payoff from a risky choice is *not* necessarily the most likely outcome, and need not even be remotely likely. Rather, it's the amount you would earn, on average, if you were to make the same risky choice many times. To illustrate, take Ilya and Napoleon's coin flip. Were they to make the same bet, say, 10,000 times, the frequency of heads and tails would be very close to 50 percent, so their average payoff would be very close to zero.

Application 11.1

The Development of New Drugs

Pharmaceutical manufacturers have drawn widespread criticism by charging high prices for life-saving drugs. For example, the drugs used to treat HIV, the virus that causes AIDS, can cost a patient tens of thousands of dollars a year, placing treatment beyond the reach of many, including millions in third world countries. Critics point out that manufacturers could make these drugs available at lower prices and still cover their costs of production.

The companies respond that drug prices must be high enough to cover the costs not only of production, but of development, including expensive clinical trials. Otherwise, they would have no incentive to develop new drugs. In evaluating the cost of development, they emphasize, it's essential to account for the fact that success isn't assured. Only a minority of experimental drugs eventually win approval by Health Canada and only after clinical testing. Companies won't develop new drugs unless, on average, their profits cover their development costs.

How much does the typical approved drug need to earn to cover a company's development costs? Let's say that a company has to spend an average of $50 million on development costs for each experimental drug, and that the probability of approval by Health Canada is 20 percent. If each approved drug generates P dollars in profits (ignoring development costs), then using formula (1) the expected payoff from each experimental drug is

$$\text{Expected payoff} = (0.2 \times \$P + 0.8 \times \$0) - \$50 \text{ million}$$

Setting $P = \$250$ million, we find that the expected payoff is exactly zero. So on average, a successful drug has to generate a profit of at least $250 million after its approval to justify the company's development of experimental drugs. Merely covering the $50 million in development costs for the approved drug isn't enough.

Experts disagree sharply about the costs of drug development. According to one controversial study by economists Joseph DiMasi, Ronald Hansen, and Henry Grabowski, the average successful drug in the United States must generate $802 million in profits after regulatory approval to cover a company's development costs.[1] Other studies have arrived at lower figures.[2] In Canada those profits are often hard to come by as the Patented Medicine Prices Review Board is charged with making sure that the prices of prescription drugs are not excessive. Patented drug prices are regulated and their price is constrained to be in the range of other drugs used to treat the illness. The cost of developing the drug is not included as one of the factors affecting the cost of prescription medicines.[3]

Variability

The **variability** of payoffs is an indication of risk. With little variability, the actual payoff is almost always close to the expected payoff. With substantial variability, the two amounts can differ significantly.

Economists gauge financial risk by measuring the **variability** of gains and losses. Roughly speaking, variability is low when the range of likely payoffs is narrow, and high when the range is wide. With little variability, the actual payoff is almost always close to the expected payoff. With substantial variability, the two amounts can differ significantly.

Histograms can help us to visualize variability. For example, look again at Figure 11.1, which summarizes the possible financial consequences of New Stuff's proposed factories. Notice that the blue bars in Figure 11.1(b) are closer together—and closer to the expected payoff of $0.5 million—than the red bars in Figure 11.1(a). That means the payoffs from the small factory are less variable than the payoffs from the large one.

A **deviation** is the difference between the actual payoff and the expected payoff.

The difference between the actual payoff and the expected payoff is called a **deviation**. Greater variability is associated with larger deviations. Figures 11.2(a) and (b) illustrate the possible deviations from the expected payoff for New Stuff's proposed factories. We've indicated the expected payoff for each of the proposed factories, $0.5 million, on the horizontal axes. As Figure 11.2(a) shows, for the large factory there is an 80 percent chance that the deviation will be −$2 million (the horizontal distance between the tall red bar and a vertical line drawn at the expected payoff), and a 20 percent chance that the deviation will be +$8 million (the horizontal distance between the short red bar and a vertical line drawn at the expected payoff). In contrast, for the small factory there is an 80 percent chance that the deviation will be −$1 million, and a 20 percent chance that it will be +$4 million.

---

[1]Joseph A. DiMasi, Ronald W. Hansen, and Henry G. Grabowski, "The Price of Innovation: New Estimates of Drug Development Costs," *Journal of Health Economics* 22, March 2003, pp. 151–185.

[2]For example, a study by the Global Alliance for TB Drug Development (*The Economics of TB Drug Development*, October 2001) concludes that the average successful tuberculosis drug must generate between $115 and $250 million in profits to cover development costs.

[3]Information on the role of the Patented Medicine Prices Review Board can be found at its website: http://www.pmprb-cepmb.gc.ca.

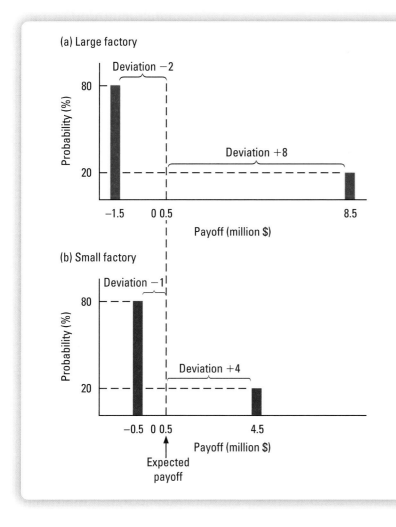

Figure 11.2

Expected Payoff and Deviations for New Stuff's Investment in the Thingamajig. The expected payoff from each of New Stuff's proposed factories is $0.5 million. However, the histograms show that the large factory's payoff is more variable—its distribution is wider, and the deviations are larger.

Often, economists measure the variability of a risky financial payoff by calculating either its variance or its standard deviation. The **variance** is the expected value of a squared deviation. The calculation of variance involves three steps: (1) compute the deviations for all possible outcomes, (2) square each deviation, and (3) find the weighted average of all the possible squared deviations, using the probability of each squared deviation as its weight. The **standard deviation** is the square root of the variance. Both the variance and the standard deviation tell us something about the size of the typical deviation.

> The **variance** is the expected value of a squared deviation.

> The **standard deviation** is the square root of the variance.

Table 11.3 calculates the variance and standard deviation of the payoffs for each of New Stuff's proposed factories. For the large factory, the variance is $16 trillion squared, and the standard deviation is $4 million. For the small factory, the variance is $4 trillion squared, and the standard deviation is $2 million. These numbers confirm what we saw in Figure 11.2; the payoffs for the large factory are much more variable than the payoffs for the small one.

Table 11.3
Variability of New Stuff's Profits on the Thingamajig

Large Factory	Probability	Deviation (million $)	Squared Dev. (trillion ^{2})	Probability × Squared Dev. (trillion ^{2})
	20%	8	64	12.8
	80%	−2	4	3.2
Variance (trillion ^{2})				16
Standard deviation (million $)				4

Small Factory	Probability	Deviation (million $)	Squared Dev. (trillion ^{2})	Probability × Squared Dev. (trillion ^{2})
	20%	4	16	3.2
	80%	−1	1	0.8
Variance (trillion ^{2})				4
Standard deviation (million $)				2

11.2 RISK PREFERENCES

Fortunately, we don't need to develop an entirely new theory to analyze decisions involving risk. We can simply apply the basic theory of consumer decision making that we learned in Chapters 4 through 6.

Consumption Bundles

In Section 10.2 we learned how to apply that theory to decisions involving time. The key was to think of a consumption bundle as a list of the quantities of each good consumed at each point in time. (If you skipped Chapter 10, take a moment to read the short section titled The Timing of Consumption, which begins on page 339.) We can handle risk in much the same way. That is, we can think of a consumption bundle as a list of the quantities of each good consumed in each possible state of nature.

To illustrate, let's start with a simple problem. A consumer, whom we'll call Julia, is uncertain about the weather at her home on the banks of the flood-prone Red River in southern Manitoba. There are only two possible states of nature, "sun" and "flood." We'll assume that Julia is familiar with the probability of each state from past experience.[4]

To keep the analysis simple, we'll assume that Julia consumes only one good, called "food," which is measured in kilograms. Julia needn't consume the same amount of food when it's sunny and when there's a flood. Indeed, if a flood were to inundate some of her property, forcing her to spend some of her money on repairs, she would most likely consume less. Therefore, her consumption bundle must list both the amount of food she eats when it's sunny and the amount she eats when there's a flood.

Figure 11.3 illustrates Julia's potential consumption bundles. The horizontal axis measures her consumption if it's sunny, and the vertical axis measures her consumption if

---

[4]We'll assume that it cannot be sunny and flooding at the same time although that is often the case in southern Manitoba if the rainfall occurs in the North Central United States.

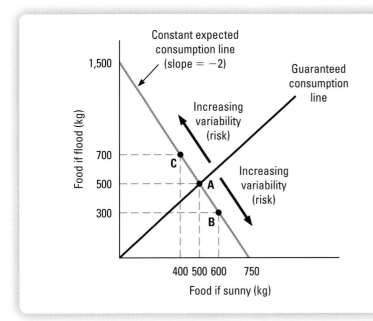

Figure II.3

Consumption Bundles. Each point on this graph corresponds to a different risky alternative. At point B, for example, Julia eats 600 kilograms of food if it's sunny and 300 kilograms if there's a flood. For points like A on the 45-degree line (also called the *guaranteed consumption line*), she eats the same amount, rain or shine. Julia's expected consumption is the same (500 kilograms) for all points on the green line (also called a *constant expected consumption line*). As Julia moves away from point A in either direction along the green line, variability (risk) increases.

there's a flood. Each point on the graph corresponds to a distinct alternative. For example, point B represents the consumption bundle consisting of 600 kilograms of food if it's sunny and 300 kilograms of food if there's a flood.

Guaranteed Consumption   For some bundles, the level of consumption is guaranteed in the sense that it does not depend on the state of nature. In Figure 11.3, those bundles all lie along the 45-degree line through the origin, also known as the **guaranteed consumption line**. Notice, for example, that point A provides Julia with the same amount of food, 500 kilograms, if it's sunny and if there's a flood. At all points below the guaranteed consumption line, like point B, Julia eats more food if it's sunny; at all points above that line, like point C, she eats more food if there's a flood.

> The **guaranteed consumption line** shows the consumption bundles for which the level of consumption does not depend on the state of nature.

Expected Consumption and Variability   For bundles that don't lie on the guaranteed consumption line in Figure 11.3, Julia's payoff (the amount of food she consumes) is uncertain. Given any particular bundle, we can compute her expected consumption (abbreviated EC) by applying formula (1). Let's use F_S to stand for the amount of food she consumes if it's sunny, F_F for the amount she consumes if there's a flood, and π for the probability of sun (so that the probability of a flood is $1 - \pi$). Then

$$EC = \pi \times F_S + (1 - \pi) \times F_F \qquad (2)$$

For example, if the probability of sun is 2/3, F_S is 600 kilograms, and F_F is 300 kilograms, then expected consumption is 500 kilograms.

Many of the bundles in Figure 11.3 share the same level of expected consumption. Which ones? Let's rearrange formula (2) as follows:[5]

$$F_F = \frac{EC}{1 - \pi} - \left(\frac{\pi}{1 - \pi}\right) F_S \qquad (3)$$

---

[5] To obtain formula (3) from formula (2), first subtract $\pi \times F_S$ from both sides, and then divide through by $1 - \pi$.

Formula (3) implies that risky consumption bundles with the same level of expected consumption (that is, the same value of EC) lie along a straight line with a slope of $-\pi/(1-\pi)$. We call this a **constant expected consumption line**.

To illustrate, let's suppose that $\pi = {}^2\!/_3$. For all of the bundles on the green line in Figure 11.3, expected consumption is 500 kilograms. Therefore, this is a constant expected consumption line. Notice that the slope of this line is $-\pi/(1-\pi) = -2$. The line would be steeper for a higher value of π and flatter for a lower value.

Although every point on the green line in Figure 11.3 has the same level of expected consumption, the *variability* of consumption differs. At point A, consumption doesn't depend on the weather, so there is no variability. As Julia moves away from point A in either direction along the constant expected consumption line, her consumption becomes increasingly variable. (Pick a point on this line and draw the histogram for the probability distribution of Julia's consumption. Notice that as your chosen point moves farther away from point A the bars corresponding to sun and flood move farther apart.)

Preferences and Indifference Curves

If one consumption bundle guarantees more of every good than a second bundle, a consumer should prefer the first bundle to the second. This assumption reflects the More-Is-Better Principle, which we introduced in Chapter 4. Notice that a consumption bundle does not have to guarantee a particular level of consumption to guarantee more consumption than a second bundle. For example, point D in Figure 11.4(a) guarantees a higher level of food consumption than point B: with point D, consumption is higher in every

Figure 11.4

Julia's Preferences for Risky Consumption Bundles. The indifference curves show Julia's preferences for risky consumption bundles. A high probability of a flood leads to relatively flat indifference curves, like the red ones shown in figure (a), and a low probability leads to relatively steep indifference curves, like the blue ones shown in figure (b).

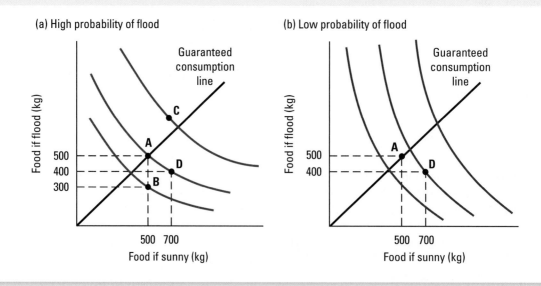

state of nature—both if it's sunny (700 kilograms versus 500 kilograms) and if there's a flood (400 kilograms versus 300 kilograms). Julia must therefore prefer point D to point B.

Assuming that more is better, we can illustrate Julia's preferences for consumption bundles by drawing indifference curves, exactly as we did in Chapter 4. For the reasons discussed in Section 4.2, her indifference curves must be downward sloping lines, and those that are farther from the origin must correspond to higher levels of well-being. For example, the indifference curves in Figure 11.4(a) show that Julia prefers point C to point A, and point A to point B. She is indifferent between points A and D. Given a choice between these four alternatives, she'll pick point C.

The slope of an indifference curve indicates the consumer's willingness to shift consumption from one state of nature to another. For example, the indifference curve that runs through points A and D in Figure 11.4(a) implies that, starting from point D, Julia is willing to give up 200 kilograms of food if it's sunny in order to secure an additional 100 kilograms if there's a flood.

Usually, a consumer's willingness to shift consumption from one state of nature to another depends on the probabilities of those states. Therefore, a change in probabilities changes the slopes of the consumer's indifference curves. In Julia's case, a high probability of a flood leads to relatively flat indifference curves, like the red ones shown in Figure 11.4(a), and a low probability leads to relatively steep indifference curves, like the blue ones shown in Figure 11.4(b). To understand why, suppose that Julia starts out with point D. When the probability of a flood is high [Figure 11.4(a)], she is indifferent between points A and D, and willing to swap 200 kilograms of food if it's sunny for an additional 100 kilograms if there's a flood. When the probability of flood falls, she becomes less concerned about consumption if there's a flood and more concerned about consumption if it's sunny. Therefore, as shown in Figure 11.4(b), the same swap makes her worse off; she prefers point D to point A. Since she now requires *more* than 100 kilograms of food if there's a flood to compensate for the loss of 200 kilograms of food if it's sunny, her indifference curve is steeper. In other words, reducing the probability of a flood increases her marginal rate of substitution for food if it's sunny with food if there's a flood.

The Concept of Risk Aversion

Most people don't like uncertainty. They pay money to eliminate or reduce risk—for example, by purchasing an insurance policy. They also avoid accepting a new risk unless they're adequately compensated. We say that a person is **risk averse** if, in comparing a riskless bundle to a risky bundle with the same level of expected consumption, he prefers the riskless bundle. This definition captures the idea that, by itself, variability is a bad thing.

What does risk aversion imply about the shape of an indifference curve? Figure 11.5 reproduces the constant expected consumption line from Figure 11.3. This line crosses the guaranteed consumption line at point A. Therefore, point A is the only riskless bundle on the constant expected consumption line. If Julia is risk averse, she will prefer point A to all other points on this line. This implies that one of her indifference curves lies tangent to the constant expected consumption line at point A, and above all other points on that line, as shown.

Risk-averse individuals do not avoid risk at all costs. Starting from a riskless position, they are usually willing to accept some risk, provided that they receive adequate compensation in the form of higher expected consumption. For example, in Figure 11.5, Julia will prefer bundle B to bundle A, even though bundle B involves more variability, and in the event of a flood, lower consumption than bundle A.

> A person is **risk averse** if, in comparing a riskless bundle to a risky bundle with the same level of expected consumption, he prefers the riskless bundle.

Figure 11.5

Risk Aversion. The constant expected consumption line crosses the guaranteed consumption line at point A. Therefore, point A is the only riskless bundle on the constant expected consumption line. If Julia is risk averse, she prefers point A to all other points on this line. This implies that her indifference curve lies tangent to the constant expected consumption line at point A, and above all other points on this line, as shown.

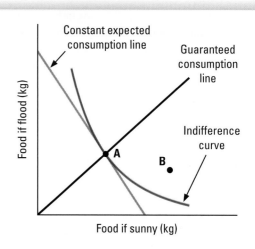

Figure 11.6

The Certainty Equivalent and the Risk Premium. The fixed level of food consumption associated with point C is the certainty equivalent of the risky consumption bundle B. The risk premium for bundle B is the difference between the expected level of consumption at B and B's certainty equivalent. It's also the amount by which the consumer is willing to reduce expected consumption to eliminate all risks. Since the expected level of consumption is the same at points A and B, the risk premium for bundle B equals the horizontal distance (also the vertical distance) between points C and A.

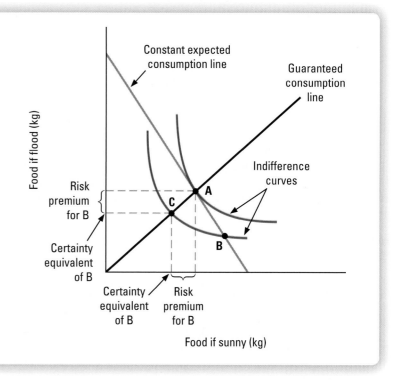

The **certainty equivalent** of a risky bundle is the amount of consumption which, if provided with certainty, would make the consumer equally well off.

Certainty Equivalents and Risk Premiums
For risk-averse individuals, exposure to risk reduces well-being. How do we measure that cost? To answer this question, we'll introduce the concept of a certainty equivalent. The **certainty equivalent** of a risky bundle is the amount of consumption which, if provided with certainty, would make the consumer equally well off. Figure 11.6 illustrates this concept. Let's take any risky bundle, like bundle B, and draw the consumer's indifference curve through it. This curve intersects the 45-degree line at point C, which guarantees a fixed level of consumption.

This guaranteed level, which we can read from either the horizontal or vertical axis (as shown in the figure), is the certainty equivalent of bundle B.

A risky bundle's certainty equivalent tells us exactly what it's worth to the consumer. When faced with a choice between two risky bundles, the consumer always chooses the one with the higher certainty equivalent. So if one risky bundle is worth $5 for sure and another is worth only $4 for sure, the first is plainly better than the second.

For a risk-averse individual, the certainty equivalent of a risky bundle is always less than expected consumption. Why? Providing the same expected consumption with no risk would clearly make the individual better off. In the figure, Julia prefers point A to point B. To make Julia indifferent between bundle B and a riskless bundle, we have to *reduce* her guaranteed consumption from the level associated with point A to the level associated with point C.

The **risk premium** of a risky bundle is the difference between its expected consumption and the consumer's certainty equivalent. In other words, it's the amount by which the consumer is willing to reduce expected consumption to eliminate all risk. In Figure 11.6, the risk premium corresponds to the horizontal distance (equivalently, the vertical distance) between point A (which has the same expected level of consumption as the risky bundle B) and point C. The size of the risk premium reflects the psychological cost of risk.

The **risk premium** of a risky bundle is the difference between its expected consumption and the consumer's certainty equivalent.

WORKED-OUT PROBLEM 11.1

The Problem   Suppose Julia's indifference curves are given by the formula

$$\frac{2}{3}\sqrt{F_S} + \frac{1}{3}\sqrt{F_F} = C$$

where C is a constant (the value of which differs from one indifference curve to another). Julia receives 36 kilograms of food when it's sunny and 81 kilograms when there's a flood. If the probability of sunshine, π, equals $2/3$, what is her expected food consumption? What is the certainty equivalent of this risky bundle? What is the risk premium?

The Solution   Expected consumption is $2/3 F_S + 1/3 F_F = 2/3 \times 36 + 1/3 \times 81 = 51$. To compute the certainty equivalent, we need to find a level of guaranteed food consumption, F, that places Julia on the same indifference curve as the risky bundle.

$$\frac{2}{3}\sqrt{36} + \frac{1}{3}\sqrt{81} = \frac{2}{3}\sqrt{F} + \frac{1}{3}\sqrt{F}$$

Simplifying, we get $4 + 3 = \sqrt{F}$, or $F = 49$. So the certainty equivalent is 49 kilograms. Since $51 - 49 = 2$, the risk premium is 2 kilograms.

IN-TEXT EXERCISE 11.1   **Repeat the calculation in worked-out problem 11.1 for each of the following risky consumption bundles.**
   (a) 81 kilograms when it's sunny, and 36 kilograms when it rains.
   (b) 225 kilograms when it's sunny, and 144 kilograms when it rains.
   (c) 9 kilograms when it's sunny, and 900 kilograms when it rains.

Figure 11.7

Degrees of Risk Aversion. The red indifference curve belongs to Julia, the blue one belongs to Arnold. Julia is less risk averse than Arnold. Neither would trade the riskless consumption bundle A for risky alternatives that lie below both of their indifference curves, like bundle B. Both would trade bundle A for risky alternatives above both of their indifference curves, like bundle C. However, Julia will trade bundle A for risky bundles between the two indifference curves, like bundle D, while Arnold will not.

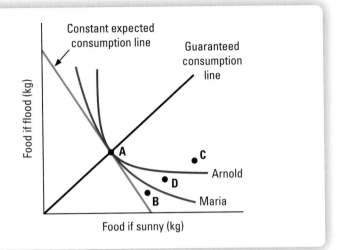

Degrees of Risk Aversion   Some people need relatively little encouragement to take a risk. Others prefer safe alternatives unless the cards are heavily stacked in their favour. What do these differences imply about the shapes of their indifference curves?

Figure 11.7 reproduces Julia's indifference curve (shown in red), along with an indifference curve for another consumer, Arnold (shown in blue). Since Julia and Arnold are both risk averse, both curves lie tangent to the constant expected consumption line at point A. However, Arnold's curve bends more sharply at the 45-degree line, and it lies above Julia's everywhere else. That means Arnold is more risk averse than Julia, starting from point A.

To understand why, notice that the two indifference curves divide the set of possible alternatives into three parts. First, there are points below Julia's indifference curve, like point B. Neither Julia nor Arnold will swap bundle A for any risky bundle in this part of the figure. Second, there are points above Arnold's indifference curve, like point C. Both Julia and Arnold will swap bundle A for any risky bundle in this part of the figure. Finally, there are points between the two indifference curves, like point D. Julia will exchange bundle A for a risky bundle in this part of the figure, but Arnold will not. Since Julia is willing to take on a wider range of risk than Arnold, she's less risk averse.

Greater risk aversion implies that for any risky bundle, the certainty equivalent is lower and the risk premium higher than it is for less risk-averse consumers. In other words, the psychological cost of risk exposure is greater for more risk-averse consumers. As an example, take point D in Figure 11.7. Since Julia prefers point D to point A, her certainty equivalent for point D must be *larger* than the level of consumption that point A guarantees. Since Arnold prefers point A to point D, his certainty equivalent for point D must be *smaller* than the level of consumption that point A guarantees. Julia's certainty equivalent is therefore larger than Arnold's, and her risk premium is smaller.

A person is **risk loving** if, in comparing a riskless bundle to a risky bundle with the same level of expected consumption, she prefers the risky bundle.

Alternatives to Risk Aversion

Some people actually like to take risks, at least in some situations. We say that a person is **risk loving** if, in comparing a riskless bundle to a risky bundle with the same level of expected consumption, she prefers the risky bundle. This definition captures the idea that variability is

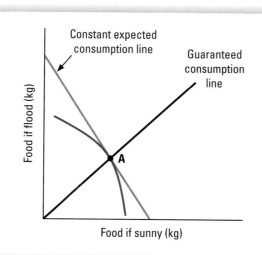

Figure 11.8
A Risk Loving Consumer. As before, point A is the only riskless bundle on the constant expected consumption line. If Julia is risk loving, she must prefer all other points on this line to point A. This implies that her indifference curve lies tangent to the constant expected consumption line at point A and below all other points on this line, as shown.

in itself a good thing. A risk-loving individual will voluntarily accept higher variability even if it isn't associated with a higher level of expected consumption.

What would Julia's indifference curves look like if she were risk loving? Figure 11.8 reproduces the constant expected consumption line from Figure 11.3. Recall that point A is the only riskless bundle on this line. If Julia is risk loving, she will prefer every other point on this line to point A. This implies that one of her indifference curves lies tangent to the constant expected consumption line at point A, and below all other points on that line, as shown.

Conceivably, some consumers may not care about risk one way or the other. As a result, they are indifferent between all bundles with the same level of expected consumption. In comparing two risky bundles, they simply select the one with the highest level of expected consumption. The indifference curves of these **risk neutral** consumers therefore coincide with the constant expected consumption lines.

A person is **risk neutral** if he is indifferent between all bundles with the same level of expected consumption.

Application 11.2

Betting on Sports

Canada has one of the most widespread legal sporting networks in the world. Bets on sporting events can be made at lottery centres throughout Canada and online. One can make wagers on hockey, Canadian and American football, baseball, and European soccer. Wagers can only be made on the outcome of two to six contests, depending on the province in which the wager is made, and cannot be made on single matches.

Why is sports betting so popular? Evidence shows that most individuals are risk averse: for example, they buy insurance. Two risk-averse individuals will never bet against

each other if they agree on the probabilities of the outcomes. Being risk averse, neither will bet unless they think the wager yields a positive expected payoff. But since their payoffs always add up to zero (one wins what the other loses), any wager that has a positive expected payoff for one person has a negative expected payoff for the other.

In contrast, if two risk-averse people disagree about the probabilities of the outcomes, they may want to bet against each other. Let's say Germany is playing Brazil in the World Cup Final. Helga and Luiz disagree about Germany's likelihood of winning; Helga thinks it's 70 percent, while Luiz thinks it's

30 percent. What if they bet $100 on the outcome, with Helga taking Germany and Luiz taking Brazil? From Helga's perspective, her expected payoff is $40 (since 0.7 × 100 − 0.3 × 100 = 40). From Luiz's perspective, his expected payoff is also $40. Both think they're getting a positive expected payoff.

Is this a good explanation for sports betting? Not necessarily. It begs the question of *why* Helga and Luiz disagree about the likely outcome. Certainly, they could come to different objective conclusions if they had different information. However, two rational, risk-averse people should never be willing to wager with each other for that reason alone.

To see why, let's change the example. Suppose Helga and Luiz agree that Germany has a 30 percent chance of beating Brazil. The day after the game, Helga picks up the sports section of the newspaper while having coffee with Luiz and reads that, despite the odds, Germany has won. Assuming that Luiz hasn't yet heard the result, they now have different beliefs that reflect different information. Even so, Luiz should refuse to take any gamble that Helga proposes.

Suppose she says, "I'll bet you $100 that Germany beat Brazil yesterday." Her willingness to make this bet after reading the paper should convince Luiz that Germany did indeed win. By proposing the gamble, Helga effectively reveals her information, thereby eliminating the difference in beliefs that might have sustained a wager.

Even after considering what each might learn from the other's willingness to make the bet, Helga and Luiz could both think they're getting a better-than-fair deal if they start out with different *subjective* beliefs. Maybe Helga has a gut feeling that Germany will win, or Luiz is feeling lucky. In other words, differences in feelings—unlike differences in hard information—could explain sports betting.[6]

Of course, many people also gamble for entertainment. For example, some think that placing a bet heightens the excitement they feel when watching a game. But while that is certainly part of the explanation, it isn't the whole story. People also place bets on the outcomes of games they don't watch, and many regular gamblers are convinced they can consistently pick winners.

Expected Utility

In Chapter 4 we learned that it's possible to represent a consumer's indifference curves with a utility function, which assigns a numerical index of well-being to each consumption bundle. In Julia's case, a consumption bundle consists of the amount of food she eats if it's sunny, F_S, and the amount of food she eats if there's a flood, F_F. Thus, we can represent her indifference curves, like the ones in Figure 11.4(a) or (b), with a utility function of the form $U(F_S, F_F)$.

When we write a utility function like $U(F_S, F_F)$, we are allowing for a very wide range of possibilities. That flexibility may make it difficult to determine consumers' preferences by observing their choices. To narrow down the range of possibilities, economists usually make some additional assumptions.

Expected Utility Functions   Let's assume that the benefit Julia derives from food depends only on the amount she eats, and not on the weather. The function $W(F)$ will tell us the size of that benefit. When it's sunny, Julia eats F_S kilograms and receives a benefit of $W(F_S)$. When there's a flood, she eats F_F kilograms and receives a benefit of $W(F_F)$. It is then natural to assume that Julia's utility is simply her expected benefit.

$$U(F_S, F_F) = \pi \times W(F_S) + (1 - \pi) \times W(F_F) \tag{4}$$

(Recall that π is the probability of sun and $1 - \pi$ is the probability of a flood.)

---

[6]Another possibility is that each thinks the other may not understand the implications of the information they possess.

Formula (4) is an example of an **expected utility function**.[7] It assigns a benefit level to each possible state of nature based only on what is consumed, and then takes the expected value of those benefits. In other words, it's a weighted average of all the possible benefit levels, using the probability of each benefit level as its weight.

What if Julia's enjoyment of food depends on the weather? For example, what if she tends to have a larger appetite when it's sunny (perhaps because she gets more exercise)? In that case, we may not be able to represent her indifference curves with an expected utility function like formula (4). Most (but certainly not all) economists nevertheless think that the assumptions behind expected utility functions are reasonably accurate in most circumstances.

> An **expected utility function** assigns a benefit level to each possible state of nature based only on what is consumed, and then takes the expected value of those benefits.

WORKED-OUT PROBLEM   11.2

The Problem Suppose we can represent Julia's preferences with an expected utility function, and that $W(F) = \sqrt{F}$. Suppose also that the probability of sun is 2/3, and the probability of a flood is 1/3. Plot the indifference curve that runs through the point $(F_S, F_F) = (400, 400)$. Plot the constant expected consumption line that runs through this same point. Is Julia risk averse, risk loving, or risk neutral?

The Solution Julia's expected utility function is

$$U(F_S, F_F) = \frac{2}{3}\sqrt{F_S} + \frac{1}{3}\sqrt{F_F}$$

Using this formula, we see that $U(400, 400) = 20$. So points on the indifference curve through the point $(F_S, F_F) = (400, 400)$ satisfy the formula $\frac{2}{3}\sqrt{F_S} + \frac{1}{3}\sqrt{F_F} = 20$. After multiplying through by 3, subtracting $2\sqrt{F_S}$ from both sides, and squaring, we can rewrite this formula as

$$F_F = (60 - 2\sqrt{F_S})^2$$

We've plotted this indifference curve in Figure 11.9 by plugging in several numerical values: for $F_S = 300$ we have $F_F = 643$; for $F_S = 350$ we have $F_F = 510$; for $F_S = 400$ we have $F_F = 400$; for $F_S = 450$ we have $F_F = 309$; and for $F_S = 500$ we have $F_F = 233$.

Points on the constant expected consumption line that runs through the point $(F_S, F_F) = (400, 400)$ satisfy the formula $\frac{2}{3}F_S + \frac{1}{3}F_F = 400$, which we can rewrite as $F_F = 1200 - 2F_S$. We've also plotted that line in Figure 11.9. Notice that the indifference curve lies tangent to the constant expected consumption line at the point $(F_S, F_F) = (400, 400)$, and above all other points on that line. Julia is therefore risk averse.

  IN-TEXT EXERCISE 11.2 **Repeat the calculation in worked-out problem 11.2, but assume that $W(F) = F^2$.**

---

[7]More than 60 years ago, a mathematician named John von Neumann and an economist named Oskar Morgenstern proved an important theorem concerning expected utility: as long as someone's choices satisfy a few simple assumptions (also known as the von Neumann-Morgenstern *axioms*), they will behave as if they maximize an expected utility function when making choices involving risk. Many economists think von Neumann and Morgenstern's assumptions are reasonable; others disagree. We describe some alternatives in Section 13.4.

Figure 11.9

Solution to Worked-Out Problem 11.2.
Julia's indifference curve is shown in red. The constant expected consumption line is shown in green. Since her indifference curve lies tangent to the constant expected consumption line where it crosses the guaranteed consumption line, and above the constant expected consumption line at all other points, Julia is risk averse.

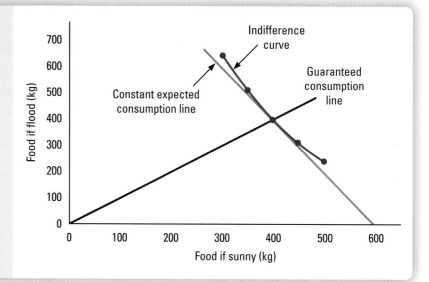

Expected Utility and Risk Aversion Assuming that it's possible to represent Julia's preferences with an expected utility function, we can determine her attitude toward risk from the shape of her benefit function, $W(F)$. If $W(F)$ is concave (that is, if it flattens as F increases), she's risk averse; if it's convex (that is, if it steepens as F increases), she's risk loving; and if it's linear (that is, a straight line), she's risk neutral.

Let's examine the case where the benefit function $W(F)$ is concave. Look at Figure 11.10, in which we've graphed the benefit function from worked-out problem 11.2, $W(F) = \sqrt{F}$. This is a typical concave function: as F increases, it becomes flatter. As we have already seen in worked-out problem 11.2, this benefit function implies risk aversion. Figure 11.10 shows that this is a consequence of the function's concavity.

Figure 11.10

Expected Utility for a Risk-Averse Consumer. If Julia's benefit function is concave, she is risk averse. Consider a consumption bundle consisting of F_S kilograms of food if it's sunny, yielding a benefit of $W(F_S)$, and F_F kilograms of food if there's a flood, yielding a benefit of $W(F_F)$. The coordinates of point C, which lies on the straight line between points A and B, correspond to expected consumption and expected benefit. Since the concave benefit function bows upward, a riskless bundle with the same level of expected consumption yields a larger benefit (point D). Therefore, Julia prefers it to the risky bundle.

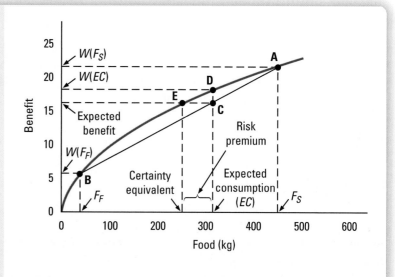

Let's consider a consumption bundle consisting of F_S kilograms of food if it's sunny and F_F kilograms of food if there's a flood. In the event of sun, Julia's benefit is $W(F_S)$, shown as point A in Figure 11.10. In the event of a flood, her benefit is $W(F_F)$, shown as point B in the figure. Now consider point C. Its horizontal coordinate is the level of expected consumption, and its vertical coordinate is the expected benefit. By definition, the coordinates of point C are weighted averages of the coordinates of points A and B, where the probabilities of sun and flood are used as the weights. Therefore, point C must lie on the straight line that connects points A and B, as shown.

Now let's consider a second consumption bundle with the same level of expected consumption, but no risk. The benefit that Julia receives from this bundle is the vertical coordinate of point D. Point D has the same horizontal coordinate as point C. However, since the concave function $W(F)$ bows upward between points A and B, point D's vertical coordinate is larger than point C's. Julia is therefore risk averse: she prefers the safe bundle, which provides a benefit equal to point D's vertical coordinate, to the risky one, which provides an expected benefit equal to point C's vertical coordinate.

Let's check this conclusion numerically. In the figure, $F_S = 441$, $F_F = 36$, $\pi = 2/3$, and $W(F) = \sqrt{F}$. You can verify that $W(F_S) = 21$, $W(F_F) = 6$. Expected consumption (EC) is 306, and Julia's expected benefit is 16. For a riskless bundle providing 306 kilograms of food in both states of nature, her benefit is approximately 17.5. Since 17.5 exceeds 16, Julia prefers the riskless bundle.

Concavity of the benefit function is linked to the idea that scarcity makes a commodity more valuable. For instance, the marginal benefit of extra food in Figure 11.10 (equivalently, the slope of the benefit function) is greater at a low level of consumption like F_F than at a high level of consumption like F_S. That is precisely why Julia is risk averse. Starting with a risky consumption bundle, she is willing to give up some food in a state of nature where food has low incremental value because it's plentiful, for extra food in a state of nature where food has high incremental value because it's scarce.

Now let's consider the case where the benefit function $W(F)$ is convex. We can evaluate a risky bundle using a diagram similar to Figure 11.10. With a convex benefit function, the red curve would bow downward rather than upward. As a result, point D would be lower than point C, rather than higher. (Check your understanding by drawing the figure.) This configuration implies a preference for the risky bundle over a riskless one with the same level of expected consumption. In other words, the consumer is risk loving. You have already seen an example of this principle: the consumer from in-text exercise 11.2 is risk loving because the benefit function $W(F) = F^2$ is convex (check this by graphing the function).

What if the benefit function $W(F)$ is linear? Once again, we can evaluate a risky bundle using a diagram similar to Figure 11.10. With a linear benefit function, the red curve would be a straight line. As a result, point D would be the same as point C. (Check your understanding by drawing the figure.) This configuration implies indifference between the risky bundle and a riskless one with the same level of expected consumption. In other words, the consumer is risk neutral.

Certainty Equivalents, Risk Premiums, and Degrees of Risk Aversion Figure 11.10 illustrates another way to find the certainty equivalent and risk premium for a risky consumption bundle. The horizontal line between point C and the vertical axis intersects the function $W(F)$ at point E. The horizontal coordinate of point E is the certainty equivalent of the risky bundle. Why? If Julia consumes that amount of food with certainty, her benefit will be the same as her expected benefit from the risky bundle. As shown in the figure, Julia's risk premium, which we defined previously as the difference between

Figure 11.11

Expected Utility and the Degree of Risk Aversion. The red benefit function is for Julia, and the blue benefit function is for Arnold. The blue curve is more bowed than the red curve; it's more concave. Julia's certainty equivalent is the horizontal coordinate of point E and Arnold's is the horizontal coordinate of point F. Julia's risk premium is the horizontal gap between points C and E; Arnold's is the horizontal gap between points C and F. Since Arnold's certainty equivalent is smaller and his risk premium larger than Julia's, he is more risk averse.

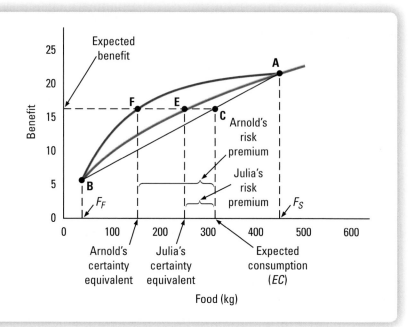

expected consumption and the certainty equivalent, corresponds to the horizontal gap between points C and E. Returning to our numerical example, we see that Julia's certainty equivalent, CE, solves the formula $W(CE) = 16$. This implies that $CE = 16^2 = 256$ kilograms. Since expected consumption is 306 kilograms, Julia's risk premium is 50 kilograms.

How does the shape of the benefit function $W(F)$ relate to the degree of risk aversion? Since concavity implies risk aversion, you won't be surprised to learn that the greater the concavity, the greater the risk aversion. To see why, look at Figure 11.11, which analyzes the same risky bundle as Figure 11.10. We've reproduced a number of elements from Figure 11.10, including Julia's benefit function (in red), certainty equivalent, and risk premium. The preferences of a second consumer, Arnold, correspond to the blue benefit function. Notice that the blue curve is more bowed than the red curve: it's more concave. Using the same logic as before, we see that Arnold's certainty equivalent is the horizontal coordinate of point F, and his risk premium is the horizontal gap between points C and F. Since Arnold's certainty equivalent is smaller and his risk premium larger than Julia's, he is more risk averse.

11.3 INSURANCE

Much of life is inherently risky. While we can take some measures to improve the odds of staying safe, secure, and healthy, many events are outside our control. To protect ourselves against the financial consequences of these risks, we sometimes purchase insurance.

The Nature of Insurance

An **insurance policy** is a contract that reduces the financial loss associated with some risky event, like a burglary, an accident, an illness, or death.

People address a wide range of risks by purchasing **insurance policies**. An insurance policy is a contract that reduces the financial loss associated with some risky event, like a burglary, an accident, an illness, or death. The simplest type of insurance policy specifies a **premium**, which is the amount of money the policyholder pays for the policy, and a **benefit**, which is the amount the policyholder receives if a specific loss occurs.

> An insurance **premium** is the amount of money a policyholder pays for an insurance policy.

The purchaser of an insurance policy is essentially placing a bet. Let's use the symbol M to stand for the size of the premium, and the symbol B to stand for the size of the promised benefit. Having paid M, the policyholder receives B if a loss occurs, for a net gain of $B - M$. If a loss doesn't occur, he loses the premium, M. Since the policy pays off only when a loss occurs, in a sense the consumer is betting that the loss will happen.

> An insurance **benefit** is the amount of money a policyholder receives if a specific loss occurs.

When the expected net payoff from an insurance policy is zero, we say that it's **actuarially fair**. Sometimes we simply call it *fair insurance*. Purchasing an actuarially fair insurance policy does not change the purchaser's expected consumption, it simply raises consumption in some states of nature and reduces it in others. Let's use the Greek letter π to stand for the probability of avoiding a loss, in which case the probability of sustaining a loss is $1 - \pi$. Actuarial fairness requires that

> An insurance policy is **actuarially fair** if its expected net payoff is zero.

$$\pi \times (-M) + (1 - \pi) \times (B - M) = 0$$

which implies that $M = B(1 - \pi)$. That is, an actuarially fair insurance premium equals the promised benefit times the probability of a loss; the price of insurance per dollar of coverage is $(1 - \pi)$.

Insurance policies are usually less than actuarially fair. That is, the premium typically exceeds the promised benefit times the probability of a loss ($M > B(1 - \pi)$). This is because insurance companies must come out ahead to cover their costs of operation. On average, then, policyholders lose money; purchasing an actuarially unfair policy reduces the purchaser's expected consumption.

The Demand for Insurance

Considered in isolation, the typical insurance policy seems unattractive. Its payoff is uncertain, and it reduces expected consumption. Risk-averse consumers are nevertheless willing to make actuarially unfair bets by purchasing insurance because an insurance policy cancels out other risks.

To illustrate, let's suppose Julia earns $500 and would like to spend as much as possible on food, which costs $1 per kilogram. As before, the weather is uncertain; the probability of sun (π) is two thirds, and the probability of a flood ($1 - \pi$) is one third. If it's sunny, Julia spends all $500 on food. If there's a flood, she sustains a loss of $300 due to property damage from flooding, and can spend only $200 on food. Thus, she starts out with the risky consumption bundle labelled A in Figure 11.12. She can protect herself from this serious risk by purchasing flood insurance (which pays off in the event of a flood). Let's see how the process works.

The Demand for Fair Insurance
In Figure 11.12, we've drawn the constant expected consumption line through point A, and labelled it L. (From formula (3) on page 375, we know that the slope of L is $-\pi/(1 - \pi) = -2$.) Since a fair insurance policy doesn't change Julia's expected consumption, it moves her from point A to some other bundle on L.

We've marked the point where L crosses the guaranteed consumption line as point B. To reach point B, Julia can purchase an insurance policy with a benefit level of $300 for a premium of $100.[8] In that case, the promised benefit equals the potential loss, giving

---

[8]We've seen that $M = B(1 - \pi)$ with actuarially fair insurance. Here, with full insurance, $B = \$300$. Since $\pi = 2/3$, the actuarially fair insurance premium is $\$300 \times (1 - 2/3) = \$100$.

Figure 11.12

The Demand for Fair Insurance.
Julia starts out with a risky consumption bundle, at point A. By purchasing actuarially fair insurance, she can reach any point on the solid green line segment connecting points A and B. If she's risk averse, she'll choose point B, representing full insurance.

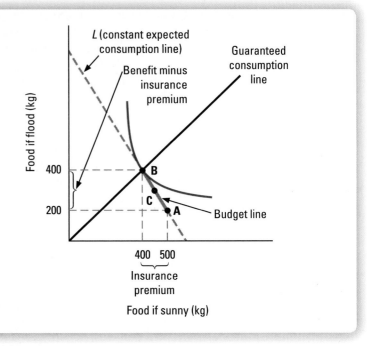

With **full insurance,** the promised benefit equals the potential loss.

With **partial insurance,** the promised benefit is less than the potential loss.

Julia **full insurance**. With full insurance, consumption is the same regardless of whether a loss occurs. Here, Julia spends $400 on food—the amount she has left after paying her insurance premium—regardless of the weather.

To reach any other point on the solid line connecting points A and B, Julia can buy an insurance policy with a benefit that's smaller than her potential loss. For example, she might pay $50 for a policy that promises a $150 benefit, obtaining the midpoint between A and B, marked as C in the figure. Because the promised benefit is less than the potential loss, this type of policy is called **partial insurance**. With partial insurance, Julia's consumption still depends on the weather, but it varies less than without insurance. At point C, she consumes 450 kilograms of food if it's sunny (spending her $500 income minus the $50 insurance premium) and 300 kilograms when there's a flood (spending her $500 income minus the $50 premium, minus the $300 loss, plus the $150 benefit).

Julia cannot obtain any point on L to the left of point B or the right of point A. Points to the left of point B would require an insurance contract that promises benefits in excess of losses. Generally, insurance policies cover policyholders only up to the amount of the actual loss; otherwise, policyholders would have incentives to create losses. Points to the right of point A would require Julia to pay the insurance company in the event of a flood, which is contrary to the definition of flood insurance.

Through fair insurance, Julia can therefore obtain any risky bundle on the solid green line connecting points A and B. Consequently, that is her budget line.

If Julia is risk averse, she will purchase full insurance. To understand why, remember that for risk-averse consumers, points of tangency between indifference curves and constant expected consumption lines lie on the guaranteed consumption line (as in Figure 11.5 on page 378). In Figure 11.12, we've drawn Julia's indifference curve through point B. Since point B is her most preferred point on L, it is certainly her best choice on the solid portion of L between points A and B.

Notice that this conclusion doesn't depend on the degree of Julia's risk aversion. Whether she's slightly or severely risk averse, point B is her best choice on the constant expected consumption line through point A, so she fully insures.

The Demand for Less-than-Fair Insurance

What if insurance is less than actuarially fair? Let's suppose that the insurance company charges a premium of R dollars per dollar of coverage (in other words, $M = BR$), where $R > 1 - \pi$. If Julia increases B by one dollar, her consumption falls by R dollars if it's sunny and rises by $1 - R$ dollars if there's a flood. Therefore, by purchasing insurance, Julia can obtain bundles on a straight line through her starting point, A, with a slope of $-(1 - R)/R$.

To illustrate, let's assume that Julia pays 50 cents for each dollar of promised benefit (that is, $R = 0.5$), rather than the actuarially fair price of $33^1/_3$ cents. Then $-(1 - R)/R = -1$. In Figure 11.13, we've drawn a straight green line with a slope of -1 between points A and D. That is Julia's budget line. To reach point D, she must fully insure by purchasing a policy with a benefit level of $300. She pays a premium of $150, or $50 more than her premium for fair insurance. As a result, her food consumption is 50 kilograms lower, regardless of the state of nature (350 kilograms instead of 400 kilograms). To reach any consumption level between points A and D, she must partially insure. For example, she can achieve point E by spending $100 to purchase a policy with a promised benefit of $200.

With less-than-fair insurance, Julia definitely won't insure fully. Why not? The constant expected consumption line that runs through point D, shown as a broken green line in the figure, has a slope of -2, so it's steeper than the budget line. Because the indifference curve that runs through point D is tangent to this constant expected consumption line, it passes below the budget line to the right of point D. So Julia's best choice on that line must lie to the right of point D. Point E is the best choice. Julia partially insures by purchasing a policy with a benefit equal to two-thirds of her potential loss.

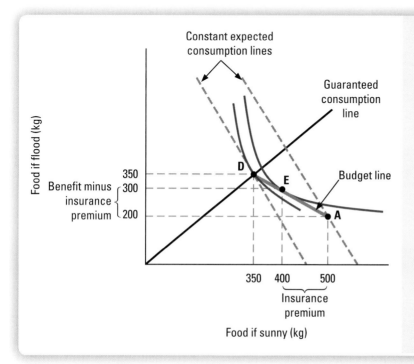

Figure II.13

The Demand for Unfair Insurance. Julia starts out with a risky consumption bundle, at point A. By purchasing actuarially unfair insurance, she can reach any point on the solid green line connecting points A and D. Her best choice, point E, lies to the right of point D, which means she partially insures.

In contrast to fair insurance, the amount of less-than-fair insurance purchased *does* depend on the policyholder's degree of risk aversion. For example, a risk-neutral consumer will buy no insurance. Why? His indifference curves coincide with the constant expected consumption lines in Figure 11.13. Point A is therefore his best choice. The same is true if the consumer is slightly risk averse; his indifference curves will still be steeper than the budget line (since they will bend only slightly as they move away from the guaranteed consumption line), so point A will remain the best choice.

The Value of Insurance

Insurance makes people better off by protecting them from the consequences of a loss. One way to measure the benefits it offers is to compare certainty equivalents.

Let's start with fair insurance. Figure 11.14 reproduces points A and B from Figure 11.12, along with the budget line that runs between them. With fair insurance, Julia chooses point B. Since this bundle involves no risk, its certainty equivalent is the same as the amount consumed, 400 kilograms. Without insurance, Julia is stuck with point A. We've drawn the indifference curve that runs through point A and marked its intersection with the guaranteed consumption line as point G. The certainty equivalent of point A is the horizontal (equivalently, vertical) coordinate of G, 300 kilograms. Fair insurance raises the certainty equivalent of Julia's best choice from 300 kilograms to 400 kilograms. The difference between these two numbers, 100 kilograms, is the net value of fair insurance, considering both the benefits and the premiums.

Now let's turn to less-than-fair insurance. Figure 11.14 also reproduces points A, D, and E from Figure 11.13, along with the budget line that runs between points A and D, and the indifference curve that runs through point E. We've marked the point where this indifference curve crosses the guaranteed consumption line as point H. Julia chooses the risky bundle E by partially insuring. The certainty equivalent of point E is the horizontal (equivalently, vertical) coordinate of point H, 375 kilograms. As before, without insurance, Julia is stuck with

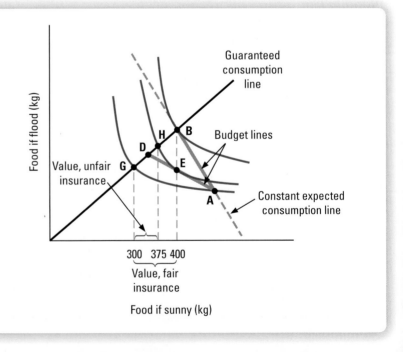

Figure II.14

The Value of Insurance. Julia starts out with a risky consumption bundle at point A. The certainty equivalent of this risky bundle, given by the level of consumption at point G, is 300 kilograms. With actuarially fair insurance, Julia obtains point B, which has a certainty equivalent of 400 kilograms. The value of actuarially fair insurance is therefore 400 kg − 300 kg = 100 kg. With actuarially unfair insurance, Julia obtains point E. The certainty equivalent of this risky bundle, given by the level of consumption at point H, is 375 kilograms. The value of actuarially unfair insurance is therefore 375 kg − 300 kg = 75 kg.

point A, which has a certainty equivalent of 300 kilograms. Less-than-fair insurance raises the certainty equivalent of her best choice from 300 kilograms to 375 kilograms. The difference between these two numbers, 75 kilograms, is the net value of less-than-fair insurance. It isn't as great as the value of fair insurance, but it contributes significantly to Julia's well-being.

Application 11.3

The Value of Life Annuities

None of us know how long we'll live. This uncertainty is the source of significant financial risk. Most obviously, the unexpected death of a family's primary breadwinner can have major financial consequences. That is why people buy life insurance.

But uncertainty concerning the length of one's life also creates a second type of risk: the possibility that you will outlive your resources. Imagine for the moment that you're 65 years old and newly retired. How well can you afford to live? The answer depends on how long you live. If you expect to live a long time, you'll have to watch your spending to make sure you won't run out of money. Even then you may find yourself in trouble. For example, you might plan your spending at age 65 on the assumption that you'll probably die by age 90. But what if you live to 95? Will you have enough money to get by in those final years? Alternatively, you could be extremely conservative and plan your spending at age 65 on the assumption that you'll live forever. But you probably won't get to spend a large chunk of your wealth in that case.

To address the risk of living "too long," people can purchase an insurance policy called a *life annuity*. The policyholder pays a premium (either in a lump sum or in installments), and in return receives a constant income for the rest of his life starting at some specified age. If he dies quickly, his premium exceeds the present value of the benefits received. But if he lives to a ripe old age, the present value of the benefits received exceeds his premium. So in effect, he is betting on living a long life. (With life insurance, he is betting on dying quickly.)

Life annuities make planning easier. A new retiree can lock in a living standard without worrying about outliving his resources. And he can achieve a higher living standard than if he conservatively planned his spending based on the assumption that he'll live forever.

How valuable is this form of insurance? According to economists Olivia Mitchell, James Poterba, Mark Warshawsky, and Jeffrey Brown, people who behave according to the Life Cycle Hypothesis (discussed in Section 10.2) would give up 30 to 38 percent of their wealth at age 65 in exchange for the ability to purchase actuarially fair life annuities![9]

Most of us end up relying heavily on life annuities, because the Canada Pension Plan (or the Quebec Pension Plan in that province) and many private pension plans provide benefits in that form. However, relatively few people buy life annuities directly. In light of the enormous potential value of these policies, their lack of popularity is something of a puzzle. A number of explanations have been proposed. First, annuities aren't actuarially fair. Second, since the Canada Pension Plan and private pensions partially insure people against living too long, additional insurance is less valuable than the figures in the previous paragraph would suggest. Third, since benefits are usually paid in nominal terms, the policyholder is exposed to inflation risk. Fourth, people may be reluctant to lock up their funds in annuities. Once money is invested in an annuity, it becomes unavailable to heirs (since income is received only while the investor lives), and the investor usually can't withdraw funds to cover unplanned expenses like uninsured nursing home care. Consequently, the demand for annuities may be low among those who want to leave bequests, or who are concerned about large uninsured expenses.

Mitchell and her coauthors found that the first two explanations are reasonably important, but fail to tell the whole story. Because annuity premiums are actuarially unfair, the typical person can expect to receive 15 to 20 percent less in benefits than she pays in premiums. However, that gap would have to be significantly larger (23 to 31 percent) to offset the advantages of annuity insurance, even taking the Canada Pension Plan and private pensions into account. The study also concludes that the third consideration—inflation risk—is of little importance. Other evidence suggests that the fourth explanation plays a more central role.[10]

[9]Olivia S. Mitchell, James M. Poterba, Mark J. Washawsky, and Jeffrey R. Brown, "New Evidence on the Money's Worth of Individual Annuities," *American Economic Review* 89, December 1999, pp. 1299–1318.

[10]See B. Douglas Bernheim, "How Strong Are Bequest Motives? Evidence Based on the Demand for Life Insurance and Annuities," *Journal of Political Economy* 99, October 1991, pp. 899–927.

WORKED-OUT PROBLEM　　　　　　　　　　　　　　　　　　　11.3

The Problem　The probability of sun is two-thirds, and the probability of a flood is one-third. Julia's indifference curves are given by the formula[11]

$$F_F F_S^2 = C$$

where F_S is the amount of food she consumes if it's sunny, F_F is the amount of food she consumes when there's a flood, and C is a constant (the value of which differs from one indifference curve to another). For indifference curves in this family, the marginal rate of substitution for food if it's sunny with food if there's a flood is

$$MRS_{SF} = 2\frac{F_F}{F_S}$$

Without insurance, Julia can spend $400 if it's sunny but only $75 if there's a flood (due to property losses from flooding). Food costs one dollar per kilogram. She can purchase flood insurance for a premium of 40 cents for each dollar of promised benefit. How much insurance will she purchase? What will she pay for it? What is its value?

The Solution　Julia's available choices lie on a budget line like the one connecting points A and D in Figure 11.14. In this case, $R = 0.4$, so the slope of the budget line is $-(1 - R)/R$, is -1.5. The formula for the budget line is therefore $F_F = C - 1.5F_S$, where C is a constant. Since the budget line must pass through Julia's starting point, $(F_S, F_F) = (400, 75)$, we know that $75 = C - (1.5 \times 400)$, so $C = 675$.

Julia's best choice is a point of tangency between the budget line and an indifference curve, like point E in Figure 11.14. At any such point, the slope of the budget line is the same as the slope of her indifference curve. Thus,

$$-1.5 = -MRS_{SF} = -2\frac{F_F}{F_S}$$

From this formula, we can conclude that at any point of tangency, $F_F = 0.75F_S$.

We know that Julia's best choice satisfies both $F_F = 675 - 1.5F_S$ (it's on the budget line) and $F_F = 0.75F_S$ (it's a point of tangency), so we can solve for it algebraically. Substituting the second expression into the first, we get $0.75F_S = 675 - 1.5F_S$, so $F_S = 675/2.25 = 300$. In other words, she consumes 300 kilograms of food if it's sunny, at a cost of $300. Since Julia starts with $400 if it's sunny, she must spend $100 on insurance. That means her insurance benefit must be $250 (since $0.4 \times 250 = 100$). If there's a flood, she consumes $F_F = 75 + 250 - 100 = 225$ kg of food.

After purchasing insurance, Julia's risky bundle is $(F_S, F_F) = (300, 225)$. Points on the indifference curve that runs through this bundle satisfy the formula $F_F F_S^2 = 225 \times 300^2 = 20{,}250{,}000$. To find a riskless bundle on this indifference curve (one for which F_S and F_F have the same value), we solve the formula $F^3 = 20{,}250{,}000$. The solution is $F = 272.6$. This is the certainty equivalent of Julia's risky bundle after purchasing insurance.

---

[11] These are Julia's indifference curves when her preferences correspond to an expected utility function of the form $U(F_S, F_F) = 1/2 \log(F_S) + \frac{2}{3} \log(F_F)$ [that is, $W(F) = \log(F)$].

Julia's initial bundle is $(F_S, F_F) = (400, 75)$. Points on the indifference curve that runs through this bundle satisfy the formula $F_F F_S^2 = 75 \times 400^2 = 12{,}000{,}000$. To find a riskless bundle on this indifference curve, we solve the formula $F^3 = 12{,}000{,}000$. The solution is $F = 228.9$. This is the certainty equivalent of Julia's initial risky bundle. Since $272.6 - 228.9 = 43.7$, the value of insurance is $43.70.

IN-TEXT EXERCISE 11.3   **Repeat worked-out problem 11.3 assuming that flood insurance costs 50 cents for each dollar of promised benefit. Repeat it again assuming that flood insurance costs $8/11 for each dollar of promised benefit. What happens if the premium is higher than that amount?**

11.4 OTHER METHODS OF MANAGING RISK

People often take risks voluntarily. For example, they invest in the stock market, start new businesses, take jobs in start-up companies, and try out new products. Companies invest in research and development, build new factories despite uncertain demand, and bring new, untried products to market. In these cases, the expected reward is high enough to justify risk-taking.

Often, we can make risky activities more attractive by taking steps to moderate potential losses while preserving much of our potential gains. Such steps are known as **risk management**. As we've seen, one way to manage risks is to purchase insurance. When a company builds a factory, for example, managers buy insurance to guard against losses due to fire, theft, lawsuits, and other unforeseen events. In this section, we'll investigate four other strategies for managing risk: risk sharing, hedging, diversification, and information acquisition. We'll see how each of these strategies influences the demand for risky assets. To learn more about the demand for risky assets, read Add-On 11A.

> The object of **risk management** is to make risky activities more attractive by taking steps to moderate the potential losses while preserving much of the potential gains.

Risk Sharing

One way to make a risky prospect more attractive is to divide it among several people, a strategy known as **risk sharing**. A simple example will illustrate.

Suppose Julia earns $600 regardless of the weather, which she's free to spend on food. In other words, she starts out at point A in Figure 11.15 (we'll continue to assume that one kilogram of food costs $1). Suppose she's offered the opportunity to acquire a sunscreen concession at the local beach for an investment of $300. If it's sunny, she makes $600 (net of her investment), which means she can spend $1200 on food (her earnings, $600, plus her net profit, $600). If there's a flood, she sells nothing and loses her investment. In that case, she can spend only $300 on food (her earnings, $600, minus her investment, $300). So if Julia makes the investment, she obtains the risky consumption bundle labelled B in the figure.

> **Risk sharing** involves dividing a risky prospect among several people.

If the probability of sun is two-thirds, this investment has an expected payoff of $300 (Julia comes out ahead by $600 with a probability of two-thirds, and behind by $300 with a probability of one-third). Since this expected return is positive, point B lies above the constant expected consumption line that runs through point A, shown as the broken green line in Figure 11.15. So while the investment would expose Julia to risk, it would also provide her with a higher level of expected consumption.

Figure 11.15

Risk Sharing. Julia starts out with a riskless consumption bundle at point A. By making an investment, she can swap bundle A for bundle B, which provides higher expected consumption. Given her preferences, however, she prefers bundle A. If she can find partners to split the investment and the profits, she can reach points on the solid green line. In that case, she would want to take a share. Point D would be her best choice.

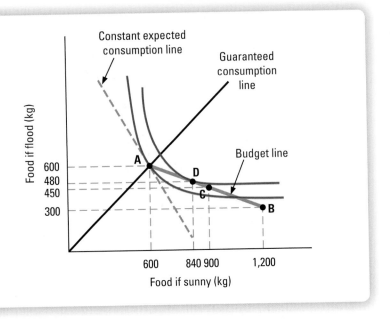

Even so, Julia does not want to make the investment. As her indifference curves show, she prefers bundle A to bundle B. The higher expected consumption offered at point B is simply not enough to offset the risk of having little to eat if there's a flood. In other words, the investment looks attractive from the perspective of expected profit, but it's just too big a risk for Julia to take on alone.

Now let's suppose Julia has a friend, Arnold, who has the same earnings and the same preferences. What if the two of them make the investment as equal partners? That is, each invests $150 and receives $300 in net profit if it's sunny. This strategy allows both Julia and Arnold to reach point C in Figure 11.15 ($600 + $300 = $900 if it's sunny, and $600 − $150 = $450 if there's a flood), which lies above the indifference curve that runs through point A. Both Julia and Arnold prefer point C to point A. Risk sharing allows both to benefit from an investment that neither would find attractive alone.

By taking on more partners, Julia can create more opportunities for risk sharing. With three equal partners, she would invest $100 and receive $200 in net profit if it's sunny; with four equal partners, she would invest $75 and receive $150 if it's sunny; and so forth. Julia could also take on unequal partners. For example, she could arrange a 60–40 split of the investment and net profits with Arnold.

In practice, owners of companies often take on partners by issuing **equity shares**. An equity share is a proportional claim on the ownership of a company. As an example, suppose the sunscreen concession has issued 1000 shares, each of which sells for 30 cents and gives its owner a claim on 1/1000 of any profit earned. Julia could buy the entire concession by acquiring all 1000 shares for $300, which would place her at point B. Or she could buy half of the concession by acquiring 500 shares for $150, which would put her at point C. In fact, by purchasing the appropriate number of

"I was spreading some risk around, and apparently it all wound up in your portfolio."

An **equity share** is a proportional claim on the ownership of a company.

shares, Julia could come very close to any point on the green line connecting points A and B in Figure 11.15. In effect, that line becomes Julia's budget line. Her best choice is point D where she spends $120 on 400 shares to acquire 40 percent of the concession (leaving her with $600 + 0.4 × $600 = $840 if it's sunny and $600 − $120 = $480 if there's a flood).

The logic of Figure 11.15 leads us to a remarkable conclusion. Even if Julia is extremely risk averse and the expected profit from the investment is very small, she will still want to invest *something* in it. Why? First, as long as Julia is risk averse, her indifference curve will lie tangent to the expected consumption line at point A. Increasing her risk aversion will only cause her indifference curve to bend more sharply at that point. Second, as long as the investment's expected profit is positive, Julia's budget line will extend above the expected consumption line through point A. Combining these two observations, we see that the budget line must always pass above the indifference curve, just as in the figure. A small enough investment therefore necessarily makes Julia better off.

Application 11.4

Insurance Coverage for Satellites

Every time someone reduces exposure to financial risk by purchasing an insurance policy, some other entity (usually an insurance company) accepts a new risk by selling the policy. Why is the insurance company willing to take on the policyholder's risk? As long as the policy is less-than-actuarially fair, the company comes out ahead on average.[12] If the risk is sufficiently small, the company may be willing to absorb all of it at terms that are only slightly worse than actuarially fair.

But what if the risk is extremely large? Take the case of commercial satellites. The costs of building and launching a single satellite regularly exceed $250 million, and satellite owners have been known to seek more than $400 million in coverage. Historically, roughly 1 out of every 10 satellites is either destroyed on launch or fails within a year of reaching orbit, so these ventures are extremely risky propositions for insurers. For example, estimates place satellite insurers' collective losses for 1998 at $1.9 billion, against only $860 million in premiums.

Not surprisingly, individual insurers are generally unwilling (and often simply unable) to accept responsibility for such catastrophic losses. Nevertheless, insurance for satellites is readily available, and the premiums do not appear to be wildly out of line with the expected benefits.[13] Insurance companies manage to provide satellite coverage at reasonably attractive rates by sharing risks. Even if a company is unwilling to take on a 10 percent risk of losing $250 million for a premium of $40 million, it might be perfectly content with ¹⁄₂₅ of that policy—that is, a 10 percent risk of losing $10 million for a premium of $1.6 million. If 25 companies will accept these terms, the satellite owner can piece together the desired coverage.

In practice, insurance companies often save satellite owners the trouble of making these arrangements. Sometimes they form syndicates to insure large-scale projects. Sometimes one company takes on a large policy and then sells interests in it to others through "reinsurance" agreements. These types of arrangements allow insurers to spread the risk more evenly through the industry, so that no single insurer faces the prospect of a catastrophic loss.

---

[12]The seller may also care less about absorbing the risk than the policyholder, for two reasons. First, by insuring many unrelated risks, the seller can benefit from diversification, discussed in the next section. Second, the seller may be less risk averse to begin with. Of course, sellers must also cover operating costs.

[13]Historically, seven percent of launches fail. Between 1995 and 2002, average premiums for launch insurance ranged from 7 to 15 percent of the covered amount.

Hedging and Diversification

Another way to make risky activities more attractive is to combine them appropriately with other risky activities. We'll discuss two versions of this strategy, hedging and diversification.

First, we need to introduce the statistical concept of correlation. Two variables are **positively correlated** if they tend to move in the same direction. For example, the number of minutes of sunshine per day is positively correlated with average temperature. Two variables are **negatively correlated** if they tend to move in the opposite directions. The number of minutes of sunshine per day is negatively correlated with rainfall (and the possibility of flooding). Two variables are **uncorrelated** if their movements tend to be unrelated. The number of minutes of sunshine per day is uncorrelated with earthquake activity. Finally, two variables are **perfectly correlated** if one is simply a multiple of the other. The number of inches of rain and the number of millimetres of rain are perfectly correlated.

Hedging   **Hedging** refers to the practice of taking on two risky activities with negatively correlated financial payoffs. We'll illustrate this strategy by adding a new twist to the example we discussed in the last section.

As before, we'll assume Julia has the opportunity to buy the entire sunscreen concession, allowing her to reach point B in Figure 11.16. In addition, we'll assume that Julia can invest \$300 in a portable generator distributorship. In the event of excessive rainfall leading to a flood, the generator distributorship will turn a net profit of \$600. In the event of sun, Julia will lose her investment. Assuming as before that the probability of sun is two-thirds, the expected payoff from this investment is zero [(\$^1/_3 \times \$600) - (\$^2/_3 \times \$300) = \$0]. If Julia invests in the generator distributorship but not the sunscreen concession, she obtains point E in Figure 11.16.

> Two variables are **positively correlated** if they tend to move in the same direction. Two variables are **negatively correlated** if they tend to move in the opposite direction. Two variables are **uncorrelated** if their movements tend to be unrelated. Finally, two variables are **perfectly correlated** if one is simply a multiple of the other.
>
> **Hedging** is the practice of taking on two risky activities with negatively correlated financial payoffs.

Figure 11.16

Hedging a Risky Venture. Julia starts out with a riskless consumption bundle at point A. By making an investment, she can swap point A for point B, which provides a higher level of expected consumption, or point A for point E, which provides the same level of expected consumption. Neither investment is attractive by itself. However, since each succeeds when the other fails, Julia can hedge her bets by making both investments. That strategy allows her to reach point F, which is better than point A. With perfect information concerning the weather, she could reach point G.

Taken individually, both these investments look unattractive to Julia (in Figure 11.16 points B and E lie on lower indifference curves than point A). Both investments are associated with substantial risk premiums. Indeed, no risk-averse individual would ever consider the generator investment, which creates risk without offering a higher expected level of consumption.

Yet what if Julia bought *both* concessions? Doing so would require an investment of $600, but would *guarantee* an overall net profit of $300 ($600 from the successful project minus $300 from the unsuccessful one). Regardless of the weather, Julia would be able to spend $900 on food (the $600 she earns plus $300 in net profit). In other words, Julia would be able to reach point F in the figure, which is obviously better than point A. Taken together, these investments are *riskless*: When Julia combines them, their risk premiums disappear!

The critical feature of this example is that the profits from the two concessions are perfectly negatively correlated. Julia hedges her bet on the sunscreen concession by investing in the generator distributorship, and vice versa. That way, bad news on one investment is always more than offset by good news on the other, so that she comes out ahead.

Insurance is actually a form of hedging. That is, the benefit paid by a flood insurance policy is perfectly negatively correlated with a loss from flooding. If Julia buys flood insurance, she is hedging against the possibility of a flood.

Diversification   **Diversification** refers to the practice of undertaking many risky activities, each on a small scale, rather than a few risky activities (or just one) on a large scale. The simplest argument for diversification is the old adage that it's unwise to put all your eggs in one basket. Dividing them among many baskets reduces risk.

Diversification is the practice of undertaking many risky activities, each on a small scale, rather than a few risky activities (or just one) on a large scale.

To illustrate, let's suppose that Julia wants to invest $300. She is thinking about two start-up companies, Go for Broke, Inc., and Shoot the Moon, Inc. An investment in Go For Broke, Inc., triples in value with 50 percent probability and becomes worthless with 50 percent probability. The same is true of an investment in Shoot the Moon, Inc. However, the payoffs for these investments are uncorrelated.

One alternative is for Julia to invest all of her money ($300) in a single company. The histogram in Figure 11.17(a) shows the probability distribution of her payoff. Her expected payoff is $450 ($\frac{1}{2} \times \$900 + \frac{1}{2} \times \$0 = \$450$), which exceeds her investment by $150. However, the risk is considerable—there's a 50 percent chance that she'll lose everything. The standard deviation of her payoff is $450 (the square root of the expected squared deviation, $\frac{1}{2} \times 450^2 + \frac{1}{2} \times 450^2$).

Alternatively, Julia could diversify, investing half of her money ($150) in each company. If both companies succeed, her payoff will be $900. Since each company succeeds with 50 percent probability, the probability that both succeed at the same time is $\frac{1}{2} \times \frac{1}{2} = \frac{1}{4}$. If both companies fail, Julia's payoff will be zero. Since each company fails with 50 percent probability, the probability that both fail at the same time is $\frac{1}{2} \times \frac{1}{2} = \frac{1}{4}$. If one company succeeds and the other fails, Julia's payoff will be $450, an outcome that occurs with a probability of $\frac{1}{2}$. (The probability that Go for Broke succeeds while Shoot the Moon fails is $\frac{1}{4}$, as is the probability that Shoot the Moon succeeds while Go for Broke fails.) Julia's overall expected payoff is still $450 ($\frac{1}{4} \times \$900 + \frac{1}{2} \times \$450 + \frac{1}{4} \times \$0 = \$450$), but the standard deviation is lower, $318 (the square root of $\frac{1}{4} \times 450^2 + \frac{1}{4} \times 450^2$).

The histogram in Figure 11.17(b) shows this information graphically. Compared with Figure 11.17(a), the payoff is less variable. Investing in two companies instead of one moves half the bar at $0 to $450, and half the bar at $900 to $450. Extreme outcomes

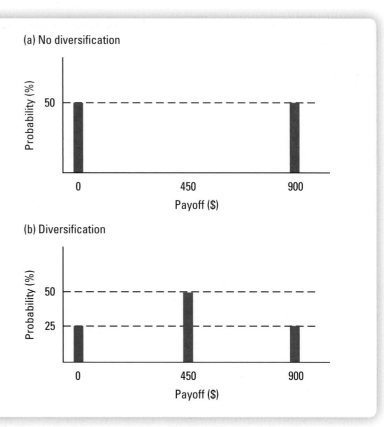

Figure 11.17

Diversification of Risk. If Julia invests $300 in Go for Broke, Inc., her payoff will be $900 with 50 percent probability, and $0 with 50 percent probability, as shown in figure (a). If she diversifies by investing $150 in Go for Broke, Inc., and $150 in Shoot the Moon, Inc. (the returns from which are uncorrelated with those from Go for Broke, Inc.), she shifts probability to an intermediate payoff ($450), reducing variability without changing her expected payoff, as shown in figure (b).

become less likely, and a moderate outcome becomes more likely. So diversification reduces risk without changing the expected payoff.

In this example, the payoffs from the two investments are uncorrelated. What if they were perfectly positively correlated? In that case, Shoot the Moon would succeed when Go for Broke succeeds and fail when Go for Broke fails. Investing $150 in each company would then be equivalent to investing $300 in one of the companies. With perfect positive correlation, there's no benefit to diversification.

What if the payoffs from the two investments were perfectly negatively correlated? In that case, Shoot the Moon would succeed when Go for Broke fails and fail when Go for Broke succeeds. By investing in both companies, Julia would perfectly hedge her bets. The risks would cancel out, delivering a payoff of $450 with certainty.

Comparing these three cases (no correlation, perfect positive correlation, and perfect negative correlation), we see that as the correlation between the payoffs increases, the risk-reducing effect of diversification decreases. Intuitively, diversification reduces risk because a gain sometimes offsets a loss, leading to an intermediate outcome. When the correlation is lower, offsetting outcomes are more likely, so diversification is more valuable. Hedging is simply a case in which diversification is particularly effective at reducing risk because the payoffs from the hedged activities are negatively correlated, so that gains usually offset losses.

This discussion underscores the point that it's dangerous to evaluate risky activities in isolation. The desirability of undertaking a risky project depends on *other* actual and potential risks, including opportunities for hedging and diversification. One of the most important functions of the stock market, in fact, is that it allows people to diversify their risky investments by purchasing small interests in many companies, instead of betting everything on a single business. Application 11.5 describes one easy way to diversify.

Application 11.5

Diversification through Mutual Funds

In principle, diversification through the stock market seems like a good idea. But in practice, many small investors find it rather difficult. Picking the right companies requires a good deal of research. Each investment has to be monitored and adjusted as prices rise and fall. Brokerage fees can add up, particularly if transactions involve only a few shares. For someone who is putting, say, $10,000 in the stock market, these costs are potentially prohibitive.

Mutual funds make diversifying investments easy. A mutual fund raises money from investors by selling shares in the fund and then invests the proceeds. Investors share in the fund's gains and losses until they either redeem their shares from the fund or sell them to other investors.

There are several different types of mutual funds. For example, equity funds invest only in common stocks, bond funds invest only in bonds, and balanced funds invest in both. Some funds specialize in certain types of stocks or bonds, while others do not. Some funds are actively managed, which means that the manager tries to choose investments that will outperform some recognized index, like the S&P/TSX 60 (which is published by the Canadian Standard and Poor's Index Committee and tracks the performance of 60 of the largest companies on the Toronto Stock Exchange). Other funds, known as index funds, try to match the performance of an index, usually by holding the stocks that make up the index.

Since the 1990s, total Canadian mutual fund investments have exploded, growing from $25 billion at the end of 1990 to over $550 billion by 2009. In large part, that growth resulted from the increased popularity of retirement savings accounts, which allow individual investors to allocate their savings among particular mutual funds. As of mid-year 2009, equity funds and balanced funds each accounted for approximately 40 percent of all mutual funds. The Canadian/Foreign asset mix of the funds was roughly 60/40. Approximately 10 percent of mutual funds were fixed income funds. The final 10 percent of mutual funds were short-term money market funds.

While mutual fund companies tout a long list of advantages over direct investment, some of their claims are disputed. For example, there is little evidence that active management improves investment outcomes. Actively managed funds do outperform index funds some of the time, but we would expect this to occur purely by chance, and there is little evidence that anything more than chance is involved. Nevertheless, mutual funds do offer individual investors at least one indisputable advantage: convenient, low-cost diversification.

WORKED-OUT PROBLEM   11.4

The Problem   Suppose Julia starts out with $300, and that she seeks to maximize her expected benefit, $\sqrt{X}$, where X measures her resources in dollars. She has three options: keep the $300, invest it all in Go for Broke, Inc., or invest $150 each in Go for Broke, Inc., and Shoot the Moon, Inc. Compute the certainty equivalent of each option assuming that the investments are uncorrelated with one another. Which is best? What is the benefit of diversification?

The Solution   Keeping $300 guarantees a benefit of 17.3 (the square root of 300); the certainty equivalent is clearly $300. Investing $300 in Go for Broke produces an expected benefit of

$$\frac{1}{2}\sqrt{0} + \frac{1}{2}\sqrt{900} = 15$$

Her certainty equivalent is the amount X that solves $\sqrt{X} = 15$, so $X = 225$. Investing in both companies produces an expected benefit of

$$\frac{1}{4}\sqrt{0} + \frac{1}{2}\sqrt{450} + \frac{1}{4}\sqrt{900} = 18.1$$

Her certainty equivalent is the amount X that solves $\sqrt{X} = 18.1$, so $X = 328$.

Julia's best choice is to invest in both companies. Her second best choice is not to invest. The benefit of diversification is $103 ($328 − $225) compared with no diversification, and $28 ($328 − $300) compared with the next best choice (no investment).

 IN-TEXT EXERCISE 11.4   Repeat worked-out problem 11.4 assuming that Julia seeks to maximize the expected value of $2000X − X^2$ (for values of X less than 1000).

Information Acquisition

People often try to reduce or eliminate risk by acquiring information. Because better information about probable events leads to better decisions, it can reduce the likelihood of undesirable outcomes.

To illustrate this point, let's return to the example we used in our discussion of hedging. As before, Julia can invest in a sunscreen concession, a generator distributorship, or both. She starts out at point A in Figure 11.16 (page 396); her investment options allow her to reach points B, E, and F. As we've said, her best choice is to buy both concessions (point F), yet that isn't the ideal solution. Because the sunscreen concession does poorly if there's a flood and the generator distributorship does poorly if the sun shines, one concession or the other will always do poorly, so Julia wastes the $300 she invests in it. Can she do better?

If Julia could predict the weather perfectly, she would always make the right investment, investing in the sunscreen concession only when the sun is about to shine and the generator distributorship only when a flood is about to hit. Rain or shine, she would earn a net profit of $600, leaving her with $1200 (including her earnings) to spend on food. In other words, with perfect information, Julia would reach point G in Figure 11.16, which is significantly better than point F. Clearly, Julia has a strong incentive to gather information about likely weather patterns.

Suppose Julia knows of a meteorological consultant who can predict the weather perfectly. How much would she pay for his services? We know she ends up with $1200 for sure if she can predict the weather, and only $900 for sure (through hedging) if she can't. That means she should be willing to pay up to $300 for perfect weather prediction. In this example, the value of information is $300.

CHAPTER SUMMARY

1. **What is risk? (LO1)**

   a. Sometimes we can assess the probability of a state of nature by determining the frequency with which it has occurred in the past. This concept is known as *objective probability*. At other times, we may assess the probability of a state of nature by using subjective judgment, a concept known as *subjective probability*.

   b. If we know the probability and payoff associated with each state of nature, we can find the probability distribution of the payoffs. We can also calculate the expected payoff, as well as the standard deviation and the variance, two measures of variability.

2. **Risk preferences (LO2)**

   a. To analyze decisions involving risk, we can apply the theory developed in Chapters 4 through 6, thinking of a consumption bundle as a list of the amount of each good consumed in each state of nature. Indifference curves represent the consumer's preferences for consumption in different states of nature.

   b. With only two possible states of nature, a risk-averse consumer's preferred point on any constant expected consumption line lies on the guaranteed consumption line.

   c. With only two possible states of nature, we can find the certainty equivalent of a risky consumption bundle by identifying the indifference curve that runs through the bundle and determining the level of consumption that corresponds to the point where the curve crosses the guaranteed consumption line.

   d. The difference between a bundle's expected level of consumption and its certainty equivalent, known as the *risk premium*, reflects the psychological cost of exposure to risk.

   e. At greater levels of risk aversion, indifference curves bend more sharply where they cross the guaranteed consumption line. The certainty equivalent of any risky bundle is lower and the risk premium higher with greater levels of risk aversion.

   f. With only two possible states of nature, a risk-loving consumer's least preferred point on any constant expected consumption line lies on the guaranteed consumption line. For risk-neutral consumers, indifference curves coincide with the constant expected consumption lines.

   g. Under some conditions, we can use an expected utility function to describe a consumer's risk preferences.

   h. For expected utility, a concave benefit function implies risk aversion; a convex function implies risk-loving preferences. A linear benefit function implies risk neutrality.

3. **Insurance (LO3)**

   a. If insurance is actuarially fair, a risk-averse consumer will purchase full insurance.

   b. If insurance is less than actuarially fair, a risk-averse consumer will purchase partial insurance or no insurance at all. The amount of insurance purchased will depend on the degree of risk aversion. Those who are not very risk averse will purchase no insurance.

   c. The value of insurance equals the difference between the certainty equivalent of the consumer's consumption bundle after purchasing insurance and the certainty equivalent of the bundle before purchasing insurance. The greater the risk aversion, the higher the value of the insurance.

4. **Other methods of managing risks (LO4, 5)**

   a. One way to make a risky investment more attractive is to share the risk by dividing it among several people. Companies can expand the opportunities for risk sharing by issuing equity shares. As long as an investment's expected payoff is positive, even an extremely risk-averse person will benefit from taking a small share of it.

   b. Hedging reduces risk, because when the payoffs from two activities are negatively correlated, the gains offset the losses.

   c. Diversification reduces risk because it creates opportunities for gains to offset losses, raising the likelihood of intermediate outcomes. The risk-reducing effects of diversification are smaller when the payoffs are more positively correlated, making offsetting gains and losses less likely. One of the most important functions of the stock market is to allow people to diversify their risky investments by purchasing small interests in many companies, instead of betting everything on the performance of a single business.

   d. Better information about probable events leads to better decisions, reducing the likelihood of a loss. The value of information equals the difference between the certainty equivalent of the risky outcome when an individual is informed and the certainty equivalent of the risky outcome when he is uninformed.

Exercise 11.1: List as many types of financial risk as possible for each of the following activities: driving a car, going to college or university, trying out a new brand of breakfast cereal, taking a vacation in Europe, and hiring a new employee. (LO1)

Exercise 11.2: Compute the expected payoff and the standard deviation for each of the following probability distributions. (LO1)

a. A payoff of 200 with a probability of 0.4 and 500 with a probability of 0.6

b. A payoff is 110 with a probability of 0.2; 130 with a probability of 0.3; 150 with a probability of 0.1; and 170 with a probability of 0.4

c. Every possible payoff that's a whole number between (and including) 100 and 200, each with the same probability (use a spreadsheet)

Exercise 11.3: As in Figure 11.3 (page 375), draw the constant expected consumption line through point A under the assumption that the probability of a flood is each of the following. (LO2)

a. 50 percent

b. 25 percent

c. 75 percent

Exercise 11.4: Suppose that consumption when it's sunny and consumption when there's a flood are perfect complements. The investor's indifference curves are L-shaped, and the corner of each L lies on the 45-degree line. Using graphs, explain why these assumptions imply infinite risk aversion. (LO2)

Exercise 11.5: Repeat worked-out problem 11.1 (page 379), assuming that the indifference curves are L-shaped, as in exercise 11.4. (LO2)

Exercise 11.6: The risk premium for a risky consumption bundle is never larger than the difference between expected consumption and the lowest payoff that occurs with a positive probability. Explain why this statement is true. Assuming there are only two possible outcomes, illustrate with a graph. (LO2)

Exercise 11.7: Using a graph like the one in Figure 11.6 (page 378), show the risk premium and certainty equivalent for a risky consumption bundle, assuming that the consumer is risk-loving. Explain why the certainty equivalent exceeds the expected level of consumption, and why the risk premium is negative. (LO2)

Exercise 11.8: Suppose that Julia seeks to maximize the expected value of the benefit function $W(F) = 1000F - F^2$ (for values of F below 100). Julia consumes 50 kilograms of food when it's sunny and 30 kilograms when there's a flood. There's a 25 percent chance of a flood. Compute her expected payoff, her expected utility, the certainty equivalent of her risky consumption bundle, and the risk premium. (LO2)

Exercise 11.9: Show graphically that a risk-loving consumer would never purchase actuarially fair insurance. (LO3)

Exercise 11.10: You've seen that the consumer's degree of risk aversion doesn't affect the quantity of actuarially fair insurance purchased (since all risk-averse consumers will fully insure). Using graphs, show that the degree of risk aversion does affect the *value* of insurance. Is the value of fair insurance smaller or larger to a more risk-averse consumer? (LO3)

Exercise 11.11: Initially, Julia consumes 400 kilograms of food when it's sunny and 75 kilograms of food when there's a flood (due to property losses from flooding). Her indifference curves are L-shaped, as in exercise 11.4. Suppose that flood insurance is available, and that the premium, M, for each dollar of promised benefit is less than a dollar (but greater than zero). Solve for Julia's best choice as a function of M. How much insurance will she buy, and how much food will she consume? (Hint: Draw a graph. Does she partially insure or fully insure?) Does your answer depend on the probability of a flood? Explain. (LO3)

Exercise 11.12: Why might it make sense for the same risk-averse person to both eliminate risk by purchasing insurance and take on new risk by investing in the stock market? (LO4)

Exercise 11.13: Recall the risk-sharing problem illustrated in Figure 11.15 (page 394). Show graphically that if Julia is less risk averse, she'll want to buy a larger fraction of the sunscreen concession (represented by a point to the right of point D). (LO4, 5)

Exercise 11.14: Consider again the risk-sharing problem illustrated in Figure 11.15 (page 394). If the sunscreen concession becomes more profitable when the sun shines, what happens to Julia's best choice? Show your answer graphically. Can you say whether she will want to own a larger or smaller share of the concession? (LO4, 5)

Exercise 11.15: Suppose a consumer can buy equity shares in any of several risky projects, all of which have the same net expected payoff and the same variability. Suppose too that the payoffs from the various projects are uncorrelated. If the consumer is risk loving, should she diversify? What if she's risk neutral? Explain. (LO4, 5)

Exercise 11.16: Jeffrey, who is risk neutral, is thinking about investing in one of two mutually exclusive projects. Project A requires an investment of $200 up front. It pays $600 if it rains, $800 if it snows, $400 if it hails, and $0 if it's sunny. Project B requires an investment of $300 up front. It pays $200 if it rains, $0 if it snows, $600 if it hails, and $700 if it's sunny. The probability of each outcome is 0.1 for rain, 0.3 for snow, 0.2 for hail, and 0.4 for sun. (LO4, 5)

a. What is the net expected payoff from each project? Which is better for Jeffrey, and by how much?

b. Suppose that a meteorologist can forecast the weather with perfect accuracy. How much will Jeffrey pay for the information?

Choices Involving Strategy

On June 6, 1944, 15,000 Canadians joined 135,000 other troops, 5000 ships, and 11,000 aircraft as the Western Allies invaded Nazi-occupied France along five beaches in Normandy codenamed Utah, Omaha, Gold, Juno, and Sword. Hitler was aware of the impending invasion, but thought it would more likely occur at Calais 200 kilometres to the northeast, not Normandy. Calais required shorter supply lines from England. It also offered access to an extensive road network, which would permit more rapid troop deployment toward Germany.

On the advice of his strategists, General Dwight D. Eisenhower, Supreme Commander of the Allied Expeditionary Force, reinforced Hitler's preconceptions through deception and misdirection. The Allies stationed squadrons of plywood airplanes and inflatable tanks near the port of Dover, directly across the English Channel from Calais. They located a fleet of rubber landing craft nearby, at the mouth of the Thames River. Allied operatives passed the Germans false information through known enemy agents and coded radio transmissions intended for interception. To reinforce the misinformation, Allied commanders held actual military manoeuvres near the decoy forces and dropped more bombs on Calais than on Normandy. As a result, Hitler ordered his generals to fortify German defenses at Calais, leaving Normandy comparatively vulnerable. According to General Alfred Jodl, Hitler's chief of staff, this was Germany's fatal strategic error.

Eisenhower's attempt to mislead Hitler prior to D-Day is an example of strategic decision making. A choice involves strategy whenever its effects depend on the actions and reactions of other people. Even in non-military situations, sound decision making frequently requires careful strategic thought. People often mull over strategies for getting dates, obtaining extensions on their assignments, securing jobs, and achieving a host of other objectives in which success or failure hinges on others' choices. Strategy is particularly important in business because the outcome of choices regarding investment, research and development, product design, pricing, and marketing depends on the decisions of other companies in the same line of business. For example, investing heavily in the development of a new product can turn out to be wildly profitable if your company is the first to market, or disastrous if another company beats yours to it.

In examining strategic decisions, economists rely on tools taken from a field called *game theory*. This chapter provides an introduction to the theory of games, particularly with respect to economic decisions. We'll study five topics:

1. *What is a game?* We'll introduce the concept of a game, and distinguish between one-stage games and multiple-stage games.

2. *Thinking strategically in one-stage games.* Strategic situations require us to think about what other people will do. We'll see that it's sometimes possible to reason out the likely choice of a sensible opponent by thinking about the game from your opponent's perspective.

3. *Nash equilibrium in one-stage games.* In Chapter 2, you learned that competitive markets have equilibria that balance supply and demand. Games have equilibria of a different kind. We'll introduce and explore an important notion of strategic equilibrium, and explain why a decision maker might choose an equilibrium strategy.

4. *Games with multiple stages.* When a game involves a sequence of decisions, people have opportunities to reward and punish each others' choices. By studying those games, we'll learn how to determine whether a threat is credible. We'll also see how people with competing interests manage to cooperate with each other.

*5. *Games in which different people have different information.* When people have different information, their choices often reveal something about what they know. We'll explain how someone can learn from the choices of other decision makers, and we'll see how this affects their behaviour.

12.1 WHAT IS A GAME?

A **game** is a situation in which a number of individuals make decisions, and all care both about their own choices and about others' choices.

A **game** is a situation in which a number of individuals make decisions, and all care both about their own choices and about others' choices. This definition isn't limited to recreational games and sports, like poker and curling; it includes any situation in which strategy plays a role, from military planning to dating.

Economists study an enormous variety of games. For example, game theory provides the foundation for understanding competition in industries with only a few producers. We devote Chapter 19 to that topic. Auctions, which we discuss at various points in this chapter, are games. Every negotiation—such as a buyer and a seller haggling over price, an entrepreneur and a venture capitalist arranging financing for a start-up company, or two countries bargaining over trade restrictions—is a game. There are many other examples. We devote a separate chapter to game theory because it has become such a central and broadly applicable component of the modern economist's toolkit.

Two Types of Games

Some games are easier to analyze than others. In the simplest games, known as **one-stage games**, participants make all of their choices before observing any choice by any other participant. Rock Paper Scissors—a game familiar to most schoolchildren—is a good example. Two players face off with one fist extended toward each other. Together, they raise and lower their forearms three times. As a player's fist descends for the third time, he forms it into one of three shapes: rock, paper, or scissors. Ideally, the two players make their choices at the same moment. The winner depends on the choices: rock smashes scissors, scissors cut paper, and paper covers rock.

> In a **one-stage game**, participants make all of their choices before observing any choice by any other participant.

In contrast, in a **multiple-stage game**, at least one participant observes a choice by another participant before making some decision. Complex multiple-stage games allow for elaborate sequences of moves and countermoves. Tic-tac-toe, chess, and poker are all examples of multiple-stage games.

> In a **multiple-stage game**, at least one participant observes a choice by another participant before making some decision.

In economics, multiple-stage games are much more common than one-stage games. For example, when companies compete with one another, each learns about its competitors' choices over time (prices, advertising expenditures, and so forth) and adjusts its own choices in response. That form of competition is therefore a multiple-stage game. Even so, as we'll see in Chapter 19, we can still learn a great deal about competitive strategy by examining simplified one-stage games.

For a practical illustration of the distinction between one-stage and multiple-stage games, let's compare two different types of auctions: the open-outcry auction and the sealed-bid auction. When people think about auctions, they usually picture the open-outcry format in which an auctioneer solicits bids from a crowd and pounds a gavel to declare the winner. These auctions are multiple-stage games, as they involve sequences of bids and counterbids. In contrast, the less flashy sealed-bid format, which calls for each potential buyer to submit a single bid privately and provides no opportunity for rebidding or counterbids, is a one-stage game.

The World RPS Society, based in Toronto, Canada, sponsors an annual Rock Paper Scissors world championship, at which more than a thousand screaming fans watch the master players showcase techniques such as "paper clipping" and "priming the chump" while competing for a cash prize ($7000 in 2006).

Though multiple-stage games are often more complex than single-stage games, we'll see that many of the same principles apply in both contexts. To keep things simple, we'll start with one-stage games and then move to multiple-stage games.

How to Describe a Game

To teach someone how to play a game, we typically start by explaining the rules and the players' objectives. Sometimes there are written rules. For example, organized sports have rule books; recreational games have instruction manuals. The decision-making meetings of many clubs and civic organizations are governed by *Robert's Rules of Order*, and attorneys must abide by the *Canada Evidence Act* when introducing evidence in

Canadian courts. In other contexts, however, the rules governing social interaction are informal and unwritten; we learn the ropes from others and through experience.

To analyze a game, we also start with a description of the game's rules and the players' objectives. However, our description usually involves fewer details than someone would need if they intended to play the game. For example, to analyze Rock Paper Scissors we need to know that each participant chooses one of three alternatives and that they make their decisions simultaneously. We don't need to know that they raise and lower their forearms three times before choosing.

We'll explain how to describe multiple-stage games in Section 12.4; here, we'll focus on one-stage games. To describe the essential features of a one-stage game, we follow two steps. First, we identify the players and list the actions available to each. For one-stage games, we use the words *action* and *strategy* interchangeably; however, this will not be the case for multiple-stage games (see Section 12.4). Second, for every possible combination of strategies (one for every player), we identify each player's payoff, be it a reward or penalty. As Example 12.1 illustrates, we can usually summarize all of the relevant information in a simple table.

Example 12.1

The Battle of Wits

In the classic children's novel *The Princess Bride* by William Goldman (known to many from the 1987 movie of the same title), the hero, Westley, disguised as "the man in black," attempts to rescue his sweetheart, Buttercup, from a clever kidnapper named Vizzini. In a battle of wits, Westley presents Vizzini with two goblets of wine, explaining that one contains an odourless, tasteless, and lethal poison called iocane powder. Then he challenges Vizzini to a toast.

"Your guess," says Westley. "Where is the poison?"

"*Guess?*" Vizzini cries. "I don't guess. I think. I ponder. I deduce. Then I decide. But I never guess."

"The battle of wits has begun," says Westley. "It ends when you decide and we drink the wine and find out who is right and who is dead . . ."

The Battle of Wits is a one-stage game: though Vizzini chooses after Westley, he can't observe Westley's choice. Figure 12.1 summarizes the game's essential features. Westley has two choices: put the poison in the goblet on the left or put it in the goblet on the right. The table contains one row for each strategy. Vizzini also has two choices: drink from the goblet on the left or drink from the goblet on the right. The table contains one column for each of these strategies. Each of the four cells represents a pair of strategies. For example, the yellow-shaded cell lies in the "left goblet" row and the "right goblet" column, so it means that Westley places the poison in the left goblet, while Vizzini drinks from the right goblet.

We've divided each cell into two halves. The number in the southwest half indicates Westley's prize (or penalty); the number in the northeast half indicates Vizzini's. The numbers in the yellow-shaded cell, for example, tell us that, when Westley puts the poison in the left goblet and Vizzini drinks from the right goblet, Westley's payoff is −1 (he dies), while Vizzini's payoff is 1 (he survives and keeps Buttercup). The magnitudes of these payoffs are unimportant; they simply indicate a preference for surviving over dying.

This example, though whimsical, captures the essence of many important strategic problems. With a bit of relabelling, for example, we can view it as a simple version of the game that preceded D-Day. Think of Westley as Eisenhower. Putting the poison in the left goblet corresponds to invading Normandy; putting it in the right goblet corresponds to invading Calais. Now think of Vizzini as Hitler. Drinking from the left goblet corresponds to defending Calais; drinking from the right goblet corresponds to defending Normandy. If the same location is attacked and defended, Hitler wins; otherwise, Eisenhower wins.

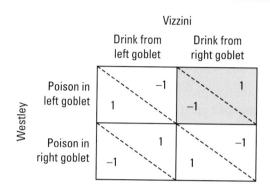

Figure 12.1

The Battle of Wits. This table contains one row for each of Westley's alternatives and one column for each of Vizzini's. Each cell corresponds to a pair of strategies. In the yellow cell, for example, Westley chooses the left goblet and Vizzini chooses the right one. The number in the southwest half of each cell indicates Westley's prize (or penalty); the number in the northeast half indicates Vizzini's.

IN-TEXT EXERCISE 12.1   **Bob and Brian square off for the World Rock Paper Scissors Championship. The winner will take home $7000, the loser receives nothing, and they split the prize in the event of a tie. Draw a table (like Figure 12.1) showing the players' possible choices, and the payoffs that result from each pair of actions.**

12.2 THINKING STRATEGICALLY IN ONE-STAGE GAMES

How should someone go about making a strategic decision? For example, let's think about how Vizzini might make his choice in the Battle of Wits. He knows his payoff will depend in part on what Westley does. That suggests he should start by putting himself in Westley's shoes, so he can figure out what Westley might do. Then he can think about his own choice, taking Westley's view into account.

What happens when Vizzini puts himself in Westley's shoes? He quickly notices that Westley's payoff depends in part on what Vizzini does. The implication dawns on him: Westley will start by putting himself in Vizzini's shoes so that he can form a view of what Vizzini will do. That means Vizzini has to think about what will run through Westley's mind when Westley puts himself in Vizzini's shoes.

It gets worse. Vizzini realizes that when Westley puts himself in Vizzini's shoes, he will recognize that Vizzini starts out by putting himself in Westley's shoes. So Vizzini has to think about what will run through Westley's mind when Westley thinks about what will run through Vizzini's mind when Vizzini thinks about Westley's choice.

It doesn't stop there. In fact, it doesn't stop *anywhere*. Vizzini can always take this line of reasoning to the next level.

Not surprisingly, thinking through strategic choices in this way is often a dead end. If, in the Battle of Wits, Westley can reason out what Vizzini will choose by putting himself in Vizzini's shoes, then Westley must win. Likewise, if Vizzini can reason out what Westley has done by putting himself in Westley's shoes, then Vizzini must win. Since they can't both win, it must not be possible to reason out each others' choices in this way. Let's see what happens when Vizzini tries:

"It's all so simple," says Vizzini. "All I have to do is deduce, from what I know of you, the way your mind works. Are you the kind of man who would put the poison into his own glass, or into the glass of his enemy?"

"Now a great fool," he continues, "would place the poison in his own goblet, because he would know that only another great fool would reach first for what he was given. I am clearly not a great fool, so I will clearly not reach for your wine."

"That's your final choice?"

"No. Because you knew I was not a great fool, so you would know that I would never fall for such a trick. You would count on it. So I will clearly not reach for mine either."

"Keep going," says Westley.

"I intend to." After reflecting for a moment, Vizzini continues. "We have now decided the poisoned cup is most likely in front of you. But the poison is powder made from iocane and iocane comes only from Australia and Australia, as everyone knows, is peopled with criminals and criminals are used to having people not trust them, as I don't trust you, which means I can clearly not choose the wine in front of you. But again, you must have suspected I knew the origins of iocane, so you would have known I knew about the criminals and criminal behavior, and therefore I can clearly not choose the wine in front of me."

"Truly you have a dizzying intellect," whispers Westley.

Vizzini's two contradictory conclusions—that he "will clearly not reach for your wine" and that he "will clearly not reach for mine either"—underscore the limitations of reasoning strategically by putting oneself in another's shoes, at least in the context of the Battle of Wits.

Fortunately, the problem isn't as hopeless as it might appear. The problem of strategic thinking may be a thorny one, but we can still make useful progress. Next we'll examine some special cases in which the issues are more straightforward.

Dominant Strategies

The **best response** is a strategy that provides a game player with the highest possible payoff, assuming that other players behave in a specified way.

A strategy is **dominant** if it is a player's only best response, regardless of other players' choices.

Sometimes, there's no need for one player to think through what another will do. To explain why, we need to introduce two new concepts. The first is known as a **best response**. This term refers to a strategy that provides a player with the highest possible payoff, assuming that other players behave in a specified way. For example, if Vizzini assumes that Westley put the poison in the left goblet, his best response is to drink from the right goblet. The second concept is known as a dominant strategy. A strategy is **dominant** if it is a player's only best response, regardless of other players' choices.

In discussing Vizzini's thought process, we said that Vizzini should start by putting himself in Westley's shoes so he could form an idea of what Westley might do. Strictly speaking, that is only necessary because Vizzini doesn't have a dominant strategy; his best response depends on what Westley does. (Check this!) If Vizzini and Westley were playing a game in which Vizzini had a dominant strategy, then Vizzini wouldn't need to forecast Westley's decision. Every conceivable forecast would lead him to the same conclusion: play the dominant strategy. To illustrate this point, we consider a new game, known as the Prisoners' Dilemma (Example 12.2).

Example 12.2

The Prisoners' Dilemma

Oskar and Roger are both enrolled in Microeconomics. While grading the midterm, Professor Getalife notices suspicious similarities between their answers. They truthfully attribute this coincidence to the fact that they always study together, but Getalife is unconvinced. Though they are actually innocent, he accuses them of cheating and asks for a disciplinary review.[1]

The disciplinary committee meets with Oskar and Roger separately, forbidding them to speak with each other until the process is complete. In each meeting, the head of the committee, Dean Windbag, presents the student with a simple choice. He explains that the university would like to send a clear message to the student body by making an example of a cheater. He says that the circumstantial evidence against them is strong enough to suspend them for only two semesters, which in his mind does not send a sufficiently powerful message. So he offers each a deal: squeal on your friend so that we can suspend him for six semesters, and we'll reduce your suspension by one semester. If your friend denies cheating, you'll get off with one semester instead of two; if he also squeals on you, you'll get off with five semesters instead of six.

Figure 12.2 summarizes the crucial features of this game. Oskar has two choices, deny or squeal; the table contains a row for each. Roger has the same two choices; the table contains a column for each. All together there are four cells, each of which represents a pair of actions. The yellow-shaded cell, for example, is in the "squeal" row and the "deny" column, so it represents the pair of choices (squeal, deny), meaning that Oskar squeals and Roger denies. Again, we've divided each cell into two halves. The number in the southwest half indicates Oskar's payoff; the number in the northeast half indicates Roger's. The numbers in the yellow-shaded cell tell us that Oskar is suspended for one semester (a payoff of -1) and Roger is suspended for six (a payoff of -6).

In Figure 12.3(a) we investigate whether Oskar's best response depends on Roger's decision. First, assume that Roger will definitely deny cheating. In that case, only the first column is relevant. For Oskar, denial results in a penalty of -2, while squealing results in a penalty of -1. Clearly, -1 is a better outcome than -2, so squealing is his best response. We've used green shading to show that -1 is Oskar's highest payoff in the first column.

Next, assume that Roger will definitely squeal. In that case, only the second column is relevant. For Oskar, denying results in a penalty of -6, while squealing results in a penalty of -5. Clearly, -5 is a better outcome than -6, so squealing is again his best response. We've used green shading to show that -5 is Oskar's highest payoff in the second column.

Notice that Oskar's best response doesn't depend on Roger's decision. Even without knowing Roger's choice, he knows he's better off squealing. Roger is in the same boat. In Figure 12.3(b), we've used red shading to indicate that squealing is Roger's best response to each of Oskar's choices. (To check this, notice that squealing, the second column, delivers Roger's highest payoff in each row.) Even without knowing Oskar's choice, Roger is clearly better off squealing. For both students, squealing is a dominant strategy.

---

[1]Usually descriptions of this game involve two individuals who stand accused of committing a crime, which is why it's called the "Prisoners' Dilemma."

Our analysis leads to a rather startling conclusion: despite their innocence, Oskar and Roger will both squeal on each other, and each will be suspended for five semesters. If they both denied cheating, both would be better off. Unfortunately, they can't achieve that preferred outcome because each has a strong incentive to sell the other out.

Is this rather nasty outcome likely in practice? Undoubtedly, you can think of many reasons why one student might be reluctant to squeal on another—concern for a friend, fear of retribution, loss of face among fellow students. That doesn't mean we've made a mistake in solving the game. Rather, it means that in an actual disciplinary situation, there is usually more going on. To capture this complexity, we would have to construct a more elaborate game. You'll see how this is done in Section 12.4.

Figure 12.2

The Prisoners' Dilemma. This table contains one row for each of Oskar's alternatives and one column for each of Roger's. Each cell corresponds to a pair of strategies. In the yellow cell, for example, Oskar squeals and Roger denies. The number in the southwest half of each cell indicates Oskar's payoff; the number in the northeast half indicates Roger's.

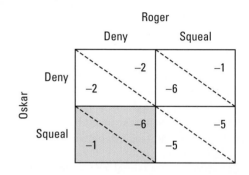

Figure 12.3

Best Responses in the Prisoners' Dilemma. In figure (a), the green shading indicates Oskar's highest payoff in each column. We see that Oskar's best response is to squeal, regardless of what he thinks Roger will do. In figure (b), the red shading to indicates Roger's highest payoff in each row. We see that Roger's best response is to squeal, regardless of what he thinks Oskar will do. Squealing is therefore a dominant strategy for both students.

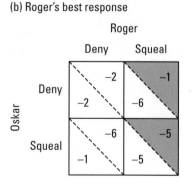

When a player has a dominant strategy, as Oskar and Roger do, he doesn't need to think about what others will choose. But what if he doesn't have a dominant strategy? In that case, he *does* need to think about what others will choose because his best choice depends on their decisions. Even so, there are some situations in which his ideal strategy is obvious. For example, if *everyone else* has a dominant strategy, their choices are predictable. In that case, a player should simply assume that everyone else will play their dominant strategies, and choose his best response accordingly. Our next example illustrates this point.

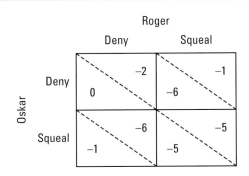

Figure 12.4

The Provost's Nephew. The choices and payoffs in the Provost's Nephew are the same as in the Prisoners' Dilemma, except that Oskar receives a payoff of zero (instead of −2) if both students deny cheating.

Dominated Strategies

Example 12.3 shows that we can make some headway as long as at least one player has a dominant strategy. But what if no one has a dominant strategy? Even when we can't immediately say which strategies players *will* choose, we can often make progress by identifying strategies they definitely *won't* choose.

Example 12.3

The Provost's Nephew

Let's modify the preceding example ever so slightly by imagining that Oskar is the provost's nephew. As long as no one confesses, he's untouchable. However, if he confesses or if Roger squeals, his uncle can't protect him.

Figure 12.4 illustrates this game. Notice that it's exactly the same as Figure 12.2, except for one detail. We've changed Oskar's payoff in the upper-left-hand cell from −2 to zero, signifying that if both students deny cheating, Oskar will avoid suspension.

Figure 12.5(a) shows Oskar's best responses. Notice that zero is his highest payoff in the first column (indicated by the green shading). So assuming that Roger denies cheating, denial is Oskar's best response. As before, −5 is Oskar's highest payoff in the second column (indicated again by green shading). So assuming that Roger squeals, squealing is Oskar's best response.

In this case, Oskar doesn't have a dominant strategy. His best response depends on Roger's choice. Even so, we can still identify Oskar's best strategic choice because Roger's decision is predictable.

To understand why, look at Figure 12.5(b), which shows Roger's best responses. Since we haven't changed Roger's payoffs, the red shading is the same as in Figure 12.3(b). Squealing is Roger's best response regardless of what Oskar does—it's his dominant strategy. So Roger necessarily squeals.

We know that Oskar would be willing to deny cheating if he thought Roger would do likewise. But in fact, he knows that Roger will squeal, which means his best choice is to squeal as well. Though squealing isn't a dominant strategy for Oskar, it's his only sensible choice. Therefore, despite their innocence and despite Oskar's connection to the provost, both students will end up with a five-semester suspension.

Figure 12.5

Best Responses in the Provost's Nephew. In figure (a), the green shading indicates Oskar's highest payoff in each column. We see that Oskar's best response is to deny if he expects Roger to deny, and to squeal if he expects Roger to squeal. Neither choice is a dominant strategy. In figure (b), the red shading indicates Roger's highest payoff in each row. We see that Roger's best response is to squeal, regardless of what he thinks Oskar will do. Squealing is therefore Roger's dominant strategy.

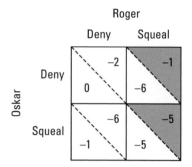

We say that a strategy is **dominated** if there is some other strategy that yields a strictly higher payoff regardless of others' choices.[2] This second strategy need not be a *dominant* strategy—that is, it may not be the player's best response in all instances (or even in any single instance). It is always better than the strategy it dominates, however. When a player does have a dominant strategy, all other strategies are dominated.

No sane player would ever select a dominated strategy. Why not? If the player switched to the strategy that dominates it, he would definitely end up with a higher payoff, regardless of how anyone else played. Thus, dominated strategies are completely irrelevant. A player with access to a dominated strategy will never choose it, and everyone else knows that he will never choose it. Nothing is lost by simply removing that strategy from the game.

Once we've removed a dominated strategy, we have a new, simpler game. Of the remaining strategies, some that weren't dominated in the original game may be dominated in the new game. (We'll provide an example of this in the next paragraph.) If so, we should remove them as well, because everyone knows they will never be played. Doing so leaves us with an even simpler game. We can repeat this procedure until there are no more dominated strategies left to remove, a process known as **iterative deletion of dominated strategies**.

In essence, we solved the Provost's Nephew game in Example 12.3 by iteratively deleting dominated strategies. To see why, look at Figure 12.6(a), which starts on the left by replicating Figure 12.4. As we've said, squealing is a dominant strategy for Roger, which means that denying is dominated. Roger won't choose deny, and Oskar knows it, so that strategy is irrelevant; we might as well remove it from the game. Doing so leaves the simpler game shown in Figure 12.6(b). Roger actually has no choice in this game; only Oskar makes a decision. In this simplified game, denying is a dominated strategy for Oskar (it yields a lower payoff than squealing, given the only choice Roger can

---

[2]Technically, a strategy is also dominated if there is a way of randomizing over other strategies that yields a higher expected payoff regardless of others' choices. To keep the analysis simple, we'll avoid discussing randomizations here. The same qualification applies to the notion of weak dominance, introduced later in this section.

Figure 12.6

Deletion of Dominated Strategies in the Provost's Nephew. In figure (a), deny is a dominated strategy for Roger, so we can remove it from the game, leaving the simpler game in figure (b). In figure (b), deny is a dominated strategy for Oskar, so we can remove it from the game, leaving only one choice for each student in figure (c).

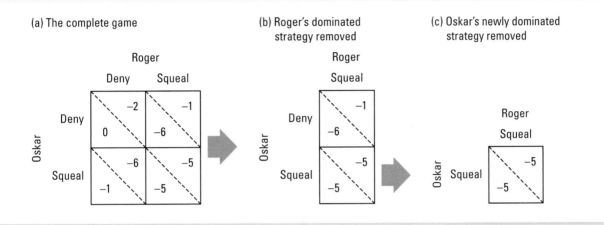

make). Oskar won't choose to deny, so it's irrelevant; we might as well remove it, leaving the game shown in Figure 12.6(c). Now there is only one possible outcome: both students squeal.

In Example 12.3, one of the players had a dominant strategy. As Example 12.4 shows, the iterative deletion of dominated strategies sometimes allows us to solve strategic problems even when *no player* has a dominant strategy.

Example 12.4

Guessing Half the Median

Imagine that five people are playing a one-stage guessing game. Each is asked to choose a number between 1 and 8 (inclusive), trying to come as close as possible to half the median choice. (The median is the middle value—here, the third highest choice.) After the players privately select their numbers, a referee finds the median and divides by two. Each player pays a penalty (in dollars) equal to the gap between this number and his own guess.

To illustrate, suppose the chosen numbers are 2, 3, 6, 7, and 7. The median is 6, so half the median is 3. The player who chose 2 pays a penalty of $1 (having missed the target by one unit), the player who chose 3 pays no penalty (having hit the target). The player who chose 6 pays a penalty of $3 (having missed the target by three units), and the players who chose 7 pay a penalty of $4 (having missed the target by four units).

Before reading further, think a bit about this game. If you were a player, what number would you choose?

Notice that in this game, no player has a dominant strategy. Why? Each player's best response depends on others' choices. For example, if everyone else chooses 6, the best choice is 3 (the median is 6, so half the median is 3). But if everyone else chooses 4, the best choice is 2 (the median is 4, so half the median is 2). No single choice is always best regardless of what others do.

Even though no player has a dominant strategy, every player has some dominated strategies. Since the median choice can be no higher than 8, half the median can be no higher than 4. Therefore, choosing 4 dominates any number greater than 4. No one should choose any number greater than 4, and everyone knows it. Those choices are irrelevant, so we might as well remove them from the game. When we do, we end up with the same guessing game as before, except that now each player must choose a number between 1 and 4.

Now let's think about the game in which each player chooses a number between 1 and 4. Again, no player has a dominant strategy. For example, if everyone else selects 4, the best choice is 2. But if everyone else chooses 2, the best choice is 1. Even so, every player has some dominated strategies. Since the median choice can be no higher than 4, half the median can be no higher than 2. Therefore, choosing 2 dominates any choice greater than 2. No one should choose any number greater than 2, and everyone knows it. Those choices are irrelevant, so we might as well remove them, just as we removed the numbers 5 through 8. When we do, we end up with the same guessing game as before, except that now each player must choose a number between 1 and 2.

Now let's think about the game in which each player chooses either 1 or 2. Since the median choice can be no higher than 2, half the median can be no higher than 1. Choosing 1 is therefore the best available alternative, regardless of what others do. In other words, in this simplified game, 1 is the dominant strategy.

In sum, iteratively deleting dominated strategies has led us to a clear and unambiguous conclusion: *All players should choose the number 1.* The same logic will lead to the same conclusion when the range of potential choices is 1 to 100, 1 to 1000, or even 1 to 1,000,000, regardless of the number of players.

Weakly Dominated Strategies

We've had some success in reasoning out strategic decisions by identifying strategies that players definitely won't select. So far, we've focused on dominated strategies. Arguably, we can go further and rule out strategies that are *weakly* dominated. We say that a strategy is **weakly dominated** if there is some other strategy that yields a strictly higher payoff in some circumstances, and that never yields a lower payoff regardless of others' choices.

A strategy is **weakly dominated** if there is some other strategy that yields a strictly higher payoff in some circumstances, and that never yields a lower payoff regardless of others' choices.

To see an illustration of this concept, look at Figure 12.7, which shows a game played by Susan, who chooses up or down, and Myrna, who chooses left or right. The green shading indicates Susan's highest payoff in each column. Notice that down is a best response for Susan no matter what Myrna does, but it isn't the only best response when Myrna plays left. Since both of Susan's choices yield the same payoff when Myrna selects left, down doesn't dominate up. However, since Susan is strictly better off with down than with up when Myrna chooses right, down weakly dominates up.

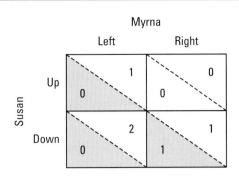

Figure 12.7

A Weakly Dominant Strategy. Myrna chooses left or right and Susan chooses up or down. The green shading indicates Susan's highest payoff in each column. For Susan, down is just as good as up when Myrna chooses left; it is better than up when Myrna chooses right. That is, for Susan, down weakly dominates up.

It may be a stretch to claim that no sane player would ever select a weakly dominated strategy. If, for example, Susan is sure that Myrna will play left, up is a perfectly reasonable choice. Even though it is weakly dominated, Susan can't improve her payoff by switching to down. Even so, down seems a safer choice. If Susan is right about Myrna, she won't end up any worse off; if she's wrong, she'll fare better. This reasoning suggests that it's usually wise to avoid weakly dominated strategies.

Example 12.5

Voting by Secret Ballot under Plurality Rule

Three candidates, Mr. Left, Ms. Right, and Ms. Maverick, are running for the same public office. There are 1000 voters, each of whom either casts a secret ballot naming one of the candidates or abstains. The candidate with the most votes wins, even if he or she does not receive a majority of the votes. For example, if 400 ballots name Ms. Right, 350 name Mr. Left, and 250 name Ms. Maverick, then Ms. Right wins. In the event of a tie, a coin flip determines the winner. This procedure is known as *plurality rule*. It is also a simple one-stage game. What does game theory tell us about how people ought to vote?

Notice that there are no dominant strategies in this game, nor are there any dominated strategies. For example, if every other citizen votes for Mr. Left, then Mr. Left will win regardless of how you vote. Therefore, all of your strategies are best responses.

However, voting for your least favourite candidate is weakly dominated by abstention. Switching to abstention reduces the vote total for your least favourite candidate. This can't make you worse off, and in some situations you're better off, because your vote makes the difference. Similarly, abstention is weakly dominated by voting for your favourite candidate. (Can you explain why?)

However, voting for your second favourite candidate is not weakly dominated. In fact, it can be a perfectly reasonable choice. To illustrate, suppose you prefer Ms. Maverick to Mr. Left, and Mr. Left to Ms. Right. Assume that 496 of your fellow citizens will vote for Mr. Left, 496 for Ms. Right, and only 7 for Ms. Maverick. In that case, you're better off breaking the tie by voting for Mr. Left, even though you prefer Ms. Maverick. In real elections involving three or more candidates, people are indeed frequently reluctant to cast their votes for a favoured candidate with little or no chance of victory.

Application 12.1

Second-Price Sealed-Bid Auctions

At the beginning of this chapter, we mentioned that sealed-bid auctions—in which each potential buyer submits a single bid privately, and there is no opportunity for rebidding or counterbids—are one-stage games. Typically, the object for sale is awarded to the highest bidder, but different sealed-bid auction formats have different rules for determining how much the winner pays. In a first-price sealed-bid auction, the selling price is the winning bid. In a second-price sealed-bid auction, the selling price is the *second* highest bid. This arrangement is also known as a *Vickrey auction*, named for William S. Vickrey, who received the 1996 Nobel Prize in Economics for his work on this topic.

William Vickrey (1914–1996) received the 1996 Nobel Prize in Economics in part for his pioneering work on the theory of auctions.

The first known second-price sealed-bid auction was held in 1893 for the purpose of selling a collection of postal stamps. During the first half of the 20th century, the format came into widespread use among companies that organized postage stamp auctions. Today, second-price auctions are less common than their first-price cousins, but they have gained popularity with the growth of eBay and other Internet auction services. At first blush, most of these services appear to use a format called the *English* or *ascending-price* auction, in which potential buyers best each others' bids until only one bidder is left. In many cases, however, buyers can make proxy bids. On eBay, for example, you can enter a maximum bid, and eBay will bid on your behalf up to your maximum. If you submit a maximum bid and win, you pay the price at which the next highest bidder drops out—in other words, the second highest bid (plus the minimum bid increment). Consequently, an ascending-price English auction with proxy bids amounts to a second-price sealed-bid auction.

Suppose you're participating as a buyer in a second-price sealed-bid auction. How much should you bid? It turns out that bidding the maximum amount you're willing to pay weakly dominates all your other possible choices. That is, if you're willing to pay $100 for an object but not a penny more, you should bid exactly $100. The same principle holds for proxy bids submitted on eBay. Why?

Let's think about what happens if you submit a lower bid—say $95—instead of $100. If your competitors' bids are all less than $95, you'll win and pay the same price—the second highest bid—bidding either $95 or $100. If at least one of your competitors bids more than $100, you'll lose in both cases. But if none of your competitors bids more than $100 and at least one bids more than $95, your $95 bid will lose while your $100 bid will win the object at a price below its value to you. So bidding $95 instead of $100 can't make you better off, and sometimes makes you worse off.

Now let's think about what happens if you submit a higher bid—say $105—instead of $100. If your competitors' bids are all less than $100, or if at least one bids more than $105, you fare equally well bidding either $100 or $105. (Why?) But if none of your competitors bids more than $105 and at least one bids more than $100, your $100 bid loses, while your $105 bid wins the object at a price above its value to you. So bidding $105 instead of $100 can't make you better off, and sometimes makes you worse off.

Why might a *seller* prefer a second-price sealed-bid auction to a first-price sealed-bid auction? Wouldn't he collect more money by requiring the winner to pay the highest bid instead of the second highest bid? The answer is, not necessarily, because bids tend to be lower in first-price auctions than in second-price auctions. As we've seen, in a second-price auction, each potential buyer should bid the maximum price he is willing to pay. But in a first-price auction, that same strategy is weakly dominated. It guarantees that the bidder won't come out ahead—even if he wins, he'll give up as much value as he gets. If instead he submits a lower bid, he may be able to buy the good for less than it's worth to him. Because bids will be lower in the first-price auction, the seller might not receive more revenue than in the second-price auction. We will return to this comparison in Application 12.2.

12.3 NASH EQUILIBRIUM IN ONE-STAGE GAMES

To this point, we've managed to reason out strategic decisions in some special situations by thinking about dominance. Unfortunately, that line of attack will only take us so far. In many one-stage games, no choice dominates any other, even weakly. What happens in those games?

The Concept of Nash Equilibrium

The life of John Nash (1928–), was the subject of the critically acclaimed film *A Beautiful Mind*, which received four Academy Awards.

In 1950, a 22-year-old mathematician named John Nash published an article based on his Princeton Ph.D. thesis, for which he later received the Nobel Prize in Economics. His article proposed a new tool for thinking about strategic decisions, known today as Nash equilibrium. While the idea took a while to catch on, over the last three decades it has become one of the most central and important concepts in microeconomics.

In a **Nash equilibrium**, the strategy played by each individual is a best response to the strategies played by everyone else. In other words, everyone correctly anticipates what everyone else will do and then chooses the best available alternative.

Let's look for a Nash equilibrium in the Prisoners' Dilemma. Figure 12.8 combines the red and green shading from the two parts of Figure 12.3 (page 410). Remember that green shading indicates Oskar's best response within each row, while red shading indicates Roger's best response within each column. Notice that the southeast cell is shaded half red and half green. The two-tone shading implies that this cell is a Nash equilibrium: since the cell is half green, the row choice is Oskar's best response to Roger's column choice; since it is also half red, the column choice is Roger's best response to Oskar's row choice. In this equilibrium, both players squeal. Squealing is Oskar's best response if Roger squeals, and it's Roger's best response if Oskar squeals. Because there are no other two-tone cells, the southeast cell is the *only* Nash equilibrium.

> In a **Nash equilibrium**, the strategy played by each individual is a best response to the strategies played by everyone else.

IN-TEXT EXERCISE 12.2   Using a diagram like Figure 12.8, explain why the pair of choices (squeal, squeal) is the only Nash equilibrium in the Provost's Nephew.

Justifications for Nash Equilibrium   Why are Nash equilibria of interest? The combination of strategies chosen in a Nash equilibrium is stable. Every participant is content

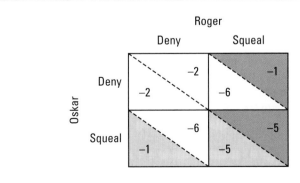

Figure 12.8

Nash Equilibrium in the Prisoners' Dilemma. As in Figure 12.3, green shading indicates Oskar's best responses and red shading indicates Roger's. The Nash equilibrium is the cell that is shaded both red and green. In this equilibrium, both Oskar and Roger squeal.

with his choice; no one wants to play anything else. All other outcomes are unstable, in the sense that at least one participant would want to change his strategy. As you learned in Chapter 2, we study the equilibria of competitive markets for a similar reason: the competitive price is stable, in the sense that there is no pressure for it to either rise or fall.

Why would we necessarily expect a group of people to settle on a stable combination of strategies? One explanation has to do with the effect of experience on the accuracy of participants' expectations. When people play games, they try to guess what their opponents will do and then play their best responses. As they gain experience (possibly with different opponents), they learn how others tend to play. If they eventually learn to make accurate guesses, they will choose best responses to their opponents' actual decisions. If in addition all players are experienced, then each will have reasonably accurate expectations and each will tend to select a best response to the others' choices. In short, they'll play a Nash equilibrium. In fact, laboratory experiments have confirmed that, for certain types of games, experienced players do tend to select Nash equilibrium strategies.

Some economists prefer to think of Nash equilibria as **self-enforcing agreements**. An agreement is self-enforcing if each party to the agreement has an incentive to abide by it, assuming that others do the same. The strategies that make up a Nash equilibrium have this property. That is, if the parties agree to play Nash equilibrium strategies, no one has an incentive to break the agreement. In some situations, people can formalize agreements by writing contracts and rely on the courts for enforcement. In those cases their agreements don't have to be self-enforcing. When that isn't possible, however, agreeing to an arrangement is pointless unless it's self-enforcing.

> In a **self-enforcing agreement**, every party to the agreement has an incentive to abide by it, assuming that others do the same.

Take the Provost's Nephew, for example. Imagine for the moment that Oskar and Roger have a chance to speak with each other immediately before their disciplinary hearings. Although they would like to agree not to squeal, that isn't self-enforcing. Oskar knows that Roger has a strong incentive to break their agreement. Knowing this, he'll probably squeal as well.

Why Nash Equilibrium Is a Useful Concept   The concept of a Nash equilibrium doesn't lead to any new conclusions in the Prisoners' Dilemma or the Provost's Nephew. By thinking about dominance, we've already figured out that both players will squeal in those games. In many other games, however, we can say a great deal more about strategic behaviour by studying Nash equilibria than by examining dominance. That is why Nash equilibrium is a useful concept. Example 12.6 and Application 12.2 illustrate this point.

Example 12.6

The Battle of the Sexes

Tony and Maria are planning an evening at the movies. Tony wants to see an action-adventure film, *Revenge of Chomp and Chew*, while Maria favours a romantic comedy, *Chickflick: The Sequel*. Neither cares much for the other's suggestion, and neither can force the other to attend a particular movie, but both want to spend the evening together, even if it means suffering through the other's preferred film.

Figure 12.9(a) shows Tony and Maria's possible choices and payoffs. The table contains two rows, one for each of Maria's choices—see the action-adventure film or see the romantic comedy. It also contains two columns, one for each of Tony's choices. The northwest cell represents attending the action-adventure film together, which makes Tony happy (a payoff of 5) and Maria more or less content (a payoff of 2). The southeast cell represents attending the romantic comedy together, which makes Maria happy and Tony more or less content. In the southwest corner, each attends his or her preferred movie alone, which isn't much fun (a payoff of 1 for both). In the northeast corner, each attends the other's preferred movie alone, which is downright unpleasant (a payoff of −1 for both).

Figure 12.9(b) uses green shading to indicate Maria's best response within each column and red shading to indicate Tony's best response within each row. Notice that each prefers to go wherever he or she believes the other will go. As a result, no choice is dominated, and we learn nothing about strategic behaviour in this game by examining dominance.

What about Nash equilibria? In Figure 12.9(b), the northwest and southeast cells are shaded half red and half green. Seeing either film together is therefore a Nash equilibrium—Tony's film choice is a best response to Maria's and Maria's is a best response to Tony's. Both equilibria are self-enforcing agreements: If Tony and Maria agree to meet at the action-adventure film, each can count on the other to follow through, and likewise if they agree to meet at the romantic comedy. Since there are two equilibria, the concept of Nash equilibrium can't pin down which film the couple will see, but it does tell us they'll attend a film together.

"As a matter of fact, you did catch us at a bad time."

Figure 12.9

The Battle of the Sexes. Figure (a) contains one row for each of Maria's alternatives and one column for each of Tony's. The number in the southwest half of each cell indicates Maria's payoff; the number in the northeast half indicates Tony's. In figure (b), the green shading indicates Maria's best response in each column, and the red shading indicates Tony's best response in each row. We see that their best responses depend on each others' choices. The two cells that are shaded half red and half green are Nash equilibria.

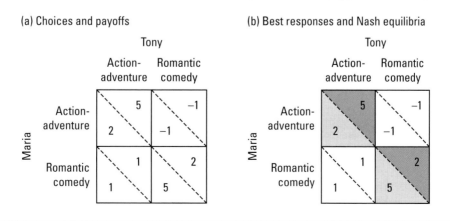

(a) Choices and payoffs

(b) Best responses and Nash equilibria

Application 12.2

Comparing First-Price and Second-Price Auctions

At the end of Application 12.1 (page 416), we asked whether first-price or second-price auctions will tend to generate more revenue for sellers. Using the concept of weak dominance, we can figure out what people will bid (and therefore what the seller will earn) in a second-price auction, but not in a first-price auction. The concept of Nash equilibrium is useful here because it allows us to project the outcome of a first-price auction and thus to compare the revenues generated by the two auction formats.

To illustrate, suppose there are three potential buyers, William, Eva, and Paul. The object they want is worth $103 to William, $100 to Eva, and $95 to Paul. For now, let's assume that everyone knows everyone else's valuation. Bids must be made in even pennies. In the event of a tie, the winner is determined at random (possibly by a coin flip).

Suppose first that the object is sold through a second-price sealed-bid auction. From Application 12.1, we know that each potential buyer should bid his actual valuation.[3] William bids $103, Eva bids $100, and Paul bids $95. William wins and pays the seller $100 (Eva's bid).

Next suppose that the object is sold through a first-price sealed-bid auction. Here's one Nash equilibrium: William bids $100, Eva bids $99.99 (a penny less than her valuation), and Paul bids $94.99 (a penny less than his valuation). William wins and pays the seller $100 (his own bid).[4] Let's check that

each participant's bid is a best response to the others' bids. Given that Eva bids $99.99 and Paul bids $94.99, William can't do any better. If he bid higher, he would have to pay more; if he bid less, he would either lose for sure (by offering less than $99.99) or win with only 50 percent probability (by offering exactly $99.99). Given that William bids $100 and Eva bids $99.99, Paul can't buy the good for less than it's worth to him ($95), so he can't do any better. Similarly, given that William bids $100 and Paul bids $94.99, Eva can't buy the good for less than it's worth to her ($100), so she can't do any better.

Notice that the seller receives *exactly the same revenue* under the first-price and second-price formats. William is the winner in each case. He bids less in the first-price auction than in the second-price auction ($100 instead of $103), but pays the same amount ($100) regardless of the format.

We've assumed here that everyone knows everyone else's valuation. Usually that isn't realistic. At this point, we're not equipped to study auctions in which people don't know one another's valuations; we'll address that topic in Section 12.5. Under reasonably general conditions, however, the conclusion we've reached here remains valid: on average, first-price and second-price sealed-bid auctions should raise exactly the same amount of revenue. This conclusion is known as the *revenue equivalence theorem*.

Nash Equilibria and Welfare   In both the Prisoners' Dilemma and the Provost's Nephew, the Nash equilibrium leads to a rather bad outcome: the players are worse off than they would be if both denied the allegations. Why does this unfortunate result happen? When comparing the desirability of squeal and deny, Oskar thinks about his own payoff, but ignores Roger's; likewise, Roger thinks about his own payoff, but ignores Oskar's. By choosing squeal, each player helps himself by doing greater harm to the other, with the result that both are worse off. (Similar problems will come up in Chapter 20, where we'll explain how "externalities" can lead to poor resource allocation.)

Keep in mind, however, that Nash equilibria can also lead to good outcomes. Think about the Battle of the Sexes. One Nash equilibrium produces the best possible outcome for Maria; the other produces the best possible outcome for Tony. Moreover, both Maria and Tony are better off in either equilibrium than they would be with the other two

---

[3]While some Nash equilibria lead to other outcomes, all of those involve weakly dominated strategies.

[4]This isn't the only possible Nash equilibrium. However, for any equilibrium in which the bidders avoid weakly dominated strategies, William buys the object for $100. See if you can figure out why.

alternatives, which involve spending the evening apart. Therefore, depending on the game, Nash equilibrium can involve either good outcomes or bad ones.

Nash Equilibria in Games with Finely Divisible Choices

So far, we've studied games in which players have a small number of choices. Yet economists typically examine situations in which the number of choices is quite large. Indeed, strategic decisions often involve finely divisible quantities, like time or money. How do we find the Nash equilibria in these settings?

Let's address this question by examining a concrete economic problem. Businesses frequently assign tasks to teams of employees rather than to individuals. When the employer can't identify the separate contributions of each team member, the members' choices become strategic. Some individuals will seek to "free ride" on others' contributions (see Chapter 20). Suppose, for example, that two employees, Liz and Scott, are writing a report together. They have 24 hours to do background research. The quality of their research will affect their prospects for raises and promotions. The more time they spend on the research, the better, but each wants the other to do most of the work.

Let's assume that Liz and Scott must conduct their research simultaneously and separately. Neither will learn how hard the other has worked until both are finished. In that case, their task is a one-stage game. Each chooses the amount of time he or she devotes to research without observing the other's choice.

Figure 12.10(a) shows Liz and Scott's potential choices. The horizontal axis measures the number of hours Scott spends on research; the vertical axis measures the number of hours Liz spends. For example, at point A, Liz and Scott each spend 15 hours on research.

Figure 12.10

Free Riding in Groups. In figure (a), the green line shows the relationship between Scott's hours and Liz's best response. The red line shows the relationship between Liz's hours and Scott's best response. In figure (b), point N is a Nash equilibrium because it lies on both the red line and the green line. In this Nash equilibrium, Scott and Liz both put in eight hours.

(a) Best responses

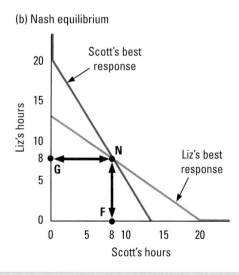

(b) Nash equilibrium

If we know Liz's objectives, then for each choice that Scott might make, we can figure out Liz's best response. Doing so allows us to plot the relationship between Scott's choices and Liz's best responses. (For an example of how this is done, see worked-out problem 12.1, below.) Let's suppose that relationship corresponds to the green line in Figure 12.10(a). For example, if Scott spends five hours on research, Liz's best choice is to put in 10 hours (follow the vertical arrow from point B to the green line and the horizontal arrow from the green line to point C). Notice that the green line is downward sloping; if Liz can count on Scott to work longer hours, she will "free ride" by working fewer hours.

Likewise, if we know Scott's objectives, we can plot his best responses to each of Liz's choices. Suppose that relationship corresponds to the red line in Figure 12.10(a). For example, if Liz spends five hours on research, Scott's best choice is to put in 10 hours (follow the horizontal arrow from point D to the red line, and the vertical arrow from the red line to point E). Since Scott would like to "free ride" on Liz's work, the red line is also downward sloping. The red and green curves are known as **best response functions** (or **reaction functions**); each shows the relationship between one player's choice and the other's best response.

> A **best response function**, also known as a **reaction function**, shows the relationship between one player's choice and the other's best response.

Notice that the layout of Figure 12.10(a) resembles that of Figure 12.9(b). Liz chooses the vertical coordinate in Figure 12.10(a), which is just like choosing a row in Figure 12.9(b). Likewise, Scott selects the horizontal coordinate in Figure 12.10(a), which is just like choosing a column in Figure 12.9(b). The main difference is that Figure 12.10(a) shows each pair of choices as a point rather than a cell. The green and red lines in Figure 12.10(a) play exactly the same role as the green and red shading in Figure 12.9(b). In both figures, green indicates one participant's best response and red indicates the other participant's best response. In Figure 12.9(b), a pair of choices is a Nash equilibrium if it corresponds to a cell that is shaded half red and half green. In Figure 12.10(a), a pair of choices is a Nash equilibrium if it corresponds to a point that lies on both the red line and on the green line. There is one such point, which we've labelled N (for "Nash equilibrium") in Figure 12.10(b).

As we've drawn the figure, the Nash equilibrium involves both employees spending eight hours on research. Let's confirm that this is indeed a Nash equilibrium. Suppose that Scott chooses eight hours. Following the vertical arrow in Figure 12.10(b) from point F to the green line and the horizontal arrow from the green line to point G, we see that Liz's best response is to put in eight hours. Now suppose that Liz chooses eight hours. Following the horizontal arrow from point G to the red line and the vertical arrow from the red line to point F, we see that Scott's best response is to put in eight hours. At point N, each employee makes a best response to the other's choice; therefore, point N is a Nash equilibrium.

WORKED-OUT PROBLEM   12.1

The Problem   Let's use the symbol X to indicate the number of hours Scott spends on research and the symbol Y to indicate the number of hours Liz spends. Both these numbers must be positive and neither can exceed 24. Suppose we can measure Scott and Liz's costs and benefits on a utility scale (recall the discussion of utility in Section 4.4). When Scott works for X hours and Liz works for Y hours, each receives a total benefit of $40(X + Y) - (X + Y)^2$. That means the marginal benefit of spending extra time is $40 - 2(X + Y)$, regardless of who puts in the time. Notice that the marginal benefit of time declines as total time rises. Let's assume that the cost of their effort is $X^2/2$ for Scott and $Y^2/2$ for Liz. The marginal cost of extra time is then X for Scott and Y for Liz. Find the Nash equilibrium of this game. Is it a good outcome for Liz and Scott? Could they do better?

The Solution   Suppose that Scott puts in X hours. To find Liz's best response, we need to set her marginal benefit equal to her marginal cost: $40 - 2(X + Y) = Y$. Solving for Y, we obtain a formula that describes the relationship between Scott's choices and Liz's best responses.

$$Y = \frac{40}{3} - \frac{2X}{3}$$

This is the formula for the green line in Figure 12.10. (Check this.)

Now suppose that Liz puts in Y hours. Through a similar calculation, we obtain a formula that describes the relationship between Liz's choices and Scott's best responses.

$$X = \frac{40}{3} - \frac{2Y}{3}$$

This is the formula for the red line in Figure 12.10. (Again, check this.)

To solve for the Nash equilibrium, we need to identify the point at which the red and green lines intersect. Doing so amounts to finding the values of X and Y that satisfy both best response formulas at the same time. Substituting the first formula into the second gives us

$$X = \frac{40}{3} - \frac{2}{3}\left[\frac{40}{3} - \frac{2X}{3}\right]$$

Solving for X, we find that $X = 8$. Plugging this value for X into the first formula, we discover that $Y = 8$. So in the Nash equilibrium, Liz and Scott each put in eight hours.

This result is not the best possible outcome. Liz and Scott would be happier if they both worked harder. Suppose, for example, that they each put in nine hours. In that case, each would receive a total benefit of $40(9 + 9) - (9 + 9)^2 = 396$, and would incur total costs of $9^2/2 = 40.5$, for a net payoff of 355.5. In contrast, when they both put in eight hours, each receives a total benefit of $40(8 + 8) - (8 + 8)^2 = 384$, and incurs a total cost of $8^2/2 = 32$, for a net payoff of only 352. Clearly, both would be better off if they worked for nine hours.

IN-TEXT EXERCISE 12.3   **Repeat worked-out problem 12.1, changing the assumptions as follows. When Scott works for X hours and Liz works for Y hours, each receives a total benefit of $60(X + 2Y) - (X + 2Y)^2$. The marginal benefit of Scott's extra time is $60 - 2(X + 2Y)$, while the marginal benefit of Liz's extra time is $120 - 4(X + 2Y)$. The cost of their effort is X^2 for Scott and $4Y^2$ for Liz, so the marginal cost is $2X$ for Scott and $8Y$ for Liz.**

Mixed Strategies

While the concept of a Nash equilibrium helps us understand strategic decision making in some games, it isn't always useful.[5] Figure 12.11 reproduces the Battle of Wits game from Figure 12.1 (page 407), with green shading to indicate Westley's best response in each column, and red shading to indicate Vizzini's best response in each row. Notice that no cell is shaded half red and half green. Consequently, if Westley's choice is a best response to Vizzini's, then Vizzini's isn't a best response to Westley's. For example, Westley will poison the left goblet if he expects Vizzini to drink from the left goblet, but Vizzini will do so only if he thinks Westley has poisoned the right goblet. We conclude that there is no Nash equilibrium in the Battle of Wits. Using a similar diagram, you should be able to explain why there is no Nash equilibrium in Rock Paper Scissors.

Playing Unpredictably   How do we think about strategic decisions in games like the Battle of Wits and Rock Paper Scissors? The key to success in such games is unpredictability. As soon as a player's choices become predictable, he loses. How can a player become unpredictable? The most obvious way is to make choices randomly. (If you skipped Chapter 11, you should pause to read Section 11.1, in which we explained some basic concepts concerning probability, risk, and expected payoff.)

> When a player chooses a strategy without randomizing, we call it a **pure strategy**. When a player uses a rule to randomize over the choice of a strategy, we call it a **mixed strategy**.

When a player chooses a strategy without randomizing, we say that he is playing a **pure strategy**. When he uses a rule to randomize over the choice of a strategy, we say he is playing a **mixed strategy**. For example, in the Battle of Wits, a mixed strategy might call for Westley to poison the left goblet with 60 percent probability and poison the right goblet with 40 percent probability. Technically, a pure strategy is a special kind of mixed strategy in which all probability is placed on a single choice.

> In a **mixed strategy equilibrium,** players choose mixed strategies, and the mixed strategy chosen by each is a best response to the mixed strategies chosen by the others.

So far, we've studied Nash equilibria in which players use pure strategies. We've seen that not all games have equilibria of this type. This problem may have a simple solution. Since behaving unpredictably is sometimes an advantage, it makes sense to look for Nash equilibria in which players introduce a degree of randomness by playing mixed strategies. This kind of equilibrium is known as a **mixed strategy equilibrium**.[6] In such an

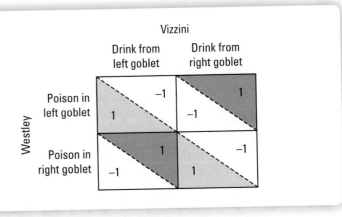

Figure 12.11
A Game with No Nash Equilibrium in Pure Strategies. We have reproduced the Battle of Wits from Figure 12.1. The green shading indicates Westley's best response in each column and the red shading indicates Vizzini's best response in each row. No cell is shaded half red and half green, so there is no Nash equilibrium in pure strategies.

[5]Technically, this paragraph refers to Nash equilibria in which players do not randomize over their choices. As explained below, the problem described in this paragraph disappears if we assume that players can make random choices.

[6]A Nash equilibrium in mixed strategies is sometimes called a *mixed strategy Nash equilibrium*, while a Nash equilibrium in pure strategies is sometimes called a *pure strategy Nash equilibrium*.

equilibrium, the mixed strategy chosen by each player is a best response to the mixed strategies chosen by the others. As it turns out, virtually all games have mixed strategy equilibria.

Take the Battle of Wits, for example.[7] Suppose Westley and Vizzini both make their choices randomly, selecting each alternative with 50 percent probability. This pair of mixed strategies is an equilibrium. To see why, first think about the problem from Westley's perspective. Suppose Vizzini drinks from each goblet with 50 percent probability. No matter which goblet Westley chooses, he receives a payoff of 1 half of the time, and -1 half of the time, so his expected payoff is zero.

$$\text{Expected payoff} = [0.5 \times 1] + [0.5 \times (-1)] = 0$$

Even if he randomizes between the goblets, his expected payoff is still zero. Selecting each goblet with 50 percent probability is therefore one of many best responses to Vizzini's mixed strategy. For exactly the same reasons, Vizzini's mixed strategy is a best response to Westley's. Since each player's mixed strategy is a best response to the other's, we have a mixed strategy equilibrium.

How to Find a Mixed Strategy Equilibrium

How do we find mixed strategy equilibria? That is, how do we know which probabilities will work? If a player is willing to decide between two alternatives based on a coin flip, he must like them equally well; otherwise he'd simply pick the one he prefers. Thus, if he chooses a mixed strategy, his opponent must be behaving in a way that makes him indifferent between the strategies over which he's randomizing. In a mixed strategy equilibrium, his opponent's probabilities are therefore chosen to make sure that he's indifferent and consequently willing to randomize, while his own probabilities are chosen to make sure that his opponent is indifferent and consequently willing to randomize.

Let's see how this works in the Battle of Wits. Let's use P to stand for the probability that Westley will poison the left goblet, in which case $1 - P$ is the probability that he will poison the right goblet. Similarly, let's use Q to stand for the probability that Vizzini will drink from the left goblet, which means that he will drink from the right goblet with a probability of $1 - Q$.

Since Westley randomizes between the left and right goblets, he must be indifferent between them. Given how Vizzini randomizes, Westley's expected payoff from poisoning the left goblet is $[Q \times 1] + [(1 - Q) \times (-1)]$, and his expected payoff from poisoning the right goblet is $[Q \times (-1)] + [(1 - Q) \times 1]$. Since he's indifferent, we know these two expressions must be equal.

$$Q - (1 - Q) = -Q + (1 - Q)$$

The only solution to this equation is $Q = \frac{1}{2}$. In other words, Westley is indifferent between the two goblets only if he thinks Vizzini is equally likely to choose either of them.

Likewise, since Vizzini randomizes between the left and right goblets, he too must be indifferent between them. Given how Westley randomizes, Vizzini's expected payoff from drinking out of the left goblet is $[P \times (-1)] + [(1 - P) \times 1]$, and his expected payoff from drinking out of the right goblet is $[P \times 1] + [(1 - P) \times (-1)]$. These expressions are equal only if $P = \frac{1}{2}$. In other words, Vizzini is indifferent between the two goblets only if he thinks Westley is equally likely to choose either of them.

---

[7]To keep the analysis simple, we'll assume here and throughout the rest of the chapter that players are risk neutral. Alternatively, we could assume that the players have expected utility functions, and that the payoffs correspond to the values of their benefit indexes rather than to dollars (see the section titled "Expected Utility" starting on page 382).

We conclude that the Battle of Wits has a single mixed strategy equilibrium. In effect, both Westley and Vizzini choose between the goblets by flipping a coin (so that both goblets are equally likely to be chosen).

Of course, this solution to the Battle of Wits assumes that cheating is impossible. In *The Princess Bride*, Westley was unwilling to trust to chance:

[Vizzini] picked up his own wine goblet.

The man in black [Westley] picked up the one in front of him.

They drank.

"You guessed wrong," said the man in black.

"You only *think* I guessed wrong," said [Vizzini], his laughter ringing louder. "That's what's so funny. I switched glasses when your back was turned . . ."

He was quite cheery until the iocane powder took effect.

The man in black stepped quickly over the corpse, then roughly ripped the blindfold from the Princess's eyes . . .

"To think," she murmured, "all that time it was your cup that was poisoned."

"They were both poisoned," said the man in black. "I've spent the past two years building up immunity to iocane powder."

IN-TEXT EXERCISE 12.4   Solve for a mixed strategy equilibrium in Rock Paper Scissors.

Application 12.3

Mixed Strategies in Sports

In most sports, predictability is a serious weakness, so contestants work hard to avoid it. In baseball, pitchers mix their pitches, alternating between fastballs, curves, and change-ups to keep batters guessing. In football, offenses set up the passing game with the running game—that is, they try to induce their opponents to defend against running plays so that passing plays will be more effective. In tennis, players vary the direction, speed, and spin of their serves so their opponents don't know what's coming. In soccer, players vary the direction of their penalty kicks so goalies won't know which way to dive.

When people make these decisions, are they in fact playing mixed strategy equilibria? How can we tell? As we've emphasized, in any mixed strategy equilibrium, players must be indifferent between the choices over which they're randomizing. In some situations, we can actually check whether this condition holds.

Take tennis. When Roger Federer serves to Rafael Nadal, each has a clear objective: win the next point. Federer can serve to the left or to the right. Nadal can prepare for a forehand return or a backhand return. Both mix up their choices to avoid becoming predictable. Could they be playing a mixed strategy equilibrium? If so, each must be indifferent toward his potential choices. That is, each choice must yield the same probability of winning the point; otherwise it would be better to pick the alternative with the highest probability of winning.

Two economists, Mark Walker and John Wooders, have tested this implication using data on 10 high-profile tennis matches between top professional players, held between 1974 and 1997.[8] Their analysis confirms the key feature of mixed strategy equilibria. While players served toward the left side of the court more frequently than toward the right (54 versus 46 percent overall), they won points with virtually the same

[8]Mark Walker and John Wooders, "Minimax Play at Wimbledon," *American Economic Review* 91, December 2001, pp. 1521–1538.

frequency, regardless of their choices (64 percent when serving to the left and 65 percent when serving to the right).[9]

The same principles apply to penalty kicks in soccer. A team of three economists, Pierre-Andre Chiappori, Steven Levitt, and Timothy Groseclose, carefully examined data on virtually every penalty kick in the elite French and Italian leagues over a three-year period, to determine if contestants were playing mixed strategy equilibria.[10] Their results confirmed the key implications of the theory. Most notably, they found that kickers scored with roughly the same frequency whether aiming at the left, right, or centre of the goal.

WORKED-OUT PROBLEM   12.2

The Problem   Dorothy and Henry are playing the one-stage game shown in Figure 12.12. Dorothy has three possible choices (left, middle, and right), as does Henry (up, middle, and down). Assume that $A = 1$, $B = 0$, $C = 6$, and $D = 3$. Find all of the Nash equilibria in pure strategies and mixed strategies.

The Solution   Focusing first on pure strategies, there are two Nash equilibria in this game: (1) Dorothy and Henry both pick middle, and (2) Dorothy picks right and Henry picks down. In each case, the choices are best responses to each other. It is easy to check that no other cell is a Nash equilibrium. For example, (up, left) isn't a Nash equilibrium because Henry and Dorothy would both switch to middle.

Are there any mixed strategy equilibria in this game? In an equilibrium, no one ever uses a dominated strategy (it's never a best response). For Henry, up is dominated by middle; for Dorothy, left is dominated by right. Henry must therefore randomize over middle and down, and Dorothy must randomize over middle and right. Let's use P to stand for the probability Henry will choose middle, and Q to stand for the probability Dorothy will choose middle. Dorothy's expected payoff from choosing middle is $7P + 1(1 - P)$, while her expected payoff from choosing right is $5P + 3(1 - P)$. Since Henry's choice of P has to make Dorothy indifferent between middle and right (so that she's willing to randomize between the two), we know that $5P + 3(1 - P) = 7P + (1 - P)$, which means that $P = \frac{1}{2}$. Henry's expected payoff from choosing middle is $8Q + 5(1 - Q)$, while his expected payoff from choosing down is $4Q + 6(1 - Q)$. Since Dorothy's choice of Q has to make Henry indifferent between middle and down (so that he's willing to randomize between the two), we know that $8Q + 5(1 - Q) = 4Q + 6(1 - Q)$, which means that $Q = \frac{1}{5}$. The following is therefore a mixed strategy equilibrium: Henry chooses middle and down with 50 percent probability each (since $P = \frac{1}{2}$); Dorothy chooses middle with 20 percent probability and right with 80 percent probability (since $Q = \frac{1}{5}$).

IN-TEXT EXERCISE 12.5   **Repeat worked-out problem 12.2 using these values: $A = 3$, $B = 1$, $C = 4$, and $D = 0$.**

---

[9]The data do not match the theory in all respects. Most servers change from left to right too frequently, making their choices somewhat predictable.

[10]Pierre-Andre Chiappori, Steven Levitt, and Timothy Groseclose, "Testing Mixed-Strategy Equilibria When Players are Heterogeneous: The Case of Penalty Kicks in Soccer," *American Economic Review* 92, September 2002, pp. 1138–1151.

Figure 12.12

Worked-Out Problem 12.2. This table contains a column for each of Dorothy's choices (left, middle, and right) and a row for each of Henry's (up, middle, and down). The number in the southwest half of each cell is Henry's; the one in the northeast half is Dorothy's.

Reinhard Selten (1930–), who shared the Nobel Prize in Economics with John Nash, pioneered the study of credible behaviour in multiple-stage games.

In a game with **perfect information** players make their choices one at time, and nothing is hidden from any player.

12.4 GAMES WITH MULTIPLE STAGES

In most strategic settings, events unfold over time, and actions can provoke responses and counter-responses. Even the simplest recreational games, like tic-tac-toe, have this feature. Clearly, then, we need to move beyond one-stage games. In this section, we provide an introduction to games with multiple stages. We focus on two important issues: how to recognize whether threats are credible, and how to establish and sustain cooperation between people with conflicting interests. To learn more about multiple-stage games, read Add-On 12A.

Credible Threats in Games with Perfect Information

How might you discourage someone from taking an action that's harmful to you? One possibility is to issue a threat. In other words, you could promise to deliver damaging consequences in return. Some threats are believable and effective, while others are empty and ineffective. What makes a threat credible?

In this section, we'll study the credibility of threats in simple multiple-stage games with **perfect information**. A game falls into this category if players make their choices one at time, and nothing is hidden from any player. Tic-tac-toe and chess are good examples of such games. Rock Paper Scissors is *not* a game of perfect information because the players make their choices at the same time. Neither is poker, because some information is hidden from each player—for example, which cards other players are dealt, and which ones they discard. To learn how to identify credible threats in more elaborate multiple-stage games, read Add-On 12A.

Describing a Game with Perfect Information   The simplest way to describe a multiple-stage game of perfect information is to draw a tree diagram that identifies the players and shows every possible sequence of decisions, along with the resulting payoffs. To illustrate this procedure, let's consider an example.

Figure 12.13

The Lopsided Battle of the Sexes. This tree diagram describes a version of the Battle of the Sexes in which Tony chooses first and Maria learns what he did before making her own choice. Solving the game by reasoning in reverse, we identify the best choice (indicated by a green arrow) at each point. Our analysis tells us that Tony will choose the action-adventure film, and Maria will follow him wherever he goes.

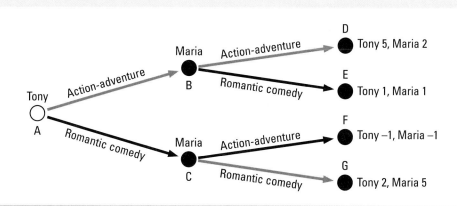

Earlier, we introduced a one-stage game called the Battle of the Sexes (see Example 12.6, page 418). We can turn the Battle of the Sexes into a two-stage game with perfect information by making one small change. We'll assume that Tony chooses a film before Maria, and that Maria learns what he chose before making her own decision (perhaps because he leaves her a note). For reasons that will become clear, we'll call this game the Lopsided Battle of the Sexes.

Figure 12.13 represents the Lopsided Battle of the Sexes graphically. The figure looks a bit like a tree turned on its side, growing from the left to the right. The tree is constructed from points and arrows. For the moment, ignore the fact that some arrows are black and some are green; we will explain the significance of these colours below. There is one unfilled point, labelled A. That's where the game starts. Tony's name appears next to point A because he chooses first. Two arrows run from point A, one for each of Tony's alternatives. The one labelled "action-adventure" ends at point B; the one labelled "romantic comedy" ends at point C. Maria's name appears next to points B and C, which means that she chooses next.

Two arrows, representing Maria's two alternatives should Tony pick the action-adventure film, run from point B. Two more arrows, representing Maria's two alternatives should Tony pick the romantic comedy, run from point C.[11] These four arrows end at the points D, E, F, and G. Tony and Maria's payoffs appear next to those points. So, for example, if Tony goes to the action-adventure film and Maria follows, play will progress from point A to point B to point D; Tony's payoff will be 5 and Maria's will be 2.

Figure 12.13 is a complete description of the Lopsided Battle of the Sexes. It identifies the players (Tony and Maria), all the possible sequences of decisions (paths from point A to point D, E, F, or G), and each player's objectives (payoffs). Everything we need to know about the game is contained in that figure.

---

[11]In this game, Maria's alternatives do not depend on Tony's choice. In other games, the choices of one player may affect the alternatives available to another player.

Thinking Strategically in a Game with Perfect Information   How should Tony go about making his decision in the Lopsided Battle of the Sexes? Clearly, his best choice depends on how he expects Maria to behave. Suppose for the moment that Maria phones Tony before the game starts and says, "You can watch whatever film you want, but I'm going to the romantic comedy no matter what." Then she hangs up without allowing Tony to reply. Tony would rather watch the romantic comedy with Maria than see the action-adventure film alone, so if he believes Maria's threat, he'll pick the romantic comedy. The question is, should he believe her?

To think strategically in a game with perfect information, a player should reason in *reverse*, starting at the *end* of the tree diagram and working back to the beginning. Why? Even before deciding what to do, an early mover (like Tony) can figure out how a late mover (like Maria) will *react* if actually confronted with a situation. Knowing those reactions, the early mover can then identify the best choice. The process of solving a strategic problem by reasoning in reverse is known as **backward induction**.

Backward induction is the process of solving a strategic problem by reasoning in reverse, starting at the end of the tree diagram that represents the game, and working back to the beginning.

Let's use this technique to solve the Lopsided Battle of the Sexes. We'll start by determining Maria's reaction to each of Tony's possible choices. In Figure 12.13, we've used green arrows to indicate those reactions. First suppose Tony chooses the action-adventure film, placing Maria at point B. If Maria chooses the action-adventure film, her payoff will be 2 (at point D); if she chooses the romantic comedy, it will be 1 (at point E). The action-adventure film is a better choice. That is why the arrow that runs from point B to point D in Figure 12.13 is coloured green. Next suppose Tony chooses the romantic comedy, placing Maria at point C. Here, the romantic comedy is Maria's better choice; it gives her a payoff of 5 (at point G), rather than -1 (at point F). That is why the arrow running from point C to point G in Figure 12.13 is coloured green. As the figure shows, Maria will react to Tony's choices by following him wherever he goes.

Having determined Maria's reactions, let's turn to Tony's choice. Taking Maria's reactions into account, Tony knows he can achieve a payoff of 5 by choosing the action-adventure film (since this will lead to point D), versus a payoff of 2 by choosing the romantic comedy (since this will lead to point G). We've used a green arrow to show that the action-adventure film is Tony's best choice.

We conclude that Tony will go the action-adventure film and that Maria will follow him wherever he goes. Even if Maria has threatened to see the romantic comedy "no matter what," she'll recognize that she can't change Tony's decision after the fact. If Tony calls Maria's bluff by going to the action-adventure film, she won't follow through on her threat, because she prefers to be with him. Knowing that, Tony will ignore the threat and count on Maria to act in her own interest when the time comes.

At this point, you're probably thinking of reasons why Maria might follow through on her threat. For example, she might be concerned that if she gives in, Tony will take advantage of her in the future. That's a valid point, but it doesn't mean that our analysis of the game is wrong. Rather, it means that the game is too simple to capture many aspects of real relationships. Most significantly, in this game there is no future. To think about what Maria might do in a relationship with a future, we'd have to consider a more elaborate game.

Nash Equilibria in a Game with Perfect Information   The concept of Nash equilibrium that we introduced in Section 12.3 applies equally well to single-stage and multiple-stage games. In fact, as we'll explain in this section, the behaviour described in the previous section is a Nash equilibrium.

Before applying the concept of Nash equilibrium to a multiple-stage game, we first have to clarify the meaning of the word *strategy*. In game theory, a **strategy** is one player's detailed plan for playing the game. For every situation that might come up during the course of play, it tells us what the player will do. In a one-stage game, a strategy simply indicates a player's chosen action. But in a multiple-stage game, a strategy can prescribe different actions depending on what a player observes.

How would we describe the players' strategies in the Lopsided Battle of the Sexes? Since Tony chooses first, his strategy simply tells us what he chooses—either the action-adventure film, or the romantic comedy. What about Maria? Since she chooses second, two situations can come up during the course of play: either she'll learn that Tony has chosen the action-adventure film, or she will learn that Tony has chosen the romantic comedy. A strategy indicates what she will choose in each of these situations. For example, the following rule is a strategy:

> If Tony chooses the action-adventure film, then choose the action-adventure film. If Tony chooses the romantic comedy, then choose the action-adventure film.

Altogether, Maria has four strategies to choose from. Here are the other three:

> If Tony chooses the action-adventure film, then choose the action-adventure film. If Tony chooses the romantic comedy, then choose the romantic comedy.

> If Tony chooses the action-adventure film, then choose the romantic comedy. If Tony chooses the romantic comedy, then choose the action-adventure film.

> If Tony chooses the action-adventure film, then choose the romantic comedy. If Tony chooses the romantic comedy, then choose the romantic comedy.

A Nash equilibrium for the Lopsided Battle of the Sexes consists of a pair of strategies, one for Tony and one for Maria, such that Tony's strategy is a best response to Maria's and Maria's is a best response to Tony's. In the previous section, we concluded that Tony and Maria will play according to the following strategies:

Tony's strategy: Choose the action-adventure film.

Maria's strategy: If Tony chooses the action-adventure film, then choose the action-adventure film. If Tony chooses the romantic comedy, then choose the romantic comedy.

In other words, Tony picks his favourite film, knowing that Maria will follow him wherever he goes. As it turns out, this pair of strategies is a Nash equilibrium.

Let's check that each player's strategy in this equilibrium is a best response to the other's. We'll start with Tony. Knowing that Maria will follow him wherever he goes, Tony is clearly better off choosing the action-adventure film. Therefore, Tony's strategy is a best response to Maria's.

Is Maria's strategy a best response to Tony's? As we've seen, a strategy tells Maria what to do in two situations: when Tony chooses the action-adventure film, and when Tony chooses the romantic comedy. From Tony's equilibrium strategy, Maria knows that the first situation will definitely come up (that is, Tony will choose the action-adventure film). Therefore, if she changes her choice in the first situation from the action-adventure film to the romantic comedy, she'll be worse off—her payoff will be 1 instead of 2. From Tony's equilibrium strategy, Maria also knows that the second situation definitely won't come up (that is, Tony won't choose the romantic comedy). Therefore, if she changes her

A **strategy** is one player's detailed plan for playing a game. For every situation that might come up during the course of play, it tells us what the player will do.

choice in the second situation from the romantic comedy to the action-adventure film, she'll be neither better off nor worse off. Because no change in Maria's strategy would make her better off, her strategy is a best response to Tony's. Since Tony's strategy is also a best response to Maria's, these strategies form a Nash equilibrium.

For a game with perfect information, we can *always* find a Nash equilibrium by reasoning in reverse, as in the previous section. As it turns out, this needn't be the game's only Nash equilibrium. In fact, for the Lopsided Battle of the Sexes, there are other equilibria. However, by reasoning in reverse, we always identify the most reasonable equilibrium—one in which no one makes the mistake of believing a threat that isn't credible. For an explanation of this point, read Add-On 12A.

Sometimes, games of perfect information are simply too complicated to solve by reasoning in reverse. Chess is a good example. Using powerful supercomputers, chess enthusiasts have applied the approach outlined here to solve endgames involving relatively few pieces. However, the number of possible configurations explodes exponentially as the number of pieces increases. While in principle it is possible to solve chess, no one has yet solved it in practice.

Even so, by solving simple games of perfect information in reverse, we can gain a great deal of practical insight into credible strategic behaviour. Application 12.4 provides an illustration.

Application 12.4

British Satellite Broadcasting versus Sky Television

Until recently, television was a relatively staid affair in Great Britain. In 1988, British consumers were limited to four stations, two of them government-operated through the British Broadcasting Corporation. Cable TV was available to only two percent of households in the United Kingdom, compared with 60 percent in the United States.

Drawn by the opportunities associated with this virtually untapped market, a company called British Satellite Broadcasting (BSB) began developing plans to provide British consumers with satellite TV service. Then, in June 1988, the Australian media mogul Rupert Murdoch announced that his company, Sky Television, would follow suit.[12]

Unfortunately, as the two companies recognized, the market wasn't big enough for both of them. Unless one exited, neither would be able to cover the necessary costs. But which one would go, and how long would the shakeout take? Could Murdoch drive BSB from the market by credibly threatening to stick around at all costs? Could BSB credibly confront Sky with the same threat? Economists call this type of competition a *war of attrition*—a situation in which two rivals incur losses until one concedes, after which the survivor becomes profitable.

The two firms were in rather different positions. BSB planned to use a superior technology, and as a result projected higher costs and longer delays before launching its service, drawbacks that provided Sky Television with an edge. Table 12.1 displays the estimated profits and losses for both companies. As we saw in Chapter 10, investment decisions should depend on the net present value (NPV) of anticipated profits. The last column in the top half of the table shows the NPV of the profits each company expected to earn with the other as a competitor (losses of £747 million for BSB and losses of £117 million for Sky). The last column in the bottom half shows the NPV of the profits each expected to earn without a competitor (£137 million for BSB and £673 million for Sky). The table also shows the flow of profits and losses broken down between two periods, 1989–90 and after 1990. For example, without a competitor, Sky would lose £356 million in 1989–90, but would earn £1029 million afterward, for a total gain of £673 million.

[12]This application is based on the Harvard Business School Case "Sky Television versus British Satellite Broadcasting" # 9-792-039. See also www.vintagebroadcasting.org.uk/bsb.htm and www.museum.tv/archives/etv/B/htmlB/britishskyb/britishskyb/htm.

Table 12.1

British Satellite Broadcasting versus Sky Television

	1989–90	After 1990	All years
NPV of profits (million £) with competitor present			
BSB	−637	−110	−747
Sky	−363	246	−117
NPV of profits (million £) with no competitor			
BSB	−595	732	137
Sky	−356	1029	673

Figure 12.14 represents the conflict between BSB and Sky as a multiple-stage game with perfect information. For the moment, ignore the fact that some arrows are black and others are green. Notice that a broken vertical line divides the tree diagram into two halves. Decisions to the left of this line took place in 1989; decisions to the right of it took place in 1991. In 1989, each firm had to decide whether to stay in the market or exit. We assume here that BSB went first, and Sky observed its choice. In 1991, the remaining firm or firms once again had to decide whether to stay or exit. If both were still active at the start of 1991, BSB would have once again moved first, and Sky would have observed its choice.

Figure 12.14

British Satellite Broadcasting versus Sky Television. This figure represents the competition between BSB and Sky as a multiple-stage game with perfect information. Solving the game by reasoning in reverse, we identify the best choice (indicated by a green arrow) at each point. Our analysis tells us that BSB should exit in 1989 after which Sky can operate profitably as the only provider of satellite TV service in Britain.

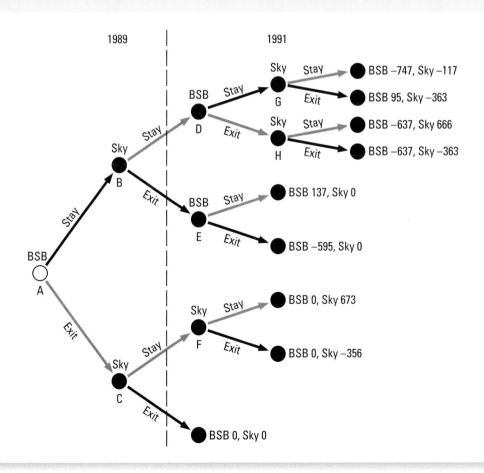

We've computed the payoffs based on the data in Table 12.1; BSB's payoff appears first and Sky's second. For example, if BSB survived until 1991 but then dropped out, while Sky stayed in the market through the end of the game, BSB's payoff would be −£637 million (it would lose that amount competing against Sky in 1989–90), while Sky's payoff would be £666 million (it would lose £363 million competing against BSB in 1989–90 but earn £1029 million after 1990).

We can identify credible strategies by solving this game in reverse. We'll use green arrows to indicate best choices at each point in the game. Let's start with Sky's decision in 1991. At point G, Sky will choose to stay, earning a payoff of −£117 million, compared to −£363 million if it exits. Sky will also choose to stay at points H (£666 million exceeds −£363 million) and F (£673 million exceeds −£356 million). In other words, having reached 1991, Sky will stay in the market regardless of whether BSB stays or exits. These decisions are shown by the green arrows.

Next, let's look at BSB's decision in 1991. Taking Sky's choices at points G and H into account, we see that BSB will choose to exit at point D (−£637 million exceeds −£747 million). In contrast, BSB will choose to stay at point E (£137 million exceeds −£595 million). In other words, having reached 1991, BSB will drop out if Sky is still around, but will stay if Sky has exited. Again, these decisions are shown by the green arrows.

Now let's turn to 1989. We'll start with Sky's decision at point B. In light of BSB's choices at points D and E, as well as Sky's own choices at points G and H, Sky should stay in the market (£666 million exceeds zero). Sky knows that if it stays in, BSB will drop out. Similarly, at point C, Sky will anticipate its own choice at point F and choose to stay (£673 million exceeds zero). In other words, in 1989 as in 1991, Sky will stay in the market regardless of BSB's decision. Again, these decisions are shown by the green arrows.

Finally, we come to BSB's initial choice at point A. In light of everything we've learned about the firms' subsequent decisions, the best choice here is to exit and accept a payoff of zero (as shown by the green arrow running from point A to point C). If instead BSB remains in the market, Sky will stay, forcing BSB to exit in 1991, with a loss of £637 million.

By reasoning in reverse, we've arrived at a sensible Nash equilibrium. Our analysis tells us that BSB should have exited in 1989, and that Sky should have operated profitably as the only provider of satellite TV services in Britain. A threat by Sky to stay in the market regardless of BSB's choices was credible, but a threat by BSB to stick around regardless of Sky's choices was not.

What actually happened? As we predicted, Sky was the eventual winner in this competition. To avoid serious losses, the two companies merged in November 1990, forming British Sky Broadcasting with Murdoch in control. The next year, Murdoch effectively shut down BSB, firing its staff and selling its satellites.[13]

WORKED-OUT PROBLEM   12.3

The Problem   Agatha challenges Danielle to a game of matchsticks (which some readers may recognize as a simplified version of Nim). The game begins with four matchsticks in a pile; the players take turns removing them from the pile. On each turn they must remove either one or two matchsticks. The player who removes the last stick wins and receives one dollar from the loser. Danielle has the first move. Illustrate this game by drawing a tree and solve it by reasoning in reverse.

The Solution   The tree for this game appears in Figure 12.15. We can solve it by reasoning in reverse, using green arrows to indicate the best choices at each point in the game. There is no decision to make at points E, F, or G—only one stick remains, so the next player to move must take it and win. At point D, two sticks are left, and Danielle wins by taking both of them. The same is true for Agatha at point C. At point

---

[13]BSB's departure didn't occur quite as quickly as our analysis led us to expect. Uncertainty about the market's potential and BSB's own competitive position probably caused executives to keep it afloat a bit longer, in hopes of a better outcome.

B, with three sticks left, Agatha doesn't care whether she takes one or two sticks; in light of Danielle's decision at point D, Agatha will lose in either case, so both are best choices. Taking all this into account, Danielle knows that at point A, she'll win if she takes one matchstick, but lose if she takes two. She therefore takes one.

IN-TEXT EXERCISE 12.6   **Repeat worked-out problem 12.3, changing the rules as follows. To begin, there are six matchsticks in the pile. At each turn a player can remove one, two, or three matchsticks.**

Cooperation in Repeated Games

Why do people make personal sacrifices to help others? Altruism certainly plays a role; sometimes we help people we like or for whom we feel compassion. But in other situations we recognize the benefits of mutual cooperation and help people out of self-interest.

Cooperation is usually sustained by the threat of a punishment for bad behaviour or the promise of a reward for good behaviour. Efforts to establish cooperation will fail

Nobel Laureate Robert Aumann (1930–) pioneered the study of cooperation and conflict in repeated games.

Figure 12.15

A Game of Matchsticks. This figure represents the game of matchsticks described in worked-out problem 12.3. At the start, there are four matchsticks in a pile; players take turns removing either one or two of them on each turn. The player to take the last stick wins one dollar from the loser. Solving the game by reasoning in reverse, we identify the best choices (indicated by green arrows) at each point. Our analysis tells us that Danielle should start the game by taking one stick. Regardless of whether Agatha responds by taking one or two sticks, Danielle can then take all that remain.

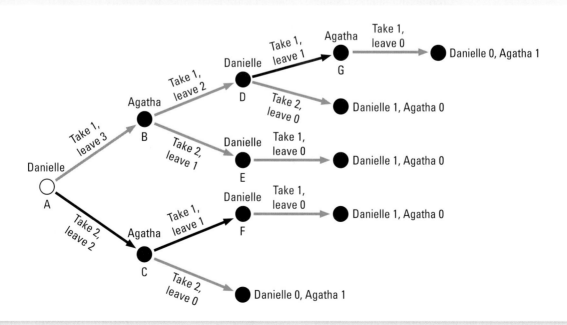

Figure 12.16

The Spouses' Dilemma. Marge and Homer simultaneously choose to clean the house or loaf. According to this table, both prefer loafing to cleaning, regardless of what the other chooses. However, when one of them cleans the house, the other is happier. Moreover, they are better off if both clean than if both loaf.

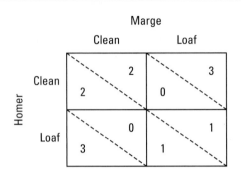

unless those threats and promises are credible. To illustrate this point, we'll study an example involving a married couple, Marge and Homer. On any given day, each can choose to either clean the house or loaf. Figure 12.16 shows their payoffs for that day. Notice that both prefer loafing to cleaning, regardless of what the other chooses. However, when one of them cleans the house, the other is happier. Moreover, they are better off if both clean than if both loaf.

Let's consider a one-stage game in which Marge and Homer simultaneously choose between cleaning and loafing on a single day. This game is a variant of the Prisoners' Dilemma (Figure 12.2, page 410); we'll call it the Spouses' Dilemma. Because loafing is a dominant strategy for both spouses, no one cleans, and each receives a payoff of 1. If Marge and Homer could cooperate and clean the house together, both would be happier. But neither has a reason to cooperate in the one-stage game.

Marriage is not, however, a one-stage game. (If you think it is, we recommend remaining single.) Spouses interact with each other repeatedly through time. They have ample opportunity to reward each other for considerate choices and punish each other for inconsiderate choices. Those opportunities foster cooperation.

To see how cooperation can emerge in a multiple-stage game, let's suppose that Marge and Homer play the Spouses' Dilemma repeatedly; each day, they simultaneously choose to clean or loaf. This is an example of a **repeated game**, one that's formed by playing a simpler game many times in succession. In some contexts, economists study games that are repeated a fixed number of times, and then end. These settings are known as **finitely repeated games**. In other contexts, economists study **infinitely repeated games**, in which the repetitions can continue indefinitely. When economists model strategic problems as infinitely repeated games, they don't literally mean that the players will interact with each other until the end of time. Rather, they simply mean that there isn't a known, fixed point in time at which the players will stop interacting with each other; instead, there is always a possibility of further interaction.

A Nash equilibrium in a repeated Spouses' Dilemma game is a pair of strategies, one for Marge and one for Homer, such that Marge's strategy is a best response to Homer's and Homer's is a best response to Marge's. As before, a strategy tells us what a player will do for every situation that might come up during the course of play. *Always clean* is a strategy. So is *loaf if my spouse loafed yesterday, otherwise clean*. In fact, any rule that specifies a choice based on the history of past choices can serve as a strategy.

A **repeated game** is formed by playing a simpler game many times in succession.

A **finitely repeated game** is formed by repeating a simpler game a fixed number of times, after which the game ends.

An **infinitely repeated game** is formed by repeating a simpler game indefinitely.

An Equilibrium without Cooperation   When a one-stage game is repeated, it's always possible that the participants will simply play the equilibrium of the one-stage game over and over. In fact, that method of playing is always a Nash equilibrium for the repeated game, regardless of whether the game is finitely or infinitely repeated.

We'll illustrate this point in the context of the Spouses' Dilemma. Without repetitions, the only Nash equilibrium in this game is for Marge and Homer to loaf. Consequently, there is a Nash equilibrium for the repeated Spouses' Dilemma in which Marge and Homer both choose the strategy, always loaf. If Homer chooses that strategy, then always loaf is a best response for Marge. Why? On any given day, loafing will give her a higher payoff than cleaning, and her choice won't affect Homer's future behaviour. For the same reason, if Marge chooses the strategy always loaf, then always loaf is a best response for Homer. This equilibrium involves no cooperation.

In a finitely repeated Spouses' Dilemma, there is no other reasonable equilibrium. The players can't cooperate because threats of punishment and promises of reward aren't credible. Suppose, for example, that Marge and Homer plan to part ways after 100 days. To determine what they will do, we reason in reverse, starting from the end of the game. On the last day, they'll both know that they have no future together. Since neither will have a chance to reward or punish the other, both will loaf. On the second-to-last day, they'll both know that they have one day left together, and that they'll spend it loafing. Since neither will choose to reward or punish the other when the final day arrives, both will loaf on the second-to-last day. On the third-to-last day, they'll both know that they have two days left together, and that they'll spend both days loafing. Since neither will choose to reward or punish the other when those final days arrive, both will loaf on the third-to-last day. Reasoning in this manner, we reach the conclusion that Homer and Marge will loaf every day. The same conclusion follows regardless of whether they plan to part after 10 days, 100 days, or 10,000 days. Any definite stopping point causes cooperation to unravel.

Equilibria with Cooperation   Can Marge and Homer manage to cooperate if the game has no fixed stopping point? As long as they care enough about the future, the answer is yes. One relatively simple possibility is to use strategies that threaten *permanent* punishment for selfish behaviour, also known as **grim strategies**. For the infinitely repeated Spouses' Dilemma, we'll examine the following grim strategies (one for Homer, one for Marge):

> Clean on the first day. On subsequent days, clean as long as my spouse and I have an unbroken history of cleaning on every previous day; otherwise loaf.

What happens when Marge and Homer both play these strategies? Obviously, they both clean on the first day. That means they will have an unbroken history of cleaning at the start of the second day, so they'll both clean again. The same thing happens at the start of the third day, and so forth. In other words, the couple will clean every day. However, if one of them ever departs from that plan and loafs, their history of cleaning will be broken, and neither will ever clean again. In that sense, the punishment for loafing is permanent.

Assuming Marge and Homer use these strategies, will either be tempted to loaf? Suppose they have an unbroken history of cleaning. According to their strategies, both are supposed to clean, receiving a payoff of 2 in every period moving forward. But what if Homer decides to loaf? He'll increase his payoff to 3 for one day, but at a cost. Marge's strategy will tell her to retaliate by loafing on all subsequent days, reducing Homer's best available payoff from 2 to 1. Therefore, if Homer cares enough about his future

With **grim strategies**, the punishment for selfish behaviour is permanent.

interactions with Marge, he'll clean. Marge will reason the same way. Accordingly, we have a Nash equilibrium in which the threat of a punishment—mutual loafing—causes Homer and Marge to cooperate.

Does the equilibrium described in the last two paragraphs involve credible threats? The answer is yes. Suppose either Homer or Marge has loafed, setting off the punishment. In that case, according to their strategies, each will always loaf in the future, no matter what the other does. If Homer thinks Marge will follow this strategy, his best choice is to loaf, and vice versa. Consequently, each of them has incentive to follow through with the punishment.

The fact that Marge and Homer *can* cooperate doesn't mean that they *will* cooperate. Remember that there is also an equilibrium in which they both always loaf. But let's suppose that Marge and Homer can discuss their strategies before playing. In that case, we can interpret Nash equilibria as self-enforcing agreements. Marge and Homer have a mutual interest in reaching an agreement that produces cooperation. Therefore, they are likely to play a cooperative equilibrium.

Even so, Marge and Homer may not agree upon the cooperative equilibrium described above. In practice, the use of grim strategies is potentially risky. If the players have a misunderstanding—for example, if Marge becomes convinced that Homer has loafed, even though he has cleaned—cooperation can fall apart forever. For that reason, it may be better to reach a self-enforcing agreement that relies on *temporary* punishments. Homer and Marge might, for example, use strategies that tell them to punish selfish choices by loafing for a few days, and then to start cleaning again. Those strategies are less risky than grim strategies (in the sense that misunderstandings will only have temporary consequences), but they're also less powerful. The less Homer and Marge care about the future, the longer punishments must last to deter selfish choices.

Application 12.5

A Crude Cartel

Worldwide, the uneven geographic distribution of crude oil deposits has had a profound effect on the economic and political landscape. For countries with abundant petroleum resources, oil represents a critical source of wealth and economic prosperity. These exporters of petroleum have a strong interest in maintaining high oil prices, which creates conflict with nations that depend on imported oil.

Maintaining high oil prices is a challenging objective, however. Since the worldwide demand curve for oil is downward sloping, high prices require low output. But why should any single oil-exporting country restrict its production? Though the price of oil will go up, other oil exporters will reap much of the benefit, as they continue producing at high levels. In other words, even though all oil exporters would benefit if they reduced production, each may lack the incentive to do so unilaterally.

The simple one-stage game shown in Figure 12.17 captures the essence of the oil exporters' quandary. Let's focus on two large exporters, Saudi Arabia and Iran, ignoring other sources for the sake of simplicity. Each country has two strategies, a low production level and a high one. High production corresponds roughly to actual levels in 2004; nine million barrels per day (bbl/day) for Saudi Arabia and four million bbl/day for Iran. Low production represents a 10 percent reduction, to 8.1 million bbl/day for Saudi Arabia and 3.6 million bbl/day for Iran. The figure includes a column for each of Saudi Arabia's choices and a row for each of

Iran's. The number in the northeast half of each cell shows Saudi Arabia's profit from the corresponding strategies; the number in the southwest half of each cell is Iran's profit.[14]

According to these figures, both countries will be better off if they both choose low production than if they both choose high production. (profits will rise from $135 to $138 million per day for Saudi Arabia and from $60 to $61 million per day for Iran.) The resulting price increase will more than compensate for the reduction in volume.

Nevertheless, each country will unilaterally choose high production. Why? In Figure 12.17, we have used green shading to indicate Iran's best responses, and red shading to indicate Saudi Arabia's. Notice that high production is a dominant strategy for both countries. For Iran, cutting production will reduce profit regardless of the Saudi production level. The price increase resulting from low production will not be enough to compensate Iran for the loss of volume, because Iran is ignoring the benefits to the Saudis. Similar reasoning applies to Saudi Arabia, though the numbers differ. In short, this game has essentially the same structure as the Prisoners' Dilemma (Figure 12.2, page 410) and the Spouses' Dilemma (Figure 12.16, page 436).

In practice, of course, Saudi Arabia and Iran don't play a one-stage game. They produce and sell oil month after month, year after year. Let's suppose they play the game in Figure 12.17 repeatedly. Can they achieve a more profitable outcome through cooperation? Our discussion of the Spouses' Dilemma suggests that they can, as long as they attach sufficient importance to their future interaction. In a cooperative Nash equilibrium, each will begin by choosing low production and will continue to do so unless one of them "cheats" by choosing high production. At that point, both will switch to high production. Though cheating increases current profits, it draws retaliation, which reduces future profits. Fear of retaliation keeps both countries in line.

What have oil-rich countries done in the past? In 1960, Iran, Iraq, Kuwait, Saudi Arabia, and Venezuela formed the Organization of Petroleum Exporting Countries (OPEC). Their object was to agree on mutually beneficial prices and production levels. Since then, they've been joined by six other countries—Algeria, Indonesia, Libya, Nigeria, Qatar, and the United Arab Emirates.

OPEC's efforts to maximize its members' profits have met with mixed success. The organization sets voluntary production targets (quotas) for its members, but compliance is imperfect. In the 1970s, oil exporters worked in concert to increase prices tenfold, precipitating an economic crisis in western countries. However, the high prices proved impossible to sustain. Cheating exploded during the second half of the 1980s, with actual production exceeding total quotas by as much as 25 percent. Oil prices plummeted, eliminating most of the gains from the 1970s. By the end of 1990, cheating on quotas subsided, but only because OPEC, acknowledging the inevitable, had allowed quotas to increase in 1989. Even so, most studies suggest that OPEC has been at least moderately successful at maintaining prices above levels that would otherwise prevail.

OPEC's chequered record illustrates the difficulties that people, companies, and countries encounter when they attempt to cooperate. Cooperation necessarily creates the temptation to cheat. When that temptation is sufficiently strong, a mutually beneficial course of action is unsustainable.

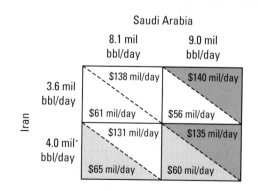

Figure 12.17

Cooperation among OPEC Nations. This game represents the interaction between oil producers Saudi Arabia and Iran as a Prisoners' Dilemma. Each nation chooses either low or high oil production. As the green shading indicates, high production is a dominant strategy for Iran. And as the red shading indicates, high production is a dominant strategy for Saudi Arabia. Yet if both chose low production, both would be better off. If both nations interact repeatedly and care enough about their future interaction, they can cooperate.

---

[14]We've assumed that the cost of production is $15 per barrel and that oil sells for $30 per barrel at high production levels (for a profit margin of $15 per barrel). Lower production raises prices and therefore profit margins. The price of oil rises by $1.2 per barrel when Saudi Arabia reduces production unilaterally; by $0.5 per barrel when Iran reduces production unilaterally; and by $1.9 per barrel when both countries reduce production at the same time.

John Harsanyi (1920–), who shared the Nobel Prize in Economics with John Nash and Reinhard Selten, pioneered the study of games in which at least one party is uncertain about another's preferences, and consequently its objectives.

*12.5 GAMES IN WHICH DIFFERENT PEOPLE HAVE DIFFERENT INFORMATION

In many strategic settings, people have difficulty predicting each others' choices because they don't share the same information. For example, when someone negotiates the price of a used car, the potential buyer typically knows less than the seller about the car's quality. When a new company enters a market, it usually has limited information about the production costs of existing firms. And when the leaders of two countries find themselves at odds, each may be unsure of the other's willingness to risk war.

Games in which different people have different information fall into two broad categories. The first category involves situations, such as the first two examples in the previous paragraph, in which objective information is available to one party, but not to another. The second category involves situations, such as the last example in the previous paragraph, in which at least one party is uncertain about another's preferences and objectives.[15]

When people have different information, whether about objective facts or about preferences, their choices can reveal something about what they know. Two important points follow. First, each participant in a game can potentially learn important information from the behaviour of other participants. Second, when participants know that others are trying to learn from their choices, they may have an incentive to mislead others by acting contrary to their immediate interests. We will illustrate the first point by describing a phenomenon known as *the winner's curse*, and the second point by discussing the creation and maintenance of reputations.

The Winner's Curse

Olivia attends an automobile auction in the hope of purchasing a used car at a low price. After carefully examining a 2000 Ford Mustang convertible, she feels reasonably confident that the car is in good shape and worth at least $10,000, its Blue Book value. To her surprise, she comes out on top with a winning bid of $6000. Her first reaction is delight. Her second reaction: what's wrong with the car?

Olivia's experience illustrates the principle that, in certain types of auctions, unsophisticated bidders tend to overpay whenever they win. This phenomenon, known as the **winner's curse**, potentially arises whenever the item's commonly perceived value depends on information that may become available to some but not all bidders. For example, in an automobile auction, some bidders may discover a mechanical problem that others overlook. Because the winner will tend to be a bidder who overlooked the problem, the winning bid will often be too high.

A sophisticated bidder—even one who potentially overlooks pertinent information—needn't fall prey to the winner's curse. For example, before bidding $6000 for the Mustang, Olivia should ask herself: "If no one bids more than $6000, does this mean they've noticed something that I've overlooked? If so, is the car really worth $6000?"

The **winner's curse** is the tendency, in certain types of auctions, for unsophisticated bidders to overpay whenever they win.

---

[15]Games in the second category are known as *games of incomplete information*.

In other words, to avoid overpaying, Olivia should try to figure out what winning at any given price would imply about what others know. The following example shows how this is done.

Example 12.7

The Winner's Curse in a Second-Price Auction

A Ford Mustang is offered for sale through a second-price auction. There are three bidders, Melissa, Olivia, and Elvis. There's a 50 percent chance that the car has a serious mechanical problem, in which case it's worth $2000 to all bidders, and a 50 percent chance that it's problem-free, in which case it's worth $10,000. Melissa has had an opportunity to inspect the car and knows whether or not it has a problem. Olivia and Elvis have had no such opportunity. Given their uncertainty, they are willing to pay only $6000.

In this game, a strategy for Melissa must specify one bid if the car has a problem and another if it's problem-free. A strategy for Olivia or Elvis simply specifies a single bid.

For the same reasons as in Application 12.1 (page 416), each participant should bid whatever he or she thinks the car is worth. Because Melissa is fully informed, her best strategy is to bid $2000 if the car has a problem and $10,000 if it's problem-free. If neither Olivia nor Elvis accounts for the winner's curse, each will naively bid $6000. Because the second highest bid will be $6000 regardless of Melissa's bid, the car will sell for $6000. When it is problem-free, Melissa will win and underpay for it. When it has a problem, either Olivia or Elvis will win and overpay for it.

To avoid the winner's curse, Olivia and Elvis must become more sophisticated. In light of Melissa's strategy, no bid between $2000 and $10,000 can possibly win if the car is problem-free. Therefore, Olivia and Elvis both know that if they win with such a bid, the car will be worth only $2000—in other words, less than their bid.

Suppose Olivia and Elvis bid $2000 instead of $6000, and Melissa bids as described above. That combination of strategies is a Nash equilibrium. When the car has a problem, all three participants bid $2000. The car sells for $2000, the buyer is selected at random, and everyone's net payoff is zero. When the car is problem-free, Melissa bids $10,000 while Olivia and Elvis bid $2000. Melissa buys the car for $2000 and receives a net payoff of $8000. The payoff to Olivia and Elvis is again zero.

To confirm that this is a Nash equilibrium, let's make sure that no participant can do better. No matter what Olivia bids, she will either win or lose. If she loses, her payoff will be zero. If she wins, the second highest bid will necessarily be $2000 if the car has a problem, and $10,000 if it's problem-free (given the strategies used by Elvis and Melissa). In either case, she will pay exactly what the car is worth and receive a net payoff of zero. Therefore, Olivia can't improve on her equilibrium payoff. The same reasoning applies to Elvis. What about Melissa? If she loses, her payoff will be zero. If she wins, the second highest bid will necessarily be $2000 whether or not the car has a problem. Therefore, her net payoff cannot exceed zero when the car has a problem and $8000 when it's problem free. Since this is what she receives in equilibrium, Melissa can't improve on her equilibrium payoff.

By avoiding the winner's curse, Olivia and Elvis achieve better results. Notice that Melissa benefits from their sophistication: when the car is problem-free, she pays a lower price. Because the car sells for $2000 instead of $6000 (regardless of whether it's problem-free), the seller is worse off.

Application 12.6

The Winner's Curse in Auctions for Offshore Oil Leases

In Canada companies that drill for oil and natural gas in offshore waters lease the rights to explore and develop particular territories, known as *tracts*, from the federal government. Historically, the government has sold these rights through auctions.

Sales of offshore drilling rights can be considered to fall into two main categories, drainage sales and wildcat sales. In a drainage sale, the government auctions off tracts that are adjacent to areas with known deposits. A wildcat sale involves tracts in areas where no drilling has occurred. In either instance, potential bidders attempt to evaluate a tract's potential through seismic tests. However, in the case of a drainage sale, the firms that hold leases on adjacent tracks (which we'll call *neighbour firms*) can also use their knowledge of local geological conditions. In auctions for drainage leases, non-neighbour firms may therefore have inferior information, in which case they are potentially exposed to the winner's curse (just like Olivia and Elvis in Example 12.7).

Do neighbour firms in fact have better information about a tract's potential than non-neighbour firms? If so, are non-neighbour firms aware of their handicap? Do they adequately compensate for this disadvantage and avoid the winner's curse? A study by economists Kenneth Hendricks and Robert Porter addresses these questions by examining a collection of federal auctions for drainage leases that took place between 1959 and 1969 in the United States.[16] The study contains a number of significant findings.

First, neighbour firms did indeed have better information than non-neighbour firms. We know this because the ultimate profitability of the typical tract was more highly correlated with the participation and bids of neighbour firms than of non-neighbour firms. Neighbour firms won most of the auctions for profitable drainage tracts, and they earned substantially higher profits than non-neighbour firms.

Second, Hendricks and Porter found evidence of the winner's curse. Notably, when the neighbour firms chose not to bid, the winning non-neighbour firm typically suffered significant losses.

Finally, there were strong indications that non-neighbour firms were aware of the winner's curse and that they attempted to compensate for it. Despite being at an informational disadvantage, non-neighbour firms managed to break even on average by behaving conservatively. Because they often declined to participate, the typical drainage tract auction had fewer competitors than the typical wildcat tract auction. Participating non-neighbour firms also bid conservatively, reducing competitive pressure on neighbour firms. As a result, the government collected only 66 percent of the typical drainage tract's value, compared with 77 percent for wildcat tracts.

Open auctions are those in which bidders get indirect information of their competitors' valuation can reduce the size of the winner's curse when compared to sealed tender auctions. When Industry Canada designed frequency spectrum (telecommunications) auctions they used an ascending multiple round auction that allowed bidders to gather information about their competitors' value estimates from their open bids. Open bidding encourages more confident bidding by reducing the uncertainty surrounding rival's valuation. As Industry Canada describes the process, "For a multiple round auction to reduce the probability that a bidder overestimates a licence's value, bidders must have time to process information during the auction, so the pace of bidding must not be too fast. A measured pace allows bidders to evaluate bidding information and review strategy. Such pacing can be achieved by using a multiple round auction format, with the results of the previous round announced before the next one begins."[17]

Reputation

A reputation is a widely held belief about a characteristic of a person or company that predisposes them to act in a particular way.

A **reputation** is a widely held belief about a characteristic of a person or company that predisposes them to act in a particular way. Usually, reputations are acquired through patterns of behaviour. Recognizing this fact, people often choose to act in ways that build or

---

[16]Kenneth Hendricks and Robert H. Porter, "An Empirical Study of an Auction with Asymmetric Information," *American Economic Review* 78, December 1988, pp. 865–883.

[17]Industry Canada "Consultation on Issues Relating to Spectrum Auctioning", August 1, 1997. See http://www.ic.gc.ca/eic/site/smt-gst.nsf/eng/home.

maintain good reputations. For example, people act kindly toward others both because they are kind, and because they like to cultivate reputations for kindness.

Concerns over reputation influence a wide variety of important economic decisions. As an illustration, let's suppose you've finished your schooling and taken an entry-level position with a good company. You're hoping to stay with the company as you build a career. You know that your boss tries to promote the type of people who like to work hard.

As a result, you'd like to develop a reputation as someone who enjoys lots of challenging assignments.

To learn if you like to work hard, your employer will pay attention to the number of hours you put in, the amount of effort you show, and your level of productivity. Consequently, you can try to enhance your reputation by working long hours, seeking difficult assignments, and making sure your contributions to team projects are visible. In fact, if career advancement would provide you with opportunities to take it easy, you may wish to follow that strategy even if, at heart, you're actually not such a hard worker.

Of course, sophisticated employers will not be completely fooled. They will understand that the same level of apparent devotion to work may reflect either a true love of challenges or a desire to disguise less productive tendencies. Even so, the ruse may succeed for some pretenders. By working hard to make visible contributions, they may prevent their bosses from discovering their true inclinations, and thereby secure desired promotions. This is why law firms sometimes worry that associates will become less productive after making partner, and some universities fear that faculty will publish fewer research papers after receiving tenure. (See Chapter 21 for further discussion of these issues.)

CHAPTER SUMMARY

1. **What is a game? (LO1)**

   a. Some strategic situations correspond to one-stage games, other correspond to multiple-stage games. In economics, multiple-stage games are more common.

   b. To describe the essential features of a one-stage game, we follow two steps. First, we identify the players and list the actions available to each. Second, for every possible combination of actions (one for every player), we identify each player's payoff, be it a reward or penalty.

2. **Thinking strategically in one-stage games (LO2)**

   a. Strategic situations require us to think about what other people will do. We can try to do so by putting ourselves into others' shoes, but that approach frequently leads to unproductive circular reasoning. Even so, in some situations it is possible to reason out the likely choice of a sensible opponent.

   b. If a player has a dominant strategy he ought to play it, regardless of what he thinks others might do. In some games, like the Prisoners' Dilemma, all players have a dominant strategy.

   c. Sometimes it is possible to reason out the likely choice of a sensible opponent by iteratively deleting dominated strategies.

   d. It's usually a good idea to avoid weakly dominated strategies. In some cases, this dictum leads to a clear choice. For example, it implies that people should bid their true valuations in second-price sealed-bid auctions.

3. **Nash equilibrium in one-stage games (LO3, 4)**

   a. Given a table that summarizes a one-stage game with two players, we can find a Nash equilibrium by looking for a cell that (a) gives the row player the highest payoff in the same column, and (b) gives the column player the highest payoff in the same row.

   b. The combination of strategies chosen in a Nash equilibrium is stable. All participants are content with their choices; no one wants to play anything else. All other outcomes are unstable, in the sense that at least one participant would want to change strategies.

   c. One justification for focusing on Nash equilibria is that when all players are experienced, they should have reasonably accurate expectations of what the others will do, and should therefore tend to make their best responses to one another's choices.

d. A Nash equilibrium is also a self-enforcing agreement—one in which every party to the agreement has an incentive to abide by it, assuming that others do likewise.

e. In many games, no strategy dominates any other, even weakly. The concept of Nash equilibrium allows us to analyze strategic behaviour in those games.

f. Depending on the game, Nash equilibrium can involve either good outcomes or bad ones.

g. In two-player games in which the choices are finely divisible, we can plot curves that show each player's best response as a function of the other's choice. To find the Nash equilibria, we then identify the points where the curves intersect.

h. In many games involving pure strategies, there are no Nash equilibria, but virtually all games have mixed-strategy equilibria.

i. Players are most likely to use mixed strategies in situations in which unpredictability is a key to success.

j. In any Nash equilibrium involving mixed strategies, players must be indifferent among the choices over which they randomize. This principle helps us to solve for the equilibria.

4. **Games with multiple stages (LO5)**

a. We can describe a game with perfect information by drawing a tree diagram that shows the sequence of decisions and indicates the players' payoffs.

b. The best way to identify credible strategies and sensible Nash equilibria in a game with perfect information is to reason in *reverse*; that is, to start at the end of the tree diagram and work back to the beginning, identifying the choices that each player will make as they go.

c. For a finitely repeated game, backward induction implies that punishments and rewards may not be credible, and cooperation may not be possible, in any reasonable Nash equilibrium.

d. For an infinitely repeated game, punishments and rewards are credible, and cooperation is possible, provided that the players care enough about the future.

5. **Games in which different people have different information (LO6)**

a. In many strategic settings, people have difficulty predicting each others' choices because they don't share the same information. One player may receive objective information that is not available to some other player, or one player may be uncertain about another's preferences.

b. In certain types of auctions, unsophisticated bidders tend to overpay whenever they win. A sophisticated bidder anticipates this winner's curse and bids more conservatively.

c. Other people often learn things about us by observing our actions. As a result, a pattern of behaviour can create a reputation. Knowing this, people may intentionally adopt patterns of behaviour that help to build or maintain desirable reputations.

ADDITIONAL EXERCISES

Exercise 12.1: Consider the game shown in Figure 12.7 (page 415). What are Myrna's best responses? Does she have a dominant strategy? What are the Nash equilibria in this game? If there is more than one, which do you think is the most plausible? Why? (LO1, 2, 3)

Exercise 12.2: Paul and Susie each pick an integer between one and five (inclusive). They make their choices simultaneously. If they pick the same number, each receives a payoff (in dollars) equal to the number they named. If they pick different numbers, they receive nothing. Draw a table representing this game, showing the players' strategies and payoffs. Does either player have a dominant, weakly dominated, or dominated strategy? Identify all the Nash equilibria. Are all equally plausible? Why or why not? (LO2, 3)

Exercise 12.3: Fred and Barney are negotiating with each other to divide $4. Simultaneously, each proposes an integer between zero and four (inclusive) to represent the amount that Fred gets. If they propose the same number, Fred receives the proposed amount and Barney receives the rest. If they propose different numbers, neither gets anything. Does either player have a dominant, weakly dominated, or dominated strategy? Identify all the Nash equilibria. Is there an equilibrium in which Fred and Barney don't reach an agreement (that is, in which they make different proposals)? If such an equilibrium exists, is it reasonable? Why or why not? (LO2, 3)

Exercise 12.4: Repeat exercise 12.3, but change the problem as follows. Fred and Barney each have an additional option: to withdraw from the negotiation. If either one withdraws, he receives a payoff of $1.50. Everything else is the same as in exercise 12.3. (LO2, 3)

Exercise 12.5: Two companies, Green, Inc. and Red, Inc., produce granfalloons. Each can produce zero, one, two, three or four granfalloons (they can't produce fractions of granfalloons). Let X be the number of units produced by Green, Inc., and Y be the number of units produced by Red, Inc. Given X and Y, granfalloons sell at a price equal to $\$(14 - X - Y)$. Every granfalloon costs $5 to produce. The companies choose X and Y simultaneously, each trying to maximize profits. Draw a table representing this one-stage game, showing the players' strategies and payoffs. Does either company have a dominated strategy? Can you solve this game by the iterative deletion of dominated strategies? Find the Nash equilibrium. Would the companies do better if they both reduced production (starting from the equilibrium point) by one unit? Why or why not? (LO2, 3)

Exercise 12.6: Alice and Tiffany are playing a simple one-stage game. Each simultaneously chooses either 1 or 2. If they both choose 1, Alice pays Tiffany $1. If they both choose 2, Alice pays Tiffany $2. If they choose different numbers, Tiffany pays Alice $1. Draw a table showing the two players' strategies and payoffs. Are any strategies dominant, weakly dominated, or dominated? Indicate each player's best responses. Is there a Nash equilibrium? Solve for a mixed-strategy equilibrium. (LO2, 3)

Exercise 12.7: Wilma and Betty are contractors who are bidding for a job. The client will hire the contractor who submits the lower bid; if the bids are tied, he'll hire Wilma. The winning contractor will incur $900 in costs. The two contractors are allowed to submit bids of $1000, $2000, or $3000. For the winner, profit equals the difference between the bid and cost; for the loser, profit is zero. Wilma and Betty submit their bids simultaneously. Draw a table representing this game, showing the players' strategies and payoffs. Are there any dominant, weakly dominated, or dominated strategies? Can you solve this game by the iterative deletion of dominated strategies? Find the Nash equilibrium. (LO2, 3)

Exercise 12.8: Consider the plurality rule election described in Example 12.5 (page 415). Suppose that *all* voters prefer Ms. Maverick to Ms. Right, and Ms. Right to Mr. Left. Is there a Nash equilibrium in which Ms. Maverick wins? Is there one in which Ms. Right wins? Is there one in which Mr. Left wins? In each case, either describe an equilibrium or explain why there isn't one. Also, for each equilibrium that you describe, say whether any voters use weakly dominated strategies. (LO2, 3)

Exercise 12.9: Suppose Westley and Vizzini play the Battle of Wits according to the following rules: Westley moves first, and Vizzini is allowed to watch what he does; then Vizzini drinks from a goblet. Illustrate this game by drawing a tree and solve it by reasoning in reverse. (LO5)

Exercise 12.10: Suppose John and Reinhard play Rock Paper Scissors according to the following rules: John chooses first, and Reinhard is allowed to watch what he does before making his own decision. Illustrate this game by drawing a tree and solve it by reasoning in reverse. (LO5)

Exercise 12.11: A firm has an unprofitable factory. Managers decide to close the factory, but only after operating it for an additional six months to meet existing contractual obligations. They can inform workers immediately or just prior to closure. If they tell workers immediately, the typical worker has a choice: try to line up a new job that will start when the factory closes or get a new job immediately.

If the typical worker gets a new job immediately, avoiding unemployment, the firm will have to use temporary employees, who are inefficient. The payoffs of this outcome are $40,000 for each worker and −$10 million for the firm.

If the typical worker lines up a new job that will start when the factory closes, the worker will experience a short period of unemployment, but the firm will be able to wind down its operations efficiently. The payoffs of this outcome are $38,000 for each worker and −$5 million for the firm.

If the firm closes the factory without warning, the typical worker will experience a long period of unemployment. The firm will be able to wind down its operations efficiently, but will create a costly public relations problem. The payoffs of this outcome are $30,000 for each worker and −$8 million for the firm.

Illustrate this game (between the firm and a typical worker) by drawing a tree and solve it by reasoning in reverse. Is there a better outcome? How might the firm and worker achieve it? (LO5)

Exercise 12.12: Fred and Barney are playing the centipede game, which works as follows: Each player starts with a pile of money containing $2. Fred moves first, then they alternate turns. On each turn, a player says either stop or continue. If he says stop, the game ends and each player keeps the money in his own pile. If he says continue, $1 is removed from his own pile and $2 is added to the other player's pile, after which the next player takes his turn. The game must end when each player's pile contains $10 (which the players keep). Illustrate this game by drawing a tree and solve it by reasoning in reverse. Do you think people would actually play the game this way? Why or why not? How would your answer change if the game ended only when each pile contained $100? (LO5)

Exercise 12.13: Wilma and Betty must split $10 by playing the ultimatum game, which works as follows: First, Wilma proposes an integer between zero and 10 (inclusive), representing the amount she will keep for herself (Betty gets the rest). Second, Betty either accepts or rejects the proposal. If she accepts it, the money will be divided as proposed. If she rejects it, neither will receive anything. Illustrate this game by drawing a tree and solve it by reasoning in reverse (there may be more than one equilibrium). Do you think people would actually play the game this way? Why or why not? (LO5)

Exercise 12.14: We know that chess has at least one Nash equilibrium. Even though we can't solve for it, we can still reach some conclusions. Specifically, if there is a Nash equilibrium in which the first-mover wins, then the first-mover wins in every Nash equilibrium. Likewise, if there is an equilibrium in which the second-mover wins, then the second-mover wins in every equilibrium. And if there is an equilibrium that results in a draw, then every equilibrium results in a draw. Can you figure out why? (LO3, 5)

Exercise 12.15: Suppose that Homer and Marge plan to play the Spouses' Dilemma on 10,000 consecutive days, and then

part ways forever. Do you agree with the prediction that they'll be unable to cooperate? If not, how and why might they be able to sustain cooperation? (LO5)

Exercise 12.16: Let's change Example 12.7 (page 415) as follows: With 20 percent probability, Melissa's examination of the car definitely reveals whether or not it's problem-free. With 80 percent probability, she learns nothing from her examination. In that case, given her uncertainty, she will be willing to pay $6000, just like Olivia and Elvis. Neither Olivia nor Elvis knows whether Melissa learns anything from her examination. Does Melissa have a weakly dominant strategy? If so, what is it? If Olivia and Elvis bid naively, will they still suffer from the winner's curse? (LO6)

Behavioural Economics

Early in 2001, pop icon Britney Spears signed a deal with PepsiCo to serve as spokesperson for the company's products. Pepsi reportedly paid Spears tens of millions of dollars for television commercials and other promotional activities. The company clearly expected Spears's ads to boost sales—but why? Her endorsement provided consumers with little if any useful information. They certainly didn't learn anything about their own preferences for Pepsi. As it happens, they didn't learn anything about Spears's preferences, either. According to reports, a technical rider to the contract for Spears's 2000 world tour required promoters to stock her dressing room with Coke, and tabloid journalists periodically spotted her with the product. But

Britney Spears served as a spokesperson for PepsiCo products during 2001 and 2002.

advertising speaks more often about psychology than about substance. Spears's endorsement wasn't intended to "prove" anything. Rather, in linking Pepsi to the pop star in consumers' minds, the company hoped to create a positive image by association.[1]

Many economists seek to gain a better understanding of such phenomena by studying the psychology of decision making, a field of inquiry known as *behavioural economics*. Some behavioural economists view psychology as offering an alternative to the standard economic theory of decision making described in Chapters 3 through 12. However, most believe that economics and psychology are fundamentally compatible. These scholars use insights from psychology to modify, supplement, and enrich the economic approach.

Much like the field of behavioural economics, this chapter presents a collection of noteworthy observations concerning decision making and offers specialized theories to explain a number of them. In contrast to previous chapters, it does not build from a few fundamental principles to a single general theory. Some behavioural economists hope their field will become more unified over time as they gain new insights into decision making, while others expect it to remain compartmentalized.

This chapter provides an overview of some important research in behavioural economics. We'll address six topics:

1. *Objectives and methods of behavioural economics*. In seeking to enrich economic theory through insights drawn from psychology, behavioural economists use the same tools as other economists. However, as we'll see, they tend to rely more heavily on experiments with human subjects.

2. *Departures from perfect rationality*. No one is completely rational all of the time. Many behavioural economists believe that departures from perfect rationality tend to occur in certain types of circumstances and take certain forms. We'll discuss some of the evidence offered in support of these conclusions and discuss its implications. (This material complements Chapters 4 through 9.)

3. *Choices involving time*. In Chapter 10, we studied the standard economic theory of decisions involving time. Many behavioural economists see that theory as too restrictive because it rules out certain patterns of behaviour that are sometimes observed in practice. We'll review some of the relevant evidence and discuss its implications.

4. *Choices involving risk*. In Chapter 11 we studied the standard economic theory of decisions involving risk. Many behavioural economists see that theory as requiring modification in light of evidence concerning the beliefs that people actually hold and the choices they actually make. Again, we'll review some of the relevant evidence and discuss its implications.

5. *Choices involving strategy*. In Chapter 12 we studied the field of game theory, which provides powerful tools for understanding choices involving strategy. Sometimes, strategic decisions appear to be motivated not only by material self-interest but also by social concerns such as altruism, fairness, and prestige. We'll discuss the potential importance of accounting for these social motives when analyzing strategic decisions.

6. *Neuroeconomics: a new frontier*. Some economists believe that it may be possible to develop a new unified theory of decision making by studying the human neural system, including brain processes. We'll summarize some provocative findings in this emerging branch of economics.

---

[1]In hindsight, Spears's troubled life has not conveyed the positive image that Pepsi would have wanted and is often used as example of celebrity endorsement gone bad. In fact Pepsi dropped all celebrity endorsements including the contract with Britney Spears in 2003.

13.1 OBJECTIVES AND METHODS OF BEHAVIOURAL ECONOMICS

What is the need for behavioural economics? What are the field's objectives? How is it related to the standard economic approach to decision making, which we studied in Chapters 4 through 12? How is behavioural economics different from and similar to standard economics? This section provides brief answers to each of these questions.

Motivations and Objectives

There are two main motivations for research in behavioural economics, both of which concern apparent weaknesses in the standard economic theory of decision making. First, people sometimes make choices that are inconsistent with—or at least very difficult to reconcile with—standard economic theory. Second, in some situations, standard economic theory leads to seemingly unreasonable conclusions about consumer welfare.

Here's a hypothetical example that illustrates the first concern. Suppose that on any given night, Ethan's favourite restaurant serves two of the following three dishes: hamburgers, tacos, and pizza. On his way to the restaurant, Ethan thinks about the various possibilities. He concludes that between hamburgers and tacos, he'd choose tacos; between tacos and pizza, he'd choose pizza; and between pizza and hamburgers, he'd choose hamburgers. The preferences that are implied by these choices violate the Ranking Principle, which holds that consumers can rank their alternatives from best to worst (see Section 4.1).[2] To see why, look at Figure 13.1. The arrow between each pair of alternatives points to the one that Ethan chooses. With this circular configuration, there's no way to rank the choices from best to worst. As we'll see in Section 13.2, experimental evidence suggests that problems like this sometimes arise in everyday decision making.

With respect to the second concern, standard theory tells us to evaluate consumer welfare by applying the principle of *revealed preference* (see Section 5.6). In other words,

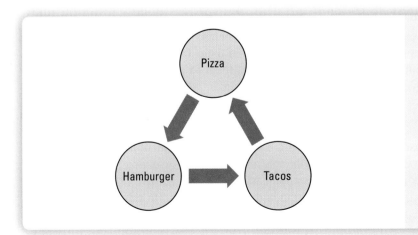

Figure 13.1
Inconsistent Choices. Between hamburgers and tacos, Ethan prefers tacos; between tacos and pizza, he prefers pizza; and between pizza and hamburgers, he prefers hamburgers. The preferences implied by these circular choices would violate the Ranking Principle, according to which consumers can rank their alternatives from best to worst.

---

[2]Technically, they violate the assumption of transitivity, which we defined in footnote 1 on page 94.

it assumes that the alternative the consumer chooses makes him at least as well off as any other alternative he could have chosen. But indiscriminate application of this principle sometimes leads to unreasonable conclusions. For example, Canadian tourists in London suffer injuries and fatalities because they often look only to the left before stepping into the street, even though they know traffic approaches from the right. Should we conclude that these people prefer to throw themselves into the path of oncoming cars? Obviously not. Their objective—to cross the street safely—is clear, but their choices are plainly mistakes. What about eating disorders? Should we assume that an anorexic's refusal to eat is an expression of valid preferences, or is it a medical problem that requires intervention? And what about addiction? Do addicts use addictive substances because they want to, or because they've lost the ability to control their own self-destructive tendencies?

The field of behavioural economics grew out of research in psychology. In a long succession of scholarly studies, researchers identified and investigated various puzzling forms of behaviour, often with the objective of disproving key premises of economic theory. Today, however, most behavioural economists recognize that economic theory is remarkably powerful and flexible and can account for behaviour in a wide range of contexts. Their objective is to modify, supplement, and enrich the theory—not to overturn it—by adding insights from psychology.

In keeping with the two main motivations for behavioural economics listed at the beginning of this section, modifications of the standard theory usually take one of two forms. In some instances, behavioural economists suggest that people care about things that standard theory ignores, like fairness or status. In other instances, they allow for the possibility that certain actions—like the use of a highly addictive substance—can be mistakes.

Methods

Because behavioural economics is an extension of standard economics, for the most part it employs the same tools as standard economics within the same methodological framework. Behavioural economists have much in common with other economists:

- They usually assume that each individual has well-defined objectives, that there is a connection between an individual's objectives and actions, and that the actions chosen affect an individual's well-being.
- They rely heavily on mathematical models of behaviour, which requires them to state their assumptions precisely, and discourages them from relying on incomplete or loose reasoning. This approach also allows them to answer important quantitative questions that arise in business and government.
- They subject their theories to careful, thorough empirical tests using objective data, replicable methods, and standard statistical tools.

Despite these similarities between the two approaches, there are also some differences. The most important concerns the role of experiments involving human subjects. In testing their theories, behavioural economists tend to rely primarily (though not exclusively) on experimental data, while standard economists tend to rely primarily (though not exclusively) on data drawn from the real world.

The Advantages of Experiments
In a typical economic experiment, subjects make decisions with monetary consequences under conditions that the experimenter

controls. Compared to the analysis of real world data, experimental methods offer several advantages, some of which are particularly important for research in behavioural economics.

First, through laboratory experiments, it's easier to determine whether people's choices are consistent with standard economic theory.[3] The real world is extremely complex; numerous factors can influence every significant decision. Even when human behaviour looks peculiar, economists can often come up with subtle explanations. Take the hypothetical example just discussed, in which Ethan's preferences violated the Ranking Principle. If the chef tends to overcook pizza while making hamburgers but not while making tacos, Ethan's preferences would make perfect sense. In a laboratory setting, in contrast, all the influences on decision making are potentially knowable and controllable. A good experiment can rule out alternative explanations (like systematic variation in the quality of pizza).

Second, with laboratory experiments, it's often easier to establish causality. For example, think about the problems we encounter in estimating a demand curve using real-world data on quantities and prices. As we discussed in the appendix to Chapter 2, such data reflect the interplay of supply and demand. Separating supply effects from demand effects is a tricky procedure that requires the use of subtle statistical techniques. In the laboratory, it's possible to avoid these difficulties altogether. The experimenter simply sets a price and measures the associated demand.

Third, with laboratory experiments, researchers can double check their assumptions and conclusions by testing and debriefing subjects. Careful questioning can reveal whether a subject has properly understood a task and interpreted options and outcomes as intended. It can also shed light on subjects' thought processes and their reasons for making particular choices.

Finally, in the laboratory, it's often possible to obtain information that isn't available in the real world. For example, experimentation offers reliable ways to measure subjects' plans and expectations.

The Disadvantages of Experiments   Experiments aren't perfect. While the advantages of the experimental method are undeniable, there are also some disadvantages. First, decisions made in the laboratory differ from decisions made in the real world. In the laboratory, tasks and settings are usually artificial, and often somewhat unfamiliar. Since behavioural economists have limited research budgets, the subjects typically don't have much at stake. Some scholars argue that these differences are too large to justify generalizations to real-world decisions. Experimental economists have attempted to address these concerns in a number of ways. Some have run experiments with both small and large stakes to determine whether the size of the stake matters. Others have conducted field experiments in which the tasks and settings are both natural and familiar, and the stakes meaningful. Some experimental results turn out to be representative of behaviour outside the lab; others don't.

Second, laboratory experiments introduce influences on decision making that are difficult to measure or control. For example, there is strong evidence that subjects often try to conform to what they think are the experimenter's expectations. Psychologists frequently attempt to overcome this difficulty through deception. That is, they invent a false

---

[3]For example, in Application 2.1 (page 33), we described a famous laboratory experiment that was designed to determine whether the theory of supply and demand accurately predicts prices and the amounts bought and sold.

explanation for the experiment's purpose. Experimental economists rarely engage in deception, however. In a university setting, students quickly learn that experiments involve deception; as subjects, they begin to second-guess an experiment's purpose, introducing unknown and uncontrolled influences on their decision making. Instead of using deception, most experimental economists try to avoid telegraphing their expectations to subjects by describing the subjects' tasks in neutral terms.

Third, in most cases, experimental subjects are students at colleges and universities, which means that by and large they are unrepresentative of the general population. They are also relatively inexperienced at making important economic decisions. To determine if results obtained from student subjects are representative, economists sometimes repeat their experiments with subjects recruited from other settings (for example, the workplace).

Fourth, as a practical matter, the scale of any given experiment is limited by the available resources. As a result, the typical experimental trial involves a relatively small number of subjects, which makes it difficult to apply the results to economic behaviour in very large groups. For example, an experiment involving a market consisting of fifteen buyers and fifteen sellers may not tell us much about markets with thousands of buyers and sellers.

How to Evaluate Behavioural Evidence

Much of behavioural economics is controversial. Some economists are convinced that certain aspects of the standard model are flawed; others think the evidence against it is weak and overstated. In evaluating behavioural research, we recommend a mix of open-mindedness and healthy skepticism. Each time we read about a pattern of behaviour that is allegedly inconsistent with standard theory, we should ask ourselves the following critical questions:

- Is the evidence convincing? If it is from a laboratory study, for example, was the experiment well-designed? Were the subjects provided with clear instructions? Did they have appropriate incentives? Were they being guided (perhaps unintentionally) to select certain choices?

- Is the observed behavioural pattern robust? Does it show up in many studies, under a variety of conditions? Are there some conditions under which it *isn't* observed? For example, does the pattern appear with certain experimental procedures and disappear with others?

- If the pattern is observed in the laboratory, how—if at all—would we expect it to translate to the real world? Did the experimental tasks involve common choices and familiar situations? Are the stakes usually different in the real world, and if so, does it matter? Does the pattern survive after people have gained experience and received feedback? Is it likely to survive in a market, where competition favours those who make better decisions?

- What are the possible explanations for the observed pattern? Can we reconcile the pattern with standard theory? For example, if an experimental subject appears to make a series of inconsistent choices, could it be that the experimenter unintentionally allowed some condition, like the quality of one of the alternatives, to vary?

- If evidence suggests that standard economic theory fails to account for a behavioural pattern in economically significant situations, how should we modify the theory?

Does the observed pattern reflect preferences or mistakes? Is it possible to tell the difference between the two? What are the larger implications for economic analysis?

We make no attempt to answer every one of these questions for every pattern we discuss. To do so would require a book, not a chapter. Rather, our object is to bring a collection of interesting and potentially important behavioural patterns to your attention, so that you can start the process of critical evaluation. Here you will find much food for thought, but few definitive answers.

13.2 DEPARTURES FROM PERFECT RATIONALITY

No one is completely rational all of the time. Psychologists and behavioural economists have identified some apparent departures from perfect rationality that tend to occur in certain types of situations, and take certain forms. In this section, we'll examine some of the pertinent behavioural evidence and discuss implications for economic analysis.

Incoherent Choices

The idea that choices reflect preferences is central to the theory of consumer decision making, described in Chapters 4 through 6. But do people actually make choices that reflect sensible preferences? According to some psychologists and behavioural economists, the answer is no, at least in some situations.

Choice Reversals   If Ethan's preferences satisfy the Ranking Principle, he will not make the circular choices illustrated in Figure 13.1. Consequently, those choices do not reflect sensible preferences. Yet laboratory subjects sometimes display this type of incoherent behaviour when confronted with certain types of choices.

In one series of experiments, subjects were asked to make decisions involving two different bets. The first involved a high probability of winning a small amount of money. For example, the subject might win $4 with 97 percent probability, or lose $1 with 3 percent probability. We'll call this type of bet the *low stakes bet*. The second bet involved a low probability of winning a larger amount of money. For example, the subject might win $16 with 30 percent probability, or lose $1.50 with 70 percent probability. We'll call this type of bet the *high stakes bet*.

Subjects were asked first to choose between a low stakes bet and a high stakes bet. Second, they were asked to state a dollar amount that was just as good as the low stakes bet—no better or worse.[4] Third, they were asked to state a dollar amount that was just as good as the high stakes bet—no better or worse.

Table 13.1 summarizes the results of a trial involving 46 subjects, each of whom considered six different pairs of low stakes bets and high stakes bets (for a total of 276 comparisons). As shown in the line labelled *low stakes bet*, in 99 comparisons subjects chose the low stakes bet over the high stakes bet. Yet for 69 of these, he or she assigned a higher dollar value to the high stakes bet than to the low stakes bet. In other words, in

---

[4]In Chapter 11, we referred to this amount as the *certainty equivalent*.

Table 13.1

Choice Reversals

Chosen Alternative	Frequency	Value of Low Stakes Bet Is Higher	Value of High Stakes Bet Is Higher	Values Equal
Low stakes bet	99	26	69	4
High stakes bet	174	22	145	7
Indifferent	3			

Source: David M. Grether and Charles R. Plott, "Economic Theory of Choice and the Preference Reversal Phenomenon," *American Economic Review* 69, September 1979, pp. 623–638. Subjects were all undergraduates at the California Institute of Technology.

those cases, subjects selected the alternative regarded as less valuable.[5] Similar inconsistencies occurred in cases in which the subject chose the high stakes bet over the low stakes bet, though with much lower frequency (only 22 out of 174 cases, as shown in the line labelled *high stakes bet*).

Even though this experiment involved bets rather than dinners, the problem with the subjects' choices is exactly the same as in Figure 13.1. To see why, consider a subject who chose a low stakes bet over a high stakes bet. Assume he valued the high stakes bet at $3.60 and the low stakes bet at $3.40, which means that he preferred the high stakes bet (valued at $3.60) to $3.50, and $3.50 to the low stakes bet (valued at $3.40). Figure 13.2 illustrates these choices. Between each pair of alternatives, the arrow points to the one chosen. With this configuration, just as in Figure 13.1, there is no way to rank the three choices (the low stakes bet, the high stakes bet, and $3.50) from best to worst.

Does this finding undermine the validity of standard economic theory? The answer to this question may depend on context. It seems unlikely that among people who would choose the Honda Prelude over the Toyota Camry, many would be willing to pay more for

Figure 13.2

A Choice Reversal. An experimental subject who chooses a low stakes bet over a high stakes bet, but who attaches a higher dollar value to the high stakes bet than to the low stakes bet, violates the Ranking Principle. In this illustration, we assume that he values the low stakes bet at $3.40 and the high stakes bet at $3.60. In that case, he chooses the high stakes bet over $3.50, and $3.50 over the low stakes bet. Yet he chooses the low stakes bet over the high stakes bet. As shown, his choices among these three options (the low stakes bet, the high stakes bet, and $3.50) are circular.

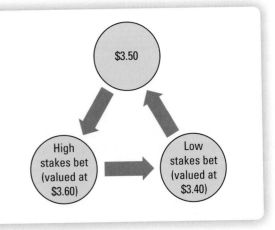

---

[5]This phenomenon was first reported by Sarah Lichtenstein and Paul Slovic, "Reversals of Preferences Between Bids and Choices in Gambling Decisions," *Journal of Experimental Psychology* 89, July 1971, pp. 46–55, and by H. R. Lindman, "Inconsistent Preferences Among Gambles," *Journal of Experimental Psychology* 89, August 1971, pp. 390–397.

the Camry than the Prelude. More likely, the reversal just described has something to do with the way people think about certain kinds of bets. There is also some evidence that the frequency of such reversals declines considerably when decisions are repeated in market settings, where people can learn from the consequences of their choices.[6] For these reasons, many economists question whether the phenomenon of choice reversal is relevant to familiar and significant economic choices.

Anchoring   Another line of research suggests that some choices are fundamentally arbitrary, and therefore can't reflect meaningful preferences. Support for this view comes from experiments in which subjects' choices depended on prominent but plainly irrelevant information, a phenomenon known as **anchoring**.[7]

In one study, 55 subjects were shown a series of six common products with an average retail price of about $70. For each product, the experiment involved two steps. First, subjects were asked if they would be willing to purchase the product at a price equal to the last two digits of their Social Insurance Numbers. Second, subjects were asked to state the highest amount they would be willing to pay for the object. The experiment was designed so that each subject had an incentive to respond truthfully.

Table 13.2 shows subjects' average willingness to pay for each product in the second step. The table separates subjects into five groups of equal size based on the last two digits of their Social Insurance Numbers. For example, if subjects' Social Insurance Numbers ended in "02," they would be placed in the group labelled *lowest fifth*; if they ended in "98," subjects would be placed in the group labelled *highest fifth*. According to the table, the subjects' willingness to pay in the second step were closely related to the last two digits of their Social Insurance Numbers. For example, those in the lowest fifth were willing to pay an average of $11.73 for a rare bottle of wine, while those in the highest fifth were willing to pay an average of $37.55—more than

> **Anchoring** occurs when someone's choices are linked to prominent but patently irrelevant information.

Table 13.2
Anchoring Effects on Economic Valuation

Rank of SIN	Cordless Trackball	Cordless Keyboard	Average Wine	Rare Wine	Design Book	Belgian Chocolate
Lowest fifth	$8.64	$16.09	$8.64	$11.73	$12.82	$9.55
Second lowest fifth	11.82	26.82	14.45	22.45	16.18	10.64
Middle fifth	13.45	29.27	12.55	18.09	15.82	12.45
Second highest fifth	21.18	34.55	15.45	24.55	19.27	13.27
Highest fifth	26.18	55.64	27.91	37.55	30.00	20.64

Source: Dan Ariely, George Loewenstein, and Drazen Prelec, "'Coherent Arbitrariness': Stable Demand Curves Without Stable Preferences," *Quarterly Journal of Economics* 118, February 2003, 73–105. Subjects were all MBA students at MIT's Sloan School of Management. The study used Social Security numbers which are the U.S. equivalent of Social Insurance Numbers.

---

[6]In one experiment involving involving auctions, choice reversals tended to disappear after five repetitions. See James C. Cox and David M. Grether, "The Preference Reversal Phenomenon: Response Modes, Markets, and Incentives," *Economic Theory* 7, April 1996, pp. 381–405.

[7]Anchoring was first documented by Amos Tversky and Daniel Kahneman, "Judgment Under Uncertainty: Heuristics and Biases," *Science* 185, September 27, 1974, pp. 1124–1131.

three times as much. Obviously, the last two digits of a Social Insurance Number should have nothing to do with a preference for wine and are indeed unrelated to a person's willingness to pay for the wine when the first step of the experiment is omitted. But apparently, by calling attention to those digits in the context of a purchase decision (the first step), the experimenters created an anchor for the subjects' subsequent valuations (the second step).

In this experiment, subjects displayed extreme sensitivity to the power of suggestion. Skeptics might suggest that the typical MBA student (the subject pool for this experiment) has relatively little experience purchasing or consuming the items listed in Table 13.2. They suggest that these same subjects might have been less sensitive to suggestion with respect to the value of familiar products, like soda or wireless phone service. The significance of anchoring effects for both everyday economic choices and major decisions calling for careful deliberation remains unclear.

Bias toward the Status Quo

The **endowment effect** refers to the observation that people tend to value something more highly when they own it than when they don't.

The **default effect** refers to the fact that when confronted with many alternatives, people sometimes avoid making a choice and end up with the option that is assigned as a default.

In some situations, people exhibit a strong attachment to the status quo. From an economic point of view, there are two potentially important manifestations of this tendency. One is called the **endowment effect**, which refers to the observation that people tend to value something more highly when they own it than when they don't. The other is called the **default effect**, which refers to the fact that when confronted with a menu of alternatives, people sometimes avoid making a choice and end up with the option assigned as a default.

The Endowment Effect　　Table 13.3 summarizes the results of an experiment illustrating the endowment effect. Forty-four students were gathered together in a classroom. Half (22) were given mugs, which were available at the campus bookstore for $6 each. The other half were allowed to examine the mugs. Each student who had a mug was asked to name the lowest price at which he or she would be willing to sell it (we'll call this amount the *owner valuation*). Each student who did not have a mug was asked to name the highest price at which he or she would be willing to buy it (we'll call this amount the *nonowner valuation*). The experimenter used the answers to construct supply and demand curves and identify the equilibrium price. Willing buyers actually purchased the mugs

Table 13.3
The Endowment Effect

Round	Equilibrium Price	Median Non-Owner Value	Median Owner Value
1	$4.25	$2.75	$5.25
2	4.75	2.25	5.25
3	4.50	2.25	5.25
4	4.25	2.25	5.25

Source: Daniel Kahneman, Jack L. Knetsch, and Richard H. Thaler, "Experimental Tests of the Endowment Effect and the Coase Theorem," *Journal of Political Economy* 98, December 1990, pp. 1325–1348. The subjects were undergraduates at Cornell University.

Figure 13.3

The Endowment Effect and the Shape of Indifference Curves. In figure (a), Angelica starts out at bundle A. The blue indifference curve running through bundle A is kinked at A because of the endowment effect. As a result, over a wide range of prices (for example, those corresponding to the green budget lines L_1 and L_2), Angela simply keeps her endowment. If the price of mugs falls far enough, however, she will trade T-shirts for mugs. For example, bundle B is her best choice on the budget line labelled L_3. After she adjusts to her trade psychologically, her indifference curve running through bundle B develops a kink at B [as shown in figure (b)]. She sticks with bundle B even when the price of mugs rises to its original level (rotating the budget line to L_4, which is parallel to the original budget line, L_1).

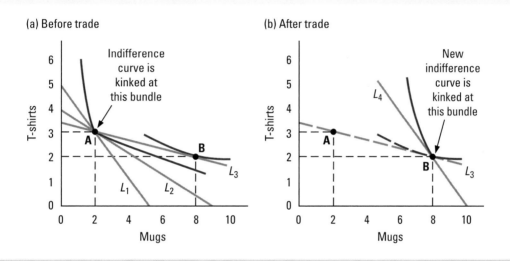

from willing sellers at that price.[8] Students repeated the exercise four times in succession (with one round selected at random as binding) to see if learning and market experience might affect their behaviour.

Since the mugs were assigned randomly, standard economic theory would predict that the average owner valuation should be the same as the average nonowner valuation. But the results shown in Table 13.3 contradict this prediction. The median owner value was roughly twice as large as the median nonowner value. In other words, when a subject is randomly chosen to receive a mug, receipt of the mug appears to double his or her valuation of it. This result did not change much as subjects gained experience through successive rounds.

Some economists think the endowment effect reflects something fundamental about the nature of preferences. How might we incorporate it into consumer theory? Look at Figure 13.3(a). Let's suppose that Angelica likes to collect mugs and T-shirts. Initially, she has two mugs and three T-shirts, putting her at bundle A in Figure 13.3(a). The endowment effect implies that her indifference curve running through bundle A (the blue curve) is kinked at that point. Here's why:

* In moving southeast from bundle A, Angelica gives up T-shirts in exchange for mugs. Since she already owns the T-shirts but doesn't yet own the additional mugs, the

---

[8]With this procedure, subjects may not have had an incentive to tell the truth about their valuations, because a subject's reported valuation could affect the price. Even with procedures that provide an incentive for truth-telling, however, the same patterns still emerge.

T-shirts seem especially valuable to her compared to the mugs. Thus, it takes many new mugs to compensate for the loss of one T-shirt. That is why this portion of the curve is relatively flat.

- In moving northwest from bundle A, Angelica gives up mugs in exchange for T-shirts. Since she already owns the mugs but doesn't yet own the additional T-shirts, the mugs seem especially valuable to her compared to the T-shirts. Thus, it takes many new T-shirts to compensate for the loss of one mug. That is why this portion of the curve is relatively steep.

With these preferences, Angelica is reluctant to trade at all. For a wide range of prices, she simply hangs onto her endowment. Consider, for example, the budget lines labelled L_1 and L_2, which reflect different prices. Bundle A is her favourite alternative on both budget lines.

There are, of course, circumstances in which Angelica will trade away part of her endowment. If the price of mugs falls far enough, she will sell a T-shirt so she can buy some extra mugs. For example, suppose that a reduction in the price of mugs rotates Angelica's budget line from L_1 to L_3. Since L_3 crosses into the area above Angelica's indifference curve, she will swap point A (two mugs and three T-shirts) for some other alternative, like bundle B (eight mugs and two T-shirts).

By trading, Angelica changes what she owns, from bundle A to bundle B. Once she adjusts to the trade psychologically, her indifference curve running through bundle B develops a kink at that point, as shown in Figure 13.3(b). So even if the price of mugs rebounds to its original level, producing the budget line labelled L_4 (which is parallel to the original budget line L_1), she hangs onto her eight mugs. With the endowment effect, smooth fluctuations in price therefore produce "jerky" changes in consumption.

Some economists think that the endowment effect reflects systematic mistakes rather than actual preferences. In support of this view, they point to evidence showing that the effect can be switched on and off by varying the experimental procedure. According to one study, the effect disappears entirely when sufficient care is taken to make sure that the subjects fully understand those procedures.[9]

The Default Effect   Experimental evidence suggests that people are sometimes less likely to make a choice and more likely to end up with a default option when they are confronted with several alternatives at once. In one study, 80 subjects were asked to fill out a short questionnaire in return for a payment of $1.50.[10] At the end of the experiment, half were offered the chance to swap the $1.50 for a Zebra pen, worth roughly $2. The other half were offered the chance to exchange the $1.50 for *either* a Zebra pen *or* two Pilot pens, also worth roughly $2.

According to standard economic theory, the introduction of a second option (the Pilot pens) should *reduce* the number of subjects who keep the $1.50. Why? Anyone who was willing to trade the $1.50 for a Zebra pen still has that option when the Pilot pens are available. In addition, some subjects who were unwilling to swap the $1.50 for the Zebra pen may be willing to trade for the Pilot pens. Therefore, fewer subjects overall should choose to keep the cash.

Yet precisely the opposite pattern was observed in the laboratory. When the only choice was a Zebra pen, only 25 percent kept the cash. When the choice included either a

---

[9]See Charles R. Plott and Kathryn Zeiler, "The Willingness to Pay–Willingness to Accept Gap, the 'Endowment Effect,' Subject Misconceptions, and Experimental Procedures for Eliciting Values," *American Economic Review* 95, June 2005, pp. 530–545.

[10]Amos Tversky and Eldar Shafir, "Choice Under Conflict: The Dynamic of Deferred Decision," *Psychological Science* 3, November 1992, pp. 358–361. The subjects were undergraduate students.

Zebra pen or two Pilot pens, 53 percent kept the cash. One possible explanation is that, when many alternatives are available, decision making entails greater psychological costs, increasing the number of people who accept the default alternative.

Choices involving pens and small amounts of cash show only that the costs of decision making outweigh the benefits when relatively little money is at stake. Do people also avoid making choices when the stakes are high? Application 13.1 suggests that the answer is yes.

Application 13.1

Saving for Retirement by Default

Financial consultants typically advise workers that they will need 60 percent to 80 percent of their pre-retirement income after retirement. That income can come from three sources: personal saving, the Canada Pension Plan, and private pension plans sponsored by employers. Historically, private pension plans didn't offer employees many choices. Today, employees have a great deal of control over their contribution levels and their pension investment portfolios. By the end of the second quarter of 2009, Canadian employers offered over 15,000 Registered Pension Plans (RPPs) to 5.9 million covered workers who had accumulated $830 billion in assets. The typical RPP allows each employee to contribute whatever she wants (up to a legal maximum) and to invest in a wide variety of mutual funds.

When people are free to choose among many complex alternatives, it's natural to wonder whether default options matter. In the vast majority of voluntary pension plans, nonparticipation is the default option, one many people end up with. Does their non-participation reflect intentional and deliberate choice, or are they simply overwhelmed by the wide range of saving and investment options available to

them? To answer that question, two economists, Brigitte Madrian and Dennis Shea, studied field data on the effects of a change in the default provisions for one particular type of U.S. private pension plan, the 401(k) plan, of a Fortune 500 company. Prior to April 1, 1998 the default option was nonparticipation. After that date, all new employees were immediately enrolled in the plan at a three percent default contribution rate, and contributions were invested in money market funds unless the employee specified something else. Since the plan's other alternatives were unchanged, standard economic theory tells us that the new default provisions should have had no impact on employees' behaviour.

What actually happened? Table 13.4 compares the contribution rates after 3 to 15 months of employment for two groups of workers: those hired during the year prior to the change (for whom the default provision was nonparticipation) and those hired during the year after the change (to whom the new default provisions applied). The new default provision reduced the rate of non-participation from 63 percent to 14 percent. It increased the fraction of workers choosing a 3 percent contribution rate from 4 percent to

65 percent. It also reduced the fraction of workers contributing *more* than 3 percent from 30 percent to 20 percent.

The study also documented the effects of the change in default provisions on employees' investment portfolios. Under the new default provisions, the fraction of assets invested in money market funds was 80 percent, compared to less than 10 percent under the old provisions. Roughly 75 percent of workers placed *all* their assets in money market funds under the new provisions, compared to 6.1 percent under the old provisions. Overall, 61.1 percent of employees followed all aspects of the new default provisions *exactly*, while less than 1 percent made those choices when the default was nonparticipation.

Can standard economic theory account for these patterns? Possibly. Typical employees may be roughly indifferent toward many of the choices available to them, simply because they don't have the expertise to determine whether one is better than another. If resolving this question requires a great deal of time or money (for example, to consult an expert advisor), going with the default provision may be the best choice.[11]

Table 13.4
Default Effects in Pension Plan Choices

Contribution Rate	Fraction of Employees (default: no participation)	Fraction of Employees (default: participation)
0%	63%	14%
1–2	3	1
3	4	65
4–5	4	2
More than 5	26	18

Source: Brigitte C. Madrian and Dennis F. Shea, "The Power of Suggestion: Inertia in 401(k) Participation and Savings Behavior," *Quarterly Journal of Economics* 116, November 2001, pp. 1149–1187.

Narrow Framing

To some extent, all the decisions we make are interrelated. Whenever we spend money or time on something, less remains to spend on everything else. At times, many of us seem to ignore these interrelationships, however. Instead, we sometimes simplify the process of decision making by compartmentalizing. When shopping for groceries, we may think only about our food purchases. When shopping for sweaters, we may think only about our clothing purchases. We tend to group related items into categories and draw artificial boundaries around those categories. In making certain types of choices, we tend to consider other items in the same category and may ignore items in different categories—a phenomenon known as **narrow framing**.

Narrow framing is the psychological tendency to group related items into categories, and, in making a choice, to consider other items in the same category while ignoring items in different categories.

In some situations, narrow framing can lead to behaviour that is hard to justify objectively. For example, in one study subjects were asked the following questions:[12]

"Imagine that you have decided to see a play where admission is $10 per ticket. As you enter the theatre you discover that you have lost a $10 bill. Would you still pay $10 for a ticket for the play?"

[11]Information about Canadian Registered Pension Plans can be found at www.statcan.gc.ca/daily-quotidien/091215/ dq091215d-eng. htm; www.nupge.ca/node/2825; and www. statcan.gc.ca/daily-quotidien/090608/dq090608c-eng.htm).

[12]Amos Tversky and Daniel Kahneman, "The Framing of Decisions and the Psychology of Choice," *Science* 211, January 30, 1981, pp. 453–458.

"Imagine that you have decided to see a play and paid the admission price of $10 per ticket. As you enter the theatre you discover that you have lost the ticket. The seat was not marked and the ticket cannot be recovered. Would you pay $10 for another ticket?"

As long as additional tickets are available, there's no meaningful difference between losing $10 in cash before buying a ticket, and losing the $10 ticket after buying it. In both cases, you're out $10. Yet far more subjects say they would see the play in response to the first question than in response to the second (88 percent versus 56 percent).

The leading explanation for this pattern attributes it to narrow framing. In the first scenario, there is no immediate connection between the thing that is lost (a $10 bill) and the play. Because the loss of the money has nothing *directly* to do with the evening's entertainment, subjects unconsciously assign these items to different mental accounts. In the second scenario, there is an immediate connection between the lost ticket and the play. Because subjects assign these items to the same mental account, they see themselves as $10 poorer for the evening and are less likely to replace the ticket than they were to buy one in the first scenario.

Narrow framing can also influence how we evaluate the factors we *do* consider in making our decisions. For example, the same study posed the following two questions:

"Imagine that you are about to purchase a jacket for $125 and a calculator for $15. The calculator salesman informs you that the calculator you wish to buy is on sale for $10 at the other branch of the store, located a 20-minute drive away. Would you make the trip to the other store?"

"Imagine that you are about to purchase a jacket for $15 and a calculator for $125. The calculator salesman informs you that the calculator you wish to buy is on sale for $120 at the other branch of the store, located a 20-minute drive away. Would you make the trip to the other store?"

Objectively, these two scenarios are identical. You plan to spend a total of $140, and can save $5 by making a 20-minute trip to another store. Yet far more subjects say they would make the trip in the first scenario than in the second (68 percent versus 29 percent).

In each case, subjects should ask themselves the same question: does saving $5 justify a 20-minute trip? However, most people tend to think of savings in relative terms. They see a steep 33 percent discount ($5 off the $15 price) in the first scenario, compared to a modest 4 percent discount ($5 off the $125 price) in the second. In both cases, narrow framing links the potential savings to the calculator but not to the jacket.

Are some of the choices described here mistakes, or do all of them reflect the subjects' true preferences? The answer to this question isn't entirely obvious. Even if two situations are objectively identical, they may *feel* different. For example, the person who loses a $10 ticket to a play may become irritable (compared to the person who loses a $10 bill), and thus may not enjoy himself. If he ignores his reaction and tries to behave rationally by replacing his ticket, he may end up feeling worse off.

Is there some way to tell whether these choices are mistakes? One strategy is to make subjects aware of what they're doing (for example, by pointing out that losing a $10 bill is objectively identical to losing a $10 ticket) and then see whether they continue the pattern. If they change their behaviour and eliminate the apparent inconsistencies, then it may be reasonable to conclude that some of their earlier choices were mistaken.

Application 13.2

Driving a Cab ... One Day at a Time

In Section 6.4, we saw that an increase in the wage rate can either raise or lower the amount of labour supplied. The substitution effect is positive (leisure becomes more expensive, so people buy less of it), but the income effect is negative (with greater resources, people buy more leisure). Based on theory alone, there's no way to tell which effect is larger.

But what if someone's wage were to increase for only a *single day*? If she's free to vary her hours, she would definitely supply more labour on that day. Why? Since earnings on any given day are trivial in comparison to total lifetime resources, the income effect is very small. The overall impact of the wage increase is therefore determined almost entirely by the substitution effect. At a higher wage, leisure becomes more expensive *on that day*, so the worker buys less of it.

Do people actually behave that way? This question is surprisingly difficult to answer. Most people don't experience day-to-day variation in their wages, nor do they have the freedom to vary their hours on extremely short notice. However, taxicab drivers' hourly compensation varies considerably from day to day. If the weather is bad, a large convention has come to town, or transit workers are on strike, a cab driver knows that passengers will be easy to find. And typical taxicab drivers are free to shorten or lengthen their shifts on any given day. According to standard economic theory, then, drivers should work longer shifts on busy days.

Is that how taxicab drivers actually behave? This question was the focus of a study by a team of four economists, Colin Camerer, Linda Babcock, George Loewenstein, and Richard Thaler.[13] The study examined roughly 2000 trip sheets submitted by New York City cab drivers during 1988, 1990, and 1994. The authors found that on any given day, the length of the shift was *negatively* related to hourly compensation. In fact, much of their analysis suggested that the elasticity of hours worked with respect to hourly compensation was approximately −1.

For the reasons just discussed, a negative relationship between labour supply and hourly compensation on a single day is inconsistent with the implications of standard economic theory. If cab drivers aren't following consumer theory, what are they doing? The estimated elasticity of labour supply may provide an important clue. It implies that a one percent increase in hourly compensation leads to a roughly one percent decrease in hours. As hourly compensation changes, then, total income—the product of the hours worked and hourly compensation—remains fixed. (See Section 2.4.) In other words, typical cab drivers appear to have daily income targets. When they reach the target, they quit for the day.

Daily income targeting is highly inefficient. To see why, let's think about the following example. Martha works 20 days each month and needs to earn $2000, or an average of $100 per day, to cover her expenses. On good days, she earns $20 per hour; on bad days she earns $10 per hour. Good and bad days occur with equal frequency. Suppose Martha sets a target of $100 per day and works until she reaches it. She works five hours on good days and 10 hours on bad days, putting in a total of 150 hours over the course of the month. What if instead she worked 10 hours on good days and five hours on bad days? For the entire month, she would earn $2500—25 percent more than with daily targeting—without putting in any extra time. Alternatively, she could reach her monthly goal of $2000 by working 10 hours on good days and taking bad days off, putting in a total of only 100 hours per month rather than 150.

Cab drivers appear to ignore the sizable inefficiencies associated with daily income targeting. Why? According to the authors of the study, most approach their jobs one day at a time. That is, they make their decisions about how many hours to work within the narrow frame of a single day. This narrow frame prevents them from noticing that they would be better off over the course of a typical month if they worked longer hours on days when they earn more money per hour. This conclusion has been challenged by another study using different data and remains controversial.[14]

[13]Colin Camerer, Linda Babcock, George Loewenstein, and Richard Thaler, "Labor Supply of New York City Cab Drivers: One Day at a Time," *Quarterly Journal of Economics* 112, May 1997, pp. 407–441.

[14]Henry Farber, "Is Tomorrow Another Day? The Labor Supply of New York City Cab Drivers," Working Paper #473, Industrial Relations Section, Princeton University, 2003.

Salience

The salience of any particular fact depends on the way it is presented. Some psychologists and behavioural economists argue that people are more likely to consider a fact when its presentation is more attention-grabbing. As a result, two different presentations of the same information can lead to different choices.

In one experiment, a group of randomly selected subjects answered the following policy question:[15]

> Imagine that the U.S. is preparing for the outbreak of an unusual Asian disease, which is expected to kill 600 people. Two alternative programs to combat the disease have been proposed. Assume that the exact scientific estimates of the consequences of the programs are as follows:
>
> If program A is adopted, 200 people will be saved.
>
> If program B is adopted, there is a one-third probability that 600 people will be saved, and a two-thirds probability that no people will be saved.
>
> Which of the two programs would you favour?

A second randomly selected group answered the same question, with the following two alternatives replacing programs A and B:

> If program C is adopted 400 people will die.
>
> If program D is adopted there is a one-third probability that no one will die, and a two-thirds probability that 600 people will die.

Objectively, program A is identical to program C, and program B is identical to program D. Yet 72 percent of the first group said they preferred A to B, while 78 percent of the second group said they preferred D to C. What explains these results? The first presentation emphasizes lives saved, while the second emphasizes deaths. As a result, the salient information is different. Program A sounds attractive because it saves lives for sure; program C sounds unattractive because it guarantees deaths. But programs A and C are the same. Whether subjects love or hate this alternative depends on how they look at it.

Were some of the choices subjects made mistakes, or did they all reflect the subjects' true preferences? Once people have been made aware of their sensitivity to the presentation of information, they tend to correct for it, and their choices become much more consistent across objectively equivalent decision problems. This finding suggests that their earlier inconsistencies were probably mistakes.

Rules of Thumb

Many economic decisions are quite complex, so that thinking through all of the possible consequences for every alternative is extremely difficult. Most of us don't try. Instead, we often rely on simple rules of thumb that have served us or others reasonably well in the past.

Take the example of saving. The appropriate rate of saving for any particular person depends on a long list of factors—age, marital status, income, expected growth in income,

---

[15]Amos Tversky and Daniel Kahneman, "The Framing of Decisions and the Psychology of Choice," *Science* 211, January 30, 1981, pp. 453–458.

likelihood of unemployment, expected age at retirement, Canadian Pension Plan contributions, private pensions, number and ages of children, expected college expenses, potential medical expenses, and so forth. Even in simple economic models, finding the best rate of saving involves complex mathematical calculations. No wonder that most people take shortcuts. In a best-selling book on personal finance called *The Wealthy Barber* Canadian author David Chilton simply advises readers (through the sage musings of a fictitious barber named Roy) to "pay yourself first" by saving 10 percent of every paycheck.

In practice, people do seem to follow simple rules of thumb for saving. According to one survey, among Americans who actually try to save some of their income, 62 percent think about their saving target as a percentage of income. The vast majority of these (73.6 percent) report targets that are even multiples of 5 percent. Nearly one-third of them attempt to save *exactly* 10 percent of their income, just as Roy the barber recommends. Moreover, these simple targets appear to be insensitive to factors that standard economic theory indicates should significantly affect saving, such as expected future income.[16]

It's important to emphasize that a person who uses a rule of thumb isn't necessarily making a mistake. A good rule of thumb is arrived at through trial and error or by imitating other people who have made successful decisions. As a result, popular rules of thumb may represent choices that are *nearly* optimal for the decisions to which they're usually applied. Given the costs and difficulty of solving complex problems, further improvements may not be worth the effort.

Some economists think that the widespread tendency to rely on rules of thumb invalidates laboratory experiments that appear to document inconsistent or irrational behaviour (including many of the ones discussed earlier). They argue that whenever we confront a new or unfamiliar task, we look for analogies to other problems we've faced in an effort to identify an applicable rule of thumb. According to this view, psychologists and behavioural economists may find evidence of irrational behaviour in the laboratory because their experiments trick subjects into applying good rules of thumb to the wrong situations.

Application 13.3

Rules of Thumb in Portfolio Allocation

Add-On 11A provided a brief introduction to the economic and financial principles governing portfolio allocation. If you read that add-on, and if you're like most readers, you probably found the material challenging. In fact, it's one of the toughest topics in this book. That's why many people rely on trained financial consultants for advice and guidance and why others resort to simple rules of thumb.

A study by economists Gur Huberman and Wei Jiang examined the accounts of nearly 38,000 individuals who began contributing to a 401(k) plan in 2001. The study concluded that rules of thumb frequently govern the allocation of 401(k) pension assets.[17] A majority of individuals (53.6 percent) invest their money in more than one but fewer than six mutual funds. Of those, nearly two out of five (38.3 percent) divide their contributions *equally* among the mutual funds to which they contribute. It is extremely unlikely that equal division would lead to the best portfolio for such a high fraction of investors. It is far more likely that equal division is a rough rule of thumb, which many investors adopt to simplify the complex problem of portfolio allocation.

---

[16]B. Douglas Bernheim, "Personal Saving, Information, and Economic Literacy: New Directions for Public Policy," in Charles E. Walker, Mark Bloomfield, and Margo Thorning (eds.), *Tax Policy for Economic Growth in the 1990s*, American Council for Capital Formation, March 1994.

[17]Gur Huberman and Wei Jiang, "Offering vs. Choice in 401(k) Plans: Equity Exposure and Number of Funds," *Journal of Finance*, April 2006, Vol. 61, pp. 763–801.

13.3 CHOICES INVOLVING TIME

In Chapter 10, we studied the standard economic theory of decisions involving time. Many behavioural economists see that theory as too restrictive, because it rules out certain patterns of behaviour that are sometimes observed in practice. For example, some people may have difficulty following through on carefully formulated plans because of lapses in self-control. They may also make systematic errors in forecasting the future, and they may be reluctant to abandon projects after incurring substantial sunk costs, even when the chances of success are low. In this section, we review some of the evidence that points to these violations of the standard theory, and discuss their implications for economic analysis.

Maintaining Self-Control

From time to time, most people encounter situations in which they have difficulty maintaining self-control. Some of us start diets and then succumb to chocolate cake. Others draw up budgets and then splurge on new clothes. Still others swear off cigarettes, alcohol, or drugs and then fall off the wagon. How do behavioural economists think about such problems?

The Problem of Dynamic Inconsistency
Standard consumer theory assumes that a person's preferences over the alternatives available at some future date don't change as the date approaches or once it arrives. This property is called **dynamic consistency**. A person with dynamically consistent preferences always wants to follow through on his plans and intentions. Lapses of self-control never occur. If dynamically consistent consumers swear off alcohol, they'll feel the same way when the moment of truth arrives, and they'll never fall off the wagon.

People are **dynamically inconsistent** if they change their ranking of the alternatives available at some future date as the date approaches, or once it arrives. Dynamic inconsistency is usually thought to reflect a bias toward immediate gratification, known as **present bias**. A person with present bias often suffers from lapses of self-control. On any given day, for example, a dieter might prefer to eat small portions at his next meal, but might nevertheless choose large portions at mealtime.

Many laboratory experiments have documented the existence of present bias. In a typical study, subjects choose between receiving a small reward after some initial delay and a large reward after some additional delay. To illustrate, suppose the subject chooses on Monday, the small reward is available on Thursday, and the large reward is available on Friday. The initial delay is three days (the time elapsed between Monday and Thursday), and the additional delay is one day (the time elapsed between Thursday and Friday). If subjects are dynamically consistent, their choices shouldn't depend on the length of the initial delay. As long as the same rewards remain available on Thursday and Friday, they will make the same choices on Monday (with an initial delay of three days), Tuesday (with an initial delay of two days), Wednesday (with an initial delay of one day), and Thursday (with no initial delay). But if subjects are present biased they will be more likely to pick the smaller reward if they choose on Thursday, when there is no initial delay and gratification is immediate, than if they choose on Monday, when gratification is delayed regardless of the subject's choice. Therefore, to determine if subjects are dynamically consistent, the

A person is **dynamically consistent** if his preferences over the alternatives available at some future date don't change as that date approaches or once it arrives. When this condition doesn't hold, preferences are **dynamically inconsistent**.

Present bias is a form of dynamic inconsistency involving a bias toward immediate gratification.

Table 13.5

Present Bias in Choosing Rewards

Initial Delay	Percentage of trials in which the smaller, more immediate reward is chosen (median across subjects)
0 seconds	80%
7.5 seconds	40
15 seconds	10

Source: Jay V. Solnick, Catherine H. Kannenberg, David A. Eckerman, and Marcus B. Waller, "An Experimental Analysis of Impulsivity and Impulse Control in Humans," *Learning and Motivation* 11, February 1980, pp. 61–77. The subjects were undergraduates at the University of North Carolina.

experimenter examines whether a change in the length of the initial delay affects choices, holding the size of the rewards and the length of the additional delay fixed.

In one classic study, 60 subjects were exposed continuously to a loud (90 decibel) noise, and were rewarded with intervals of silence.[18] The small reward lasted 60 seconds, the large reward 120 seconds. The initial time delay (prior to the start of the small reward) was either zero, 7.5, or 15 seconds. The additional delay (between the end of the small reward and the start of the large reward) was held fixed at 60 seconds. Each subject repeated the task ten times.

Table 13.5 summarizes some of the experiment's results. The shorter the initial delay, the more often the subjects chose the small reward. This general pattern, which has been replicated in many experiments with both human and animal subjects and with different kinds of rewards, is evidence of present bias.

Odysseus, lashed to the ship's mast, listens to the Sirens' songs.

A **precommitment** is a choice that removes future options.

The Solution: Precommitment   If people are dynamically inconsistent, unable to follow through on plans and intentions, what can they do about it? For an answer to this question, we turn to classical literature. In Homer's *Odyssey*, Odysseus sails his ship near the island of the Sirens, mythical creatures whose beautiful singing lures sailors to their deaths. Though he wants to hear the Sirens' songs, he also wants to survive and knows he won't be able to resist their deadly call. So he instructs his men to block their ears with beeswax, to bind him to the ship's mast, and to ignore his demands for release until the Sirens' land is well out of sight.

Odysseus' decision to have himself bound to the ship's mast is an example of a **precommitment**—that is, a choice that removes future options. Precommitments are useful in situations in which, because of dynamic inconsistency, people don't trust themselves to follow through on their plans and intentions. Everyday life offers many illustrations. A smoker decides to quit and throws away her cigarettes. A student who wants to avoid driving while intoxicated hands his car keys to a friend before joining

---

[18]To enhance the value of the rewards, subjects were asked to solve math problems during the experiment. See Jay V. Solnick, Catherine H. Kannenberg, David A. Eckerman, and Marcus B. Waller, "An Experimental Analysis of Impulsivity and Impulse Control in Humans," *Learning and Motivation* 11, February 1980, pp. 61–77.

a party. A worker with a history of procrastination wants to avoid falling behind on a major project, so she promises a series of presentations showing her work in progress. In each case, the decision maker's object is to avoid "bad" choices by restricting future options.

Precommitments have been observed in the laboratory. Take the experiment described in the last section. Given the opportunity, will subjects who appear to be dynamically inconsistent choose to restrict their future options? Another version of the experiment examined this possibility.[19] Subjects were told that they would choose between the small and large rewards with no initial delay. Then, 15 seconds before making this choice, they were offered the chance to rule out the possibility of choosing the small reward. Overall, subjects took the opportunity 57 percent of the time, precommitting themselves to the large reward.

Implications for Saving People who suffer from present bias may have difficulty exercising the self-control required to save money. To study the effect of present bias on saving, economists have modified the tools discussed in Section 10.2. Their approach is to assume that a consumer applies one set of preferences when the alternatives under consideration involve only future consequences and another set of preferences when at least one of those alternatives involves an immediate consequence.

To illustrate, suppose Myra's employer sends her on a three-day trip, providing her with a $60 meal allowance. As long as she sticks to the overall budget, she's free to spend as much or as little as she likes on each day. Assuming that Myra suffers from present bias, what will she do?

To make a choice on the first day of her trip (Monday), Myra has to figure out how she would spend any remaining balance on Tuesday and Wednesday. Figure 13.4 illustrates. The horizontal axis shows the amount of food she eats on Tuesday, and the vertical

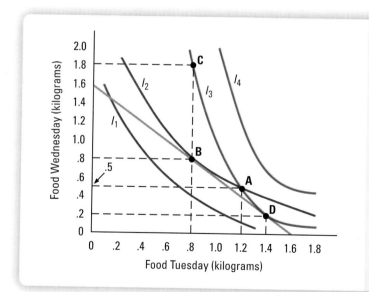

Figure 13.4

Dynamic Inconsistency in Saving. Myra's dining preferences for Tuesday and Wednesday change from Monday to Tuesday. The blue indifference curves correspond to her preferences on Monday; the red ones correspond to her preferences on Tuesday. Wherever a blue curve crosses a red one, for example at bundle A, the red one is steeper, meaning that Myra shows less patience concerning Wednesday's dining on Tuesday than on Monday. If she has $40 to spend on Tuesday and Wednesday, and if food costs $25 per kilogram., she can pick any bundle on the green budget line. From Monday's perspective, she would like to choose bundle B, but on Tuesday she will choose bundle D. Myra lacks the self-control to follow through on Monday's plan.

---

[19]This version of the experiment involved 15 subjects. See Jay V. Solnick, Catherine H. Kannenberg, David A. Eckerman, and Marcus B. Waller, "An Experimental Analysis of Impulsivity and Impulse Control in Humans," *Learning and Motivation* 11, February 1980, pp. 61–77.

axis shows the amount she eats on Wednesday. The blue indifference curves (labelled I_1 and I_2) reflect Myra's preferences as of Monday; the red indifference curves (labelled I_3 and I_4) reflect her preferences as of Tuesday.

Myra's preferences change from Monday to Tuesday because Tuesday's meals provide her with immediate gratification on Tuesday but not on Monday. As we've drawn the figure, the red indifference curves are steeper than the blue ones wherever they intersect, implying that Myra suffers from present bias. Why? Suppose Myra starts out at bundle A (1.2 kilograms on Tuesday and 0.5 kilograms on Wednesday). According to Monday's preferences, she would require an extra 0.3 kilograms on Wednesday—0.8 in total—to compensate for the loss of 0.4 kilograms on Tuesday (because bundles A and B lie on the same blue indifference curve, I_2). But according to Tuesday's preferences, she would require an extra 1.3 kilograms on Wednesday—1.8 in total—to compensate for the same loss (because bundles A and C lie on the same red indifference curve, I_3).

Now suppose food costs $25.00 per kilogram, and that Myra spent $20 for 0.8 kilograms of food on Monday, leaving her with $40 to spend on Tuesday and Wednesday. That means she can pick any bundle on the green budget line. According to her preferences on Monday, she'd like to pick bundle B, splitting her remaining allowance equally between Tuesday and Wednesday. On Tuesday, however, she prefers bundle D. Though her best plan as of Monday is to spend $20 on Tuesday and $20 on Wednesday, she ends up spending $35 on Tuesday (to purchase 1.4 kilograms of food) and only $5 on Wednesday (enough for 0.2 kilograms of food). From Monday's perspective, Tuesday's bias toward instant gratification causes her to save too little for Wednesday.

On Monday, present bias affects Myra's decisions in two ways. The first is obvious: as on Tuesday, consumption provides her with immediate gratification while saving doesn't, so Myra saves less than she would if she didn't suffer from present bias. The second consideration is a bit more subtle. Knowing that she will blow most of her remaining funds once Tuesday arrives, she may think that it's pointless to save much. Or she may feel the need to compensate for Tuesday's poor choices by saving more, to make sure she doesn't go hungry on Wednesday. In most models, present bias reduces saving overall.

From Myra's perspective on or before Monday, her employer provides her with too much flexibility. A precommitment to save more and spend less would improve her situation. Given the opportunity, for example, she might choose a meal allowance that provides $20 each day, rather than $60 for three days.

This simple example suggests some important lessons concerning retirement saving. People who suffer from present bias may save less for retirement than those who are time consistent. They may indulge their whims when young and then regret it when they are old. If they're aware of their tendencies, they may look for ways to save automatically, to lock up funds for retirement. Many pension plans, including RPPs, provide such opportunities (see Applications 13.1 and 13.3). Employees fix their contributions in advance and aren't allowed to change them on short notice. In some cases, early withdrawals from these plans are not permitted; in other cases they are heavily penalized. These features may help to explain why most households do much of their saving through pensions.[20]

---

[20]Pension plans also receive favourable tax treatment, and this is another reason for their popularity.

Application 13.4

Paying Not to Go to the Gym

For most people, relaxation provides immediate gratification; strenuous physical activity doesn't. Present bias therefore makes fitness objectives difficult to achieve. Many people who would like to maintain a regular exercise program lack the willpower to follow through.

We've seen that people often deal with present bias by making precommitments. Short of joining the armed services, there's no fool-proof way to guarantee that you'll exercise regularly. However, there are ways to make partial commitments that either reduce the marginal cost of exercise or create costs for skipping it. If you join a soccer team or schedule tennis games with your friends, for example, social pressure will help you to follow through.

Many people try to get fit by joining a health club. In 2009 nearly 6000 fitness facilities were operating in the Canada, boasting more than four million members. Most health clubs offer monthly and annual membership contracts for a recurring fee. Some also require initiation fees. Many health clubs also allow nonmembers to use their facilities on a pay-per-visit basis. In some cases, customers can pay up front for a fixed number of visits.

Why do so many customers choose memberships rather than paying for actual visits? One possible explanation is that memberships can be less expensive, depending on the frequency of a customer's visits. If the recurring membership fee is $80 per month and a single visit costs $10, a customer must exercise more than eight times a month to come out ahead with a monthly contract.

Another possible explanation has to do with present bias. A customer who suffers from present bias fears that, in the future, he will attach too much importance to the costs of

"I'll be at lunch. If anyone calls say I'm at the health club."

exercise, most of which will be immediate, and not enough importance to the benefits, most of which will be delayed. Purchasing a membership can counteract that bias by reducing the marginal cost of future exercise. When the future arrives, a member will be more likely to go to the club than a non-member because the member's visits cost nothing on the margin, rather than $10. Also, once a customer pays for a membership, skipping an exercise session may become psychologically costly. As a result, some customers may become members hoping that they'll exercise more often.

How do health club customers actually behave? Economists Stefano Della Vigna and Ulrike Malmendier studied the choices made by nearly 8000 members of three New England health clubs over a four-year period, starting in 1997.[21] Table 13.6 provides some information about costs and attendance for monthly members during each of the first six months after enrolment. In every single month, the average price per visit (final column) exceeded the pay-per-visit fee of $10 by a wide margin. Clearly, customers weren't choosing memberships because they were less expensive!

To some extent, this pattern could reflect excessive optimism at the time of enrolment. Were that the only explanation, however, we would expect to see cancellations by members with lower-than-expected attendance. As a result, the average attendance among continuing members would tend to rise with the passage of time after enrolment, and the average price per visit would fall. The data in Table 13.6 are not consistent with this prediction. Among those who remained members after six months, the average price per visit ($18.90) was nearly *double* the pay-per-visit price, and higher than during the first five months of membership.

[21]Stefano Della Vigna and Ulrike Malmendier, "Paying Not to Go to the Gym," *American Economic Review* 96, June 2006, pp. 694–719.

Based on the evidence presented in their study, Della Vigna and Malmendier concluded that many people become health club members—and end up paying more per visit—at least in part because this strategy can counteract the effects of present bias.

Table 13.6
The Cost to Members of Going to the Gym

Months after Enrolment	Average Price per Month	Average Attendance per Month	Average Price per Visit
1	$55.10	3.45	$16.00
2	80.50	5.45	14.80
3	70.00	4.97	14.10
4	81.70	4.61	17.70
5	81.90	4.43	18.50
6	81.90	4.32	18.90
Nonmembers	—	—	10.00

Source: Stefano Della Vigna and Ulrike Malmendier, "Paying Not to Go to the Gym," *American Economic Review* 96, June 2006, pp. 694–719.

WORKED-OUT PROBLEM   13.1

The Problem   It's Sunday and Matt is making plans for the week. He has to do an unpleasant chore by Thursday at the latest. On the day he does the chore, his payoff will be -4, but he will receive a benefit on the next day. If he does the chore on Monday, his payoff on Tuesday will be 12; if he does it on Tuesday, his payoff on Wednesday will be 10; if he does it on Wednesday, his payoff on Thursday will be 8; and if he does it on Thursday, his payoff on Friday will be 5. Matt behaves as follows. On any given day, he wants to maximize the utility function $2P_N + P_F$, where P_N is his payoff on that day, and P_F is the sum of his payoffs on future days. To illustrate, suppose he does the chore on Wednesday. Then his utility from Tuesday's perspective will be $[2 \times 0] + (-4 + 8) = 4$, but his utility from Wednesday's perspective will be $[2 \times (-4)] + 8 = 0$. When deciding whether to do the chore on any given day, Matt correctly anticipates how he will behave on subsequent days. As of Sunday, when would Matt like to do the chore? When will he actually do the chore? Does he procrastinate? Is he dynamically consistent?

The Solution   From Sunday's perspective, Matt's utility will be $12 - 4 = 8$ if he does the chore on Monday, $10 - 4 = 6$ if he does it on Tuesday, $8 - 4 = 4$ if he does it on Wednesday, and $5 - 4 = 1$ if he does it on Thursday. Therefore, as of Sunday, he would like to do it on Monday.

Now let's determine what Matt will actually do. Suppose he reaches Wednesday without having done the chore. He can either do it on Wednesday or delay until Thursday. If he does it on Wednesday, his utility (from Wednesday's perspective) will be $[2 \times (-4)] + 8 = 0$. If he delays until Thursday, his utility (from Wednesday's perspective) will be $5 - 4 = 1$. Since $0 < 1$, he won't do the chore on Wednesday.

Next, suppose Matt reaches Tuesday without having done the chore. He can either do it on Tuesday or delay. If he does it on Tuesday, his utility (from Tuesday's perspective) will be $[2 \times (-4)] + 10 = 2$. If he delays, he knows he will end up doing it on Thursday (as explained in the previous paragraph), so his utility (from Tuesday's perspective) will be $5 - 4 = 1$. Since $2 > 1$, he'll do the chore on Tuesday.

On Monday, Matt can either do the chore or delay. If he does it, his utility (from Monday's perspective) will be $[2 \times (-4)] + 12 = 4$. If he delays, he knows he will end up doing it on Tuesday (as explained in the previous paragraph), so his utility (from Monday's perspective) will be $10 - 4 = 6$. Since $4 < 6$, he won't do the chore on Monday.

Based on this reasoning, we conclude that Matt will procrastinate doing the chore until Tuesday. Since he is dynamically inconsistent, he won't follow through on Sunday's intention to do it on Monday.

IN-TEXT EXERCISE 13.1 **Repeat worked-out problem 13.1, but assume that Matt wants to maximize the utility function $3P_N + P_F$.**

Ignoring Sunk Costs

In Section 3.3, we saw that in making decisions, it's important to ignore sunk costs. This dictum is one of the most basic and fundamental principles in microeconomics. But do people always follow it?

Suppose that within a few days of buying a new pair of shoes, you discover they're extremely uncomfortable and stop wearing them. At that point, you can either throw them away or stow them in the back of your closet. Does your action depend on how much you paid for them? For example, are you less likely to throw the shoes away if you paid $200 for them than if you paid $30? According to standard microeconomic principles, the amount you paid is a sunk cost, so it shouldn't affect your decision. But some people would be less likely to throw the shoes away if they paid the higher price. Those people suffer from the incorrect belief that if they paid more for something it must be more valuable to them. That belief is known as the **sunk cost fallacy**.

Experiments have confirmed that people are sometimes susceptible to the sunk cost fallacy. One study involved the first 60 people to approach the ticket window at Ohio University's theatre with the intention of buying 1982–83 season tickets.[22] One-third of the subjects were charged the normal ticket price ($15), one-third unexpectedly received discounts of $2, and another third unexpectedly received discounts of $7. Once the tickets were purchased, the amount paid became a sunk cost. According to standard economic theory, the size of this sunk cost should have had no effect on whether customers subsequently chose to attend the plays. Yet Table 13.7 shows customers who paid more for their tickets, and who therefore incurred higher sunk costs, attended significantly more

> The **sunk cost fallacy** refers to the belief that if you paid more for something it must be more valuable to you.

---

[22]Hal R. Arkes and Catherine Blumer, "The Psychology of Sunk Cost," *Organizational Behavior and Human Decision Processes* 35, February 1985, pp. 124–140.

Table 13.7

Effect of Sunk Costs on Theatre Attendance

Season Ticket Discount	Attendance, First 5 Plays	Attendance, Last 5 Plays
None	4.11	2.28
$2	3.32	1.84
$7	3.29	2.18
Difference statistically significant?	Yes	No

Source: Hal R. Arkes and Catherine Blumer, "The Psychology of Sunk Cost," *Organizational Behaviour and Human Decision Processes* 35, February 1985, pp. 124–140. The subjects were season ticket holders for the Ohio University Theater.

performances than others during the first half of the season. This pattern suggests that they valued the plays more highly simply because they paid more for their tickets. However, this difference had largely disappeared by the second half of the season, suggesting that while sunk costs do influence people's valuations, their effect shrinks over time.

Application 13.5

Do Investors Hang On to Losing Stocks?

Suppose you purchase some stock in a publicly traded company for $50 per share. After a month, the share price falls to $40. Should you sell your shares or hang on to them? Would your answer change if you had originally paid $30 per share, and the price *rose* to $40 after a month?

The amount you paid for the stock is a sunk cost. According to economic theory, it shouldn't affect your decision—at least not directly.[23] There are some indirect considerations involving taxes. Accounting for taxes, you actually have a strong incentive to sell your shares more quickly if your have losses than if you have gains.[24] For the example described in the previous paragraph, you should therefore be *more* willing to sell the stock if you bought it for $50 than if you bought it for $30. But if you suffer from the sunk cost fallacy, you'll attach *more* value to the stock, and you'll therefore be *less* willing to sell it for $40, if you bought it for $50 than if you bought it for $30.

What do investors actually do? To answer this question, economist Terrance Odean examined trading data for 10,000 randomly selected customers of a nationwide discount brokerage firm.[25] He found that, on average, investors realized 14.8 percent of their gains (by selling the stock on which the gains were earned) but only 9.8 percent of their losses. In other words, typical investors are more reluctant to let go of a stock if they paid more for it. This finding is consistent with the view that investors are susceptible to the sunk cost fallacy. In fact, it suggests that the sunk cost fallacy is so powerful that it overcomes the desire to reduce taxes by realizing losses. Odean considered and rejected a number of other explanations. He also found that the strategy of hanging on to losing stocks has significant costs. According to his calculations, the typical investor's after-tax return over the subsequent year would have been about 4.4 percentage points higher on average if he had sold a losing stock rather than a winning one.

---

[23]You might think that after a loss, further losses are more likely to occur, or alternatively, that losing stocks are more likely to rebound. In fact, there is almost no correlation between past returns and future returns.

[24]Because you pay taxes on your net investment income (the difference between gains and losses), you're better off using your losses to reduce your taxes as soon as possible.

[25]Terrance Odean, "Are Investors Reluctant to Realize Their Losses?" *Journal of Finance* 53, October 1998, pp. 1775–1798.

Forecasting Future Tastes and Needs

Whenever our actions have future consequences, the quality of our decisions will depend in part on the accuracy of our forecasts. Among other things, we need to forecast our own tastes and needs. For example, if we expect to be hungry, we'll favour alternatives that provide food; if we expect to be thirsty, we'll lean toward choices that provide water.

Evidence suggests that people sometimes have trouble forecasting how they'll feel about different outcomes in the future. Instead of making reasonable forecasts, they evaluate future consequences based on their tastes and needs at the moment of decision making. In other words, they *project* their current states of mind into the future. For example, when they're hungry they may project their hunger into the future, causing them to favour alternatives that provide food in the future, even if there's no objective reason to think they'll still be hungry. This tendency is known as **projection bias**.

When a consumer suffers from projection bias, a temporary mood or state of mind can exert a powerful influence on decisions that have only long-term consequences. For example, in controlled experiments that manipulate subjects' hunger prior to grocery shopping, those who are hungry have a greater tendency to stock up on supplies than those who are sated.[26]

Projection bias can also lead people to underestimate their adaptability. Experiments have shown that people tend to overestimate the intensity and duration of unhappiness caused by a wide variety of events, including a romantic breakup, failure to receive a promotion or to be hired by a potential employer, the defeat of a preferred political candidate, and negative feedback on their performance.[27] Before these events, people tend to forecast their reactions based on current states of mind. But after the events occur, they adjust and come to view them as much less disturbing.

> **Projection bias** is the tendency to evaluate future consequences based on tastes and needs at the moment of decision making.

13.4 CHOICES INVOLVING RISK

In Chapter 11, we studied the standard economic theory of decisions involving risk. Many behavioural economists believe that theory requires modification in light of evidence concerning the beliefs that people actually hold and the choices they actually make. For example, some people may have trouble assessing probabilities. Others may attach disproportionate significance to low-probability events or to potential losses. In this section, we review some of the evidence that points to these violations of the standard theory and discuss their implications for economic analysis.

Trouble Assessing Probabilities

In making risky choices, people tend to attach more importance to likely outcomes than to unlikely ones. In that sense, probabilities definitely factor into their decisions. But the laws of probability are complicated, and few of us are trained statisticians. Research suggests that people tend to make specific errors in assessing probabilities.

---

[26]Daniel T. Gilbert, Michael J. Gill, and Timothy D. Wilson, "The Future Is Now: Temporal Correction in Affective Forecasting," *Organizational Behavior and Human Decision Processes* 88, May 2002, pp. 430–444.

[27]Daniel T. Gilbert, Elizabeth C. Pinel, Timothy D. Wilson, Stephen J. Blumberg, and Thalia P. Wheatley, "Immune Neglect: A Source of Durability Bias in Affective Forecasting," *Journal of Personality and Social Psychology* 75, September 1998, pp. 617–638.

Two Common Fallacies   When you flip a coin, the probability of heads is 50 percent. But suppose you flip the coin 10 times in a row and it comes up heads every time. What's the probability of heads on the eleventh flip? Students of statistics know that the correct answer is exactly 50 percent. But some people suffer from the **hot-hand fallacy**, the belief that once an event has occurred several times in a row, it is *more* likely to repeat. This fallacy leads to the false conclusion that after you've flipped heads 10 times in a row, the probability of heads is greater than 50 percent because "you're on a run." Other people suffer from the **gambler's fallacy**, the belief that once an event has occurred, it is less likely to repeat. This fallacy leads to the false conclusion that after a streak of 10 consecutive heads, the probability of heads is less than 50 percent, because tails is "due."

Even if you understand probability in the context of coin flips, you may nevertheless fall prey to these two fallacies in other contexts. The hot-hand fallacy tends to arise in situations in which people can easily invent explanations for streaks. Take basketball. The overwhelming majority of fans, players, coaches, and commentators believe that from time to time, a player has the "hot hand"—in other words, he or she practically can't miss. Some players even develop reputations as "streak shooters." Those who believe in the hot-hand phenomenon attribute it to a variety of plausible factors, such as changes in a player's level of confidence. But we know that some streaks will occur purely by chance. For example, if the probability of making any given shot is 50 percent, the odds are 1 in 16 that a player will hit four in a row. Do players in fact run hot and cold, or are streaks just an illusion created by the luck of the draw?

Table 13.8 shows the shooting percentages for members of a professional basketball team, the Philadelphia 76ers, based on 48 home games played during the 1980–81 season.[28] The first row shows the frequency with which players made their shots ("hits") after missing three in a row; the second row shows the frequency of hits after missing two in a

The **hot-hand fallacy** is the belief that once an event has occurred several times in a row, it is *more* likely to repeat.

The **gambler's fallacy** is the belief that once an event has occurred, it is *less* likely to repeat.

Table 13.8
The Myth of the "Hot Hand"

After a Run of:	Shooting Percentage on the Next Shot for:		
	Entire Team	Julius Erving	Andrew Toney
3 misses	56%	52%	52%
2 misses	53	51	53
1 miss	54	51	51
1 hit	51	53	43
2 hits	50	52	40
3 hits	46	48	34

Source: Thomas Gilovich, Robert Vallone, and Amos Tversky, "The Hot Hand in Basketball: On the Misperception of Random Sequences," *Cognitive Psychology* 17, July 1985, pp. 295–314.

[28]Thomas Gilovich, Robert Vallone, and Amos Tversky, "The Hot Hand in Basketball: On the Misperception of Random Sequences," *Cognitive Psychology* 17, July 1985, pp. 295–314.

row, and so forth. The table reports results both for the team as a whole and for two players, Hall of Famer Julius Erving ("Dr. J") and notorious "streak shooter" Andrew Toney. If players run hot and cold, we would expect to see higher shooting percentages after runs of hits and lower shooting percentages after runs of misses. In fact, the table shows *precisely the opposite pattern* for the team as a whole and for Toney. A hit was *more* likely after a run of misses, and *less* likely after a run of hits. (Erving's shooting percentage was, for the most part, unrelated to his recent hits and misses.) A variety of other statistical tests failed to turn up any evidence of the "hot hand."

The gambler's fallacy tends to arise in situations in which people can't easily invent explanations for streaks. State lotteries provide good illustration. Several studies have shown that many people stop betting on a number right after it wins. This phenomenon occurs even in parimutuel lotteries, in which people have a strong incentive to bid on unpopular numbers (because multiple winners must split the prize). Take New Jersey's pick-three parimutuel lottery game. A study of nearly 1800 daily drawings between 1988 and 1992 found that after a number came up a winner, bettors tended to avoid it. As a result, recent winning numbers were much better bets than other numbers. For two weeks after a win, a number's expected payoff was elevated by 33 percent; over the next two months, it gradually returned to normal.[29]

The hot-hand fallacy and the gambler's fallacy have potentially important implications for economic behaviour. They are clearly relevant in the context of investing, for instance. Some investors assume that a rising stock will continue to rise (the hot-hand fallacy); others assume that a falling stock is due for a rebound (the gambler's fallacy). Investors may also make mistakes in evaluating financial analysts and advisors. For example, they may conclude that a broker who has recommended four or five good stocks in a row is "on a roll," and decide to invest a great deal on his or her next pick.

The Danger of Overconfidence Studies show that many people have overly inflated views of their own abilities. In a variety of studies, for example, researchers have asked people to evaluate themselves in relation to a reference group. If people were objective about themselves, 10 percent would say that they fall within the top 10 percent of the group, 20 percent would say that they fall within the top 20 percent, and so forth. But in fact, on virtually every personal and professional characteristic, people rate themselves much more favourably. In one survey of students with an average age of twenty-two, 82 percent ranked their driving ability among the top 30 percent of their age group.[30]

In the context of decisions involving risk, overconfidence causes people both to overstate the likelihood of favourable events and to understate the uncertainty involved. As Application 13.6 illustrates, this tendency has important implications for economic behaviour.

---

[29]D. Terrell, "A Test of the Gambler's Fallacy—Evidence from Parimutuel Games," *Journal of Risk and Uncertainty* 8, May 1994, pp. 309–317.

[30]O. Svenson, "Are we all less risky and more skillful than our fellow drivers?" *Acta Psychologica* 47, February 1981, pp. 143–148.

Application 13.6

Overconfidence and Business Failure

Relatively few new businesses are successful. In the manufacturing sector, more than 60 percent of new entrants exit within five years; nearly 80 percent exit within 10 years. In most cases, their exit results from business failure.

There are many possible explanations for the high rate of business failure. In some cases, entrepreneurs may launch new businesses in response to temporary profit opportunities, intending to shut them down when the opportunities evaporate. In other cases, the profits from a successful start-up company may be so large that despite the high failure rate, the expected return on entry is still positive. But it is also possible that overconfidence causes new business owners to overestimate their chances of success.

Surveys of entrepreneurs suggest that overconfidence may indeed play a role. In one study, 81 percent of nearly 3000 new business owners assessed their chances of success at more than 70 percent or better, though only 39 percent thought a business like theirs would be that likely to succeed.[31] One-third described their success as *certain*. Judging from actual experience, those expectations were wildly off the mark. In addition, entrepreneurs' self-assessed chances of success were largely uncorrelated with objective factors that might predict business survival, such as their education, prior experience, and initial capital.

Economists Colin Camerer and Dan Lovallo have investigated these issues using an experiment involving a simple game of entrepreneurship.[32] At the start of the game, each entrepreneur decides whether or not to enter a fictitious industry. Participants are told that their profits will depend on their position in some ranking relative to other entrants; a higher ranking implies higher profits. In one version of the game, those who enter are ranked randomly. In another, the ranking depends on the entrepreneur's skill at solving brainteaser puzzles or answering trivia questions. In trials with random rankings, total payoffs per round averaged $16.87. But in trials with skill-based rankings, considerably more entry occurred, causing the average subject to *lose* money (total payoffs averaged −$1.56). Because overconfidence only comes into play when skill is a factor, it provides a natural explanation for this pattern. When potential subjects were told at the time of recruitment that their payoffs would be partly skill-based (which presumably discouraged participation by less confident students), the results were even more striking. Total payoffs per round averaged $13.96 with random rankings and −$13.13 with skill-based rankings. Apparently, overconfidence in one's skill leads to excessive optimism, and consequently, too much entry, causing the average entrant to lose money.

Preferences toward Risk

In Section 11.2 we presented the standard economic theory of risk preferences. Some economists have expressed doubts that the standard theory can account adequately for observed behaviour. To address its perceived shortcomings, they've also proposed modifications of the theory. One of the main alternatives is motivated primarily by two behavioural puzzles, one involving low probability events, and the other involving aversion to very small losses.

A Puzzle Involving Low Probability Events   Experimental subjects definitely show an aversion to risk in gambles involving moderate odds. For example, most choose $2500 for sure over a 50 percent chance of winning $5000, coupled with a 50 percent

---

[31]See A. Cooper, C. Woo, and W. Dunkelberg, "Entrepreneurs' perceived chances for success," *Journal of Business Venturing* 3, Spring 1988, pp. 97–108.

[32]Colin Camerer and Dan Lovallo, "Overconfidence and Excess Entry: An Experimental Approach," *American Economic Review* 89, March 1999, pp. 306–318. Subjects included 118 MBA and undergraduate students from the University of Pennsylvania's Wharton School and the University of Chicago.

chance of winning nothing. When gambles offer very high payoffs with very low probabilities, however, some subjects appear to become risk loving.

To illustrate, suppose someone offered you the following choice:

Option A: Win $5 for sure.

Option B: Win $5000 with odds of 1 in 1000; otherwise win nothing.

Which option would you pick? In laboratory experiments, a sizable majority of subjects say they would pick option B.[33] They prefer a small chance of winning a large sum to the certainty of receiving a very small sum. This choice is puzzling because options A and B have the same expected payoff ($5), but option B clearly involves greater risk. If subjects are risk averse, they should pick option A.

This puzzle isn't confined to the laboratory. The expected payoff on a lottery ticket is only a fraction of its price, and the odds against winning a large prize are astronomical. Yet every year, millions of Canadians spend billions of dollars on lottery tickets. Other evidence suggests that most of these people are risk averse; for example, they insure a wide variety of risks. So why are they so attracted to lotteries?

A Puzzle Involving Aversion to Very Small Risks   Suppose you were offered the following gamble:

Option C: Win $1010 with 50 percent probability; otherwise, lose $1000 with 50 percent probability.

Would you be willing to take it? Most people say they wouldn't. Because the expected payoff is only $5, risking $1000 doesn't seem worthwhile to them. However, in Section 11.4, you learned that a risk-averse individual will always be willing to accept a sufficiently small share of any gamble that provides a positive expected payoff. The following gamble is a 1/100 share of option C:

Option D: Win $10.10 with 50 percent probability; otherwise, lose $10 with 50 percent probability.

Would you be willing to take it? Again, most people say they wouldn't. Because the expected payoff is only 5 cents, risking $10 doesn't seem worthwhile to them.

As this example suggests, many people appear reluctant to take even very tiny shares of certain gambles that have positive expected payoffs. That reluctance implies a level of risk aversion so high that it becomes impossible to explain the typical person's willingness to take larger financial risks.

Prospect Theory: A Potential Solution   In the late 1970s two psychologists, Daniel Kahneman (then at the University of British Columbia and who in 2002 won the Nobel Prize in economics) and Amos Tversky, proposed an alternative to the standard economic theory of risk preference. Their approach, known as **prospect theory**, was intended to resolve a number of puzzles related to risky decisions, including the ones just mentioned.

> **Prospect theory** is an alternative to expected utility theory that may resolve a number of puzzles related to risky decisions.

To explain the basic elements of prospect theory, we need a bit of mathematical notation. Suppose a consumer starts out with resources R. We'll focus our discussion on a gamble with two potential payoffs, X_1 and X_2, which may be positive or negative. Let's

---

[33]In one experiment, 72 percent of subjects said they would choose option B. The subjects were all students at an Israeli university, and the amounts given referred to Israeli pounds rather than U.S. dollars. See Daniel Kahneman and Amos Tversky, "Prospect Theory: An Analysis of Decision Under Risk," *Econometrica* 47, March 1979, pp. 263–291.

say the gamble pays out X_1 with probability P and X_2 with probability $1 - P$ (where P is greater than zero and less than 1). Using expected utility theory (which we covered in Section 11.2), we'd assume that the decision maker takes this gamble when

$$U(R) < [P \times U(R + X_1)] + [(1 - P) \times U(R + X_2)], \qquad \textbf{(1)}$$

where U is his benefit function. The left-hand side of this expression is the utility associated with the resource level R, while the right-hand side is the expected utility when the decision maker takes the gamble. Using prospect theory, however, we assume that the decision maker takes this gamble when

$$V(0) < [W(P) \times V(X_1)] + [W(1 - P) \times V(X_2)], \qquad \textbf{(2)}$$

where W assigns a weight to each probability and V assigns a value to gains and losses.[34] The left-hand side of this expression is the value associated with the status quo (that is, neither a gain nor a loss), while the right-hand side is a weighted average of the values associated with the gamble's gains and losses.

There are two differences between expressions (1) and (2). First, using expected utility theory, we evaluate an outcome based on total resources (that is, R, $R + X_1$, or $R + X_2$). Using prospect theory, we evaluate an outcome based on the *change* in total resources (that is, 0, X_1, or X_2). In other words, prospect theory holds that we judge alternatives according to the gains and losses they generate, relative to the status quo. Kahneman and Tversky justified this assumption as follows:

> "Our perceptual apparatus is attuned to the evaluation of changes or differences rather than to the evaluation of absolute magnitudes. When we respond to attributes such as brightness, loudness, or temperature, the past and present context of experience defines an adaptation level, or reference point, and stimuli are perceived in relation to this reference point."

The second difference between expressions (1) and (2) is that in expression (1), we multiply each valuation by its probability, whereas in expression (2), we multiply each valuation by the weight assigned to its probability. According to prospect theory, the weighting function has the shape shown in Figure 13.5(a). For low values of P, the weight $W(P)$ exceeds P; for high values of P, P exceeds the weight $W(P)$. In other words, people assign disproportionate weight to low-probability outcomes.

Prospect theory also makes some assumptions about the shape of the value function, $V(X)$; see Figure 13.5(b). First, there is a kink at zero, so that the function is steeper to the left of the origin than to the right. This kink means that people are more sensitive, per dollar, to small losses than to small gains, a feature of the theory known as **loss aversion**. The endowment effect can be seen as a form of loss aversion. In fact, the indifference curves in Figure 13.3 (page 457) and the value function in Figure 13.5(b) are kinked for similar reasons. Notice that in Figure 13.5(b), the value function bows upward to the right of the origin but downward to the left of the origin. In both directions—gain or loss—the marginal impact of enlarging a change from the status quo declines with the size of the change. This property is known as **diminishing sensitivity**. Think about buying and selling objects of different value. When you buy (or sell) a coffee mug, you probably care whether the price is $5 or $15, but when you buy (or sell) a car, do you really care whether

Two pioneers in the field of behavioural economics, Nobel Laureate Daniel Kahneman (above, 1934–) and Amos Tversky (below, 1937–1996)

Loss aversion occurs when the consumer's valuation of an outcome is more sensitive, per dollar, to small losses than to small gains.

The property of **diminishing sensitivity** holds when the marginal impact of enlarging a change from the status quo declines with the size of the change.

---

[34]If an alternative yields a payoff of $X with certainty, expected utility theory tells us the decision maker ranks it against other alternatives according to the value $U(R + X)$; prospect theory tells us the decision maker ranks it according to the value of $V(X)$.

Figure 13.5

Prospect Theory. Figure (a) shows a weighting function. The weight exceeds the probability when the probability is low; when the probability is high, it exceeds the weight. Figure (b) shows a valuation function. Valuation depends on changes (gains and losses) starting from the origin, which represents the consumer's status quo. The kink at the origin generates loss aversion. The curve bows upward to the right of the origin and downward to the left, reflecting diminishing sensitivity to gains and losses.

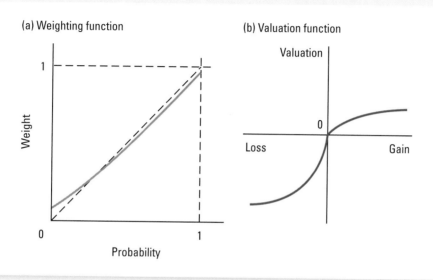

(a) Weighting function

(b) Valuation function

the price is $15,530 or $15,540? In each case the difference is $10, but in the second case you may be less sensitive to this difference because you're considering a larger change from the status quo.

Prospect theory can account for each of the puzzles described in this section. (See worked-out problem 13.2 and in-text exercise 13.2 on page 481 for numerical examples of these points.)

- In the puzzle involving low-probability events (page 477), why do people prefer option B to option A? To evaluate option B using expected utility theory, we would assign a weight of 0.001 to the utility level associated with winning $5000, and a weight of 0.999 to the utility level associated with winning nothing. In contrast, to evaluate option B using prospect theory, we would assign a weight greater than 0.001 to the value associated with winning $5000, and a weight less than 0.999 to the value associated with winning nothing. Compared with expected utility theory, prospect theory makes option B look more attractive because it shifts weight toward the low probability outcome, winning $5000. Similarly, prospect theory implies that people buy lottery tickets because they attach disproportionate weight to prizes that are received with low probability. According to prospect theory, people who buy lottery tickets also demand insurance because they assign disproportionate weight to large losses that occur with low probability.

- Why are people averse to small gambles with positive expected payoffs? Prospect theory attributes this puzzle to loss aversion. Because of the kink in the value function, each dollar lost counts more than each dollar gained.

Prospect theory remains controversial. Some critics have challenged the evidence, arguing that despite a few puzzles, expected utility theory accounts rather well for most risky choices. Others suggest that the evidence reflects systematic mistakes that consumers might correct through experience and awareness. Still others complain that, instead of *explaining* behavioural puzzles, prospect theory merely *summarizes* them by cobbling together a collection of unrelated assumptions.

With respect to this last point, advocates of prospect theory point to success in explaining new puzzles discovered since the theory was proposed. Application 13.7 is sometimes offered as an example.

Application 13.7

The Equity Premium Puzzle

In the appendix to Chapter 11, we noted that stocks (corporate equities) are riskier than Canadian government bonds. To compensate for their greater risk, investors demand a higher return on stocks than on safe bonds. The difference between the annual returns on a broad portfolio of stocks and safe bonds is known as the *equity premium*. For most of the twentieth century, the equity premium averaged around eight percentage points. In other words, when safe bonds pay two percent per year, the rate of return for stocks will be roughly 10 percent, on average.

In 1985, economists Edward C. Prescott (who later received the Nobel Prize in Economics) and Rajnish Mehra published a famous study in which they attempted to reach conclusions about investors' risk preferences based on historical asset returns.[35] To everyone's surprise, they discovered that only an absurdly risk-averse investor would demand an eight percent equity premium. Someone with that level of risk aversion would be indifferent between flipping a coin for a payoff of either $50,000 or $100,000, and receiving $51,209 for sure. Yet most people would strongly prefer the coin flip. This finding, known as the *equity premium puzzle*, suggests that standard economic models can account for the historical equity premium only if investors are absurdly risk averse.

Edward Prescott (1940–) received the Nobel Prize in Economics in 2004. He and Rajnish Mehra were the first economists to describe the equity premium puzzle.

The discovery of the equity premium puzzle sent shockwaves through the economics profession. For the last two decades, finding a good explanation for the puzzle has been one of the central objectives of financial economists. Many explanations have been proposed. One of them involves loss aversion, a central feature of prospect theory. The idea is simple: unlike bond returns, annual stock returns are frequently negative. Loss-averse investors would demand compensation for exposure to such losses.

How much loss aversion is required to explain the equity premium puzzle? The answer depends on whether investors focus on short- or long-term returns. If investors are worried primarily about returns over the next year, moderate levels of loss aversion can produce an equity premium of eight percent. Specifically, in Figure 13.5(b) (page 479), the slope of the valuation function slightly to the left of the origin must be 2.25 times as large as the slope slightly to the right of the origin.[36] Over longer time horizons, equity returns are less likely to be negative, so much greater loss aversion is required to produce an eight percent equity premium. If investors focus on returns over, say, 20 or 30 years, loss aversion cannot explain the equity premium.

[35]Rajnish Mehra and Edward C. Prescott, "The Equity Premium: A Puzzle," *Journal of Monetary Economics* 15, March 1985, pp. 145–161.

[36]Shlomo Benartzi and Richard Thaler, "Myopic Loss Aversion and the Equity Premium Puzzle," *Quarterly Journal of Economics* 110, February 1995, pp. 73–92.

WORKED-OUT PROBLEM   13.2

The Problem   Rosa evaluates risky alternatives based on prospect theory (see expression (2), page 478). For positive values of X (up to \$5000), her valuation function is $V(X) = 20,000X - X^2$. For negative values of X (closer to zero than $-\$5000$), it's $V(X) = 40,000X + 2X^2$. Rosa's probability weighting function is $W(P) = 0.001 + 0.998P$. By graphing these functions, you can see that they look like the ones shown in Figure 13.5.

A. With respect to the first puzzle described on page 477, show that Rosa prefers option B over option A.

B. There is a 0.2 percent chance Rosa will need automobile repairs costing \$2000. She can buy insurance for \$5. Since her expected loss is \$4, the insurance is actuarially unfair. Rosa has just learned of this risk, and still thinks of the status quo as involving neither repairs nor insurance premiums. Show that she will buy this insurance.

The Solution   To answer each of these questions, we need to solve for the expected valuation of each risky prospect using expression (2).

A. Option A provides a valuation of $V(5) = 99,975$. Option B provides a valuation of either $V(5000) = 75,000,000$ or $V(0) = 0$. The weight attached to $V(5000)$ is $W(0.001) = 0.001998$, while the weight attached to $V(0)$ is $W(0.999) = 0.998002$. The value Rosa attaches to option B is therefore $[0.001998 \times 75,000,000] + [0.998002 \times 0] = 149,850$. Since $149,850 > 99,975$, Rosa picks option B.

B. Rosa's valuation for auto insurance is $V(-5) = -199,950$. No insurance provides a valuation of either $V(-2000) = -72,000,000$ or $V(0) = 0$, depending on whether she has an accident. The weight attached to $V(-2000)$ is $W(0.002) = 0.002996$, while the weight attached to $V(0)$ is $W(0.998) = 0.997004$. The value Rosa attaches to option B is therefore $[0.002996 \times (-72,000,000)] + [0.997004 \times 0] = -215,712$. Since $-199,950 > -215,712$, Rosa buys insurance.

IN-TEXT EXERCISE 13.2   Show that Rosa will not take the gamble labelled option C on page 477. Show that she will nevertheless risk losing \$1000 against winning \$5000 based on a coin flip.

13.5 CHOICES INVOLVING STRATEGY

In Chapter 12, we studied the field of game theory, which provides powerful tools for understanding choices involving strategy. How well do those tools perform in practice? The evidence is mixed. However, as we will see in this section, some of game theory's apparent failures may be attributable to faulty assumptions about people's preferences, rather than to fundamental problems with the theory itself. Many applications of the theory assume that people are motivated only by material self-interest. But strategic decisions are inherently social, in the sense that they involve more than one person. When making strategic decisions, some people appear to be motivated in part by social concerns such as altruism, fairness, and prestige. In some situations, it may be important to account for these social motives when analyzing strategic decisions.

Possible Shortcomings of Game Theory

Game theory tends to predict behaviour most accurately once players have gained some experience with a game, particularly if the rules are relatively simple. However, even experienced players of simple games sometimes make decisions that seem contrary to their own interests.

To illustrate these points, we'll examine the types of choices that people tend to make in **voluntary contribution games**. In such a game, each member of a group receives a fixed number of tokens. Players are invited to contribute some or all of their tokens to a central pool. They choose their contributions simultaneously, then the game ends. The following formula determines each player's payoff:

> In a **voluntary contribution game,** each member of a group makes a contribution to a common pool. Each player's contribution benefits everyone, but the cost exceeds the contributor's benefit.

$$\text{Player's payoff (\$)} = \text{Player's remaining tokens} + [M \times \text{Tokens in common pool}]$$

where M is some number between zero and one. So when a player contributes a token to the common pool, everyone else gains $\$M$. The contributor gains $\$M$ through the growth of the common pool, but loses \$1 in the form of the donated token.

Problems like the voluntary contribution game come up in the real world all the time. Think of the common pool as a joint project, in which contributions can take the form of money or effort. Each person's contribution to the project benefits everyone else.

Before reading further, imagine yourself playing this game with three other people. Suppose everyone starts with 20 tokens, and $M = 0.4$. What would you do?

For each token you contribute to the central pool, your payoff changes by $\$(0.4 - 1)$, or $-\$0.60$. No matter what you expect others to do, your best choice is to contribute nothing. In other words, giving nothing is a dominant strategy. Standard game theory predicts that every player should keep all his tokens.

But what if *every* player were to contribute one token? In that case, everyone's payoff would change by $\$(4 \times 0.4 - 1)$, or $+\$0.60$. Everyone would come out ahead. If the players could reach a binding agreement with each other, they would no doubt decide to contribute *all* their tokens. That way, each would end up with $\$4 \times 0.4 \times 20$, or \$32, rather than \$20.

In essence, the voluntary contribution game creates a conflict between individual interests and collective interests. Think of it as a multiple-player version of the Prisoners' Dilemma. Each player has a dominant strategy, but playing those strategies is bad for the group as a whole.

What do people do when they play this game for the first time? Many focus on their individual economic incentives and give nothing. Many others focus on the collective interest and give all of their tokens. Relatively few give something in between. The overall contribution rate is usually around 30 percent to 50 percent—rather far from what game theory would predict.

What happens, though, when people gain experience with this game? In one experiment, subjects played the voluntary contribution game described above 20 times in a row. Playing a game repeatedly can sometimes change the subjects' strategic opportunities and incentives—for example, by introducing the possibility of retaliation or reciprocation (recall Section 12.4). To avoid this possibility, the experimenters assigned players to a new group in each round, so that each round involved a group of "strangers." Subjects were not told what other members of their group had contributed in past rounds.

Figure 13.6 shows the average contributions by round. For the moment, let's focus on the results for the first 10 rounds. Note that contributions dropped steadily as players gained experience. By the tenth round, players were contributing only about 10 percent of their tokens (two tokens), on average. Other studies confirm that contributions dwindle as players become more familiar with the voluntary contribution game. Though there is usually a small core of determined contributors, game theory predicts the behaviour of experienced subjects reasonably well.

What about rounds 11 through 20? The experimenters changed the game by adding a second stage in which any player could punish any other player. To inflict a punishment, a player had to give up some tokens. For example, reducing another player's payoff by 30 percent cost four tokens. Before reading further, think about what you would do in this two-stage voluntary contribution game. Would you contribute more? Would you punish someone who didn't contribute to the common pool?

With a *credible* threat of punishment, you'd expect people to contribute more. However, in this game, self-interest should guarantee that no one will punish anyone else. Inflicting a punishment is costly. And while it may change the punished player's *future* behaviour, it doesn't benefit the punisher because the group assignments change each round. Since the threat of punishment *isn't* credible here, game theory tells us that the addition of punishments shouldn't change the results. (Recall our discussion of strategic credibility in Section 12.4.) Players should contribute nothing and then leave each other alone.

Figure 13.6

Average Contributions in the Voluntary Contribution Game. In a voluntary contribution game, the amount given dropped steadily as players gained experience. By the 10th round, players contributed only about 10 percent of their tokens (2 tokens), on average. As soon as punishments became available (round 11), the contribution rate leaped to nearly 40 percent (8 tokens). As players gained experience with punishments, the contribution rate continued to increase. By the 20th round, the average contribution rate was about 65 percent (13 tokens).

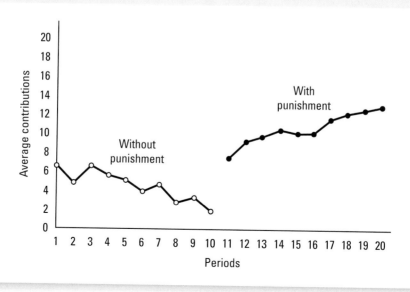

Source: Ernst Fehr and Simon Gachter, "Cooperation and Punishment in Public Goods Experiments," *American Economic Review* 90, September 2000, pp. 980–994.

How do people actually play the two-stage voluntary contribution game? Look again at Figure 13.6. As soon as punishments became available (round 11), the contribution rate leaped to nearly 40 percent (eight tokens). As players gained experience with the new stage, *the contribution rate continued to increase.* By the twentieth round, the average contribution rate was about 65 percent (13 tokens). So for the two-stage voluntary contribution game, our predictions based on standard game theory are quite far off, even for experienced players.

Does this result mean that game theory is wrong? That's one possibility. Another possibility is that our assumptions about players' preferences are incorrect. In solving the voluntary contribution game with and without punishments, we've assumed that players care only about their own monetary rewards. In fact, they may also care about other things, like fairness. To make sensible predictions, we must take all their motives into account.

The Importance of Social Motives

Games that involve more than one person are necessarily social. In social situations, monetary gain usually isn't the only motive. Some people are altruistic, some value fairness. Others are attracted to efficient outcomes that avoid waste. Some worry about status, and try to create a favourable impression. If treated badly by others, some people react angrily.

An important objective of behavioural economics is to understand these social motives and the ways in which they influence strategic choices. In the following sections we'll highlight some important insights, based on experimental studies of three simple two-player games: the dictator game, the ultimatum game, and the trust game.

The Dictator Game   In the **dictator game**, one player (the dictator) divides a fixed prize—say $10—between himself and another player (the recipient) who is a passive participant. The dictator and the recipient usually don't know each other, and they have no direct contact during or after the game. Strictly speaking, this isn't really a game at all, since only one player makes a choice. Before reading further, think about what you would do if you played this game in the role of dictator.

> In the **dictator game**, one player (the dictator) divides a fixed prize between himself and another player (the recipient) who is a passive participant.

If people care only about their own monetary payoffs, every dictator should keep the entire prize. That is not the way people actually behave, however. In one experiment involving $10 prizes and 24 pairs of subjects, only 21 percent of the dictators kept everything for themselves. The same fraction of subjects—21 percent—gave away half the prize ($5). Of the rest, 17 percent ceded $1 to the recipient, 13 percent ceded $2, and 29 percent ceded $3. No one gave away more than half the prize.[37] The specific results have varied a bit from experiment to experiment, depending on the nature of the subject pool, the size of the prize, and other conditions. But most studies have found evidence of significant generosity, even as subjects gained experience. Indeed, a sizable fraction of subjects almost always divides the prize equally.

Results of the dictator game clearly illustrate the potential importance of social motives. Possible explanations include altruism, fairness, and egalitarianism. Concerns about status may also play a role—subjects may want to be *perceived* as generous or fair. Indeed, dictators are considerably less generous when their anonymity is assured.

---

[37]Robert Forsythe, Joel L. Horowitz, N. E. Savin, and Martin Sefton, "Fairness in Simple Bargaining Experiments," *Games and Economic Behavior* 6, May 1994, pp. 347–369. The experiment involved undergraduates and MBA students at the University of Iowa.

The Ultimatum Game   The **ultimatum game** (also known as **ultimatum bargaining**) starts out just as the dictator game: one player (the proposer) offers to give a second player (the recipient) some share of a fixed prize. The recipient then decides whether to accept or reject the proposal. If the recipient accepts, the pie is divided as specified. If the recipient rejects, both players receive nothing. In other words, this game involves a take-it-or-leave-it offer. Before reading further, think about what you would offer as the proposer (given a prize of, say, $10) and what you would accept as the recipient.

In the **ultimatum game** (also known as **ultimatum bargaining**), one player (the proposer) offers to give the second player (the recipient) some share of a fixed prize. The recipient then decides whether to accept or reject the proposal.

You might expect people to give more under a threat of rejection. But as long as the proposer offers the recipient *something*, a recipient who cares only about his monetary payoff will be better off accepting the offer than rejecting it, so a threat to reject isn't credible. In that case, game theory tells us that the proposer will offer only a tiny fraction of the prize, which the recipient will accept.

How do people actually play this game? When the proposer makes an offer below 20 percent, the recipient rejects it about half of the time. Higher offers are also rejected, but with lower frequency. The threat of rejection results in larger offers than in the dictator game, and recipients enjoy significantly higher payoffs on average, even though some offers are rejected. In an ultimatum game experiment that was otherwise identical to the dictator game experiment discussed in the previous section (the same prize, subject pool, and sample size), 71 percent of proposers divided the $10 prize equally; none proposed keeping it all for themselves. Of the rest, four percent offered $1, four percent offered $2, 17 percent offered $4, and four percent offered $6.[38] As with the dictator game, specific results have varied a bit from experiment to experiment. Even so, virtually every study confirms that many subjects reject very low offers, and the threat of rejection produces larger offers.

Choices in the ultimatum game suggest that in social situations, emotions such as anger and indignation influence economic decisions. People can and often do reject offers that offend their sense of fair play, even if doing so runs contrary to their monetary interests. As a result, many people are careful to avoid giving offense to others.

The Trust Game   In the **trust game**, one player (the trustor) starts out with a fixed amount of money, $X, which he can keep or invest. The investment yields $R for every dollar invested (where $R > 1$), but the principal and earnings are controlled by a second player (the trustee). The game ends just as the dictator game: the trustee divides the principal and earnings between herself and the trustor. Before reading further, think about what you would invest as the trustor (assuming that $X = 10$ and $R = 3$) and what you would return as the trustee.

In the **trust game**, one player (the trustor) decides how much money to invest. A second party (the trustee) divides up the principal and earnings.

You might think that players are more likely to return the money if someone entrusts them with it. But if the trustee cares only about her monetary payoff, she'll keep all the principal and earnings for herself. Anticipating this response, a selfish trustor invests nothing. Since $R > 1$, this result is inefficient. In other words, if players have no motives other than monetary gain, game theory tells us that trustees will be untrustworthy and trustors will forgo potentially profitable investments.

How do people actually play this game? In one experiment involving $10 prizes and 32 pairs of subjects, only two trustors invested nothing and five of them invested everything. Overall, trustors invested about half their initial funds. Trustees varied widely in their choices. Twenty percent returned nothing and another 27 percent returned only $1.

---

[38]Ibid.

But others paid back large amounts. Among the 30 trustees who invested something, 11 received more than their investments, 16 received less, and three received the same amount. Overall, trustors received about $0.95 in return for every dollar invested.[39] These results are fairly typical of experimental trust games. Trustors show trust by investing sizable amounts. Some trustees prove trustworthy, while others don't. On average, trustors usually come close to breaking even on their investments.

Why is the trust game important? In the real world, people can sometimes enter into binding contracts, which eliminate the need for trust. Here, a contract might specify that the trustor is to provide investment funds of $10, and the trustee is to return $15, keeping $15 for herself. Both parties would come out ahead. But binding contracts don't work well in all situations. A great deal of business is conducted on the basis of handshakes and verbal agreements. The trust game helps us to understand one reason why this approach works. Many (but not all) people do feel obliged to justify the trust shown in them by others. As a result, many are willing to extend trust to others.

13.6 NEUROECONOMICS: A NEW FRONTIER

Neuroeconomics studies the human neural system, including brain processes, with the object of discovering new principles of economic decision making.

Like the previous sections of this chapter, the field of behavioural economics is highly compartmentalized. It catalogues noteworthy observations concerning decision making and offers specialized theories to explain many of them. Unlike standard economic theory, it does not proceed from overarching principles, nor does it provide a single unified theory of decision making. Some behavioural economists believe that it may be possible to develop a new unified theory of economic decision making by studying the human neural system, including brain processes. Such speculation has led to a new field of microeconomic research called **neuroeconomics**. Progress to date has been limited, but the field is still in its infancy and the pace of discovery is accelerating.

How can the study of human neural processes help with economic modelling? Take the issue of self-control, discussed in Section 13.3. Neuroeconomic research has identified a plausible neurological source of dynamic inconsistency. In one experimental study, subjects made choices involving immediate and delayed rewards while undergoing brain scans.[40] The results suggest that when someone chooses between, say, $10 in two weeks and $12 in six weeks, the brain evaluates both alternatives using the same neural circuitry. However, when someone chooses between $10 immediately and $12 in four weeks (that is, the same alternatives two weeks later), the brain appears to use different circuitry. All alternatives—whether delayed or immediate—activate a portion of the brain that is well-suited to evaluating and comparing abstract rewards (the lateral prefrontal cortex and related structures). But immediate rewards produce more pronounced responses in a part of the brain that is thought to play an important role in many of our emotional responses (the limbic system).

Figure 13.7(a) provides a composite image of multiple brain scans. It highlights areas in which activity is elevated during decision making. Figure 13.7(b) shows how the level of activity in four areas of the brain changes over time once the subject has been asked to

---

[39]Joyce Berg, John Dickhaut, and Kevin McCabe, "Trust, Reciprocity, and Social History," *Games and Economic Behavior* 10, July 1995, pp. 122–142.

[40]Samuel M. McClure, David I. Laibson, George Loewenstein, and Jonathan D. Cohen, "Separate Neural Systems Value Immediate and Delayed Monetary Rewards," *Science* 306, October 15, 2004, pp. 504–507.

choose between two alternatives. Three of these areas are considered limbic structures. The red lines show the level of activity when one of the alternatives provides an immediate reward ("d = today," where d indicates when the earliest reward is available), while the green and blue lines show the level of activity when both alternatives provide delayed rewards ("d = 2 weeks" and "d = 1 month"). Activity in each of these brain structures is considerably higher when one of the alternatives provides an immediate reward than when rewards are delayed (compare the red lines to the green and blue lines). However, as long as the earliest reward is not immediate, the amount of delay doesn't seem to matter (compare the green lines to the blue lines).

Earlier in this chapter, we emphasized that it is often difficult to determine whether a particular behavioural pattern reflects preferences or mistakes. As Application 13.8 illustrates, another potential benefit of neuroeconomics is that it may help us resolve this issue in particular instances.

Figure 13.7

Brain Activity during Choices Involving Time. Figure (a), a composite image of multiple brain scans, shows four areas of the brain that are disproportionately activated by immediate rewards. Figure (b) tracks the level of activation in each of these structures in response to various choices. Here, "d" refers to the time delay before the earlier of two rewards. Immediate rewards (d = Today) produce higher activation in all four areas.

Source: Samuel M. McClure, David I. Laibson, George Loewenstein, and Jonathan D. Cohen, "Separate Neural Systems Value Immediate and Delayed Monetary Rewards," *Science* 306, October 15, 2004, 504–507.

Application 13.8

Addiction

The consumption of addictive substances is an important social issue that affects members of all socioeconomic strata in virtually every nation. According to estimates for Canada in 2002, nearly 37,000 deaths each year are attributable to cigarettes, more than 8000 to alcohol, and roughly 1700 to various narcotics. The social cost of substance abuse in Canada in 2002 has been estimated at almost $40 billion with $5.4 billion of that in direct law enforcement costs.[41]

One school of thought, known as the *theory of rational addiction*, holds that the consumption of addictive substances is simply an expression of consumer preferences.[42] According to this view, addictive substances are distinguished only by the particular pattern of benefits and costs they deliver over time; otherwise, they're just like other goods. While it's true that addictive substances are potentially dangerous, so are hang-gliding, rock climbing, and eating too much fast food. And while it's true that the use of addictive substances sometimes harms other people, the same can be said of the use of automobiles, electricity, and matches. What is the justification for treating addictive substances differently?

There is a growing consensus among neuroscientists that addictive substances interfere with the normal operation of a neural system that generates forecasts of near-term pleasure. Normally, this system learns through feedback—that is, it forecasts pleasure based on past experience. Addictive substances "short circuit" this system, causing it to malfunction. With repeated use of a substance, the cues associated with past consumption cause the system to forecast grossly exaggerated pleasure responses, creating a powerful (and disproportionate) impulse to use.[43]

This new consensus within neuroscience has potentially important implications for the economic analysis of addictive substances. Normally, economists infer consumers' preferences from their choices, and evaluate policies based on these inferred preferences. But in the case of addictive substances, some choices may be attributable to malfunctions of the brain's forecasting circuitry. As a result, they may not reveal consumers' preferences reliably. Indeed, many addicts say they want to quit, and many of them try to quit, but report that they are unable to control their use.

CHAPTER SUMMARY

1. **Objectives and methods of behavioural economics (LO1)**

   a. There are two main motivations for research in behavioural economics. First, people sometimes make choices that are inconsistent or at least very difficult to reconcile with standard economic theory. Second, in some situations, standard economic theory leads to seemingly unreasonable conclusions about consumer welfare.

   b. The main objective of behavioural economists is to modify, supplement, and enrich standard economic theory by adding insights from psychology. Usually they modify the theory either by making different assumptions about preferences or by assuming that certain actions are mistakes.

   c. For the most part, behavioural economists employ the same tools as other economists, though they tend to rely more on experiments. Experiments offer several potential advantages and disadvantages over other methods.

2. **Departures from perfect rationality (LO2)**

   a. Some experiments call into question the assumption that people have coherent preferences. In some situations, subjects consistently violate the Ranking Principle; in others, their judgments appear to depend on patently irrelevant information.

   b. In some situations, people exhibit a strong attachment to the status quo. For example, they tend to value

---

[41]The Canadian Centre on Substance Abuse (www.ccsa.ca) provides information on a variety of topics related to substance abuse and addiction.

[42]See Gary Becker and Kevin Murphy, "A Theory of Rational Addiction," *Journal of Political Economy* 96, August 1988, pp. 675–700.

[43]For a review of the evidence, as well as an elaboration of the policy implications, see B. Douglas Bernheim and Antonio Rangel, "Addiction and Cue-Triggered Decision Processes," *American Economic Review* 94, December 2004, pp. 1558–1590.

something more highly when they own it than when they don't. Moreover, when confronted with a menu of alternatives, they sometimes avoid making a choice and end up with the default option. Default effects are apparent in decisions about retirement saving.

c. People tend to group related items into categories and to draw artificial boundaries around those categories. In making a choice, they tend to consider other items in the same category, and may ignore items in different categories.

d. Sometimes, people's choices seem to depend on the way the alternatives are presented. Different presentations may convey precisely the same objective information while calling attention to different facts.

e. When confronted with complex problems, people often rely on simple rules of thumb that have performed reasonably well in the past. Rules of thumb appear to play an important role in decisions concerning saving and portfolio allocation.

3. **Choices involving time (LO3)**

a. Some people change their rankings of the alternatives available at some future time as that time approaches. This phenomenon reflects a bias toward immediate gratification, which creates problems involving self-control. That, in turn, leads people to restrict future choices.

b. People who suffer from present bias may have difficulty exercising the self-control required to save money. If they're aware of their tendencies, they may look for ways to save automatically and lock up funds for retirement—for example, through pension plans.

c. Though microeconomic theory tells us to ignore sunk costs, people sometimes have difficulty following that principle. For example, they may behave as if the value they attach to an object depends on the price they paid for it.

d. In some situations, people appear to have trouble accurately forecasting how they'll feel about different outcomes in the future. Instead of making reasonable forecasts, they tend to evaluate future consequences based on their tastes and needs at the moment of decision making.

4. **Choices involving risk (LO3)**

a. People tend to make several types of errors in assessing probabilities. Some think that once an event has occurred several times in a row, it is more likely to repeat; others think it is less likely to repeat. Overconfidence causes people to overestimate their abilities and underestimate the uncertainty involved in decisions. This tendency may contribute to the high frequency of business failure.

b. In some situations, people seem to place disproportionate weight on low-probability events, and are noticeably risk averse, even toward gambles involving very low stakes. These and other puzzles have led to the development of prospect theory.

c. Prospect theory assumes (1) that people evaluate an outcome based on the change in total resources, rather than on the level of total resources; (2) that a person's valuation of an outcome is more sensitive, per dollar, to small losses than to small gains; (3) that the impact of enlarging a change on a valuation declines with the size of the change; and (4) that the weight associated with each potential outcome is greater than its probability for small probabilities and smaller than its probability for large probabilities.

5. **Choices involving strategy (LO4)**

a. Predictions of behaviour that are based on game theory tend to become more accurate once players have gained some experience with a game, particularly if the rules are relatively simple. However, even experienced players of simple games sometimes appear to behave contrary to their own interests. Many of these failures may be attributable to assumptions about players' payoffs (in particular, that they care only about their own monetary rewards) rather than to problems with game theory itself.

b. An important objective of behavioural economists is to understand the ways in which social motives influence strategic choices. Results for the dictator game illustrate the potential importance of social motives such as altruism, fairness, egalitarianism, and status. Results for the ultimatum game suggest that emotions such as anger and indignation can also influence economic decisions. Results for the trust game help us to understand one reason why it's possible to conduct a great deal of business based on only handshakes and oral agreements.

6. **Neuroeconomics: a new frontier (LO5)**

a. Some economists believe that they will eventually learn to build better models of economic behaviour, and perhaps develop a new unified theory of decision making, by studying relevant aspects of the human neural system, including brain processes. For example, researchers have identified a plausible neurological source of dynamic inconsistency.

b. Neuroeconomics may help us determine whether particular behavioural patterns, such as the consumption of addictive substances, reflect preferences or mistakes.

Exercise 13.1: What are the characteristics of a good economic experiment? What characteristics make an experiment convincing? (LO1)

Exercise 13.2: Some people use behavioural economics constructively to identify patterns they should watch out for in their own behaviour. Based on the material in this chapter, what patterns do you think you should watch out for? Why? How would you detect them? (LO1–5)

Exercise 13.3: Some countries (including Canada) require explicit consent for an organ donation; others presume that an individual consents unless he or she explicitly opts out. In countries that require explicit consent, fewer than 30 percent of adults are eligible for organ donation. In most opt-out countries, more than 98 percent are eligible. Interpret this observation in light of the default effect. Why do you think the effect is so strong with regard to organ donation? Can you reconcile this pattern with standard economic theory? (LO2)

Exercise 13.4: Describe three situations (not including the examples given in the text) in which people use rules of thumb to make complex decisions. What rules do they tend to use? Do those rules strike you as reasonable? Why or why not? (LO2)

Exercise 13.5: Application 13.4 (on health clubs) shows how a business can make a profit by taking advantage of customers' dynamic inconsistency. Why do health club members allow health clubs to take advantage of them? What else might they do? Can you think of other examples of profitable business strategies (either actual or potential) designed to take advantage of the behavioural patterns discussed in this chapter? For example, do businesses sometimes try to exploit the endowment effect? The anchoring effect? How? Think about advertising and marketing strategies, among other things. (LO3)

Exercise 13.6: Describe three situations (not including the examples given in the text) in which people may make precommitments. Do they do so because they don't trust themselves to follow through on their plans or intentions, or for some other reason? (LO3)

Exercise 13.7: Try to think of a situation in which a sunk cost influenced a decision you made. Do you think the decision was a mistake? If you had the opportunity to make a similar decision today, would you choose differently? Why or why not? (LO3)

Exercise 13.8: Think about a voluntary contribution game with nine players, in which each player receives 20 tokens.

Suppose $M = 0.2$. Let's use R to stand for a player's remaining tokens and C to stand for the number of tokens in the common pool. The dollar payoff is $D = R + 0.2C$, but players are altruistic and rank outcomes according to the value $D + AD^0$, where A is a positive number and D^0 stands for the total dollar payoff to every other player. The value of A differs from one player to another. Suppose $A > 0.5$. Will the players have a dominant strategy? What is it? What if $A < 0.5$? (LO4)

Exercise 13.9: Think about a dictator game in which one player divides $10 between himself and someone else. Let's use S to stand for the amount he keeps for himself and F for the absolute value of the difference between the amount he keeps, and the amount he gives the other player. For instance, if he keeps $8, then $F = 6$ (because he gives $2 to the other player); if he keeps $4, then $F = 2$ (because he gives $6 to the other player). Suppose the dictator ranks the outcomes according to the value $S - AF$, where A is a positive number. That is, he cares about both his own dollar payoff and the fairness of the outcome (where greater equality implies greater fairness). What will he do if $A < 0.5$? What will he do if $A > 0.5$? (LO4)

Exercise 13.10: Think about an ultimatum game in which the proposer divides $10 and the recipient decides whether to accept or reject the proposal. If the recipient rejects the proposal, neither player receives anything. Let's use F to stand for the absolute value of the difference between the two players' payoffs, as in the last question. Suppose the proposer is selfish and cares only about his own dollar payoff. The receiver, however, cares about fairness—she ranks the outcomes according to the value $R - 0.5F$, where R is her dollar payoff. Which proposals will she accept? Which ones will she reject? Knowing that information, what will the proposer offer? (LO4)

Exercise 13.11: Think about a trust game in which the trustor starts out with $10, and an investment yields $3 for each dollar invested. Let's use F to stand for the absolute value of the difference between the two players' payoffs, as in the last two questions. Suppose the trustor is selfish and cares only about his own dollar payoff. The trustee, however, cares about fairness—she ranks the outcomes according to the value $R - 2F$, where R is her dollar payoff. What will the trustee do if the trustor invests $2, $4, $6, $8, or $10? What is the trustor's payoff in each case? What is the trustor's best choice? How would your answer change if the investment yielded $1.50 for each dollar invested? (LO4)

Markets

Part III In the next eight chapters we turn our attention to markets. Our objective is to understand how the economic decisions of consumers and firms determine market outcomes, including the prices of goods and the quantities bought and sold. Part IIIA studies perfectly competitive markets, in which consumers and firms treat market prices as fixed. We'll see that perfectly competitive markets achieve desirable economic outcomes. Part IIIB studies imperfectly competitive markets which fall short of the competitive ideal.

Part IIIA Competitive Markets 491

Part IIIB Market Failures 613

Competitive Markets

In Chapter 2 we provided a brief introduction to the analysis of competitive markets. The next three chapters examine the nature of competitive equilibrium in greater depth. In Chapter 14 we'll investigate the differences between market equilibrium in the short run and the long run. We'll also analyze the welfare properties of competitive equilibrium outcomes. We'll see that perfectly competitive markets allocate resources efficiently in the sense that it is impossible to make any individual better off without making others worse off. Chapter 15 uses the tools that we develop to study the effects of various government policies. In Chapter 16 we'll broaden the scope of our analysis beyond a single market, and examine competitive equilibrium in many markets simultaneously. We'll see how developments in one market affect others, and how those effects ripple between markets and produce feedback into the original market. We'll also extend our conclusion regarding the efficiency of competitive markets to this more general setting.

14 Equilibrium and Efficiency 492

15 Market Intervention 533

16 General Equilibrium, Efficiency, and Equity 568

14

Equilibrium and Efficiency

On the night of November 9, 1989, the Berlin Wall came down. Its fall marked the culmination of a revolution in Central Europe, one that gave political and economic freedom to millions who had lived for years under Soviet controlled communist regimes. Soon after, the Soviet Union would itself break apart, unable to sustain high military spending and a collapsing economy.

The collapse of communism marked a turning point for the economies of the former Soviet-bloc nations. In the years that followed, many would move from state-controlled to free-market economies. State-owned firms would be privatized and new businesses would be allowed to form without hindrance. The economies of those nations that aggressively embraced free markets and privatization soon began to grow rapidly. In Poland, for example, the share of gross domestic product produced by private firms increased from 19 percent

The fall of the Berlin Wall (above) and soon after (below)

in 1988 to 65 percent in 1997. Gross domestic product per capita rose over 150 percent in the ten years from 1990 to 2000.

Economists put a lot of faith in markets. In this chapter, we'll see why. As we noted in Section 1.1, there are many ways for a society to determine what goods are produced, how they are produced, and who consumes them. In the former Soviet-bloc countries, those decisions were made largely by government edict. In a market economy, most of those decisions are made instead by individuals who face market prices. When markets are perfectly competitive, this process, which Adam Smith called the "invisible hand" of the market, produces an outcome that maximizes society's net benefit from the production and consumption of goods. That is not to say that markets always perform flawlessly. In Part IIIB (Chapters 17–21), we'll study circumstances in which markets fail to achieve this ideal, in some cases justifying government intervention.

This chapter covers five topics concerning competitive markets:

1. *What makes a market competitive?* We'll start by discussing the factors that make a market competitive, so that individuals and firms act as price takers and supply-and-demand analysis is appropriate.

2. *Market demand and market supply.* In Parts IIA and IIB (Chapters 4–9) we discussed *individual* demand and supply. To find the market demand and market supply, we need to add up those individual demands and supplies. We'll see how to do so, both when the number of firms is fixed, and when firms can freely enter and exit a market.

3. *Short-run and long-run competitive equilibrium.* Once we know the market demand and supply, we can determine the market equilibrium, as discussed in Chapter 2. Here we'll study a topic not covered in Chapter 2, the short-run and long-run adjustments in markets that are characterized by free entry and exit in the long run.

4. *Efficiency of perfectly competitive markets.* A market is only one of many possible ways to allocate a society's scarce resources. Yet with all those possibilities, economists tend to put their faith in markets. We'll show that in a perfectly competitive market, an equilibrium is efficient in the sense that it maximizes "aggregate surplus," society's net benefit from the production and consumption of a good or service.

5. *Measuring surplus using market demand and supply curves.* We'll study how to use market demand and supply curves to measure aggregate surplus, as well as the surpluses enjoyed by consumers and firms. These techniques will prove very useful when we consider applications of competitive equilibrium theory in Chapter 15.

14.1 WHAT MAKES A MARKET COMPETITIVE?

When we apply supply-and-demand analysis to study a market, we assume that buyers and sellers act as price takers. When is this reasonable?

Let's consider buyers first. Usually, a consumer's demand for a good, or a firm's demand for an input, is just a tiny fraction of the overall amount bought and sold. A change in the amount a consumer or firm purchases has a negligible effect on the balance between total supply and demand, so price remains virtually unchanged. Put slightly differently, because their needs are small relative to the market, each consumer or firm can greatly increase the amount they buy with only a negligible increase in the price they offer to pay sellers. As a result, it is usually reasonable to assume that buyers are price takers. (We discuss some exceptions in Section 17.6.)

What about sellers? Conditions for sellers in markets for their outputs are more varied. Sometimes they act as price takers, and at other times not. We'll study both cases in the remaining chapters of this book.

Economists call the idealized setting in which both buyers and sellers have absolutely no effect on price a *perfectly competitive* market. Three factors cause a market to be perfectly competitive. The first factor is the *absence of transactions costs*. Transactions costs are absent when sellers can easily communicate their prices, buyers can easily locate suppliers and learn their prices, and buyers and sellers can arrange transactions without significant obstacles. This means that when different sellers produce the same product buyers will have no difficulty identifying and purchasing from the seller who offers it at the best terms.

The second factor is **product homogeneity**. Wheat is wheat. For the most part, buyers of wheat don't care who grew it. If any one farmer tries to charge more than the others, buyers will simply get their wheat elsewhere. This means there's only one market for wheat, with a price that applies for wheat grown by every farmer. In contrast, consider a situation in which a small town has two local car dealers, one selling General Motors cars, and the other selling Fords. Consumers are likely to view Ford and General Motors cars as **differentiated products**, products that are not the same. Because consumers will differ in their desire to buy from one dealer versus another, the prices of the dealers' cars need not be the same for both to make sales.

The third factor is the presence of a *large number of sellers*, *each of whom accounts for a small fraction of the market supply*. With many small sellers, a single firm can substantially increase or decrease the amount it sells (say doubling it, or halving it) with its profit affected in only a trivial way by the negligible changes in price this may cause. As a result, it will act like a price taker, selling a unit if the price is greater than the marginal cost of producing it (see Section 9.3). Economies of scale play a key role in determining when this situation can arise (see Section 8.8 for a review of economies of scale). For many small firms to produce efficiently in a market, the efficient scale of production must be small compared to the total amount produced and consumed in the market. The efficient scale in wheat production is indeed a tiny fraction of the overall amount of wheat produced. In contrast, consider the market for concrete in a small town. Because concrete production involves economies of scale, a small town may have only a single concrete producer. If so, and if the market demand curve is downward sloping, that firm will recognize that the more it wants to sell, the lower its price must be. It will not be a price taker.[1]

When all three of these factors are present, consumers have many options and buy from the firm that offers the lowest price. No firm can charge more than the price offered by other firms—the market price—without losing virtually all of its customers. Moreover, even substantial changes in the amount a firm sells involve only negligible changes in price. As a result, each firm can essentially take the market price as given and focus only on how much it wants to sell at that price, which leads the firm to sell a unit precisely when the marginal cost of producing it is no greater than the market price.

> Products are **homogeneous** when they are identical in the eyes of purchasers. They are **differentiated** when some purchasers view the products as different.

---

[1] In Section 19.6, we'll see more explicitly how the number of firms grows as economies of scale shrink, driving the market toward the outcome predicted by supply and demand analysis.

Factors That Make a Market Perfectly Competitive

1. Buyers and sellers face no transactions costs.

2. Products are homogeneous.

3. There are many suppliers, each accounting for a small fraction of the overall supply of the good.

Few markets, if any, are *perfectly* competitive. Consumers usually face at least some transactions costs, the products of different firms usually differ at least a little bit, and many markets have quite a few firms but not an extremely large number (say, 20 firms rather than 100). As a result, firms usually think that their decisions have at least a small effect on price. Economists nonetheless devote a fair amount of attention to models of perfectly competitive markets for two reasons. First, many markets are highly competitive and behave almost as if they're perfectly competitive. Our model of perfect competition therefore helps us predict outcomes in these markets. It provides a useful tool for analyzing how changes in input costs, prices of substitutes, taxes, and other market factors affect the price and quantity sold. Second, we'll see in Section 14.4 (and Chapter 16) that perfect competition leads to outcomes that are, in an important sense, very desirable from the perspective of market participants. As a result, it serves as a useful benchmark against which to compare the performance of markets that are not perfectly competitive, the subject of Part IIIB (Chapters 17–21).

14.2 MARKET DEMAND AND MARKET SUPPLY

In Chapters 4–9 we studied how price-taking consumers and firms determine their individual demand and supply. But to analyze the competitive market for a good, we need to determine the good's *market* demand and *market* supply. Let's start with market demand.

Market Demand

At any given price, the **market demand** for a product is the sum of the demands of all the individual consumers. (For simplicity, in this section we'll assume that all demand comes from consumers and all supply comes from firms.) Graphically, the **market demand curve** is the horizontal sum of the individual demand curves. Example 14.1 illustrates how to add up individual demand to get market demand.

> The **market demand** for a product is the sum of the demands of all the individual consumers. Graphically, the **market demand curve** is the horizontal sum of the individual demand curves.

Example 14.1

The Market Demand for Ice Cream Cones

Juan and Emily are the only consumers of ice cream cones. Figure 14.1(a) shows their demand curves, labelled D_{Juan} and D_{Emily}, respectively. Juan's demand function is $Q^d_{Juan} = 10 - 4P$ (the inverse demand function being $P = 2.5 - (1/4)Q^d_{Juan}$) at prices below $2.50, and zero at prices above $2.50.[2] Emily's demand function is $Q^d_{Emily} = 6 - 2P$ (the inverse demand function being $P = 3 - (1/2)Q^d_{Emily}$) at prices below $3, and zero at prices above $3. Figure 14.1(b) shows the market demand curve for ice cream cones. At prices equal to or greater than $2.50, only Emily wants to buy ice cream, so the market demand curve is the same as her individual demand curve. For example, at a price of $2.50, the market demand is one cone, which is the number Emily demands. Juan demands nothing at that price. At prices below $2.50, Emily and Juan both want to buy ice cream so the market demand equals the sum of their demands at each price. For example, when the price is $1.50, Emily wants three cones and Juan wants four cones, so the market demand is seven cones. Since Juan and Emily's demand curves both slope downward, so does the market demand curve.

We can find the market demand function using algebra. At prices below $2.50, the market demand is $Q^d = Q^d_{Juan} + Q^d_{Emily} = (10 - 4P) + (6 - 2P) = 16 - 6P$. For prices between $2.50 and $3.00, only Emily buys ice cream, so the market demand function is $Q^d = Q^d_{Emily} = 6 - 2P$. At prices above $3.00, neither Emily nor Juan wants a cone. So we can write the market demand function as

$$Q^d = \begin{cases} 0 \text{ for } P > 3.00 \\ 6 - 2P \text{ for } 2.50 < P \le 3.00 \\ 16 - 6P \text{ for } P \le 2.50 \end{cases}$$

Figure 14.1

Individual and Market Demand Curves for Ice Cream Cones. Figure (a) shows Juan's and Emily's weekly demand curves for ice cream cones. Figure (b) shows the market demand curve, equal to the horizontal sum of Juan's and Emily's individual demand curves.

(a) Individual demand

(b) Market demand

---

[2]Whenever a demand curve is shown hitting the vertical axis at some price, this should be understood as meaning that demand is zero for all higher prices.

Suppose Juan's demand function for ice cream cones changes to $Q^d_{Juan} = 20 - 5P$ at prices below \$4, and zero at prices above \$4. Emily's demand function is $Q^d_{Emily} = 6 - 2P$ at prices below \$3, and zero at prices above \$3. What is the market demand function? Graph the individual and market demand curves.

In Chapter 5 we discussed how a consumer's demand for a product can differ in the short and long run. To find the market demand in the short run, we just add up consumers' short-run demand curves. Similarly, to find the market demand in the long run, we add up consumers' long-run demand curves. Thus, when consumers' demand curves differ in the short and long run, the market demand curve is likely to do so as well.

Market Supply

At any given price, the **market supply** of a product is the sum of all the individual sellers' supplies. Graphically, the **market supply curve** is therefore the horizontal sum of the individual supply curves. Example 14.2 illustrates how to add up individual supplies to get market supply. The procedure is very similar to the way we constructed market demand.

> The **market supply** of a product is the sum of the supply of all the individual sellers. Graphically, the **market supply curve** is the horizontal sum of the individual supply curves.

Example 14.2

The Market Supply of Ice Cream Cones

Anitra and Robert are the only sellers of ice cream cones. Figure 14.2(a) shows their supply curves, labelled S_{Anitra} and S_{Robert}, respectively. Anitra's supply function is $Q^S_{Anitra} = 8P - 8$ (the inverse supply curve being $P = 1 - (1/8)Q^S_{Anitra}$) at prices above \$1, and zero at prices below \$1.[3] Robert's supply function is $Q^S_{Robert} = 3P - 1.50$ (the inverse supply curve being $P = (1/2) - (1/3)Q^S_{Anitra}$) at prices above \$0.50, and zero at prices below \$0.50. Figure 14.2(b) shows the market supply curve. At prices below \$0.50, neither of them wants to sell any ice cream. At prices between \$0.50 and \$1, only Robert wants to sell ice cream, so the market supply curve is the same as his individual supply curve. For example, when the price is \$1, the market supply is 1.5 cones per week; all of that supply comes from Robert. At prices above \$1, both Anitra and Robert want to sell ice cream, so the market supply equals the sum of their individual supplies at each price. For example, when the price is \$1.50, Anitra wants to sell four cones and Robert wants to sell three cones. Market supply is therefore seven cones. Since both their supply curves slope upward, so does the market supply curve.

We can find the market supply function using algebra. At prices above \$1, the market supply function is $Q^S = Q^S_{Anitra} + Q^S_{Robert} = (8P - 8) + (3P - 1.50) = 11P - 9.50$. At prices between \$0.50 and \$1, it is $Q^S = Q^S_{Robert} = 3P - 1.50$. At prices below \$0.50, neither Robert nor Anitra wants to supply any ice cream. So we can write the market supply function as

$$Q^S = \begin{cases} 11P - 9.50 \text{ for } P \geq 1.00 \\ 3P - 1.50 \text{ for } 0.50 \leq P < 1.00 \\ 0 \text{ for } P < 0.50 \end{cases}$$

---

[3]Whenever a supply curve is shown hitting the vertical axis at some price, this should be understood as meaning that supply is zero for all lower prices. In some cases, however, to avoid any possible confusion, we'll explicitly show the portion of a supply curve that reflects zero supply (as we did in Chapter 9 when a firm's supply jumped from zero to a positive quantity when the price reached the lowest level of average cost, AC_{min}).

Figure 14.2

Individual and Market Supply Curves for Ice Cream Cones. Figure (a) shows Anitra's and Robert's weekly supply curves for ice cream cones. Figure (b) shows the market supply curve, equal to the horizontal sum of Anitra's and Robert's individual supply curves.

IN-TEXT EXERCISE 14.2   **The supply function of each firm that makes fudge brownies is $Q^s = 100P - 50$ at prices above \$0.50, and zero at prices below \$0.50. Suppose there are 50 brownie manufacturers. What is the market supply function for brownies? Graph the market supply curve. Repeat the exercise supposing instead that there are 100 brownie manufacturers.**

Application 14.1

Canadian Exports and the U.S. Softwood Lumber Supply in 1998

In Application 9.3 (page 314) we saw how the Softwood Lumber Agreement (SLA) between the United States and Canada affected the export supply curve of lumber producers in Alberta, British Columbia, Ontario, and Quebec. Now let's look at the U.S. market supply of softwood lumber in 1998 when augmented by Canadian and other exports, one of the five years the agreement was in effect.

The softwood lumber consumed in the United States comes from three sources: domestic (U.S.) producers, Canadian producers in the four provinces subject to the SLA, and other foreign producers (including other Canadian provinces not covered by the SLA). In 1998, U.S. consumption of softwood lumber was 52.9 billion board feet (bbf). U.S. firms produced 65 percent of that total, Canadian firms in the four SLA provinces produced 29 percent, and other imports accounted for the rest.

Figure 14.3 shows the supply curves for these three groups, labelled $S_{U.S.}$ for U.S. producers, S_{Cdn} for the Canadian producers subject to the SLA, and S_{other} for other foreign producers. Each of those curves is the horizontal sum of the individual supply curves of all producers in the group. The light-red dashed line shows what the Canadian supply curve would have looked like at prices above $240 without the Softwood Lumber Agreement.

The supply curve for the Canadian producers who were subject to the SLA reflects the features we studied in Application 9.3. The SLA specified that those producers could freely export in total up to 14.7 bbf per year to the United States; that the next 0.65 bbf would be subject to a tariff of $50 per thousand board feet (collected by the Canadian government); and that any further exports would be subject to a tariff of $100 per thousand board feet. As a result, the SLA shifted the supply curve of those Canadian producers, S_{Cdn}, up by $50 at 14.7 bbf and another $50 at 15.35 bbf.[4] Those jumps imply that there are price ranges over which exports by those producers are insensitive to the price. For example, at all prices between $240 and $290, Canadian producers would export 14.7 bbf to the United States. Only if the price exceeded $290 would it become worthwhile for Canadian producers to incur the $50 tariff in order to sell more lumber in the United States. Similarly, they would export 15.35 bbf at all prices between $304 and $354.

The U.S. market supply curve of softwood lumber, labelled S in Figure 14.3, is equal to the horizontal sum of the supply curves of the three groups. It is steeper in the price ranges $240–$290 and $304–$354, where Canadian producers from the four affected provinces would not have changed their exports in response to price changes. The medium-red dashed line shows what the U.S. market supply curve would have looked like at prices above $240 without the Softwood Lumber Agreement.

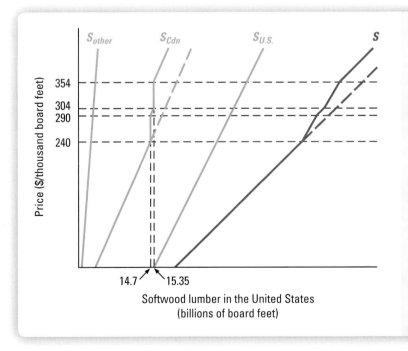

Figure 14.3

Canadian Exports and the U.S. Market Supply Curve of Softwood Lumber, 1998.
The market supply curve S is the sum of the supply curves of three groups: U.S. domestic producers (curve $S_{U.S.}$), Canadian producers subject to the Softwood Lumber Agreement (curve S_{Cdn}), and other foreign producers not subject to the agreement (curve S_{other}). The dashed red lines show what the Canadian and market supply curves would have been at prices above $240 without the Softwood Lumber Agreement.

---

[4]The precise shape of the supply curve S_{Cdn} depends on how the Canadian government distributes the quota limits among the individual suppliers in the four provinces. In constructing it, we've made the simplifying assumption that all of those producers were identical and faced the same fee-free and low-fee limits, so that they had identical individual supply curves like the one in Application 9.3. (For example, with 100 producers, each would face the $50 and $100 tariffs once their production reached 1.47 bbf and 1.535 bbf, respectively.)

Short-Run versus Long-Run Market Supply   In Section 9.4 we saw that a firm's short-run and long-run supply curves may differ. Since the market supply curve for a product is just the sum of individual sellers' supply curves, the short-run and long-run market supply curves may differ as well.

Short-run and long-run market supply curves may also differ for another reason. Over time, the set of firms that operate in a market may change. In the short run, only those firms that are currently active in the market can produce output. But in the long run other firms may be able to begin producing if it is profitable for them to do so. This means that the short-run market supply curve is found by summing the short-run supply curves of the currently active firms, while the long-run market supply curve is found by summing the long-run supply curves of all *potential* suppliers.

Sometimes the number of potential firms is limited; there may be only a small number of firms that are able to produce a product, even in the long run. (End-of-chapter exercise 14.4 asks you to consider such a case.) However, since technological knowledge diffuses over time and patents on production processes, which can prevent others from copying a firm's technology, eventually expire, we can usually assume that technology is freely available over the long run. When that is so, anyone who wishes to start a firm and enter a market has access to the same technology and opportunities as everyone else—a situation called **free entry**. With free entry there are, in effect, an unlimited (that is, infinite) number of firms that can produce a good in the long run.

> There is **free entry** in a market when technology is freely available to anyone who wishes to start a firm and entry is unrestricted. In that case, the number of potential firms is unlimited.

How do we add up the supply curves of an unlimited number of potential firms to find the long-run market supply curve with free entry? Figure 14.4 illustrates the procedure. Suppose everyone has access to the same technology for producing garden benches. The (long-run) marginal cost, average cost, and individual firm supply curves are shown in Figure 14.4(a). The level of minimum average cost, AC_{min}, is $100 per unit. It is achieved at the efficient scale of production, equal to 200 benches per month. (We studied these concepts in Section 8.5.) As the firm's supply curve shows, a firm will produce zero benches if the price is below $100 and either zero or 200 benches if the price equals $100. It will produce the amount indicated by the marginal cost curve if the price is above $100 (that is, the quantity where MC equals the price).

Figure 14.4(b) shows the short-run market supply curves if there are five firms, 10 firms, and an unlimited number of firms that can produce in the long run. The market supply curve with five firms, labelled S_5, is the horizontal sum of five of the supply curves in Figure 14.4(a). At prices below $100, supply is zero. At prices above $100, each of the five firms produces the quantity on its marginal cost curve corresponding to that price. So the market supply curve at prices above $100 is the horizontal sum of the individual firms' marginal cost curves. What happens when the price equals $100? Then every firm is willing to supply either zero or 200 benches. As a result, there are several possibilities for market supply. One firm could produce 200 benches, while the other four firms produce zero. In that case, market supply would be 200 benches, indicated by the dot labelled "A" in Figure 14.4(b). Or two firms could each produce 200 benches, while the other three firms produce zero. Then market supply would be 400, indicated by the dot labelled "B" in Figure 14.4(b). In fact, market supply could be any multiple of 200 benches up to 1000, which would be the market supply if all five firms produced 200 benches. Those amounts are shown by the set of five dots running up to 1000 benches.

Figure 14.4

The Long-Run Market Supply Curve for Garden Benches with Free Entry. Figure (a) shows the marginal and average costs and supply curve for an individual firm. With 5 or 10 such firms, the short-run market supply curves would be S_5 or S_{10} respectively, in figure (b). With free entry, the number of potential firms is unlimited, so the long-run market supply curve becomes the horizontal line at a price of $100 (equal to AC_{min}), labelled S_∞ in figure (b).

The same idea applies when there are 10 firms; the market supply curve is then S_{10}. Supply is zero at prices below $100. At prices above $100, it coincides with the horizontal sum of the 10 firms' marginal cost curves. At a price of exactly $100, the market supply curve is shown by the set of 10 dots (spaced in multiples of 200 benches) running up to 2000.

If we increase the number of firms further, we get more and more dots at a price of $100. With an unlimited number of potential firms, the long-run market supply curve is the set of dots spaced in multiples of 200 benches that lie along the light red horizontal line at a price equal to $100, the level of AC_{min}. When the distance between the dots that make up the long-run market supply curve is small compared to total market production, we can safely approximate the long-run market supply curve by the infinitely elastic, horizontal line S_∞.

The fact that with free entry, the long-run market supply curve is a horizontal line at the price AC_{min} makes sense. At any price below AC_{min} no firm can make a profit, so supply is zero. At any price above AC_{min} every firm with access to the technology can make a profit, so with an unlimited number of potential firms, supply is infinite. When the price exactly equals AC_{min}, a firm with access to the technology can break even (earn zero profit) by producing at its efficient scale, the level at which average cost equals AC_{min}. In that case the market supply can be anything, depending on how many firms choose to produce at the efficient scale and how many choose to produce nothing.

WORKED-OUT PROBLEM   14.1

The Problem   Consider the pizza market in Vancouver, where the (long-run) daily costs for a pizza company are the same as for Dan's Pizza Company in worked-out problems 9.2 and 9.3 (pages 308 and 310). They include $845 in avoidable fixed costs and variable costs equal to $VC = 5Q + Q^2/80$, where Q is the number of pizzas produced each day. Marginal cost when producing Q pizzas is $MC = 5 + Q/40$. Suppose that in the long run there is free entry into this market. What is the long-run market supply curve?

The Solution   In answering worked-out problem 9.3, we found that the efficient scale of production was 260 pizzas per day. (Recall that we determined that level by finding the output level at which average cost equals marginal cost—look back at worked-out problem 9.3.) At the efficient scale, average cost (AC_{min}) equals $11.50. Thus, the long-run market supply curve is a horizontal line at $11.50. At prices below $11.50, long-run supply is zero; at prices above $11.50, it is infinite. When the price exactly equals $11.50, long-run supply can be any positive quantity (strictly speaking, any positive quantity that is a multiple of 260).

IN-TEXT EXERCISE 14.3   **Suppose that, in the long run, a pizza firm's variable costs are $VC = Q^2/2$ (where Q is the number of pizzas produced each day), its marginal cost is $MC = Q$, and there is an avoidable fixed cost of $50 per day. In the long run, there is free entry into the market. What is the long-run market supply curve?**

The time horizon required for long-run adjustments in the number of active firms can differ across products. It may take a matter of months, for example, to set up a new retail coffee shop. But in the automobile industry, it can take years to open a new plant. The time required for long-run adjustments in a given market may also depend on the types of adjustments required; for example, it may be shorter when existing firms need to shut down than when new ones need to enter.

14.3 SHORT-RUN AND LONG-RUN COMPETITIVE EQUILIBRIUM

Once we've determined market supply and demand, we can find the equilibrium price and quantity (the amount bought and sold), just as we did in Chapter 2. At the equilibrium price, the amounts supplied and demanded are equal. The market clears at that price, with buyers and sellers making all their desired purchases and sales.

To illustrate, consider the market for ice cream cones in Examples 14.1 and 14.2 (pages 495 and 497). Figure 14.5 shows the market demand curve from Figure 14.1(b), labelled D, and the market supply curve from Figure 14.2(b), labelled S. The market clearing price is $1.50, the price at which the demand and supply curves intersect. At that price, seven cones are bought and sold each week.

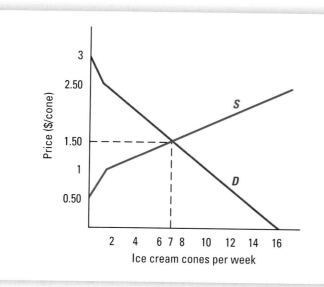

Figure 14.5

Market Equilibrium. The market for ice cream cones clears at a price of $1.50 per cone. At that price demand equals supply, and there is no tendency for the price to either increase or decrease.

Before you read further, review (or read for the first time) Section 2.3 on the basics of market equilibrium, including how to use algebra to find the market equilibrium and determine changes in the equilibrium in response to shifts in demand or supply. In this section, we'll discuss an issue not covered in Section 2.3, the short-run and long-run adjustment to changes in market conditions in markets with free entry in the long run. We'll begin by considering some of the properties of long-run competitive equilibrium with free entry. (The chapter's appendix examines another issue not covered in Section 2.3: equilibrium in factor markets, the markets for firms' inputs.)

Long-Run Competitive Equilibrium with Free Entry

In Section 14.2 we saw that, with free entry, the supply curve is horizontal at the level of AC_{min}, the minimum average cost. Figure 14.6 depicts a long-run competitive equilibrium in the garden bench market when there is free entry and all firms have access to the technology shown in Figure 14.4(a) (page 501), so that AC_{min} is $100 and the efficient scale is 200 garden benches per month. The market demand curve is the medium blue curve, labelled D. The long-run market supply curve is S_∞. The long-run equilibrium price is $100 and 2000 garden benches are bought and sold per month. Since each active firm must be producing at its efficient scale of 200 garden benches, there are 10 active firms.

More generally, free entry has three important implications for market equilibrium:

Three Properties of Long-Run Competitive Equilibrium with Free Entry

1. The equilibrium price must equal AC_{min}.

2. Firms must earn zero profit.

3. Each active firm must produce at its efficient scale of production.

Figure 14.6

Long-Run Market Equilibrium with Free Entry. This figure shows a long-run competitive equilibrium in the garden bench market when there is free entry and all firms have access to the technology in Figure 14.4(a). The equilibrium price equals AC_{min} and 2000 garden benches are bought and sold each month. Since each firm must produce at its efficient scale (200 garden benches per month), there are 10 active firms.

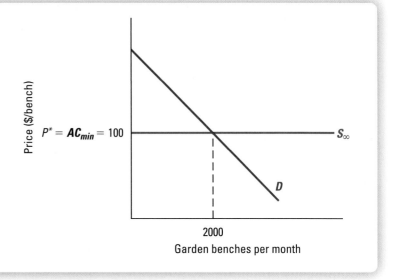

Figure 14.6 shows why the first implication is true. Because the market supply curve with free entry is a horizontal line at the price AC_{min}, the equilibrium price must equal AC_{min} regardless of the location or shape of the demand curve.

The second and third points follow from the first. When the price equals AC_{min} a firm can't make a positive profit: there is no output level it might choose at which the price would exceed its average cost. The most it can earn is zero profit, which it does by producing at its efficient scale, the quantity at which average cost equals AC_{min}.

A firm that earns zero economic profit is not doing badly. Remember that economic costs include opportunity costs (see Section 8.2). For example, the firm's economic costs include the opportunity cost of any time the owner spends running the firm. If the firm earns zero economic profit, the owner is being compensated fully for her opportunity cost, which means she can't make more money doing anything else. While the owner would of course prefer to make a positive economic profit, she is earning as much return on her investment of time in the firm as she could earn in other ways. Likewise, if the firm is using capital assets, it is earning exactly the opportunity cost of those assets—that is, the amount it could earn by deploying them in some other way, such as renting them to other firms.

Short-Run and Long-Run Responses to Changes in Demand

To predict the short-run and long-run responses to changes in market conditions, we need to determine how market equilibrium changes in the short run when the number of firms is fixed, as well as in the long run when conditions of free entry hold.

Consider the garden bench market again. Suppose that initially the market is in the long-run equilibrium depicted in Figure 14.6, with 10 active firms, but that the demand curve then shifts outward to the curve labelled $\hat{D}$ in Figure 14.7(a). In the short run, the number of firms is fixed at 10 (its original equilibrium level), so the short-run supply curve is S_{10}. This curve is the sum of the 10 active firms' short-run supply curves (we assume that these firms' fixed costs are sunk in the short run, so these curves coincide with the marginal cost curve in Figure 14.4(a), even at prices below AC_{min}). So in the short

Figure 14.7

Short-Run and Long-Run Responses to a Change in Demand. In the long run, all firms have access to the technology for producing garden benches shown in Figure 14.4(a) (page 501), and can enter or exit the market. In the short run, however, the number of firms is fixed (and active firms' fixed costs are sunk). Initially, in both figures, the market is in a long-run equilibrium at point A, with 10 firms each producing 200 units. When demand changes from D to $\hat{D}$, the short-run equilibrium shifts to point B. In figure (a), where demand increases, the price rises above $100 and active firms earn a positive profit. In figure (b), where demand decreases, the price falls below $100 and active firms earn a negative profit. In the long run, however, in both cases the equilibrium shifts to point C in the respective figures and the price returns to $100. Once again, each active firm produces 200 benches per month and earns zero economic profit. The new long-run equilibrium involves 20 firms in figure (a) and 5 firms in figure (b).

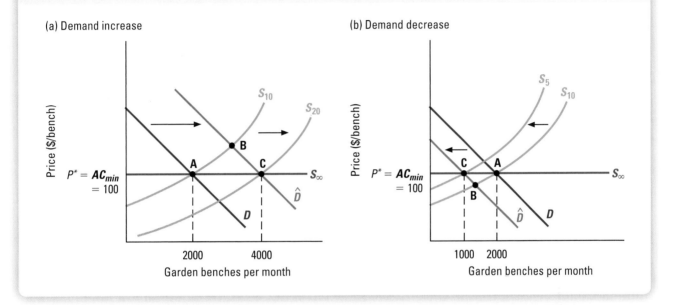

run the market equilibrium shifts from point A to point B. The price rises above $100. Because the equilibrium price exceeds the firms' minimum average cost, AC_{min}, they make positive economic profits.

In the long run, however, new firms are free to enter the market. More firms become active in response to the profit opportunity that emerges when the short-run equilibrium price rises above AC_{min}. This entry eventually pushes the price down to a new long-run equilibrium at point C. The price is once again $100, but the total amount bought and sold is now 4000 benches. Since each active firm must be producing at its efficient scale, there are now 20 active firms.

Figure 14.7(b) shows the short-run and long-run response to a *reduction* in the demand for garden benches. When demand decreases from D to $\hat{D}$, the market equilibrium adjusts from its initial long-run equilibrium at point A to a new short-run equilibrium at point B. The price falls below $100, and the active firms incur losses (in the short run, their fixed costs are sunk and they cannot avoid them by exiting). Over time, however, some firms exit and the market adjusts to a new long-run equilibrium at point C. The price is once again $100 and 1000 benches are produced and sold each month. Since each active firm must be producing at its efficient scale of 200 benches per month, only five of the ten original firms remain active; the other five have exited.

We can aso solve for short and long-run changes using algebra instead of graphs. Worked-out problem 14.2 provides an example.

WORKED-OUT PROBLEM   14.2

The Problem   Consider again the pizza market in Vancouver. Assume the daily demand for pizza is $Q^d = 32{,}900 - 600P$, where P is the price of a pizza. The daily costs for a pizza company are the same as in worked-out problem 14.1 (page 496). They include \$845 in fixed costs and variable costs equal to $VC = 5Q + Q^2/80$, where Q is the number of pizzas produced in a day. Marginal cost is $MC = 5 + Q/40$. Suppose that in the long run, there is free entry into the market and the fixed cost is avoidable. What are the long-run market equilibrium price and quantity? How many firms are active, and how much does each produce?

Now suppose that demand doubles to $Q^d = 65{,}800 - 1200P$. If in the short run the number of firms is fixed (so that neither entry nor exit is possible) and fixed costs are sunk, what is the new short-run market equilibrium? What is the new market equilibrium in the long run?

The Solution   Recall from worked-out problem 14.1 that the efficient scale of production is 260 pizzas per day, and that AC_{min} equals \$11.50, so that the long-run market supply curve is horizontal at a price of \$11.50.

Step 1:   Finding the initial long-run market equilibrium. In a long-run equilibrium, the market price equals AC_{min}, so the price in the initial long-run equilibrium must be \$11.50. The next step is to find out how many pizzas are produced and sold each day in this equilibrium. We can find this quantity from the demand function: when the price is \$11.50, the total quantity demanded is $Q^d = 32{,}900 - 600(11.50) = 26{,}000$ pizzas per day. Finally, in a long-run equilibrium, each active firm produces 260 pizzas per day, its efficient scale. That means there are 100 active firms in the initial long-run equilibrium.

Step 2:   Finding the new short-run market equilibrium. Now suppose that demand doubles. In the short run, the number of active firms is fixed at 100. To find the short-run market supply, we need to first find the supply function for each of these individual firms. In the short run, their fixed costs are sunk. Each of the firms therefore has the same supply function that we solved for in worked-out problem 9.3 (page 310), in the case with no avoidable fixed cost:

$$S(P) = \begin{cases} 40P - 200 \text{ if } P \geq 5 \\ 0 \text{ if } P \leq 5 \end{cases}$$

Since there are 100 such firms, the short-run market supply function is

$$S(P) = \begin{cases} 4000P - 20{,}000 \text{ if } P \geq 5 \\ 0 \text{ if } P \leq 5 \end{cases}$$

To find the new short-run market equilibrium, we equate supply and demand and solve for the equilibrium price.

$$65{,}800 - 1200P = 4000P - 20{,}000$$

The solution is $P^* = \$16.50$. The total number of pizzas produced and sold each day in this short-run equilibrium is 46,000 and each active firm sells 460 pizzas. Since the price is above $AC_{min} = \$11.50$, the active firms each make a positive profit.[5]

Step 3: Finding the new long-run market equilibrium. In the long run, the price falls back to $AC_{min} = \$11.50$. Since demand has doubled, the total number of pizzas produced and sold must double to 52,000 a day. And since each active firm is again producing at its efficient scale of 260 pizzas a day, the number of active firms doubles to 200.

IN-TEXT EXERCISE 14.4   **The daily demand for pizzas is $Q^d = 750 - 25P$, where P is the price of a pizza. The daily costs for a pizza company include \$50 in fixed costs, and variable costs equal to $VC = Q^2/2$, where Q is the number of pizzas produced in a day. Marginal cost is $MC = Q$. (These are the costs in in-text exercise 14.3 on page 502.) Suppose that in the long run there is free entry into the market and the fixed cost is avoidable. What are the long-run market equilibrium price and quantity? How many firms are active, and how much does each produce? If demand doubles to $Q^d = 1500 - 50P$ and, in the short run, the number of firms is fixed (so that neither entry nor exit is possible) and fixed costs are sunk, what is the new short-run market equilibrium? What is the new market equilibrium in the long run?**

Short-Run and Long-Run Responses to Changes in Cost

Let's look now at the short and long-run response to a change in firms' costs. Suppose that, starting from the long-run equilibrium in Figure 14.6, a garden bench firm's fixed costs decrease while variable costs remain the same. For example, the firm's monthly rent may have decreased, or the opportunity cost of its owner's time may have fallen. Figure 14.8(a) shows that this decrease in fixed cost shifts the average cost curve downward from AC to $\hat{AC}$, decreasing minimum average cost from \$100 to \$70 per table. The firm's minimum efficient scale decreases from 200 to 160.

Figure 14.8(b) shows the resulting short-run and long-run changes in market equilibrium. After the decrease in costs, the short-run market supply curve is S_{10}, the horizontal sum of the firms' marginal cost curves (again, in the short run, the fixed cost is sunk). Since firms' marginal costs have not changed and the number of active firms is fixed, the market equilibrium remains at point A in the short run. Active firms make a positive profit because the price is greater than the now-lower minimum average cost level of \$70 per table.

In the long run, however, firms enter the market in response to this profit opportunity. The long-run supply curve is now the horizontal line $\hat{S}_\infty$, and the market equilibrium shifts to point B. The price falls to \$70 per table and 2720 garden benches are produced and sold each month. Since each firm's efficient scale is now 160 benches per month, all active firms must be producing that quantity. Thus, there are 17 active firms in this new long-run equilibrium.

---

[5]Specifically, each of the 100 active firms earns revenue of $460 \times 16.50 = \$7590$ per day, incurs variable costs of $5(460) + (460)^2/80 = \$4945$, and has a fixed cost of \$845. Thus, they each earn \$1800 per day.

Figure 14.8

Short-Run and Long-Run Responses to a Decrease in Fixed Costs. In the long run, all firms have access to the technology whose cost curves are shown in figure (a), and can enter or exit the market at will. In the short run, however, the number of firms is fixed. Initially, each firm's average cost curve is AC, but when fixed costs fall, the average cost curve drops to $\hat{AC}$ and the efficient scale of production falls from 200 to 160 benches per month. Initially, the market is in equilibrium at point A in figure (b), with 10 active firms. When fixed costs decrease, the market equilibrium remains at point A in the short run, but shifts to point B in the long run. The price falls to $70 in the long run.

(a) Change in average cost

(b) Change in market equilibrium

When instead firms' variable costs change, a firm's marginal and average cost curves both shift. This causes the short-run supply curve to shift, in contrast to what happened in Figure 14.8. The basic procedure for identifying short-run and long-run responses is similar, however. Find the new short-run equilibrium using the new short-run supply curve of the initially active firms, and then find the new long-run equilibrium using the new long-run market supply curve (which reflects free entry). End-of-chapter exercises 14.8 and 14.9 ask you to identify the short-run and long-run responses to changes in costs using algebra.

Price Changes in the Long Run

In reaching the conclusion that, with free entry, the long-run competitive price is unaffected by changes in demand (always equal to AC_{min}), we've assumed that the prices of firms' inputs do not change. This assumption will be a reasonable one if any increases in the amounts of inputs used are small compared to the sizes of the overall input markets. Then the prices of the inputs will likely not change. Our assumption will also be reasonable when the supply in those input markets is very elastic (see Section 2.4 for a discussion of elasticity), since then even large changes in the demand for those inputs will cause only very small changes in their prices. In this case the long-run supply curve is horizontal, as in Figures 14.7 and 14.8, and the industry is referred to as a *constant cost industry*. In general, though, when the demand for a product increases, the prices of the inputs used to make it may change. This phenomenon is an example of a *general equilibrium effect*—that is, an effect that arises because the market we are studying and the markets for its inputs must *all* be in equilibrium.

We'll study general equilibrium effects in Chapter 16. In the context of input prices, the basic idea is fairly straightforward. Figure 14.9(a) considers again what happens when the demand for garden benches increases. Now, however, we suppose that this drives up the price of the inputs used in producing them. For example, garden bench production might require a special kind of wood that has few other uses, so that a large portion of the demand for that particular wood comes from firms producing garden benches. The increase in the price of this wood causes the long-run market supply curve to slope upward. This is because the average cost curves and marginal cost curves of individual firms shift upward as input prices increase. These shifts occur even if the firm is able to change its input mix as a result of the input price change. In particular, the minimum point on each firm's average cost curve increases as a result of the input price change. The new long-run equilibrium is point C. Thus, once we take account of the induced change in input prices, the increase in demand raises the price of garden benches in the long run. Note the impact on the long-run supply curve from a change in variable costs when compared to the change in fixed costs considered earlier. In the case of a change in fixed costs the long-run supply curve shifts upward while with a change in variable costs the long-run

Figure 14.9

Price Changes in the Long Run. Figure (a) shows a case in which an increase in the demand for garden benches from D to $\hat{D}$ drives up firms' input costs, inducing the long-run market supply curve to slope upward and causing the price to increase in the long run. Figure (b) shows a case in which instead input prices fall, inducing the long-run supply curve to slope downward and causing the price of garden benches to fall in the long run. Before additional firms enter in response to the increase in price caused by demand increasing, firms make economic profits at short-run equilibrium B. The short-run supply curves before and after firms enter are given by S and $\hat{S}$.

(a) Increasing-cost industry

(b) Decreasing-cost industry

supply curve slopes upward. When input costs increase as the total output in the market increases we call the industry an *increasing cost industry*.

Sometimes an increase in demand for an input can cause its price to fall. This can't happen if the input market is competitive (since increases in input demand would cause the input price to increase, as we saw in Section 2.3), but we'll see in Section 19.5 that it can happen in an oligopolistic input market. In that case, the long-run market supply curve for the final product would slope downward in response to the increase in demand for garden benches, causing the price of garden benches to fall in the long run, as illustrated in Figure 14.9(b). In this case we would call the industry a *decreasing cost industry*.

If marginal costs increase for reasons unrelated to the demand for inputs by garden bench producers the impact on the short- and long-run equilibrium is simplified. If marginal costs increase by a fixed amount the average cost and marginal cost curve of an individual firms exhibit a parallel shift upward by the amount of the change in marginal costs. The long-run supply curve shifts upward by that same amount, rather than sloping upward.

14.4 EFFICIENCY OF PERFECTLY COMPETITIVE MARKETS

A market system is only one of many possible ways for a society to determine what goods are produced and consumed, and who consumes and produces them. Instead of privately owned firms producing and selling goods, state-owned firms might produce them, as they did in the former Soviet Union and other Eastern-bloc countries. And instead of consumers buying the goods they desire at market prices, the government could allocate goods by edict, a lottery, or on a first-come first-served basis.

Of all the possibilities, why do economists usually prefer markets? Could another economic system achieve a better allocation of resources? In this section we'll provide an answer to this question. We'll see that a perfectly competitive market produces an outcome that is economically efficient, in the sense that it generates the largest possible net benefit from the production and consumption of the good.

Before showing why this statement is true, however, we need to define more carefully what we mean by economic efficiency. For the sake of simplicity, we'll assume that all the buyers in the market are consumers and all the sellers are firms. (The same conclusions would hold even if some or all buyers were firms and some or all sellers were consumers, as in a labour market.)

Aggregate Surplus and Economic Efficiency

If an economic system works well, it creates net benefits: consumers' benefits from the goods they consume exceed the costs of producing them. Economists measure the net benefit created by the production and consumption of a good using the concept of **aggregate surplus** (also called *total surplus* or *social surplus*), which is the total benefit from consumption less the total avoidable cost of production.

Aggregate surplus =

$$\text{Total benefit from consumption} - \text{Total avoidable cost of production} \quad \textbf{(1)}$$

Consider, first, the total benefits from consumption, the sum of the benefits enjoyed by all of the consumers of the good. In Section 6.2, we saw that economists measure an

Aggregate surplus equals consumers' total willingness to pay for a good less firms' total avoidable cost of production. It captures the net benefit created by the production and consumption of the good.

Figure 14.10

Juan's and Emily's Willingness to Pay for Ice Cream Cones. Juan's and Emily's willingness to pay for four and three ice cream cones per week, respectively, is shown by the shaded areas under their demand curves. Juan's willingness to pay is $8; Emily's is $6.75.

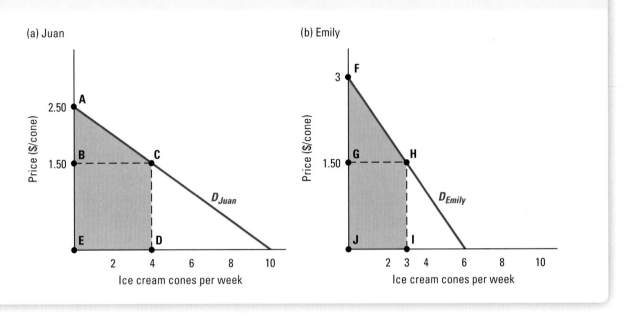

individual's benefit from consuming a good by calculating her willingness to pay for the amount she consumes. It follows that

Aggregate surplus = Total willingness to pay − Total avoidable cost of production (2)

In Section 6.2 we also saw that a consumer's willingness to pay for a particular amount of the good equals the area under the consumer's demand curve up to that quantity.[6] By extension, we can calculate the total willingness to pay of all consumers of a good by adding the areas under those consumers' individual demand curves up to the quantities they each consume. Figure 14.10 shows the total willingness to pay for ice cream cones in Example 14.1 (page 495) when Juan buys four ice cream cones and Emily buys three. Juan's total willingness to pay is $8 (the area of the triangle ABC is two, and the area of the rectangle BCDE is six), while Emily's is $6.75 (the area of the triangle FGH is 2.25, and the area of the rectangle GHIJ is 4.50). Their total willingness to pay is therefore $14.75.

Now consider the second part of aggregate surplus in formulas (1) and (2), the total avoidable cost of production. This is the sum of all producers' avoidable costs of producing the good. Avoidable costs include all of a firm's costs other than its sunk costs. Since sunk costs are incurred even if *none* of the good is produced and consumed, by considering only avoidable costs aggregate surplus truly measures the net benefit from production and consumption of the good.

---

[6] In general, the consumer's willingness to pay equals the area under her compensated demand curve (see Section 6.5). However, when the consumer's demand for the good is insensitive to her income, so that there are no income effects, her compensated and uncompensated (ordinary or Marshallian) demand curves coincide, and we can use the area under the consumer's ordinary demand curve. For simplicity, throughout this section we'll assume that there are no income effects, so that we can use uncompensated demand curves.

Figure 14.11

Anitra's and Robert's Avoidable Costs of Producing Ice Cream Cones. Anitra's and Robert's avoidable costs of producing four and three ice cream cones per week, respectively, are shown by the shaded areas under their supply curves. Anitra's avoidable cost is $5; Robert's is $3.

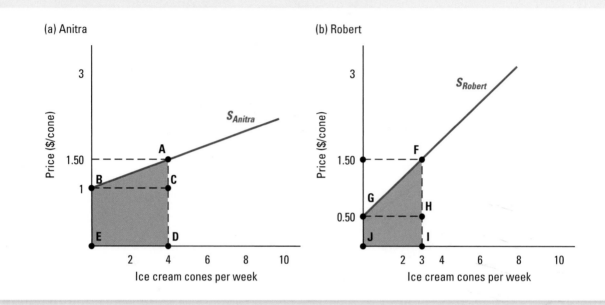

In Section 9.5 we saw that a firm's avoidable cost of production equals the area under its supply curve up to its production level. Figure 14.11 shows the avoidable cost of production when Anitra sells four ice cream cones and Robert sells three. Anitra's avoidable cost is $5 (the area of the triangle ABC is $1 and the area of the rectangle BCDE is $4), while Robert's is $3 (the area of the triangle FGH is $1.50 and the area of the rectangle GHIJ is $1.50). The total avoidable cost is therefore $8. Aggregate surplus therefore equals $6.75 (this is consumers' total willingness to pay, $14.75, minus total avoidable costs, $8).

An economic system that maximizes aggregate surplus creates the largest possible net social benefit to be distributed among society's members. Indeed, if an economic outcome maximizes aggregate surplus, it is economically efficient in the following sense: any alternative outcome that makes some members of society better off must make someone else worse off. To see why, think of aggregate surplus as a pie. If an economic system maximizes the size of the pie, any other outcome must make the pie smaller. And if the pie grows smaller, *someone* has to get a smaller slice—that is, someone must be worse off. We'll discuss this notion of economic efficiency, called *Pareto efficiency*, in more detail in Chapter 16.

How Perfectly Competitive Markets Maximize Aggregate Surplus

Economists have long marvelled at the workings of competitive markets. Adam Smith, whose insights into the specialization of labour we discussed in Application 7.1, is best known for his observations concerning the efficiency of competitive markets. In his book

The Wealth of Nations (1776) he commented on the "invisible hand" of the market, through which the self-interested actions of each individual lead to economic efficiency:

> [An individual] generally, indeed, neither intends to promote the public interest, nor knows how much he is promoting it. By preferring the support of domestic to that of foreign industry, he intends only his own security; and by directing that industry in such a manner as its produce may be of the greatest value, he intends only his own gain, and he is in this, as in many other cases, led by an invisible hand to promote an end which was no part of his intention. Nor is it always the worse for the society that it was no part of it. By pursuing his own interest he frequently promotes that of the society more effectually than when he really intends to promote it.

Because price equals marginal cost in a perfectly competitive market, a buyer who contemplates consuming one more unit of a good must pay exactly the marginal cost of producing it. Likewise, a seller who contemplates producing another unit of a good foresees receiving a payment equal to each buyer's marginal willingness to pay for it. Intuitively, this fact means that buyers and sellers face exactly the social costs and benefits of their actions, leading them to make efficient decisions.

In the rest of this section we'll show that perfectly competitive markets do indeed maximize aggregate surplus. Imagine that a competitive market is in equilibrium, with an equilibrium price of P^*. Given that price, consumers and firms each decide how much to consume or produce. We'll show that there is no way to increase aggregate surplus by changing either consumption or production. There are three different ways that we could make such changes:

1. We could change who consumes the good.
2. We could change who produces the good.
3. We could change how much of the good is produced and consumed.

"Look, all I'm asking is that we let market forces bring a greater degree of efficiency into our marriage."

Let's examine the effect of each of these changes on aggregate surplus.[7]

Effects of a Change in Who Consumes the Good

Let's think first about changing who consumes the good. Recall that in the market for ice cream cones, the competitive equilibrium involved a price of $1.50. Juan consumed four cones per week and Emily consumed three. Let's see if there is another way to divide up those seven cones that increases aggregate surplus.

Suppose we try to take one cone from Juan and give it to Emily. Could that change increase aggregate surplus? Figure 14.12 demonstrates that the answer is no. Figure 14.12(a) shows Juan's willingness to pay for that ice cream cone (his fourth), represented by the red-shaded area under his demand curve. (We'll use red shading to indicate changes that reduce aggregate surplus and green shading to indicate changes that increase it.) To keep Juan just as happy as he would be at the market equilibrium, we would need to pay him that amount when we take away the fourth ice cream cone. Figure 14.12(b) shows

---

[7]While we'll continue to assume that income effects are absent, the result holds even with income effects. Indeed, the result follows from the same argument, but using consumers' compensated demand curves (discussed in Section 6.5) instead of their uncompensated (ordinary or Marshallian) ones.

Figure 14.12

Effects of a Change in Who Consumes an Ice Cream Cone. What happens to aggregate surplus if we change the person who consumes an ice cream cone starting from a competitive market equilibrium? When we transfer one ice cream cone from Juan to Emily, Juan's willingness to pay for the cone he loses [equal to the red-shaded area in figure (a)] exceeds Emily's willingness to pay for the cone she gains [equal to the green-shaded area in figure (b)]. Aggregate surplus declines as a result of this change.

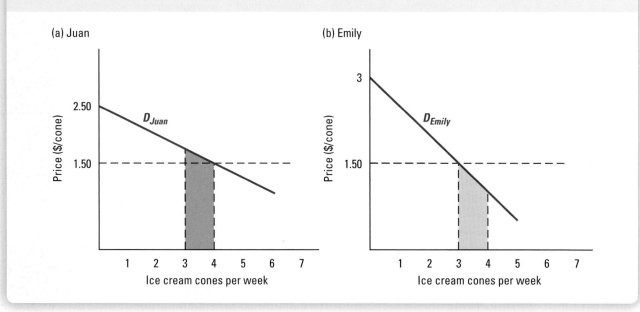

Emily's willingness to pay for one more ice cream cone (her fourth), represented by the green-shaded area under her demand curve. Notice that Emily's green-shaded area is smaller than Juan's red-shaded area. The width of each area equals one, so the green-shaded area is less than $1.50, while the red-shaded area is greater than $1.50. If we take an ice cream cone from Juan and give it to Emily, the total willingness to pay for the seven cones falls, and aggregate surplus falls with it.

A similar kind of argument applies for *any* number of ice cream cones we might transfer from Juan to Emily, as well as for *any* number we might transfer from Emily to Juan. (Try it.) The reason is that in a competitive equilibrium, the economic value that Juan and Emily attach to any ice cream cones they choose not to buy must be *less* than the market price, $1.50—otherwise they would have bought those cones. Likewise, the value that Juan and Emily attach to any cones they do choose to buy must be greater than the market price: otherwise they would not have bought those cones. Therefore, if we take cones from someone who chose to purchase them at the market price, and give them to someone who chose not to purchase them at the market price, aggregate surplus must fall.

Effects of a Change in Who Produces the Good

Changing who produces the cones, like changing who consumes them, can't increase aggregate surplus. Recall that in the competitive equilibrium of the ice cream market, Robert sells three cones and Anitra sells four cones. Can we reassign those sales in a way that would lower the total cost of production and increase aggregate surplus?

Figure 14.13 shows that we cannot. Suppose we reduce Anitra's sales from four to three cones and increase Robert's from three to four cones. Figure 14.13(a) shows Anitra's

Figure 14.13

Effects of a Change in Who Produces an Ice Cream Cone. What happens to aggregate surplus if we change the person who produces an ice cream cone starting from a competitive market equilibrium? When we transfer production of one cone from Anitra to Robert, Anitra's cost of producing that cone [equal to the green-shaded area in figure (a)] is less than Robert's cost of producing it [equal to the red-shaded area in figure (b)]. Aggregate surplus declines as a result of this change.

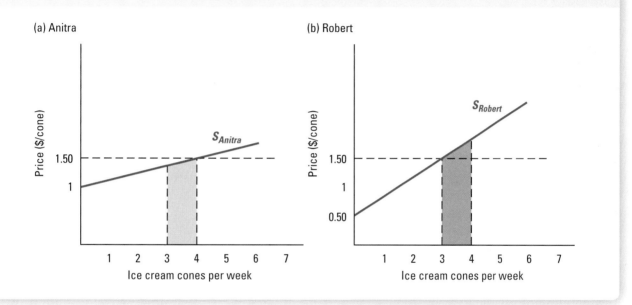

(a) Anitra

(b) Robert

cost of producing that ice cream cone, her fourth, as the green-shaded area under her supply curve. Figure 14.13(b) shows Robert's cost of producing an extra cone, his fourth, as the red-shaded area under his supply curve. Since the green-shaded area is smaller than the red-shaded one, the total cost of production increases, so aggregate surplus falls. The same would be true of any change in production that keeps total supply fixed. The cost of producing any ice cream cone that a firm chooses to sell must be less than the equilibrium price of $1.50, and the cost of any cone that a firm chooses not to sell must exceed $1.50. So any shift in production from one firm to another must raise the total cost of production and lower aggregate surplus.

Effects of a Change in the Number of Goods Produced and Consumed

Finally, let's see whether we can increase aggregate surplus by changing the total number of ice cream cones produced and consumed. Suppose, for example, that Robert produces one extra ice cream cone, which Juan consumes. Figure 14.14 shows that this change, too, lowers aggregate surplus. Figure 14.14(a) shows Robert's extra cost of producing that cone, his fourth, as the red-shaded area. Figure 14.14(b) shows Juan's willingness to pay for the extra cone, his fifth, as the green-shaded area. Since the red-shaded area exceeds the green-shaded area, the extra cone costs Robert more to produce than Juan is willing to pay for it. The change therefore lowers aggregate surplus.

The same result holds for any change in the total number of cones. Any cones that are produced and consumed in a competitive market equilibrium must be worth more than the market price of $1.50 to the consumers who buy them. If not, those consumers wouldn't have bought them. They must also cost less than the market price to produce; otherwise the firms

Figure 14.14

Effects of an Increase in the Number of Ice Cream Cones Produced and Consumed. This figure shows the effect on aggregate surplus of an increase in the number of ice cream cones produced and consumed starting from a competitive market equilibrium. If Robert produces an additional cone that Juan consumes, Robert's cost of producing that cone equals the red-shaded area in figure (a), and Juan's willingness to pay for it equals the smaller green-shaded area in figure (b). Aggregate surplus declines as a result of this change.

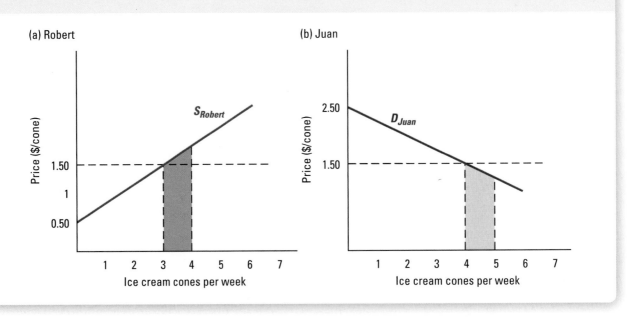

that produced them wouldn't have done so. Those cones must therefore make a positive contribution to aggregate surplus. Similarly, any cones that aren't produced and consumed in a competitive market equilibrium must be worth less than the market price to consumers and must cost more than the market price to produce; otherwise they would have been demanded or produced. Producing and consuming those cones would therefore lower aggregate surplus.

Putting these observations about the effects of the three possible changes in consumption and production together, we can see that a perfectly competitive market equilibrium does indeed maximize aggregate surplus. Any change in who consumes the good, which firms produce it, or the amount that is produced and consumed must lower aggregate surplus and make someone worse off in the process.

This analysis of perfectly competitive market outcomes explains economists' tendency to favour the market over other ways of making production and consumption decisions. At the same time, it does not address questions of *distribution*. If we care about *who* is made better or worse off, we might favour a change that lowers aggregate surplus, as long as it makes the *right* individuals (those considered most deserving) better off.

Need our concerns about equity and efficiency conflict? In principle, no. If the government can transfer wealth from the rich to the poor without cost, and allow the markets for goods to operate freely, it can get the best of both worlds: aggregate surplus would still be maximized, and we could use transfers to achieve an equitable distribution of resources. Intuitively, if we can slice the pie any way we want, making the pie bigger by allowing markets to operate freely is desirable because it means that we can give *everyone* a bigger slice.

Unfortunately, in practice, redistribution often interferes with the workings of markets. For example, if the government tries to transfer wealth, it will discourage individuals from saving. As a result, equity and efficiency concerns can conflict, and balancing them can involve some difficult trade-offs for society. We'll return to this point in Chapter 16.

Application 14.2

The Market for SO₂ Emissions

Acid rain forms when sulfur dioxide (SO₂) and nitrogen oxides (NOx) react in the atmosphere to form sulfuric and nitric acids. Those acids then fall to the earth when it rains, damaging both fragile ecosystems and man-made structures. In Canada, the main source of acid rain is the SO₂ produced by coal-fired electric power plants in the northeast and midwest United States as well as the eastern provinces of Canada. The SO₂ produced by those plants can cause acid rain to fall hundreds of kilometres away. The Canadian government aggressively cut SO₂ emissions to less than half their 1980 levels by the mid 1990s. This

An acid-rain-damaged forest

was insufficient to stop the environmental damage because roughly half of the acid rain problem was caused by emissions south of the border. In 1991 Canada and the U.S. signed the Canada–United States Air Quality Agreement in which the United States agreed to reduce its SO₂ emissions. Environment Canada predicted that by 2010 the United States will have reduced its SO₂ emissions by 40 percent compared to 1980.[8]

There are two ways to reduce SO₂ emissions. A power plant can switch to more expensive low-sulfur coal or it can install so-called scrubbers, which reduce the amount of SO₂ that the power plant emits. Traditionally, the U.S. government has regulated SO₂ pollution by limiting the amount of pollution each individual plant can generate.[9] The problem with this type of regulation is that because of differences in location, design, and production rates, power plants differ greatly in the ease

and cost with which they can switch to low-sulfur coal or install scrubbers. For example, the cost of switching to low sulfur coal depends on the cost of transporting it from the nearest low-sulfur coal mine.

In the 1990 Clean Air Act amendments, the United States government tried a new approach to the problem. The amendments established a program that relied on tradable emissions permits, called *allowances,* to control pollution. Under the program, each generating unit (the typical power plant contains several generating units) receives a certain number of allowances, each of which entitles it to emit one ton of SO₂ per year. The total number of allowances distributed places a cap on the total amount of emissions per year.[10] Once the allowances have been distributed, generators can buy or sell them without restriction.

The idea behind the program is that, through trading, the same degree of emissions reduction can be accomplished at a lower cost. In fact, if this market is perfectly competitive (there are, in fact, many buyers and sellers), abatement targets will be reached at the *lowest possible* cost. Why? The value that a power plant places on an emissions allowance is exactly equal to the cost it would incur if it had to buy low-sulfur coal or install scrubbers to reduce its emissions by one ton. We know that every power plant values the allowances it retains or buys in the market equilibrium more than the equilibrium price of an allowance; it values any additional allowances less than the market price. Thus, any transfer of

---

[8]Information on the Canada–United States Air Quality Agreement can be found in the most recent progress report (2008), available at http://www.ec.gc.ca/air/default.asp?lang=En&n=AF1043BE-1.

[9]We'll discuss why government regulation may be desirable in Chapter 20.

[10]The program also allows plants to save unused allowances for future use.

an allowance from a plant that bought or retained it to a plant that did not must increase the total cost of emissions reduction.

Figure 14.15, based on work by economists Richard Schmalensee, Paul Joskow, Denny Ellerman, Juan Pablo Montero, and Elizabeth Bailey shows the dramatic effects of allowing tradable permits.[11] The black curve represents the predicted amount of SO_2 that different generating units would have emitted in 1996 if the permits had *not* been tradable. The generating units are ordered from left to right along the horizontal axis in terms of their predicted "no trading" emissions, from lowest to highest. The gray vertical bars show the *actual* levels of emissions at each plant in that

year after trading of SO_2 allowances. These levels differed dramatically from the no-trading emissions levels. Some generating units bought allowances and used them to produce more SO_2 than their own allowances would have permitted (for those generating units, the gray vertical bar extends above the black curve). Others sold some of their allowances and either bought low-sulfur coal or installed scrubbers to reduce their emissions (for those generating units, the gray vertical bar is below the black curve). Schmalensee et al. estimate that the trading of pollution allowances lowered the cost of reducing SO_2 emissions by 225 to 375 million dollars per year.[12]

Figure 14.15

The Effects of Tradable SO_2 Allowances. The black curve shows the levels of SO_2 that different electric generating units would have emitted in 1996 if allowances were not tradable. The generating units are ordered from left to right from the lowest to the highest predicted "no-trading" emission rate. The gray-shaded vertical lines show the *actual* emission rates that occurred in 1996 after the trading of SO_2 allowances. Some generating units bought permits to allow them to increase their emissions (for those units, the gray vertical bar extends above the black curve). Others sold permits and emitted less SO_2 (for those units, the gray vertical bar is below the black curve).

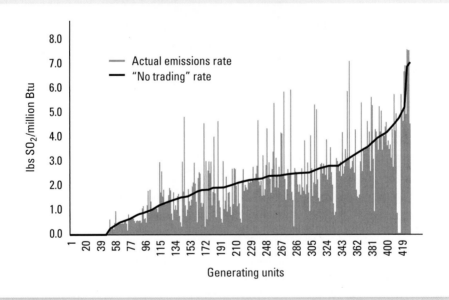

[11]Richard Schmalensee et al., "An Interim Evaluation of Sulfur Dioxide Emissions Trading," *Journal of Economic Perspectives* 12, Summer 1998, pp. 53–68.

[12]There is one important caveat to the use of such markets: While allowance markets minimize the costs of compliance, the market outcome is insensitive to any differences in the harm caused by emissions from different sources. (For example, the damage from one tonne of SO_2 emissions may depend on whether the plant is near a city, or whether prevailing winds carry the emissions over sensitive wildlife areas.) The reason these differences don't affect the equilibrium outcome is that the power plants do not care directly about the harm done by their emissions. (In economists' language, there is still an "externality"—see Chapter 20.) For an allowance market to deliver a desirable outcome, emissions from different sources should create roughly the same level of harm.

14.5 MEASURING SURPLUS USING MARKET DEMAND AND SUPPLY CURVES

We've seen that it's possible to measure aggregate surplus using each consumer's demand curve and each firm's supply curve. That procedure can be cumbersome with large numbers of consumers and firms. Fortunately, there's a more direct and simple procedure. In this section, we explain how to compute aggregate surplus, and the division of that surplus between aggregate benefits to consumers and aggregate benefits to producers, using market demand and supply curves. This method will prove very convenient when we discuss the effects of market interventions in Chapter 15.

First let's see how to use the market demand curve to measure total willingness to pay. Figures 14.16(a) and (b) show Emily's and Juan's demand curves for ice cream from Figure 14.1(a). Their willingness to pay for each cone is shown with a shaded vertical bar. For example, in Figure 14.16(a), the heights of the blue vertical bars represent Emily's willingness to pay for each cone, while in Figure 14.16(b), the heights of the red vertical bars represent Juan's willingness to pay for each cone.

Figure 14.16(c) shows the market demand curve [from Figure 14.1(b)] and total willingness to pay for ice cream cones. The willingness to pay for each cone is shown by a vertical bar whose colour corresponds to the consumer who demands it. Whenever cones are consumed by the individuals with the highest willingness to pay for them, we can measure the total willingness to pay for the cones they consume by the area under the

Figure 14.16

Measuring Total Willingness to Pay Using the Market Demand Curve. Figures (a) and (b) show Emily's and Juan's demand curves for ice cream cones. The coloured bars represent their willingness to pay for each cone. Figure (c) shows the market demand curve and the corresponding willingness to pay for each cone. The colour of each vertical bar indicates whose willingness to pay it represents. At any price, the area under the market demand curve up to the quantity demanded at that price equals consumers' total willingness to pay for the cones they consume.

market demand curve up to that quantity. To illustrate, suppose that three cones are consumed, with Emily consuming two and Juan consuming one. In this arrangement, the three cones are consumed by the individuals with the highest willingness to pay for them: Emily has the highest willingness to pay for a cone, $2.75; Juan has the second highest, $2.38; and Emily's willingness to pay for her second cone, $2.25, is the third highest. Their total willingness to pay for these cones is $7.38, which equals the area under the market demand curve up to three cones.

Cones will always be consumed by the individuals with the highest willingness to pay for them whenever all consumers face the same market price. This follows because the willingness to pay for each cone that is purchased is at least the market price, while the willingness to pay for any cone not purchased is below the market price. For example, if the price of cones in Figure 14.16(c) was $2.20, three cones would be purchased, two by Emily and one by Juan. The three cones are therefore consumed by the individuals with the highest willingness to pay for them, and the total willingness to pay equals the area under the market demand curve up to three cones.

In similar fashion, whenever cones are produced by the firms with the lowest avoidable cost of producing them (as occurs whenever all firms in a market face the same price for the goods they sell) we can measure the total avoidable cost by the area under the market supply curve up to that quantity. We won't draw another set of figures to illustrate, but the reasoning is basically the same as for measuring total willingness to pay.

In sum:

Using Market Demand and Supply Curves to Measure Total Willingness to Pay and Total Avoidable Cost

- Whenever the units of a good are consumed by those individuals with the highest willingness to pay for them, we can measure consumers' total willingness to pay for the units they consume by the area under the market demand curve up to that quantity.

- Whenever the units of a good are produced by the firms with the lowest avoidable cost of producing them, we can measure firms' total avoidable cost for the units they produce by the area under the market supply curve up to that quantity.

Aggregate Surplus

In light of this observation, we can use the market demand and supply curves to measure aggregate surplus whenever a good is consumed by the individuals with the highest willingness to pay and produced by the firms with the lowest avoidable costs of production.

To illustrate, Figure 14.17(a) shows a situation in which the market demand function for corn is $Q^d = 15 - 2P$ and the market supply function is $Q^s = 5P - 2.50$, both quantities measured in billions of bushels per year, and the market reaches a competitive equilibrium. The demand curve hits the vertical axis at a price of $7.50 per bushel, while the supply curve hits the vertical axis at a price of $0.50 per bushel. The equilibrium price is $2.50 per bushel, and 10 billion bushels of corn are bought and sold.

Figure 14.17

Aggregate Surplus, Consumer Surplus, and Producer Surplus in the Market for Corn. Figure (a) shows that aggregate surplus at the market equilibrium for corn, equal to the green-shaded area, is $35 billion per year. Figure (b) shows that this surplus is composed of $25 billion of consumer surplus and $10 billion of producer surplus.

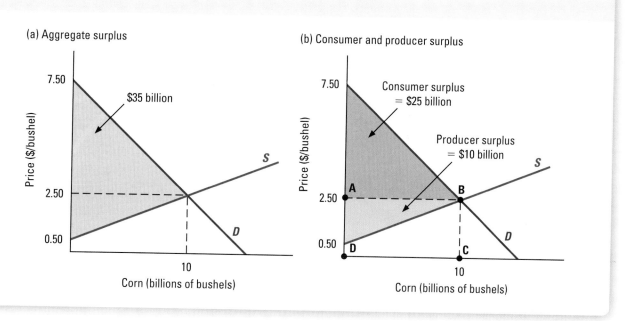

The figure shows the aggregate surplus in that equilibrium. Since all consumers and firms face the same price, we can measure total willingness to pay and total avoidable costs—and therefore aggregate surplus—using these curves. Consumers' total willingness to pay for the equilibrium quantity is the area under the demand curve up to 10 billion bushels, while firms' total avoidable cost is the area under the supply curve up to that same quantity. Since aggregate surplus is the difference between those two areas, it equals the green-shaded region between the demand and supply curves up to the equilibrium quantity of 10 billion bushels, the point at which the demand and supply curves cross. That region is a triangle, whose area is $35 billion (looking at it sideways, the base of the triangle along the vertical axis has length seven, and the height is 10 billion). So aggregate surplus is $35 billion per year.

In Chapter 15 we'll use market demand and supply curves to measure the loss in aggregate surplus associated with various market interventions. Economists call a reduction in aggregate surplus below its maximum possible value a **deadweight loss**. In a competitive market without any interventions, aggregate surplus is maximized, so there is no deadweight loss. Figure 14.18(a) illustrates the deadweight loss that occurs in the corn market if the amount produced differs from 10 billion bushels. Suppose that only seven billion bushels are produced and consumed, with production being done by the lowest cost farmers and consumption by the individuals with the highest willingness to pay for those bushels. (We'll see examples of how this can happen in Chapter 15.) Because aggregate surplus then equals the area between the demand and supply curves up to only seven

> A **deadweight loss** is a reduction in aggregate surplus below its maximum possible value.

Figure 14.18

Deadweight Loss and Aggregate Surplus. Figure (a) shows the deadweight losses if either 7 billion or 13 billion bushels of corn are produced and consumed each year (shaded light red and dark red respectively). In each case, the deadweight loss is $3.15 billion per year. Figure (b) shows the relationship between aggregate surplus, deadweight loss, and the amount produced and consumed. Aggregate surplus is largest at 10 billion bushels per year. At that quantity, the deadweight loss is zero.

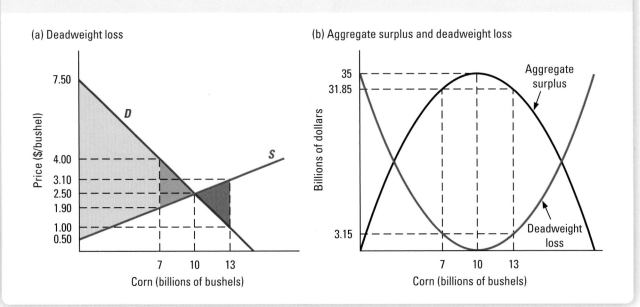

(a) Deadweight loss

(b) Aggregate surplus and deadweight loss

billion bushels (the green-shaded area), the deadweight loss would equal the area of the light red-shaded triangle, $3.15 billion per year. That loss arises because the economy fails to produce three billion bushels whose value exceeds their cost. If 13 billion bushels per year were instead produced and consumed, aggregate surplus would equal the sum of the green and light red-shaded areas *less* the dark red-shaded triangle (we subtract the area of the dark red triangle because above 10 billion bushels the willingness to pay is *less* than the avoidable cost of production). The deadweight loss therefore equals the area of the dark red-shaded triangle, again $3.15 billion per year. This time the loss occurs because the economy produces three billion bushels whose cost exceeds their value to consumers.

Figure 14.18(b) shows how aggregate surplus and deadweight loss depend on the amount produced and consumed. Aggregate surplus is largest at 10 billion bushels, the equilibrium quantity (recall Section 14.4). At that quantity, the deadweight loss is zero. At other quantities, the deadweight loss equals the difference between $35 billion, the largest possible aggregate surplus, and the aggregate surplus at the given quantity. For example, the figure shows that when 7 billion bushels are produced and consumed, aggregate surplus is $31.85 billion per year and the deadweight loss is $3.15 billion per year.

Consumer and Producer Surpluses

In Section 6.2 we introduced the notion of consumer surplus. An individual's consumer surplus is equal to her willingness to pay for the goods she consumes less her expenditure on those goods. *Aggregate* consumer surplus is the sum of individual consumers' surpluses, which equals the sum of consumers' total willingness to pay less their total expenditure. Where doing so does not create confusion, we'll call this concept simply the **consumer surplus**.

We can use the market demand curve to measure consumer surplus. Figure 14.17(b) shows the consumer surplus in the competitive equilibrium of the corn market. Total expenditure equals the area of rectangle ABCD (it's $25 billion, the equilibrium price of $2.50, times the total amount of corn bought, 10 billion bushels). Since consumer surplus each year is the difference between the total willingness to pay and the total expenditure, each year it equals the area of the blue-shaded triangle, $25 billion.

In Section 9.5, we introduced the notion of a firm's producer surplus, equal to the firm's total revenue less its avoidable cost. (The firm's profit equals its producer surplus less its sunk costs.) *Aggregate* producer surplus equals the sum of the individual firms' producer surpluses, which equals the sum of firms' revenues less their avoidable costs. Where doing so does not create confusion, we'll refer to this concept simply as **producer surplus**. (Aggregate profit is this amount less firms' sunk costs.)

We can use the market supply curve to measure producer surplus. Figure 14.17(b) shows the producer surplus in the equilibrium of the corn market. Total revenue, which is the same as the total expenditure by consumers, is the area of the rectangle ABCD. Since producer surplus is the difference between firms' revenue and their avoidable costs, each year it equals the area of the yellow-shaded triangle, $10 billion.

Comparing Figures 14.17(a) and (b), we can see that the green-shaded area in Figure 14.17(a) equals the sum of the blue and yellow-shaded areas in Figure 14.17(b), which represent consumer surplus and producer surplus, respectively. So

$$\text{Aggregate surplus} = \text{Consumer surplus} + \text{Producer surplus} \qquad \textbf{(3)}$$

Formula (3) shows that the aggregate surplus, the total net benefit pie, is composed of the slice consumers get (consumer surplus) plus the slice that firms get (producer surplus).[13] When we study government intervention into markets in Chapter 15, however, we'll also need to take into account the slice of the pie that government gets. Nonetheless, our ability to use market demand and supply curves to measure consumer and producer surplus will prove very helpful.

> **(Aggregate) consumer surplus** equals the sum of consumers' total willingness to pay less their total expenditure.

> **(Aggregate) producer surplus** equals the sum of firms' revenues less their avoidable costs.

IN-TEXT EXERCISE 14.5 **The market demand function for corn is $Q^d = 15 - 2P$ and the market supply function is $Q^s = 5P - 6$, both quantities measured in billions of bushels per year. What are the aggregate surplus, consumer surplus, and producer surplus at the competitive market equilibrium?**

---

[13]Formula (3) can be derived directly from formula (2) on page 511 by adding and subtracting total expenditure to rewrite formula (2) as Aggregate surplus = (Total willingness to pay − Total expenditure) + (Total expenditure − Total avoidable cost of production). The first expression in parentheses is consumer surplus; the second is producer surplus (since consumers' total expenditure exactly equals firms' total revenue).

Application 14.3

The Transition from Communism to Capitalism

The transition of many former Soviet-bloc countries from communism to capitalism represented an enormous change in the organization of their economic systems. This was most true of the countries of eastern Europe, many of which aggressively embraced market-based reforms. For decades in these countries, production decisions had been made by government bureaucrats and communist party officials, who were influenced primarily by political concerns. Those officials also set the prices that consumers faced. Goods they considered necessities were priced low; those they considered luxuries (such as cars) were priced extremely high. When not enough of a good was available to satisfy demand at those prices, the available goods were rationed according to the priorities of those officials.

With the transition to capitalism, all of this changed. Goods were traded in markets at market-determined prices. Government-owned firms were sold (or sometimes given) to private investors, managers, and workers. Individuals were allowed to start their own businesses. As Table 14.1 shows, these changes dramatically increased the share of gross domestic product (GDP) produced by private firms in those countries. Indeed, for some of them, that share was approaching the level in western Europe and North America by 1997.

Market reforms increased economic efficiency in three ways. First, competitive markets pushed firms to become efficient. In state-run firms, production decisions had often reflected political rather than economic motives. Moreover, the state had often heavily subsidized large firms, giving managers little incentive to produce efficiently. In

Table 14.1
Percentage of GDP Derived from Private Sources, Six Countries

	1980	1988	1994	1997
Czech Republic	< 1.0	< 1.0	65	75
Hungary	3.5	7.1	55	75
Poland	15.6	18.8	55	65
Romania	4.5	—	35	60
Slovakia	< 1.0	< 1.0	55	75
United States	79.4	79.6	81.1	82

Source: J.L Saving, "Privatization and the Transition to a Market Economy," Federal Reserve Bank of Dallas *Economic Review*, 1998, pp. 17–25.

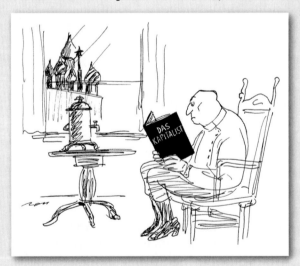

privately owned firms, the desire to maximize profit drives firms to use efficient production technologies (see Chapter 7) and choose least-cost input combinations (see Chapter 8). Second, competitive markets result in an efficient allocation of production across firms. Third, with competitive markets, the amount of each good that is produced and consumed maximizes aggregate surplus, given consumers' willingness to pay and the costs of production. Finally, competitive markets allocate goods to the consumers who value them most.

Figure 14.19 shows the change in aggregate surplus for a good considered a necessity, whose price had been set very low by government officials. For simplicity, it focuses on only the first and third type of gain listed above by assuming that the government had efficiently allocated production and consumption across firms and consumers prior to the transition. (If this assumption is not correct, then the efficiency gains from market reforms are even greater.) Originally, the marginal cost curve was MC_H, the price was $\underline{P}$, and the amount produced and consumed was Q (there was no rationing for this good). After the transition to capitalism, the marginal cost of production fell to MC_L and the market reached equilibrium at point B.

The transition increased aggregate surplus by an amount equal to the sum of the green- and red-shaded areas. We can find this change in aggregate surplus in two steps. First, without any change in the marginal cost curve, the transition to a market would shift the amount produced and consumed to point A, with Q_0 units produced and consumed. The red-shaded area represents the increase in aggregate surplus due to that change. The last $(Q - Q_0)$ units produced under communism were worth less to consumers than they cost to produce; aggregate surplus increases when those units are no longer produced. Second, the reduction in marginal cost shifts the market equilibrium from point A to point B, further increasing aggregate surplus by the green-shaded area.

The gains from a transition to capitalism don't materialize overnight. It can take time for market institutions to develop, for new firms to enter the market, and for consumers and producers to adjust to the new system. Nonetheless, in a relatively short period, many of the Eastern European countries began to grow rapidly. Figure 14.20 shows the growth of GDP per capita in five of those countries from 1990 to 1996. Unfortunately, not all of these countries experienced these benefits. Romania, for example, embraced market reforms only half-heartedly. The situation was even worse in many of the former Soviet Republics (not shown in the figure). The collapse of the Soviet system disrupted their already inefficient economies, causing their per capita GDPs to fall precipitously. Most of these countries adopted less ambitious market reforms than countries such as Poland, Hungary, and the Czech Republic and in many cases their GDPs still haven't recovered to the levels achieved before the fall of communism. One important lesson from this experience is that the transition to a healthy market economy requires many interrelated developments—steps to assure the free formation of businesses, the protection of private property, the ability of shareholders to hold managers accountable, and the general rule of law, among others.

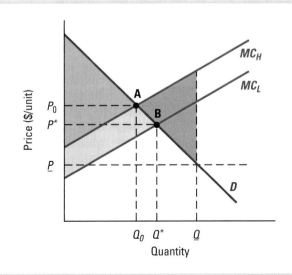

Figure 14.19

Effects of the Transition from Communism to Capitalism. Under communism, the price was set at $\underline{P}$ and the amount consumed was Q. After the transition to capitalism, an increase in the efficiency of production resulted in a decline in the marginal costs of production. The combination of declining marginal costs, in conjunction with the removal of price controls, caused the equilibrium price to rise to P^*, and Q^* units were bought and sold. Aggregate surplus increased by an amount equal to the sum of the red- and green-shaded areas.

Figure 14.20

The Growth of Real GDP per Capita in Former Soviet-Bloc Countries, 1990–1996. This figure shows the changes in gross domestic product per capita in five former Soviet-bloc countries following the transition to capitalism.

Source: Saving (1998).

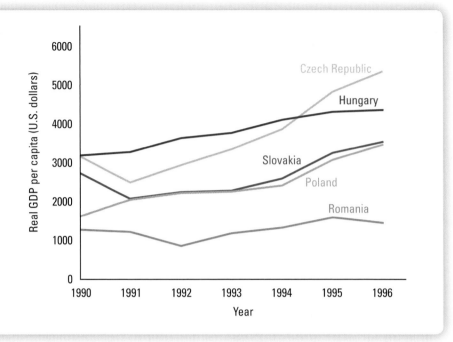

CHAPTER SUMMARY

1. **What makes a market competitive? (LO1)**

   a. A market is perfectly competitive, with firms acting as price takers, when (1) buyers and sellers face no transactions costs, (2) products are homogeneous, and (3) there are many suppliers, each accounting for a small fraction of the overall supply of the good.

   b. For many small firms to produce efficiently in a market, the efficient scale of production must be small compared to the overall size of the market, the total amount produced and consumed.

2. **Market demand and market supply (LO2)**

   a. The market demand for a product is the sum of the demands of all the individual consumers (or firms, in a factor market). The market demand curve is the horizontal sum of all the individual demand curves.

   b. The market supply for a product is the sum of the supplies of all the individual sellers. The market supply curve is the horizontal sum of all the individual supply curves.

   c. In the short run, the market supply curve includes the supply of all active firms; in the long run it includes the supply of all potential firms.

   d. In the long run, many markets are characterized by free entry, because in the long run technology is freely available to anyone who wishes to start a firm and entry is unrestricted. When this is so, the long-run market supply curve is a horizontal line at the lowest average cost, AC_{min}.

3. **Short-run and long-run competitive equilibrium (LO3)**

   a. The equilibrium price equates demand and supply.

   b. In a long-run competitive equilibrium with free entry: (1) the equilibrium price must equal AC_{min}, (2) firms must earn zero profit, and (3) each active firm must produce at its efficient scale of production.

   c. The short-run effect of a change in demand or costs is determined using the short-run market supply curve (which includes the supply of all active firms), while in the long run it is determined using the long-run market supply curve (which includes the supply of all potential firms).

   d. When there is free entry in the long run, changes in demand have no effect on the price of the good in the long run, assuming input prices are fixed.

   e. When a change in the demand for a good affects the price of an input, the good's price can change in the long run even when there is free entry.

4. **Efficiency of perfectly competitive markets (LO4)**

   a. The aggregate surplus from the production and consumption of a good equals consumers' total willingness to pay for the goods they consume less firms' total avoidable cost of producing those goods. It captures the net benefit created by the production and consumption of the good.

   b. If an economic outcome maximizes aggregate surplus, then any alternative outcome that makes some members of society better off must make someone else worse off.

   c. A perfectly competitive equilibrium results in the largest possible level of aggregate surplus.

   d. There are three different ways to change consumption or production starting from a perfectly competitive equilibrium: (1) change who consumes the good; (2) change who produces the good; and (3) change the quantity of the good that is produced and consumed. Any of these changes will lower aggregate surplus.

5. **Measuring surplus using market demand and supply curves (LO5)**

   a. Whenever the units of a good are consumed by those individuals with the highest willingness to pay for them, we can measure consumers' total willingness to pay for the units they consume by the area under the market demand curve up to that quantity.

   b. Whenever the units of a good are produced by the firms with the lowest avoidable cost of producing them, we can measure firms' total avoidable cost for the units they produce by the area under the market supply curve up to that quantity.

   c. Under these conditions, we can use market demand and supply curves to measure aggregate surplus. Aggregate surplus equals the area between these curves up to the quantity produced and consumed. (If the quantity is above the efficient quantity, we *subtract* the area between the curves above the efficient quantity, where the willingness to pay is less than the avoidable cost of production.)

   d. We can use the market demand curve to measure the (aggregate) consumer surplus from a good, which equals the total willingness to pay less total expenditure.

   e. We can use the market supply curve to measure the (aggregate) producer surplus, which equals total revenue less firms' total avoidable costs of production.

   f. Aggregate surplus equals the sum of consumer surplus and producer surplus.

ADDITIONAL EXERCISES

Exercise 14.1: Juan's demand function for ice cream cones is $Q^d_{Juan} = 10 - 2.5P$ at prices below $4 and zero at prices above $4. Emily's demand function is $Q^d_{Emily} = 6 - 1.5P$ at prices below $4 and zero at prices above $4. What is the market demand function? Graph the individual and market demand curves. (LO2)

Exercise 14.2: Anitra's supply function for ice cream cones is $Q^s_{Anitra} = 6P - 4$ at prices above $1.50 and zero at prices below $1.50. Robert's supply function is $Q^d_{Robert} = 4P - 8$ at prices above $2 and zero at prices below $2. What is the market supply function? Graph the individual and market supply curves. (LO2)

Exercise 14.3: The daily cost of producing pizza in St. John's is $C(Q) = 4Q + (Q^2/40)$; the marginal cost is $MC = 4 + (Q/20)$. What is the market supply function if there are 10 firms making pizza? If 20 firms are making pizza? What is the market supply curve under free entry?(LO3)

Exercise 14.4: Suppose the price of bagels in Waterloo is currently $0.75 per bagel. There are 10 low-cost bakeries that can produce bagels, each of which has the supply function $Q^s = 200P - 100$. There are 10 high-cost bakeries that can produce bagels, each of which has the supply function $Q^s = 200P - 200$. (These individual supply functions apply in the short run and the long run.) Which bakeries will be active when the price is $0.75? If the price rises to $1.25, what will be the market supply in the short run? In the long run? Graph the short-run and long-run market supply curves. (LO3)

Exercise 14.5: The daily cost of making pizza in Edmonton is $C(Q) = 4Q + (Q^2/40)$, plus an avoidable fixed cost of $10; marginal cost is $MC = 4 + (Q/20)$. In the long run firms may enter the market freely. What is the long-run market supply curve? (LO3)

Exercise 14.6: What are the equilibrium price and amount bought and sold when individual demand and supply are as in exercises 14.1 and 14.2? (LO3)

Exercise 14.7: Suppose the daily demand function for pizza in Regina is $Q^d = 1,525 - 5P$. The variable cost of making Q pizzas per day is $C(Q) = 3Q + 0.01Q^2$, there is a $100 fixed cost (which is avoidable in the long run), and the marginal cost is $MC = 3 + 0.02Q$. There is free entry in the long run. What is the long-run market equilibrium in this market? Suppose that demand increases to $Q^d = 2125 - 5P$. If, in the short run, the number of firms is fixed (so that neither entry nor exit is possible) and fixed costs are sunk, what is the new short-run market equilibrium? What is the new long-run market equilibrium if there is free entry in the long run? How many firms are there at the new equilibrium? What if instead demand decreased to $Q^d = 925 - 5P$? (LO3)

Exercise 14.8: The daily demand for pizzas is $Q^d = 750 - 25P$, where P is the price of a pizza. The daily costs for a pizza company initially include $50 in fixed costs (which are avoidable in the long run), and variable costs equal to $VC = Q^2/2$, where Q is the number of pizzas produced in a day. Marginal cost is $MC = Q$. Suppose that in the long run there is free entry into the market. If fixed costs fall to $18 and, in the short run, the number of firms is fixed (so that neither entry nor exit is possible) and fixed costs are sunk, what is the new short-run market equilibrium? What is the new market equilibrium in the long run? How many firms are there at the new long-run equilibrium? (LO3)

Exercise 14.9: The daily demand for pizzas is $Q^d = 750 - 25P$, where P is the price of a pizza. The daily costs for a pizza company initially include $50 in fixed costs (which are avoidable in the long run), and variable costs equal to $VC = Q^2/2$, where Q is the number of pizzas produced in a day. Marginal cost is $MC = Q$. Suppose that in the long run there is free entry into the market. If marginal costs rise by $6 per pizza and, in the short run, the number of firms is fixed (so that neither entry nor exit is possible) and fixed costs are sunk, what is the new short-run market equilibrium? What is the new market equilibrium in the long run? (LO3)

Exercise 14.10: Firms can often exit a market more quickly than they can enter one. What would change in the answers to exercises 14.8 and 14.9 if active firms could shut down in the short run avoiding all costs, but inactive firms could enter only in the long run? (LO3)

Exercise 14.11: After Henry Ford invented the assembly line for manufacturing automobiles, other automobile firms copied his invention. The new technology increased the economies of scale in automobile manufacturing. In the long run, how would it have changed the size of the typical automobile firm? (LO3)

Exercise 14.12: Suppose the costs of production fall by $1 per unit at every output level. If the number of firms is fixed in the short run but not in the long run, how would such a change affect the market equilibrium in the short and long run? (LO3)

Exercise 14.13: At some universities and business schools, lotteries have long been used to assign seats in highly popular lecture courses. Recently, some schools have switched to systems in which students receive points that they can use to bid for seats in their favourite classes. Why might this new system be more efficient? (LO4)

Exercise 14.14: For some rock concerts thousands of fans stand in line for hours to purchase tickets. What is the likely effect on aggregate surplus if resale of those tickets in a competitive market is possible? Would aggregate surplus be higher if the concert tickets were priced to begin with at the resale market's equilibrium price? (LO4)

Exercise 14.15: The market demand function for corn is $Q^d = 21 - 4P$, and the market supply function is $Q^s = 5P - 6$, both quantities measured in billions of bushels per year. What are the aggregate surplus, consumer surplus, and producer surplus at the competitive market equilibrium? (LO5)

APPENDIX

EQUILIBRIUM IN FACTOR MARKETS

A **factor market** is a market for an input, such as labour, physical capital goods (machines), or financial capital. In a factor market, firms are the buyers. Either firms or individual consumers may be the suppliers. For example, many of Dell's personal computers are sold to other firms, which use those computers to produce their own products. In a labour market, however, individuals are the sellers of their labour services. Similarly, when a firm needs to raise financial capital, individuals are often the suppliers of that capital.

> A **factor market** is a market for an input.

In many ways, factor markets work just like the markets for consumption goods that we've been studying. Figure 14.21, for example, shows two examples of equilibrium in a factor market. Figure 14.21(a) shows the demand and supply curves in the labour market for nurses in a large city. The demand for nurses comes from the hospitals and nursing homes that need nurses to take care of their patients and residents. The demand curve is downward sloping: the lower the wage, the more nurses they will want to hire. As the wage decreases, for example, they may decide to provide care with more nurses and fewer doctors, or may decide to offer improved services that require relatively intensive supervision (taking nursing

Figure 14.21

Equilibrium in Factor Markets. Figure (a) shows equilibrium in a labour market for nurses, where the equilibrium weekly wage rate W^* brings the supply and demand for nurses into balance. Figure (b) shows equilibrium in a market for financial capital, where the equilibrium interest rate R^* brings the supply and demand for financial capital into balance.

(a) Labour market

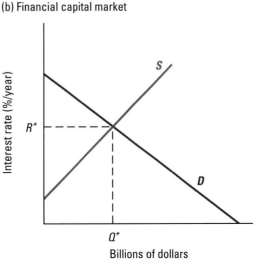

(b) Financial capital market

home residents on more walks). They may also decide to increase the number of patients or residents they care for. The supply curve of nurses in Figure 14.21(a), on the other hand, is upward sloping. As the wage increases, more trained nurses may decide to work (rather than stay home), and some may accept a job in this city rather than others. As in other competitive markets, the equilibrium wage brings this supply and demand into balance.

Figure 14.21(b) shows an equilibrium in the market for financial capital (money provided today in return for promised repayments in the future). Here demand arises from entrepreneurs and firms with investment projects. The suppliers are individuals and financial institutions with money to lend. As we discussed in Chapter 10, the price of financial capital is the interest rate. In Figure 14.21(b), the demand curve for financial capital is downward sloping. As the interest rate rises, fewer projects are profitable (have a positive net present value), so the quantity of financial capital demanded falls. In Figure 14.21(b), the supply curve of financial capital is upward sloping. As the interest rate rises, some investors find that lending to others is more lucrative than using the cash for their own projects, and some individuals decide to save more for the future by lending money to firms today (or by putting money in banks, which then lend it to firms). The equilibrium interest rate brings this supply and demand into balance.

Backward-Bending Supply Curves in Factor Markets

The factor demand and supply curves in Figure 14.21 look just like those we've studied in Chapter 2 and this chapter. However, this need not always be the case. One important difference from our previous analysis of competitive markets can arise in factor markets: in some cases, the supply curve can bend backwards in a factor market. That is, the amount supplied can *fall* when the price rises. For example, in Section 6.4, we saw that the supply curve for labour may bend backwards. A similar phenomenon can occur in the markets for financial capital. Firms need money to finance investment. They obtain this money both from other firms and from consumers, who can choose to save some of their money and supply it to the firms, either directly or through banks. We saw in Section 10.2 that saving—and consequently the supply of financial capital from consumers—can either rise or fall when the interest rate rises. Thus, the supply curve for financial capital can also bend backwards. In both of these cases, a similar mechanism is at work: an increase in the price of the input has a positive income effect for consumers, who respond by supplying less of it.

How does a backward-bending supply curve affect supply and demand analysis? Figure 14.22(a) shows the demand and supply curves in a labour market with a backward bending supply curve. In this situation, shifts in the demand for labour can have effects that differ from those we discussed in Chapter 2. In Figure 14.22(b), for example, the labour demand curve shifts outward from the dark blue curve labelled D to the light blue curve labelled $\hat{D}$. Following this increase in labour demand, however, firms actually employ *less* labour: the amount of labour hired falls from Q^* to $\hat{Q}^*$. The reason is that the increase in the wage rate from W^* to $\hat{W}^*$ raises workers' incomes, causing them to supply less labour.

Multiple Equilibria

Another consequence of a backward-bending supply curve is that there may be more than one potential market equilibrium. Figure 14.23 shows an example of this phenomenon in a labour market. Note the triple intersection of the demand and supply curves, one at a high wage (W^{***}) and low employment, one at a medium wage (W^{**}) and medium

Figure 14.22

Equilibrium in a Labour Market with a Backward-Bending Supply Curve. Because of income effects, the labour supply curve can be backward bending, as in figure (a). As figure (b) shows, this shape can lead to the surprising result that an increase in the demand for labour can reduce the amount of labour that firms employ.

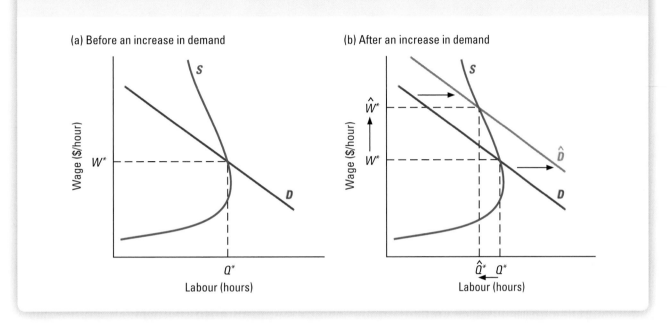

employment, and one at a low wage (W^*) and high employment. What determines which of these equilibria will arise?

One factor is the stability of the various equilibria. An equilibrium is **stable** if market pressures near the equilibrium tend to push the market price toward its equilibrium level and **unstable** if they tend to push it away.

The low-wage equilibrium in Figure 14.23 is a stable one. When the wage rate is a little above W^*, supply exceeds demand. Because workers who can't get jobs are willing to work for less, the wage tends to fall back toward W^*. Likewise, when the wage is a little below W^*, demand exceeds supply. Because firms that can't hire enough workers are willing to pay them a little more, the wage tends to rise back toward W^*. The same is true of the high wage equilibrium, which is also stable.

In contrast, the medium-wage equilibrium in Figure 14.23 is not stable. When the wage is a little below W^{**}, supply exceeds demand, causing the wage to fall further below W^{**} as unemployed workers offer to accept lower wages. When the wage is a little above W^{**}, demand exceeds supply, causing the wage to rise further above W^{**} as firms with vacancies try to attract workers. In general, a market equilibrium is stable if demand is greater than supply at prices a little below the equilibrium price, and less than supply at slightly higher prices. A market is unlikely to settle into an unstable equilibrium, since the market price will tend to move away from the price level in an unstable equilibrium whenever it is close to it.

Another factor that may influence which equilibrium prevails is the recent price level. For example, in Figure 14.23, if the wage has recently been below W^{**}, the balancing of supply and demand tends to push the wage toward W^*. If instead the wage has recently been above W^{**}, that balancing tends to push the wage toward W^{***}.

A market equilibrium is **stable** if market pressures near the equilibrium point tend to push the price toward its equilibrium level; it is **unstable** if they tend to push it away.

Figure 14.23

Multiple Equilibria in a Labour Market. When the labour supply curve is backward bending, the demand for labour can equal the supply at more than one wage rate. Here, the high and low-wage equilibria are stable, but the medium-wage equilibrium is not.

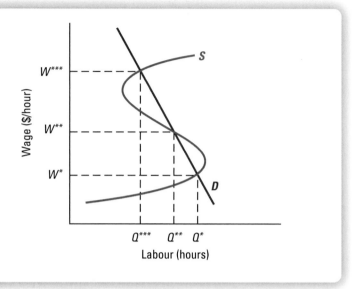

IN-TEXT EXERCISE 14.6   Graph the demand and supply in a factor market with three equilibrium prices. Suppose there is a small increase in demand. What will be the effect of this change on each of the three equilibria? Will it differ for stable and unstable equilibria?

Welfare Analysis in Factor Markets

Section 14.4 discussed the welfare properties of competitive markets. How are these properties affected by the presence of a backward-bending supply curve in a factor market? They aren't. A market equilibrium in a perfectly competitive factor market always maximizes aggregate surplus, just as in Section 14.4. In fact, the logic is exactly the same as there: buyers find any units of the factor that they purchase worth more than the equilibrium price and any units that they do not purchase worth less. What about sellers? We can always think of sellers' "costs" in a factor market as the opportunity cost of selling the factor to a buyer. For example, in a labour market this opportunity cost may be the individual's value from leisure or her wage in her best alternative employment. Any units of the factor that are sold must cost less than the equilibrium price, and any units that are not sold must cost more. Thus, as in Section 14.4, any change in who uses the factor, who supplies the factor, or the total amount of the factor bought and sold must lower aggregate surplus. (The analysis in Chapter 16 also leads to this same conclusion.)

What about using market demand and supply curves to measure aggregate, consumer, and producer surpluses as in Section 14.5? Does a backward-bending supply curve interfere with doing this? No. To understand why, think of a labour market. The supply of labour can bend backwards only if there are sizable income effects in the demand for leisure. But, as we saw in Section 6.5, to properly measure surplus when income effects are large, we need to use *compensated* demand curves. In the context of factor markets, this translates into using a compensated factor supply curve. Because the compensation removes income effects, compensated factor supply curves always slope upwards, so we can measure surplus using those curves just as in Section 14.5.

Market Interventions

LEARNING OBJECTIVES

After reading this chapter, students should be able to

LOI Describe the effects of a tax or subsidy in a competitive market.

LO2 Explain what determines who bears the burden of a tax and the difference between the statutory and economic incidence of the tax.

LO3 Compare the results of policies designed to raise prices, including price floors, price supports, production quotas, and voluntary price programs.

LO4 Show the effects of price ceilings designed to lower prices below their equilibrium levels.

LO5 Define domestic aggregate surplus and determine the effects of import tariffs and quotas.

Since the Canadian Dairy Commission (CDC) was established in 1966, supply management of the dairy industry in Canada has enjoyed support from both liberal and conservative politicians. The CDC regulates both the production and price of milk with the aim of providing stability in prices and ensuring a fair return to producers. The program is not without its critics; milk prices are higher in Canada than they are in the United States as a result of CDC initiatives. This has necessitated the introduction of extraordinary high tariffs on imported dairy products. The egg, poultry, and grain producers of Canada also benefit from an array of government programs designed to bolster the incomes of farmers.

In Chapter 14 we saw that a perfectly competitive market leads to an efficient outcome, maximizing the level of aggregate surplus generated by the production and consumption of a good. This conclusion suggests that the best government policy would be to let markets function without interference provided they are competitive and don't suffer from any of the forms of market failure that we'll consider in Part IIIB (Chapters 17–21). Despite the logic of this prescription, however, governments often intervene in competitive markets that have no obvious market failures. Sometimes intervention is necessary, as when government needs to raise tax revenue to finance essential programs. But often intervention results from a political process that benefits certain constituencies.

Whether government interventions are or are not necessary, and whether they benefit groups in need of protection or groups that make large campaign donations, those interventions usually alter market outcomes. In so doing, they often also reduce efficiency and aggregate surplus. In this chapter we'll use the tools we developed in Chapter 14 to examine the effects of market interventions. We'll study three types of intervention:

1. *Taxes (and subsidies).* Governments tax goods to raise the revenue needed to pay for various public expenditures. We'll see that in a perfectly competitive market, taxation reduces aggregate surplus, creating a deadweight loss. We'll explore the factors that determine the size of the loss, and ask who truly bears the burden of a tax. We'll also examine subsidies, which governments use to encourage certain activities, or to benefit buyers and sellers in a market.

2. *Policies designed to raise prices.* Many government interventions are designed to assist those who sell certain goods by raising their prices. Price floors, price supports, production quotas, and voluntary production reduction programs are all meant to raise prices, whether by mandating minimum prices, raising demand, or reducing supply. We'll compare the effects of these different policies. (We'll also briefly discuss policies that are designed to benefit buyers by reducing prices, for which similar principles apply.)

3. *Import tariffs and quotas.* Governments also try to assist those who sell certain goods by reducing competition from foreign producers, usually through tariffs or quotas. We'll discuss these policies, paying particular attention to the distinction between overall economic efficiency and the maximization of domestic aggregate surplus.

15.1 TAXES (AND SUBSIDIES)

In many markets, consumers or firms pay taxes to the government when they buy or sell a good. In Canada, the federal government imposes a goods and services tax (GST) in some provinces and a harmonized sales tax (HST) in others. In provinces without an HST all provincial governments except Alberta collect a provincial sales tax (PST). Currently this includes the provinces of Saskatchewan (five percent PST), Manitoba (seven percent PST), Prince Edward Island (ten percent PST), and Quebec (seven-and-a-half percent QST). In provinces with an HST the federal government collects the provincial sales tax along with the five-percent GST and returns the provincial portion to the provinces. Both the federal and provincial governments collect income tax on workers' earnings from the sale of their labour. In this section we'll study the effects of such taxes on the equilibrium of a perfectly competitive market.

Economists distinguish between specific taxes and *ad valorem* taxes. A **specific tax** is a fixed dollar amount that must be paid on each unit bought or sold. The Canadian federal gasoline tax is a type of specific tax called an excise tax; currently it is 10 cents per litre. Excise taxes are also collected on alcohol and tobacco products where they are often referred to as *sin* taxes. An ***ad valorem* tax** is a tax that is stated as a percentage of the good's price. Examples of *ad valorem* taxes include sales taxes, value added taxes, and property taxes. An HST is one type of *ad valorem* tax. Ontario, for example, charges an HST of 13 percent on most goods sold within the province, while in British Columbia the

A **specific tax** is a fixed dollar amount that must be paid on each unit bought or sold.

An ***ad valorem* tax** is a tax that is stated as a percentage of the good's price.

HST is 12 percent. For the sake of simplicity, we'll focus here mainly on specific taxes. The appendix to the chapter discusses *ad valorem* taxes.

The Burden of a Tax

Let's consider the effects of a specific tax of T dollars per litre paid by gas stations on their sales of gasoline. In studying the effects of taxes, it's important to distinguish between the amount a buyer pays for a good and the amount a seller receives. We'll use P_b to stand for the amount a buyer pays and P_s to stand for the amount a seller receives after paying the tax. In the case of gasoline, for example, P_b is the amount posted at the pump. The amount the gas station receives, P_s, equals $P_b - T$.

Figure 15.1 shows one way to determine the tax's effect. The blue and red curves labelled D and S are the market demand and supply curves with no government intervention. Without the tax, consumers pay and firms (stations) receive the equilibrium price P_0 and Q_0 litres are bought and sold. What happens with the tax? We'll first determine the new price paid by consumers, P_b. To do that, we need to determine the demand and supply for each possible level of P_b and then find the price P_b that equates the quantities demanded and supplied.

Figure 15.1 also graphs the demand and supply curves with the tax. For this purpose, the vertical axis measures the price paid by consumers rather than the price received by firms. The demand curve is still D. What about the supply curve? Intuitively, for any price

Figure 15.1

The Effects of a Specific Tax. This figure shows the effects of a specific tax of T dollars per litre of gas. Without the tax, the market price would be P_0 and Q_0 litres would be bought and sold. With the vertical axis measuring the price paid by consumers, the tax causes the supply curve to shift upward by the distance T at each quantity. With the tax, consumers pay P_b per litre, firms receive $P_s = P_b - T$ per litre, and Q_T litres are bought and sold. The total tax collected is the gray-shaded area, which equals $T \times Q_T$. The tax causes the price per litre paid by consumers to increase and the price per litre received by firms to fall. The sum of the two changes equals T, the amount of the tax.

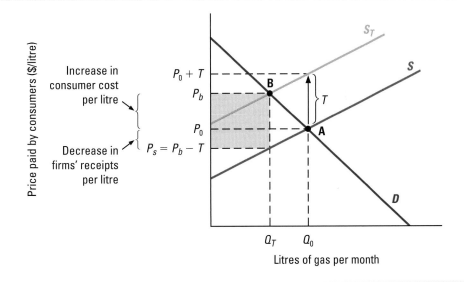

paid by consumers, firms receive less than when there is no tax, so they won't be willing to supply as much. That is, the supply curve must shift. How do we construct the new supply curve? Consider, for example, the price that elicits a supply of Q_0. Without the tax, a price of P_0 did that. With the tax, the price paid by consumers must be T dollars higher (that is, equal to $P_0 + T$) if firms are to receive the P_0 per litre that induces them to supply Q_0 litres. The same idea applies at *every* quantity. Graphically, this means that at each quantity, the supply curve with the tax is located a distance T above the original supply curve: the tax shifts the supply curve up to the light red curve S_T.

The new equilibrium price paid by consumers, P_b, is the price at which the curves D and S_T cross. The tax shifts the market equilibrium from point A to point B, causing the quantity bought and sold to fall from Q_0 to Q_T. The amount that firms receive per litre net of the tax is simply $P_s = P_b - T$, also shown in Figure 15.1.

Since P_b is greater than P_0 and P_s is less than P_0, the amount paid by consumers per litre increases, while the amount received by firms (after paying the tax) decreases. However, even though firms pay the tax, the total amount they receive per litre decreases by less than the amount of the tax, T. Indeed, as Figure 15.1 shows, if we add the extra amount that consumers pay per litre and the decrease in the amount that firms receive per litre, the total comes to T dollars, the amount of the tax. Thus, in a perfectly competitive market, the burden of the tax is shared by consumers and firms.

What determines how much of the tax burden is borne by consumers versus firms? Economists call the division of a tax's burden among market participants the tax's **incidence**. The incidence of a tax depends on the shapes of the demand and supply curves. Figure 15.2 shows four extreme cases in which all of the tax is borne by just one side of the market. In Figure 15.2(a), demand is perfectly elastic, so that the tax causes no change in the price paid by consumers; all of the tax is borne by firms. Firms bear all of the tax in Figure 15.2(b) as well. There, the tax leaves the supply curve unchanged (because it is perfectly inelastic, it remains in the same location when it shifts upward by T dollars). In Figures 15.2(c) and (d), the entire burden of the tax falls instead on consumers, who pay T dollars more per litre than without the tax. In Figure 15.2(c), consumer demand is perfectly inelastic, while in Figure 15.2(d), firms' supply is perfectly elastic.

As a general matter, the more elastic is demand and the less elastic is supply, the more of the tax is borne by firms. In the appendix to this chapter, we'll show that for small taxes the share of the tax borne by consumers is given by the formula

> The **incidence** of a tax indicates how much of the tax burden is borne by various market participants.

$$\text{Consumers' share of tax} = \frac{E^s}{E^s - E^d} \tag{1}$$

where E^d and E^s are the elasticities of demand and supply, respectively. Consumers bear the larger share of the tax when demand is less elastic than supply, and the smaller share when demand is more elastic than supply (meaning that it is larger in absolute value; recall that E^d is a negative number). For example, if $E^s = 2$ and $E^d = -1$, then consumers bear two-thirds of the tax's burden, meaning that their price rises by $(2/3)T$ dollars, while firms receive $T/3$ dollars less per litre. (Check for yourself that the formula gives the right answer for the four cases shown in Figure 15.2.)

The two groups bear the tax equally when demand and supply are equally elastic (so that $E^s = -E^d$). This is because consumer and producer prices must change with the tax in a way that causes the quantities supplied and demanded to change by the same amount—otherwise, the quantities supplied and demanded would no longer be equal after the tax. When the demand and supply elasticities are equal (in absolute value), the

> *Optional Using the definition of the price elasticity of demand and supply, equation (1) can also be rewritten as
>
> Consumer's share of tax
> $$= \frac{1}{1 - \dfrac{dP/dQ^s}{dP/dQ^D}}$$
>
> where dP/dQ^S and dP/dQ^D are the slopes of the supply curve and demand curve respectively (evaluated where the demand and supply curve intersect).

Figure 15.2

Incidence of a Specific Tax: Four Cases. Figures (a) and (b) show two cases in which firms bear the entire burden of the tax. Figures (c) and (d) show two cases in which consumers bear the entire burden of the tax.

(a) Perfectly elastic demand

(b) Perfectly inelastic supply

(c) Perfectly inelastic demand

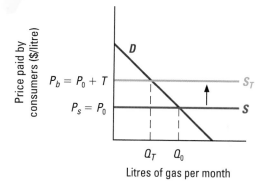

(d) Perfectly elastic supply

quantities demanded and supplied will change by the same amount only if consumer and producer prices change by the same amount. That's why the burden is equally shared. When one group has a larger elasticity than the other (one farther away from zero), a smaller change in its price is required to produce the same change in quantity, which means that group bears a smaller share of the burden.

So far we've focused on a tax paid by firms. What difference would it make if the tax was instead paid by consumers? Surprisingly, perhaps, the answer is *none*. To see why, suppose that for each litre of gas a consumer buys, she must send T dollars to the government. Let's use demand and supply curves to look at the effect of this tax. We'll continue to let P_b stand for the amount paid by consumers. Now, though, it is the *total* amount paid per litre, including both the amount the consumer pays to the firm, P_s, and the tax, T. Let's again graph demand and supply curves as a function of P_b (which now includes the tax) and find the price P_b at which the amounts demanded and supplied are equal. The demand curve is exactly the same as the one shown in Figure 15.1. What about the supply curve?

Just as when firms paid the tax, if consumers pay (in total) P_b per litre, firms receive $P_s = P_b - T$ per litre. So the supply curve is once again S_T. Thus, Figure 15.1 also describes the situation in which consumers pay the tax. As a result, the market equilibrium is still point B. Regardless of who hands the tax money over to the government, the incidence of the tax is the same. Another way to put this is that the "statutory incidence" (who by law must pay the tax) has no effect on the "economic incidence" (who really bears the burden of the tax).

Upon reflection, this result is less surprising than it might seem at first. Suppose that instead of having consumers send T dollars to the government for each litre of gas they buy, the government adopts an "easy pay" program in which gas stations are required to collect and remit consumers' tax payments. Since the consumer is still the one paying the tax, this change (which involves only the person who puts the envelope in the mail) shouldn't matter. But this new way of collecting taxes is exactly the same as imposing the tax on firms!

The method we have followed in Figure 15.1 is not the only way to determine graphically the effect of the tax. Figure 15.3 shows a second way to do so. There the vertical axis measures the price received by firms, net of any taxes, P_s. In that case, the tax leaves the supply curve unchanged, but shifts the demand curve down by a distance of T at each quantity to the curve D_T. Why? For any amount per litre received by firms, the tax increases the cost to consumers by T dollars per litre. The price received by firms with the tax (P_s), and the amount bought and sold (Q_T) correspond to the intersection of the curves D_T and S, while the price paid by consumers is T higher than the price received by firms ($P_b = P_s + T$). This outcome is the same as in Figure 15.1.

Figures 15.1 and 15.3 also suggest a third way to determine the effect of a specific tax, regardless of who pays it. We can find the amount bought and sold with the tax, Q_T,

Figure 15.3

The Effects of a Specific Tax: Shifting the Demand Curve. The figure shows another way to find the effect of a specific tax. Now the vertical axis measures the price received by firms, so the tax shifts the demand curve downward by the distance T at each quantity. The outcome identified here is the same as in Figure 15.1.

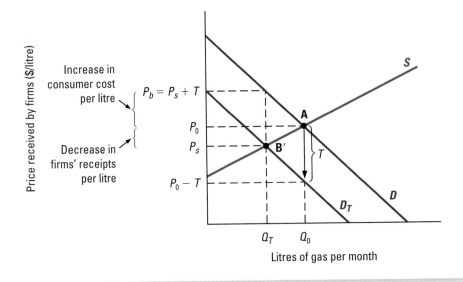

by finding the quantity at which the no-tax demand curve, D, is exactly the distance T above the no-tax supply curve, S. Once we have done so, we can read the amounts per litre that consumers pay and firms receive, P_b and P_s, from the no-tax demand curve D and no-tax supply curve S.

This third approach to finding the effect of a specific tax highlights the fact that the tax creates a "wedge" between the amounts that consumers pay and firms receive. We'll see later in this section that this wedge leads to an inefficiency, because the value of the marginal unit to consumers is T dollars higher than firms' marginal cost of producing that unit.

Application 15.1

Statutory versus Economic Incidence: The Evidence

In practice, is the statutory incidence of a tax really irrelevant? Unfortunately, there isn't much evidence on this point. That's because policymakers haven't provided the "experiment" that economists need to study this question empirically: a case in which the legal obligation to pay a tax was switched from buyers to sellers, or vice versa, without any other changes that might confuse the results.

Given the lack of a real-world example to study, economists have taken the question into the laboratory. In one laboratory experiment, Canadian economist Bradley Ruffle created a competitive market environment much like Vernon Smith's experimental markets (see Application 2.1 on page 33).[1] Ruffle first ran the market experiment several times without any taxes. Then he introduced a tax, sometimes requiring buyers to pay it and sometimes requiring sellers to pay.

Figure 15.4 shows the results of Ruffle's experiments. Each line shows the fluctuations in the median price paid by buyers to sellers (not including any tax that buyers paid) during a single experimental session, each of which involved a sequence of 20 experimental markets. In all there were 12 sessions, which differed in the numbers of buyers and sellers and in whether buyers or sellers had to pay the tax. In the first eight experimental markets of each session, there was no tax. Given the demand and supply conditions Ruffle created, the predicted market equilibrium price was between 31 and 33 Israeli shekels.[2] Then, starting with the ninth experimental market in each session and continuing through

the twentieth, a 10-shekel tax was imposed on either the buyers or the sellers. In both cases, the predicted market equilibrium price paid by buyers to sellers was between 36 and 38 shekels when sellers paid the tax, and between 26 and 28 shekels when buyers paid the tax (bringing their total cost per unit again to 36–38 shekels).

The accompanying figure shows that prices converged fairly rapidly to the predicted ranges. As the theory suggests, the statutory incidence of the tax led to only minor differences in who actually bore its burden.

The prediction that statutory incidence is irrelevant to economic incidence can be extended to market settings that aren't perfectly competitive (see, for example, Exercise 17.21). In some of those settings, however, the theoretical predictions turn out to be less accurate. For example, economists Rudolf Kerschbamer and Georg Kirchsteiger studied the relevance of statutory incidence when sellers face a buyer in one-on-one bargaining, with the power to make take-it-or-leave-it offers (paralleling the ultimatum game discussed in Section 13.5).[3] They found that a seller or buyer who had to pay the tax did worse than the other party. Why might this be the case? In this one-on-one setting, people appear to care about fairness (see Section 13.5). The statutory incidence of a tax may affect their views about what's fair. When a tax is imposed on one party, this may foster a belief that it's fair for that party to bear a larger share of the total burden.

[1]Bradley J. Ruffle, "Tax and Subsidy Incidence Equivalence Theories: Experimental Evidence from Competitive Markets," *Journal of Public Economics* 89, August 2005, pp. 1519–1542. Ruffle's experimental procedure did differ somewhat from Smith's, in that it allowed buyers and sellers to engage in direct negotiations. (Smith used an "open outcry" procedure, which resembles commodity trading markets.)

[2]Because the demand and supply curves had a steplike form, all prices in this range were equilibrium prices.

[3]Rudolf Kerschbamer and Georg Kirchsteiger, "Theoretically Robust but Empirically Invalid? An Experimental Investigation into Tax Equivalence," *Economic Theory* 16, November 2000, pp. 719–734.

Figure 15.4

An Experimental Study of Tax Incidence. Each line shows the changes in the median price paid by buyers to sellers (not including any tax buyers paid) during a single session of the experiment, each consisting of 20 experimental markets. The 12 sessions differed in the number of buyers and sellers who participated, and in who paid the 10-shekel tax starting in the 9th experimental market. For example, in session "tax13b10," the 10th session, there were 13 buyers and sellers, and the buyers had to pay the tax. The predicted equilibrium price without the tax was in the range of 31–33 shekels. With the tax, the predicted prices paid by buyers to sellers were in the range of 36–38 shekels when sellers paid the tax and 26–28 shekels when buyers paid the tax. As the figure shows, prices converged rapidly to the predicted levels.

Application 15.2

The Incidence of the Payroll Tax

If you've ever received a paycheque, you've probably noticed that a significant chunk of your pay was deducted under the heading "CPP" or "QPP" (if you live in Quebec). CPP stands for the Canada Pension Plan. The CPP is an earning-related social insurance program that is levied on all workers 18 and older. Ever since its enactment, both workers and employers have had to make equal contributions. Currently, workers and employers must each pay the federal government 4.95 percent of the worker's total earnings above $3500 and below $46,300. Self-employed individuals pay the entire 9.9 percent themselves. CPP taxes are often referred to as payroll taxes, a category of taxes that also include employment insurance, or EI.

EI deductions are also matched by contributions from employers.

When legislators enacted the tax for CPP, they decided that it was "fair" for workers and employers to split the tax equally. Economic analysis, however, tells us that the statutory obligation to pay the tax doesn't matter. The statutory incidence may be 50-50, but what is the economic incidence of the tax?

Most of the available evidence suggests that, in Canada, workers bear nearly all the burden of employment-based taxes, such as the payroll tax. Morely Gunderson at the University of Toronto, in a paper titled "Payroll Taxes: Killers of jobs, killers of wages," argues that the burden of the payroll tax is especially high on the poor.[4] This is to be expected, because the elasticity of labour supply is quite low. Among men, for example, there is almost no variation in hours worked in response to changes in the wage, and estimates of the elasticity of women's labour supply are around 0.4. Workers who have full-time jobs simply don't vary their hours of work very much.

For some occupations, however, labour supply is more elastic. For example, those who are employed part time, working in some weeks but not in others, are more responsive than others to increases in the wage. As a result, formula (1) predicts that in occupations staffed largely by this type of worker (for example, cab drivers or temporary help), firms may bear a larger share of the payroll tax than in other types of businesses.

The Welfare Effects of a Tax

Now let's examine the welfare effects of a tax.[5] Figure 15.5 shows the change in aggregate surplus caused by the tax of T dollars per litre. The no-tax demand curve D and no-tax supply curve S are the same as those in Figures 15.1 and 15.3. The tax reduces the amount bought and sold from Q_0 to Q_T, the quantity at which the distance between the curves D and S is T. We can use the D and S curves to measure aggregate surplus. The area under the no-tax demand curve reflects consumers' willingness to pay, while the area under the no-tax supply curve reflects the avoidable costs of production.[6] As in Section 14.5, aggregate surplus is the area between these curves, up to the equilibrium quantity (the amount bought and sold).

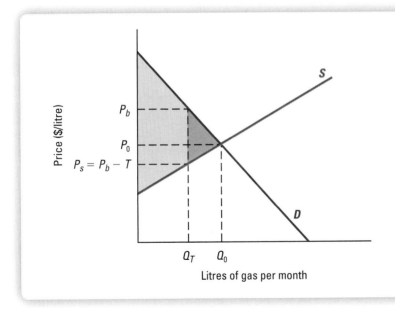

Figure 15.5

The Deadweight Loss of Taxation. This figure shows the deadweight loss from a specific tax of T dollars per litre of gas. Without the tax, aggregate surplus is the sum of the green-shaded area and the red-shaded area. With the tax, it is the green-shaded area. The deadweight loss (the reduction in aggregate surplus) is therefore the red-shaded area.

---

[4]See the "Primer on Payroll Taxes in Canada" by Human Resources and Skills Development Canada (www.hrsdc.gc.ca). Morely Gunderson's paper appeared in the Atlantic Institute for Market Studies Labour Market Commentary Series on December 11, 2008 on pages 1–8. Several empirical studies on payroll taxes have been conducted in the United States including, for example, Jonathan Gruber, "The Incidence of Mandated Maternity Benefits," *American Economic Review* 84, June 1994, pp. 622–641 and Jonathan Gruber and Alan Krueger, "The Incidence of Mandated Employer-Provided Insurance: Lessons from Workers' Compensation Insurance," in *Tax Policy and the Economy* 5, edited by David Bradford, Cambridge, MA: MIT Press, 1991.

[5]Here and throughout the remaining sections of this chapter, we'll assume that there are no income effects, or that they're small so that we can get approximately the right answer using ordinary (uncompensated or Marshallian) demand curves. Add-On 15A shows how to measure the welfare effects of a tax when income effects complicate the analysis.

[6]Note that we need to use the no-tax supply curve S for this purpose, *not* the with-tax supply curve S_T. The area under the latter curve includes the cost of the tax, which is not a true social cost of production because the tax is collected by the government. For similar reasons, we need to use the no-tax demand curve, D.

Initially, Q_0 litres are bought and sold, so aggregate surplus is the sum of the green-shaded area and the red-shaded area. With the tax, only Q_T litres of gas are bought and sold. So the aggregate surplus with the tax is the green-shaded area. The tax decreases aggregate surplus by an amount equal to the red-shaded area. That area is the **deadweight loss of taxation**. This deadweight loss arises because the $Q_T - Q_0$ litres of gas that are not being produced and consumed with the tax cost firms less to produce than consumers are willing to pay.[7]

> The **deadweight loss of taxation** is the lost aggregate surplus due to a tax.

Figure 15.6 shows how consumers, producers, and the government fare as a result of the tax. Without the tax, consumer surplus equals areas C + D + E; with the tax, it is only C. So the loss to consumers is D + E. Producer surplus equals areas F + G + H without the tax, but only H with the tax, so the loss to producers is F + G. (See Section 14.5 for a discussion of how to use market demand and supply curves to measure consumer and producer surpluses.) The government receives tax revenue equal to areas D + F. Of the amount consumers give up, D + E, the government gets only D. Of the amount producers give up, F + G, the government gets only F. The lost amount, E + G, is the deadweight loss. Taxation is therefore a "leaky bucket"; though it can be used to move resources from the private sector to the government, the government receives less than private parties give up.

Of course, the effect of the tax on welfare depends on what the government does with the revenue. The previous calculation assumes, in effect, that a dollar spent by the government has the same social value as a dollar spent by the typical consumer. (This would be

Figure 15.6

The Welfare Effects of a Specific Tax. A specific tax lowers consumer surplus from the sum of areas C + D + E to area C; it lowers producer surplus from the sum of areas F + G + H to area H. The tax revenue collected is the sum of areas D + F. The amount lost by consumers and firms but not gained by the government equals areas E + G, the deadweight loss of the tax.

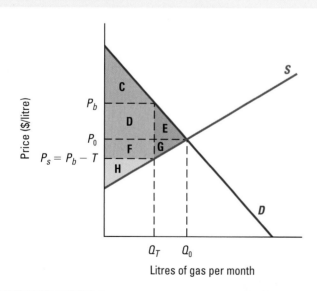

	Without tax	With tax	Gain/Loss with tax
Aggregate surplus	C + D + E + F + G + H	C + D + F + H	E + G
Consumer surplus	C + D + E	C	D + E
Producer surplus	F + G + H	H	F + G
Tax revenue	0	D + F	D + F

Litres of gas per month

---

[7]For simplicity, we haven't included any administrative costs of collecting the tax, which would increase the deadweight loss.

the case, for example, if the government simply handed the revenues back to consumers.) If the government wasted the money, then the tax would create an even larger social loss—it would include areas D + F. The loss associated with the tax could be smaller, however—indeed, the tax might even be beneficial—if government spending were more socially valuable on the margin than private spending. This is sometimes possible when there are market failures; see, for example, the discussion of public goods in Chapter 20.

Worked-out problem 15.1 shows how to calculate the welfare effects of a tax.

WORKED-OUT PROBLEM   15.1

The Problem   The market demand function for corn is $Q^d = 15 - 2P$ and the market supply function is $Q^s = 5P - 2.5$, both measured in billions of bushels per year. Suppose the government imposes a $0.70 tax on each bushel of corn. What will be the effects on aggregate surplus, consumer surplus, and producer surplus? What will be the deadweight loss caused by the tax?

The Solution   We can find the answer in three steps:

Step 1: Find the market equilibrium without the tax.   The equilibrium price without the tax is $2.50 per bushel, and 10 billion bushels of corn are bought and sold each year. (These are the same demand and supply curves that we considered in Figure 14.19 on page 525.) Aggregate surplus is $35 billion, consumer surplus is $25 billion, and producer surplus is $10 billion per year.

At this market equilibrium the elasticity of demand is -0.5 and the elasticity of supply is 1.25. (Check this!) So we should expect that more of the tax will be borne by consumers, and that because demand is relatively inelastic, the tax will cause a small deadweight loss.

Step 2: Find the new market equilibrium with the tax.   The tax changes the market supply function to

$$Q^s = 5(P_b - 0.70) - 2.5 = 5P_b - 6$$

where P_b is the price paid by buyers. To find the equilibrium level of P_b, we set demand equal to supply.

$$15 - 2P_b = 5P_b - 6$$

Solving, we find that $P_b = $3 per bushel, which means that sellers receive $P_s = $2.30 per bushel (the price buyers pay, less the tax). So buyers pay $0.50 more per bushel, and sellers receive $0.20 less because of the tax. Substituting $P_b = $3 into the demand function tells us that 9 billion bushels are bought and sold each year with the tax. Figure 15.7 shows the new equilibrium.

Step 3: Calculate the new levels of aggregate surplus, consumer surplus, and producer surplus.   Figure 15.7 shows the areas that we need to measure. Consumer surplus, equal to the area of the blue triangle, is $20.25 billion per year. Producer surplus, equal to the area of the yellow triangle, is $8.1 billion per year. Government revenue, equal to the area of the gray rectangle, is $6.3 billion per year. Adding these three amounts tells us that aggregate surplus is $34.65 billion per year. Since aggregate surplus without the tax is $35 billion per year, the deadweight loss from the tax must be $0.35 billion per year—a relatively small fraction of the original aggregate surplus. Indeed, the tax collects 18 percent of the original aggregate surplus as government revenue, losing only one percent of it as deadweight loss. The ratio of deadweight loss to tax revenue is 0.056 (0.35/6.3), so the lost aggregate surplus amounts to 5.6 percent of every tax dollar collected.

We could have calculated aggregate surplus with the tax in two other ways. First, we could have determined the area of the trapezoid formed by the blue, gray, and yellow areas. Viewed sideways, this trapezoid has a bottom base of 7, a top base of 0.7, and a height of 9, so its area equals ½ × (bottom base + top base) × height, or 34.65. Alternatively, we could have calculated the area of the red deadweight loss triangle, which has a base of 0.7 and a height of 1, so that its area is 0.35. Aggregate surplus with the tax equals the no-tax aggregate surplus ($35 billion) less this deadweight loss ($0.35 billion).

IN-TEXT EXERCISE 15.1 **The market demand function for corn is $Q^d = 15 - 2P$ and the market supply function is $Q^s = 5P - 2.5$, both measured in billions of bushels per year. Suppose the government imposes a $1.40 tax on each bushel of corn. What will be the effects on aggregate surplus, consumer surplus, and producer surplus? What will be the deadweight loss caused by the tax?**

Which Goods Should the Government Tax?

The size of the deadweight loss from taxation of a good depends on the shapes of the demand and supply curves. Look at Figure 15.8(a), in which demand is perfectly inelastic, and Figure 15.8(b), in which supply is perfectly inelastic. In both these cases, there is no deadweight loss from taxation, because the tax doesn't change the amount bought and sold. More generally, if either the demand or supply curve is very inelastic, even if not perfectly so, the deadweight loss caused by a tax will be low.

Figure 15.7

The Welfare Effects of a Tax on Corn. The figure shows the welfare effects of a $0.70 per bushel tax on corn. Consumer surplus falls from $25 billion per year without the tax (see Figure 14.17 on page 521) to $20.25 billion with it. Producer surplus falls from $10 billion per year without the tax to $8.1 billion with it. The government collects $6.3 billion per year in tax revenue. Aggregate surplus therefore falls from $35 billion per year without the tax to $34.65 billion with it, creating a deadweight loss of $0.35 billion per year.

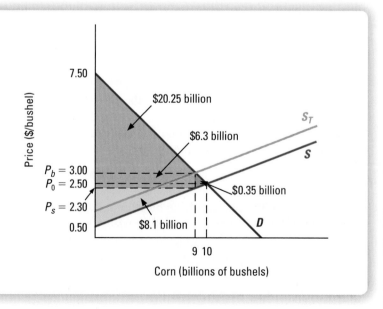

Figure 15.8

Two Cases of Taxation with No Deadweight Loss. In figure (a), demand is perfectly inelastic; in figure (b), supply is perfectly inelastic. In both cases, a tax causes no change in the amount bought and sold. Aggregate surplus, which equals the green-shaded areas with and without the tax, remains the same.

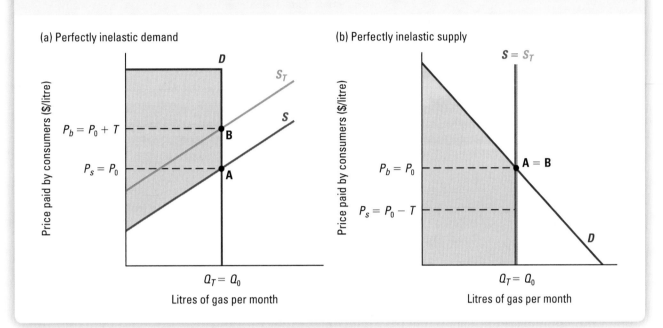

(a) Perfectly inelastic demand

(b) Perfectly inelastic supply

Governments use tax revenue to finance a number of programs, including road and highway improvements, military expenditures, and the administrative functions of government. What goods should the government tax, and in what amounts, to raise this revenue? One important objective should be to tax goods for which the deadweight loss of taxation will be low. Figure 15.8 suggests that this involves choosing goods with inelastic demand or supply. For example, we saw in Chapter 2 that the demand for gasoline is fairly inelastic, which would make gasoline a good product to tax.[8] In Add-On 17B we'll confirm this general observation by deriving a formula for minimizing the deadweight loss of taxation. As an example, suppose that two goods X and Y have the same, constant marginal cost, MC (because marginal cost is constant, the supply curve is infinitely elastic). That formula tells us that the taxes on these two goods, T_X and T_Y, should satisfy

$$\left[\frac{\left(\dfrac{T_X}{MC + T_X} \right)}{\left(\dfrac{T_Y}{MC + T_Y} \right)} \right] = \left(\frac{E_Y^d}{E_X^d} \right)$$

If good X's demand is less elastic than good Y's, the ratio on the right-hand side of this formula is greater than one. So the taxes on the two goods should have $T_X/(MC + T_X) > T_Y/(MC + T_Y)$, which implies that $T_X > T_Y$: the good with the less elastic demand should face a larger tax.

---

[8] In fact, since both gasoline consumption and driving create externalities, there are also other reasons to tax gasoline (see Chapter 20).

© Eric Allie. Used by permission.

While minimizing deadweight losses is an important objective, it may not be the only one. Distributional considerations can also affect the choice of goods to tax. Many goods with inelastic demand are necessities, such as milk. Taxes on such goods will place a heavy burden on low-income consumers. If there isn't any way to redistribute income without causing deadweight losses, it may make sense to instead tax other goods with more elastic demands.

Finally, for some goods, taxation can actually raise aggregate surplus. In Chapter 20, for example, we'll discuss taxes on pollution. Markets don't necessarily produce efficient outcomes where pollution is concerned. Because polluters don't personally bear all the costs of their actions, they may choose to pollute excessively. (This type of market failure is known as an externality.) Taxes can promote efficiency by making activities that generate pollution more costly to polluters. So-called sin taxes on addictive substances such as alcohol or cigarettes may also promote efficiency. One reason is that an addict's substance abuse can harm others (again, an externality). Another possible social benefit is that these taxes discourage youths from developing tastes for addictive substances. In these cases, taxes not only improve efficiency, but also raise revenue at the same time, eliminating the need to tax other goods where the taxation would cause deadweight losses.

Government Subsidies and Their Effects

A subsidy is a payment that reduces the amount that buyers pay for a good or increases the amount that sellers receive.

In some circumstances, governments offer a **subsidy**—a payment that reduces the amount that buyers pay for a good or increases the amount that sellers receive. Subsidies can be either specific (that is, a dollar amount per unit) or *ad valorem* (that is, a percentage of price). Like taxes, subsidies are sometimes imposed to restore efficiency in response to market failures. Unlike taxes, which routinely are observed in competitive markets without significant market failures because of the government's need to raise revenue, subsidies in such markets often result from extensive lobbying efforts on behalf of the beneficiaries. For example, the Canadian government subsidizes the production and use of ethanol in gasoline, increasing the incomes of ethanol producers, gasoline refiners, and the farmers who grow the corn that is its primary input. Canada, as a member of the World Trade Organization (WTO), is entitled to provide up to $4.3 billion in agricultural subsidies that are directly related to production quantities (the overall subsidy level is termed the "aggregate measure of support" or AMS).[9] In 2000, the latest year in which Canada submitted a report to the WTO, the actual subsidy level was $848 million. Although directly comparable data on production distorting subsidies is not currently available, Agriculture and Agri-Food Canada estimate 2009 agricultural transfers to be $1.89 billion.[10]

---

[9]Michael Holden, Economics Division, Sept. 20, 2005, Library of Parliament, "Canada's Domestic Agricultural Supports and the World Trade Organization."

[10]Agriculture and Food Canada, "Summary of Three-Year Plan (2009–2012) for Transfer Payments."

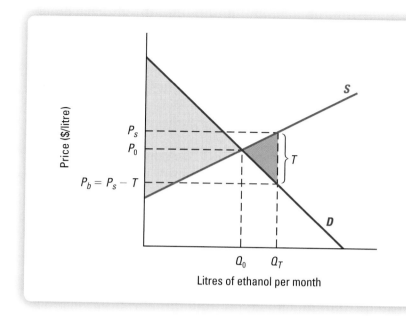

Figure 15.9

The Deadweight Loss from a Per-Unit Subsidy on Ethanol. With a subsidy of T dollars per unit, the amount bought and sold increases from Q_0 to Q_T, producing a deadweight loss equal to the area of the red triangle. As a result of the subsidy, consumers pay less and firms receive more for every litre of ethanol sold.

Unlike taxes, subsidies usually *increase* sales of the subsidized good. Like taxes, however, they cause deadweight losses. Figure 15.9 shows the effect of a government subsidy of T dollars for each litre of ethanol produced.[11] Just as with a tax, we can find the equilibrium with the subsidy by shifting either the supply or demand curve (for example, when we measure the price paid by consumers on the vertical axis, the supply curve shifts *down* by a distance of T, since supply increases with the subsidy) or by looking for the quantity at which the no-subsidy demand curve lies a distance of T below the no-subsidy supply curve (since consumers pay T dollars less than firms receive). In the figure, the subsidy increases the amount bought and sold from Q_0 to Q_T.

Without the subsidy, aggregate surplus is the green-shaded area. With the subsidy, it is the green-shaded area minus the red-shaded deadweight loss. This deadweight loss arises because the last $Q_T - Q_0$ litres of ethanol cost more to produce than consumers are willing to pay.

Consumers and firms both benefit from this subsidy. As with a tax, the sum of the reduction in the price paid by consumers and the increase in the price received by firms equals exactly T.

CALVIN AND HOBBES © 1993 Watterson. Dist. By UNIVERSAL PRESS SYNDICATE. Reprinted with permission. All rights reserved.

[11]Subsidies for ethanol in Canada have typically been targeted at production infrastructure rather than a subsidy per litre of ethanol. In August of 2008 Husky Energy received a $72.8 million subsidy for its ethanol plant in Manitoba.

How much each group's price changes depends again on the shape of the demand and supply curves. In general, the side of the market where the response is less elastic has a larger price change. Formula (1) on page 536 still describes consumers' share of the total price change, but now getting a larger share is good since a subsidy reduces the amount paid by consumers and increases the amount received by firms. Since aggregate surplus falls even though both consumers and firms are better off, someone must be worse off. That "someone" is the government, which incurs an expense equal to $T \times Q_T$.

IN-TEXT EXERCISE 15.2   Graph the changes in consumer surplus, producer surplus, and government revenue caused by a subsidy of T dollars per litre of ethanol.

15.2 POLICIES DESIGNED TO RAISE OR LOWER PRICES

Governments often attempt to interfere in markets with the intention of benefiting a particular group. When politicians want to help the sellers in a market, they turn to a variety of policies meant to raise prices. Such policies are particularly prevalent in agricultural markets, where they are intended to raise farmers' incomes. We'll discuss four such policies: price floors, price supports, production quotas, and voluntary production limits. A particular country will typically only use one of the four policies in any particular agricultural market. Canada has historically used production quotas or price supports to achieve its agricultural policy objectives.

Price Floors

A price floor is the minimum price that sellers can charge.

A **price floor** is the minimum price that sellers can charge. For example, the Canadian provinces have minimum wage laws specifying the minimum hourly wage for an employee. Minimum wages in March 2010 ranged from a low of $8.00 per hour in British Columbia (where a "First Job/Entry Level" wage of $6.00 can be paid for the first 500 hours) up to a high of $10.00 in Nunavut. The province of Alberta has a minimum wage of $8.80, Quebec and Manitoba have minimum wages of $9.00, and Ontario has a minimum wage of $9.50 per hour.

In the agricultural sector supply and prices are regulated in the poultry and dairy industries. As an example, the Canadian Milk Supply Management Committee, chaired by the Canadian Dairy Commission, determines the national supply of domestic milk and regulates the price at which it is sold to processors. Production quotas and price supports are commonly used for agricultural products, such as milk, rather than price floors. However, in the examples that follow we trace the impact of a hypothetical price floor, in addition to price supports and production quotas, in the dairy industry.

Figure 15.10(a) shows (hypothetical) yearly demand and supply curves for milk. Absent any intervention, the competitive price would be P_0. Suppose the government sets a price floor above that level, at $\underline{P}$. At that price, the amount supplied exceeds the amount demanded. Since trade requires that both parties agree, the amount of milk bought and sold is Q_1 litres, determined by the demand curve. (Farmers would like to sell more than Q_1 litres, but no one is willing to buy them.)

Figure 15.10

Three Ways to Raise the Price of Milk. The figure shows three ways to raise the price of milk to $\underline{P}$. In figure (a), the government imposes a price floor of $\underline{P}$, which results in Q_1 litres being bought and sold. In figure (b), the government increases demand through a price support program in which it buys $Q_2 - Q_1$ litres a year. Total sales of milk are Q_2 litres, of which Q_1 litres are bought by private buyers. In figure (c), the government reduces the supply by convincing farmers to limit their production to Q_1 litres per year, either by imposing a quota or by instituting a voluntary production reduction program.

Figure 15.11 shows the welfare implications of this policy (see both the figure and the accompanying table). Aggregate surplus without any intervention, described in the first row of the first column of the table, is the sum of areas A + B + C + D + E. What about with the price floor? Since farmers want to sell Q_2 litres of milk at a price of $\underline{P}$, the total cost of production depends on *which* farms produce the Q_1 litres of milk that are bought and sold. If they are the least-cost producers, the total avoidable cost of production is given by the area under the supply curve up to Q_1 litres (see Section 14.5).[12] In that case, the aggregate surplus is areas A + B + D (see the first row of the "Price Floor" column in the table). The deadweight loss from this policy is then areas C + E (shown in the second row of that same column).

Consumers are worse off, because consumer surplus falls from A + B + C without the price floor to only A with it. What about farmers? Certainly, any farmer who is no longer able to sell his milk is worse off, while a farmer who still sells the same amount is better off. What about farmers as a whole? Surprisingly, they may be either better or worse off. With the floor, producer surplus is area B + D; without the floor, it is area D + E. So farmers are better off if area B exceeds area E. In the figure that is so, but it need not be in other cases. (Try redrawing the figure with different price floors. You'll see that if the price floor is very high, farmers will make very little money.)

The reason producer surplus need not increase is simple; it relates to our discussion of profit maximization in Chapter 9 (see also Chapter 17). It's just a matter of whether or

---

[12]This means that each farm produces those units for which the marginal cost is below $\hat{P}$ in Figures 15.12(a) and 15.13.

Figure 15.11

The Welfare Effects of Four Policies Designed to Raise the Price of Milk. All policies represented in this figure raise the price of milk from P_0 to $\underline{P}$, and all create a deadweight loss. The least efficient is the price support program, which causes unused milk to be produced. The other three policies all create the same deadweight loss, but they differ in their benefits to farmers and their cost to the government. The price floor and production quota have the same effects. The voluntary production reduction system gives farmers a larger profit, but is more costly for the government. Farmers do as well under the voluntary production reduction system as under the price support program, but at a lower cost to the government.

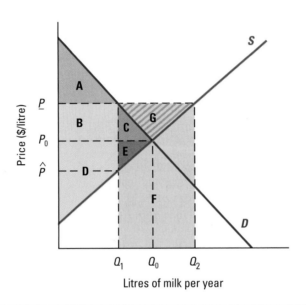

Litres of milk per year

	No intervention	Price floor	Price support	Production quota	Voluntary production reduction
Aggregate surplus	$A + B + C + D + E$	$A + B + D$	$A + B + D - F$	$A + B + D$	$A + B + D$
Deadweight loss	0	$C + E$	$C + E + F$	$C + E$	$C + E$
Consumer surplus	$A + B + C$	A	A	A	A
Producer surplus	$D + E$	$B + D$	$B + C + D + E + G$	$B + D$	$B + C + D + E + G$
Government revenue	0	0	$-(C + E + F + G)$	0	$-(C + E + G)$

not industry profits go up when the price goes up. As we saw in Chapter 9, the highest possible profit occurs where marginal revenue (derived from the market demand curve) equals the marginal cost (which is given by the industry supply curve, S). However, the government may set the price floor above or below this profit-maximizing level. If the price floor is too high, it may yield a *lower* profit than the original market equilibrium. (That said, since these policies are often introduced in response to political pressure from the affected farmers, it's a safe bet that they'll suggest price floors that do, in fact, raise their profits.)

In some cases, the welfare effects of a price floor can be worse than we have indicated. First, the Q_1 litres sold with a price floor might not be produced by the least-cost producers. This would raise the costs of production, lowering aggregate surplus. Second, with a binding price floor, producers aren't able to sell as much as they want. Sometimes, they resort to inefficient actions designed to increase their chances of making a sale. For example, under a minimum wage policy that raises the wage above its market equilibrium level, there will be more willing workers than there are jobs. This excess supply of labour can lead to additional inefficiencies, such as workers waiting in line for jobs or filling out excessive numbers of job applications.

Price Supports

Price floors require that the government monitor transactions, since sellers who cannot make sales at the mandated price have an incentive to sell at a lower price. To avoid the need for monitoring, governments often try to increase prices through other means, such as increasing market demand. This policy, known as a **price support** program, is used primarily in the dairy industry in Canada (skim milk and butter); the United States government has traditionally used price supports to raise prices for many agricultural crops. For example, in the United States the government buys milk powder at an elevated price to support the price of milk. (Unlike liquid milk, milk powder can be stored.)

> A **price support** program raises the market price by making purchases of the good, thereby increasing demand.

When a government implements price supports, it may end up buying a lot of the supported good, for which it may have little or no use. In 2010 the Canadian Dairy Commission support prices for butter and skim milk powder were $7.10 per kilogram and $6.18 per kilogram respectively.

Suppose the government decides to increase the price of milk to P using a price support program. As Figure 15.10(b) shows, at that price the demand is Q_1 litres per year, while the supply is Q_2 litres per year. For P to be the equilibrium price, the government must therefore buy $Q_2 - Q_1$ litres of milk each year. By doing so, it shifts the demand curve to $\hat{D}$, as shown in the figure. The amount bought and sold in the new equilibrium is Q_2 litres. Private parties buy Q_1 litres, and the government buys the rest.

The welfare effects of this policy depend on what happens to the litres that the government buys. If the government has no use for the milk, it will just go to waste. (Officials can't distribute the milk to anyone who would otherwise be willing to buy it at price P without undermining the effect of the program.) Figure 15.11 shows the welfare effects of the policy in this case. Aggregate surplus with the price support program is A + B + D − F, so the deadweight loss is C + E + F. The deadweight loss is larger than it is under the price floor by area F because, under the price support program, society incurs the cost of producing an extra $Q_2 - Q_1$ litres of milk that will not be used. Consumers are just as well off as with a price floor, but farmers are better off by areas C + E + G because they sell Q_2 instead of Q_1 litres at price $\underline{P}$. (They are also better off than they would be at the unregulated market equilibrium, by areas B + C + G.) The government, on the other hand, incurs the expense of buying the extra milk, equal to areas C + E + F + G.

Application 15.3

The Market for Taxi Permits: What Does $600,000 Buy in Vancouver?

The right to drive a taxi in one of Canada's larger cities has never been more expensive. In 2008 the cost of a taxi permit in Toronto was a staggering $150,000. The cost was even higher in Montreal where a permit costs $220,000, and in Vancouver the cost is between $450,000 and an astronomical $600,000. The cost of a permit dwarfs the average salary of a taxi driver, which is just $35,000 a year. The number of taxis in most Canadian cities is regulated by law, and the number increases gradually over time. Usually the only way to obtain a taxi permit is to purchase one from an existing holder.[13]

The situation is no different in other major world cities. Victor Salazar, a 40-year-old Ecuadorian immigrant, was a nervous man in April 2004, just before the City of New York's auction of 126 new taxi medallions.[14] The auction was a rare opportunity to become his own boss, as opposed to just driving for a taxi company. Over the next three years, New York would auction off 900 medallions—the largest increase in the number of medallions since the end of World War II—increasing the total number of cabs from 12,187 to 13,087. Salazar won a medallion in the auction, with a bid that was almost $300,000. The average price of the medallions sold that day was $292,580.86.

The amount Salazar and others were willing to pay tells us that the taxi fares set by New York City's Taxi Commission are a good deal higher than those that would prevail in an unregulated competitive market equilibrium. How much profit would justify spending $292,580.86 on a medallion? If

banks paid six percent interest in 2004, a potential medallion owner could make approximately $17,500 per year by putting that money in the bank. So it's safe to assume that the yearly profit the bidders anticipated was at least that amount.[15]

This knowledge tells us a lot about the degree to which taxi fares in New York City and elsewhere exceed the cost of providing taxi service. In 2002, 237 million taxi trips were taken in New York. Total taxi revenue was $1.4 billion, split among 12,187 taxicabs. Thus, the average fare was $5.90 per trip, and each taxi made on average 19,447 trips. If each taxi generated $17,500 per year in profit, it earned a profit of $0.90 per trip. The average cost per trip must therefore be about $5.

Figure 15.12 shows the demand and supply curves for taxi services in New York City. The production of taxi service is simple, requiring little more than a driver and a car. We'll assume, as an approximation, that the supply curve is perfectly elastic. The results of one study of the New York City taxi industry suggest that the elasticity of demand is about -1.2 at the regulated price.[16] We have plotted a linear demand curve that is consistent with the price of $5.90 per trip and the 237 million trips taken in 2002, along with an elasticity of -1.2. (The demand function is $Q^d = 520 - 48\,P$, where Q^d represents millions of trips demanded per year.[17]) As the figure shows, if the price of a taxi trip were instead equal to the $5 marginal cost, 280 million trips would have been taken. The deadweight loss, equal to the area of the red triangle, is therefore $19.35 million per year.

Production Quotas

Another way to raise prices without causing the overproduction that occurs under a price support program is to institute **production quotas**. Rather than raising demand, the government restricts supply by imposing limits on the quantity that individual firms can produce. For example, the government might pass a law that limits a dairy's production

---

[13]The Canadian Press as reported by CBC news, "Cabbie costs climb across Canadian cities," Monday, March 3 2008.

[14]Source: "126 Medallions, 126 Dreams," *The New York Times*, April 24, 2004, p. A11.

[15]This profit represents the amount bidders could earn above what they would earn if they didn't own a cab and instead worked for a taxi company. That is, it is their profit net of any opportunity cost.

[16]Bruce Schaller, "Elasticities for Taxicab Fares and Service Availability," *Transportation*, 1999, pp. 283–297; Schaller Consulting, *The New York City Taxicab Fact Book*, 2004.

[17]If the demand function has the form $Q^d = A - BP$ and the elasticity of demand is -1.2, then $-1.2 = -B(P/Q) = -B(5.90/237)$, so $B = 48$ (see Section 2.4). Given that, $A = 237 + 48(5.90) = 520$.

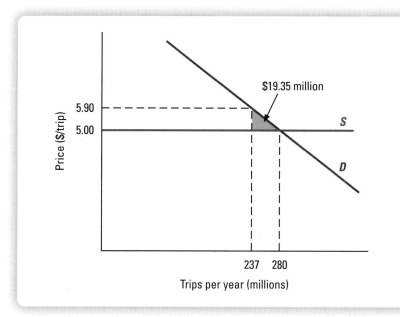

Figure 15.12

The Deadweight Loss from Regulated Taxi Fares. Taxi fares set by the New York City Taxi Commission in 2002 raised the price 90 cents above the level that would have prevailed in a perfectly competitive market and lowered the number of trips taken by 43 million per year, resulting in an annual deadweight loss of $19.35 million.

to a certain number of litres per year. Restriction of production is the most commonly used measure that Canadian federal and provincial governments use to support agricultural prices. As mentioned earlier, the Canadian Milk Supply Management Committee decides each year how much milk will be produced as well as the provincial production shares. The February 2010 revision of the annual production target for milk was set at 5.002 billion litres with Quebec and Ontario receiving the largest shares at 45.4 and 31.4 percent respectively. In Ontario individual farmers having dairy quotas can only sell milk to the Dairy Farmers of Ontario (DFO) and processors can only purchase milk from the DFO. The retail price of dairy products is unregulated. Additional marketing boards governing the production of chicken, turkey, eggs, and tobacco operate at the federal and provincial level.

Figure 15.10(c) shows the effect of a production quota that limits farmers to producing a total of Q_1 litres per year. It raises the price to $\underline{P}$ and lowers the amount bought and sold to Q_1. What are the welfare effects of such a quota? The answer depends on how the individual quotas are distributed across individual producers. As long as the individual quotas are assigned to the least-cost producers of the Q_1 units, the total avoidable cost of production will equal the area under the market supply curve up to Q_1 litres.[18] As Figure 15.11 shows, in that case aggregate surplus is exactly the same as with a price floor of $\underline{P}$. However, if the quota isn't assigned to the least-cost producers (which could well happen in practice), then the cost of production would be higher and aggregate surplus lower.

One way to ensure that the Q_1 litres will be produced at the lowest possible cost is to allow producers to trade their quotas, just as in the SO_2 allowance market discussed in Application 14.3 (page 524). In Ontario, dairy quotas are bought and sold through a quota exchange where the price of a quota is based on the butterfat content of milk. In early 2010 the price of a quota allowing the dairy farmer to sell milk with a kilogram of butterfat

---

[18]Specifically, each farm would be assigned a quota equal to the amount it would supply were the price equal to $\hat{P}$ in Figure 15.12(c). Thus, the total supply would be Q_1, and every litre supplied would be produced at a marginal cost below $\hat{P}$.

content daily was \$25,000. In the summer of 2008 a kilogram of dairy quota sold for almost \$34,000. The efficiency of a perfectly competitive market will guarantee that the quotas will end up in the right hands. Another measure of the gain to producers from the imposition of a quota is termed **quota rent**. In Figure 15.11 it is the area between $\hat{P}$ and $\underline{P}$ up to the quota amount Q_1. It is the revenue received by the industry above the amount necessary for the quota amount to be supplied. In the case of no market intervention the quota rents would be zero as marginal cost would equal price.

> A **quota rent** per unit output is the difference between the marginal cost of production at the quota amount and the price that results from the imposition of the quota.

Voluntary Production Reduction Programs

> A **voluntary production reduction** program offers firms inducements to reduce their production voluntarily.

Sometimes the government tries to reduce supply through a **voluntary production reduction** program. In such a program, the government offers inducements to firms to limit their production voluntarily.

To induce a market price of $\underline{P}$, the government must persuade farmers to produce only Q_1 litres. How much money must it offer farmers to reach that goal? Since farmers want to produce Q_2 litres when the price is $\underline{P}$, they will collectively forgo a profit equal to area C + E + G in Figure 15.11 if they agree to limit their production to Q_1 litres. That is the amount the government must pay them in total to accept this limit voluntarily.

With this program, the amount bought and sold is Q_1, just as with the quota program. What about the welfare effects? Figure 15.11 shows that aggregate surplus and consumer surplus are the same as they are under a price floor or quota system (with least-cost production) because the same amount is being produced and consumed in the two cases. But farmers do better than under a price floor or quota system by an amount equal to the government payment. In fact, they do exactly as well as under the price support program since the government compensates them to give them the same profit they would earn if they sold their desired output level at price $\underline{P}$. The government, though, does worse under the quota system since it must make payments to the farmers. Those payments are smaller than under the price support program. Under the voluntary production reduction program the government must pay farmers only an amount equal to their forgone profit (area C + E + G); it need not compensate them for the cost of actually producing an additional $Q_2 - Q_1$ litres (area F).

All these policies create a deadweight loss. The price support program is the worst, because it causes farmers to produce unused milk. The other three programs all create the same deadweight loss (assuming there is least-cost production under the price floor and quota policies). Consumer surplus is the same in all the programs. Farmers do better with price supports or a voluntary production reduction program than with a price floor or quota, but the government does worse since it incurs expenses with those programs. The government's expense, however, is lower under a voluntary production reduction program than under a price support program.

If all these policies create a deadweight loss, why are they ever enacted? The benefits of raising the price of a good are usually concentrated among a relatively small, easily identified set of people or firms. In contrast, the costs are usually widely dispersed, with only a minute portion borne by each injured party. For example, by one estimate, the U.S. government paid farmers roughly \$3 billion from 1995 to 2005 under its various dairy programs. Yet that amounted to only about \$10 for each American. As a result, those who are negatively affected by such policies may have little economic incentive to oppose them, while those who benefit have an incentive to lobby for them. (Those who are harmed by the policy face a "free rider" problem, as we'll discuss in Chapter 20.)

Application 15.4

Canadian Marketing Boards

Canadian agricultural policy for dairy and poultry products has for many years been regulated by marketing boards at both the federal and provincial levels. The Canadian Dairy Commission (established in 1966), the Chicken Farmers of Canada (established in 1978), the Turkey Famers of Canada (established as the Canadian Turkey Marketing Agency in 1974), and the Egg Farmers of Canada (established as the Canadian Egg Marketing Agency in 1973) all participate in national supply management programs. Agreements among the provinces establish provincial quotas based on historical market shares and are set to meet production targets consistent with support price objectives. For example, the Dairy Industry Act of 2000 regulates the price at which dairy products can be sold, sets production limits, and places limits on the transfer and sale of quotas. Support prices are maintained by augmenting domestic production quotas with high tariff barriers against imported dairy and poultry products (see section 15.3).

The effect of marketing boards is to increase the price paid by consumers above the market equilibrium price as we saw in Figures 15.10(c) and 15.11. Reality is a bit more complicated than our simple analysis, as most Canadian marketing boards use both production quotas and price supports simultaneously. As a result, the welfare effects from the use of price supports in Canadian agricultural markets is closer to that of a production quota or price floor. There have been several attempts to estimate the cost to consumers and the benefits to producers of supply management. Roger Beck, Colin Hoskins, and Glen Mumey estimated that the loss to consumers from supply management in the poultry and egg industry was over $500 million in 1991 dollars. After deducting quota rents the social loss was estimated to be approximately $100 million.[19]

The economic impact of dairy marketing boards has been even greater. A 2004 report by the Organisation for Economic Co-operation and Development (OECD) estimated that supply management accounted for between 50 and 60 percent of gross farm receipts from 1986 to 2002. The OECD estimated in 2003 that if the dairy industry were deregulated the benefit to consumers would be approximately $2.1 billion. Dairy farm households would see a decline of almost $1.4 billion, of which the majority would be a reduction in quota rents. The net benefit to the Canadian economy of $700 million is about one third of the value of production in the dairy sector.[20]

WORKED-OUT PROBLEM   15.2

The Problem   The market demand function for corn is $Q^d = 15 - 2P$ and the market supply function is $Q^s = 5P - 2.5$, both measured in billions of bushels per year. Suppose the government wants to raise the price to $3 per bushel. Describe how it could do this with a price ceiling, a price support program, a quota, and a voluntary production reduction program. What would be the welfare consequences of each of these policies?

The Solution   As in worked-out problem 15.1 (page 543), the equilibrium absent intervention has a price of $2.50 per bushel and 10 billion bushels bought and sold each year. At a price of $3 per bushel, consumers demand 9 billion bushels while farmers want to supply 12.5 billion bushels. The price ceiling policy would simply state that corn can't be sold for less than $3 per bushel. The price support program

[19]Roger Beck, Colin Hoskins and Glen Mumey, "The Social Welfare Loss from Egg and Poultry Marketing Boards, Revisited," *Canadian Journal of Agricultural Economics* 42, July 1994, pp. 149–158.

[20]OECD Joint Working Party on Agriculture and Trade, "An Analysis of Dairy Policy Reform and Trade Liberalization," COM/AGR/TD/WP(2004)20/FINAL, 2004.

would have the government purchase 3.5 billion bushels each year, the difference between the quantities supplied and demanded at a price of $3. The quota would distribute permits to farmers to sell 9 billion bushels (ideally in a manner that minimizes the cost of producing those bushels). In the voluntary production reduction program, the government would pay farmers to reduce their production from 12.5 to 9 billion bushels per year. To calculate the required payment we need to find the area corresponding to C + E + G in Figure 15.11 (using the supply curve for corn). Figure 15.13 shows that the sum of those areas is $1.23 billion.

The welfare effects from each policy can be found by calculating the areas corresponding to areas A–G in Figure 15.11. Figure 15.13 shows these amounts.

IN-TEXT EXERCISE 15.3   The market demand function for corn is $Q^d = 15 - 2P$ and the market supply function is $Q^s = 5P - 6$, both measured in billions of bushels per year. Suppose the government wants to raise the price to $4 per bushel. Describe how it could do this with a price ceiling, a price support program, a quota, and a voluntary production reduction program. What would be the welfare consequences of each of these policies?

Figure 15.13

Welfare Effects of Raising the Price of Corn. The figure shows the sizes of the areas labelled A–G in Figure 15.13 for the demand and supply curves in worked-out problem 15.2.

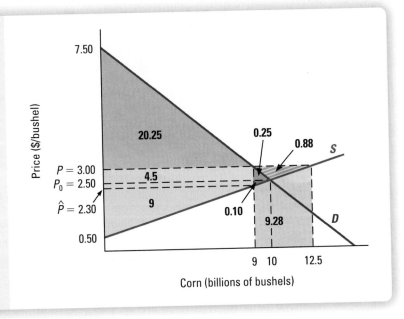

Policies that Lower Prices

In this section we've focused on policies designed to raise prices. Sometimes governments adopt policies that are designed instead to *lower* prices, in order to improve the well-being of buyers. For example, some Canadian cities have rent control laws that put a ceiling on rent increases for apartments.

We can analyze the effects of these policies in much the same way that we evaluated the effects of policies that raise prices. As an illustration, Figure 15.14 shows the effects

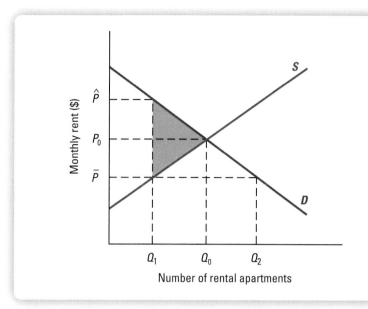

Figure 15.14

A Price Ceiling. If the government imposes a price ceiling on apartment rents equal to $\overline{P}$, the number of available apartments—and hence the number rented—falls from Q_0 to Q_1. The resulting deadweight loss equals the red-shaded area.

of a price ceiling equal to $\overline{P}$, which is below the unregulated competitive equilibrium monthly rent for an apartment, P_0. (In reality, most cities' rent control policies apply to some, but not all rental apartments; for simplicity, we assume it applies to all apartments here.) Figure 15.14 shows that the policy reduces the number of apartments landlords make available for rent to Q_1. Some former rental apartments may be sold, and fewer new apartments will be built.[21] Since supply is less than demand at the price $\overline{P}$, the amount supplied determines the equilibrium quantity (trade requires both sides to agree). That quantity falls from Q_0 to Q_1. Figure 15.14 also shows the red-shaded deadweight loss, assuming that the Q_1 apartments are rented by the consumers whose willingness to pay for them is greatest.[22] If they are not, then the deadweight loss would be greater.

IN-TEXT EXERCISE 15.4 **Draw a graph to show the effect on the consumer and producer surpluses of the price ceiling in Figure 15.14, assuming that the Q_1 apartments are rented by the consumers whose willingness to pay for them is greatest.**

Because buyers can't buy all that they want at the ceiling price, sometimes they take inefficient actions that increase the deadweight loss. For example, with rent control, renters who want to secure an apartment may wake up at five in the morning to scan the apartment rental ads before others do. There is also another loss that can occur with price ceilings: since sellers face excess demand for their products, each will be able to make sales even if their products are not as good as those of competitors. As a result, sellers have too little incentive to maintain or enhance the quality of their products. For example, a common complaint about rent-controlled apartments is that they receive little maintenance and no renovations.

---

[21]Cities adopting rent control often try to limit this reduction by prohibiting currently rented apartments from being sold. Even so, over the long run, the supply of rental apartments is reduced as the policy leads to fewer new apartments being built.

[22]Specifically, the consumers who rent the apartments should be those whose willingness to pay exceeds $\hat{P}$ in the figure.

IMPORT TARIFFS AND QUOTAS

A **tariff** is a tax on imports. A **quota** directly limits the total quantity of a good that can be imported.

Many countries discourage the importation of goods through tariffs or quotas. A **tariff** is a tax on imports while a **quota** directly limits the total amount of a good that can be imported. Canada has at times used both. The World Trade Organization, of which Canada is a member, has required that countries eliminate quotas and replace them with tariffs so that the cost of trade protection is more transparent. This has created a hybrid type of trade protection called a tariff-rate quota (TRQ) under which imports below the quota qualify for a low (or no) tariff, while imports above the quota are subject to a higher tariff. The North American Free Trade Agreement (NAFTA) has a two-tiered tariff schedule for several agricultural commodities. For example, Canada imposes a low tariff rate of 5 percent on cuts of poultry for those imports below 7.5 percent of domestic production. For imports above the so-called access commitment to the Canadian market the tariff rate jumps to 249 percent and adds a minimum of $3.78 per kilogram to the price of cuts of poultry. Although Canada does not formally impose a quota on poultry imports, the low access commitment amount coupled with high tariff rates effectively introduces a quota on imports. Canada's TRQ on poultry in 2004 was some 69,000 tonnes based on Canadian production of 946,000 tonnes. Actual imports were closer to 100,000 tonnes as an outbreak of avian influenza caused a partial shutdown of British Columbia's poultry industry.

The import fee structure in the Canada–U.S. Softwood Lumber Agreement (discussed in Applications 9.3 and 14.1, as well as later in this section) is another example of this type of a TRQ.

Tariffs

A tariff is a tax on sellers in a market. Unlike the taxes we studied in Section 15.1, however, a tariff is imposed only on *some* sellers—the foreign ones.

Consider the domestic market for sugar. Figure 15.15(a) shows the market supply curve without a tariff or quota. The domestic producers' supply curve is S^d. We'll assume that this country consumes a small share of the world's production of sugar, so that it doesn't affect the world price. As a result, the import supply curve is horizontal at some price P_W. If the domestic price is below P_W, foreign producers won't want to sell anything in this country. If it's above P_W, they'll want to sell all their production here. Without the tariff, the market supply curve is therefore the dark red curve S_0.

Figure 15.15(b) shows the effect of a tariff of T dollars per tonne. The vertical axis measures the domestic price (the price paid by consumers and received by domestic firms). The tariff shifts the import supply curve upward by the distance T since foreign firms must receive a price of $P_W + T$ to be willing to sell anything in the country. The new market supply curve is therefore the dark red curve S_T. Without the tariff, the domestic equilibrium price equals P_W, and domestic consumers buy Q_0 tonnes of sugar. Of those tonnes, Q_0^d are supplied by domestic producers; foreign producers supply the remaining $(Q_0 - Q_0^d)$ tonnes. With the tariff, the domestic equilibrium price rises to $P_T = P_W + T$, and domestic consumers buy only Q_T tonnes of sugar. However, the amount sold by domestic producers increases to Q_T^d. Imports decline to $(Q_T - Q_T^d)$.

Figure 15.15

The Effects of a Tariff. Figure (a) shows the market supply curve of sugar without a tariff. The domestic producers' supply curve is S^d. Because the country's production is only a small share of world demand, it doesn't affect the world price. The import supply curve is horizontal at price P_W. The market supply curve is the dark red curve S_0. Figure (b) shows the effect of a tariff. It shifts the import supply curve upward by the distance T, which shifts the market supply curve to S_T. Without the tariff, the price is P_W, and Q_0 tonnes are bought and sold, of which Q_0^d are supplied by domestic firms. With the tariff, the price rises to $P_W + T$, and Q_T tonnes are bought and sold, of which Q_T^d are supplied by domestic firms.

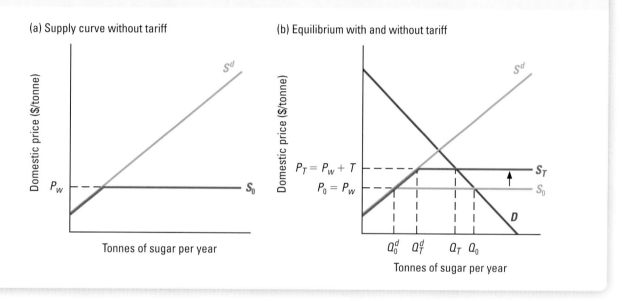

(a) Supply curve without tariff

(b) Equilibrium with and without tariff

Figure 15.16 shows the welfare effects of this policy. We'll take the perspective of the domestic government, which is concerned only with **domestic aggregate surplus**, the sum of consumer surplus, domestic producer surplus, and government revenue. (A dollar of government revenue counts as a dollar of aggregate surplus.) Without the tariff, consumer surplus equals the area A + B + C + D + E; with the tariff it is only area A. So consumers are worse off under the tariff. Domestic firms, though, are better off: their producer surplus equals area B + F with the tariff, compared to area F without it. The government receives revenue equal to the area of rectangle D, which is the quantity of imports $(Q_T - Q_T^d)$ times the tariff T.

While consumers lose areas B + C + D + E under the tariff, only areas B and D are captured by domestic firms and the government. The remaining part of their loss, areas C plus E, is the domestic deadweight loss from the tariff. Area E represents the surplus lost because of the reduction in total consumption: it is the difference between consumers' willingness to pay for the $(Q_0 - Q_T)$ tonnes of sugar they no longer purchase and the cost of that sugar. Since those units are imported, their cost per unit equals P_W. This loss is similar to the deadweight loss from taxation that we encountered in Section 15.1. Area C represents the loss that arises because $(Q_T^d - Q_0^d)$ tonnes that were previously imported at a cost of P_W per unit are now produced by domestic firms at a higher cost. That is, the tariff causes production to be allocated inefficiently away from foreign producers and toward domestic producers.

> **Domestic aggregate surplus** is the sum of consumer surplus, domestic producer surplus, and government revenue.

Figure 15.16

The Welfare Effects of a Tariff. This figure and the accompanying table summarize the welfare effects of a tariff on sugar. Because of the price increase, consumer surplus decreases by an amount equal to area B + C + D + E. Domestic firms' producer surplus increases by area B, and the government gains tariff revenue equal to area D. Domestic aggregate surplus shrinks by an amount equal to areas C + E.

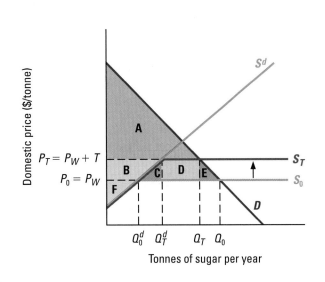

	Without tariff	With tariff
Domestic aggregate surplus	A + B + C + D + E + F	A + B + D + F
Domestic deadweight loss	0	C + E
Consumer surplus	A + B + C + D + E	A
Domestic producer surplus	F	B + F
Government revenue	0	D

Quotas

A quota limits the supply of imports to some maximum $\overline{Q}$. As Figure 15.17 shows, if the government limits imports to a maximum of $(Q_T - Q_T^d)$ tonnes [the same amounts as in Figure 15.15(b)], the domestic price of sugar will be the same $(P_T = P_W + T)$ as if it imposed a tariff of T dollars per tonne. That quota produces the market supply curve labelled S_Q in the figure. (If the price is below P_W, only domestic producers are willing to supply sugar; if the price is above P_W, foreign supply will equal the quota level.)

Consumers and domestic firms are both exactly as well off with the quota as with the tariff. The difference is that with a quota, the government doesn't receive any revenue. Instead, that revenue is earned by whichever foreign firms are lucky enough to be allowed to import their goods. So a quota yields a lower aggregate domestic surplus than a tariff.

If instead, the government were to allocate the right to import those $(Q_T - Q_T^d)$ tonnes to domestic firms that can buy the good abroad at the world price, then those revenues would increase domestic firms' producer surplus. Aggregate domestic surplus would then be the same with a tariff as with a quota. Another approach with equivalent consequences would be to sell the rights to import those $(Q_T - Q_T^d)$ tonnes to foreign firms for T dollars per tonne.

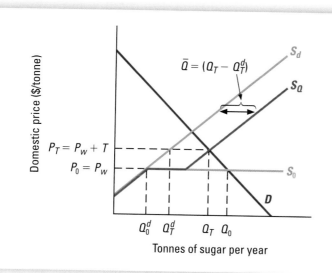

Figure 15.17

The Effects of a Quota. By limiting imports to $(Q_T - Q_T^d)$ tonnes, a quota produces the same equilibrium price, consumption, and production levels as a tariff of T dollars per tonne [compare Figure 15.15 (b)]. Consumers and domestic firms are equally well off with a quota as with a tariff. The government, however, earns no tariff revenue with a quota. Instead, that gain goes to the foreign producers who are allowed to import their goods.

Beneficial Trade Barriers

When the supply of imports is perfectly elastic, tariffs and quotas must lower aggregate domestic surplus. Sometimes, however, the import supply curve is upward sloping. For example, a large share of Canadian softwood lumber production is exported to the United States. Due to the high cost of shipping lumber overseas, there is not much other foreign demand for that lumber. As a result, changes in U.S. imports from Canada affect the price of Canadian softwood lumber, and the import supply curve of softwood lumber into the United States is upward sloping (see Application 14.1 on page 498). When the import supply curve is upward sloping, a country can sometimes increase its domestic aggregate surplus by imposing a tariff or quota.

To see why, consider a situation with *no* domestic producers of a good. In that case, a tariff is just a tax on all sellers. Look back now at Figure 15.6 (page 542). The effects of a tariff will be exactly the same as the effects of the tax in that figure. The difference, however, is that this government cares only about domestic aggregate surplus, here the sum of consumer surplus and government revenue (it doesn't count foreign firms' producer surplus). Domestic aggregate surplus is area C + D + E without the tariff, and area C + D + F with the tariff (consumer surplus is area C, and the government's tariff revenue is D + F). If area F is larger than area E, the tariff will increase domestic aggregate surplus.

This idea applies even if there are some domestic producers. The key point is that when the import supply curve is upward sloping, a government can reduce the amount that foreign firms receive for their goods by imposing a tariff.[23] Sometimes the domestic benefit from this effect exceeds the deadweight loss that the tariff creates.

---

[23] In essence, the domestic government is in the position of a monopsonist relative to the foreign suppliers (see Section 17.6 for a discussion of monopsonists).

Application 15.5

The Effects of the Canada–U.S. Softwood Lumber Agreement

In Application 14.1 (page 498), we saw how the Canada–U.S. Softwood Lumber Agreement (SLA) affected the market supply curve for softwood lumber in the United States in 1998. Let's see now what effect it had on market equilibrium and social welfare.

Figure 15.18 shows again the market demand curve and various supply curves, both with and without the SLA from Figure 14.3 (page 499). As before, the dark red curve labelled S is the market supply curve with the SLA, and the dashed dark red line shows how it would differ at prices above $240 without the SLA. The other supply curves are those of U.S. producers, Canadian producers in the four provinces affected by the SLA, and other foreign producers. The market supply curve is the sum of those three supply curves.

Under the SLA, the market equilibrium in 1998 resulted in a price of $354 per thousand board feet (point B in Figure 15.18). U.S. consumers bought 52.9 billion board feet of softwood lumber that year. U.S. producers supplied 34.2 billion of that total. Canadian producers from the affected provinces exported 15.35 billion board feet to the United States, coinciding with the quantity at which the fee rises from $50 to $100 per thousand board feet. The remaining 3.35 billion came from other foreign sources.

To determine the effects of the SLA, we first need to determine the equilibrium that would have prevailed in its absence. The market demand curve in Figure 15.18 represents the linear function

$$Q^d = 61.9 - 0.0254P$$

This demand function has an elasticity of $-.17$ at the market equilibrium, which matches published elasticity estimates. The supply curves represent linear supply functions chosen to match published elasticity estimates.[24] The U.S. producers' supply function is

$$Q^S_{U.S.} = 15.4 + 0.0531P$$

and the other foreign producers' supply function is

$$Q^S_{other} = 0.8 + 0.0076P$$

Without the SLA, the Canadian producers' supply function would have been

$$Q^S_{Cdn} = 3.5 + 0.0465P$$

and the market supply function would have been $Q^s = 19.7 + 0.1072P$, the sum of the no-SLA supply functions of the three groups of producers. Setting demand equal to supply, and solving the equation

$$61.9 - 0.0254P = 19.7 + 0.1072P$$

we find that the no-SLA equilibrium price would have been $318 per thousand board feet. Substituting that price into the demand function, we see that U.S. consumers would have bought 53.8 billion board feet of softwood lumber without the SLA (point A in Figure 15.18). Substituting the same price into the three groups' supply functions, we see that 32.3 billion of that amount would have been supplied by U.S. producers, 18.3 billion by firms in the four affected Canadian provinces, and 3.2 billion by other foreign producers.

Consumer surplus fell by $1.9 billion as a result of the SLA. (To calculate this amount, first convert the prices into dollars per board foot. The lost consumer surplus then equals the area of a trapezoid with a height of $0.036 = (0.354 - 0.318)$, one base of 52.9 billion, and another base of 53.8 billion.) Domestic producer surplus increased by $1.2 billion (equal to the area of a trapezoid with a height of $0.036, one base of 32.3 billion, and another base of 34.2 billion). Under the agreement, the Canadian government, not the U.S. government, collected the tariff, so U.S. domestic aggregate surplus fell by $700 million. So this is a case in which the trade barrier lowered domestic aggregate surplus, even though the import supply curve was upward sloping. (In fact, the Canadian government collected only $49 million in tariff fees, so domestic aggregate surplus would have fallen even if the U.S. government had received these payments.)

What about Canadian domestic aggregate surplus? Canadian producers from the four affected provinces earned an additional $606 million (U.S.), not including the SLA fees. Since the $49 million in fees were just a transfer to the Canadian government, they had no effect on Canada's domestic aggregate surplus. Other foreign producers' profits, some of which are in other Canadian provinces, increased by $118 million. So by raising the price of softwood lumber in the United States, the SLA increased Canada's domestic aggregate surplus by more than $606 million. (This analysis ignores any welfare effects arising from induced changes in the market for softwood lumber in Canada.)

---

[24]See D. Zhang, "Welfare Impacts of the 1996 United States—Canada Softwood Lumber (Trade) Agreement," *Canadian Journal of Forest Research* 31, November 2001, pp. 1958–1967.

Figure 15.18

The Effects of the Canada–U.S. Softwood Lumber Agreement in 1998. In 1998, the Canada–U.S. Softwood Lumber Agreement shifted the market equilibrium from point A to point B. U.S. producer surplus increased by $1.2 billion, but consumer surplus fell by $1.9 billion, reducing domestic aggregate surplus by $700 million. Canadian aggregate surplus, on the other hand, increased by more than $606 million.

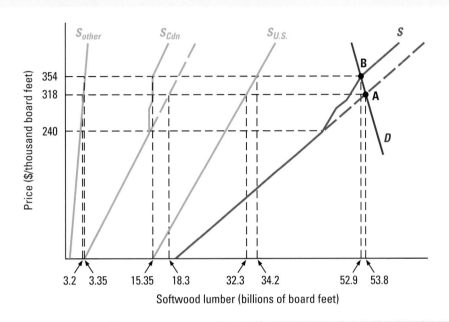

CHAPTER SUMMARY

1. **Taxes (and subsidies) (LO1, 2)**

    a. A specific tax is a fixed dollar amount that must be paid for each unit bought or sold. An *ad valorem* tax is a tax that is stated as a percentage of the good's price.

    b. The effects of a tax are independent of who is legally required to pay it, whether buyers or sellers.

    c. A tax lowers the amount of a good bought and sold, raises the total amount that buyers pay per unit, and lowers the amount that sellers receive per unit. It also causes a deadweight loss because some units that buyers value more than the cost of production are not produced.

    d. The economic incidence of a tax depends on the shapes of the demand and supply curves. The more elastic is demand and the less elastic is supply, the smaller the share of the tax borne by consumers. For small taxes, consumers' share of the tax is $E^s/(E^s - E^d)$.

    e. Consumer surplus and producer surplus both fall because of a tax. The sum of these losses is greater than the government's revenue from the tax. The difference between the two amounts is the deadweight loss.

    f. To minimize the deadweight loss from taxation, goods that have more inelastic demands and supplies should be taxed more heavily than other goods.

    g. A subsidy is a payment that reduces the amount buyers need to pay or increases the amount sellers receive. Subsidies increase the amount of a good bought and sold. They also create a deadweight loss, because some units that consumers value less than the cost of production are produced and consumed.

2. **Policies designed to raise or lower prices (LO3, 4)**

    a. A price floor establishes a minimum price that sellers can charge. If it is above the equilibrium price without the floor, sellers will want to supply more than buyers are willing to purchase at that price. In principle, a price floor may either raise or lower sellers' total profits.

b. A price support program raises the price of a good by increasing the demand for it. Price supports can result in the government buying units for which it has little or no use.

c. A production quota imposes limits on the amount of a good that individual firms can produce.

d. A voluntary production reduction program offers firms an inducement to voluntarily reduce their production.

e. All these ways of raising the price create a deadweight loss. The price support policy creates the largest deadweight loss; the other programs create the same deadweight loss (assuming that quotas are distributed efficiently or can be traded and that production is efficient with the price floor).

f. Sometimes governments instead want to lower the price of a good. A price ceiling is one example of a policy that governments use for this purpose. With a binding price ceiling, sellers will want to supply less than buyers

are willing to purchase at the ceiling price. The equilibrium quantity falls, creating a deadweight loss.

3. Import tariffs and quotas (LO5)

a. A tariff is a tax on imports. A quota places direct limits on the total amount of a good that can be imported.

b. Domestic aggregate surplus is the sum of consumer surplus, domestic firms' producer surplus, and government revenue.

c. If the import supply curve is horizontal at the world price (that is, if it is infinitely elastic), a tariff will lower domestic aggregate surplus.

d. An appropriately chosen quota can produce the same market equilibrium as a tariff. The only difference is that the government does not receive any revenue with a quota (unless it sells the rights to import the good). Instead, foreign firms lucky enough to import their goods receive the benefit.

e. If the import supply curve is upward sloping, a tariff (or quota) can increase domestic aggregate surplus.

ADDITIONAL EXERCISES

Exercise 15.1: The market demand function for corn is $Q^d = 15 - 2P$ and the market supply function is $Q^s = 5P - 2.5$, both measured in billions of bushels per year. Suppose the government imposes a $2.10 tax per bushel. What will be the effects on aggregate surplus, consumer surplus, and producer surplus? What will be the deadweight loss created by the tax? (LO2)

Exercise 15.2: Compare your answers to exercise 15.1 and in-text exercise 15.1 (page 544) with the answer to worked-out problem 15.1 (page 543). In each case, compute the ratio of the deadweight loss to tax revenue. What happens as the tax grows larger? (LO2)

Exercise 15.3: Is a tax on luxury cars a more efficient way to raise revenue (in the sense of creating a small deadweight loss) than a tax on all car purchases? Why or why not? (LO2)

Exercise 15.4: In a market with free entry and exit, who bears the burden of a tax? Given this fact, how might tax incidence differ in the short and long run? (LO2)

Exercise 15.5: Consider again worked-out problem 14.2 (page 506). Suppose that starting at the initial long-run equilibrium with a price of $11.50 and 100 active firms, the government requires firms to pay a tax of $11.50 per pizza. What is the effect of the tax on the amounts paid by buyers and sellers in the short run? What is the government revenue? What is the deadweight loss? What about in the long run? (LO2)

Exercise 15.6: Use a graph to show that, when the government increases the tax on a good, the sum of the change in consumer surplus plus the change in producer surplus plus the change in government revenue equals the change in the deadweight loss. Verify that this relationship holds by comparing the answers to worked-out problem 15.1 and in-text exercise 15.1 (pages 543 and 544). (LO2)

Exercise 15.7: The market demand and supply functions for corn are the same as in exercise 15.1. Suppose the government gives corn farmers a $0.70 subsidy per bushel of corn. What will be the effects on aggregate surplus, consumer surplus, and producer surplus? What will be the deadweight loss created by the subsidy? (LO2)

Exercise 15.8: Suppose the government enacts a tax that requires each active firm in a market to pay an annual fee of F dollars. What effect will this tax have in the short run? In the long run? (LO2)

Exercise 15.9: The market demand and supply functions for corn are the same as in exercise 15.1. Suppose the government wants to raise the price of corn to $3. What are the welfare effects of a price floor, price support, production quota, and voluntary production reduction program? (LO3)

Exercise 15.10: Suppose that the demand function for pizzas is $Q^d = 65,800 - 1200P$ and the supply function is $Q^s = 4000P - 20,000$. Suppose the pizza parlour lobby is effective at lobbying the government, which institutes a price floor of $15 on pizzas. Assuming that the least-cost pizza producers are the ones to produce the demanded pizzas, what is the effect on the aggregate, consumer, and producer surpluses? What if instead the government raised the price to $15 using a price support program? (LO3)

Exercise 15.11: Suppose that the demand function for pizzas is $Q^d = 65,800 - 1200P$ and the supply function is $Q^s = 4000P - 20,000$. Suppose the University Student Party is elected and places a price ceiling on pizza of $10 per pizza. How many pizzas will be bought and sold? Assuming that the highest willingness to pay consumers are the ones to consume the supplied pizzas, what will the effect be on the aggregate, consumer, and producer surpluses? (LO4)

Exercise 15.12: The market demand and supply functions for corn are the same as in exercise 15.1. What would be the welfare effects of a policy that put a cap of $2 per bushel on the price farmers can charge for corn? (LO4)

Exercise 15.13: The market demand and domestic supply functions for corn are the same as in exercise 15.1. Suppose the import supply curve is infinitely elastic at a price of $1.50 per bushel. What would be the welfare effects of a $0.50 per bushel tariff? (LO5)

Exercise 15.14: Suppose the import supply curve of a good is infinitely elastic at the world price. Draw a graph to show the welfare effect of a subsidy on imports. (LO4)

Exercise 15.15: Suppose the supply curve of imports is infinitely elastic at the world price. Using a graph, show how high a tariff the country must set to prevent imports from coming into the country. (LO4)

Exercise 15.16: Is there any benefit to a country (in terms of its domestic aggregate surplus) from subsidizing firms that export to another country when the market in that other country is perfectly competitive? (LO4)

APPENDIX

TAX INCIDENCE AND *AD VALOREM* TAXES

In this appendix we discuss two topics. First, we derive formula (1) on page 536, showing the share of the tax burden borne by consumers with a specific tax. Then, we show how to analyze *ad valorem* taxes.

Tax Incidence with a Specific Tax

When the government imposes a specific tax of T dollars per unit, the reduction in quantity demanded must equal the reduction in quantity supplied. For small taxes, the reduction in quantity demanded is equal to the elasticity of demand times the percentage change in the price buyers pay, $(\Delta P_b/P_0)$, where P_0 is the initial no-tax equilibrium price and $\Delta P_b = P_b - P_0$ is the increase in the amount buyers pay per unit. So

$$\text{Change in quantity demanded} = E^d\left(\frac{\Delta P_b}{P_0}\right)$$

Likewise, the change in quantity supplied is equal to the elasticity of supply times the percentage change in the price firms receive.

$$\text{Change in quantity supplied} = E^s\left(\frac{\Delta P_s}{P_0}\right)$$

Since $\Delta P_s = P_s - P_0 = (P_b - T) - P_0 = \Delta P_b - T$, we can rewrite the change in quantity supplied as

$$\text{Change in quantity supplied} = E^s\left[\left(\frac{\Delta P_b}{P_0}\right) - \left(\frac{T}{P_0}\right)\right]$$

Since the change in quantity demanded must equal the change in quantity supplied we know that

$$E^d\left(\frac{\Delta P_b}{P_0}\right) = E^s\left[\left(\frac{\Delta P_b}{P_0}\right) - \left(\frac{T}{P_0}\right)\right]$$

Solving this formula for ΔP_b we find that

$$\Delta P_b = \left(\frac{E^s}{E^s - E^d}\right)T$$

That is, the increase in the total amount that buyers pay per unit, ΔP_b, is the fraction $E^s/(E^s - E^d)$ of the per-unit tax T.

Tax Incidence with an *Ad Valorem* Tax

An *ad valorem* tax, whether it is paid by consumers or firms, is usually stated as a percentage of the amount received by firms. For example, if a store charges $100 for a sweater, a five percent sales tax requires that the consumer pay $105 in total.

Figure 15.19 shows the effects of an *ad valorem* tax on gasoline that requires consumers to pay t percent of the amount firms charge. As before, we can find the effect of the tax by identifying the total price paid by consumers, P_b, at which demand equals supply. With the vertical axis measuring the price paid by consumers, the tax shifts the supply curve upward to the curve labelled S_t. For example, without the tax firms supply Q_0 litres when the price is P_0. With the tax, consumers must pay $P_b = (1 + t)P_0$ for firms to receive P_0 per litre. So, with the tax, firms supply Q_0 litres at the price $(1 + t)P_0$.

Note that the higher the price, the larger the shift in the supply curve. To the left of Q_0 (for example, at Q_t), the supply curve shifts upward by less than it does at Q_0. This is because the prices needed to induce firms to supply those smaller quantities are lower, so the fixed-percentage tax produces a smaller payment. To the right of Q_0, the shift upward is larger, because the fixed-percentage tax produces a greater payment at the higher prices needed to induce firms to supply those larger quantities.

With an *ad valorem* tax, then, the tax collected per litre depends on the equilibrium price. In Figure 15.19, at the equilibrium point B consumers pay P_b per litre, including the tax. Firms receive $P_s = P_b/(1 + t)$ per unit. The difference between those two amounts, $P_b - [P_b/(1 + t)] = t[P_b/(1 + t)] = tP_s$, is the tax consumers pay on each litre of gas they buy. The total tax collected by the government (indicated by the gray-shaded area in the figure) is the tax per litre times the number of litres consumers buy, Q_t. As before, consumers pay more in total for each litre of gas they buy because of the tax (P_b exceeds P_0), and firms receive less for each litre they sell [$P_s = P_b/(1 + t)$ is less than P_0]. As the figure shows, the sum of these two amounts equals the tax collected per litre.

As with a specific tax, the effect of an *ad valorem* tax is the same no matter who pays it. If firms were to pay a tax of t percent on the amount they charge consumers, the shift in the supply curve would be exactly the same as that shown in Figure 15.19, and the equilibrium with the tax would also be the same.

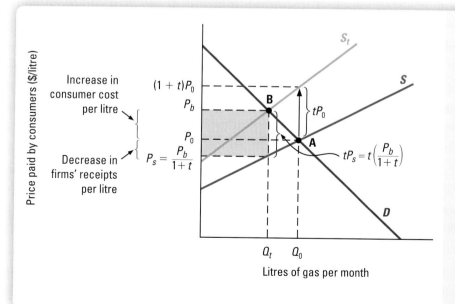

Figure 15.19

The Effects of an *Ad Valorem* Tax. Without the *ad valorem* tax of t percent, the market price would be P_0, and Q_0 litres of gas would be bought and sold. The tax causes an upward shift in the supply curve that is larger at higher prices. With the tax, consumers pay P_b per litre, while firms receive $P_s = P_b/(1 + t)$ per litre. The gray-shaded area represents the total tax collected. The tax causes consumers to pay more per litre and firms to receive less per litre. The sum of those changes equals the tax per litre at the new market equilibrium, tP_s.

General Equilibrium, Efficiency, and Equity

LEARNING OBJECTIVES

After reading this chapter, students should be able to

LO1 Explain how general equilibrium analysis helps economists to understand interdependence among markets.

LO2 Use a simple general equilibrium model to answer positive economic questions.

LO3 Identify criteria for answering normative economic questions.

LO4 Describe how competitive markets achieve efficient exchange and efficient production in general equilibrium.

LO5 Discuss how the goals of equity and efficiency can come into conflict.

etween January 2004 and October 2005, a span of only 19 months, the average price of regular gasoline in the Canada nearly doubled, from $0.68 to $1.21 per litre. The impact on the market for new automobiles was dramatic. Canadian car buyers reconsidered their long-term love affair with gas-guzzling pickup trucks and sport utility vehicles (SUVs), turning instead to smaller, more fuel-efficient models. This development spelled trouble for North American car manufacturers like General Motors, Chrysler, and Ford, for which pickup trucks and SUVs had long been a mainstay. Asian rivals like Toyota and Honda, which had placed much greater emphasis on developing more economical vehicles, suddenly found themselves in far better competitive positions. Toyota was unable to keep pace with the booming demand for its ground-breaking hybrid car, the Prius, and even Camrys flew out of showrooms as quickly as dealers could stock them.

In July 2006, Toyota overtook Ford as the world's second-largest automobile manufacturer and set its sights on General Motors. By the end of 2008 the International Organization of Motor Vehicle Manufacturers reported that Toyota had become the world's largest producer of cars, followed by General Motors, Volkswagen, and Ford. The seeming inability of North American car companies to adapt to changing consumer preferences for more fuel efficient cars contributed to the collapse and subsequent bailout of General Motors and Chrysler in early 2009 during the worldwide recession.

Just as the popularity of pickup trucks and SUVs stimulated the demand for gasoline and contributed to the longer-term rise in gasoline prices, over time the shift to more fuel-efficient cars will reduce the demand for gasoline (or at least moderate the rate of increase) and relieve some of the pressure on gasoline prices. Thus gasoline and automobile markets are highly interdependent.

General equilibrium analysis—the subject of this chapter—provides tools for thinking about the ways in which developments in one market affect others, and how these effects ripple between markets and produce feedback into the original market. It also leads to some important conclusions about the performance of competitive markets and the appropriate economic roles for government. In this chapter we'll cover six topics:

1. *The nature of general equilibrium.* General equilibrium analysis is the study of competitive equilibrium in two or more markets at the same time. As we'll see, it allows us to understand the consequences of interdependence between markets.

2. *Positive analysis of general equilibrium.* Economists are often asked to determine how prices and quantities will respond to changes in the economic environment. Answers based on partial equilibrium analysis are often incomplete. We'll explain how to answer these positive questions more accurately through general equilibrium analysis.

3. *Normative criteria for evaluating economic performance.* Good economic institutions avoid waste while treating all members of society fairly. We'll explain how economists think about these two dimensions of economic performance.

4. *General equilibrium and efficient exchange.* Competitive markets allocate consumption goods efficiently among consumers. We'll show why any reallocation of goods in a competitive market hurts at least one consumer.

5. *General equilibrium and efficient production.* Competitive markets also assure efficient production. We'll explain why any other use of the available inputs in a competitive market reduces the output of at least one good, and hurts at least one consumer.

6. *Equity and redistribution.* A competitive equilibrium is only as fair as the initial distribution of resources. We'll investigate the potential for achieving more equitable outcomes through redistribution, and we'll explain how the goals of equity and efficiency can come into conflict.

16.1 THE NATURE OF GENERAL EQUILIBRIUM

In Chapters 14 and 15 we studied the nature of competitive equilibrium in a single market, considered in isolation. That approach is known as **partial equilibrium analysis**. The word *partial* means that the market under consideration is only one part of the economy.

Partial equilibrium analysis generates many valuable insights concerning competitive markets. It's especially useful when the supply and demand for a good are largely independent of activities in other markets. In practice, however, markets are often interdependent, as when a change in the price of a good affects the demand for its complements and substitutes.

General equilibrium analysis is the study of competitive equilibrium in many markets at the same time. Unlike partial equilibrium analysis, it allows us to understand the consequences of interdependence among markets. This advantage is important for two reasons.

Partial equilibrium analysis concerns competitive equilibrium in a single market, considered in isolation.

General equilibrium analysis is the study of competitive equilibrium in many markets at the same time.

The 19th century French economist Léon Walras (1834–1910) is widely viewed as the father of general equilibrium theory.

First, factors that affect supply and demand in one market can have significant ripple effects in other markets. In the context of policy making, those ripples can create unintended consequences. Second, the interdependence of markets produces feedback. When a change in price and quantity in one market affects a second market, the resulting change in price and quantity in the second market can in turn affect the first. General equilibrium analysis accounts for this feedback between markets; partial equilibrium analysis does not.

Sometimes markets are linked because the price of one good affects the demand for another; sometimes they're linked because the production of one good affects the cost of producing another. For an illustration of a demand-side linkage, consider the case of pie and ice cream. These goods could be either complements (pie is often served a la mode) or substitutes (both are desserts in their own right). Therefore, the location of the demand curve for ice cream depends on the price of pie, and the location of the demand curve for pie depends on the price of ice cream. If we know the price of pie, we can find a partial equilibrium in the ice cream market by looking for the intersection of the supply and demand curves. If we know the price of ice cream, we can find a partial equilibrium in the pie market in exactly the same way. In a general equilibrium, the same pie and ice cream prices clear both markets at the same time.

Figure 16.1 illustrates a general equilibrium in the markets for pie and ice cream. Figure 16.1(a) shows the ice cream market. Assuming that pie costs $12 per pie, the weekly demand curve for ice cream is D^I. With an ice cream price of $6 per carton, the amounts of ice cream supplied and demanded are equal. Figure 16.1(b) shows the pie

Figure 16.1

General Equilibrium in the Markets for Pie and Ice Cream. Figure (a) shows the ice cream market. When the price of pie is $12 per pie, the demand curve for ice cream intersects the supply curve at a price of $6 per carton. Figure (b) shows the market for pie. When the price of ice cream is $6 per carton, the demand curve for pie intersects the supply curve at a price of $12 per pie. At these prices, both markets are in equilibrium.

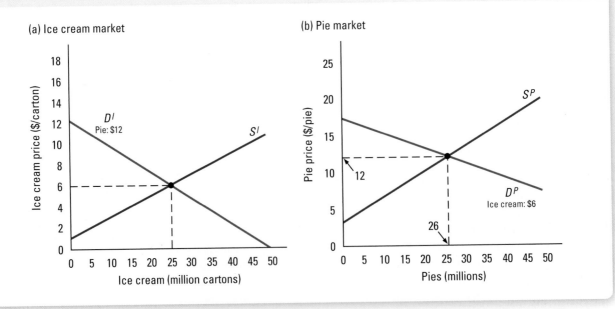

market. Assuming that ice cream costs $6 per carton, the weekly demand curve for pie is D^P. With a pie price of $12 per pie, the amounts of pie supplied and demanded are equal. Therefore, when the price of ice cream is $6 per carton and the price of pie is $12 per pie, both markets clear; in other words, we have a general equilibrium. In this equilibrium, there is neither upward nor downward pressure on the price of either good. In contrast, when a general equilibrium does not prevail, the prices of goods will tend to change, rising when demand exceeds supply, and falling when supply exceeds demand.

To be *completely* general, equilibrium analysis would need to encompass every market in the world economy. For most purposes, such an undertaking is obviously impractical. Instead, economists usually focus on markets that are clearly linked, ignoring others. For example, if we're interested in understanding the effect of some development affecting the supply or demand for pie, we might need to consider feedback effects from the ice cream market, but probably not from the market for light bulbs.

16.2 POSITIVE ANALYSIS OF GENERAL EQUILIBRIUM

Economists are often asked to determine how prices and quantities will respond to changes in the economic environment, including the types of policy interventions we studied in Chapter 15. In many cases, answers based on partial equilibrium analysis are incomplete because they ignore the interdependencies between markets. In this section, we explain how to answer positive questions more accurately through general equilibrium analysis.[1]

For the purpose of illustration, we will examine the effects of a sales tax on ice cream. We'll assume here that pie and ice cream are complements. (In-text exercise 16.1 asks you to assume that those goods are substitutes.) We'll also assume that there are no supply linkages between these markets—that is, pie-making costs are independent of ice cream production, and vice versa. (The first exercise at the end of this chapter asks you to consider a case with supply-side linkages.)

The modern treatment of general equilibrium was pioneered by economists Kenneth Arrow (1921–), above, and Gerard Debreu (1921–2004), below, both Nobel laureates.

The partial equilibrium effects of an ice cream tax are easy to determine: the tax shifts the supply curve upward, causing its intersection with the demand curve, and therefore price and quantity, to change (as in Figure 15.1, page 535). In contrast, the general equilibrium effects of an ice cream tax are more difficult to evaluate. First, there is the direct (partial equilibrium) effect on the ice cream market: the price of ice cream rises, and the quantity of ice cream falls. This direct effect produces an indirect effect on the pie market: since the price of ice cream has risen, and since pie and ice cream are complements, the demand curve for pie shifts downward, causing the price of pie to fall. This indirect effect produces a feedback effect on the ice cream market: the falling pie price shifts the demand curve for ice cream upward, causing the price of ice cream to rise further. This feedback effect produces another indirect effect on the pie market, which produces another feedback effect on the ice cream market, which produces another indirect effect on the pie market, and so forth. The effects of the tax ripple back and forth between the two markets in an unending sequence. How can we account for all of those ripples?

In this section, we'll introduce a new tool that helps us determine the prices that prevail in a general equilibrium, accounting for the interdependencies between markets. Then we'll use this tool to evaluate the general equilibrium effects of a sales tax on ice cream.

---

[1]As we explained in Chapter 1, a positive question concerns what did, will, or would happen; it calls for a factual, descriptive answer.

Figure 16.2

The Market-Clearing Curve for Ice Cream. Figure (a) shows an ice cream supply curve (S^I), three ice cream demand curves (D_1^I, D_2^I, and D_3^I) corresponding to three different pie prices ($6, $12, and $18), and three partial equilibria in the ice cream market (points A_1, A_2, and A_3). Each partial equilibrium shown in figure (a) is associated with a price combination that clears the ice cream market in figure (b): points B_1, B_2, and B_3, respectively. The market-clearing curve for ice cream passes through those points.

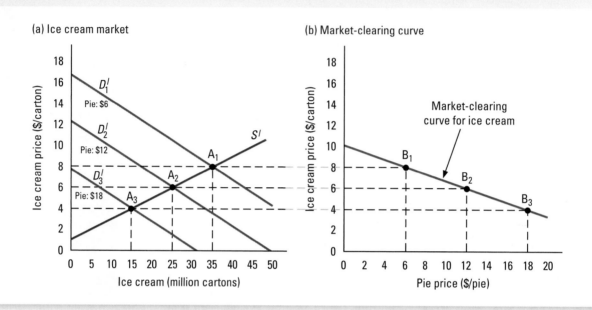

Market-Clearing Curves

The first step in our search for a general equilibrium is to identify, for each good, the combinations of prices (both for that good and for other related goods) that bring supply and demand for the good into balance. The **market-clearing curve** for a good shows these price combinations graphically.

The **market-clearing curve** for a good shows the combinations of prices (both for that good and for other related goods) that bring supply and demand for the good into balance.

Let's start with the ice cream market. Figure 16.2(a) shows a supply curve for ice cream, S^I (in blue), as well as three demand curves (in red). Each demand curve is associated with a different pie price. Since ice cream and pie are complements, the demand curve for ice cream shifts downward as the price of pie rises. When pies cost $6 per pie, the demand curve is D_1^I. The ice cream market clears at point A_1, where consumers purchase 35 million cartons at $8 per carton. When pies cost $12 per pie, the demand curve is D_2^I and consumers purchase 25 million cartons at $6 per carton (point A_2). And when pies cost $18 per pie, the demand curve is D_3^I, consumers purchase 15 million cartons at $4 per carton (point A_3).

Figure 16.2(b) shows the market-clearing curve for ice cream. The horizontal axis shows the price of pie; the vertical axis shows the price of ice cream. Point B_1 corresponds to point A_1 in Figure 16.2(a). It tells us that when the price of pie is $6 per pie, the ice cream market clears at a price of $8 per carton. Similarly, point B_2 corresponds to point A_2 in Figure 16.2(a). It tells us that when the price of pie is $12 per pie, the ice cream market clears at a price of $6 per carton. And point B_3 corresponds to point A_3 in Figure 16.2(a). It tells us that when the price of pie is $18 per pie, the ice cream market

Figure 16.3

The Market-Clearing Curve for Pie. Figure (a) shows a pie supply curve (S^P), three pie demand curves (D_1^P, D_2^P, and D_3^P) corresponding to three different ice cream prices ($2, $6, and $10), and three partial equilibria in the pie market (points C_1, C_2, and C_3). Each partial equilibrium shown in figure (a) is associated with a price combination that clears the pie market in figure (b): points E_1, E_2, and E_3, respectively. The market-clearing curve for pie passes through those points.

(a) Pie market

(b) Market-clearing curve

clears at a price of $4 per carton. By considering the effects of other pie prices, we can trace the brown market-clearing curve. At any combination of prices on this curve, the supply of ice cream matches the demand.

Notice that the market-clearing curve for ice cream is downward sloping. Because we've assumed that ice cream and pie are complements, an increase in the price of pie reduces the demand for ice cream, which in turn lowers the partial equilibrium price of ice cream. When the goods in question are substitutes, however, the market-clearing curve is upward sloping (see in-text exercise 16.1, page 578).

Now let's examine the market for pie. Figure 16.3(a) is similar to Figure 16.2(a): it shows a pie supply curve (S^P); three pie demand curves (D_1^P, D_2^P, and D_3^P) corresponding to three different ice cream prices ($2, $6, and $10 per carton); and three partial equilibria in the pie market (C_1, C_2, and C_3). Each partial equilibrium shown in Figure 16.3(a) is associated with a price combination that clears the pie market in Figure 16.3(b) (points E_1, E_2, and E_3). The green market-clearing curve for pie passes through those price combination points.

A General Equilibrium in Two Markets

At all price combinations on the brown market-clearing curve in Figure 16.2(b), the ice cream market is in equilibrium. At all price combinations on the green market-clearing curve in Figure 16.3(b), the pie market is in equilibrium. If a price combination lies on *both* market-clearing curves, then *both* markets are in equilibrium. In other words, we have a general equilibrium.

Figure 16.4

The General Equilibrium Price Combination. The market-clearing curves for pie and ice cream intersect at a single point, where the pie price is $12 and the ice cream price is $6. These are the general equilibrium prices. According to the market clearing curves, they clear both the pie market and the ice cream market.

To find a general equilibrium price combination, we can plot both market-clearing curves on the same graph; see Figure 16.4. As in Figure 16.2(b), the horizontal axis shows the price of pie and the vertical axis measures the price of ice cream. The market-clearing curve for pie looks steeper in Figure 16.4 than in Figure 16.3(b) because, compared to Figure 16.3(b), we've reversed the axes. (To confirm that the two curves are the same, check that points E_1, E_2, and E_3 correspond to the same price combinations in both figures.)

Notice that the two market-clearing curves in Figure 16.4 intersect at a single point (labelled B_2 on the ice cream curve and E_2 on the pie curve), where the ice cream price is $6 per carton and the pie price is $12 per pie. These are the general equilibrium prices. According to the market-clearing curves, the ice cream market and the pie market clear at these prices, exactly as illustrated in Figure 16.1.

The Effects of a Sales Tax

We've said that partial equilibrium analysis, though useful, sometimes overlooks important general equilibrium effects. To illustrate this point, let's examine the effects of a $3 per carton sales tax on ice cream. First we'll determine the partial equilibrium effects of the tax, starting from the general equilibrium price and quantity described in the previous section. Then we'll find the new general equilibrium.

Let's start with the partial equilibrium effects of the tax. Figure 16.5(a) shows prices and quantities in the ice cream market. The numbers on the vertical axis indicate the price paid by consumers, including the tax, if any. Without a tax, the supply curve S^I (shown in dark blue) intersects the demand curve D_2^I (shown in dark red) at point A_2, producing an initial equilibrium price of $6 per carton, as in the last section. A $3 per carton tax on ice cream shifts the ice cream supply curve upward by $3, from S^I to S_T^I, shown in light blue (recall the discussion of sales taxation in Section 15.1). With the price of pie held fixed at $12, the new partial equilibrium is point F_2, where the demand curve D_2^I crosses the new

Figure 16.5

The General Equilibrium Effect of a Tax on Ice Cream, Part 1. In figure (a), a $3 tax on ice cream shifts the supply curve upward by $3, from S^I to S^I_T. For the three ice cream demand curves (D^I_1, D^I_2, and D^I_3) corresponding to three different pie prices ($6, $12, and $18), we now have three new partial equilibria (F_1, F_2, and F_3). Each partial equilibrium shown in figure (a) is associated with a price combination that clears the ice cream market, plotted in figure (b) (points G_1, G_2, and G_3, respectively). The market-clearing curve shifts upward by $1\frac{2}{3}$ per carton, as shown. Point G_4 is the new general equilibrium. The tax increases the price of ice cream by $2 per carton (from $6 to $8), and reduces the price of pie by $1 per pie (from $12 to $11).

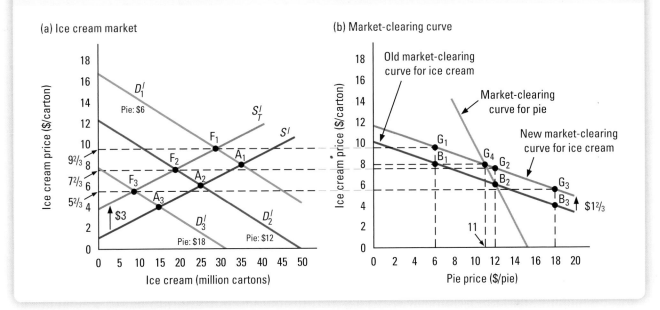

(a) Ice cream market (b) Market-clearing curve

supply curve S^I_T. The price of ice cream therefore rises by $1\frac{2}{3}$ per carton (from $6 to $7\frac{2}{3}$), which is less than the amount of the tax ($3).

To determine the general equilibrium effects of the ice cream tax, we need to plot a new market clearing curve for ice cream. Notice that Figure 16.5(a) reproduces (in light red) the demand curves D^I_1 (corresponding to a pie price of $6) and D^I_3 (corresponding to a pie price of $18) from Figure 16.2(a), as well as the points at which they intersect the supply curve S^I (points A_1 and A_3). When the supply curve shifts from S^I to S^I_T, the partial equilibrium point on D^I_1 moves from A_1 to F_1, and the one on D^I_3 moves from A_3 to F_3. In each case, the tax-inclusive price of ice cream rises by $1\frac{2}{3}$ per carton.

As shown in Figure 16.5(b), taxing ice cream shifts the market-clearing curve for ice cream upward. The new market clearing curve (shown in green) lies exactly $1\frac{2}{3}$ above the old one (shown in brown as in Figure 16.2(b)), which means that the magnitude of the shift equals the partial equilibrium effect of the tax. Point G_1 corresponds to point F_1 in Figure 16.5(a); it tells us that when the price of pie is $6 per pie, the ice cream market clears at a price of $9\frac{2}{3}$ per carton. Similarly, point G_2 corresponds to point F_2 in Figure 16.5(a), and point G_3 corresponds to point F_3 in Figure 16.5(a).

Figure 16.5(b) also includes the same (green) market-clearing curve for pie that appeared in Figure 16.4. To find the new general equilibrium, we look for an intersection between this curve and the new (rose-coloured) market-clearing curve for ice cream.

Figure 16.6

The General Equilibrium Effect of a Tax on Ice Cream, Part 2. Figure (a) shows the ice cream market. When pies cost $11 each, the demand curve for ice cream, D_4^I (shown in light red) intersects the supply curve, S_T^I (shown in light blue), at a price of $8 per carton. Figure (b) shows the market for pie. When the price of ice cream is $8 per carton, the demand curve for pie, D_4^P (shown in light red), intersects the supply curve, S^P (shown in blue) at a price of $11 per pie. At these prices, both markets are in equilibrium.

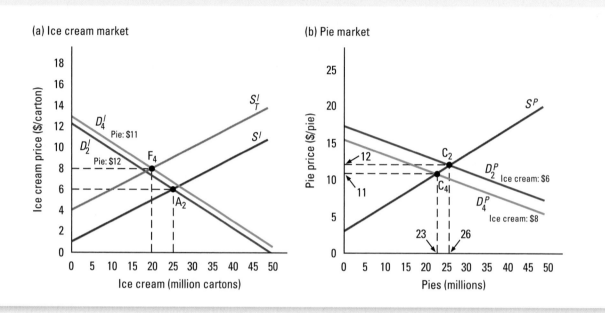

(a) Ice cream market

(b) Pie market

These curves intersect at point G_4, where the pie price is $11 and the ice cream price is $8. These are the new general equilibrium prices: according to the market-clearing curves, they clear both the pie market and the ice cream market.

Figure 16.6 illustrates the new general equilibrium (points F_4 and C_4). We have determined that both markets clear when the price of ice cream is $8 per carton and the price of pie is $11 per pie. Figure 16.6(a) shows the ice cream market. With pies priced at $11 each, the demand curve for ice cream is D_4^I (shown in light red). With an ice cream price of $8 per carton, the amounts of ice cream supplied and demanded are equal. Figure 16.6(b) shows the pie market. With ice cream priced at $8 per carton, the demand curve for pie is D_4^P (shown in light red). With a pie price of $11 per pie, the amounts of pie supplied and demand are equal. Notice that as a result of the tax, the demand curves for both goods shift, moving the general equilibrium from points A_2 and C_2 to points F_4 and C_4.

In this example, we've reached two important conclusions from general equilibrium analysis. First, a sales tax on ice cream reduces the price of a pie by $1 (from $12 to $11). This price reduction occurs because pie and ice cream are complements—a tax on ice cream increases the price of ice cream, which reduces the demand for pie [the shift from D_2^P to D_4^P in Figure 16.6(b)], causing the price of pie to fall. Second, partial equilibrium analysis *understates* the effect of the sales tax on the price of ice cream. According to partial equilibrium analysis, the price rises by $1²/₃, from $6 to $7²/₃, per carton. But according to general equilibrium analysis, it rises by $2, from $6 to $8 per carton.

Why is the general equilibrium effect of the sales tax larger than the partial equilibrium effect in this example? We've concluded that a tax on ice cream causes the pie price to fall. Because ice cream and pie are complements, a lower pie price leads to greater demand for ice cream [the shift from D_2^I to D_4^I in Figure 16.6(a)], which *reinforces* the pressure for the ice cream price to rise. General equilibrium analysis accounts for this feedback from the pie market, but partial equilibrium analysis doesn't.

WORKED-OUT PROBLEM   16.1

The Problem Suppose the following formulas describe the weekly supply and demand for ice cream (where Q_I^d stands for millions of cartons demanded, Q_I^s stands for millions of cartons supplied, P_I stands for the price of ice cream per carton, and P_P stands for the price per pie).

$$Q_I^d = 85 - 4P_I - 3P_P \tag{1}$$

$$Q_I^s = 5P_I - 5 \tag{2}$$

Also suppose the following formulas describe the supply and demand for pie (where Q_P^d stands for millions of pies demanded and Q_P^s stands for millions of pies supplied).

$$Q_P^d = 110 - 5P_P - 4P_I \tag{3}$$

$$Q_P^s = 3P_P - 10 \tag{4}$$

These formulas correspond to the supply and demand curves in Figures 16.2(a) and 16.3(a) (you should check this).[2] Solve algebraically for the partial and general equilibrium effects of a $3 sales tax on ice cream.

The Solution When $85 - 4P_I - 3P_P = 5P_I - 5$, the quantity of ice cream demanded equals the quantity supplied. Solving for P_I, we find that

$$P_I = 10 - \frac{1}{3}P_P \tag{5}$$

This is the formula for the market-clearing curve for ice cream. It corresponds to the brown line in Figure 16.2(b).

Similarly, when $110 - 5P_P - 4P_I = 3P_P - 10$, the quantity of pie demanded equals the quantity supplied. Solving for P_P, we find that

$$P_P = 15 - \frac{1}{2}P_I \tag{6}$$

This is the formula for the market-clearing curve for pie. It corresponds to the green line in Figure 16.3(b).

Now let's solve for the prices that satisfy both market-clearing formulas at the same time. Substituting formula (5) into (6), we have

$$P_P = 15 - \frac{1}{2}\left(10 - \frac{1}{3}P_P\right)$$

---

[2]Because quantity cannot be negative, if any of these formulas yields a negative value, the quantity is actually zero.

Solving for P_P yields $P_P = 12$. Substituting this value into formula (5), we find that $P_I = 6$. Plugging these values into either the demand formulas, (1) and (3), or the supply formulas, (2) and (4), we learn that in the general equilibrium, consumers purchase 25 million cartons of ice cream and 26 million pies.

The tax changes the supply function for ice cream from formula (2) to

$$Q_I^s = 5(P_I - 3) - 5 \qquad (7)$$

The difference between the supply formulas (7) and (2) reflects the fact that, once the tax is imposed, sellers receive $\$(P_I - 3)$ per carton, rather than the price consumers pay, $\$P_I$. (If this isn't clear to you, review Section 15.1, including worked-out problem 15.1 on page 543). The quantity of ice cream demanded equals the quantity supplied when $85 - 4P_I - 3P_P = 5(P_I - 3) - 5$. Solving for P_I, we find that

$$P_I = 11^{2}/_{3} - \frac{1}{3} P_P \qquad (8)$$

This is the formula for the new market-clearing curve for ice cream. It corresponds to the tan line in Figure 16.5(b). Comparing formulas (8) and (5), we see that at any pie price, the market-clearing ice cream price is now $\$1^{2}/_{3}$ per carton higher. This is the partial equilibrium effect of the sales tax.

The market-clearing curve for pie, which corresponds to formula (6), is unchanged. We can solve for the prices that satisfy both market-clearing formulas by substituting formula (8) into (6).

$$P_P = 15 - \frac{1}{2}\left(11^{2}/_{3} - \frac{1}{3}P_P\right)$$

Solving for P_P gives us $P_P = 11$. Substituting this value into formula (8), we find that $P_I = 8$. So in general equilibrium, the ice cream price rises by $\$2$ and the pie price falls by $\$1$. Plugging these new prices into either the demand formula, (1) and (3), or the supply formulas, (7) and (4), we learn that in the new general equilibrium, consumers purchase 20 million cartons of ice cream and 23 million pies.

IN-TEXT EXERCISE 16.1   Suppose that the formula for ice cream demand is $Q_I^d = 85 - 4P_I + 6P_P$ and the formula for pie demand is $Q_P^d = 110 - 5P_P + 2P_I$. Here, pie and ice cream are substitutes instead of complements. Continue to assume that formulas (2) and (4) describe the supply of ice cream and pie. **(a)** Solve for and graph the market-clearing curves for pie and ice cream. Are they downward sloping, as in Figures 16.2(b) and 16.3(b), or upward sloping? Why? **(b)** Find the general equilibrium prices and levels of consumption. Show the general equilibrium graphically. **(c)** Solve for the partial and general equilibrium effects of a $\$3$ sales tax on ice cream. Illustrate these effects graphically. Is the general equilibrium effect on the price of ice cream larger or smaller than the partial equilibrium effect? Why? Does the pie price in general equilibrium rise or fall? Why?

Application 16.1

Do Investment Tax Breaks Benefit the Working Class?

People earn income by supplying labour and/or capital to firms. Most governments raise substantial revenue by taxing that income. Because capital income flows disproportionately to wealthy individuals, many people feel that the tax rate for capital income should be at least as high as the tax rate for labour income. In response, political conservatives often argue that low tax rates for capital income benefit virtually all members of society, including the working class. They reason that a favourable investment climate stimulates business activity, thereby increasing the demand for labour and driving up wage rates. General equilibrium analysis provides the tools we need to assess the validity of this position.

For the sake of simplicity let's suppose that all workers are the same, and that there is only one type of capital. These assumptions allow us to focus our attention on just two markets: one for labour and the other for capital. An individual's labour income is simply the payment she receives when she sells her labour to a firm. Therefore, we can think of a labour income tax as a sales tax on labour. Similarly, because capital income is the payment received when supplying capital to a firm, we can think of a capital income tax as a sales tax on capital. In effect, conservatives argue that a sales tax on capital reduces the price of labour (that is, the wage rate). To evaluate this argument, we can simply apply what we've learned in the previous section.

The price of labour will affect firms' demand for both labour and capital, as will the price of capital. But are labour and capital complements or substitutes? When the price of capital rises, firms substitute labour for capital, which increases the amount of labour demanded. But they also scale back production, which reduces the amount of labour demanded. If the scale effect is large relative to the substitution effect, the demand for labour falls, which means capital and labour are complements. If the opposite is true, the demand for labour rises, which means capital and labour are substitutes.

Let's suppose for the moment that capital and labour are complements. In that case, all we need to do is relabel Figures 16.1 through 16.6. "Ice cream" becomes capital and the "price of ice cream" becomes the cost of capital; "pie"

becomes labour and the "price of pie" becomes the wage rate. As Figures 16.5 and 16.6 show, when two goods are complements, a tax on one reduces the general equilibrium price of the other, so a tax on capital will reduce the wage rate. In this case, reducing the tax burden on capital would raise the wage rate, just as political conservatives claim.

Now let's suppose that capital and labour are substitutes. From in-text exercise 16.1, we know that when two goods are substitutes, a tax on one increases the general equilibrium price of the other. So in this case reducing the tax burden on capital would reduce the wage rate, contrary to the politically conservative view. Thus, theory alone cannot resolve whether the conservatives are right or wrong.

A number of economists have attempted to calculate the general equilibrium effects of capital income taxes on wage rates, using estimates of the supply and demand curves for labour and capital. As you might expect, their economic models are more complicated than the one discussed here. For example, a pioneering study by economist Lawrence Summers accounts for the fact that capital accumulates and depreciates gradually over time.[3] It also recognizes that if the government reduces one tax, it must increase another in order to maintain the same total revenue. Still, the basic principles of his analysis are essentially the same as those we discussed in this section.

Suppose we replace a tax on capital with a tax on wages that generates the same amount of revenue. What might happen to the wage rate in the long run? According to Summers' calculations, the lower cost of capital would stimulate a great deal of additional investment. Ultimately, the ratio of total capital to total labour would rise by about 78 percent. With capital more plentiful, labour would become more productive, leading to a 15.5 percent increase in the pre-tax wage rate. Of course, to maintain revenues, the government would need to tax wages at a higher rate. Still, the after-tax wage rate would fall by only 0.25 percent—a tiny fraction of the incremental tax burden that workers would appear to bear if we ignored the general equilibrium effects. If the government balanced its budget by imposing higher taxes on consumption goods instead of on wages, some of those taxes would fall on purchases made by the

---

[3]Lawrence H. Summers, "Capital Taxation and Accumulation in a Life-Cycle Growth Model," *American Economic Review* 71, September 1981, pp. 533–544.

owners of capital, and workers would actually *benefit* from a reduction in the capital income tax rate.

Some of Summers' assumptions about the supply and demand for capital and labour are controversial. Other economists have reached different conclusions based on alternative assumptions. General equilibrium analysis is useful because it allows us to see how different assumptions lead to different outcomes. It shows that the debate over the taxation of capital boils down to scale effects, substitution effects, and supply elasticities, and underscores the importance of measuring those effects accurately.

16.3 NORMATIVE CRITERIA FOR EVALUATING ECONOMIC PERFORMANCE

The most commonly-used notion of economic efficiency originated in the writings of the Italian economist Vilfredo Pareto (1848–1923).

Historically, societies have allocated their scarce resources through a wide variety of procedures, including barter, free trade in open markets, restricted trade in regulated markets, central planning, and mixed approaches (such as using markets and central planners to allocate different resources). Every society must set up institutions to govern the allocation of resources. Are there reasons to prefer a free market?

As we noted in Section 14.4, Adam Smith believed that markets are desirable because they lead each individual "by an invisible hand to promote an end which was no part of his intention." Does society in fact benefit from the way in which markets allocate scarce resources? Modern economists have spent a great deal of time and energy investigating this question. The rest of this chapter—and indeed much of the rest of this book—summarizes some key findings concerning the performance of free markets.

Before proceeding, however, it's important to establish criteria for answering normative questions concerning economic performance.[4] Ideally, we would like to achieve an allocation of society's resources that is efficient, in the sense that it avoids waste. But we would also like to achieve an allocation that is equitable, in the sense that it is fair to all members of society. Economists have developed clear criteria for measuring efficiency. However, as we explain, equity and fairness are far more difficult to define and evaluate.

Efficiency

An economy is wasteful (or inefficient) if we can reallocate resources in a way that will make at least one consumer better off without hurting anyone else.[5] An economy is efficient if there is no waste—that is, if it's *impossible* to make any consumer better off without hurting someone else. This notion of efficiency, known as **Pareto efficiency**, was first proposed by the Italian economist Vilfredo Pareto.

How do we judge whether one allocation makes a consumer better off or worse off than another allocation? With few exceptions, economists use the consumer's own preferences. In other words, we assume that individuals know what's best for them; we don't

An allocation of resources is **Pareto efficient** if it's impossible to make any consumer better off without hurting someone else.

---

[4]As we explained in Chapter 1, a normative question concerns what *should* happen; it calls for judgment.

[5]In most situations, this is the equivalent of saying that we can make everyone better off. To see why, suppose there is an allocation that makes one person better off and no one worse off. If we take a sufficiently small amount of some good away from the person who's better off, he'll remain better off. If we then divide what we've taken from him among everyone else, everyone ends up better off.

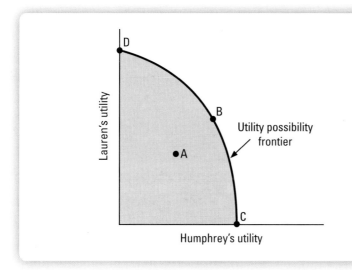

Figure 16.7

Pareto Efficient Outcomes. The green-shaded area shows the utility levels associated with every possible allocation of resources. The northeast boundary of this area, called the utility possibility frontier, contains all the Pareto efficient allocations. Point A is inefficient, while points B, C, and D are all efficient.

second-guess any consumer's personal judgment. For example, no matter what we may think of television, we don't take the position that watching television is a waste of time. If someone chooses to watch television, we conclude that doing so must make her better off than the available alternatives.

Figure 16.7 illustrates the concept of Pareto efficiency. Let's assume that the economy consists of two people, Humphrey and Lauren. Suppose we know their preferences, which we can represent with utility functions. Each allocation of society's resources leads to a pair of utility levels, one for Humphrey and one for Lauren. We can plot each of those outcomes as a point in Figure 16.7, like A or B. The green-shaded area shows the utility levels associated with every possible allocation of resources.

The northeast boundary of this area, shown in black, is known as the **utility possibility frontier**.[6] Any allocation associated with a point below this frontier is inefficient. Starting from point A, for example, we can make both Humphrey and Lauren better off by moving to point B. Point A may be inefficient because there's a better way to distribute goods among consumers, or because firms could produce more outputs from the same inputs. Any allocation associated with a point on the utility possibility frontier is Pareto efficient. Starting from point B, for example, we can make Lauren better off only by hurting Humphrey, and we can make Humphrey better off only by hurting Lauren.

As the figure shows, there are many efficient outcomes. Some (like point C) favour Humphrey, while others (like D) favour Lauren. To choose among them, we must rely on normative criteria other than efficiency, like equity.

The **utility possibility frontier** shows the utility levels associated with all efficient allocations of resources.

Equity

Equity is much harder to define and measure than efficiency, because it's a very subjective concept. Different people have different views of what's fair.

---

[6]As we have drawn it, the utility possibility frontier is concave; that is, it bows outward from the origin. However, since the scale used to measure utility is completely arbitrary (as discussed in Section 4.4), this frontier need not be concave.

Process-oriented notions of equity focus on the procedures used to arrive at an allocation of resources rather than on the allocation itself.

Some notions of equity are **process-oriented**. That is, they focus on the procedures used to arrive at an allocation of resources rather than on the allocation itself. The familiar principle of equal opportunity is an example; it focuses on what people *could* choose rather than on what they *actually* choose.

Some people believe that the free market system is a fair process. They maintain that it fairly rewards people for their effort and ingenuity. Others think that, in practice, markets are unfair. They point out that some people have less opportunity than others to obtain education and marketable skills. They also insist that a person is not less deserving of a comfortable life merely because he or she was born with less talent or intelligence than others.

Outcome-oriented notions of equity focus on whether the process used to allocate resources yields fair results.

Other notions of equity are **outcome-oriented**. That is, they require us to determine whether the process used to allocate resources yields fair results. Most people would agree that some outcomes—like giving everything to a single person—are not fair. Still, there's a lot of room here for subjective judgment and disagreement.

Some outcome-oriented notions of equity focus on the distribution of well-being. In Section 4.4 we mentioned the British moral philosopher Jeremy Bentham, who argued that society should place equal weight on the well-being of every individual. This principle is called **utilitarianism**. John Rawls, a famous contemporary philosopher, has taken a radically different view, arguing that society should maximize the well-being of its least advantaged member, a principle known as **Rawlsianism**. Utilitarianism and Rawlsianism reflect different subjective judgments concerning equity.

According to the principle of **utilitarianism**, society should place equal weight on the well-being of every individual.

According to the principle of **Rawlsianism**, society should maximize the well-being of its least advantaged member.

Unfortunately, no one has yet discovered a reliable way to measure an individual's well-being. Indeed, many economists believe that this is an unachievable objective. While the notion of consumer utility is obviously related to well-being, a utility function provides only ordinal information about one individual's preferences, rather than cardinal information (see the discussion beginning on page 118). That is, it assigns higher numbers to preferred alternatives according to some arbitrary scale. Whether one allocation is judged more or less equitable than another shouldn't depend on these arbitrary scales.

This difficulty definitely spells trouble for Rawlsians and utilitarians. Rawlsians assume there's a way to identify society's least happy member. Utilitarians assume it's possible to say if a change in resource allocation will increase the well-being of one individual more than it decreases the well-being of another. But if we have only ordinal information concerning individual preferences, we can't compare happiness across consumers. For example, we can't say whether Humphrey will be happier with three kilograms of food than Lauren will be with two kilograms. We can say only that a particular individual likes one consumption bundle better than another.

According to the principle of **egalitarianism**, equal division of society's resources among all members of the population is the most equitable outcome.

Other outcome-oriented notions of equity focus on the distribution of consumption. According to the principle of **egalitarianism**, for example, equal division of society's resources among all members of the population is the most equitable outcome. Unfortunately, egalitarian distributions tend to be extremely inefficient. If you love Coke and hate Pepsi, while your friend loves Pepsi and hates Coke, it makes no sense to give each of you the same amount of Coke and the same amount of Pepsi.[7]

---

[7]Some people would argue that from a process-oriented perspective, free markets are fair as long as everyone *starts out* with exactly the same resources. Since people have different preferences, they'll make different trades, and the outcome won't be egalitarian. However, everyone will have the same opportunities. Still, the outcomes may seem unfair. If you like Coke and your friend likes Pepsi, starting both of you off with exactly the same resources may seem fair. But what if the prices turn out to be $2 per quart for Pepsi and $20,000 per quart for Coke—does the process still seem fair?

Social Welfare Functions

Economists often use **social welfare functions** to summarize judgments about resource allocations. For each possible allocation, the function assigns a number that indicates the overall level of social welfare. Higher numbers reflect greater social well-being.

Sometimes, economists break up the calculation of social welfare into two steps. First, they assign utility levels to every consumer using utility functions that represent the consumers' preferences. Second, they apply a function, call it W, that converts those utility levels into social welfare:

$$\text{Social welfare} = W(U_1, U_2, \ldots, U_N) \qquad (9)$$

In formula (9), U_i is the level of utility enjoyed by the ith individual, and N is the number of individuals. Typically, economists assume that higher levels of individual utility imply higher levels of social welfare. The function W is sometimes called a Bergson-Samuelson social welfare function, after economists Abram Bergson and Paul Samuelson who pioneered this approach.

A Bergson-Samuelson social welfare function can capture concerns for both efficiency and outcome-oriented notions of equity. Let's start with efficiency. Notice that formula (9) is a lot like a utility function. Instead of assigning utility levels to consumption bundles, it assigns welfare levels to "utility bundles." With this analogy in mind, let's return to the problem of allocating resources between Humphrey and Lauren, depicted in Figure 16.7. We've reproduced the feasible outcomes in Figure 16.8, and added social indifference curves to represent the judgments associated with a given social welfare function. Indifference curves that are farther from the origin correspond to higher levels of social welfare. It follows that point A delivers the highest feasible level of social welfare. Since that point lies on the utility possibility frontier, it's Pareto efficient. Thus, the social welfare function reflects a preference for efficiency.

A **social welfare function** summarizes judgments about resource allocations. For each possible allocation, the function assigns a number that indicates the overall level of social welfare.

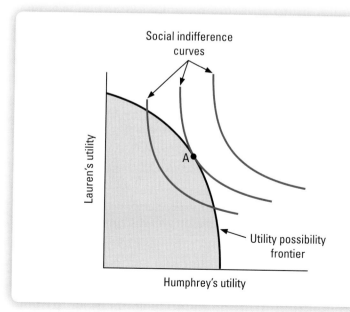

Figure 16.8

Applying Social Welfare Functions. For the social welfare function corresponding to the red social indifference curves, point A is the best possible outcome. Since it lies on the utility possibility frontier, it is Pareto efficient.

It's tempting to interpret a Bergson-Samuelson social welfare function as capturing concerns for outcome-oriented notions of equity that focus on the distribution of well-being.[8] But as we emphasized in the previous section, the utility scale used to measure each individual's well-being is completely arbitrary. How then are we to judge whether one person's "utils" are more or less important than another's?

Instead, economists usually interpret Bergson-Samuelson social welfare functions as capturing concerns for outcome-oriented notions of equity that focus on the distribution of consumption, rather than well-being. We choose the function W in combination with utility scales to summarize judgments about the relative desirability of giving extra goods to different people. For example, a particular Bergson-Samuelson social welfare function, along with particular utility scales, might reflect the judgment that a kilogram of food received by someone with an income of $20,000 per year is just as socially valuable as 10 kilograms of food received by someone with an income of $100,000 per year.

How do we arrive at the value judgments captured by a social welfare function? That's a matter for politicians and philosophers. Efforts to develop general economic principles for evaluating and comparing efficient social alternatives have been largely unsuccessful. Indeed, a result known as Arrow's Impossibility Theorem (named after economist Kenneth Arrow, whom we mentioned earlier in this chapter) suggests that such efforts are doomed to fail. To learn about Arrow's theorem and the conceptual issues it raises, read Add-On 16A.

16.4 GENERAL EQUILIBRIUM AND EFFICIENT EXCHANGE

In Section 14.4 we learned that in a single competitive market, partial equilibrium is efficient in the sense that it maximizes the sum of consumer and producer surplus. But what about a general equilibrium with many perfectly competitive markets? When all markets balance at the same time, is the allocation of resources Pareto efficient? In this section, we'll address this question in the context of **exchange economies**—economies in which consumers own and trade goods, but no production takes place. In Section 16.5, we'll expand the analysis to include production.

> In an **exchange economy**, people own and trade goods, but no production takes place.

General Equilibrium in Exchange Economies

In an exchange economy, each individual starts out with a bundle of goods called an **endowment**. To meet their needs, consumers buy and sell goods at market prices. A consumer who has too much of one good and too little of another will supply the first and demand the second. If the quantity supplied matches the quantity demanded for every good, the economy is in general equilibrium.

> An **endowment** is the bundle of goods an individual starts out with before trading.

A Simple Example   Suppose Humphrey and Lauren are the only consumers in the economy, and they consume only two goods, food and water. Humphrey starts out with an endowment of eight kilograms of food and three litres of water. Lauren starts out with

---

[8]To capture utilitarianism, the function W would sum up the utility levels of all consumers. That way, an additional unit of utility would be equally valuable regardless of who received it. To capture Rawlsianism, W would equal the lowest level of utility enjoyed by any consumer. That way, an additional unit of utility would be valuable only if it was received by society's worst-off member.

Figure 16.9

General Equilibrium in an Exchange Economy. Humphrey starts at point A_H and Lauren starts at point A_L. When food costs $1 per kilogram and water costs $1 per litre, Humphrey prefers point B_H—he wants to swap 3 kilograms of food for 3 litres of water. Lauren prefers point B_L—she wants to swap 4 kilograms of food for 4 litres of water. Supply doesn't match demand, so this is not an equilibrium. When food costs $2 per kilogram and water costs $1 per litre, Humphrey prefers point C_H—he wants to swap 2 kilograms of food for 4 litres of water. Lauren prefers point C_L—she wants to swap 4 litres of water for 2 kilograms of food. Supply matches demand, so the economy is in equilibrium.

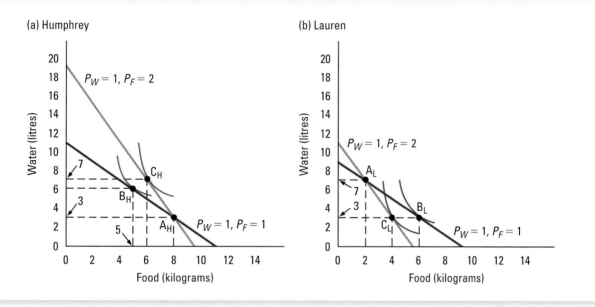

two kilograms of food and seven litres of water. In Figure 16.9(a), Humphrey's endowment corresponds to point A_H; in Figure 16.9(b), Lauren's corresponds to A_L.

For the moment, let's assume that food sells for $1 per kilogram and water sells for $1 per litre.[9] At those prices, each consumer can trade one kilogram of food for one litre of water, or vice versa. The figure shows the resulting budget lines in brown. Judging by the red indifference curves in Figure 16.9(a), Humphrey's favourite point on his budget line is B_H (five kilograms of food and six litres of water). He supplies three kilograms of food (eight kilograms minus five kilograms) and demands three litres of water (six litres minus three litres). Judging by the blue indifference curves in Figure 16.9(b), Lauren's favourite point on her budget line is B_L (six kilograms of food and three litres of water). She demands four kilograms of food (six kilograms minus two kilograms) and supplies four litres of water (seven litres minus three litres). Supply doesn't match demand in either market: Humphrey supplies three kilograms of food but Lauren demands four kilograms, and Humphrey demands three litres of water but Lauren supplies four litres. Consequently, this is not a general equilibrium.

---

[9]We'll assume too that Humphrey and Lauren are both price takers. With only two consumers in the economy, that is a bit of a stretch—both Humphrey and Lauren should realize that their choices will influence the prices at which markets clear. (If this assumption troubles you, just assume that the economy consists of many identical Humphreys and many identical Laurens, all of whom behave as described in the text.)

Now let's assume that food sells for $2 per kilogram and water sells for $1 per litre. Consumers can swap one kilogram of food for two litres of water or vice versa. The figure shows the resulting budget lines in green. Humphrey chooses point C_H in Figure 16.9(a) (six kilograms of food and seven litres of water), supplying two kilograms of food (eight kilograms minus six kilograms) and demanding four litres of water (seven litres minus three litres). Lauren chooses the point C_L in Figure 16.9(b) (four kilograms of food and three litres of water), demanding two kilograms of food (four kilograms minus two kilograms) and supplying four litres of water (seven litres minus three litres). Because supply and demand match in both markets, this *is* a general equilibrium.

The Edgeworth Box   Economists often illustrate equilibrium in a simple exchange economy using a diagram known as the **Edgeworth box**. First introduced by the British economist Francis Ysidro Edgeworth in the late nineteenth century, the Edgeworth box is useful because it shows two consumers' opportunities and choices in a single figure.

> The **Edgeworth box** is a diagram that shows two consumers' opportunities and choices in a single figure.

Figure 16.10 shows the Edgeworth box for the exchange economy discussed in the last section. The box is 10 units wide and 10 units high. Each unit of width represents a kilogram of food, and each unit of height represents a litre of water. The width is 10 units because Humphrey and Lauren start out with 10 kilograms of food in total (eight for Humphrey and two for Lauren). Similarly, the height is 10 units because the two start out with 10 litres of water in total (three for Humphrey and seven for Lauren).

Each point in the Edgeworth box describes an allocation of resources between Humphrey and Lauren. That is, it specifies the division of food and water between them. For Humphrey, the bottom of the box serves as an axis measuring the amount of food, and the left side serves as an axis measuring the amount of water. For Lauren, the *top* of the box serves as an axis measuring the amount of food, and the *right* side serves as an axis measuring the amount of water. Notice that the numbers on Lauren's axes are read *backward*. On the top, they run from right to left; on the right side, they run from top to bottom.

To illustrate, consider point A. We read Humphrey's consumption from Humphrey's axes: eight kilograms of food and three litres of water. We read Lauren's consumption

Figure 16.10

Equilibrium in an Edgeworth Box. Humphrey and Lauren start out at point A. When food costs $1 per kilogram and water costs $1 per litre, Humphrey prefers point B_H and Lauren prefers point B_L. Supply doesn't match demand, so this economy isn't in equilibrium. When food costs $2 per kilogram and water costs $1 per litre, Humphrey and Lauren both prefer point C. They swap four litres of water and two kilograms of food. Supply matches demand, so this economy is in equilibrium.

from Lauren's axes: two kilograms of food and seven litres of water. These are their endowments. In other words, using Humphrey's axes, point A corresponds to point A_H in Figure 16.9(a); using Lauren's axes, point A corresponds to point A_L in Figure 16.9(b).

Next, we'll add budget lines. Suppose food costs $1 per kilogram and water costs $1 per litre. Starting from their endowments, either consumer can swap food for water at the rate of one kilogram per litre, or vice versa. To represent these opportunities, we can draw a brown line through the endowment point, A, with a slope of -1. Each consumer can choose any point on this line. Viewed from Humphrey's perspective, this line is identical to the brown one in Figure 16.9(a). Viewed from Lauren's perspective, it's identical to the brown one in Figure 16.9(b). In effect, we've constructed the Edgeworth box by rotating Figure 16.9(b) 180 degrees, and superimposing it on Figure 16.9(a).

From Figures 16.9(a) and (b), we know that at these prices, Humphrey will trade to point B_H and Lauren will trade to point B_L. We reproduce these points (using Humphrey's axes to plot B_H and Lauren's to plot B_L), as well as the two consumers' indifference curves, in Figure 16.10. (Remember that for Lauren, the picture is upside down, which is why her indifference curve appears to bend the wrong way. If you turn your book upside down, you'll see that it's a normal indifference curve.) We can tell immediately that this economy isn't in equilibrium because points B_H and B_L don't lie on top of each other. At these prices, Humphrey and Lauren together want to consume 11 kilograms of food (more than is available), and nine litres of water (less than is available).

Now let's suppose that food costs $2 per kilogram and water costs $1 per litre. Starting from his or her endowment, either consumer can swap food for water at the rate of one kilogram for every two litres, or vice versa. To represent these opportunities, we've drawn a green line through the endowment point, A, with a slope of -2. From Humphrey's perspective, this line is the same as the green budget line in Figure 16.9(a); from Lauren's perspective it's the same as the green budget line in Figure 16.9(b). From Figure 16.9, we know that Humphrey will trade to point C_H and Lauren will trade to point C_L. Those choices correspond to the *same point*, labelled C, in Figure 16.10. As shown, Humphrey supplies and Lauren demands two kilograms of food (the horizontal distance between points A and C); likewise, Humphrey demands and Lauren supplies four litres of water (the vertical distance between points A and C). Since supply matches demand in both markets, this economy is in general equilibrium.

In 1881, British economist Francis Ysidro Edgeworth (1845–1926) published *Mathematical Psychics: An Essay on the Application of Mathematics to the Moral Sciences*. Though the book was path-breaking, it was also nearly impenetrable. William Jevons, another famous economist of the era, wrote of Edgeworth that "his style, if not obscure, is implicit, so that the reader is left to puzzle out every important sentence like an enigma."

The First Welfare Theorem

We started this section by asking whether in a general equilibrium with many perfectly competitive markets, the allocation of resources is necessarily Pareto efficient. The answer to this question is yes. This important result, known as the **first welfare theorem**, clarifies the sense in which, as Adam Smith put it, the "invisible hand" of the market guides people toward socially desirable choices.

To understand why the first welfare theorem holds for exchange economies, look at the Edgeworth box in Figure 16.11. It reproduces the initial allocation (point A) and the equilibrium allocation (point C) from Figure 16.10. Since Humphrey and Lauren face *the same equilibrium prices*, the green line that runs through points A and C serves both as Humphrey's budget line, and as Lauren's budget line. From this critical observation, we can deduce that point C is Pareto efficient:

The **first welfare theorem** tells us that, in a general equilibrium with perfect competition, the allocation of resources is Pareto efficient.

1. Moving to any allocation to the left of the budget line, like point D, hurts Humphrey. Why? Point D is below Humphrey's budget line (from the perspective of Humphrey's

Figure 16.11

The First Welfare Theorem in an Exchange Economy. Suppose that point C is a competitive equilibrium allocation, and that, in equilibrium, the consumers share the green budget line. Humphrey must like point C better than all points to the left of the budget line, like point D. Lauren must like point C better than all points to the right of the budget line, like point E. Both of them must like point C at least as well as all other points on the budget line, like point F. So point C is Pareto efficient.

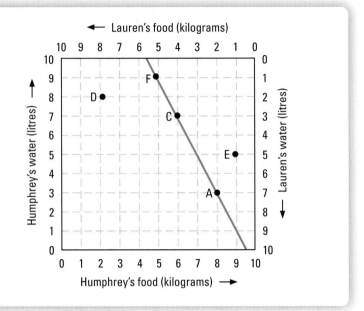

axes). He could have purchased bundle D, plus a little extra food or water, but he chose bundle C instead. So Humphrey must like bundle C better than bundle D.[10]

2. Moving to any allocation to the right of the budget line, like point E, hurts Lauren. Why? Point E is below Lauren's budget line (from the perspective of Lauren's axes). She could have purchased bundle E, plus a little extra food or water, but she chose bundle C instead. So Lauren must like bundle C more than bundle E.

3. Moving to any other allocation on the budget line, like point F, doesn't help either Humphrey or Lauren. Why not? Either one could have chosen point F, but they both chose point C instead. So they must like point C at least as well as point F.

We conclude that it's impossible to help Humphrey without hurting Lauren, and impossible to help Lauren without hurting Humphrey. That means the general equilibrium is indeed Pareto efficient.

Efficiency in Exchange

What does efficiency entail in an exchange economy? What makes some allocations efficient and others inefficient?

Look at the Edgeworth box in Figure 16.12. Is point G efficient? Two indifference curves pass through point G. The red one (labelled I_0) is Humphrey's and the blue one (labelled I_L) is Lauren's. Because the two indifference curves cross, we can find points that lie above Humphrey's indifference curve and below Lauren's. Any point in the yellow-shaded area will do. Take point H. Since point H lies above the red indifference curve labelled I_0, Humphrey likes it better than point G. Point H also lies below the blue indifference curve labelled I_L, so Lauren also likes it better than point G (remember that the picture is upside down for Lauren). Starting from point G, then, it's possible to make both Humphrey and Lauren better off. That means that point G is inefficient.

---

[10]This observation reflects the principle of revealed preference, discussed in Section 5.6.

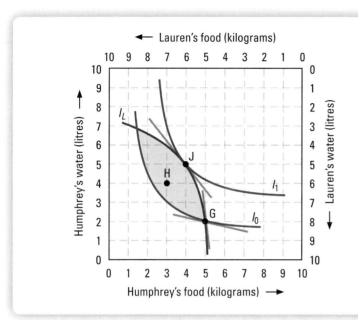

Figure 16.12

A Pareto Efficient Allocation in an Exchange Economy. At point G, Humphrey's indifference curve (in red) crosses Lauren's (in blue). Every point in the yellow-shaded area, such as H, makes both Humphrey and Lauren better off than at point G, so point G is not Pareto efficient. At point J, Humphrey's and Lauren's indifference curves touch but do not cross. This is Humphrey's favourite point on Lauren's blue indifference curve. It is also Pareto efficient. At point J, Humphrey and Lauren have the same marginal rate of substitution between food and water. At point G, their marginal rates of substitution differ.

Whenever an allocation is inefficient, there are always potential gains from trade. Starting from the inefficient point G in Figure 16.12, for example, Humphrey and Lauren can reach point H, which they both prefer, by swapping two litres of Humphrey's food for two litres of Lauren's water.

Now let's find an efficient allocation. Starting from point G, we'll redistribute resources to make Humphrey as well off as possible without making Lauren worse off. To avoid hurting Lauren, we need to stay on or below the blue indifference curve labelled I_L. Given this restriction, Humphrey's favourite point is J. Notice that one of Humphrey's red indifference curves (labelled I_1) runs through point J, and touches but does not cross the blue indifference curve.

Point J is Pareto efficient. Why? The points that Humphrey likes better than point J lie above the red indifference curve labelled I_1. But all of these points are above the blue indifference curve labelled I_L, which means that Lauren likes point J better. Similarly, the points that Lauren likes better than point J lie below the blue indifference curve labelled I_L. But all of these points are below the red indifference curve labelled I_1, which means that Humphrey likes point J better. So it's impossible to make one of the two consumers better off without hurting the other.

Whenever an allocation is efficient, there are no mutually beneficial trades. Starting from the efficient point J, for example, every conceivable trade makes either Humphrey or Lauren (or both) worse off.

A Condition for Efficiency in Exchange   In Section 4.3, we introduced a concept called the marginal rate of substitution (MRS). At point J in Figure 16.12, Humphrey's marginal rate of substitution for food with water (abbreviated MRS_{FW}) is the same as Lauren's. Why? Humphrey and Lauren's indifference curves lie tangent to the *same straight line* at point J (shown in green). The slope of this straight line tells us the rate at which *both* of them are willing to substitute for food with water when the amounts involved are tiny. In contrast, at point G in Figure 16.12, Humphrey and Lauren have different marginal rates of substitution, because their indifference curves lie tangent to different straight lines.

The **exchange efficiency condition** holds if every pair of individuals shares the same marginal rate of substitution for every pair of goods.

If every pair of individuals shares the same marginal rate of substitution for every pair of goods, we say that the allocation satisfies the **exchange efficiency condition**. As long as consumers' indifference curves are smooth (with no kinks) and have declining marginal rates of substitution (see page 111 in Section 4.3), this condition provides a simple test for Pareto efficiency. Allocations that satisfy this condition, like point J, are efficient.[11] Among allocations that assign everyone a positive amount of every good, ones that don't satisfy the exchange efficiency condition, like point G, are inefficient.[12]

We can think of the exchange efficiency condition as a test for the existence of potential gains from trade between consumers.[13] When the consumers' marginal rates of substitution differ, they can both gain by trading goods. Suppose Humphrey's MRS for food with water is $1/2$ and Lauren's is 2. That means Humphrey is willing to trade food for water at the rate of two kilograms per litre, while Lauren is willing to trade water for food at the rate of two litres per kilogram. Therefore, if they swap Humphrey's food for Lauren's water at the rate of one litre per kilogram, both will be better off. We made a similar point in Example 4.3 (page 112).

In contrast, when marginal rates of substitution are the same, as at point J in Figure 16.12, there are no potential gains to trade. Suppose Humphrey's MRS between food and water is one, and so is Lauren's. Can Humphrey improve his allocation by trading for an extra litre of water? He'll be better off only if he gives up slightly less than one kilogram of food, but Lauren is better off only if she receives slightly more than one kilogram of food. For similar reasons, Humphrey can't successfully trade for extra food. So there's no way to arrange a mutually beneficial trade.

To illustrate the use of the exchange efficiency condition, let's revisit the first welfare theorem. We've already provided one explanation for the efficiency of a general competitive equilibrium (recall Figure 16.11); here's another. Let's assume that in equilibrium, every consumer purchases a positive amount of every good. If so, then, for each consumer, the marginal rate of substitution between any two goods equals the ratio of their prices (recall formula (4) on page 577). Since every consumer faces the same prices, all their marginal rates of substitution must be the same. So the competitive allocation satisfies the exchange efficiency condition.

For a graphical illustration, look again at Figure 16.10 (page 586). Notice the similarities between the equilibrium allocation point C in Figure 16.10 and the Pareto efficient point J in Figure 16.12. At point C, each consumer's marginal rate of substitution equals the same price ratio.

$$\text{Humphrey's } MRS_{FW} = \frac{P_F}{P_W} = \text{Lauren's } MRS_{FW}$$

As a result, Humphrey and Lauren's marginal rates of substitution are the same, so the exchange efficiency condition is satisfied.

---

[11]When indifference curves do not have declining marginal rates of substitution, the allocation of consumption goods may not be efficient even if it satisfies the exchange efficiency condition. The principles at work here are similar to those discussed in connection with Figure 5.8 in Section 5.2, page 137.

[12]When at least one individual doesn't consume a positive amount of every good, a corresponding condition involves inequalities between marginal rates of substitution. The principles at work here are similar to those discussed in Section 5.2, in the subsection titled "Boundary Solutions" (page 138). We'll skip this case for the sake of brevity.

[13]To keep things simple, we'll assume here that indifference curves are smooth and that they have declining MRSs. We'll also focus on allocations in which everyone consumes a positive amount of every good.

The Contract Curve   We've seen that in Figure 16.12, point J is efficient. But is it the *only* efficient allocation? Plainly not. We found point J by locating Humphrey's favourite point on one of Lauren's indifference curves. To find other efficient allocations, we simply look for Humphrey's favourite points on Lauren's other indifference curves.

Figure 16.13 shows three of Lauren's indifference curves, I_1, I_2, and I_3, in blue. On each of these, we look for a point of tangency with one of Humphrey's indifference curves, shown in red. These three allocations—point K on I_1, point J on I_2, and point L on I_3—are all efficient. If we continued to identify other efficient allocations on Lauren's other indifference curves, we would trace out the black curve in the figure, known as the **contract curve**.[14] The contract curve shows every efficient allocation of consumption goods. At every point on the contract curve, Humphrey and Lauren's indifference curves touch but don't cross, so it is impossible to make both of them better off.

Notice that the contract curve starts at the southwest corner of the Edgeworth box (point M) and ends at the northeast corner (point N). In the southwest corner, Lauren receives all the food and all the water. While that is certainly unfortunate for Humphrey, it is nevertheless Pareto efficient. There isn't any way to help poor Humphrey without taking something away from Lauren, which would make her worse off. The allocation in the northeast corner simply reverses the situation—Humphrey consumes everything, and Lauren goes without.

There is a close relationship between the contract curve shown in Figure 16.13 and the utility possibility frontier shown in Figure 16.7 (page 581). Suppose we have a utility function representing Humphrey's preferences and another representing Lauren's. If so, we can associate each allocation in the Edgeworth box with a pair of utility levels. Every allocation on the contract curve will correspond to a point on the utility possibility frontier, and every point on the utility possibility frontier will correspond to an allocation on the contract curve. For example, an efficient allocation, like point J in Figure 16.13, will

> The **contract curve** shows every efficient allocation of consumption goods in an Edgeworth box.

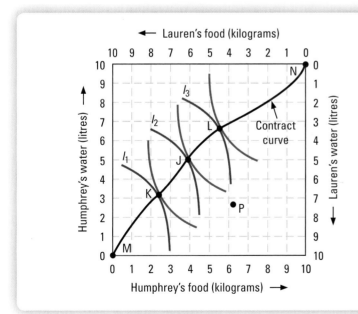

Figure 16.13

The Contract Curve. The contract curve shows every Pareto-efficient allocation of consumption goods. At every point on the contract curve, Humphrey's and Lauren's indifference curves touch but don't cross, so it is impossible to make both of them better off.

---

[14]It is called the contract curve because any efficient contract between Humphrey and Lauren would lead to an allocation on this curve.

correspond to a point on the utility possibility frontier, like point B in Figure 16.7. An inefficient allocation, like point P in Figure 16.13, will correspond to a point below the utility possibility frontier, like point A in Figure 16.7. Point M in Figure 16.13 corresponds to point D in Figure 16.7: Lauren consumes everything, achieving her highest possible level of utility, while Humphrey consumes nothing, achieving his lowest possible level of utility. Similarly, point N in Figure 16.13 corresponds to point C in Figure 16.7.

If, instead of trading through markets, Humphrey and Lauren were to select an allocation through direct negotiation, they would presumably pick a point on the contract curve. Any other proposal would be met with a counterproposal making both of them better off. The first welfare theorem tells us that a competitive equilibrium also delivers an allocation on the contract curve. To learn more about the relationship between the allocations achieved through competitive markets and through direct negotiation, read Add-on 16B.

WORKED-OUT PROBLEM   16.2

The Problem   Humphrey and Lauren must split 10 kilograms of food and 10 litres of water. Suppose we can represent Humphrey's preferences with the utility function $U_H = F_H^2 W_H$ (for which Humphrey's marginal rate of substitution for food with water is $2W_H/F_H$), and Lauren's preferences with the utility function $U_L = \min\{F_L, W_L\}$, where F_H and F_L indicate their food consumption, while W_H and W_L indicate their water consumption. Find and graph the contract curve. Suppose Humphrey and Lauren's initial endowments are $F_H = 2$, $F_L = 8$, $W_H = 5$, and $W_L = 5$. What is the ratio of the price of food to the price of water in competitive equilibrium? To which allocation will Humphrey and Lauren trade?

The Solution   In any Pareto efficient allocation, Lauren's food consumption (in kilograms) must equal her water consumption (in litres), that is, $F_L = W_L$. If $F_L > W_L$, we could transfer a small amount of food from Lauren to Humphrey, which would help Humphrey without hurting Lauren. If $F_L < W_L$, we could accomplish the same objective by transferring a small amount of water. Therefore, the contract curve is the diagonal line running between the southwest and northeast corners of the Edgeworth box, as shown in Figure 16.14. Humphrey's indifference curves are shown in red, and Lauren's in blue.

Since a competitive equilibrium is Pareto efficient, Humphrey and Lauren must trade to a point on the contract curve. At every point on that curve, $F_H = W_H$, so Humphrey's $MRS_{FW} = 2$ litres per kilogram. We know that, in a competitive equilibrium, Humphrey's $MRS_{FW} = P_F/P_W$, so we conclude that $P_F/P_W = 2$.

To find the allocations to which Humphrey and Lauren trade, we draw a budget line through their endowment point (shown as point A in Figure 16.14). The slope of the budget line is $-P_F/P_W = -2$. Where does this line cross the contract curve? If Humphrey increases his food consumption by one kilogram (from 2 to 3 kilograms), he will have to reduce his water consumption by 2 litres (from 5 to 3 litres). This exchange will place him on the contract curve, at point B. As shown in the figure, that is the allocation to which Humphrey and Lauren both wish to trade given their endowments and the equilibrium price ratio.

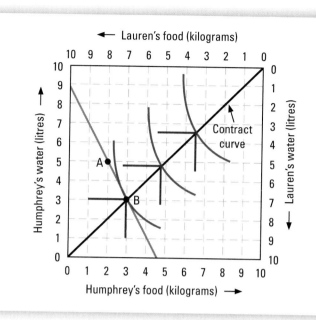

Figure 16.14
Solution to Worked-Out Problem
16.2. Humphrey's indifference curves are shown in red and Lauren's in blue. The contract curve is the diagonal line running between the southwest and northeast corners of the box. The equilibrium ratio of the price of food to the price of water will be 2. Starting from point A, Humphrey and Lauren will trade along the green budget line to point B.

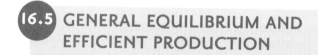

IN-TEXT EXERCISE 16.2 **Repeat worked-out problem 16.2 with the following changes: Humphrey's preferences correspond to the utility function $U_H = F_H W_H$ (which means his $MRS_{FW} = W_H/F_H$) and the consumers' endowments are $F_H = 3$, $F_L = 7$, $W_H = 9$, and $W_L = 1$.**

16.5 GENERAL EQUILIBRIUM AND EFFICIENT PRODUCTION

In Section 16.4, we learned that the competitive equilibrium of an exchange economy is Pareto efficient (the first welfare theorem). We also learned how to tell the difference between efficient and inefficient allocations (the exchange efficiency condition). In this section we'll add production to the mix and explain why competitive equilibria remain Pareto efficient. First, though, we'll introduce two new conditions that allow us to distinguish between allocations with efficient versus inefficient production.

Efficiency in Production

What does Pareto efficiency entail in a production economy? It certainly requires efficient exchange. Otherwise, we could help some consumer without hurting anyone else simply by redistributing consumption goods while holding production fixed. By itself, however, exchange efficiency is not enough; production must also be efficient. As we explain next, there are two requirements for efficient production: input efficiency and output efficiency.

Input Efficiency **Input efficiency** means that holding constant the total amount of each input used in the economy, there is no way to increase any firm's output without decreasing the output of another firm. Pareto efficiency requires input efficiency. If an

> **Input efficiency** means that holding constant the total amount of each input used in the economy, there is no way to increase any firm's output without decreasing the output of another firm.

allocation doesn't satisfy input efficiency, then it's possible to produce more of one good and at least as much of every other good using the same inputs. By splitting the extra output among consumers, we could make everyone better off. Thus, the allocation isn't Pareto efficient.

To illustrate this concept, let's examine a simple case involving two firms and two inputs. One firm, MunchieCo, uses labour and capital to produce food. The other, CribCo, uses the same inputs to produce housing. Suppose that between them, the two firms use 50 workers and 25 machines. Which input allocations will achieve input efficiency?

In Section 16.4 we used the Edgeworth box to illustrate allocations of goods between consumers. Here, we can use it to illustrate allocations of inputs between firms. Look at Figure 16.15, which shows an Edgeworth box that is 50 units wide and 25 units high. Each unit of width represents a worker, and each unit of height represents a machine. The width is 50 units because in total, MunchieCo and CribCo use 50 workers. The height is 25 units because in total, the two companies use 25 machines.

Each point in the Edgeworth box describes an allocation of the two inputs between the two firms. For MunchieCo, the bottom of the box serves as the axis that measures the number of workers, and the left side serves as the axis that measures the number of machines. For CribCo, the top of the box serves as the axis that measures the number of workers, and the right side serves as the axis that measures the number of machines.

Now let's consider whether point A, which assigns 25 workers and 8 machines to MunchieCo and 25 workers and 17 machines to CribCo, achieves input efficiency. The figure shows two isoquants crossing at that point, the red one for MunchieCo and the blue one for CribCo. Since the isoquants cross, we can find points that lie above MunchieCo's and below CribCo's, like point B. Because point B lies above the red isoquant, MunchieCo can produce more food at point B than at point A. Likewise, since point B lies below the blue isoquant, CribCo can produce more houses at point B than at point A (remember that for CribCo, the picture is upside down). So starting from point A, it's possible to squeeze more food and more housing out of the same inputs. Therefore, point A is inefficient.

Figure 16.15

Input Efficiency. This Edgeworth box shows all the possible ways to divide 50 workers and 25 machines between MunchieCo, which produces food, and CribCo, which produces housing. MunchieCo's isoquants are shown in red and CribCo's in blue. Points where the isoquants cross, like point A, are inefficient (point B, for example, allows both firms to increase production). Inputs are allocated efficiently at points C, D, E, F, and G, which lie on the production contract curve.

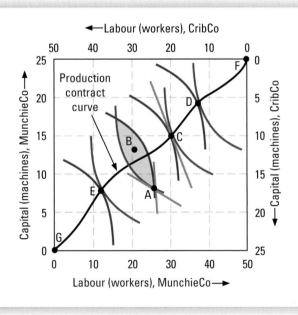

In contrast, at point C, where the two firms' isoquants touch but do not cross, the two inputs are allocated efficiently. Why? Every point other than C is either below the red isoquant that runs through point C (which means that MunchieCo produces less food), above the blue isoquant that runs through point C (which means that CribCo produces fewer houses), or both. There is no way to increase the output of one good without decreasing the output of the other.

Point C isn't the only efficient allocation of inputs. The red and blue isoquants also touch but do not cross at points D and E. These input allocations are also efficient. If we identified all such points, we would trace out the black curve in the figure, known as the **production contract curve**. The production contract curve shows every efficient allocation of inputs between the two firms.

> The **production contract curve** shows every efficient allocation of inputs between two firms in an Edgeworth box.

A Condition for Input Efficiency

In Section 7.3, we introduced a concept called the marginal rate of technical substitution (MRTS). At the efficient allocations in Figure 16.15, like point C, MunchieCo's marginal rate of technical substitution for labour with capital (abbreviated $MRTS_{LK}$) is the same as CribCo's. Why? At point C, the firms' isoquants lie tangent to the *same straight line* (shown in green). The slope of this line tells us the rate at which *both* firms can substitute labour for capital without changing their output (when the amounts involved are tiny). In other words, it defines their marginal rates of technical substitution. In contrast, at the inefficient allocations in Figure 16.15, like point A, the firms' isoquants lie tangent to different straight lines, so their marginal rates of technical substitution differ.

We say that an allocation satisfies the **input efficiency condition** if, for every pair of inputs, every pair of firms shares the same marginal rate of technical substitution. As long as the firms' isoquants are smooth (with no kinks) and have declining marginal rates of technical substitution, this condition provides a simple test for input efficiency. Allocations that satisfy this condition, like point C, are efficient.[15] Among allocations that assign every firm a positive amount of every input, ones that don't satisfy the condition, like point A, are inefficient.[16]

> The **input efficiency condition** holds if, for every pair of inputs, every pair of firms share the same marginal rate of technical substitution.

We can think of the input efficiency condition as a test for the existence of potential gains from trade between firms. When the firms' marginal rates of technical substitution differ, they can both gain by trading inputs. For example, suppose that MunchieCo can substitute 5 machines for 10 workers without changing its output, while CribCo can substitute 5 workers for 10 machines. If MunchieCo sends 10 workers to CribCo in exchange for 10 machines, both firms can increase their production. But when the two firms' marginal rates of technical substitution are the same, this potential gain from trade vanishes. As with exchange among consumers, the existence of potential gains from trade implies inefficiency, and vice versa.

Production Possibilities

In Figure 16.15 we focused on inputs. But what about outputs? Look at Figure 16.16. The horizontal axis shows weekly food production and the vertical axis shows weekly housing production. Each input allocation in Figure 16.15 is associated with a level of food production and a level of housing production. We can plot

---

[15]When isoquants do not have declining MRTSs, the allocation of inputs may not be efficient even if it satisfies the input efficiency condition. Here, declining MRTSs play the same role as did declining MRSs in our discussion of exchange efficiency.

[16]When at least one firm doesn't use a positive amount of every input, a corresponding condition involves inequalities between marginal rates of technical substitution. The applicable principles are similar to those discussed in Section 8.4, in the subsection titled "Boundary Solutions" (p. 267). We'll skip this case for brevity.

Figure 16.16

The Production Possibility Frontier. Each of the input allocations in Figure 16.15 corresponds to specific levels of food and housing production, which are plotted in this figure. For example, point A in Figure 16.15 corresponds to A′. The boundary of the green set is the production possibility frontier. Inputs are allocated efficiently at points on the frontier, and inefficiently for points below the frontier. At point C′, the marginal rate of transformation between food and clothing is one.

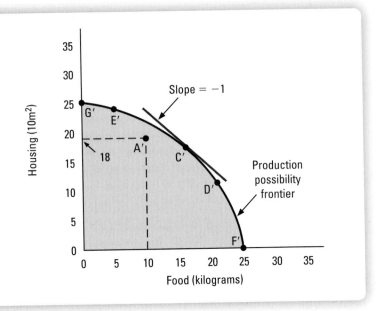

> **The production possibility frontier** shows the combinations of outputs that firms can produce when inputs are allocated efficiently among them, given their technologies and the total inputs available.

those levels in Figure 16.16. To illustrate, let's assume that with 25 workers and 8 machines, MunchieCo can produce 10 kilograms of food, and that, with 25 workers and 17 machines, CribCo can produce 180 square metres of housing. In that case, the input allocation labelled A in Figure 16.15 is associated with the outputs labelled A′ in Figure 16.16. Following this procedure for every possible input allocation generates the green-shaded area in Figure 16.16. These are the production possibilities for MunchieCo and CribCo, given their technologies and the inputs available to them.

The northeast boundary of the green-shaded area in Figure 16.16 is known as the **production possibility frontier** (abbreviated PPF). It shows the combinations of outputs firms can produce when inputs are allocated efficiently among them, given their technologies and the total inputs available. The relationship between the PPF and the production contract curve is the same as the relationship between the utility possibility frontier and the contract curve (see Section 16.4). Each input allocation on the production contract curve in Figure 16.15 is associated with a point on the PPF in Figure 16.16, and vice versa. For example, points C, D, E, F, and G in Figure 16.15 are associated, respectively, with points C′, D′, E′, F′, and G′ in Figure 16.16. Points F and F′ represent one extreme: all inputs are allocated to food, and no housing is produced. Points G and G′ represent the opposite extreme: all inputs are allocated to housing, and no food is produced. Inefficient input allocations, like point A in Figure 16.15, are associated with points below the PPF, like A′ in Figure 16.16.

As in Figure 16.16, the PPF always slopes downward. An upward slope would imply that starting at some point on the frontier, it's possible to increase the production of food *and* clothing without changing the total amount of any input. But if that's the case, the allocation of inputs is plainly inefficient. By definition, the PPF includes only those output combinations corresponding to efficient input allocations.

The Marginal Rate of Transformation

The downward slope of the PPF reflects the fact that with society's limited inputs, production involves tradeoffs. If we choose to produce more of one good, we must produce less of another. When the units involved are very small, the amount of one good, call it Y, that can be produced by sacrificing an additional unit of a second good, call it X, is known as the **marginal rate of transformation** from X to Y (abbreviated MRT$_{XY}$).

At any point on the PPF, the marginal rate of transformation is equal to the slope of a straight line drawn tangent to the frontier at that point, times negative one. For example, at point C' in Figure 16.16, the slope of the straight line drawn tangent to the PPF is -1, so the marginal rate of transformation from food to housing is 1.

The marginal rate of transformation is related to firms' marginal products. Let's say we want to increase housing production. There are many ways to do so. Here are two possibilities:

1. Shift one worker from MunchieCo to CribCo. MunchieCo's food production falls by its marginal product of labour (abbreviated MP_L^F), and CribCo's housing production rises by its marginal product of labour (abbreviated MP_L^H). The rate at which we can convert food to housing is therefore MP_L^H/MP_L^F.

2. Shift one machine from MunchieCo to CribCo. By the same reasoning, the rate at which we can convert food to housing is MP_K^H/MP_K^F. (where MP_K^F is MunchieCo's marginal product of capital and MP_K^H is CribCo's).

At first, the rate at which we can convert food to housing might appear to depend on which input we shift. But in fact, the two rates are identical at any point on the PPF. Remember from Section 7.3 that the marginal rate of technical substitution for labour with capital equals the marginal product of labour divided by the marginal product of capital (page 237). Remember too that on the PPF, inputs are allocated efficiently, so the firms' marginal rates of technical substitution are equal. Putting these facts together, we have

$$\frac{MP_L^F}{MP_K^F} = \text{MunchieCo's } MRTS_{LK} = \text{CribCo's } MRTS_{LK} = \frac{MP_L^H}{MP_K^H}$$

Rearranging this expression, we discover that $MP_K^H/MP_K^F = MP_L^H/MP_L^F$. In other words, these two ratios are indeed identical. We can therefore use either ratio, reflecting a shift of either input, to define the marginal rate of transformation from food to housing.

$$MRT_{FH} = \frac{MP_K^H}{MP_K^F} = \frac{MP_L^H}{MP_L^F} \qquad \textbf{(10)}$$

Note that the PPF in Figure 16.16 bows outward, away from the origin. As we move from left to right, the frontier becomes steeper, which means the marginal rate of transformation from food to housing rises. This change reflects decreasing returns to scale in the production technologies (Section 7.4). As we move from left to right, inputs become more productive in housing (as scale declines) and less productive in food (as scale increases). As a result, the rate at which we gain housing by sacrificing food rises. We can see this relationship in the preceding formula for the MRT_{FH}. If MP_L^H and MP_K^H both rise (due to declining scale) while MP_L^F and MP_K^F both fall (due to increasing scale), the two ratios, MP_K^H/MP_K^F and MP_L^H/MP_L^F will both rise.

Output Efficiency

Output efficiency means that, among allocations satisfying exchange efficiency and input efficiency, there is no way to make one consumer better off without harming anyone else by shifting production from one good to another. We've seen that we achieve input efficiency by choosing a point on the production contract curve, which is equivalent to choosing a point on the PPF. To achieve output efficiency, we need to choose the right point.

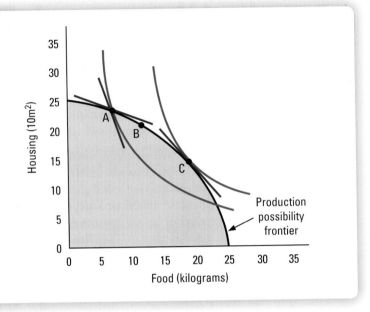

Figure 16.17

Output Efficiency. Point A doesn't achieve output efficiency, because Humphrey's indifference curve crosses the PPF at that point. Since the two curves lie tangent to different straight lines at that point, Humphrey's MRS for food with housing doesn't equal the MRT. Point C achieves output efficiency because the indifference curve touches but does not cross the PPF at that point. At point C, Humphrey's indifference curve and the PPF lie tangent to the same straight line, implying that Humphrey's MRS for food with housing equals the MRT.

Figure 16.17 illustrates the concept of output efficiency for an economy with a single consumer (Humphrey). It shows both the PPF (in black) and Humphrey's indifference curves (in red). Point A satisfies the input efficiency condition because it's on the PPF. However, it doesn't satisfy output efficiency. Why not? Since the indifference curve that runs through point A crosses the PPF, we can make Humphrey better off by moving southeast along the PPF, to a point like B. We reach point B by shifting inputs from housing to food while staying on the production contract curve.

In contrast, point C satisfies both input efficiency and output efficiency. It's on the PPF, and the indifference curve that runs through point C touches but does not cross the PPF. To make Humphrey better off, we would need to move to a point above the indifference curve. But the firms in this economy can't produce any of those points.

A Condition for Output Efficiency   At the efficient allocation in Figure 16.17, point C, Humphrey's marginal rate of substitution for food with housing equals the marginal rate of transformation. Why? The indifference curve that runs through point C lies tangent to the same straight line as the PPF. So the slope of that line (shown in dark red) defines both Humphrey's marginal rate of substitution and the marginal rate of transformation at point C.

In contrast, at the inefficient allocations on the PPF, Humphrey's marginal rate of substitution differs from the marginal rate of transformation. At point A, for example, the indifference curve and the PPF lie tangent to different straight lines (as shown in Figure 16.17). The slopes of those lines—which define, respectively, the marginal rate of substitution and the marginal rate of transformation—clearly are not the same.

In an economy with many consumers, when *any* consumer's marginal rate of substitution differs from the marginal rate of transformation, better alternatives are available. For example, suppose Humphrey is willing to give up 1 square metre of housing to get five kilograms of food. Suppose too that it's possible to produce an extra five kilograms of food while sacrificing only ½ square metre of housing. In that case, we can make

Humphrey better off without hurting Lauren: reduce both housing production and Humphrey's housing consumption by $1/2$ square metre, and increase both food production and Humphrey's food consumption by five kilograms, while leaving Lauren's consumption unchanged.

An allocation satisfies the **output efficiency condition** if for every pair of goods, every consumer's marginal rate of substitution equals the marginal rate of transformation. In our example,

$$\text{Humphrey's } MRS_{FH} = \text{Lauren's } MRS_{FH} = MRT_{FH}$$

When the exchange efficiency condition is satisfied, all consumers share the same marginal rate of substitution; therefore, if the preceding equality holds for one of them, it holds for all of them. As long as (1) the PPF and indifference curves are smooth (with no kinks), (2) indifference curves have declining MRSs, and (3) no production technology yields increasing returns to scale, this condition provides a simple test for output efficiency. Allocations that satisfy this condition, like point C, are efficient.[17] Among allocations that involve positive consumption of every good, ones that don't satisfy the output efficiency condition, like point A, are inefficient.[18]

The output efficiency condition applies both when firms produce different products (like food and housing), and when they produce the same product. For example, suppose that firms A and B both produce food, and that A's product is a perfect substitute for B's. In that case, the output efficiency condition simply tells us to allocate inputs between firms A and B so as to maximize total food production. That's because consumers are willing to give up exactly one unit of firm A's product to get one unit of firm B's product: the $MRS_{AB} = 1$. Therefore, the output efficiency condition requires that the $MRT_{AB} = 1$. Since we can increase total food output by shifting inputs from firm A to firm B when $MRT_{AB} > 1$, and from firm B to firm A when $MRT_{AB} < 1$, total food production is maximized when the $MRT_{AB} = 1$. The output efficiency condition therefore amounts to the requirement that the allocation of production among food producers maximizes total output. We learned in Section 14.4 that the total cost of producing a good is minimized when all the firms that produce it share the same marginal cost (see Figure 14.15, page 518). That property is equivalent to the output efficiency condition, applied to cases in which different firms produce the same good.[19]

The First Welfare Theorem, Again

We saw in Section 16.4 that the general equilibrium of a competitive exchange economy is Pareto efficient. The same conclusion holds for economies with production.

Intuitively, why does perfect competition guarantee Pareto efficiency? Let's suppose for the moment that the first welfare theorem is wrong, and that there's a feasible allocation

> An allocation satisfies the **output efficiency condition** if, for every pair of goods, every consumer's marginal rate of substitution equals the marginal rate of transformation.

---

[17]When indifference curves do not have declining MRSs or production technologies do not have decreasing returns to scale, production may not be efficient even if it satisfies the input and output efficiency conditions. The issues here are the same as those mentioned in the context of exchange efficiency.

[18]When a good is neither produced nor consumed, there is a corresponding condition involving inequalities between the MRS and MRT. We'll skip this case for brevity.

[19]To demonstrate this equivalence, we use the following facts: (1) $MC_A = W/MP_L^A$ and $MC_B = W/MP_L^B$ (see p. 279), and (2) $MRT_{AB} = MC_L^B/MP_L^A$ (see the previous section, formula (10)). Together, these facts imply that $MRT_{AB} = MC_A/MC_B$. In this special case, the output efficiency condition requires $MRT_{AB} = 1$, from which it follows that $MC_A = MC_B$.

that makes all consumers better off than they are in equilibrium. Then at the equilibrium prices consumers must not be able to afford the bundles they would consume in that new allocation (otherwise they would purchase those bundles instead of their equilibrium bundles). Consequently, the value of the goods they would purchase from firms must exceed the value of the inputs they would supply to firms, plus any profits they receive in equilibrium as the owners of firms.

$$\text{Value of new output bundle at equilibrium prices} > \text{Value of new input bundle at equilibrium prices} + \text{Equilibrium profits}$$

Rearranging this expression, we discover that

$$\text{Value of new output bundle at equilibrium prices} - \text{Value of new input bundle at equilibrium prices} > \text{Equilibrium profits}$$

But the difference between the value of outputs and inputs for the new allocation (at equilibrium prices) equals the profits that firms would earn by choosing those output and input levels instead of the equilibrium levels. The preceding expression therefore tells us that, if it's possible to make all consumers better off, and if consumers and firms are facing the same prices, then firms haven't really maximized their profits, which in turn implies that the original allocation isn't a competitive equilibrium after all!

To convince ourselves that a competitive equilibrium is Pareto efficient, we can also check the three efficiency conditions. The exchange efficiency condition holds for the same reasons as in Section 16.4. That leaves us with the input and output efficiency conditions.

We'll start with the input efficiency condition. Let's assume for simplicity that in equilibrium, every firm uses a positive amount of every input. If so, then for each firm the marginal rate of technical substitution for one input with another equals the ratio of their prices (as we learned in Section 8.4, p. 261). Since every firm faces the same input prices, all their MRTSs must be the same. So, in our example involving MunchieCo and CribCo

$$\text{MunchieCo's } MRTS_{LK} = \frac{W}{R} = \text{CribCo's } MRTS_{LK}$$

(where W is the price of labour, and R is the price of capital). Thus, a competitive allocation satisfies the input efficiency condition.

What about the output efficiency condition? Let's assume for simplicity that, in equilibrium, every individual consumes a positive amount of every good. Then for each pair of goods, every consumer's marginal rate of substitution must equal the price ratio (see equation (4) in Section 5.2, p. 132). In our example,

$$MRS_{FH} = \frac{P_F}{P_H}$$

As we learned in Section 9.3, competitive firms will produce up to the point where price equals marginal cost ($P_F = MC_F$ and $P_H = MC_H$), so this last equation implies

$$MRS_{FH} = \frac{MC_F}{MC_H}$$

The marginal cost of each good, in turn, equals the price of any input divided by its marginal product (see Section 8.5, p. 274). In our example, $MC_F = W/MP_L^F$, and $MC_H = W/MP_L^H$. Substituting these terms into the last equation and using formula (10) on page 597, we have

$$MRS_{FH} = \frac{W/MP_L^F}{W/MP_L^H}$$

$$= \frac{MP_L^H}{MP_L^F} = MRT_{FH}$$

This formula confirms that the output efficiency condition is indeed satisfied.

> **IN-TEXT EXERCISE 16.3** Suppose the food production by MunchieCo is given by $F = 2(L_F K_F)^{1/2}$ and housing production by CribCo is given by $H = (L_H K_H)^{1/2}$. The marginal products of labour and capital in food and housing production are $MP_L^F = (K_F/L_F)^{1/2}$, $MP_K^F = (L_F/K_F)^{1/2}$, $MP_L^H = \frac{1}{2}(K_H/L_H)^{1/2}$, and $MP_K^H = \frac{1}{2}(L_H/K_H)^{1/2}$. There are 100 units of both labour and capital so that $L_F + L_H = 100$ and $K_F + K_H = 100$. Using the input efficiency condition show that $L_F = K_F$ and that $L_H = K_H$, and that the production possibly frontier is given by $F = 200 - 2H$. What is the MRT_{FH}? Suppose consumer's preferences are identical and given by the utility function $U = F^{2/3}H^{1/3}$ with marginal utilities $MU_F = \frac{2}{3}(H/F)^{1/3}$ and $MU_H = \frac{1}{3}(F/H)^{2/3}$. Show that for output efficiency the economy produces $133\frac{1}{3}$ units of F and $33\frac{1}{3}$ units of H.

Application 16.2

The Gains from Free Trade across Countries

Government policy on international trade is highly controversial. Some people support protectionism, which usually involves tariffs and/or quotas (discussed in Section 15.3). These people believe that citizens are best served by policies that protect their jobs and businesses from foreign competition. Other people favour open markets and free trade. They contend that protectionism hurts consumers by denying them free access to desirable foreign goods. They also point out that the reduction of trade barriers worldwide would open up foreign markets to domestic companies.

General equilibrium analysis sheds some light on this debate. From a microeconomic point of view, trade between countries is really trade between individual consumers and firms who happen to be located in different countries. As individuals, all of us participate in the same world economy.

Seen in this light, trade barriers clearly get in the way of economic efficiency. When countries impose tariffs, consumers and firms face different relative prices for the same goods, depending on where they live. For example, if Canada imposes a tariff on Japanese DVD players and Japan counters with a tariff on Canadian beef, then DVD players will be less expensive relative to beef in Japan than they are in Canada. As a result, Japanese and Canadian consumers will have different marginal rates of substitution for DVD players with beef—a failure of exchange efficiency. Also, the Japanese marginal rate of transformation from DVD players to beef will differ from the marginal rate of substitution among Canadian consumers, and the Canadian marginal rate of transformation will differ from the marginal rate of substitution among Japanese consumers, both failures of output efficiency. (Can you explain why?) Similarly, protectionism can cause the relative prices of inputs to vary from country to country. As a result, firms end up with different marginal rates of technical substitution—a failure of input efficiency.

Even though every country might be better off if all reduced or eliminated their tariffs, there is frequently little incentive for any one country to abandon protectionism unilaterally. Often, groups of countries attempt to overcome this problem by reducing their trade barriers cooperatively, through international agreements like the General Agreement on Tariffs and Trade (GATT), the European Union (EU), and the North American Free Trade Agreement (NAFTA). International institutions like the World Trade Organization (WTO) generally try to promote cooperative pro-trade policies (though critics charge that they also pursue politically motivated agendas).

Figure 16.18 illustrates how an economist might measure the gains from free trade agreements. To keep the analysis simple, we'll consider a country (Humphria) consisting of a single individual (Humphrey) who consumes only food and clothing. Figure 16.18(a) shows Humphria's PPF in black and Humphrey's indifference curves in red. On its own, Humphria can do no better than point A. We've drawn the figure so that at point A, $MRS_{FC} = MRT_{FC} = 1$. In other words, at the efficient outcome, Humphria can transform one garment of clothing into one kilogram of food, or vice versa.

Now suppose the rest of the world is relatively good at producing clothing and relatively bad at producing food. As a result, other countries are willing to trade two units of clothing for each kilogram of food. Starting from point A, Humphria can achieve any point on the brown line, which includes points that Humphria could not have reached on its own. It is as if the country's production possibilities have expanded. From Humphrey's perspective, the best point on this new line is B. To reach it, Humphria produces point A and then exchanges food for clothing.

But Humphria can do even better than point B. Suppose it produces point C in Figure 16.18(b), which involves more food and less clothing than point A. In other words, Humphria specializes in producing the good for which it has a relative

advantage. Through trade, it can then achieve any point on the blue line. The best of these is D. (Since the blue line lies tangent to the PPF at point C, no other starting point provides better trading opportunities, which means that Humphria can do no better than point D.) Here, the gains from free trade correspond to the improvement in Humphrey's well-being that come with moving from point A to point D.

In practice, how large are the gains from free trade? This question remains controversial, despite the fact that trade produces measurable gains along many dimensions. According to a study by economists Christian Broda and David Weinstein, between 1972 and 1997, the increasing variety of imported goods brought about through increased trade by itself significantly raised inflation-adjusted incomes throughout the world.[20] The gain, which was equivalent to three percent of national income in the world's largest economy, the United States, was much larger in many other countries—45.6 percent of national income in Singapore, 36.9 percent in Taiwan, 26.9 percent in China, 26.8 percent in Brazil, 25.4 percent in the former Soviet Union, and 19.4 percent in Canada.

Within any given country, however, these gains were not equally distributed across the population. When economic activity moves from one country to another, businesses inevitably shut down. People lose their jobs and often encounter serious economic hardship. Some believe that the impact on poorer, lower-skilled workers is particularly severe (though that, too, is controversial). As a result, discussions of trade policy inevitably raise questions about the trade-off between efficiency and equity, as well as the need to compensate the losers through redistribution.

Efficiency as a Justification for Free Markets

Advocates of free markets from Adam Smith to the present argue that the government should not play a significant role in overseeing, directing, or conducting economic activity. Generally, they advocate a "hands off" approach to private commerce. This policy doctrine is known as **laissez-faire**, which is short for *laissez-faire, laissez passer*, a French phrase meaning "let things alone, let them pass."

The doctrine of **laissez-faire** holds that the government should adopt a "hands off" approach to private commerce.

The first welfare theorem provides some support for this position: it tells us that a perfectly competitive economy would produce an efficient outcome. However, this observation does not necessarily imply that laissez-faire is the best policy. Opponents of laissez-faire express two main types of reservations.

A **market failure** is a source of inefficiency in an imperfectly competitive economy.

First, few if any economists would describe the real economy as perfectly competitive. An imperfectly competitive economy may allocate resources inefficiently. The sources of inefficiency are known as **market failures**. When a market failure occurs, the

---

[20]Christian Broda and David Weinstein, "Variety Growth and World Welfare," *American Economic Review* 94, May 2004, pp. 139–144.

Figure 16.18

The Gains from International Trade. On its own, the country of Humphria can do no better than point A, where its MRT from food to housing and Humphrey's MRS both equal one. But if Humphria can trade with the rest of the world at the rate of two garments of clothing for one kilogram of food, it can produce point A and trade to any point on the brown line in figure (a). The best of these, point B, improves on point A. Humphria can do even better, however, by producing at point C in figure (b) and trading to point D.

government may be able to promote economic well-being by intervening in markets. However, even in cases in which improvements are possible, government interventions may introduce new inefficiencies. In some cases, the cure may be worse than the disease. In Part IV of this book, we'll examine the main forms of market failure and their implications in some depth.

Second, many people express concerns that free markets can produce inequitable outcomes. Among other things, they point out that laissez-faire leads to extreme wealth and extreme poverty (see, for example, Application 16.3). In the next section, we'll examine potential remedies.

Application 16.3

The Concentration of Wealth and Income

The actual distribution of economic resources favours some people over others. Vast fortunes are the stuff of modern legend. In 2008, the richest 100 Canadians had an average net worth of $1.65 billion, which was more than 10,000 times that of the average Canadian household. The list of the richest Canadians includes members of the Thomson (publishing) and Irving (energy) families, Galen Weston (Loblaws), Michael Lazaridis and James Balsillie

(Research in Motion), Jeff Skoll (eBay), and Guy Laliberté (Cirque de Soleil).

Many other Canadians enjoy substantial wealth and income, although not enough to place them on this exclusive list. Statistics Canada reports that during 2004 an income of more than $89,000 was enough to place individuals in the top 5 percent of earners, while an income of more than $181,000 placed an individual in the top 1 percent of earners. To be in the top 0.1 percent of taxpayers one needed to earn more than $2.8 million. Popular wisdom holds that the rich grow steadily richer. This has certainly been true in Canada over the past several decades if one considers the income shares of the highest-income individuals and families; there has been a steady trend toward greater inequality. The media have reported a growing gap between the wealthy and the middle class, supported by government statistics on the distribution of income. The share of income of the top five percent

of Canadians has grown from 21 percent in 1982 to 25.3 percent in 2004. The share of the top one percent has increased from 8.5 to 12.2 percent, and the share of the top 0.1 percent has almost doubled from 2.7 to 4.7 percent.[21]

Figure 16.19 shows the fraction of total income earned by the richest five percent, one percent, and 0.1 percent of the Canadian population from 1920 to 2000. All three curves exhibit essentially the same pattern. The concentration of wealth peaked in 1930, when the richest five percent of Canadians accounted for a little more than 40 percent of total income; the richest one percent earned 18 percent; and the richest 0.1 percent earned six percent. Their income shares declined sharply in the 1930s and 1940s due largely to effects of the Great Depression and World War II. They then remained relatively stable until the 1970s, when they dipped slightly once again before recovering during the 1980s. Since 1990 the income shares of the richest Canadians have once again started to increase.[22]

Figure 16.19

Income Shares in Canada, 1920–2000. This figure shows the fraction of income earned by the richest 5 percent, 1 percent, and 0.1 percent of the Canadian population over an 80-year period.

Source: Constructed from data appendix accompanying Emmanuel Saez and Michael Veall, "The Evolution of High Incomes in Canada, 1920–2000," *NBER Working Paper*, number 9607, 2003.

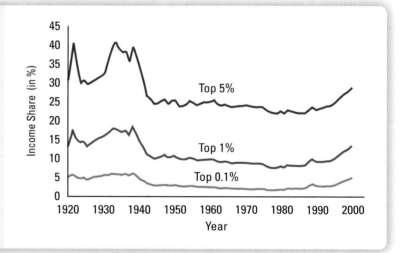

16.6 EQUITY AND REDISTRIBUTION

The first welfare theorem tells us that a competitive equilibrium is Pareto efficient. While this is certainly good news, it may not be enough to convince you that a policy of laissez-faire is desirable. Remember that efficient allocations can be extremely inequitable. Look again at the contract curve in Figure 16.13 (page 591). Every point on that curve is

[21]Taken from table 5 of Statistics Canada Perspectives on Income and Labour Volume 8, no. 9, September 2007.

[22]Emmanuel Saez and Michael Veall, "The Evolution of High Incomes in Canada, 1920–2000," *NBER Working Paper*, no. 9607, 2003.

Pareto efficient, including points M and N, which assign everything to a single consumer. Even if the competitive equilibrium allocation lies on the contract curve, there may be other points on that curve that are far more attractive from the perspective of equity. In this section, we examine some of the ways in which a government might achieve a more equitable outcome.

The Second Welfare Theorem

Can competitive markets generate allocations that are not just efficient, but equitable? Another important result, known as the **second welfare theorem**, addresses this question. The second welfare theorem tells us that every Pareto efficient allocation is a competitive equilibrium for some initial allocation of resources.

The **second welfare theorem** tells us that every Pareto efficient allocation is a competitive equilibrium for some initial allocation of resources.

From one perspective, the message of this theorem is discouraging. It tells us that competitive allocations can be extremely inequitable. If the initial distribution of endowments heavily favours certain individuals, the equilibrium will favour them as well.

From another perspective, however, the second welfare theorem carries a positive message. It tells us that in principle, societies can use competitive markets to achieve *both* efficiency *and* equity. If a competitive allocation is inequitable, the problem lies not with the market institutions, but with the initial distribution of resources. If society can redistribute those resources appropriately, then competitive markets will deliver the most equitable Pareto efficient allocation. A society need not sacrifice efficiency—for example, by regulating a market—for the sake of equity. This second interpretation requires many qualifications, and its practical relevance is controversial. We'll explain why later in this section.

To see why the second welfare theorem holds, let's focus on exchange economies. Figure 16.20 reproduces the Edgeworth box presented earlier in this chapter (see Figure 16.13, page 591). Pick any point on the curve—say point J. For which initial allocations of resources is point J a competitive equilibrium? Suppose we give point J to Humphrey and

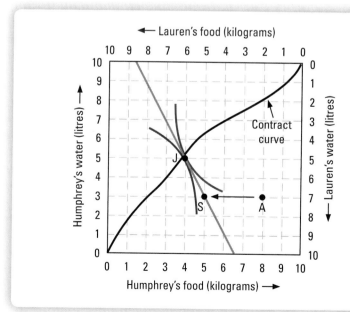

Figure 16.20

The Second Welfare Theorem. Suppose Humphrey and Lauren start out with point J as their endowments. Since point J is efficient, their indifference curves lie tangent to the same straight line at that point. At the right prices, this line is also their budget line. With this budget line, both consumers choose point J. Since neither consumer supplies or demands anything, supply matches demand, creating a competitive equilibrium. Using any other endowments on the green line, like S, the same prices would lead to the same competitive equilibrium.

Lauren as their initial endowments. We know that their indifference curves will be tangent to the same straight line (shown in green) at point J. With the right prices for food and water, this straight line will also be their budget line, and both will choose point J. Since neither consumer will supply or demand anything, supply will match demand, creating a competitive equilibrium.

Are there other initial allocations of resources for which point J is a competitive equilibrium? Indeed there are. In fact, any point on the straight green line will do. Take point S. At the same prices for food and water as before, the budget line will be unchanged, so both consumers will still pick point J. To reach point J from point S, Humphrey will supply food and demand water, while Lauren will demand food and supply water. Supply will match demand in both markets, so again we will have a competitive equilibrium.

Now let's suppose the two consumers start out with point A as their endowments. To reach point J, we can replace point A with any endowment on the straight green line, and then allow competitive markets to operate. For example, we can take three kilograms of food from Humphrey and give it to Lauren, in which case their endowments will be point S. In the competitive equilibrium that follows, Humphrey and Lauren will trade to point J.

The redistribution of food that moves Humphrey and Lauren from point A to point S is called a **lump-sum transfer**. All lump-sum transfers have the property that the amount of resources received or surrendered by each consumer is fixed; it doesn't depend on the consumer's choices. Unlike other taxes and transfers, lump-sum transfers don't compromise efficiency because they don't distort choices.

With a **lump-sum transfer,** the amount of resources received or surrendered by each consumer is fixed; it doesn't depend on the consumer's choices.

The Conflict between Equity and Efficiency

The second welfare theorem suggests that societies can use competitive markets and lump-sum transfers to achieve both efficiency and equity: we achieve an equitable outcome by transferring resources from consumers with substantial endowments to consumers with modest endowments; we achieve an efficient outcome by allowing competitive markets to operate. This policy prescription assumes, however, that we can observe consumers' endowments so that we know who to tax and who to subsidize. Is this assumption reasonable?

Since wealth is observable, we could try to achieve an equitable outcome by redistributing resources from the rich to the poor. But wealth isn't an endowment; it depends on a variety of choices involving education, employment, and saving. Therefore, transfers based on wealth aren't lump-sum transfers. While they may be equitable, they distort choices and sacrifice efficiency by reducing consumers' incentives to study, work, and save. The same comments apply to redistribution based on income.

It's difficult to imagine a measure of need that doesn't depend on *any* choice. (Can you come up with one?) As a practical matter, then, we can't use lump-sum transfers to accomplish our distributional objectives. Instead, we need to link such transfers to criteria that reflect choices. Doing so brings equity and efficiency into direct conflict, however. Contrary to the second welfare theorem, we may have to put up with a less efficient outcome to achieve a more equitable one.

Figure 16.21 illustrates the conflict between equity and efficiency in a simple exchange economy consisting of two consumers (Humphrey and Lauren) and two goods (food and water). The endowments (point A in the figure) heavily favour Humphrey, who has all the water and more than half the food. A policy of laissez-faire would lead to a competitive equilibrium at point B. When food sells for $1 per kilogram and water sells

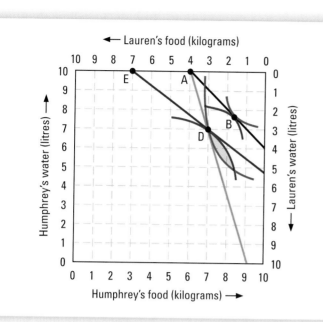

Figure 16.21

Equity versus Efficiency. Humphrey and Lauren start out at point A. Without taxes, food costs $1 per kilogram. and water costs $1 per litre; point B is the equilibrium. With a 75 percent tax on food (which takes 3 out of every 4 units of food purchased) to fund a distribution to Lauren, food costs $0.75 per kilogram and water costs $1 per litre. Humphrey's budget line, in green, passes through points A and D; he chooses D. Lauren's budget line, in brown, passes through points E and D; she too chooses D, so this is an equilibrium. Though the tax-transfer program makes Lauren better off, it is inefficient.

for $1 per litre, the slope of the budget line (shown in black) is −1. At point B, Humphrey's indifference curve (shown in red) lies tangent to the budget line, as does Lauren's (shown in blue). This equilibrium outcome is efficient, but is arguably unfair to Lauren.

What can the government do to promote a more equitable outcome? Here we'll assume that it's impossible to redistribute the endowments. As in the real world, however, the government can tax transactions and transfer revenues to Lauren.

In equilibrium, Humphrey buys food from Lauren. Therefore, the government can try to finance distributions to Lauren by taxing Humphrey's food purchases. Let's see what happens when the government imposes a 75 percent tax on food. For each kilogram of food Humphrey purchases, the government takes 0.75 kilogram, leaving him with 0.25 kilogram. It then gives this food to Lauren.

Figure 16.21 illustrates the new equilibrium. As we've drawn the figure, the equilibrium price of water remains unchanged at $1 per litre, while the equilibrium price of food falls to $0.75. Humphrey and Lauren end up at point D, rather than at point B.

Why do these new prices lead to an equilibrium allocation at point D? Let's start with Humphrey. Since he has to buy four kilograms of food in order to keep one kilogram, in effect he pays $3 (4 × $0.75) for each kilogram of food. The slope of the solid green budget line, −3, equals the after-tax price ratio that Humphrey faces ($3 per kilogram of food, divided by $1 per litre of water), times negative one. As drawn, D is Humphrey's favourite point on the solid green line. The government collects three kilograms of food in tax revenue at that point.

Now consider Lauren. She receives three kilograms of food from the government as part of her endowment. The handout shifts her endowment point from point A to E. Since Lauren *sells* food to Humphrey, she doesn't pay the sales tax. As far as she's concerned, the price of food is $0.75 per kilogram. The slope of her budget line, shown in brown, is −0.75. Like Humphrey, Lauren chooses point D in the figure, creating an equilibrium. She sells four kilograms of food to Humphrey, and buys three litres of water from him.

Notice that point D is to the southwest of both the blue and red indifference curves that run through point B. Therefore, the tax-transfer policy illustrated in Figure 16.21

makes Lauren better off and Humphrey worse off. Arguably, it produces a more equitable outcome than laissez-faire. However, it's inefficient. At point D, Humphrey and Lauren's indifference curves lie tangent to their budget lines, which have different slopes. As a result, the curves cross. Any point in the yellow-shaded area would make both of them better off. But without lump-sum transfers, there is no way to achieve one of those allocations. Thus, in making the outcome more equitable, the government sacrifices a degree of efficiency.

Application 16.4

Optimal Personal Income Taxation

The personal income tax is the Canadian government's most important source of funds. In 2008, it raised $168 billion—nearly two thirds of total federal revenue, and just over 10 percent of the Canadian gross domestic product (a common measure of total national income).

In addition to providing revenue, the personal income tax also serves the government's distributional objectives. The system is *progressive*, in the sense that the tax rate applied to the last dollar of income rises with the total amount of income received.[23] As a result, affluent people pay more than others, both in absolute terms and as a fraction of their incomes.

Figure 16.22(a) shows the tax rates applicable to income individuals received in 2008. The horizontal axis shows taxable income, equal to total income less various deductions and exemptions. The vertical axis shows the tax rate applied to the last dollar received, also known as the *marginal tax rate*. Because of deductions and exemptions, the lowest-income households pay no tax. A 15-percent tax rate applies to the first dollar of taxable income. This rate rises in several steps, reaching a peak of 29 percent for households with incomes exceeding $123,184.

Some would argue that in the interest of equity, the government should increase the top marginal tax rate and reduce rates on lower incomes. That policy would have the

"Found meat is income."

effect of redistributing resources from affluent households to the poor and middle class. Others argue that high tax rates discourage people from earning money. In their view, redistribution through the tax system comes at a high cost in terms of economic inefficiency.

At different times, lawmakers have made very different choices concerning the trade-off between equity and efficiency. As Figure 16.22(b) shows, the top marginal tax rate at the federal and provincial level has varied considerably from 1920 (personal and sales taxes were first introduced in Canada in 1917 during the first world war) through 2000.[24] The figure gives the top combined rate and the rate for the top 0.01 percent of taxpayers which differed until 1972. The combined federal and provincial marginal tax rate in 2000 was approximately 48 percent and is relatively low by historical standards, particularly when compared with the historic peak of 94 percent, reached during World War II.

How should we resolve the trade-off between equity and efficiency, and what does the answer to that question imply for the top marginal tax rate? Many economists have tried to answer these questions by studying simple general equilibrium models that attempt to capture the way income taxation affects the allocation of resources. To evaluate and compare allocations, they apply a social welfare function.

---

[23]Technically, this concept is called *marginal rate progressivity*. In contrast, *average rate progressivity* means that the ratio of total taxes to total income rises as the taxpayer's income increases.

[24]Emmanuel Saez and Michael Veall, "The Evolution of High Incomes in Canada, 1920–2000," *NBER Working Paper*, no. 9607, 2003

Using this approach, economist Emmanuel Saez has developed a general formula for the optimal value of the top tax rate.[25] For the empirically relevant cases, this formula simplifies to the following:

$$T = \frac{1}{1 + 2E_T/(1 - A)}$$

where T is the top marginal tax rate and E_T is the elasticity of taxable income with respect to $1 - T$ (averaged over the top tax bracket).[26] The remaining term, A, reflects the degree of importance placed on equity. It represents the social value of $1 given as a lump sum to the average person in the top tax bracket, divided by the social value of the same dollar given as a lump sum to the average person in the entire population. Presumably, most people would agree that A is no greater than one. When more importance is attached to equity, A is smaller.

According to Saez's formula, larger values of either E_T or A justify lower tax rates for high income individuals. The effect of E_T on the optimal tax rate reflects concerns for efficiency: when that elasticity is larger, the tax distorts taxpayers' decisions to a greater degree, which makes low tax rates more desirable. The effect of A on the optimal tax rate reflects concerns for equity: when the importance attached to low-income individuals is greater, A is smaller, which makes higher tax rates more desirable.

Many economists have tried to measure E_T empirically, with most estimates falling between 0.25 and 2.0. While reasonable people may disagree about the appropriate value of A, many would argue that it should be close to zero. Whatever values we use, Saez's formula identifies the optimal value of the top tax rate. To illustrate, let's use $A = 0$, meaning that we attach no social value to extra money received by the wealthiest individuals. In that case, you might think that the best top tax rate would be 100 percent. But such a high rate would cause the wealthy to earn much less income, reducing government revenue, and leaving the poor worse off. In fact, the formula tells us that the top tax rate should be 67 percent if $E_T = 0.25$, 50 percent if $E_T = 0.5$, 33 percent if $E_T = 1$, and 20 percent if $E_T = 2$. Nailing down the value of this elasticity would help policymakers to design the best possible system of personal income taxation.

Figure 16.22

The Federal Personal Income Tax. Figure (a) shows the marginal tax rates on different levels of taxable income in 2005. Figure (b) shows how the marginal tax rate on the highest incomes has changed over time.

(a) Federal marginal tax rates, 2008

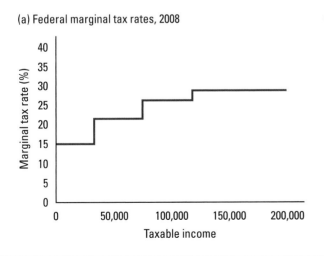

(b) Top marginal tax rate, federal and provincial including surtaxes, 1920–2000

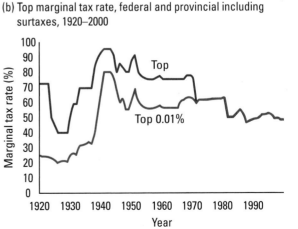

[25]Emmanuel Saez, "Using Elasticities to Derive Optimal Income Tax Rates," *Review of Economic Studies* 68, January 2001, pp. 205–229.

[26]In other words, E_T is the percentage change in taxable income that results from a one percent change in the fraction of income that the taxpayer keeps.

1. **The nature of general equilibrium (LO1)**

   a. Interdependence between markets is important for two reasons. First, factors that affect supply and demand in one market can have significant ripple effects in other markets. Second, interdependence produces feedback.

   b. To be completely general, equilibrium analysis would need to encompass every market in the world economy. For reasons of practicality, economists usually focus on markets that are clearly linked, ignoring others.

2. **Positive analysis of general equilibrium (LO2)**

   a. In a market with just two goods, general equilibrium corresponds to a point of intersection between two market-clearing curves.

   b. The general equilibrium effects of a tax may differ considerably from the partial equilibrium effects. The effect of a sales tax on the price of a good becomes larger when we account for feedback from the market for a complement, and smaller when we account for feedback from the market for a substitute.

3. **Normative criteria for evaluating economic performance (LO3)**

   a. Economists evaluate economic performance on the basis of efficiency and equity.

   b. The economy is wasteful (or inefficient) if it's possible to reallocate resources in a way that makes at least one consumer better off without hurting someone else. It is Pareto efficient if there is no waste.

   c. Pareto efficient allocations are associated with utility levels that lie on the utility possibility frontier.

   d. Some notions of equity are process-oriented—for example, the idea that markets are fair because they reward people for effort and ingenuity.

   e. Outcome-oriented notions of equity are based on the distribution of either well-being or consumption and include utilitarianism, Rawlsianism, and egalitarianism. The distribution of well-being may, however, be impossible to measure.

   f. A social welfare function can capture concerns about efficiency, as well as outcome-oriented notions of equity.

4. **General equilibrium and efficient exchange (LO4)**

   a. To illustrate allocations and competitive equilibrium in an exchange economy, economists often use an Edgeworth box.

   b. The first welfare theorem tells us that competitive general equilibria are Pareto efficient.

   c. To identify efficient allocations of consumption goods in an Edgeworth box, we look for points where two consumers' indifference curves touch but do not cross.

At efficient interior points, the two curves lie tangent to the same straight line, implying that the two consumers have the same marginal rate of substitution. This result is known as the exchange efficiency condition.

   d. Competitive equilibria satisfy the exchange efficiency condition because consumers choose a point at which their marginal rate of substitution equals the same price ratio.

   e. When an allocation is inefficient, consumers can mutually benefit from further trade. When an allocation is efficient, no further trade is mutually beneficial.

   f. In an Edgeworth box, each point on the contract curve corresponds to a point on the utility possibility frontier. The contract curve includes both equal and highly unequal allocations.

5. **General equilibrium and efficient production (LO4)**

   a. To identify efficient allocations of inputs in an Edgeworth box, we look for points where the isoquants for two firms touch but do not cross. At efficient interior points, the two curves lie tangent to the same straight line, implying that the two firms have the same marginal rate of technical substitution. This result is known as the *input efficiency condition*.

   b. In an Edgeworth box, each point on the production contract curve corresponds to a point on the production possibility frontier.

   c. To identify efficient levels of production in a one-consumer economy, we look for a point where the PPF and an indifference curve touch but do not cross. At efficient interior points, the two curves lie tangent to the same straight line, implying that the firm's marginal rate of transformation equals the consumer's marginal rate of substitution. This result, which also holds with more than one consumer, is known as the *output efficiency condition*.

   d. The first welfare theorem holds in production economies. Competitive equilibria satisfy the input efficiency condition because every firm chooses a point at which its marginal rate of substitution equals the same input price ratio. Competitive equilibria also satisfy the output efficiency condition because firms and consumers face the same prices. Consumers each choose a bundle for which their marginal rate of substitution equals the price ratio for the goods in question. Firms choose production levels at which the marginal rate of transformation equals the same price ratio.

   e. Market failures may prevent free markets from operating efficiently. Also, competitive equilibrium allocations may be extremely inequitable across consumers. Either consideration may justify government intervention in markets. However, even in cases where improvements are possible, governments may introduce new inefficiencies.

6. **Equity and redistribution (LO5)**

   a. The second welfare theorem implies that, in principle, societies can use competitive markets to achieve both efficiency and equity. Doing so requires lump-sum transfers to improve the initial allocation of consumption goods.

   b. In practice, governments cannot achieve their distributional goals through lump-sum transfers. Instead, taxes and transfers are linked to choices, which creates a trade-off between equity and efficiency.

ADDITIONAL EXERCISES

Exercise 16.1: Suppose that the demand for pie doesn't depend on the price of cake, and that the demand for cake doesn't depend on the price of pie. An increase in the price of pie, however, shifts the supply curve for cake downward, while an increase in the price of cake shifts the supply curve for pie downward (because bakers spend more time making the more profitable product). Assume that demand curves slope downward and supply curves slope upward. Using graphs, show how to construct the market-clearing curves for pie and cake. Do they slope upward or downward? Again using graphs, illustrate the effects of a sales tax on cake. Does the cake price change more in general equilibrium or partial equilibrium? (LO1, 2)

Exercise 16.2: Should society have economic goals other than equity and efficiency, as those terms are used in the text? If so, what should they be? Explain your reasoning. (LO3)

Exercise 16.3: Humphrey and Lauren are splitting 10 litres of soda and six kilograms of popcorn. Let's represent Humphrey's preferences with the utility function $U_H = 3S_H + P_H$ and Lauren's preferences with $U_L = 2S_L + 4P_L$, where S_H and S_L indicate their soda consumption, while P_H and P_L indicate their popcorn consumption. Consider the social welfare function $W(U_H, U_L) = U_H + U_L$. According to this social welfare function, which of the following two allocations is better: (1) $S_H = 1$, $S_L = 9$, $P_H = 2$, and $P_L = 4$, or (2) $S_H = 5$, $S_L = 5$, $P_H = 3$, and $P_L = 3$? Which allocation does each consumer prefer? Considering all possible allocations, which is the most socially desirable? (Hint: How is social welfare affected by shifting a litre of soda between Humphrey and Lauren? What about a kilogram of popcorn?) (LO2, 3)

Exercise 16.4: In Section 5.4 we learned about price-consumption curves. Add Humphrey and Lauren's price consumption curves to the Edgeworth Box in Figure 16.10 (page 586). Explain why the competitive equilibrium corresponds to the point at which the price-consumption curves intersect. (LO3)

Exercise 16.5: In Figure 16.10 (page 586), the competitive equilibrium must lie either to the northwest or southeast of the endowment point A, regardless of the consumers' preferences. Explain why. (LO3)

Exercise 16.6: Suppose Humphrey starts out with four kilograms of food and seven litres of water, while Lauren starts out with eight kilograms of food and five litres of water. Draw an Edgeworth box that shows all possible allocations of these goods, and plot the endowment points. Now suppose that both Lauren and Humphrey's preferences correspond to the utility function $U(F,W) = \min\{F, W\}$ (where F refers to kilograms of food and W refers to litres of water). This is a case of perfect complements. Add Humphrey and Lauren's indifference curves to the Edgeworth box. Then draw the contract curve. To which points on the contract curve is each consumer willing to trade? Suppose Humphrey starts out with six kilograms of food instead of four kilograms. How does the picture change? What does the contract curve look like? (LO4)

Exercise 16.7: For the exchange economy considered in Exercise 16.6, illustrate a competitive equilibrium by adding a budget line to your diagram. Does only one equilibrium exist or are there many? What can you say about general equilibrium prices and the consumption bundles chosen at those prices? (LO4)

Exercise 16.8: Repeat exercise 16.6, but assume that Humphrey's preferences correspond to the utility function $U(F,W) = 2F + W$, while Lauren's preferences correspond to the utility function $U(F,W) = F + 2W$. This is a case of perfect substitutes. (LO4)

Exercise 16.9: Repeat exercise 16.7, but assume that Humphrey and Lauren have the preferences described in exercise 16.8. (LO4)

Exercise 16.10: In an exchange economy with two consumers and two goods, is it possible for one of the markets to clear but not the other? Explain your answer graphically using an Edgeworth box. (LO4)

Exercise 16.11: Figure 16.17 (page 598) shows why, in an economy with a single consumer, output efficiency requires the marginal rates of substitution and transformation to be identical. How might you modify this figure to make the same point concerning an economy with many consumers? (LO4)

Exercise 16.12: Suppose an economy produces two goods, food and housing, from two inputs, capital and labour. Explain why in an otherwise competitive economy, a tax on food will violate the output efficiency condition. Illustrate using a graph like Figure 16.17 (page 598). (LO4)

Exercise 16.13: For each of the following hypothetical policies, indicate which of the three efficiency conditions (exchange, input, and output) are violated, if any. (a) The government bans orange juice. (b) The government assigns a house or apartment to each family and prohibits swapping. (c) The government subsidizes the use of capital for oil exploration. (LO4)

Exercise 16.14: If the government wanted to reach point J in Figure 16.20 (page 605), it could simply mandate this allocation through centralized control of resources. Why might it be better to set up competitive markets and allow trading? (Hint: What if the government is not completely certain of Humphrey and Lauren's preferences?) (LO5)

Exercise 16.15: After reading Section 16.6, a student proposes a system of taxes and transfers based on the intelligence quotient (IQ). She argues that intelligence is not chosen, and that it's closely related to economic success. She concludes that redistributing resources from people with high IQs to people with low IQs will promote equity without compromising efficiency. What do you think of this proposal? Why? (LO5)

Market Failures

We've seen in Part IIIA that perfectly competitive markets allocate resources efficiently. In the next five chapters we'll explain why many real-world markets fail to achieve this ideal. Chapters 17–19 examine markets in which one or more participants (usually a seller) has some control over the market price of a good. Chapter 17 considers markets in which there is a single seller, known as a monopolist. We'll see that a monopolist will usually charge a price above its marginal cost, creating a deadweight loss. Chapter 18 examines the possibility that a monopolist might profit by charging different prices to different buyers, or for different units of the same good. Chapter 19 considers markets in which a small number of sellers, known as oligopolists, engage in limited competition. In Chapter 20, we turn our attention to market failures arising from consumption or production decisions that have direct effects (other than through market transactions) on the well-being of other consumers or on the profits of other firms. Finally, in Chapter 21 (available online), we examine situations in which some market participants have better information than others concerning the goods they trade.

17

Monopoly

LEARNING OBJECTIVES

After reading this chapter, students should be able to

LO1 Define monopoly and oligopoly markets and discuss the factors that lead to monopoly markets.

LO2 Identify a monopolist's profit-maximizing price and sales quantity and determine the effect of monopoly pricing on consumer and aggregate surpluses.

LO3 Discuss how the behaviour of a monopolist differs from the behaviour of firms in a perfectly competitive market.

LO4 Define monopsony and analyze a monopsonist's profit-maximizing behaviour.

LO5 Describe the goals and difficulties involved in regulating monopolists.

LO6 Understand how monopolists set prices and quantities when they produce several related products.

U.S. Attorney General Janet Reno announcing the filing of an antitrust suit against Microsoft Corporation for monopolization.

On May 18, 1998, the U.S. Department of Justice, with the attorneys general of 20 states and the District of Columbia, filed an antitrust suit against the Microsoft Corporation, claiming it was a monopolist in the market for PC operating systems. For the next two and a half years, the case was front-page news in countries around the world. Was Microsoft really a monopolist? Had it used illegal tactics to strengthen and extend its market position? Lawyers on both sides of the case turned to economists to answer these questions.

Although the Competition Bureau in Canada did not follow its United States counterpart, in 2003 the European Commission reached a preliminary decision in a suit brought against Microsoft that also claimed abuse of its dominant position among operating systems. In March of 2004 the Commission levied the largest fine, almost €500 million, ever issued by the European Union. The Commission ordered Microsoft to offer a version of Windows® without its Windows Media Player® and to release information to competing networking firms so their software could work with the Windows operating system.

Why would government officials be concerned about the existence of a monopoly? In this chapter we'll address this and other questions about monopoly markets. How, for example, does the market outcome under monopoly differ from the market outcome under perfect competition? How can the government tell if a group of firms is colluding and acting just like a monopolist instead of competing vigorously? What can government do to improve on the outcomes of monopoly?

To answer these questions, we'll cover eight topics:

1. *Market power*. A firm enjoys market power when it can profitably charge a price that is above its marginal cost. We'll identify two kinds of markets with market power—monopoly and oligopoly markets—and explain why some markets end up as monopoly markets. (We'll discuss oligopoly markets in detail in Chapter 19.)

2. *Monopoly pricing*. We'll explain how a monopolist can find the price that maximizes profit and examine factors that determine by how much that price exceeds marginal cost.

3. *Welfare effects of monopoly pricing*. By raising the price above marginal cost, a monopolist reduces consumers' well-being. We'll see that such pricing also reduces aggregate surplus, the sum of consumer surplus and profit.

4. *Distinguishing monopoly from perfect competition*. We'll discuss the ways in which a monopolist's behaviour differs from that of firms in perfectly competitive markets. These differences provide ways of testing whether a group of firms is behaving like price takers or is instead colluding, acting jointly as a monopolist.

5. *Nonprice effects of monopoly*. Monopolists do much more than just set prices. They choose their products' quality, advertise, and engage in research and development. We'll see how a monopolist makes these choices and study some of their welfare consequences.

6. *Monopsony*. Just as a firm can exercise market power selling its output, it can exert market power buying its inputs. We'll study the market outcome and welfare consequences when a firm is the sole buyer of an input. The analysis has much in common with the analysis of monopoly.

7. *Regulation of monopolies*. To prevent the welfare loss that accompanies monopoly pricing, governments sometimes regulate the price a monopolist can charge. We'll discuss what price the government should set in principle, as well as some of the difficulties inherent in price regulation.

*8. *Multiproduct monopoly*. Most firms sell more than one product. We'll study how selling more than one product alters a monopolist's profit-maximizing price.

17.1 MARKET POWER

In Part IIIA we studied perfectly competitive markets, in which there are many buyers and sellers of a product. In such markets, any attempt by a firm to charge more than the market price results in the loss of all its sales. As a result, each firm takes the market price as given and produces to the point at which the market price equals its marginal cost.

In many situations, however, competition is not intense. A firm may produce a product that only a few other producers sell, or it may be the only seller of a product for which there are few or no close substitutes. In these circumstances, firms can increase their profit by charging a price that is above marginal cost. When a firm can profitably charge a price that is above its marginal cost, we say that it has **market power**.[1]

A firm has **market power** when it can profitably charge a price that is above its marginal cost.

Most firms have some degree of market power. Some firms' market power is only slight. In consumers' eyes, their competitors' products may be very close substitutes for the firm's product, if not perfect substitutes. In other cases, a firm may have a lot of market power. A company that faces no competitors at all can often charge a price that is substantially above marginal cost.

A **monopoly market** is a market with a single seller, who is called a **monopolist**.

An **oligopoly market** is a market with a few (but not many) sellers, who are called **oligopolists**.

Significant market power exists in two types of markets. A market with only one seller is called a **monopoly market**, and the single seller in that market is called a **monopolist**. A market with a few (but not many) sellers is called an **oligopoly market**. Firms in those markets are known as **oligopolists**. Because a monopolist's behaviour can be studied without concern for the behaviour of other firms, monopoly is conceptually simpler than oligopoly. Analyzing the interactions among firms in oligopoly markets requires the use of game theory (covered in Chapter 12). We'll study monopoly markets in this chapter and oligopoly markets in Chapter 19.

In practice, determining what is and is not a monopoly market can be trickier than these simple definitions might suggest. The reason is that to do so we need to specify what is the relevant market. When we discussed competitive markets, the definition of a market was simple: each market involved the purchase and sale of a single homogeneous product. In situations with market power, however, we often must think of a single market as containing a number of different but closely related products. For example, Coke and Pepsi are distinct products. Many consumers prefer one of those drinks to the other. Nonetheless, because they are close substitutes, each firm's profit-maximizing price depends on what its rival does. As a result, thinking about a "Coke" market wouldn't make much sense. Rather, an economist might speak of the "market for cola drinks" (or possibly the broader "pop market," or maybe even the "nonalcoholic liquid beverage market") and analyze directly the interactions among the producers in that market.

In situations with market power, economists define a market to include products that are close substitutes for one another and to exclude more distant substitutes. In practice, though, drawing a line between those products that are inside and outside of a market can be difficult. How strong must substitution between a product and other products that are in the market be to include the first product in the market? If we define the market too narrowly, we may inadvertently identify a firm as a monopolist when it actually faces significant competition. If instead we define the market too broadly, a firm that faces no significant competition may appear to have many rivals. Thus, defining the market properly requires care in determining which substitutes are so distant that we can ignore their competitive effects.

"Of course, you could try another bank, if there were any other banks."

---

[1] A word of warning: The fact that a firm has market power does not mean that government intervention is likely to improve the market outcome. Indeed, some economists would not use the term *market power* to describe a situation in which the price equals the firm's average cost, even if it exceeds marginal cost, because any lower price would be unsustainable (see Section 17.7). Here, we'll stick to our broader definition of the term, but bear in mind this caveat.

Application 17.1

Monopoly and Oligopoly Markets for Ready-Mix Concrete

Ready-mix concrete is used for sidewalks, highways, and building foundations. It's made by mixing cement, sand, gravel, and water in one of those trucks with a spinning barrel on top. Unfortunately, once mixed, the concrete must be used within an hour. The material's short life makes markets for ready-mix concrete very local. In small towns and cities, there is often only a single ready-mix concrete producer; moreover, other producers are often too far away to supply the product. Burnco Rock Products Ltd., for example, is the only ready-mix concrete producer in Medicine Hat, Alberta, a city of about 61,000 people. The nearest competitors are almost two hours away. In the rocky mountain city of Jasper, a town of less than 5000, Jasper Concrete Ltd. is the only ready-mix concrete producer. The nearest competitor is in Hinton about an hour away. Small, local markets such as these are monopoly markets.

In other places, only a few producers can supply concrete; these are oligopoly markets. Lethbridge, Alberta, a city of 85,000, has two ready-mix concrete firms. The cities of Red Deer and Lacombe, Alberta, have two firms serving the two cities. Because of the cities' proximity, each firm can sell to consumers in the other city, so it makes sense to think of a single market for concrete that includes both cities.

How Do Firms Become Monopolists?

Firms get to be monopolists in various ways. Sometimes the government grants a monopoly position to a firm. Cable TV companies, for example, usually hold the sole right to serve a local community.[2] (We'll discuss the reason for this kind of arrangement later in the chapter.) And the Canadian government awards patents to firms that have made new discoveries; these prevent competitors from selling the same good for 20 years. The company Allergan, for example, holds a patent on its small-muscle relaxant Botox, which is used to temporarily reduce facial wrinkles. Botox is the *only* drug available for this purpose; the closest substitutes are surgical procedures, facial creams, and being happy with one's appearance.

At other times, a firm achieves a monopoly position, not through a government award but because no other firm finds the market profitable. When a potential entrant foresees a profit that is

---

[2]They may, nevertheless, face significant competition from satellite television providers, in which case they would not properly be considered monopolists. In some locations, however, reception of satellite signals is poor, so the cable TV firm is effectively the sole provider of television signals.

less than the cost of entry into the market, a firm can become a monopolist by default. In extreme cases, economies of scale (see Section 8.8) imply that it is impossible for more than one firm to make a positive profit.

Figure 17.1 shows such a case, that of a firm selling concrete in a small rural town. (Note that average costs decrease as output rises, meaning that this firm enjoys economies of scale—see Section 8.8.) The figure shows both the market demand curve, labelled D, and another curve that represents half the market demand at each price, labelled D_{half}. The curve D_{half} shows how much each individual firm would sell if two firms split the market demand at a given price P. In general, a monopolist can make a positive profit if its average cost curve lies below the market demand curve at some quantity. In the figure, for example, curve D shows that when the price is $60 per cubic metre, the monopolist will sell 4000 cubic metres of concrete. Since its average cost would then be only $50 per cubic metre, a monopolist in this market can make a profit.

Suppose, however, that there are two firms in this market who split demand equally when they charge the same price. Notice that the AC curve lies entirely above the D_{half} curve. When each firm captures only half the market demand, a firm's average cost is always higher than the price. If the price is $60 per cubic metre, for example, the curve D_{half} shows that each firm sells only 2000 cubic metres of concrete. At that quantity, the firm's average cost is $70 per cubic metre—higher than the price of $60. Because the same is true at *every* price, the two firms can't help but lose money in this market. In fact, even if the firms don't split demand equally, at least one firm must get no more than half the market demand at any price. Two firms therefore can't both be profitable in this market, a fact that will discourage a second firm from entering.

In some cases, as in Figure 17.1, economies of scale alone imply that only one firm will enter the market. More generally, both economies of scale and the nature of competition will determine how many firms enter a market, and thus whether the market ends up an oligopoly or a monopoly. We'll study the entry process in more detail in Chapter 19.

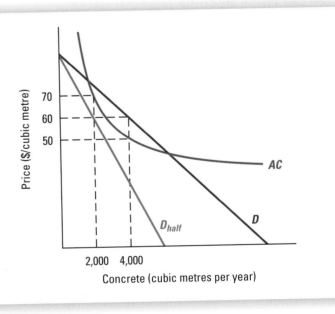

Figure 17.1
Scale Economies and Monopoly. The figure shows the demand and cost conditions for the ready-mix concrete market in a small rural town. A monopolist can make a profit because the AC curve lies below the demand curve D at some quantities. But because the AC curve lies everywhere above the curve D_{half} (representing half the market demand at each price), there is no price at which two firms can make positive profits in this market.

Firms can become monopolists or near monopolists in still other ways. Sometimes a firm can gain a monopoly position simply because it is the first to recognize an opportunity to produce a new product, or the first to produce it successfully. Apple, for example, introduced its tremendously successful iPod in 2001, grabbing the lion's share (estimated at close to 90 percent) of the portable music hard-drive business by being the first to design and produce a portable hard-drive music player with an easy-to-use and visually appealing user interface. Similarly, a firm can become a monopolist by discovering how to produce a product so cheaply that its price is below other firms' costs.

Monopolies that arise because a firm has discovered something first tend to erode over time, as other firms attempt to copy the idea. To hold on to a monopoly, the monopolist must often either continue to innovate or find a way to prevent others from copying the idea. Apple has held on to its dominant market share in part by continually improving its product. But it also continues to benefit from the advantage of being first: once iPod users have bought a lot of music from the iTunes Store, they may be reluctant to switch to other products that cannot play that music.

Sometimes a firm becomes a monopolist simply by owning all of an essential input. In the 1980s the South African diamond producer De Beers controlled more than 80 percent of the world's diamond production, which gave it a near-monopoly position in the world diamond market. That market share has since eroded to less than 60 percent, however, due to major diamond discoveries in Canada and Russia.

17.2 MONOPOLY PRICING

A monopolist will choose the price that maximizes its profit, given the demand for its product. In Sections 9.1 and 9.2 we discussed in general terms how a firm should set its price, or equivalently, determine the quantity to sell. We saw that whenever the firm's profit-maximizing sales quantity is positive, marginal revenue equals marginal cost at that quantity. This insight leads to a simple two-step procedure for finding a firm's profit-maximizing sales quantity. Here we'll apply that procedure to the case of a monopolist.

Marginal Revenue for a Monopolist

To begin, let's discuss the monopolist's marginal revenue. Recall from Section 9.2 that a firm's marginal revenue captures the additional revenue it gets from the marginal units it sells (the smallest possible increment ΔQ in its sales quantity), measured on a per unit basis. So if the firm is selling Q units of a product, its marginal revenue is $MR = \Delta R/\Delta Q$, where ΔR is the change in total revenue from selling the ΔQ marginal units.

In Section 9.2 we saw that for a firm selling Q units this change in revenue, ΔR, is composed of two effects, which are illustrated in Figure 17.2. The extra ΔQ sales at price $P(Q)$ contribute additional revenue of $P(Q) \times \Delta Q$, equal to the area of the green-shaded rectangle in the figure. This is the *output expansion effect*. If it were the *only* effect, marginal revenue would simply equal $\Delta R/\Delta Q = [P(Q) \times \Delta Q]/\Delta Q = P(Q)$, the price the firm receives for each of these marginal units.

The second effect, the *price reduction effect*, reduces marginal revenue below this level. To sell the ΔQ marginal units, the firm must reduce its price from $P(Q - \Delta Q)$ to $P(Q)$.

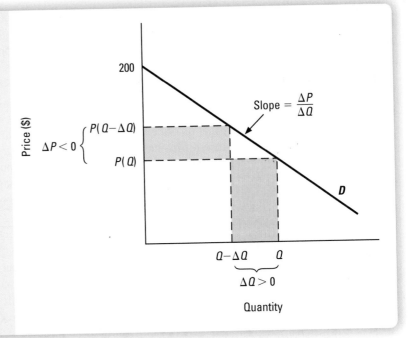

Figure 17.2

The Relationship between Marginal Revenue and Price. When a monopolist expands its sales from $Q - \Delta Q$ to Q, it earns $P(Q) \times \Delta Q$ in revenue on the extra units it sells, equal to the area of the green-shaded rectangle. It also suffers a loss in revenue on the $Q - \Delta Q$ inframarginal units because it must lower its price by the amount $\Delta P = P(Q) - P(Q - \Delta Q)$ to sell the extra units. This revenue loss equals the area of the yellow-shaded rectangle. The change in revenue equals the sum of these output expansion and price reduction effects. The price reduction effect makes the firm's marginal revenue less than the price $P(Q)$.

The resulting price change is $\Delta P = [P(Q) - P(Q - \Delta Q)]$ (a negative number) whose magnitude equals the height of the yellow rectangle in Figure 17.2. Since the firm loses ΔP on each of the $Q - \Delta Q$ inframarginal units, the price reduction effect makes revenue fall by $\Delta P \times (Q - \Delta Q)$, which is represented by the area of the yellow-shaded rectangle in the figure. (Recall from Section 9.2 that the inframarginal units are the $Q - \Delta Q$ units other than the marginal ones.)

The overall change in revenue equals the sum of the output expansion and price reduction effects: $\Delta R = [P(Q) \times \Delta Q] + [\Delta P \times (Q - \Delta Q)]$.[3] Using this expression for ΔR, we can write marginal revenue as

$$MR = \frac{\Delta R}{\Delta Q} = \frac{[P(Q) \times \Delta Q] + [\Delta P \times (Q - \Delta Q)]}{\Delta Q}$$

$$= P(Q) + \left(\frac{\Delta P}{\Delta Q}\right)(Q - \Delta Q)$$

*Optional **Marginal revenue, MR,** can be found using calculus by differentiating the revenue function with respect to output.

$$MR = \frac{dR}{dQ} = \frac{dP(Q)Q}{dQ}$$

$$= P(Q) + \frac{dP(Q)}{dQ}Q$$

Moreover, when the monopolist's output is finely divisible (as we'll assume here), $Q - \Delta Q$ is approximately equal to Q, so marginal revenue can be written simply as

$$MR = P(Q) + \left(\frac{\Delta P}{\Delta Q}\right)Q \qquad (1)$$

---

[3]Another way to derive this change in total revenue from selling the marginal units is to write it as

$$\Delta R = [P(Q) \times Q] - [P(Q - \Delta Q) \times (Q - \Delta Q)]$$
$$= [P(Q) \times \Delta Q] + [P(Q) \times (Q - \Delta Q)] - [P(Q - \Delta Q) \times (Q - \Delta Q)]$$
$$= [P(Q) \times \Delta Q] + [\Delta P \times (Q - \Delta Q)]$$

The second term in formula (1), $(\Delta P/\Delta Q)Q$, captures the price reduction effect. Since $(\Delta P/\Delta Q)$ is a negative number (because the price must be reduced to sell more), this term implies that marginal revenue is less than the price, $P(Q)$, at all positive quantities.[4] However, this difference becomes small as Q approaches zero because, when the firm is not selling many units, little revenue is lost due to the price reduction effect. Indeed, formula (1) implies that marginal revenue *equals* the price at $Q = 0$ (that is, for the firm's very first sale).

WORKED-OUT PROBLEM   17.1

The Problem   Kenora Competition-free Concrete (KCC) is a local monopolist of ready-mix concrete. Its annual demand function is $Q^d = 16{,}000 - 200P$, where P is the price, in dollars, of a cubic metre of concrete and Q is the number of cubic metres sold per year. What is KCC's marginal revenue when it sells 4000 cubic metres of concrete per year? How does KCC's marginal revenue compare to its price when it sells that amount of concrete? Graph KCC's demand and marginal revenue curves.

The Solution   KCC's inverse demand function is $P(Q) = 80 - 0.005Q$ (see Section 9.1 for a discussion of inverse demand functions) so $\Delta P/\Delta Q = -0.005$. Using formula (1) KCC's marginal revenue when it sells Q cubic metres per year is

$$MR = P(Q) + \left(\frac{\Delta P}{\Delta Q}\right)Q = (80 - 0.005Q) + (-0.005)Q$$

$$= 80 - 0.01Q$$

So KCC's marginal revenue when it sells 4000 cubic metres per year is $40 [$= 80 - (0.01)4000$]. That is less than its price at 4000 cubic metres per year, which is $P(4000) = 80 - (0.005)\,4000 = 60. Figure 17.3 shows KCC's demand and marginal revenue curves. Note that the MR curve lies below the demand curve at all positive quantities, and coincides with the demand curve where it hits the vertical axis (and sales are zero).[5]

IN-TEXT EXERCISE 17.1   **Suppose KCC's demand function is $Q^d = 10{,}000 - 100P$. What is KCC's marginal revenue when it sells 4000 cubic metres of concrete per year? How does KCC's marginal revenue compare to its price when it sells that amount of concrete? Graph KCC's demand and marginal revenue curves.**

Formula (1) expresses marginal revenue in terms of the slope of the firm's demand curve, which is one measure of the responsiveness of demand to price changes. In Section 2.4, we saw that the elasticity of demand often provides a more convenient measure

---

[4]For a firm that faces a perfectly horizontal demand curve for its product at the market price, $\Delta P/\Delta Q = 0$. In that case, formula (1) tells us that marginal revenue always equals the price, consistent with our discussion of price-taking firms in Section 9.3.

[5]In general, for a linear inverse demand function of the form $P = A - BQ$, marginal revenue is $MR = (A - BQ) - BQ = A - 2BQ$. Thus, the marginal revenue curve for a linear demand curve is also linear, with the same intercept as the demand curve and twice as steep.

Figure 17.3

KCC's Demand and Marginal Revenue Curves. The marginal revenue curve lies below the demand curve at all positive quantities. It coincides with the demand curve where it hits the vertical axis (and sales are zero).

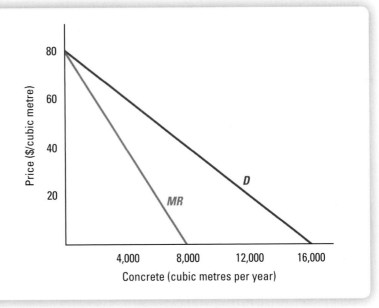

of that responsiveness. To express marginal revenue in terms of the elasticity of demand, $E^d = (\Delta Q/\Delta P)(P/Q)$, we can rewrite formula (1) as

$$MR = P(Q) + \left(\frac{\Delta P}{\Delta Q}\right)\left(\frac{P(Q) \times Q}{P(Q)}\right)$$

$$= P(Q)\left(1 + \frac{\Delta P \times Q}{\Delta Q \times P(Q)}\right)$$

$$= P(Q)\left(1 + \cfrac{1}{\underbrace{\left(\dfrac{\Delta Q}{\Delta P}\right)\left(\dfrac{P(Q)}{Q}\right)}_{=E^d}}\right)$$

Using the definition of the elasticity of demand, E^d, we can therefore write the formula for marginal revenue as

$$MR = P(Q)\left(1 + \frac{1}{E^d}\right) \qquad (2)$$

Since the elasticity of demand E^d is a negative number, formula (2) shows once again that marginal revenue is less than the price. The more elastic is demand, the closer to zero is $(1/E^d)$, and the closer is marginal revenue to the price. Intuitively, if demand is very elastic, the firm does not need to reduce its price much to increase its sales, so the price reduction effect is small.

Monopoly Profit Maximization

When a monopolist maximizes its profit by selling a positive amount, its marginal revenue must equal its marginal cost at that quantity. Why? If marginal revenue exceeded marginal cost, the monopolist would be better off selling a little more, since an additional unit sold would bring more in revenue than it cost to produce. If instead marginal revenue were less than marginal cost, selling a little less would increase its profit.

More generally, we can find a monopolist's profit-maximizing sales quantity by following the two-step procedure outlined in Section 9.2 (page 302), which we recall here.

Finding the Profit-Maximizing Sales Quantity Using Marginal Revenue and Marginal Cost

Step 1: Quantity rule   Identify any positive sales quantities at which $MR = MC$. If more than one positive sales quantity satisfies $MR = MC$, determine which one is best (which produces the highest profit).

Step 2: Shut-down rule   Check whether the most profitable positive sales quantity from Step 1 results in greater profit than shutting down. If it does, that is the profit-maximizing choice. If not, then selling nothing is the best option. If they are the same, then either choice maximizes profit.

Just as with a price-taking firm (see Section 9.3), if a firm has no sunk costs then the profit from shutting down is zero. In that case, the shut-down rule simply amounts to checking whether profit is at least zero at the best positive sales quantity: $PQ - C \geq 0$. Equivalently, dividing both sides by Q, we can apply the shut-down rule by checking whether the price is at least as large as the average cost: $P \geq C/Q = AC$.

What if the firm does have sunk costs, so that its profit, should it shut down, is negative (equal to those sunk costs)? Just as in Section 9.3, since the sunk costs don't affect a decision maker's best choice (as we discussed in Section 3.3, they are water under the bridge), we can just ignore them in calculating costs and proceed exactly as above. This amounts to comparing the price P not to average cost in making the shut-down decision but to average cost excluding any sunk costs; that is, to average avoidable cost.

Figure 17.4 shows the profit-maximizing sales quantity and price for Kenora Competition-free Concrete (see worked-out problem 17.1). In the figure, we suppose that KCC has annual variable costs of $VC = 20Q + 0.00125Q^2$ and marginal costs of $MC = 20 + 0.0025Q$, where Q is the number of cubic metres of concrete it produces per year. In addition, it has an avoidable fixed cost of $48,000 per year. Figure 17.4(a) shows the application of the quantity rule. Marginal revenue equals marginal cost at a sales quantity of 4800 cubic metres per year, which requires a price of $56 per cubic metre.

Figure 17.4(b) illustrates the shut-down rule. It includes KCC's average cost curve (KCC has no sunk costs). KCC's profit from selling 4800 cubic metres equals the area of the green-shaded rectangle: its height is the difference between the price ($56) and the average cost when KCC produces 4800 cubic metres ($36); its width is the number of cubic metres KCC sells (4800). KCC's profit is $(P - AC)Q = (56 - 36)4800 = \$96,000$. KCC prefers setting a price of $56 and selling 4800 cubic metres per year to shutting down, which would yield zero profit. KCC's monopoly price of $56 exceeds its marginal cost, which is $32 when it produces 4800 cubic metres [see Figure 17.4(a)]. It is also above the price that would prevail if KCC acted as a price taker. In that case, KCC's supply curve would coincide with the portion of its marginal cost curve that lies above its average cost curve. The market outcome would be at the intersection of its marginal cost

Figure 17.4

The Profit-Maximizing Price and Sales Quantity for a Monopolist. Figure (a) shows that KCC's best positive sales quantity, at which $MR = MC$, is 4800 cubic metres per year. To sell this amount, KCC charges $56 per cubic metre. Figure (b) adds KCC's average cost curve. The profit, which is positive here because AC is $36 at 4800 cubic metres per year, equals the area of the greenshaded rectangle, $(P - AC) \times Q = (56 - 36) \times 4800 = \$96,000$.

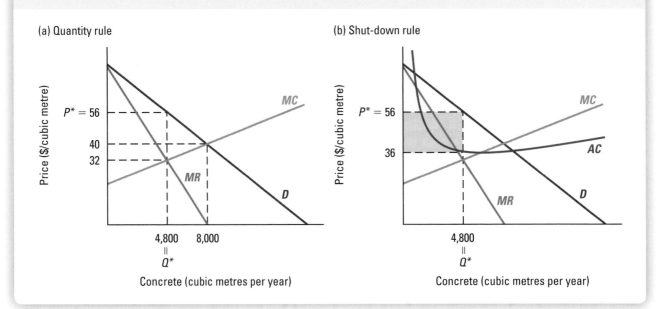

(a) Quantity rule

(b) Shut-down rule

curve and the market demand curve and would involve KCC producing 8000 cubic metres and a price of $40 per cubic metre [again, see Figure 17.4(a)].

Worked-out problem 17.2 shows how to find KCC's profit-maximizing price and quantity using algebra.

WORKED-OUT PROBLEM 17.2

The Problem Consider again Kenora Competition-free Concrete (KCC) from worked-out problem 17.1. Suppose that it has annual variable costs of $VC = 20Q + 0.00125Q^2$ and marginal costs of $MC = 20 + 0.0025Q$, where Q is the number of cubic metres of concrete it produces per year. In addition, it has an avoidable fixed cost of $48,000 per year. What are its profit-maximizing sales quantity and price?

The Solution In worked-out problem 17.1 we determined that KCC's inverse demand function is $P(Q) = 80 - 0.005Q$, and its marginal revenue is $MR = 80 - 0.01Q$. We can find its most profitable positive sales quantity and the associated price by applying the quantity rule and setting MR equal to MC.

$$80 - 0.01Q = 20 + 0.0025Q$$

Solving, we find that $Q = 4800$. Then, substituting this quantity into the inverse demand function, we find that the price required to sell that amount is

$$P(4800) = 80 - (0.005)4800 = 56$$

To apply the shut-down rule, we observe that KCC's profit at that price is $96,000 per year, which equals its total revenue of $268,800 (from selling 4800 cubic metres at a price of $56 per cubic metre) less its total cost of $172,800 (equal to its $124,800 variable cost of producing 4800 cubic metres, plus its $48,000 fixed cost). Since KCC earns nothing by shutting down, it prefers to operate at its profit-maximizing price of $56.

IN-TEXT EXERCISE 17.2   Suppose instead that KCC's demand function is $D(P) = 10,000 - 100P$, its marginal costs are $40 per cubic metre, and it has avoidable fixed costs of $40,000 per year. What are its profit-maximizing sales quantity and price?

Markup: A Measure of Market Power

We have seen that a monopolist facing a downward-sloping demand curve will set its price above marginal cost. For a firm in a perfectly competitive market, price equals marginal cost, which means that the firm has no market power. A measure of the degree of a monopolist's market power, therefore, is the extent to which its price exceeds its marginal cost. Economists typically measure this difference as a percentage of the firm's price.

$$\frac{P - MC}{P}$$

This ratio is known by several names: the **markup**, the **price-cost margin**, and the **Lerner Index**. KCC's markup at its profit-maximizing price in worked-out problem 17.2 is 0.43 since $P = 56$ and $MC = 32$.

Using formula (2) on page 622 for marginal revenue, we can relate this measure to the elasticity of demand. Since $MR = MC$, formula (2) tells us that

> A firm's **markup, price-cost margin,** or **Lerner Index** equals the amount by which its price exceeds its marginal cost, expressed as a percentage of its price.

$$P\left(1 + \frac{1}{E^d}\right) = MC \tag{3}$$

or, by rearranging terms,

$$\frac{P - MC}{P} = -\frac{1}{E^d} \tag{4}$$

Formula (4) says that a monopolist's markup at its profit-maximizing price always equals the reciprocal of the elasticity of demand, times -1. The less elastic the demand curve (the closer to zero is E^d), the greater the firm's markup over its marginal cost. Intuitively, when demand is less elastic, raising the price is more attractive because fewer sales are lost (or, equivalently, restricting output is more attractive because it enables a greater increase in price).

Formula (4) also tells us something interesting about the elasticity of demand at the monopolist's profit-maximizing price. Since the left side of the formula is less than one for a monopolist with a positive marginal cost (the numerator, $P - MC$, is less than the denominator, P), formula (4) implies that the profit-maximizing price always occurs at an elastic point on the demand curve (that is, where $E^d < -1$). This makes sense. Recall from Section 2.4 that at a price at which demand is inelastic, a small increase in price will increase total revenue. But since it also reduces the quantity the monopolist sells, that small increase in price reduces the monopolist's total cost. When revenue goes up and costs go down, profit goes up. Thus, at any price at which demand is inelastic, the monopolist will do better by raising its price. Demand must therefore be elastic at the profit-maximizing price.

This fact provides a way to check whether a firm or group of firms is acting like a profit-maximizing monopolist. If demand at the going price is inelastic, that price could not have been set by a profit-maximizing monopolist (with positive marginal cost). We'll see an example of this test a little later, in Application 17.4.

Application 17.2

The Effect of Generic Drugs on Branded Pharmaceutical Prices

In 2003 the pharmaceutical firm Pfizer earned revenues of over $9 billion worldwide from sales of Lipitor, the best-selling prescription drug of the year. No other company can produce Lipitor, because Pfizer has a patent on the key chemical contained in the drug. The patent will expire in the year 2010, when competitors are sure to rush into the market, offering generic versions of the drug at much less than the current price.[6] But if you or a family member still want to buy Pfizer's version of the drug, will the expiration of Pfizer's patent reduce your cost?

Surprisingly, it may not. Despite the loss in sales they suffer when generic manufacturers enter the market, branded pharmaceutical manufacturers often don't lower their price. In fact, they sometimes raise it.[7] Why?

Think about the elasticity of demand for a branded drug. Some consumers care a lot about brand names; they won't even consider buying a generic version. Other consumers don't care very much about brand names. Once generic versions of a drug have entered the market, a branded manufacturer has little hope of retaining this second group of customers unless it matches the generics' prices.

When many generic manufacturers enter a market, moreover, their prices quickly drop almost to the cost of production, making consumers who are not brand conscious truly unattractive to the branded manufacturer (who can retain them only by lowering its own price almost to the cost of production). In this situation, the branded manufacturer's most profitable strategy is to maximize the profit from selling to the remaining brand-conscious consumers. Often, these brand-conscious consumers have a less elastic demand than others; that is, they care more than others about the benefits of the drug and are less sensitive to price than others.

In short, the demand Pfizer will face after its patent expires may well be less elastic than the demand it faces before its patent expires. If so, formula (4) tells us that the profit-maximizing price may actually be *higher* after generic drug makers enter the market.

---

[6]Generic versions of a prescription drug are chemically identical to the branded drug, but are known by the active chemical ingredient rather than the drug's original brand name.

[7]See, for example, Richard E. Caves, Mark A. Hurwitz, and Michael D. Whinston, "Patent Expiration, Entry, and Competition in the U.S. Pharmaceutical Industry: An Exploratory Analysis," *Brookings Papers on Economic Activity, Microeconomics*, 1991, pp. 1–48.

17.3 WELFARE EFFECTS OF MONOPOLY PRICING

In a perfectly competitive market, the price equals firms' marginal cost. But in a monopoly, as we have just seen, the monopolist maximizes profit by charging a price that is above marginal cost. In doing so, the monopolist makes consumers worse off. Consumers who buy the product must pay more than they would in a competitive market, and some consumers who would have bought the product in a competitive market will not buy it at all, or will buy less, at the monopolist's elevated price.

Figure 17.5 shows the welfare effects of Kenora Competition-free Concrete's monopoly pricing. KCC charges $56 per cubic metre and sells 4800 cubic metres of concrete each year. As we noted in Section 17.2, if KCC instead acted like a price taker, it would produce 8000 cubic metres each year and the price would be $40 per cubic metre. How much worse off are consumers, in aggregate, from KCC's monopoly pricing? If the price was $40, consumer surplus would equal the sum of areas A + B + F in the figure, which equals $160,000 per year (see the table accompanying the figure).[8] At a price of $56,

Figure 17.5

The Welfare Effects of Monopoly Pricing. KCC's monopoly pricing reduces consumer surplus each year by area B + F, which equals $102,400, compared to the level of consumer surplus at a price of $40, the price that would prevail if KCC acted like a price taker. Monopoly pricing raises KCC's annual profit by $64,000, equal to area B minus area G. The deadweight loss each year is area F + G, which equals $38,400.

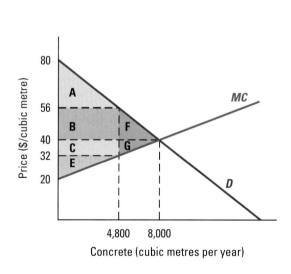

	$P = \$40$	$P = \$56$
Consumer surplus	A + B + F	A
Producer surplus	C + E + G − Avoidable fixed cost	B + C + E − Avoidable fixed cost
Aggregate surplus	A + B + C + E + F + G − Avoidable fixed cost	A + B + C + E − Avoidable fixed cost
Deadweight loss	0	F + G

Area A = $57,600	Area E = $28,800
Area B = $76,800	Area F = $25,600
Area C = $38,400	Area G = $12,800

---

[8]Here and throughout this chapter, we'll assume that there are no income effects for this good, so that we can represent consumer and aggregate surplus using ordinary (that is, uncompensated or Marshallian) demand curves: see Sections 6.2, 6.5, and 14.5.

however, consumer surplus instead equals area A, which is $57,600 per year. The difference, area B + F, equals the amount by which consumers are worse off due to monopoly pricing, $102,400 per year.

KCC is of course better off when it sets the monopoly price. As discussed in Section 9.5, we can measure its producer surplus (which equals its profit since KCC has no sunk costs) using its marginal cost curve. At a price of $40, its producer surplus equals area C + G + E, $80,000, less its avoidable fixed cost of $48,000. This equals $32,000. Its producer surplus at a price of $56 is area B + C + E, less its avoidable fixed cost. This equals $96,000 (area B + C + E, which is $144,000, less $48,000). By raising its price from $40 to $56, KCC gains area B but loses area G. That difference is a net gain of $64,000 per year.

What effect does KCC's monopoly pricing have on aggregate surplus, the *sum* of consumer and producer surplus? That sum equals the net benefit from production and consumption of the good: the difference between consumers' total willingness to pay for the amount they consume and the avoidable cost of producing those units (see Sections 14.4 and 14.5 for a discussion of aggregate surplus).

If KCC acted like a price taker, so that the price were $40, aggregate surplus would equal area A + B + C + E + F + G less KCC's avoidable fixed costs. This comes to $192,000 per year ($240,000 less the avoidable fixed cost of $48,000). As discussed in Section 14.4, this is the largest possible level of aggregate surplus. When the price is $56, aggregate surplus is instead area A + B + C + E less the avoidable fixed cost. This comes to $153,600 ($201,600 less the avoidable fixed cost of $48,000). The difference, area F + G, is known as the **deadweight loss from monopoly pricing**. In Figure 17.5, the deadweight loss is $38,400 per year. It represents the lost net benefits from the 3200 cubic metres that are not produced and consumed because of the elevated price. Notice that the deadweight loss from monopoly pricing equals the difference between the amount that consumers lose and the smaller amount that the monopolist gains: consumers lose area B + F, while the monopolist's profit increases by area B less area G. Together there is a loss of areas F and G.

> The **deadweight loss from monopoly pricing** is the amount by which aggregate surplus falls short of its maximum possible level, which is attained in a perfectly competitive market.

IN-TEXT EXERCISE 17.3   What is the deadweight loss from monopoly pricing in in-text exercise 17.2 (page 625)?

Application 17.3

Welfare Impacts of Pharmaceutical Patents in Developing Countries

Under the Agreement on Trade-Related Intellectual Property Rights (called "TRIPS") all members of the World Trade Organization must recognize and enforce product patents on pharmaceuticals. In the past, governments in many developing countries did not do so, allowing domestic producers to sell copied versions of patented drugs. Their failure to recognize patents has led to much lower pharmaceutical prices in those developing countries than in Canada and other developed countries. For example, economist Jean Lanjouw observed that in the mid-1990s, the antibiotic ciprofloxacin was roughly 15 times more expensive in the United States than in India.[9] Unfortunately, enforcing patents in developing countries, where most citizens are very poor, might drastically limit people's access to life-saving drugs. Indeed, individuals who live in developing countries rarely have any medical insurance to defray those costs; medical expenses are paid almost entirely out of pocket. On the other hand, extending patent protection to these countries might encourage pharmaceutical manufacturers to develop more drugs, which might help their citizens.

How much would the higher prices caused by patent enforcement harm individuals in developing countries? Let's consider the sale of ciprofloxacin in India. Economists Shubham Chudhuri, Pinelopi Goldberg, and Panle Jia report that in the years 1999 and 2000, over 50 firms sold versions of ciprofloxacin in India.[10] The average price of the drug was 11.24 rupees per milligram, and 283.5 million milligrams were sold. Chudhuri et al. estimate that the elasticity of Indian demand for ciprofloxacin in those years was −1.68. Given the large number of sellers, we can safely assume that the marginal cost of production was at or close to the price of 11.24 rupees per milligram, and it is reasonable to suppose that this marginal cost was independent of the level of output produced.

The amount that the price of ciprofloxacin would increase with patent enforcement depends on the shape of the demand curve. Figure 17.6 shows two hypothetical demand curves for ciprofloxacin, one linear [figure (a)] and the other with constant elasticity [figure (b)]. Both have an elasticity of −1.68 at a price of 11.24 rupees. In both cases, enforcing patent rights would replace the competitive market with a monopoly. With the linear demand curve in Figure 17.6(a), the monopoly price would rise to 14.58 rupees per milligram, and 142 million milligrams (the quantity at which $MR = MC$) would be sold. The resulting reduction in surplus for Indian consumers would be 236 million rupees

per year. With the constant-elasticity demand curve in Figure 17.6(b), the price would rise to 28.10 rupees per milligram, and only 60 million milligrams (the quantity at which $MR = MC$) would be sold. Consumer surplus would fall by 2.174 billion rupees per year. In fact, Chudhuri et al. estimate that the actual effect would be even larger, with the price rising to 37.6 rupees per milligram and consumer surplus falling by 9.47 billion rupees.[11]

These numbers show the potential effects when only *one* drug's patent protection changes. TRIPS will turn the market for *many* drugs into monopolies. To the extent that some of those drugs are substitutes for one another, we can expect even larger price increases and reductions in surplus (we'll see why in Section 17.8). For example, Chudhuri et al. have looked at the market for the broader class of antibiotics called *fluoroquinolones*, which includes ciprofloxacin and several other patented drugs. They predict that if the patents of *all* those drugs were enforced, the price of ciprofloxacin in India would rise to 65.8 rupees per milligram. Their estimate is roughly consistent with Lanjouw's observation that the price of ciprofloxacin in Pakistan, where the demand is likely similar to that in India but where patent rights *are* enforced, was roughly eight times the price in India in the mid-1990s.

Might the harm from such price increases be offset by a greater flow of new drugs? TRIPS is unlikely to make much of a difference for drugs that are used extensively in developed countries, because developing countries make up a very small portion of the worldwide revenue for those drugs. But it could matter more for drugs aimed at curing diseases like malaria and leprosy, which primarily afflict those in developing countries. The prospect of increased profits will increase pharmaceutical manufacturers' incentive to develop such drugs. The extent to which this effect will offset the loss of consumer surplus due to higher prices is difficult to predict, however.

[9]Jean O. Lanjouw, "The Introduction of Pharmaceutical Product Patents in India: Heartless Exploitation of the Poor and Suffering?" 1998, National Bureau of Economic Research Working Paper No. 6366.

[10]Shubham Chudhuri, Pinelopi K. Goldberg, and Panle Jia, "Estimating the Effects of Global Patent Protection in Pharmaceuticals: A Case Study of Quinolones in India," 2004, mimeo.

[11]Chudhuri et al. actually consider a more complicated demand structure which allows the products from different sellers (say, Indian versus foreign) to be viewed as differentiated products by consumers.

Figure 17.6

Welfare Effects of Patent Protection for Ciprofloxacin in India. Figures (a) and (b) show the effects of enforcing patent rights in India for the antibiotic ciprofloxacin with linear and constant elasticity demand curves, respectively. Patent protection transforms the market from a competitive market into a monopoly market. The resulting losses in surplus for Indian consumers are equal to the red-shaded areas.

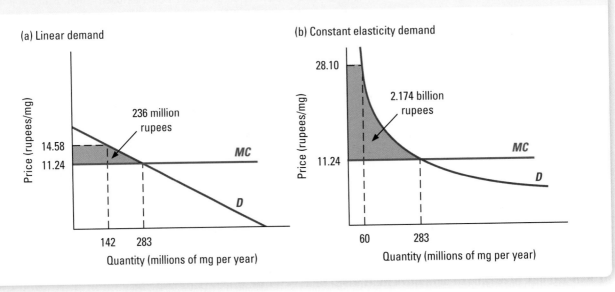

17.4 DISTINGUISHING MONOPOLY FROM PERFECT COMPETITION

In Chapter 14 we saw that perfectly competitive markets perform well, in the sense that they maximize aggregate surplus. In contrast, in Section 17.3 we saw that monopolized markets fail to achieve this ideal. Unfortunately, the existence of more than one firm in a market doesn't necessarily guarantee competition. In Chapter 19 we'll see that sometimes competitors succeed in colluding, so that they act just like a monopolist.

Suppose there are five or six firms in a given market. How can we tell whether they are behaving like price takers in a perfectly competitive market or are instead colluding, in effect acting like a monopolist? This is a question that government agencies might pose in deciding whether to intervene in the market in order to increase competition (we'll discuss the antitrust laws, which provide the means to do that, in Chapter 19).

Answering that question would be easy if we could observe firms' marginal costs; then we could compare them to the price. If the price exceeds their marginal costs, the firms are not acting like price takers. If instead the Lerner Index, $(P - MC)/P$, equals the reciprocal of the elasticity of market demand times negative one, then the firms are behaving like a monopolist.

Unfortunately, it is often difficult to learn a firm's marginal cost. Accounting statements report total and average costs but not marginal costs. And even those measures reflect accounting notions of cost, which often exclude opportunity costs. Moreover, the type of information we would need to construct better cost measures is often unavailable to people outside the firm. Is there any other way to distinguish competition from monopoly? The answer is yes: there are some significant differences in the ways in which monopolists and perfectly competitive industries respond to changes in market demand and costs.

Response to Changes in Demand

Why might a monopolist (or firms that are colluding as a monopolist) respond differently from a perfectly competitive industry to a change in demand? Intuitively, a monopolist's profit-maximizing price depends on the *elasticity* of demand. The price in a perfectly competitive market, on the other hand, depends on the *level* of demand. So if the elasticity of demand changes but the level of demand (at the initial market price) does not, then a monopolist's price will change but a competitive industry's price will not. This distinction provides a way to determine whether firms in a market are behaving like a monopoly or, instead, like highly competitive firms.

Suppose the price in a local concrete market, whose demand curve D is shown in Figure 17.7(a), is initially $60, and a quantity of 4000 cubic metres is sold each year. Imagine, first, that the firms are acting as price takers, so that the market is perfectly competitive. In that case, the industry's marginal cost curve, which coincides with its supply curve, must intersect the demand curve at a price of $60, as shown in Figure 17.7(a). Now suppose the market demand curve shifts to curve $\hat{D}$, rotating through the initial price and quantity.

Figure 17.7

Responses to a Rotation of the Demand Curve. Figure (a) shows that in a perfectly competitive market a rotation in the demand curve from D to $\hat{D}$ through an initial market equilibrium point leads to no change in the market price. In contrast, figure (b) shows the response of a monopolist to this same change in the demand curve. Because the demand elasticity falls, the profit-maximizing price increases to $68.

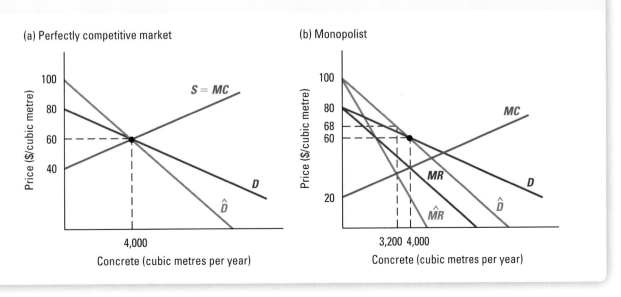

This rotation increases the elasticity of demand at a price of $60, but does not change the level of demand at that price. The intersection of the supply and demand curves therefore remains the same. In other words, in a perfectly competitive market, a rotation of the demand curve has *no effect* on the market price.

Now imagine that the firms are colluding, acting just like a monopolist. If so, then if the price is $60 when the demand curve is *D*, the industry's marginal cost curve must look like the one shown in Figure 17.7(b). That curve crosses the marginal revenue curve associated with demand curve *D*, labelled *MR*, at a quantity of 4000 cubic metres. What happens if the demand curve changes, rotating to demand curve $\hat{D}$? The marginal revenue curve shifts to $\hat{MR}$. This curve lies below curve *MR* at 4000 cubic metres. Why? Because curve $\hat{D}$ is less elastic than *D* at a price of $60, formula (4) implies that $\hat{MR}$ is less than *MR* at 4000 cubic metres. As Figure 17.7(b) shows, this implies that curve $\hat{MR}$ must intersect the marginal cost curve at a quantity less than 4000 cubic metres: with demand curve $\hat{D}$ the monopoly price is therefore greater than $60 (it is $68). Intuitively, when the demand curve rotates, a monopolist will find raising its price more attractive than before because fewer sales will now be lost with a price increase.

How likely are we to see a rotation like this? It's not very likely that from one year to the next the demand curve for concrete will change in exactly the right way to produce a rotation. But that isn't necessary. Imagine that, starting with demand curve *D*, each year there is some change in the intercept or slope of the demand curve. One year the intercept may increase due to an increase in the price of a substitute, the next year the slope may get steeper because of a fall in consumer income, and so on. All that is necessary is that eventually those changes result in demand curve $\hat{D}$. Then we can compare the prices in the two years in which demand is *D* and $\hat{D}$. An economist would actually predict the effect of a shift from *D* to $\hat{D}$ using statistical techniques, such as those discussed in the appendix of Chapter 2, to capture how the intercept and slope change in response to changes in factors such as the prices of other goods and income, and their effects on the price.

Response to Changes in Cost

How do monopolies and perfectly competitive markets differ in their response to changes in cost? To answer this question, let's think about what happens if the marginal cost increases by a given amount at every level of output. In Section 15.1 we considered exactly this type of change when we studied the response to a specific tax on firms of *T* per unit. There we saw that in a perfectly competitive market, the tax shifts the market supply curve up by *T* at each output level. In the end, as Figure 15.1 (page 535) showed, the price consumers pay rises by an amount no greater than the tax.

In a monopoly, however, the price can rise by *more* than the tax. To see why, suppose a monopolist faces a constant-elasticity demand curve. Rearranging formula (3) on page 625 we can write the relationship between price and marginal cost as

$$P = \left(\frac{E^d}{E^d + 1} \right) MC \qquad (5)$$

Formula (5) tells us that the monopolist's price is a multiple of its marginal cost. That multiple, $E^d/(E^d + 1)$, depends on the elasticity of demand. Suppose, for example, that the demand curve has a constant elasticity of $E^d = -2$. Then the monopolist will set the price equal to twice the marginal cost. If *MC* is constant (that is, if the marginal cost curve is perfectly horizontal), then in response to an increase of one dollar in marginal cost, the monopolist will raise its price by two dollars. This kind of response would never happen in a perfectly competitive market.[12]

The **pass-through rate** is the increase in price that occurs in response to a small increase in marginal cost, measured per dollar of increase in marginal cost. That is, it is the ratio $\Delta P/\Delta MC$. In a perfectly competitive market, the pass-through rate is never greater than one. In comparison, the monopolist's pass-through rate depends on the shape of the demand curve. With a constant-elasticity demand curve in which $E^d < -1$, the pass-through rate is greater than one (for example, it is two in the example just given where $E^d = -2$). If instead the monopolist faces a linear demand curve, then its pass-through rate is 0.5 (see, for example, end-of-chapter exercise 17.11). So if a firm's pass-through rate is less than one, it could be behaving either competitively or as a monopolist. But if the firm's pass-through rate is greater than one, then we know it is not behaving like a price taker.

> The **pass-through rate** is the ratio $\Delta P/\Delta MC$, the increase in price that occurs in response to a small increase in marginal cost, measured per dollar of increase in marginal cost.

Application 17.4

Pass-Through of Crude Oil Price Changes

The Canadian gasoline, diesel, and propane markets are dominated by some of the largest firms in Canada. These firms have been among the most profitable companies in Canada. Many of the firms are vertically integrated in that they are producers, refiners, distributors, and retailers of petroleum products. Over the years, many have accused the firms in this industry of behaving like a monopolist; others have defended them, arguing that active competition prevailed. Who was right?

The Canadian Agricultural Energy End Use Data and Analysis Centre is a research centre that analyzes energy use by Canadian farmers. In 1998 the centre published a study of the energy industry's competitiveness by examining how it responds to cost changes.[13] They did so by comparing gasoline and diesel prices in several cities in Saskatchewan and comparing them with other cities in Canada. In Saskatchewan three companies, Shell, Petro-Canada, and Esso, own and control the Minden pipeline which is the only pipeline delivering fuel to Saskatoon from Alberta refineries. Saskatoon is also served by tanker trucks from Regina and fuel can also be delivered from other Canadian locations as well as United States centres. Any strategic supply manipulation by the pipeline owners would require the tacit agreement of other suppliers. The study investigated the response of retail and rack (wholesale) prices to changes in crude oil prices in various centres across Canada. In particular the study looked for asymmetric response patterns to changes in crude oil prices, which would indicate that firms were likely behaving non-competitively.

The study found that for gasoline, retail prices respond the same way to decreases or increases in crude oil prices. In most Canadian cities the rack and retail price changes did not exhibit an asymmetry in the speed of pass-through, which would be consistent with active competition among firms. There was a weak asymmetry in the cities of Vancouver, Calgary, and Winnipeg, but not enough to warrant the conclusion that firms passed on an increase in crude oil prices faster than a decline in price in Saskatchewan or other Canadian centres. In the diesel market the pass-through rates are lower than for the gasoline market for rack prices and about the same for retail prices. The study found considerable asymmetry in pass-through rates for crude oil price changes in most cities other than Halifax. This is especially true in the farming provinces, such as Saskatchewan where there is considerable demand for diesel fuel. Taken together, the evidence suggests that the energy sector companies, which are in fact oligopolists, behave like competitors in the gasoline market and exercise some market power in the market for diesel fuel. (We'll study oligopoly behaviour in Chapter 19.)

---

[12]This statement assumes that partial equilibrium analysis is valid. If, instead, there are general equilibrium induced changes in prices in related markets (see Chapter 16), then the price in a competitive market could increase by more than $1 in response to a $1 increase in marginal cost.

[13]Canadian Agricultural Energy End Use Data and Analysis Centre, "Canadian Agricultural Energy Prices," December 2000.

17.5 NONPRICE EFFECTS OF MONOPOLY

To this point, we've focused entirely on the monopolist's pricing decision and the welfare consequences. But monopolists (and firms in general) make many other decisions. In this section we'll discuss some of the most important ones.

Product Quality

Sometimes the quality of a firm's product is given. When a pharmaceutical company manufactures a prescription pill, for example, the pill's disease-fighting properties depend almost exclusively on the chemicals it contains, which cannot be adjusted.[14] More typically, however, the firm can choose its products' characteristics. A car wash may offer hand washing or automated service, a gas station may provide full service or self-service, a tax accountant may provide extensive service and advice or only basic preparation of tax returns. (Sometimes a firm may decide to sell more than one product, each of a different quality. We'll discuss multiproduct firms in Section 17.8.)

When a firm raises a product's quality, it increases the consumer's willingness to pay. If doing so were costless, it would surely be a good thing to do (since at the same price, the firm could sell more units). Matters become more complicated, however, when producing a higher-quality product costs more. Then the firm must decide whether the extra benefit justifies the extra cost. From a social perspective, too, we want to balance the benefits and costs of increased quality. How does the quality the monopolist provides compare to the level of quality that would maximize aggregate surplus?

To understand the issues involved in a quality decision, let's imagine that the only car wash in town is trying to decide whether to provide hand washing. If it does so, every consumer will value a car wash by $5 more than without hand washing. Will it be profitable for the monopolist to provide the service? That depends on how much it costs. Figure 17.8(a) shows the demand, marginal revenue, and marginal cost curves in this market without hand washing (labelled D_0, MR_0, and MC_0). The car wash maximizes its profit by selling 100 washes at $15 each; its profit is $1000. Let's suppose hand washing costs $5 more per wash. Figure 17.8(b) shows the demand, marginal revenue, and marginal cost curves with hand washing (labelled D_1, MR_1, and MC_1). Each of these curves is the same as the corresponding curve in Figure 17.8(a), except that it has shifted up by $5. (Use formula (1) to see why marginal revenue has shifted up by $5 at each sales quantity.) Therefore, with hand washing, the marginal revenue and marginal cost curves still intersect at 100 washes. Now, however, the profit-maximizing price is $20, $5 higher than before. The monopolist's profit is $1000—exactly the same as without hand washing.

When hand washing costs $5 more per wash, then, the monopolist is indifferent between offering and not offering the service. If hand washing added *less* than $5 in cost per wash, then the monopolist would certainly be better off with hand washing: he could raise the price by $5, sell 100 washes, and make more money than without hand washing.

---

[14]By law, the drug's chemical composition cannot be changed. However, the manufacturer may still make some choices that affect quality. For example, it might introduce a "sustained release" pill, which offers a superior method of delivery to the body.

Figure 17.8

Profitability of a Quality Increase. In figure (a), D_0, MC_0, and MR_0 are the demand, marginal cost, and marginal revenue curves, respectively, without hand washing. With hand washing each wash costs $5 more, shifting the marginal cost curve in figure (b) up to MC_1, and consumers value each wash $5 more, shifting the demand and marginal revenue curves up to D_1 and MR_1. The profit-maximizing price increases by $5, from $15 to $20. However, the quantity sold and profit are unchanged. The figures also show that aggregate surplus, equal to the green-shaded areas, is unchanged.

Likewise, if hand washing cost *more* than $5, then the monopolist would be better off without it.[15]

How does this profit-maximizing result compare to the quality that would maximize aggregate surplus? In this special case, in which every consumer values higher quality by the same amount, the monopolist gets it right. Figures 17.8(a) and (b) show aggregate surplus, shaded green, with and without hand washing at the monopolist's profit-maximizing price. Note that when hand washing costs $5 extra aggregate surplus is exactly the same in both cases. (You can check that in both cases, it is $1500.) The reason is that each of the 100 customers values a hand wash $5 more than an automatic wash, but each of those 100 washes also costs $5 more. If hand washing cost less than $5 extra, it would raise aggregate surplus; if it cost more than $5, it would lower aggregate surplus. Just like the monopolist, if we want to maximize aggregate surplus, we want to have hand washing if it costs less than $5, but not if it costs more than $5.

If different consumers value quality differently, however, the monopolist may not choose to offer the quality that maximizes aggregate surplus. To see this point, let's suppose that consumers with a higher willingness to pay are also willing to pay more for an increase in quality. Figure 17.9 shows an example in which those car wash consumers whose willingness to pay is above $22 (there are 30 of them) value a car wash $15 more if done by hand, while all other consumers value a car wash $5 more if done by hand.

---

[15]To see this, start from the profit-maximizing price and sales level with hand washing. If the car wash removed the hand washing service and cut the price by $5, it would sell the same number of car washes. Since the cost reduction per wash would be greater than $5, the profit would be higher.

Figure 17.9

A Monopolist May Not Produce the Right Level of Quality. The figure shows an example for which higher quality is valued more by very high willingness-to-pay consumers. The monopolist car wash's profit is the same with and without hand washing when it costs $5 extra per wash, but aggregate surplus (equal to the green-shaded areas) increases when hand washing is offered. If hand washing instead cost $5.01 extra per wash, the monopolist would definitely not offer it even though it would increase aggregate surplus.

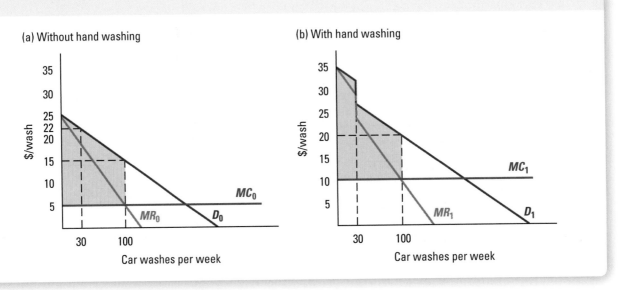

Figure 17.9(a) shows the demand, marginal revenue, and marginal cost curves without hand washing, just as in Figure 17.8(a); Figure 17.9(b) shows the same curves with hand washing. Now the willingness to pay for the first 30 hand washes is $10 higher than in Figure 17.8(b). (The marginal revenue curve in Figure 17.9(b) jumps down at 30 car washes, in accordance with formula (1) (page 620), because the price jumps down when the quantity reaches 30 washes.) The car wash's profit-maximizing sales quantity with hand washing is still 100 washes (where $MR = MC$), which it sells at a price of $20 each, exactly as in Figure 17.8(b). Its profit with and without hand washing is also the same as in Figure 17.8 ($1000). Now let's think about aggregate surplus. While the monopolist's profit is the same with and without hand washing, aggregate surplus is strictly greater with it: it is $1500 without hand washing and $1800 with it. This difference arises from the fact that hand washing is worth $10, rather than $5, to the 30 consumers with the highest willingness to pay.

Now suppose that hand washing costs a little bit more than $5 extra—say, just a penny more. In that case, the monopolist will choose not to offer it. But aggregate surplus is still strictly greater with hand washing (it will be very close to $1800 with it and very close to $1500 without it). So, in this case, the monopolist's choice does *not* maximize aggregate surplus.

What explains the difference between what is profitable and what maximizes aggregate surplus? The problem in Figure 17.9 is that the monopolist doesn't pay sufficient attention to the willingness to pay for quality of inframarginal consumers, whose purchase decisions are not affected by small changes in the price or quality. They will buy from him no matter what; his price is instead determined by the willingness to pay of the marginal consumers. A quality improvement is worthwhile to the monopolist only if it raises the willingness to pay of those marginal consumers by more than its cost.

In other cases, a monopolist can be too willing to raise quality, as in-text exercise 17.4 shows.

IN-TEXT EXERCISE 17.4   Suppose that in Figure 17.9, the 30 consumers whose willingness to pay for a car wash is above \$22 place no value on hand washing, while all other consumers are willing to pay an extra \$6 for the service. Show that the monopolist will provide hand washing in this case, even though doing so lowers aggregate surplus.

Advertising

Another important decision for many firms is how much to spend on advertising to increase sales. Firms in perfectly competitive markets have no individual incentive to advertise, because each firm perceives itself as capable of selling as much as it desires at the market price.[16] However, a monopolist (as well as any firm with market power) does have an incentive to advertise. Because the monopolist's marginal cost is less than the price, each additional sale increases its profit.

Let's consider a situation in which the demand for the monopolist's product is given by a demand function of the form *Quantity demanded* $= D(P, A)$, where A is the total amount the firm spends on advertising. This monopolist will choose a price P and an advertising expenditure A to maximize profit,

$$PQ - C(Q) - A$$

where $C(Q)$ is the cost of producing Q units, and the sales quantity Q depends on both the price and the advertising level. If the firm spends a dollar more on advertising, the marginal benefit will be

$$(P - MC)(\Delta Q/\Delta A)$$

This formula is intuitive: it says that the marginal benefit of advertising equals the increase in sales, $(\Delta Q/\Delta A)$, times the firm's profit on each additional sale, $(P - MC)$. At the profit-maximizing level of advertising, this marginal benefit must equal the extra dollar expended (the marginal cost) so

$$(P - MC)(\Delta Q/\Delta A) = 1 \tag{6}$$

To gain more insight into the profit-maximizing level of advertising, we can rewrite this formula as

$$\left[P \times \underbrace{\left(\frac{P - MC}{P} \right)}_{= -\left(\frac{1}{E^d} \right)} \right] \left[\underbrace{\left(\frac{\Delta Q}{\Delta A} \right)\left(\frac{A}{Q} \right)\left(\frac{Q}{A} \right)}_{= E_A^d} \right] = 1$$

---

[16]Sometimes firms in a competitive industry do advertise *collectively* (as when milk producers' associations run advertisements showing famous personalities drinking milk). As a group they have an incentive to expand overall demand, since this can increase the market price. (Individual producers have little incentive to expand overall demand, because doing so involves the kind of "free rider" problem we discuss in Chapter 20.)

In writing this formula, we've noted that $(\Delta Q/\Delta A)(A/Q) = E_A^d$, the elasticity of demand with respect to advertising. (See Section 2.4 for a discussion of elasticities with respect to variables other than price.) We've also noted that $(P - MC)/P = -(1/E^d)$ at the monopolist's profit-maximizing price (this is just formula (4) from page 625 again). Substituting these expressions and rearranging terms, we can rewrite the formula as

$$\left(\frac{A}{P \times Q}\right) = -\left(\frac{E_A^d}{E^d}\right) \tag{7}$$

Formula (7) says that the *advertising-sales ratio* (the ratio of the amount spent on advertising to the firm's total sales revenue) equals the advertising elasticity divided by the price elasticity of demand, times negative one. Intuitively, a higher advertising elasticity makes advertising more productive, raising the amount of advertising the firm should purchase. A lower (less negative) price elasticity of demand increases the firm's profit maximizing price, and therefore profit per unit, making the increase in sales due to advertising worth more.

The welfare analysis of advertising is controversial, because the evaluation of its effects on aggregate surplus depends on the reason it succeeds in increasing demand. If advertising conveys only useful information about a product, then it is appropriate to count the full increase in aggregate surplus indicated by the shift in the market demand curve. (As with product quality decisions, the monopolist may not have the right incentives, from a social perspective, to create such shifts in the demand curve.) On the other hand, if advertising is misleading, or causes consumers to respond in irrational ways (see Chapter 13), then its welfare consequences may be less desirable.

Application 17.5

The Effect of Generic Drugs on Pharmaceutical Advertising

In Application 17.2 we saw that branded drug manufacturers often maintain or even raise their prices when generic manufacturers enter the market following the expiration of their patents. What happens to their advertising? Prior to a patent expiration, branded manufacturers typically advertise extensively to promote their products, both in medical journals and through traveling sales representatives (not to mention giving doctors free trips to special "conferences" at expensive resorts). When a patent is about to expire, however, branded manufacturers often greatly reduce their advertising. On average, their advertising falls roughly 10 percent in the two years prior to patent expiration, and roughly 25 percent per year between the expiration and the entry of the first generic manufacturer. Advertising falls roughly 20 percent after the entry of the first generic manufacturer, another 40 percent when the number of generic entrants reaches five, and another 20 percent when the number of generic entrants reaches 10.[17]

These changes can be understood by thinking about the marginal benefit of advertising [the left-hand side of

---

[17]See again, Richard E. Caves, Michael D. Whinston, and Mark A. Hurwitz, "Patent Expiration, Entry, and Competition in the U.S. Pharmaceutical Industry: An Exploratory Analysis," *Brookings Papers on Economic Activity: Microeconomics*, 1991, pp. 1–48.

formula (6)]. While the profit a branded manufacturer earns on the marginal units, $P - MC$, often stays relatively unchanged when generics enter the market (it may rise a bit; recall Application 17.2), the responsiveness of sales to advertising, $\Delta Q/\Delta A$, often decreases sharply. Once generics are on the market, advertising to increase overall demand for the drug only partly benefits the branded manufacturer, since many of the additional sales will go to the generics. So the marginal benefit of advertising falls, causing the branded

manufacturer to reduce advertising expenditures.[18] Moreover, since in practice the impact of advertising is often long-lived (a fact we have ignored thus far), some of its benefits come in the form of effects on future profits. (In this respect, advertising is similar to the investments we studied in Section 10.3.) Thus, the imminent entry of generics lowers the marginal benefit of today's advertising, giving the branded manufacturer an incentive to reduce advertising expenditures even before entry actually occurs.

Investments Made to Become a Monopolist

The investment decisions we have just considered involved a firm that was *already* a monopolist. Firms can also make investments in an effort to *become* monopolists. For example, pharmaceutical firms invest billions of dollars each year in an attempt to make discoveries that will lead to patented drugs (see Application 11.1 on page 371). Cable TV firms may also spend money to influence government officials to award them franchises.

In a famous article, economist Gordon Tullock noted that the deadweight loss of monopoly identified in Section 17.3 may constitute only a small fraction of the loss caused by monopoly power.[19] If firms engage in competition to become a monopolist, they will spend up to the full monopoly profit (the green-shaded rectangle in Figure 17.4 on page 624 or, equivalently, area $B + C + E$ less avoidable fixed costs in Figure 17.5 on page 627) in their effort to succeed. If these expenditures are for socially useless things, such as extravagant meals and weekend getaways for local officials, then the loss from monopoly may include not only the deadweight loss, but *all* the anticipated monopoly profit. Socially useless effort devoted to securing a monopoly position is known as **rent seeking**, a term coined by economist Anne Krueger.[20] In Figure 17.5, for example, KCC's monopoly profit ($96,000) is two-and-a-half times as large as the red-shaded deadweight loss, so the loss due to monopoly could be three-and-a-half times as large as indicated in the figure.

> **Rent seeking** is socially useless effort devoted to securing a monopoly position.

While Tullock's argument is insightful, the welfare effects of monopoly need not always be so bad. The expenditures firms make to gain monopoly positions can be socially valuable. An obvious example is the R&D spending that pharmaceutical companies engage in during the search for patentable drugs. Indeed, the fact that the monopoly positions bestowed by patents create incentives for firms to conduct socially valuable R&D is exactly the idea behind the patent system.

---

[18]These changes can also be understood using formula (7). If the price and advertising elasticities of demand do not change too much after a generic entry (the advertising elasticity will not change if all consumers respond to advertising in the same way, so that the monopolist's remaining, brand-conscious consumers have the same percentage increase in demand in response to advertising as all consumers do before generic manufacturers enter the market), then the fact that its revenue $P \times Q$ declines dramatically implies that its advertising will decline as well.

[19]Gordon Tullock, "The Welfare Costs of Tariffs, Monopolies, and Theft." *Western Economic Journal* 5, June 1967, pp. 224–232.

[20]Anne Krueger, "The Political Economy of the Rent-Seeking Society." *American Economic Review* 64, June 1974, pp. 291–303.

17.6 MONOPSONY

Market power isn't limited to the sellers of a product; it also can be held by buyers. In a perfectly competitive market, buyers take the price of a product as given. They simply cannot purchase the product below the market price. In some circumstances, however, there may be only a few buyers of a product. In an extreme case, called a **monopsony market**, there is just one buyer, called a **monopsonist**. In these circumstances, buyers may not need to take the price of a good as given. Rather, they can lower the price they pay, at least if they are willing to reduce the quantity that they purchase. The Canadian Wheat Board, established by an act of Parliament in 1935, is a monopsony buyer of the wheat and barley produced in the prairie provinces. The Wheat Board does not operate in Eastern Canada and most of British Columbia, so farmers in those provinces are able to sell their grain on the open market. The monopsony also acts as an oligopolistic seller of wheat and barley both in Canada and in the world market. Supporters of the Wheat Board claim that the monopsony is able to sell grain for higher prices than an individual farmer would receive. Opponents of the Wheat Board, which include Prime Minister Harper, argue that selling grain to the Wheat Board should not be compulsory and that even if farmers do benefit, the cost to taxpayers of maintaining the monopsony is significant. Labour markets are often characterized by monopsony especially in small rural communities where the main employer might be a mine or a lumber mill.

The analysis of monopsony parallels the analysis of monopoly. A monopolist who faces a downward-sloping demand curve understands that lowering the quantity sold makes it possible to increase the purchase price. A monopsonist who faces an upward-sloping supply curve understands that lowering the quantity bought makes it possible to reduce the purchase price.

Let's see how this works. Imagine a small city in which the only employment opportunities for nurses are at a single hospital, Confederation Hospital. Figure 17.10 shows its demand curve for nurses, labelled D, along with the market supply curve for nurses,

Figure 17.10

Monopsony. The figure shows the outcome in a monopsony market for nurses in a small city. The hospital's profit-maximizing number of nurses occurs at the quantity at which its marginal expenditure curve, *ME*, crosses its demand curve, *D*, whose height equals the hospital's marginal benefit from an additional nurse. The monopsonist hospital lowers the wage by hiring fewer nurses than it would if it acted as a price taker. It hires 200 nurses rather than 300, lowering the wage from $60,000 to $50,000 per year. The resulting deadweight loss is equal to the red-shaded area ($1 million per year).

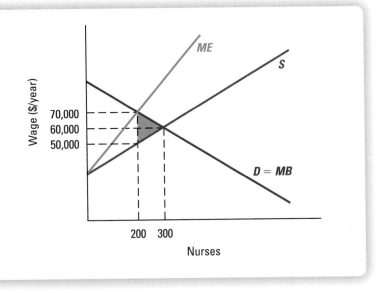

labelled *S*. The vertical axis measures the annual salary for a nurse in that city, *W*. The supply curve is upward-sloping. As the wage rises, more people will decide to accept employment as a nurse in this city. Some may choose nursing over other occupations they are trained for. Others may decide to go back to work rather than stay at home. If the wage gets high enough, nurses in other places may decide to move to this city, and enrolments at the local nursing school may begin to rise.

Like a monopolist, the monopsonist hospital's administrators can think either in terms of what wage to pay or in terms of how many nurses to employ. What are the marginal benefit and marginal cost of adding the marginal nurse? The marginal benefit, MB, equals the hospital's willingness to pay for the marginal nurse, which is measured by the height of its demand curve. The marginal cost is the extra expenditure the hospital must incur to hire that nurse. Let's look at this extra expenditure more closely.

Marginal Expenditure

The extra cost of hiring the marginal nurse is called the hospital's marginal expenditure. More generally, a monopsonist's **marginal expenditure**, *ME*, is the extra cost incurred to hire or purchase the marginal units of an input, per marginal unit. The hospital's marginal expenditure has two parts: (1) the marginal nurse costs *W*. We'll call this the *input expansion effect*. (2) hiring that marginal nurse requires administrators to raise the wage. This is the *price increase effect*.

> A monopsonist's **marginal expenditure**, *ME*, is the extra cost incurred to hire or purchase the marginal units of an input, per marginal unit.

The market supply curve tells us that to hire another nurse, the hospital must increase the wage by ($\Delta W/\Delta Q$), the supply curve's slope. Since it pays this wage to *Q* nurses, the wage increase raises the hospital's nursing costs by ($\Delta W/\Delta Q$)*Q*. Putting together the input expansion and price increase effects, we find that the marginal expenditure is

$$ME = W + \left(\frac{\Delta W}{\Delta Q}\right) Q \qquad (8)$$

The term ($\Delta W/\Delta Q$)*Q* captures the price increase effect. If the hospital were a price taker, this effect would be absent and the marginal expenditure would simply equal the market wage *W*. Since the supply curve is upward sloping, ($\Delta W/\Delta Q$) is a positive number (hiring an additional nurse increases the market wage), so the price increase effect makes *ME* larger than *W*.

Figure 17.10 shows Confederation Hospital's *ME* curve. Note that it lies above the market supply curve: At every positive number of nurses the hospital might hire, *Q*, the wage required to hire that number of workers is less than the marginal expenditure (*ME*). However, the marginal expenditure curve's vertical intercept is the same as the vertical intercept of the market supply curve because *ME* = *W* when *Q* = 0, as formula (8) shows. This is because the price increase effect will not matter when the hospital is hiring its first nurse.

The input expansion and price increase effects on marginal expenditure for a monopsonist parallel the output expansion and price reduction effects on marginal revenue for a monopolist. To sell more, a monopolist must lower its price, which makes marginal revenue smaller than the price; to hire more nurses, the monopsonist hospital must increase the wage, which makes its marginal expenditure larger than the wage.

Worked-out problem 17.3 shows how to derive the marginal expenditure using algebra.

WORKED-OUT PROBLEM   17.3

The Problem   Confederation Hospital is a monopsonist employer of nurses in a small city. The market supply of nurses is $Q^s = 0.01W - 300$, where W is the annual wage of a nurse, in dollars, and Q is the number of people who would accept employment as a nurse. What is Confederation Hospital's marginal expenditure when it hires 200 nurses? How does Confederation Hospital's marginal expenditure compare to the wage when it hires that number of nurses? Graph its supply and marginal expenditure curves.

The Solution   To find Confederation Hospital's marginal expenditure, ME, we first derive the "inverse market supply function," which gives the wage it must pay for each number of nurses it might hire. Since the market supply function is $Q^s = 0.01W - 300$, this inverse supply function is $W^s(Q) = 30,000 + 100Q$. For example, to hire 200 nurses, Confederation Hospital must pay \$50,000 per year [$=30,000 + 100(200)$]. Since $(\Delta W/\Delta Q) = 100$ for this inverse supply function, Confederation Hospital's marginal expenditure is

$$ME = W + \left(\frac{\Delta W}{\Delta Q}\right)Q = (30,000 + 100Q) + 100Q$$

$$= 30,000 + 200Q$$

So Confederation Hospital's marginal expenditure when it hires 200 nurses is \$70,000 [$= 30,000 + 200(200)$], which is more than the wage it must offer to hire 200 nurses, \$50,000 [$= 30,000 + 100(200)$]. Figure 17.10 shows the market supply and marginal expenditure curves. Note that the ME curve lies above the market supply curve at all positive quantities, and coincides with the supply curve where it hits the vertical axis (and the number of nurses hired is zero).[21]

IN-TEXT EXERCISE 17.5   **Confederation Hospital is a monopsonist employer of nurses in a small city. The market supply of nurses is $Q^s = 0.01W - 600$, where W is the annual wage of a nurse, in dollars, and Q is the number of people who would accept employment as a nurse. What is Confederation Hospital's marginal expenditure when it hires 100 nurses? How does Confederation Hospital's marginal expenditure compare to the wage when it hires that number of nurses? Graph its supply and marginal expenditure curves.**

Monopsony Profit Maximization

Confederation Hospital's profit-maximizing choice is the number of nurses at which its marginal benefit equals its marginal cost (see Section 3.2). So its profit-maximizing choice equates its willingness to pay (the marginal benefit) with its marginal expenditure (the marginal cost): $MB = ME$. Since the hospital's marginal benefit equals the height of its demand curve for nurses, it maximizes its profit by hiring the number of nurses at which its demand and marginal expenditure curves cross. In Figure 17.10, that number is

---

[21]In general, for a linear inverse supply function of the form $W = A + BQ$, marginal expenditure is $ME = (A + BQ) + BQ = A + 2BQ$. Thus, the marginal expenditure curve for a linear supply curve is also linear, with the same intercept as the supply curve and twice as steep.

200 nurses. If it was a price taker, the hospital would instead hire 300 nurses, the number where the demand and supply curves cross. By hiring 200 nurses instead of 300, the hospital lowers the wage from $60,000 to $50,000 per year.

Worked-out problem 17.4 shows how to use algebra to solve for the profit-maximizing number of nurses.

WORKED-OUT PROBLEM   17.4

The Problem Consider again Confederation Hospital from worked-out problem 17.3. Suppose that its demand for nurses is $Q^d = 900 - 0.01W$ where W is the annual wage of a nurse. What is its profit-maximizing number of nurses and wage? What would the number of nurses hired and the wage be if Confederation Hospital acted like a price taker?

The Solution In worked-out problem 17.3 we determined that Confederation Hospital's marginal expenditure is $ME = 30,000 + 200Q$. To find its profit-maximizing number of nurses, we first need to find its marginal benefit. This is given by the value of its inverse demand function at each number of nurses (which gives the height of its demand curve). Since its demand function is $Q^d = 900 - 0.01W$, its inverse demand function is $W^d(Q) = 90,000 - 100Q$, so its marginal benefit function is $MB = 90,000 - 100Q$.

We find its profit-maximizing number of nurses by setting $MB = ME$.

$$90,000 - 100Q = 30,000 + 200Q$$

Solving we find that $Q = 200$. The price required to hire that number of nurses can then be found from the inverse market supply curve (see worked-out problem 17.3); it is $W = 30,000 + 100(200) = \$50,000$.

If Confederation Hospital instead acted as a price taker, the market wage would equate demand and supply.

$$900 - 0.01W = 0.01W - 300$$

Solving, the wage would be $60,000 per year, which means (from either the demand or the supply function) that 300 nurses would be hired.

IN-TEXT EXERCISE 17.6 **Consider again Confederation Hospital from in-text exercise 17.5. Suppose that its demand for nurses is $Q^d = 900 - 0.01W$ where W is the annual wage of a nurse. What is its profit-maximizing number of nurses and wage? What would the number of nurses hired and the wage be if Confederation Hospital acted like a price taker?**

The Welfare Effects of Monopsony Pricing

Just like with monopoly, monopsony price setting creates a deadweight loss. The monopsonist uses too little of the input, meaning that some potential net benefits from the input are lost. In Figure 17.10, for example, aggregate surplus from nursing services would be maximized if the hospital hired 300 nurses. Instead, it hires only 200. The deadweight loss is the red-shaded region, the area between the hospital's demand (marginal benefit) and market supply curves. The deadweight loss in the figure equals $1 million per year.

Application 17.6

The Suncor Energy Inc. Acquisition of Petro-Canada

On March 23, 2009, Petro-Canada and Suncor Energy Ltd. announced their intention to merge and create the country's largest energy company with an estimated market value of $43 billion. At the conclusion of the merger the new company was expected to have a market capitalization only exceeded by the Royal Bank of Canada. At the time of their agreement, Suncor was the second largest producer in the Alberta oil sands, and Petro-Canada was the largest retailer of gasoline across Canada with over 1300 retail outlets.

The deal raised concerns that competition in the retail gasoline, storage, and distribution markets would be reduced. As a result of these concerns, the Canadian Competition Bureau launched an investigation of the firms' merger, to address concerns that the merger would reduce competition in the retail gas market and wholesale distribution markets. (We'll discuss antitrust laws in Chapter 19.) In the end, the companies agreed to sell some of their facilities to other firms as a condition of gaining approval of their merger. On July 21, 2009, upon receiving regulatory approval to merge, the two companies agreed to divest themselves of 104 retail gas stations in Ontario and to sell 1.1 billion litres of storage

and distribution capacity annually over a ten year period. The new company would also be required to sell 98 million litres of gasoline to independents each year for ten years. These conditions were designed to prevent the merged firm from unduly restricting competition in both retailing and distribution.

17.7 REGULATION OF MONOPOLIES

In Chapter 15 we saw that efforts to affect market prices in perfectly competitive markets generally lead to a deadweight loss. However, the deadweight loss from monopoly pricing provides a justification for government intervention in markets in which firms enjoy market power. In those markets, government actions that keep the price closer to marginal cost can not only protect consumers, but can also increase aggregate surplus.

Government intervention to limit the exercise of market power can take many forms. In Chapter 19 we'll discuss antitrust legislation, which seeks to keep prices low by ensuring that a market is as competitive as possible. Here we'll discuss another possibility, direct regulation of prices. Government price regulation is not common in Canada, but it has been more common in the past and still exists for a number of products, such as electricity, natural gas, cable, and local telephone service. It is more common in other countries. (Add-On 17A, for example, discusses Canadian drug price regulation.) In this section, we'll discuss the motives and effects of government regulation.

Why Are Some Monopolies Regulated?

Regulated monopolies arise in several ways. Sometimes regulation is a response to market dominance. As we saw in Section 17.1, a market may end up as a monopoly for a variety of reasons. Sometimes, the market is only large enough for one firm to sell a good profitably. Other times, a firm may gain a monopoly position by being the first to develop a new product. Regulation arises when there is enough economic concern and political pressure to limit the resulting prices.

At other times, as we've noted, governments actually create monopolies, such as with local cable TV franchises. When they do so, they may then regulate those monopolists to deal with the negative consequences. (We'll discuss the history of cable TV regulation in Application 17.7.) Why would the government want to create a monopoly? One reason, which we've already mentioned, is as a reward for successful innovation. Government patents do exactly that. In some countries, including Canada, patent holders may face price regulation (again, see Add-On 17A). Another reason for the creation of monopolies, which we haven't yet discussed, is to ensure that goods are produced at least cost. This motive makes sense in the case of natural monopolies.

A market is a **natural monopoly** when a good is produced most economically by a single firm. Figure 17.11 shows the demand, average cost, and marginal cost curves for cable TV in a small city. The horizontal axis measures the number of subscribers, and the vertical axis, the monthly subscriber charge. Note that average cost falls as the cable TV firm gains more subscribers, reflecting economies of scale (see Section 8.8). As a result, the cost per unit is lowest when only one firm is operating.[22]

> A market is a **natural monopoly** when a good is produced most economically by a single firm.

Even if a market is a natural monopoly, sometimes a second firm may still find it profitable to enter. Suppose that in the market shown in Figure 17.11, the price after entry of a second cable TV firm is $60 per month. If the two firms split the market demand

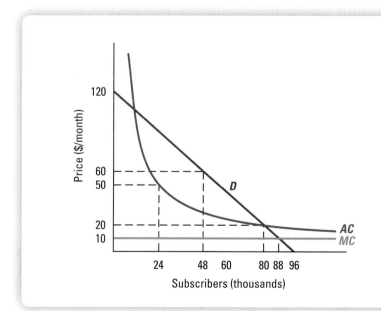

Figure 17.11
A Natural Monopoly. Because average cost falls as the number of cable TV subscribers increases, the market demand is supplied most economically when a single firm is operating. If a regulator sets the price equal to the marginal cost, the monopolist loses money. The price that maximizes aggregate surplus, while still allowing the monopolist to at least break even, is $20.

---

[22]A market can be a natural monopoly even if the average cost is not everywhere declining. As long as the quantity demanded is not much above the efficient scale of production and average cost rises steeply enough at output levels below the efficient scale, production by a single firm is most economical.

evenly (each serving 24,000 subscribers), their average cost would be $50. With a price of $60 and an average cost of $50, they would each make a profit. (We'll study the determination of prices in such oligopolies in Chapter 19.) In this case, the second cable TV firm would find it profitable to lay cable in the city, even though another company is already operating. The second firm's laying of cable would be inefficient, causing the cost per subscriber to go up. To prevent that from happening, the government can designate one firm to be the monopolist provider and bar other firms from entering the market. Once government officials have done so, however, they will likely institute price regulation to protect consumers and avoid the inefficiencies of monopoly pricing.

First-Best versus Second-Best Price Regulation

If the government is regulating a monopolist, what price should it set? In principle, the price should be the *competitive price*, the price at which the demand and marginal cost curves intersect. At that price, aggregate surplus will be maximized (recall Section 14.4). This approach is known as the *first-best* solution to the problem of price regulation.

In practice, however, at least two real-world problems may get in the way of this approach, leading to what is termed *second-best regulation*. First, the regulator may not be privy to the firm's marginal cost. In fact, most price regulation involves elaborate and costly rate hearings at which the firm tries to justify charging high prices by presenting evidence about costs, which regulators and consumer groups often challenge.

Second, even if the regulator knows the firm's marginal cost, the first-best solution would often cause the monopolist to lose money. To see why, look again at Figure 17.11. The price that maximizes aggregate surplus—where the demand and marginal cost curves intersect—is $10 per month, which results in 88,000 subscribers. But with 88,000 subscribers, the average cost is more than $10.

In principle, this problem could be solved by making a payment to the firm so that it breaks even. In practice, such transfers are often politically infeasible.[23] While rate regulators have the authority to determine the monopolist's price, they usually do not have the ability to make payments to the monopolist. As a result, the best the regulator can do is set the price that makes aggregate surplus as large as possible, while still allowing the firm to at least break even. In Figure 17.11, for example, that price is $20 per month. At that price, the monopolist breaks even: it has 80,000 subscribers at an average cost of exactly $20 per subscriber. At any lower price, it loses money. At any higher price, aggregate surplus is not as large as with a price of $20. (For a discussion of second-best price regulation when the regulated firm produces more than one product, see Add-On 17B.)

Nonprice Effects of Price Regulation

Another difficulty with price regulation has to do with the fact that regulated monopolists (just like unregulated ones) make many decisions other than about price. They decide on the mix of inputs, invest money and effort to reduce costs, and introduce new, higher-quality products. Price regulation can lead to inefficiencies in all these decisions.

Consider, for example, a regulated monopolist's incentives to lower costs. How much effort would you put into lowering your costs if your price were set so that you would earn nothing? Clearly, not very much. That is exactly what can happen under price regulation.

---

[23]Because these transfers must be financed with distortionary taxes of the kind we studied in Section 15.1, they also involve a deadweight loss.

This problem has led economists to suggest that regulators should guarantee to the firm that they will not lower the price in response to *future* cost reductions, at least not for some period. With this approach, the firm breaks even at the outset but gets to keep future gains from cost reduction.

Regulatory Failure

Another reason that regulation may not work as well in practice as it does in theory is that regulators may decide to pursue goals other than the maximization of aggregate surplus. Sometimes their official mandate includes other objectives. Energy and telephone regulators, for example, are supposed to ensure that the basic level of service is affordable even to poor consumers. Often, though, the failure to maximize surplus arises for less desirable reasons. Regulators are typically appointed; sometimes they are elected. As a result, they may behave in ways that are designed to improve their chances of reappointment or re-election, rather than to maximize economic efficiency. Because some of an elected regulator's constituents may be particularly powerful in turning out the vote or making campaign contributions, the regulator may focus more on promoting those constituents' agendas than on maximizing aggregate surplus. Because individual consumers usually have little political power or economic resources, they are typically less able to influence regulators than are large, organized interest groups.

Another concern is that regulators may be **captured** by the regulated firm and begin to promote the firm's agenda instead of maximizing aggregate surplus. Over time, for example, the regulator may become friendly with the regulated firm's executives, whom he may see at industry gatherings, golf outings, and other functions. Or he may hope to find a job in the industry once his term as a regulator is finished.

> Regulators have been **captured** when they promote the regulated firm's agenda.

The possibility of influencing a regulator to pursue the regulated firm's objectives leads to more inefficiency than just that caused by distorted regulatory decisions. The influence process itself involves real social costs, as hundreds of lawyers and lobbyists (and even some economists) work to influence regulatory decisions rather than to achieve more socially productive goals.

The Trend toward Deregulation

Historically, price regulation has been a cyclical phenomenon. The first half of the twentieth century saw a significant increase in regulation. During this period Parliament created the Canadian Transportation Agency (descended from the Board of Railway Commissioners established in 1904) to regulate railroads and subsequently air travel; the Canadian Radio-television and Telecommunications Commission, or CRTC (originally established as the Canadian Radio Broadcasting Commission in 1932) to regulate the airwaves and communication; and the Canadian Competition Bureau (established in 1986 by the Competition Act which supplanted the Combine Investigation Act of 1910). This move toward government intervention was partly a response to the industrial revolution, which dramatically increased the extent of economies of scale in many industries. The accompanying increase in market power led naturally to a greater need for regulation. But the increase in regulation was also a response to the loss of faith in markets that followed a series of well-publicized business scandals and the economic collapse known as the Great Depression. During this period, state and local governments began to regulate local telephone companies, electricity and natural gas providers, and taxicab service.

The last 30 years have seen a dramatic reversal of this trend. Today, airlines, railroads, trucking firms, electric utilities, and telecommunications firms have all been substantially or even completely deregulated. In part this shift was caused by technological changes that reduced the number of markets thought to be natural monopolies. In part it was a response to increased faith in the benefits of competition and reduced faith in the ability of regulators. Market conditions continue to evolve, along with economists' understanding of the likely results of unregulated competition in specific industries. As a result, the degree to which governments will resort to price regulation in the future is likely to evolve as well.

Application 17.7

Cable TV Regulation and Deregulation

Cable TV was first introduced in Canada in the early 1950s, as a means of increasing the quality of over-the-air reception of local and regional television. Over the years, however, cable TV has developed into much more than a technology providing high quality reception. The cable industry is now known for the diversity of its programming and for the independent content it creates.

Most cable TV firms are monopolists, designated as such by a franchise agreement with the local government. This treatment is partly a response to the fact that cable TV is a natural monopoly in most markets. Production of cable TV service requires investment in the construction of a "headend," through which satellite TV transmissions are received, as well as the much more costly laying of coaxial or fibre-optic cable to create the distribution network. Once those fixed costs have been incurred, the incremental cost of connecting a household to the network is minimal. As a result, the average cost per subscriber is lower when only one cable company serves a given area.

Since its inception, the cable TV industry has been on a roller coaster ride of regulation and deregulation. Originally, the industry was subject to price regulation by the CRTC. However in recent years the CRTC has not regulated prices because of increased competition from satellite TV. Many of the large cable and satellite companies applied for and received relief from regulation in 2002. Since then consumers—and broadcasters that receive no compensation for cable use of over-the-air signals—have complained about the rate of increase of cable and satellite service and excessive profits of that sector. Since deregulation in 2002 through early 2008

there was a 71.2 percent increase in basic cable rates of Rogers customers in Toronto Peel, Ottawa West, and Saint John while basic cable rates served by Shaw in Vancouver, Winnipeg East, and Calgary increased 67.8 percent.[24] Steve Guiton, the chief regulatory officer of CBC/Radio-Canada said in September of 2009 that Canadian cable rates had increased six times as fast as those south of the border in the past five years.

In October of 2009 the CBC complained of excessive profits in the cable and satellite industry, claiming that CRTC filings showed profits of approximately $2 billion in 2008, up 33 percent from the year before. Over the same time period broadcaster profits were only $8 million, down 92 percent from the year before. In March 2010 the CRTC ruled that broadcasters such as CTV and Canwest, but not the CBC, can choose to negotiate payments from cable and satellite companies. The CRTC specifically said that television stations will be able to "enter into negotiations to establish a fair value for the distribution of their programs." The CRTC ruling fell short of requiring cable and satellite firms to pay a fee to broadcasters. Broadcasters, excepting the CBC, can pull their signals from cable and satellite feeds if they are not satisfied with the results of the negotiations. The chairman of the CRTC, Konrad von Finckenstein, in discussing the new framework, said that "The current dispute between conventional broadcasters and distributors threatens the overall integrity of the broadcasting system...The time has come for them to put their differences aside and work together to ensure the continuation of conventional television, which Canadians clearly value."

---

[24]Friends of Canadian Broadcasting press release dated October 28, 2009 titled "CRTC decision on cable de-regulation–October 30th."

Government Ownership of Monopolies

Sometimes in response to concerns about the high prices and other social costs of monopoly, the government acquires ownership of a monopoly. The Canadian government, for example, owns Canada Post and Via Rail. Likewise, the City of Guelph, Ontario, owns the firm that supplies electricity to the city.

With government ownership, the need for elaborate regulatory hearings to set a price is eliminated. Instead, government employees or politicians set the prices. This approach to pricing can save a considerable amount of resources. It also eliminates the incentives for the owner or manager of a privately owned monopoly to overstate the firm's costs in order to justify a higher price.

At the same time, government ownership is not without problems. The most significant involve the incentives of those who control the publicly owned firm. The owners of a privately owned firm are concerned mainly with profit, as are the firm's managers, whose pay is often tied to the firm's financial success. This focus on profit drives owners and managers to produce their products efficiently. In a publicly owned firm, however, the politicians and bureaucrats who control the firm may have many other incentives. Re-election, retaining control of the firm, and a taste for the easy life all may take precedence over efficient production.

Like the regulation of privately owned monopolies, the extent of government ownership of monopolies is cyclical. The trend over the last 20 to 30 years in the Canada and many other countries has been to move away from government ownership.

*17.8 MULTIPRODUCT MONOPOLY

Most firms sell more than one product. Sometimes those products are substitutes for one another. For example, gas stations usually sell both premium and regular-grade gasoline. If the gas station lowers the price of regular gas, sales of premium gas are likely to fall, because some consumers will decide that the benefits of premium gas are no longer worth the extra cost.

At other times, a firm will sell products that are complements. For example, Microsoft sells not only the Windows® operating system, but the Office software suite, among many other software programs. If Microsoft sets the price of Windows too high, consumers may decide not to buy a computer, or they may buy fewer computers. That would reduce the demand for Microsoft Office®. Likewise, Gillette razors and razor blades are complements; so are the tickets and popcorn that movie theatres sell.

Does the fact that a monopolist sells more than one product affect its profit-maximizing price for a given product? If the demand for each product is not related to the others, then the monopolist can determine the price of each product separately, using the methods discussed in Section 17.2.[25] But that is not the case if the demand for each product is related to the others.

Consider the case of complementary products. When a monopolist's products are complements, the profit-maximizing price of any of its products typically will be lower

---

[25]The approach in Section 17.2 can be generalized easily to the case in which the costs of a firm's products are interrelated but the demands are independent. In that case, the firm should still set the marginal revenue for each product equal to its marginal cost, but where that marginal cost is the level given how much the firm is producing of its other products.

than if the firm sold only that one product. The reason is that lowering the price of any one product will increase sales of the others.

To illustrate this point, let's consider the example of the single movie theatre in a small town. The theatre sells two products, tickets and popcorn. Suppose the weekly demand for movie tickets is

$$Q^d_{tix} = 500 - 20P_{tix} - 10P_{popcorn}$$

where P_{tix} and $P_{popcorn}$ are the prices of a ticket and a bag of popcorn, respectively. Ticket sales will fall if the theatre raises the ticket price. They will also fall if the theatre raises the popcorn price, because patrons who like to eat popcorn while watching a movie will anticipate a more expensive evening at the theatre. These moviegoers may decide to stay home or to seek other forms of entertainment. Suppose that each time a moviegoer buys a ticket, his demand for popcorn at the theatre is

$$Q^d_{popcorn} = 3 - 0.4P_{popcorn}$$

where $Q^d_{popcorn}$ is the number of bags of popcorn the moviegoer buys. If the price of popcorn goes up, some moviegoers will decide not to buy it.

Suppose further that the theatre's marginal cost of a ticket is $2, while the marginal cost of a bag of popcorn is $0.50. Let's find the movie theatre's profit-maximizing ticket price if popcorn sells for $5 a bag. Given the price of popcorn, the demand for tickets can be written as

$$Q^d_{tix} = 500 - 20P_{tix} - 10(5) = 450 - 20P_{tix}$$

The inverse demand function for tickets is therefore

$$P_{tix} = 22.50 - 0.05Q_{tix}$$

and (using formula (1) on page 620) the marginal revenue earned on ticket sales is

$$MR_{tix} = 22.50 - 0.1Q_{tix}$$

As usual, the theatre's profit-maximizing ticket price equates the marginal revenue and marginal cost of a ticket. Now, however, the theatre owner needs to take into account how the sale of an additional ticket affects the profit from popcorn sales. One way to think about that effect is that it changes the true marginal cost of selling a ticket. That is, while the theatre incurs $2 of direct expenses when it sells a ticket, it also makes money on popcorn sales to that customer. If the price of popcorn is $5, each ticket buyer purchases $Q^d_{popcorn} = 3 - (0.4)5 = 1$ bag of popcorn, and the theatre makes $4.50 on that bag. So rather than incurring a $2 cost from each ticket sale, the theatre's true marginal cost of a ticket sale once popcorn profits have been taken into account is $-\$2.50$. It is as if the marginal cost of a ticket is negative.

As a result, to find the theatre's profit-maximizing number of tickets, we must set the marginal revenue from a ticket sale equal to the true marginal cost of selling a ticket.

$$22.50 - 0.1Q_{tix} = -2.50$$

Solving this equation, we find that the theatre will sell 250 tickets per week. From the inverse demand function, we see that to do so the owner will charge $10 per ticket ($= 22.50 - (0.05)250$). The profit from ticket sales will be $2000 per week (250 tickets times a profit of $8 on each ticket), and the theatre will make an additional profit of $1125 on sales of popcorn (250 bags times a profit of $4.50 on each bag). The profit earned on popcorn sales, which effectively lowers the marginal cost of selling a ticket, encourages the theatre owner to lower the ticket price in order to sell more tickets.[26]

Sometimes this kind of effect can be so strong that the profit-maximizing price of one of the firm's products is below its direct marginal cost. For example, the movie monopolist might sell a ticket for less than $2. In that case, the product is called a **loss leader**. In fact, sometimes firms even give away one of their products—for example, a razor—to encourage sales of a complementary product, like razor blades.

In this example, the two complementary products are sold to the same consumers. In some settings, however, the two products are sold to different purchasers. For example, Google's search engine produces two basic products, information searches of the World Wide Web, which are used by individuals, and advertising space on the Web site, which is used by advertisers. The more individuals who use Google to search the Web, the greater the demand for advertising space on the site. The complementarity of the two products will lower Google's profit-maximizing price for searches. In fact, Google gives away its search results, treating them as a loss leader.

When a firm's products are *substitutes* rather than complements, the opposite effect occurs. That is, the profit-maximizing price of any given product typically will be higher than it would otherwise be, because increasing the price increases the sales of the other product. Exercise 17.20 at the end of the chapter provides an example.

> A **loss leader** is a product that is sold at a price below its direct marginal cost to encourage sales of a complementary product.

Application 17.8

Why Is the Price of Microsoft Windows® So Low?

The U.S. government's antitrust case against Microsoft, referred to at the beginning of this chapter, generated tremendous controversy. The government accused Microsoft of monopolizing the market for personal computer operating systems, and of using various anticompetitive practices to protect its monopoly. One part of the controversy concerned the question of whether Microsoft could reasonably be considered a monopolist. Economist Richard Schmalensee, arguing on Microsoft's behalf, claimed that the company faced competition from several current and prospective competitors, such as Linux and Apple. Those rivals, he reasoned, forced Microsoft to keep the price of Windows lower than a monopolist would charge. Indeed, even though every personal computer must have an operating system, Microsoft earns only about $65 in revenue on each copy of Windows that is installed on a new computer, despite the fact that the computer itself might sell for thousands of dollars.

To support his claim, Schmalensee attempted to show that $65 is much less than the price Microsoft would charge for Windows if the company were really a monopolist.[27] To do that, he started by determining the elasticity of demand for Windows that would have led Microsoft to charge $65 if it were a monopolist. He included the fact that Microsoft expects to sell complementary products, such as Office, Excel, and other software, to consumers who purchase Windows. This was important for him to do because one reason that Microsoft might set a low price for Windows, even if it were a monopolist, is that it also profits from sales of these complementary products. Based on evidence from Microsoft's records, he estimated that these other purchases would generate a profit of $160 per computer.

---

[26]In this discussion, we've taken the $5 price of popcorn as a given. In general, however, the theatre owner will want to set that price so as to maximize profit as well. In doing so, the owner will need to consider how the price of popcorn affects the sale of movie tickets. When the owner has chosen both prices so as to maximize profit, the price of each product will equate that product's marginal revenue with its true marginal cost, including its effect on the profits from the other product.

[27]For further discussion of this calculation, see Richard Schmalensee, "Antitrust Issues in Schumpeterian Industries," *American Economic Review* 90, May 2000, pp. 192–196.

(This amount is the discounted present value of a future profit stream; see Chapter 10.) Since the marginal cost of selling a license to use Windows is essentially zero, we can think of Microsoft's effective marginal cost as −$160. The Lerner Index for Windows at a price of $65 is therefore 3.46 [= (65 − (−160))/65]. Formula (4) on page 625 then implies that if Microsoft is a monopolist its elasticity of demand must be −0.29.[28]

Is that elasticity of demand for Windows plausible? An elasticity of −0.29 means that a 100 percent increase in the price of Windows, an increase of $65, would reduce Windows demand by roughly 29 percent (assuming a constant-elasticity demand curve). Schmalensee argued that such a scenario was inconsistent with sensible estimates of the elasticity of demand for personal computers. Why? If Microsoft were indeed a monopolist, then every PC would need a copy of Windows. So an increase of $65 in the price of Windows would also cause a 29 percent reduction in the sales of personal computers. But since PCs sold for an average of at least $1600 (in 1990), Schmalensee argued, it is implausible that a $65 dollar increase in the total cost of purchasing a PC would reduce PC sales by 29 percent; it would mean that the elasticity of demand for PCs is −7.4, an implausibly large magnitude. However, if the elasticity of demand for PCs is much less than this value, then Microsoft's profit-maximizing price for Windows, were it a monopolist, would be much greater than $65.

Schmalensee's conclusions were challenged by the government's expert witness, economist Franklin Fisher, who argued that the average price of a PC was closer to $1000, implying that the elasticity of demand for PCs that would be consistent with the monopoly price of Windows being $65 was instead only −4.8. Fisher concluded that computer purchases might well be this price sensitive. Without firsthand access to the data these economists used, it is difficult to reach a definitive conclusion about their claims. In the end, the court dismissed Schmalensee's argument and declared Microsoft a monopolist.

CHAPTER SUMMARY

1. **Market power (LO1)**

   a. A firm has market power if it can profitably charge a price that is above its marginal cost.

   b. A monopoly market is a market with a single seller; an oligopoly market has a few (but not many) sellers.

   c. In situations in which market power exists, economists define the market to include products that are close substitutes for one another but to exclude more distant substitutes.

2. **Monopoly pricing (LO2)**

   a. A monopolist's marginal revenue is determined by both output expansion and price reduction effects. Because of the price reduction effect, a monopolist's marginal revenue is less than his price, except when his sales quantity is zero, where it equals the price.

   b. If the monopolist's profit-maximizing sales quantity is positive, it occurs at a point where marginal revenue equals marginal cost. The monopolist can find the profit-maximizing sales quantity by first identifying the most profitable positive sales quantity at which marginal revenue equals marginal cost (the quantity rule) and then checking whether that sales quantity results in a greater profit than does shutting down (the shut-down rule).

   c. At the profit-maximizing price, a monopolist's markup (or price-cost margin, or Lerner Index), $(P − MC)/P$, is equal to the reciprocal of the elasticity of market demand, times negative one.

3. **Welfare effects of monopoly pricing (LO2)**

   a. By raising the price above marginal cost, a monopolist increases profit but reduces consumers' well-being.

   b. Monopoly pricing results in a deadweight loss, because aggregate surplus fails to achieve its maximum possible level. Put differently, the harm to consumers from monopoly pricing is greater than the monopolist's gain in profit.

4. **Distinguishing monopoly from perfect competition (LO3)**

   a. A monopolist responds to changes in demand and cost differently from firms in a perfectly competitive industry. This can provide ways to tell if a group of firms is competing vigorously or is instead colluding and acting just like a monopolist.

---

[28]In Section 17.2 we observed that demand must be elastic at a monopolist's profit-maximizing price *when the marginal cost is positive*. When the marginal cost is negative as here, however, demand can be inelastic at the profit-maximizing price.

b. A monopolist's price depends on the elasticity of demand, while the price in a perfectly competitive market depends on the level of demand. As a result, a rotation of the demand curve through the initial price and sales quantity will change the monopolist's price, but not the price in a perfectly competitive market.

c. In a perfectly competitive market, an increase in marginal cost never increases the price by more than the increase in marginal cost. A monopolist's price may increase by more than the increase in marginal cost.

5. **Nonprice effects of monopoly (LO3)**

a. When all consumers value an increase in a product's quality by the same amount, a monopolist will produce the level of quality that maximizes aggregate surplus.

b. If some consumers value increases in quality more than others, the monopolist will not necessarily provide the quality level that maximizes aggregate surplus.

c. A monopolist's incentive to advertise depends on both the amount by which the price exceeds the marginal cost (which depends on the price elasticity of demand) and the responsiveness of demand to advertising.

d. Investments that are made with the aim of becoming a monopolist can be either socially beneficial or wasteful (through rent seeking).

6. **Monopsony (LO4)**

a. Sometimes the buyers in a market enjoy market power, so that they need not take the price at which a good is sold as given. In extreme cases, there may be only a single buyer for a good, known as a monopsonist.

b. The analysis of monopsony parallels the analysis of monopoly. Monopsonists can reduce the amount that they pay for a good by reducing the quantity they buy.

c. A monopsonist's marginal expenditure is determined by input expansion and price increase effects. The price increase effect makes a monopsonist's marginal expenditure greater than the input price, except when the monopsonist's purchase of the input is zero, where it equals the input price.

d. The optimal purchase quantity for the monopsonist, if positive, equates the marginal benefit from the good to the marginal expenditure.

e. The monopsonist buys less of a good than the amount that would maximize aggregate surplus, leading to a deadweight loss.

7. **Regulation of monopolies (LO5)**

a. In response to concerns about monopoly pricing, governments may decide to regulate monopolies. Some monopolies arise because the market can be profitable for only one firm. Others are created by the government. Governments sometimes create monopolies in natural monopoly markets, in which the entry of a second firm would lead to inefficient production.

b. Ideally, government regulators would set the monopolist's price at the "competitive price," which would maximize aggregate surplus. In practice, however, that price would often cause the regulated firm to lose money. In that case, they may implement second-best price regulation, which involves setting the price so as to maximize aggregate surplus, subject to the constraint that the firm not lose money.

c. In practice, price regulation can cause other problems, such as discouraging efforts at cost reduction, allowing regulators to pursue aims other than economic efficiency, and permitting regulatory capture.

d. Sometimes concern over monopoly pricing leads to government ownership, which can eliminate some problems of regulation (such as elaborate rate hearings), but may lead to other problems (such as elimination of the profit motive).

*8. **Multiproduct monopoly (LO6)**

a. When a monopolist sells products that are complements or substitutes, the profit-maximizing price of any given product takes account of the effects on sales of other products.

b. If a monopolist sells one product (say, popcorn) at a price above its marginal cost and it is a complement to another product (say, a movie ticket) the monopolist also sells, the monopolist will have an incentive to set a lower price for the second product (the movie ticket) because doing so will increase sales of the first product (popcorn). If instead the first product is a substitute for the second, the monopolist will have an incentive to set a higher price for the second product because, with substitutes, doing so increases sales of the first product.

ADDITIONAL EXERCISES

Exercise 17.1: Consider the market for canned tuna fish. The labels fall into three categories: premium imported brands (Callipo, Rio Mare), medium quality (Clover Leaf, Gold Seal), and store brand. There is chunk light tuna and solid white tuna, tuna packed in water and tuna packed in oil. Is there a single "canned tuna" market? A "premium tuna" market? What factors are important in defining this market? (LO1)

Exercise 17.2: Suppose that Noah and Naomi have a monopoly in the garden bench market. Their weekly demand is $D(P) = 500 - 4P$. What is their marginal revenue when they sell 100 garden benches a week? Graph their inverse demand and marginal revenue curves. (LO2)

Exercise 17.3: Show that a monopolist's marginal revenue will be positive at a certain sales quantity only if the demand for the firm's product at that point on its demand curve, E^d, is elastic; that is, if $E^d < -1$. (LO2)

Exercise 17.4: Consider again the problem of Kenora Competition-free Concrete in worked-out problem 17.2 (page 624). Suppose that Kenora's marginal cost is instead $20 per cubic metre and its avoidable fixed costs are $100,000 per year. What are its profit-maximizing sales quantity and price? How would your answer change if Kenora had an avoidable fixed cost of $200,000 a year? What if that fixed cost were instead sunk? (LO2)

Exercise 17.5: Suppose that Kenora Competition-free Concrete's demand function is $D(P) = 5000 - 50P$, its marginal cost is $40 per cubic metre, and it faces an avoidable fixed cost of $40,000 per year. What are its profit-maximizing sales quantity and price? (LO2)

Exercise 17.6: Consider again the problem of Kenora Competition-free Concrete in worked-out problem 17.2 (page 624). Suppose that Kenora's marginal cost is $MC = 20 + 0.02Q$. What are its profit-maximizing sales quantity and price? (LO2)

Exercise 17.7: What is the deadweight loss from monopoly pricing in exercises 17.4 and 17.5? (LO2)

Exercise 17.8: What is the deadweight loss from monopoly pricing in exercise 17.6? (LO2)

Exercise 17.9: Show that if a monopolist's marginal cost goes up at every level of output, its profit-maximizing price will go up as well. (LO3)

Exercise 17.10: There is a demand curve with a slope of -0.01125 that goes through the price and quantity chosen by Kenora Competition-free Concrete in worked-out problem 17.2 on page 624 (KCC sold 4800 cubic metres at a price of $56). What is the inverse demand function for this demand curve? With this demand curve, what are KCC's profit-maximizing sales quantity and price? How do these compare to KCC's profit-maximizing sales quantity and price in worked-out problem 17.2? How does this comparison relate to the discussion in Section 17.4? (LO3)

Exercise 17.11: A local video rental monopolist faces the weekly demand function $D(P) = 1000 - 50P$. The marginal cost of a rental is $1. Suppose the town government places a $1 tax on all video rentals. What effect will the tax have on the price the monopolist charges? What will be the pass-through rate? (LO3)

Exercise 17.12: After Apple introduced its new iPhone, the price of standard cell phones rose. A consumer advocacy group that has long claimed that standard cell phone producers are colluding like a monopolist asserts that this is further evidence of that fact. You've noticed that the elasticity of

demand for standard cell phones increased after Apple's entry. Does this shed any light on the group's claim? (LO3)

Exercise 17.13: Consider again the video monopolist in exercise 17.11. What per-unit subsidy would persuade the monopolist to sell the same quantity of rentals that would be sold in a competitive video rental industry? (LO3)

Exercise 17.14: The South African firm De Beers was responsible for the well-known ad line "A Diamond Is Forever." Notably, the firm's advertisements never mentioned the De Beers brand name. Why would only a near-monopolist such as De Beers omit its name? (LO3)

Exercise 17.15: The Happyland Hospital is a monopsonist employer of nurses in the small city of Happyland. The supply function of nurses is $S(W) = 0.1W - 100$, where W is the nurses' weekly wage. What is the hospital's marginal expenditure, ME? If the hospital's marginal benefit is $2000 per week no matter how many nurses it hires, what is the profit-maximizing number of nurses for the hospital to hire? What will the nurses' wage be? What is the deadweight loss? (LO4)

Exercise 17.16: Can you think of three examples of natural monopolies? (LO5)

Exercise 17.17: Suppose that in Exercise 17.4, the government wants to regulate Kenora Competition-free Concrete. What price will maximize aggregate surplus in this market? If the government must ensure that KCC does not lose money, what is the second-best price that maximizes aggregate surplus, subject to this constraint? (LO5)

Exercise 17.18: Suppose that in worked-out problem 17.2 (page 624), the government wants to regulate Kenora Competition-free Concrete. To do so, regulators institute a price ceiling that sets the maximum price KCC can charge. What price will KCC charge and how much will it sell if the price ceiling is set between $56 (the monopoly price) and $40 (the price if KCC acts like a price taker)? What if the price ceiling is below $40? (Assume, for simplicity, that KCC has no fixed costs.) (LO5)

*Exercise 17.19: Consider the movie ticket and popcorn example discussed in Section 17.8. If the marginal cost of popcorn is instead $1 per bag, what is the profit-maximizing price of a movie ticket? Explain intuitively why this profit-maximizing price is different from the profit-maximizing price in Section 17.8. (LO5)

*Exercise 17.20: The only gas station in a small town sells both regular and premium gasoline. The weekly demand functions for the two types of gasoline are

$$Q^d_{regular} = 10,000 - 1000P_{regular} + 250P_{premium}$$

and

$$Q^d_{premium} = 650 + 150P_{regular} - 500P_{premium}$$

where quantities are measured in litres and prices in dollars per litre. Are these products substitutes or complements? If the price of regular gas is $1.00 per litre, its marginal cost is $0.95, and the marginal cost of premium is $1.05, what is the profit-maximizing price of premium gas? (LO5)

Exercise 17.21: Suppose that the government imposes a specific tax (see Section 15.1) of T dollars on a good sold by a monopolist. Does it matter for the amount bought and sold, and the total cost per unit to consumers, whether the tax is paid by consumers or the monopolist? (LO2)

Exercise 17.22: Suppose that in April a monopolist handed out a coupon to every consumer offering a discount of T dollars off of the purchase price of its product during the

month of May. What effect will those coupons have on the amount of the product the monopolist sells in May, the final cost per unit to consumers, and the monopolist's profit? (LO4)

Exercise 17.23: The following table lists six independent scenarios for six different firms, each of which is either a monopolist or perfectly competitive. For each row, fill out the missing information and indicate, if not already indicated, whether the firm is a monopoly or a competitive firm. There are no avoidable fixed costs. "Min" means that the cost curve is at its minimum point. Assume the firm in each row is maximizing profit. (LO2, 3)

Market Structure	Price	Quantity	Cost	Variable Cost	Marginal Cost	Average Cost	Average Variable Cost	Average Fixed Cost	Marginal Revenue	Profit
Monopoly	12		220		5		5	6		
Competitive		10				5	3			−10
		15				8	6		4	0
			600			min		0	6	0
Competitive				200	8			5		−50
	16			240		15	min	7		

18

Pricing Strategies

LEARNING OBJECTIVES

After reading this chapter, students should be able to

LO1 Define price discrimination and the conditions necessary for price discrimination to be successful.

LO2 Identify various ways that a firm can price discriminate.

LO3 Describe the outcome of perfect price discrimination and its welfare effects.

LO4 Identify a monopolist's profit-maximizing prices when it can discriminate based on observable customer characteristics and calculate the welfare effects of that discrimination.

LO5 Understand how pricing based on self-selection can increase a firm's profit.

LO6 Understand how bundling and mixed bundling of several products together can increase firm profits.

An Intel 486SX chip

I n 1989 Intel introduced a new and improved generation of microprocessors called the 486. Among its other innovative features, the 486 was the first microprocessor to offer a built-in math coprocessor capable of handling complex numerical calculations. Two years later, Intel introduced another new chip called the 486SX and renamed the original the 486DX. The SX, which was less powerful than the DX, was targeted at purchasers of lower-end computers. Intel produced it by disabling the math coprocessor of an otherwise fully functional 486DX. As a result, the less powerful SX actually cost *more* to produce than the more powerful DX. Nonetheless, Intel priced the SX at just $333, compared to $588 for the 486DX.

Why would Intel spend money to disable a 486DX, which sold for $588, in order to market it as an SX at $333?

As we'll see in this chapter, this seemingly illogical decision allowed Intel to extract profit from lower-end customers without sacrificing profit from higher-end customers. As a result, Intel earned higher profits than it would have by continuing to market a single 486 processor at the monopoly price.

In this chapter we'll study the pricing tactics that firms like Intel use to increase profits beyond the levels attainable at a single monopoly price (see Chapter 17). We'll cover five topics:

1. *Price discrimination: pricing to extract surplus.* Under certain conditions, a firm with market power can increase its profit by charging different prices for different units of the same good, a practice known as *price discrimination*. We'll identify the conditions required for successful price discrimination, and discuss different ways that a firm can price discriminate.

2. *Perfect price discrimination.* We'll first examine the extreme case in which a firm's ability to price discriminate is perfect because it can observe consumers' willingness to pay for every unit it sells and can set a distinct price for each of those units. Though rarely applicable in practice, this case serves as a useful starting point for our discussion.

3. *Price discrimination based on observable customer characteristics.* Sometimes a firm that can't perfectly price discriminate can nonetheless distinguish between two or more distinct groups of customers. In such cases, it may be able to earn more by selling to different groups at different prices. We'll study the firm's profit-maximizing pricing strategy and consider the consequences for consumer and aggregate welfare.

4. *Price discrimination based on self-selection.* Sometimes a firm's managers know that different customers belong to different groups but can't distinguish among them. In such cases, the firm may be able to price discriminate by offering each customer a menu of alternatives, designed to encourage different customers to make different choices in a process known as *self-selection*. We'll see how this tactic can increase the firm's profit.

*5. *Bundling.* For firms that sell more than one product, it is sometimes profitable to make the price or availability of one good dependent on the purchase of another good. We'll consider one simple version of this approach, the practice of selling goods together as a bundle.

18.1 PRICE DISCRIMINATION: PRICING TO EXTRACT SURPLUS

In Chapter 17 we studied how a monopolist that sells all of its output at a single price chooses that price (or, equivalently, its sales quantity) to maximize profit. The monopolist does so by equating marginal revenue and marginal cost, as in Figure 17.4 (page 624). Is there a way for the monopolist to do even better?

Looking back at Figure 17.4, we can see that the monopolist's profit would be larger if two problems were solved. First, consumers who buy some of the product at the monopoly price receive some consumer surplus. That means that those units of the product are worth more to them than they are paying. If the monopolist could charge those consumers more for those same units, that would increase the monopolist's profit. Second, consumers aren't purchasing units of the good that they value less than the monopoly price but more than the monopolist's marginal cost of producing them. (These are the units that are not bought at the monopoly price but would be bought at the competitive price.) If the monopolist could charge these buyers less for the same units, but more than those units' marginal cost, its profit would be higher.

These observations suggest that the monopolist might be able to do better by charging *different* prices for different units of the good, a practice known as **price discrimination**. The idea is to charge higher prices for units for which consumers have a high willingness to pay than for those units for which the willingness to pay is low.

> A firm engages in **price discrimination** when it charges different prices for different units of the same good.

To be able to price discriminate, a firm must have some market power. If it doesn't, any attempt to set a price above marginal cost will result in no sales. In most of this chapter, we'll focus for simplicity on the extreme case in which the firm is a monopolist. Doing so will simplify the analysis of price discrimination, allowing us to defer the consideration of strategic interaction until Chapter 19. Nonetheless, the issues we discuss here apply as well to firms whose market power falls short of monopoly.

To price discriminate successfully, the firm must also be able to distinguish sales for which the purchasers have a high willingness to pay from those for which the purchasers have a low willingness to pay. In some rare cases, a firm may know perfectly a customer's willingness to pay for each unit it sells and may be able to charge a different price for each unit. This case is called **perfect price discrimination**. A monopolist that sells a production input to another firm, for example, might know the customer's willingness to pay by understanding the firm's technology and the prices of the firm's output and other inputs. For those that sell to retail consumers, knowing a customer's willingness to pay can be more difficult. Nonetheless, firms try hard to discover this information. An important part of the car salesperson's job, for example, is to discern customers' willingness to pay when they walk into the showroom. The consumer's dress, speech, family size, address, and place of employment all reveal valuable information. A good car salesperson is expert at reading these cues and basing the prices offered to the customer on that information.

> A monopolist can **perfectly price discriminate** if it knows perfectly the customer's willingness to pay for each unit and can charge a different price for each unit.

Usually, though, a customer's willingness to pay is not known perfectly by a firm. In that case, the firm may distinguish purchases for which the customer has a high versus a low willingness to pay in two different ways. In some cases, the distinguishing factor is an observable difference between customers. For example, a ski area operator might know that local residents, whose incomes are lower than those of visitors, generally have a lower willingness to pay for a lift ticket than tourists. If so, the ski area can then offer a special discount to patrons who show a local driver's license. This practice is an example of price discrimination based on **observable customer characteristics**.

> Price discrimination is based on **observable customer characteristics** when a firm can distinguish, even if imperfectly, consumers with a high versus a low willingness to pay.

Sometimes firms can effectively charge different prices to different customers even though there are no observable characteristics that reveal information about the customer's willingness to pay. They do so by offering a menu of alternatives, designed so that different customers will make different choices based on their willingness to pay. For example, passengers on the same airline flight might pay very different fares, depending on whether their return flight involves a Saturday night stay-over. Because many business travelers (who generally have a higher willingness to pay) wish to spend the weekend with their families, they will choose the higher-priced tickets. By requiring a Saturday night stay-over to qualify for the lower rate, then, airlines manage to charge business travelers more than leisure travelers—even though they cannot directly observe which consumers are booking their flights for business and which for leisure. This practice is an example of price discrimination based on **self-selection**.

One common tool that helps firms achieve price discrimination is **quantity-dependent** (or **volume-sensitive**) **pricing**, in which the price the consumer pays for an additional unit depends on how many units the consumer has already bought (see also Add-On 5D). The simplest kind of quantity-dependent pricing is evident at the supermarket, where larger bottles of ketchup, mayonnaise, and dish detergent typically sell for less per ounce than smaller bottles. More refined quantity-dependent pricing makes the price dependent on a buyer's overall purchases, which requires that the firm be able to monitor those purchases. For example, a store may offer a rebate based on a consumer's total purchases. Airline frequent flier programs are, in essence, also an example of this type of pricing.

In Section 18.2 we'll see that a monopolist that can perfectly discriminate can use quantity-dependent pricing to maximize its profit. Quantity-dependent pricing can also be an effective method of price discrimination when perfect discrimination isn't possible, as long as customers with different propensities to buy a high quantity tend to differ in their willingness to pay. We'll see how a firm can use quantity-dependent pricing to maximize its profit in those circumstances in Section 18.4.

Finally, if a firm wants to charge different prices to different consumers, the good or service must be difficult to resell. Otherwise, if the firm tries to charge Harry $100 and Ryan $80, Ryan could buy two units and resell one of them to Harry for $90. Both of them would be better off: Ryan would make a $10 profit, and Harry would pay $90 instead of $100. The firm would sell both units at $80, the lower of the two prices.

For some goods and services, resale simply isn't feasible. When a service provider such as a plumber or a doctor charges different prices to different people, there is no way for those people to resell the service. On the other hand, if the publisher of this book tried to charge economics majors more than non-majors (on the theory that majors need the book more than others), no doubt the majors would ask their non-major friends to buy their books for them. Few sales would occur at the higher price.

> Price discrimination is based on **self-selection** when the firm offers a menu of alternatives, designed so that different customers will make different choices based on their willingness to pay.
>
> In a **quantity-dependent** (or **volume-sensitive**) **pricing** plan, the price a consumer pays for an additional unit depends on how many units the consumer has bought.

"O.K. Fair enough. That's a great price for mayonnaise."

18.2 PERFECT PRICE DISCRIMINATION

Although firms rarely know *perfectly* their customers' willingness to pay, the case of perfect price discrimination is a useful place to start our discussion. To see how perfect price discrimination works in a simple setting, let's consider again the market for ice cream cones shown in Figure 14.16 (page 519). Recall that Emily and Juan are the only two consumers in this market. Figure 18.1(a) shows Emily's demand curve, reproduced from Figure 14.16(a). The shaded vertical bars represent her willingness to pay for each cone.

Now let's imagine that there is a monopolist of ice cream cones, the Ice Cream Monopoly Company, that knows Emily and Juan's exact willingness to pay for each cone. The monopolist can set the price for each cone Emily wants so that it is equal to (or maybe

Figure 18.1

Emily's Prices and Total Payments with Perfect Price Discrimination. Figure (a) shows Emily's demand curve for ice cream cones. The perfectly discriminating monopolist sets the price for each cone equal to Emily's willingness to pay for that cone, represented by the height of her demand curve at that cone. Figure (b) shows the corresponding total payments. Since prices decline as Emily buys more, she gets a quantity discount.

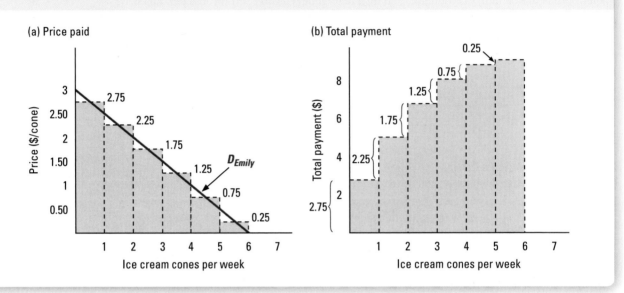

a penny less than) her willingness to pay for it. For example, when Emily buys her first cone, the monopolist can charge her $2.75, the height of the first blue bar. When she buys her second cone, the monopolist can charge her $2.25, the height of the second blue bar. It can charge $1.75 for her third cone. Emily would then pay a total of $6.75 for the three cones.[1] As she buys more, the amount she pays for a cone decreases, so that Emily receives a quantity discount. Hence, perfect price discrimination uses quantity-dependent pricing as well as pricing based on observable characteristics of the individual. Figure 18.1(b) shows the relationship between the total amount she pays (measured on the vertical axis) and the number of cones she buys. The height of each step is equal to the price paid for each additional cone. The monopolist can take the same approach to Juan's purchases.

Since a perfectly discriminating monopolist collects an amount equal to the consumer's willingness to pay for each cone it sells, its marginal revenue curve coincides with the market demand curve, as Figure 18.2 shows. (The blue- and red-shaded bars represent the cones demanded by Emily and Juan, respectively, as in Figure 14.16(c); we'll discuss the green shading between the demand and marginal cost curves shortly.) Let's suppose that the monopolist's marginal cost is $1.50 per cone. (Throughout the chapter we'll assume, to keep things simple, that the monopolist's marginal cost is constant. The same conclusions hold, though, in the more general case where the marginal cost varies with the amount produced.) In that case, the monopolist's profit-maximizing sales quantity, which occurs

---

[1]We assume here that there are no income effects for ice cream cones. If there were, we would need to use compensated demand curves to derive the amount the monopolist can charge for each cone, as described in Section 6.5.

Figure 18.2
A Perfectly Price Discriminating Monopolist's Sales Quantity. Because a perfectly discriminating monopolist's marginal revenue curve coincides with the market demand curve, it sells exactly the same number of units as would a perfectly competitive industry with the same marginal cost curve, here seven cones.

where $MR = MC$, is the quantity at which the market demand curve crosses the marginal cost curve. In Figure 18.2, this amount is seven cones, of which Emily buys three and Juan four. This observation leads us to a striking conclusion: *With perfect price discrimination, the monopolist produces exactly the same quantity, and each consumer consumes exactly the same quantity, as would occur in a perfectly competitive market.* Thus, the outcome with perfect price discrimination is efficient; there is no deadweight loss.

We can make two important inferences from this exercise. First, a price-discriminating monopoly need not be inefficient. Second, in terms of efficiency, allowing a monopolist to price discriminate may not make market outcomes worse, and may even make them better. That said, the outcome for the consumers, Emily and Juan, is not very good here, because they receive no surplus at all. The monopolist earns as profit the entire aggregate surplus, equal to the green-shaded area in Figure 18.2.

We'll see soon that when the monopolist's ability to price discriminate is less than perfect, price discrimination sometimes increases consumer and aggregate surplus and sometimes decreases them.

> **IN-TEXT EXERCISE 18.1**   **Let Elena's demand for candy bars be given by $Q^d = 10 - 2P$ and let Peter's demand for candy bars be given by $Q^d = 12 - 3P$. If a perfectly price discriminating monopolist's marginal cost is \$1 how many candy bars will be sold to Elena and Peter? How much consumer surplus is captured by the firm?**

Two-Part Tariffs

Our perfectly discriminating monopolist set a price for each cone it sold to Emily that equalled her willingness to pay for it. While that is one type of quantity-dependent pricing plan, it is not the only quantity-dependent pricing plan that allows a perfectly discriminating monopolist to maximize profit.

With a **two-part tariff**,
consumers pay a fixed fee
if they buy anything at all,
plus a separate per-unit
price for each unit they buy.

Another, simpler type of quantity-dependent pricing is known as a two-part tariff. With a **two-part tariff**, consumers pay a fixed fee if they buy anything at all, plus a separate per-unit price for each unit they buy. Two-part tariffs are commonly used by both monopolists and firms whose market power falls short of monopoly. Amusement parks may charge an entry fee plus a separate price per ride. Telephone companies (both traditional and wireless) often charge a monthly fee plus a price per minute used. Many rental car companies combine a daily charge with a price per mile. Warehouse clubs like Costco charge an annual fee as well as a separate price for each item purchased (see Application 6.5). And nightclubs often have a separate cover charge that is added to the price of food and drink. We'll study two-part tariffs in more detail in Section 18.4. Here we'll see how a perfectly discriminating monopolist can use this type of pricing plan to maximize profit. The two-part tariff has the advantage of simplicity: rather than naming a different price for every unit it sells to a customer, the monopolist can name just two charges for each consumer, a fixed fee and a per-unit price.

Suppose the Ice Cream Monopoly Company offers Emily a two-part tariff. Specifically, it creates an ice cream lovers' club that entitles members to buy cones for only $1.50 each after they have paid a weekly fixed fee. What is the largest fixed fee the monopolist can charge Emily without causing her to stop buying ice cream cones? Figure 18.3 shows the answer. Once Emily has accepted the plan and paid the fixed fee, she can buy cones for $1.50 each. At that price, she'll demand three cones. Her consumer surplus before paying the fixed fee is the light green-shaded triangle, which equals $2.25 (see Section 6.2 for a discussion of consumer surplus). That means Emily will be willing to pay a weekly fee of up to $2.25, but no more. If the monopolist charges a fixed fee of $2, for example, then Emily will find it worthwhile to pay the fixed fee, since she will get a positive net benefit (equal to $0.25) after paying the fixed fee. The same would be true if the fixed fee were $2.20, or even $2.24.

Notice that this two-part tariff results in Emily buying the same number of cones (three) as when the monopolist charged different prices for each cone based on her willingness to pay (see Figure 18.2). It also yields the same total revenue: $6.75 ($4.50 for the three cones, equal to the dark-green rectangle, plus the $2.25 weekly fee). So the Ice Cream Monopoly Company's profit from selling cones to Emily is exactly the same as

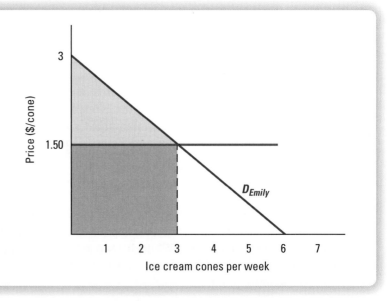

Figure 18.3

A Two-Part Tariff. If Emily faces a per-cone charge of $1.50, her consumer surplus is $2.25, the light green-shaded triangle in the figure. That is the largest fixed fee the monopolist can charge and still have Emily buy. The monopolist's total revenue on sales to Emily with this two-part tariff equals $6.75, the sum of the light- and dark-green shaded areas. (The dark green rectangle is revenue from sales of cones at the $1.50 per-cone price.)

before. It could do the same with Juan, offering him a per-cone price of $1.50 in return for a weekly fee that extracts all of his surplus. (Juan's weekly fee would be different from Emily's, however. See end-of-chapter exercise 18.2.) The consumer surplus captured from Elena and Peter by the perfectly discriminating monopolist in in-text exercise 18.1 is identical to the fixed fee charged if the firm is setting a two-part tariff.

Is there something special about the per-cone price of $1.50? Yes. That price equals the Ice Cream Monopoly Company's marginal cost, so it induces ice cream club members to buy exactly the same number of cones as they would in a perfectly competitive market (which is the same number of cones the perfectly discriminating monopolist sold earlier). At a price of $1.50 aggregate surplus is maximized and is exactly equal to consumer surplus. Worked-out problem 18.1 shows that to maximize its profit using a two-part tariff, a perfectly discriminating monopolist needs to set the per-unit charge equal to its marginal cost.

WORKED-OUT PROBLEM   18.1

The Problem   Clearvoice is a wireless telephone monopolist in a rural area. There are 100 consumers, each of whom has a monthly demand curve for wireless minutes of $Q^d = 100 - 100P$, where P is the per-minute price in dollars. The marginal cost of providing wireless service is 10 cents per minute. If Clearvoice charges 20 cents per minute, how large a fixed fee can it charge and still persuade consumers to buy its service? What will be Clearvoice's profit from each consumer? What will be its fixed fee and profit if it instead charges 10 cents per minute? Which of these two-part tariffs produces a larger profit?

The Solution   As Figure 18.4 shows, when the price is 20 cents per minute, each consumer will buy 80 minutes of service per month. The consumer's surplus before paying the fixed fee equals the green-shaded triangle with a height of $0.80 and base of 80 minutes. That area equals $32. So Clearvoice can charge a fixed fee of $32 per month without discouraging consumers from buying. In addition, Clearvoice makes $0.10 on each of the 80 minutes it sells to a consumer, for an additional profit of $8. This equals the area of the yellow-shaded rectangle. So Clearvoice makes $40 on each consumer, the sum of the green triangle and yellow rectangle. Its total profit is $4000 per month.

Repeating the calculations for the lower per-unit price, a consumer who pays 10 cents per minute will buy 90 minutes and will enjoy a surplus of $40.50 (the area of the triangle formed by the green-, yellow-, and red-shaded areas, with a height of $0.90 and a base of 90 minutes). Clearvoice can charge this amount for the fixed fee. Since 10 cents equals the marginal cost, Clearvoice won't make anything on the sale of minutes. Its profit from each consumer is therefore $40.50, and its total profit is $4050 per month. This two-part tariff yields a larger profit than the one with a per-minute price of 20 cents.

Note that the 50-cent difference in profit from each consumer between the two plans equals the area of the red-shaded triangle. This triangle represents the deadweight loss caused by the 20-cent-per-minute charge, which exceeds Clearvoice's marginal cost. Because a perfectly discriminating monopolist receives all of the surplus, any deadweight loss created by setting the per-unit price above marginal cost comes right out of its pocket.

Figure 18.4

Profit with a Two-Part Tariff and Identical Consumers. The figure shows the profit for the wireless telephone monopolist Clearvoice when its marginal cost is 10 cents per minute and it offers a consumer a two-part tariff with a per-minute price of 20 cents. The yellow-shaded area is the profit from sales of minutes. In addition, Clearvoice can charge a fixed fee equal to the green-shaded area. Its profit, equal to the sum of those two areas, falls short of the maximum possible aggregate surplus by an amount equal to the red-shaded triangle. By lowering its per-minute charge to 10 cents, equal to its marginal cost, and raising its fixed fee to equal the sum of the three shaded areas, Clearvoice can increase its profit.

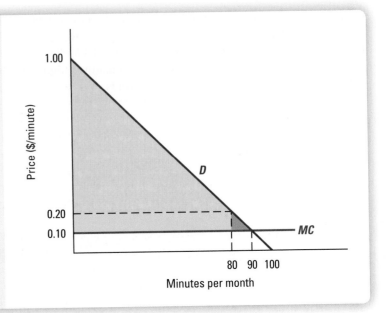

> **IN-TEXT EXERCISE 18.2**   **Suppose that Clearvoice in worked-out problem 18.1 charges 30 cents per minute. How large a fixed fee can Clearvoice charge and still persuade consumers to buy the service? What will be its profit from each consumer? What will be its total profit, and how will this amount compare to its total profit with a per-minute charge of 10 cents? Of 20 cents?**

18.3 PRICE DISCRIMINATION BASED ON OBSERVABLE CUSTOMER CHARACTERISTICS

Most often, a firm's ability to price discriminate is imperfect. Customers' observable characteristics may say something about their willingness to pay but fall short of revealing it completely. In this section, we'll see how a monopolist should price when it can sort customers into rough groups based on their observable characteristics, but knows no more about their willingness to pay and cannot engage in quantity-dependent pricing (perhaps a consumer purchases only one unit or the monopolist cannot track how much each consumer buys).

Take the simple example of a small-town movie theatre monopolist who can sort consumers into four groups: adults, children, senior citizens, and university students. Within each group, however, she cannot differentiate those who are willing to pay high prices from those who are not. Nor can she monitor how often each moviegoer attends the theatre.

How should our movie monopolist set her prices? For the sake of simplicity, we'll focus on the case in which the marginal cost of selling a seat is the same for each group, regardless of how many tickets the theatre sells.[2] Given the monopolist's inability to

---

[2]This is a reasonable assumption as long as the shows do not sell out. (Once a show sells out, the marginal cost effectively becomes infinite.) The marginal cost might equal a per-ticket payment the theatre must make to the film distributor plus the cost of cleaning up after the movie is over.

differentiate consumers within each group and to track their purchases, the most the movie monopolist can do is set a different ticket price for each group. For example, she can charge senior citizens a different price from university students.

In this case, the movie monopolist can treat the different groups as if they belong to completely separate markets. To maximize her profit, the monopolist should consider each group's demand curve separately, setting the price so as to maximize the profit earned from that group. To set the senior citizens' price, for example, she should look at the senior citizens' demand curve and find the number of ticket sales that equates senior citizen marginal revenue with marginal cost, exactly as the single-product monopolist did in Section 17.2.

The movie monopolist will want to set different prices whenever the groups have different elasticities of demand, charging a higher price to groups with less elastic demand (that is, a less negative elasticity of demand). To see why, let's think about the case of just two groups—university students and other adults—whose demand functions each have a constant elasticity. We'll let E_s^d be the students' elasticity of demand and E_s^d be the elasticity of demand of other adults. Recall from Section 17.2 that the profit-maximizing price is set so that the markup equals the reciprocal of the elasticity of demand, times -1. So,

$$\frac{P_s - MC}{P_s} = -\frac{1}{E_s^d} \tag{1}$$

where P_S is the student price. Similarly, letting P_A be the price for other adults,

$$\frac{P_A - MC}{P_A} = -\frac{1}{E_A^d} \tag{2}$$

If students have a more elastic demand than other adults, then $-(1/E_A^d) > -(1/E_s^d)$. Formulas (1) and (2) then imply that the markup for students will be less than the markup for other adults; that is, $(P_S - M_C)/P_S < (P_A - M_C)/P_A$. This statement implies, in turn, that the student price will be less than the price for other adults: $P_S < P_A$.[3]

More generally, the group that will face the higher price is the one with the less elastic demand at the profit-maximizing no-discrimination price. Starting at that price, the monopolist will want to raise the price of the less elastic group and lower the price of the more elastic group. Worked-out problem 18.2 illustrates this point.

WORKED-OUT PROBLEM 18.2

The Problem A movie monopolist sells to university students and other adults. The demand function for students is $Q_s^d = 800 - 100P$ and the demand function for other adults is $Q_A^d = 1600 - 100P$. Marginal cost is $2 per ticket. What prices will the monopolist set when she can discriminate and when she cannot? How will discrimination affect the monopolist's profit?

---

[3]If the monopolist's marginal cost depends on the number of tickets she sells, the optimal student and other adult prices will still satisfy formulas (1) and (2), but MC in those formulas will depend on the total number of tickets she sells to all of the groups. As a result, the optimal price for each group will depend on the amount sold to the other groups, and the monopolist will need to determine the optimal prices for the various groups together (see end-of-chapter exercise 18.11).

The Solution:

Step 1: Find the profit-maximizing student price and the associated profit. The inverse demand function for students is $P_S = 8 - 0.01Q_S$. So student marginal revenue is

$$MR_S = P_S + (\Delta P_S / \Delta Q_S)Q_S$$
$$= 8 - 0.01Q_S - 0.01Q_S$$
$$= 8 - 0.02Q_S$$

Setting this marginal revenue equal to marginal cost, $MR_S = MC$, we have

$$8 - 0.02Q_S = 2$$

Solving for Q_S tells us that the monopolist will maximize her profit from university students by selling 300 student tickets. To sell that number of student tickets, the monopolist will set a student price of $5 [= 8 - (0.01)300]$, as shown in Figure 18.5(a). Profit from students will be $(5 - 2) \times 300 = \$900$, the green rectangle's area. The elasticity of the student demand curve is -1.67. (This elasticity equals $(\Delta Q_S^d / \Delta P)(P/Q_S^d) = -100 \times (5/300) = -5/3$, since students demand 300 tickets at that price.) Markup equals the absolute value of the reciprocal of the elasticity of demand and is equal to 0.6.

Step 2: Find the profit-maximizing price for other adults and the associated profit. Following a similar procedure as in step 1, the inverse demand function for other adults is $P_A = 16 - 0.01Q_A$, so marginal revenue is $MR_A = 16 - 0.02Q_A$. Setting

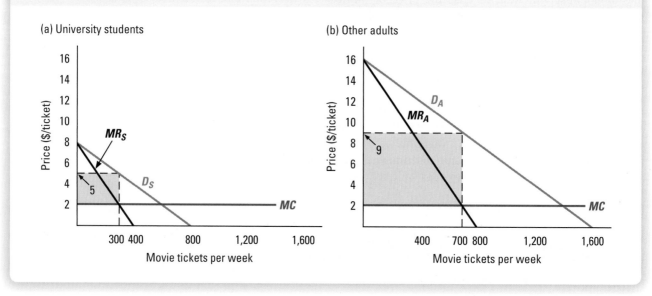

Figure 18.5

Profit-Maximizing Prices to Two Groups of Consumers. Figures (a) and (b) show the demand, marginal revenue, and marginal cost curves for university students and other adults, respectively, in worked-out problem 18.2. The monopolist maximizes her profit by setting a ticket price of $5 for university students and $9 for other adults. The profit from each group is the area of the green-shaded rectangle, $900 from students and $4900 from other adults.

other adult marginal revenue equal to marginal cost, we find that the monopolist should sell $Q_A = 700$ adult tickets to maximize the profit from other adults. Doing so requires an adult price of $9, as shown in Figure 18.5(b). The monopolist's profit from other adults will be $(9 - 2) \times 700 = \$4900$. The elasticity of the adult demand curve is -1.29. (This elasticity equals $(\Delta Q_A^d/\Delta P)(P/Q_A^d) = -100 \times (9/700) = -9/7$, since students demand 300 tickets at that price.) Markup equals the absolute value of the reciprocal of the elasticity of demand and is equal to 0.78.

Step 3: Find the profit-maximizing price without discrimination and the associated profit. The market demand function (which is the sum of the student and other adult demand functions) is

$$Q^d = \begin{cases} 1600 - 100P \text{ for } P > 8 \\ 2400 - 200P \text{ for } P \leq 8 \end{cases}$$

This demand function corresponds to the market demand curve shown in dark blue and labelled D in Figure 18.6(a). We can find the inverse demand function for curve D in two parts: one for quantities below 800, and the other for quantities above 800. The inverse demand in each of those regions is the inverse demand function for the corresponding part of the market demand function just given.

$$P = \begin{cases} 16 - 0.01Q \text{ for } Q < 800 \\ 12 - 0.005Q \text{ for } Q \geq 800 \end{cases}$$

Figure 18.6

Profit-Maximizing Price without Discrimination. Figure (a) shows the market demand curve for movie tickets (D), which is the horizontal sum of the demand curves for university students (D_S) and other adults (D_A). Figure (b) shows the market demand, marginal revenue, and marginal cost curves when the movie-monopolist cannot discriminate. Marginal revenue equals marginal cost at two sales quantities, $Q = 700$ and $Q = 1000$. Profit is higher at $Q = 1000$ (it is $5000, equal to the area of the green-shaded rectangle), which requires a price of $7 and involves both groups buying tickets.

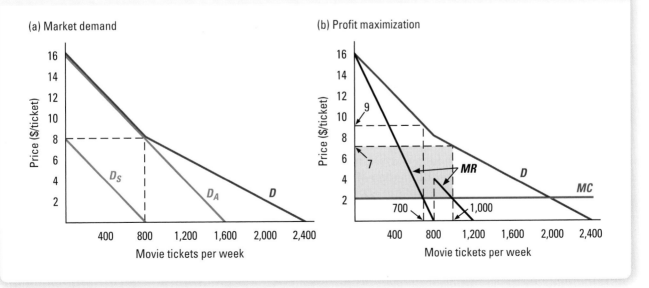

Likewise, we can find the marginal revenue by deriving the marginal revenue from this inverse demand function separately for quantities below 800 and above 800:

$$MR = \begin{cases} 16 - 0.02Q \text{ for } Q < 800 \\ 12 - 0.01Q \text{ for } Q \geq 800 \end{cases}$$

To find the profit-maximizing price, we need to look for all the sales quantities at which marginal revenue equals marginal cost, and then determine which of those quantities (if there is more than one) offers the highest profit. (This is another example of the approach we studied in Section 3.2 and the appendix to Chapter 3). Figure 18.6(b) shows the market demand, the two marginal revenue curves, and the marginal cost curve. Note that the marginal cost curve crosses both of the marginal revenue curves twice. At quantities above 800, marginal revenue equals marginal cost where

$$12 - 0.01Q = 2$$

which occurs at $Q = 1000$. This quantity requires a price of $7 and yields a profit of $(7 - 2) \times 1000 = \$5000$. Both groups buy positive amounts at that price.

At quantities below 800, marginal revenue equals marginal cost at $Q = 700$. This quantity requires a price of $9, so that only other adults will make purchases, and yields a profit of $4900. (That is the same profit the monopolist makes by selling only to other adults when discrimination is possible.) Since the profit at $Q = 1000$ exceeds the profit at $Q = 700$, the more profitable price is $7, at which the monopolist sells 1000 tickets for a profit of $5000.[4] From the demand functions, we know that students buy 100 of these tickets and other adults buy 900.

Note that the profit-maximizing price without discrimination, $7, lies between the discriminating prices that the monopolist would charge students and other adults. Observe that at the no-discrimination price of $7, the elasticity of the student demand curve is -7 (this elasticity equals $(\Delta Q_s^d / \Delta P)(P / Q_s^d) = -100 \times (7/100) = -7$, since students demand 100 tickets at that price), while the elasticity of other adult demand is -0.78 (this elasticity equals $(\Delta Q_A^d / \Delta P)(P / \Delta Q_A^d) = -100 \times (7/900) = -7/9$, since other adults demand 900 tickets at that price). Since student demand is more elastic than other adult demand, it is profitable to lower the student price and raise the price for other adults.

Step 4: Compare profits with and without discrimination. The total profit with discrimination is $5800, or the sum of the $900 profit from students and the $4900 profit from other adults. Discrimination, which allows the monopolist to price separately for each group, has increased the profit by $800, from $5000 to $5800—a 16 percent increase.

IN-TEXT EXERCISE 18.3   Suppose the demand function for other adults is the same as in worked-out problem 18.2, but the demand function for students is $Q_s^d = 2400 - 300P$. Marginal cost is still $2 per ticket. What prices will the monopolist set when she can discriminate and when she cannot? How will discrimination affect her profit?

---

[4]We must also compare the profit at a price of $7 to two other possibilities. The first is shutting down and producing nothing. Since shutting down yields a profit of zero it is less profitable than setting a price of $7. The second possibility is pricing to sell 800 tickets, the quantity at which marginal revenue jumps. (As in Application 9.3, we need to check the profits at any point where either marginal revenue or marginal cost jumps.) Selling 800 tickets requires a price of $8 and results in a profit of $4800, less than the profit with a price of $7. (Another way to see that selling 800 tickets is not profit maximizing is to use the No Marginal Improvement Principle to show that either a small increase or decrease in quantity would raise profit, because MR is greater than MC just above 800 tickets and MR is less than MC just below 800 tickets.)

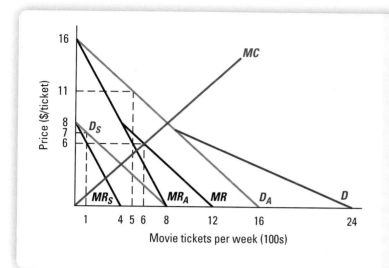

Figure 18.7

Profit-Maximizing Prices with Increasing Marginal Cost. The total marginal revenue curve for movie tickets (MR is the horizontal sum of the marginal revenue curves for college students (MR_S) and other adults (MR_A). Above $8 the total marginal revenue curve is just the marginal revenue curve for adults. The marginal cost curve intersects the total marginal revenue curve at an output of 600 tickets so that marginal cost equals $6. Equating marginal cost to the marginal revenue curves for students and adults, the theatre maximizes profits by selling 100 tickets to students at $7 each and 500 tickets to adults at $11 each.

If marginal cost is not constant, the determination of the profit-maximizing price with discrimination is not as straightforward. Previously, with marginal costs constant at two, the profit-maximizing level of output in the student and adult markets was found by equating marginal revenue to marginal cost in each market. Marginal cost did not vary with the amount of output. If marginal cost is given by

$$MC = 0.01Q$$

marginal costs vary with output and a different procedure is required. In this case marginal cost is equated with the total marginal revenue curve

$$MR = \begin{cases} 16 - 0.02Q \text{ for } Q < 400 \\ 12 - 0.01Q \text{ for } Q \geq 400 \end{cases}$$

rather than finding the intersection point of the marginal revenue curves in each market with the marginal cost curve. In Figure 18.7 the marginal cost curve would intersect the kinked total marginal revenue curve where $Q = 600$ at a marginal costs of $MC = 6$. Equating the value of marginal cost at 600 units of output to the individual marginal revenue curves for the adult and student markets gives the profit maximizing strategy for the monopolist. The theatre will sell 100 tickets to university students at a price of $7 and will sell 500 tickets to adults at a price of $11.

Application 18.1

International Price Discrimination

One form of price discrimination based on observable characteristics arises when firms sell their products at different prices in different countries. For example, some firms charge different prices for the same product in Canada and the United States. Their ability to do so depends on how readily consumers in the high-priced country can cross the border, buy the product, and bring it home, or have a friend buy at the lower price and ship it to them.

The problem of consumer border crossing is potentially acute for firms like Amazon, Office Depot, and Home Depot, which sell directly to consumers through their Web sites. To facilitate price discrimination, these firms have set up a different Web site for each country. How different are the prices listed on these Web sites? Table 18.1 shows the Canadian and U.S. prices of various goods that were featured on Amazon's Web sites on November 18, 2009. (The U.S. prices have been converted to Canadian dollars.) The final column gives the price difference as a percentage of the U.S. price.

As the table shows, most items were selling at higher prices in Canada than in the United States. However, the price differences varied substantially from one item to the next. These retail prices could reflect price discrimination by Amazon, or they could reflect discrimination by the manufacturers (who could charge Amazon a different price for units sold in each country).

Table 18.1
Amazon's Prices in Canada and the United States

Item	Canadian Price ($)	U.S. Price (Can$)	% Price Difference
Microsoft Windows 7® Home Premium Upgrade	130.49	112.32	+16.2
Canon PowerShot A480 10MP digital camera	123.99	112.11	+10.6
Paparazzi (Lady Gaga)	11.99	8.90	+34.7
Casino Royale (Blue Ray)	22.99	18.33	+25.4
Call of Duty: Modern Warfare 2 (PS3)	59.99	62.88	−4.6

Welfare Effects of Imperfect Price Discrimination

What are the welfare effects of price discrimination based on observed characteristics? Certainly, profit is at least as large with discrimination as without. After all, the monopolist is always free to charge every group the same price; she wouldn't charge different prices unless doing so benefited her. As for consumers, price discrimination affects different groups differently. A group is worse off if its price rises as a result of discrimination and better off if its price falls. For example, the price discrimination by the movie theatre monopolist in worked-out problem 18.2 made students better off and other adults worse off.

What about aggregate surplus and consumer surplus as a whole? Consider aggregate surplus. Price discrimination has two main effects on aggregate surplus. The first is bad: different consumers pay different prices. As a result, a consumer who faces a low price and decides to buy the good may have a lower willingness to pay than a consumer who faces a high price and decides *not* to buy the good. That result is inefficient. Both total consumer surplus and aggregate surplus are largest when a good is consumed by those who value it most. Indeed, we learned in Section 14.4 that a competitive equilibrium efficiently allocates goods to those consumers who value them most precisely because all consumers face the same price.

Figure 18.8 illustrates the inefficiency that arises when different consumers face different prices. The demand curves for university students, other adults, and all

Figure 18.8

Welfare Effects of Price Discrimination. Aggregate surplus falls because the same number of tickets (1000) are sold with and without discrimination but are inefficiently distributed with discrimination. Total consumer surplus is smaller with discrimination because the gain to university students (the green-shaded area) is more than offset by the loss to other adults (the red-shaded area). Aggregate surplus falls with discrimination because the gain in profit ($800) is less than the reduction in consumer surplus ($1200).

consumers are the same as in Figure 18.6. With discrimination, university students face a price of $5 per ticket and buy 300 tickets, while other adults face a price of $9 per ticket and buy 700 tickets. However, the 1000 tickets are not allocated to the consumers with the highest willingness to pay for them. In particular, the last student ticket is sold to someone who values it at $5. Among those who did not buy tickets, the other adult with the highest willingness to pay values it more highly, at just under $9.

The second effect, however, can work in the opposite direction: price discrimination may encourage the monopolist to sell more tickets. Since without discrimination, the monopolist will sell too few tickets, this effect can increase aggregate surplus. (We saw in Section 18.2, for example, that *perfect* price discrimination maximizes aggregate surplus.)

Depending on the particulars, these two opposing effects can combine to either raise or lower aggregate surplus. The same is true for consumer surplus. Worked-out problem 18.3 provides an example in which both consumer surplus and aggregate surplus are reduced by discrimination.

WORKED-OUT PROBLEM   18.3

The Problem Consider the movie monopolist in worked-out problem 18.2 (page 665). How does her price discrimination affect consumer surplus and aggregate surplus?

The Solution Price discrimination helps students, who face a lower price, and hurts other adults, who face a higher one. The gain for students, which equals the green-shaded area in Figure 18.8, is $400 (this area is a trapezoid with a height of 2, one base equal to 100, and the other base equal to 300). The loss for other adults, which equals the red-shaded area, is $1600 (this area is a trapezoid with a height of 2, one base equal to 700, and the other base equal to 900). Total consumer surplus is therefore $1200 lower with price discrimination than without.

Profit increases by $800 (as worked-out problem 18.2 showed), but consumer surplus decreases by $1200, so price discrimination lowers aggregate surplus by $400. (In fact, since 1000 tickets are sold both with and without discrimination, we know that aggregate surplus *must* fall. Those 1000 tickets are distributed efficiently only if all consumers face the same price—that is, without price discrimination.)

IN-TEXT EXERCISE 18.4 **Suppose that the demands of other adults and students are the same as in in-text exercise 18.3 (page 668). Marginal cost is $2 per ticket. How does price discrimination affect consumer surplus and aggregate surplus?**

Price discrimination doesn't always reduce consumer surplus and aggregate surplus. Figure 18.9, for example, illustrates a case in which discrimination increases both

Figure 18.9
Price Discrimination Can Increase Consumer and Aggregate Surplus. The figure shows a case in which the other adult demand curve is the same as in Figure 18.8, but there is less student demand. The profit-maximizing price when discrimination is not possible is $P = \$9$, which is the same as the adult ticket price P_A with discrimination. With discrimination, though, the monopolist also offers a student ticket for a price of $P_S = \$3$. So consumer and aggregate surplus are both increased with discrimination. In fact, both students and the monopolist are better off with discrimination, while other adults are unaffected.

aggregate surplus and consumer surplus. As before, we've assumed that a small-town movie monopolist can distinguish between university students and other adults. In this case, student demand is low, so the student demand curve D_S hits the vertical axis at $4 and shows that few tickets are sold even at a price of $2. Without price discrimination, the monopolist will find it worthwhile to sell only to other adults, setting a price of $9. No student will buy a ticket at that price. With discrimination, the monopolist will still offer an adult ticket for $9, but will add a student ticket for $3. In this case, then, the price-discriminating monopolist will sell more tickets than she would have without discrimination, and both aggregate surplus and consumer surplus are higher with discrimination. (Exercise 18.7 at the end of this chapter asks you to confirm these claims.) In fact, in this example price discrimination benefits some parties (the monopolist and those students who are willing to pay more than $3 for a ticket) and hurts no one (since other adults pay $9 per ticket regardless).

Price Discrimination and Market Power

In a competitive market, firms can't price discriminate. A competitive firm knows it can sell as much as it wants at the market price, but nothing at a higher price. As a result, every unit a competitive firm produces is sold at a price that equals its marginal cost. Thus, one way to tell whether a market is perfectly competitive is to see whether there is price discrimination.

That said, telling whether price discrimination exists can be surprisingly difficult because different prices may reflect cost differences rather than price discrimination. For example, if other adults drop more popcorn on the floor than students do, the higher price they pay for a movie ticket may just reflect the cost of cleaning up after them. Even in a perfectly competitive market, they would pay more for their tickets—the extra amount they would pay would exactly equal the extra cleanup cost.

Moreover, while the presence of price discrimination does indicate that a market isn't *perfectly* competitive, it doesn't necessarily mean that it is very far from perfectly competitive. How far from perfectly competitive must a market be for price discrimination to occur? The answer is *not very far*. Even markets that feature a good deal of competition (but aren't perfectly competitive) can exhibit a lot of price discrimination.

Oligopolists, in fact, may price discriminate *more* than monopolists. Why might that be so? A complete explanation would require some of the tools we'll develop in Chapter 19, but the basic idea is easy to grasp. Price discrimination occurs when a firm's customers have different elasticities of demand, which reflect their responsiveness to the firm's price changes. In a monopoly market, a consumer can respond to a price increase only by buying less of the product. So price discrimination occurs in a monopoly market only if consumers have different propensities to purchase the good. In an oligopoly market, however, a consumer can respond to a firm's price increase either by buying less of the product or by switching to another firm. As a result, price discrimination may occur for reasons different from those in a monopoly market: consumers may differ in their willingness to switch firms. Thus, when the strength of brand loyalties differs greatly across identifiable groups of consumers, oligopolies tend to display greater price discrimination than monopolies.

Application 18.2 discusses some evidence on this point.

Application 18.2

Price Discrimination in Airline Markets

As anyone who has ever bought an airline ticket knows, not everyone on the plane pays the same price. First-class and business-class tickets cost more than economy-class tickets. Even within economy class, however, different passengers usually pay different prices. These prices depend on when they bought their tickets, whether their tickets are one way or round trip, and (for those who are flying round trip) whether their itinerary includes a Saturday night stay-over.

Economists Severin Borenstein and Nancy Rose studied the degree of price dispersion in airline markets.[5] To do so, they examined a sample of economy-class tickets in 521 of the largest airline markets in 1986.[6] They found a substantial amount of price dispersion. On average, the tickets of two randomly drawn economy-class passengers on the same route differed by an amount equal to 36 percent of the average economy-class fare.

Borenstein and Rose also investigated the relationship between the degree of price dispersion and the extent of competition on a route. They found that the level of price discrimination was *higher* in markets with more competitors than in others. Their results imply that, on average, an airline market with two competing firms would show roughly 25 percent more price dispersion than a market with only one firm.

What caused these surprising results? Airline passengers can differ markedly in their willingness to switch carriers. Some are very loyal to a particular airline because they like the service, know the terminal configuration, or belong to the frequent flier program and therefore want to accumulate a lot of miles on one airline. Other passengers just want the cheapest seat they can find. These differences in loyalty create strong incentives to price discriminate in an oligopoly airline market. An airline's most loyal customers are typically travelling primarily for business. Restrictions on Saturday night stay-overs and discounts for advance purchases can be an effective means to charge those loyal customers higher prices.

18.4 PRICE DISCRIMINATION BASED ON SELF-SELECTION

Often, firms cannot distinguish between groups of customers based on observable characteristics. Nonetheless, price discrimination may still be possible if the monopolist is sufficiently clever. In particular, the firm may be able to discriminate by offering customers a menu of alternatives, designed so that customers with different degrees of willingness to pay will choose different alternatives.

To give a fanciful example, suppose the only movie theatre in a small university town cannot offer lower prices to students. (Maybe the practice is prohibited by law, or maybe the theatre can't tell who really is a student because of fake student IDs.) If the theatre has two screens, the management could feature music by Lady Gaga before the lights go down in one screening room, and music by Barry Manilow in the other. In that

---

[5]Severin Borenstein and Nancy L. Rose, "Competition and Price Dispersion in the U.S. Airline Industry," *Journal of Political Economy* 102, August 1994, pp. 653–683.

[6]In this case, a market is defined as travel between two specific airports. Borenstein and Rose restricted their attention to *direct* tickets—those that were either nonstop or did not require a change of plane.

case, students might find the first screening room enjoyable and the other horrific. Other adults would probably react the opposite way.[7] Even if the theatre charged different prices for tickets to the two screening rooms, each group of moviegoers would choose the room intended for it. Thus, even though the monopolist can't discriminate directly based on consumers' observed characteristics, he can still manage to do so indirectly, by carefully designing the theatre's offerings so that customers select the one intended for them.

While the movie theatre example is fanciful, in practice this type of price discrimination is quite common. Supermarkets give discounts to consumers who are willing to take the time to clip coupons. They do so because customers who are coupon clippers tend to be more price sensitive than others. Less price-sensitive consumers choose to pay more rather than clip coupons, but they save time. Similarly, wireless telephone companies offer multiple calling plans. Some, designed for consumers with a low willingness to pay, offer low monthly charges but don't include much prepaid calling time. Others, designed for consumers with a high willingness to pay, carry much higher monthly charges but offer a great deal of prepaid calling time. Application 18.3 discusses some other examples of price discrimination based on self-selection.

Application 18.3

Damaged Goods

In an effort to price discriminate, firms frequently offer different versions of a product or service so that consumers with a high or low willingness to pay can self-select. In fact, to accomplish this goal, a manufacturer will sometimes incur extra expense to produce a lower-quality version of a product. Economists Raymond Deneckere and Preston McAfee refer to such versions as *damaged goods*.[8]

Intel's 486 microprocessor, discussed in the introduction to this chapter, is one example of a damaged good. Intel hoped to sell the more powerful 486DX to consumers with a high willingness to pay for a computer (and therefore a chip), and the less powerful 486SX with the disabled math coprocessor to consumers with a low willingness to pay. Critical to the success of this strategy was the fact that consumers with a high willingness to pay would accept a higher price rather than forgo the math coprocessor, while those with a low willingness to pay wouldn't care that much about the performance difference.

To give another example from a high-tech industry, consider IBM's 1990 introduction of the LaserPrinter E, a low-cost alternative to its then-popular LaserPrinter. The two printers were virtually identical, except that the E model printed text at five pages per minute, compared to the LaserPrinter's 10 pages per minute. How did IBM achieve this critical difference? By including special controllers to slow the print speed of the E, at extra expense. Like Intel, IBM wanted a lower-priced model that could be targeted at consumers with a low willingness to pay.

Students encounter this type of strategy regularly when they buy discounted student versions of popular software programs. Despite the fact that software vendors try to verify that their customers really are students, and even though students aren't supposed to share or copy the programs, firms still worry about nonstudents purchasing them at discounted prices. As a result, they often go to the trouble of disabling some functions in the student version, so that

---

[7]Admittedly, Barry Manilow might just be very unpleasant to students rather than horrific, and some other adults might prefer Lady Gaga to Barry Manilow. For the purposes of this example, though, assume this is how the two types of consumers would react.

[8]Raymond J. Deneckere and R. Preston McAfee, "Damaged Goods," *Journal of Economics and Management Strategy* 5, Summer 1986, pp. 149–174.

consumers with a high willingness to pay will be willing to pay a higher price for the complete version.

Table 18.2 illustrates the benefits of a damaged-good pricing strategy through an example involving the sale of a software program. We'll assume that the marginal cost of providing software to another user is zero. The table considers a situation in which there are two types of consumers for a software program, who have either a high or a low willingness to pay respectively. The first row indicates that there are 100 individuals of each type. The second row shows that high willingness-to-pay consumers are willing to pay $100 for the full program; while low willingness-to-pay consumers are willing to pay only $40. Therefore, if the software firm sells only the full program, it will charge $100 and sell only to high willingness-to-pay consumers (doing so it earns $10,000, versus $8000 if it charges $40 and sells to both types of consumer).

Now suppose the firm produces a "damaged" version that omits some features. The third row of Table 18.2 shows that high willingness-to-pay consumers are willing to pay only $40 for that version, while low willingness-to-pay consumers are willing to pay $30. Suppose the monopolist charges $29.99 for the damaged version, and $89.98 for the full version. Low willingness-to-pay consumers will buy the damaged version; doing so gives them a surplus of a penny. What about high willingness-to-pay consumers? They'll each buy the full version: doing so gives them each a surplus of $10.02 (the $100 willingness to pay less the $89.98 price), while they enjoy a surplus $10.01 from buying the damaged version (the $40 willingness to pay less the $29.99 price). The software firm's profit from this strategy is $11,997, $1997 more than the profit from selling only the full version.

Table 18.2
A Damaged-Good Pricing Strategy

	High Willingness-to-Pay Consumers	Low Willingness-to-Pay Consumers
Number	100	100
Willingness to pay for full version	$100	$40
Willingness to pay for damaged version	$40	$30

Quantity-Dependent Pricing and Self-Selection

In the rest of this section, we'll explore in more detail one particular method of price discriminating through self-selection, quantity-dependent pricing (see Sections 18.1 and 18.2). Specifically, we'll consider a firm that can offer consumers two-part tariff plans and we'll examine how those plans should be designed to maximize the firm's profit.

In Section 18.2 we saw that a perfectly discriminating monopolist can maximize its profit by offering each consumer a two-part tariff plan in which the per-unit charge equals the marginal cost and the fixed fee equals the consumer's surplus at that per-unit price. Such a plan maximizes aggregate surplus and leaves the consumer no surplus—the monopolist gets all the aggregate surplus as profit. When the monopolist can't directly observe consumers' characteristics, however, this level of profit won't be achievable.

To illustrate the problem, consider again the Clearvoice wireless telephone monopolist from worked-out problem 18.1 (page 663). Now, however, suppose Clearvoice faces two types of consumers, whose demands for wireless telephone service are shown in Figure 18.10. One type has the demand curve from Figure 18.4 (page 664), labelled D_H in Figure 18.10(b). These are high-demand consumers. The second type, a low-demand consumer, has the demand curve labelled D_L in Figure 18.10(a). (Figure 18.10(b) also shows

Figure 18.10

A Two-Part Tariff with Two Types of Consumers. Figures (a) and (b) show the profits the wireless telephone monopolist Clearvoice earns from low- and high-demand consumers, respectively, if both consumer types sign up for a two-part tariff with a per-minute charge of 10 cents (equal to its marginal cost) and a fixed fee of $8, the amount that leaves a low-demand consumer with no surplus. The profit from each low- or high-demand consumer equals the green-shaded area ($8) which is the monopolist's fixed fee. The high-demand consumer enjoys a surplus equal to the grey-shaded area ($32.50) while the low-demand consumer enjoys no surplus.

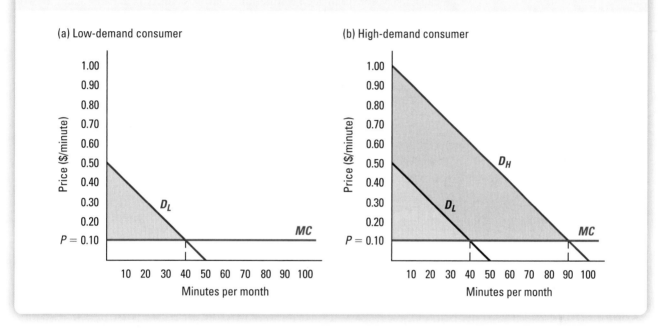

(a) Low-demand consumer

(b) High-demand consumer

demand curve D_L in black; we'll see why shortly.) A consumer with the demand curve D_H is willing to pay 50 cents more for each minute than a consumer with the demand curve D_L. For example, the first consumer's willingness to pay for the first minute is $1, compared to 50 cents for the second consumer. The figure also shows Clearvoice's marginal cost, which is 10 cents per minute.

If Clearvoice knew if a consumer had a high or low demand, it could gain all of the aggregate surplus as profit by offering each type of consumer a two-part tariff with a 10-cent-per-minute price. The fixed fee for the low-demand consumers, equal to the area of the green-shaded triangle in Figure 18.10(a), would be $8; the fixed fee for the high-demand consumers would be $40.50, as we saw in worked-out problem 18.1.

What if Clearvoice can't observe if a given consumer has a high or low demand? Suppose, for example, that in a naïve moment Clearvoice offers these same two pricing plans and asks consumers to state if they are low-demand or high-demand consumers. Individual consumers are then assigned the plan designed for their announced types. In that case, since both plans offer the same 10-cent-per-minute price, *every* consumer will claim to have a low demand so as to pay the lower ($8) fixed fee.

In effect, Clearvoice would do no better than if it had offered only the low-demand plan: it would earn $8 from each consumer (equal to the fixed fee consumers pay). In each of Figures 18.10(a) and (b), that fixed fee equals the area of the green-shaded triangle. [The black demand curve D_L in Figure 18.10(b) shows that this triangle is the same as in Figure 18.10(a).] High-demand consumers each end up with a surplus of $32.50, equal to the grey-shaded area in Figure 18.10(b). (The grey-shaded area is the portion of the area between the high-demand curve D_H and the 10-cent-per-minute MC curve that is left over after paying the fixed fee, which equals the green-shaded triangle.) This $32.50 is Clear-voice's lost profit from each high-demand consumer compared to the scenario in which it can observe consumers' types.

What can Clearvoice do in such a situation? One possibility is to offer a single two-part tariff and design it so as to maximize profit. We'll examine this possibility first. We'll see that when consumer types are not observable, Clearvoice can often do better by raising the per-minute charge above its marginal cost. Then we'll show that Clear-voice can do even better by offering consumers a *menu* of different two-part tariffs. While all consumers would opt for the plan with the lowest fixed fee if given the choice between two plans with the same per-minute price, different types of consumers may choose different plans when plans differ in their per-minute price. We'll see that by designing the menu carefully, Clearvoice can increase its profit. Some of its plans will carry high per-unit charges and low fixed fees; others will carry low per-unit charges and high fixed fees.

The Profit-Maximizing Two-Part Tariff

Let's consider first the case in which Clearvoice offers a single two-part tariff plan. When consumers have different demands, but the monopolist cannot identify which consumers are willing to pay more than others, finding the profit-maximizing two-part tariff involves carefully considering how different types of consumer will respond to various offers.

Selling to Only High-Demand Consumers   To begin, let's suppose that Clear-voice offers consumers a plan with a per-minute price of 10 cents and a fixed monthly fee of $40.50. With this plan, high-demand consumers pay the fixed fee and purchase 90 minutes of service; the monopolist makes a profit of $40.50 from each high-demand consumer. There is a potential problem with this plan, however. Since a low-demand consumer's surplus when paying 10 cents per minute is only $8, which is considerably less than the $40.50 monthly fee, a low-demand consumer will decline the offer. If there are a large number of low-demand consumers in Clearvoice's market, this two-part tariff, which attracts only high-demand consumers, may be far from profit maximizing.

Selling to Both Low- and High-Demand Consumers   Alternatively, Clearvoice could offer a two-part tariff plan that both types of consumer will accept. To do so, it must ensure that the fixed fee is no greater than the surplus that low-demand consumers enjoy at its per-minute price. We've already seen that if it charges 10 cents per minute (equal to its marginal cost), Clearvoice can charge $8 at most for the fixed fee and will earn a profit of $8 from every consumer.

How does this plan compare to offering a fixed fee of $40.50 and selling only to high-demand consumers? If there are enough low-demand consumers in the market, then the $8 fixed fee will be a better choice. For example, if there are 600 low-demand consumers and 100 high-demand consumers, then the $8 fixed fee will yield the monopolist a profit of $5600 ($8 times 700 consumers) versus $4050 from selling to only high-demand consumers at a fixed fee of $40.50. On the other hand, if there are few low-demand consumers, then selling only to high-demand consumers will be a better choice. If there are only 100 consumers of each type, for example, the $8 fixed fee will yield a profit of just $1600 versus $4050 for the $40.50 fixed fee.[9]

Among two-part tariffs that result in sales to both types of consumers, is one with a 10-cent-per-minute price the most profitable for Clearvoice? In general, the answer is no. Clearvoice can do better by raising the per-minute price above the marginal cost and lowering the fixed fee just enough to keep low-demand consumers purchasing. If it decides how much to raise the per-minute charge carefully, it will make less from low-demand consumers but will increase its profit from high-demand consumers by enough that its overall profit increases.

Let's see how this approach works. Suppose Clearvoice raises the per-minute price to 20 cents and lowers the fixed fee so that low-demand consumers are still willing to buy. The new fixed fee, equal to the area of the green-shaded triangle in Figure 18.11(a), is $4.50. Figure 18.11(a) also shows the resulting profit from a low-demand consumer. It is

Figure 18.11

Benefits of Raising the Per-Minute Price. Figures (a) and (b) show the profit from a low- and a high-demand consumer, respectively, when the per-minute price is 20 cents and the fixed fee is set to make a low-demand consumer just willing to buy. In each case, the yellow-shaded area equals the profit on sales of minutes and the green-shaded area equals the fixed fee. Total profit is the sum of these two areas. Compared to a per-minute charge of 10 cents, profit is $0.50 lower from a low-demand consumer and is $4.50 higher from a high-demand consumer. Whether overall profit is higher depends on the proportions of low- and high-demand consumers.

9This is exactly like the trade-off discussed in Chapter 17: the lower the price, the more a monopolist sells. How low Clearvoice should set the fixed fee depends on how much its sales expand as the fee falls, which depends on the number of consumers with a low willingness to pay.

composed of two parts, the area of the green triangle ($4.50), representing the fixed fee, and the area of the yellow rectangle ($3), which equals the profit Clearvoice earns on sales of minutes at the 20-cent-per-minute price (the $0.10 profit per minute times 30 minutes). The total profit from a low-demand consumer is therefore $7.50, the sum of the two amounts. Notice that this profit is less than $8, the total profit shown in Figure 18.10(a) where the monopolist sells to low-demand consumers at a per-minute price of 10 cents. The difference, $0.50, equals the deadweight loss that arises from selling to a low-demand consumer at a price that is above marginal cost.

Now let's consider high-demand consumers. Figure 18.11(b) shows the profit from a high-demand consumer. The fixed fee of $4.50, equal to the green-shaded area, is the same as for low-demand consumers. However, the profit from the sale of minutes (the yellow-shaded area) is larger than the corresponding profit from sales of minutes to a low-demand consumer because high-demand consumers buy more minutes. More important, the total profit from a high-demand consumer, equal to the sum of the yellow- and green-shaded areas, is larger than the profit the monopolist earned from a high-demand consumer in Figure 18.10(b). It is now $12.50: the $4.50 fixed fee (the green-shaded triangle) plus $8 in profit on the sale of minutes (the yellow-shaded rectangle).

By raising the per-minute price to 20 cents, then, Clearvoice makes $4.50 more from each high-demand consumer and $0.50 less from each low-demand consumer. Whether overall profit increases from this change depends on the number of high-demand consumers relative to low-demand consumers. With 600 low-demand consumers and 100 high-demand consumers, for example, profit will increase by $150. With 900 low-demand consumers and 100 high-demand consumers, Clearvoice's profit will remain the same; with more low-demand consumers than that, its profit will decrease.

Nevertheless, it is possible to show that it is *always* profitable for Clearvoice to raise the per-minute price at least a little above marginal cost if it plans on selling to both types of consumer, regardless of those types' relative proportions (see Add-On 18A). Intuitively, Clearvoice would like to extract some of the surplus of high-demand consumers without changing the surplus of low-demand consumers (whose surplus is zero). Raising the per-minute price and lowering the fixed fee is a way to accomplish this: increasing the per-minute price extracts more surplus from high-demand consumers, who buy a lot of minutes, than from low-demand consumers. Thus, if Clearvoice also adjusts the fixed fee so that a low-demand consumer's surplus is unchanged, the overall effect will be to reduce a high-demand consumer's surplus, increasing its profit.

What is the most profitable two-part tariff? Worked-out problem 18.4 compares the profitability of four different two-part tariffs. Add-On 18A discusses using algebra to find the most profitable two-part tariff among all the possibilities.

As the discussion above suggests, how much Clearvoice wants to raise the per-minute price above its marginal cost depends on the proportions of low- and high-demand consumers. The benefit of raising the per-minute price is that more profit is extracted from high-demand consumers, while the cost is that less profit is earned from low-demand consumers (because the deadweight loss for those consumers increases). Intuitively, the smaller the fraction of low-demand consumers, the smaller is the cost relative to the benefit, making it more worthwhile to raise the per-minute price. Add-On 18A discusses this effect in greater detail.

WORKED-OUT PROBLEM 18.4

The Problem   Suppose that Clearvoice serves 100 high-demand consumers, each of whose monthly demand curve for minutes of wireless service is $Q_H^d = 100 - 100P$, and 400 low-demand consumers, each of whose monthly demand curve is $Q_L^d = 50 - 100P$, where P is the per-minute price in dollars. Clearvoice's marginal cost is 10 cents per minute. If it sells to both types of consumers, which of the following per-minute prices is the most profitable: 10, 15, 20, or 25 cents? (For simplicity, assume that Clearvoice can set its fixed fee in units smaller than a penny so that it is able to extract all of the low-demand consumer's surplus.)

The Solution   Table 18.3 shows the four different per-minute prices for the quantities purchased by each type of consumer, the fixed fees, the profits from sales to each type of consumer, and the total profits. The numbers in the columns for the 10- and 20-cent-per-minute prices correspond to the amounts calculated above in the text. Those in the columns for the other two per-minute prices are calculated in the same way, where in each case the fixed fee leaves a low-demand consumer with zero surplus. (As an exercise, you should calculate these amounts for yourself.) The most profitable per-minute price is 20 cents.

IN-TEXT EXERCISE 18.5   Suppose that Clearvoice serves 100 high-demand consumers, each of whose monthly demand curve for minutes of wireless service is $Q_H^d = 100 - 100P$, and 200 low-demand consumers, each of whose monthly demand curve is $Q_L^d = 50 - 100P$, where P is the per-minute price in dollars. Clearvoice's marginal cost is 10 cents per minute. If it sells to both types of consumers, which of the following per-minute prices is the most profitable: 10, 15, 20, or 25 cents? (For simplicity, assume that Clearvoice can set its fixed fee in units smaller than a penny so that it is able to extract all of the low-demand consumer's surplus.)

Table 18.3

Profits from Four Possible Two-Part Tariffs

(400 low-demand consumers and 100 high-demand consumers)

	Per-Minute Price			
	$0.10	**$0.15**	**$0.20**	**$0.25**
Minutes purchased				
Low-demand consumer	40	35	30	25
High-demand consumer	90	85	80	75
Fixed fee ($):	8.00	6.125	4.50	3.125
Profits ($):				
Low-demand consumer	8.00	7.875	7.50	6.875
High-demand consumer	8.00	10.375	12.50	14.375
Total profit ($):	4,000	4,187.50	4,250	4,187.50

Application 18.4

Tied Sales and Price Discrimination

Sometimes the value consumers attach to a good depends on the intensity with which they expect to use it. Take printers. Consumers with a need for high-volume printing will be more willing to pay for a printer than those with a need for low-volume printing. So a printer monopolist would want to discriminate by charging a higher price to consumers with high-volume printing needs. Directly measuring (or *metering*) the number of copies a consumer prints can be costly, however.

One alternative is for the printer manufacturer to ensure that it is the only source of printing supplies. For example, an inkjet printer requires ink. If the consumer must buy ink from the manufacturer of the printer, then ink sales serve as an indirect meter of the purchaser's use of the machine. And by setting a high price for ink, the monopolist can raise the cost of the machine to those who print a lot of pages. In effect, the combination of the printer price and the ink price acts as a two-part tariff for printing services.[10]

Sometimes this kind of pricing is accomplished by means of tied sales, in which the consumer contracts to buy supplies only from the firm. (The term *tied sales* refers to the fact that the firm ties the requirement of purchasing the associated supplies to the sale of the printer.) Another way firms sometimes impose tied sales on consumers is by threatening to void the warranties of buyers who use supplies purchased from other sources.

At other times this kind of pricing is accomplished by rendering the machine technically incompatible with other manufacturers' supplies. For example, printer manufacturers often design their printers so that other manufacturers' ink cartridges won't fit. The firm can then charge a lot for replacement ink cartridges to extract some of the high-volume consumers' surplus. In fact, replacement cartridges are typically very expensive—so much so that within a couple of years, high-volume consumers find they have paid much more for replacement cartridges than they paid for the printer itself.

One example of this kind of price discrimination occurred in the early 1960s, when SCM Corporation was a leading manufacturer of electrofax copying machines. Those machines required special paper. At first SCM priced the machines at a markup of about 25 percent, and the special paper at a markup of close to 300 percent. This plan worked for a while, but before long other companies had entered the market for electrofax paper, offering it at much lower prices than SCM. The company was forced to lower the price of its paper.

SCM responded to this challenge in two ways. First, it raised the price of the copying machines. Second, it adopted a variety of practices designed to force customers to continue buying its paper, which was still more expensive than other firms' paper. For example, customers could buy replenisher (another necessary supply) only if they bought SCM's paper. Then, after chemical companies entered the replenisher market, SCM required customers to use SCM paper in order to get SCM service. Eventually, the entry of other electrofax manufacturers brought an end to SCM's attempts at price discrimination through tied sales.

Using Menus to Increase Profit

We've now seen that when Clearvoice can't distinguish high- and low-demand consumers and offers a single two-part tariff, the company does best by setting the per-minute price above its marginal cost to extract more profit from high-demand consumers. But is this the best Clearvoice can do? No—it can do even better by offering consumers a choice from a menu of two-part tariff plans. Let's see how.

---

[10]In fact, we can imagine that consumers have a downward-sloping demand for printing services, with the number of pages they will print if they have access to a printer increasing when the cost per page falls. (The cost per page is affected by the price of ink as well as the price of paper.) The amount consumers are willing to pay for the printer itself then equals the consumer surplus they get from printing at the given cost per page.

Intuitively, Clearvoice's profit from the two-part tariff in Figure 18.11 might be higher if (1) it could eliminate some of the deadweight loss caused by the per-minute price of 20 cents, and (2) it could extract more of the surplus enjoyed by high-demand consumers, which equals the grey-shaded area in Figure 18.11(b). We'll see now that Clearvoice can achieve these goals by offering consumers a choice from a pair of two-part tariffs, with each tariff plan designed to attract a specific type of consumer. First, we'll show how Clearvoice can eliminate the deadweight loss for high-demand consumers by introducing a second tariff plan. Then we'll show how Clearvoice can extract more of the high-demand consumers' surplus by making the low-demand plan less attractive to high-demand consumers.

Eliminating the Deadweight Loss of High-Demand Consumers   Suppose Clearvoice offers a pair of two-part tariffs: one with a per-minute price of 20 cents and a fixed fee of $4.50 (from Figure 18.11) and another that is designed to attract high-demand consumers only. The second plan has a per-minute price of 10 cents, equal to Clearvoice's marginal cost. Its fixed fee is the largest amount Clearvoice can charge without causing the high-demand consumer to choose instead the first two-part tariff, intended for low-demand consumers. How high can the fixed fee for this plan be?

Look at Figure 18.12(b). The grey-shaded area represents the surplus a high-demand consumer enjoys under the 20-cent-per-minute plan (it is the same area as in Figure 18.11(b), on page 679). If this consumer instead faces a per-minute price of 10 cents, he

Figure 18.12

A Menu of Two-Part Tariffs. Figures (a) and (b) show the profits from low- and high-demand consumers, respectively, when low-demand consumers choose the same plan as in Figure 18.11 but high-demand consumers instead choose a plan that has a per-minute price of 10 cents and a fixed fee that makes them indifferent between that plan and the plan in Figure 18.11 (in both cases, their surplus after paying the fixed fee equals the grey-shaded area). Each type of consumer prefers the plan designed for him. The monopolist's profits are higher since it earns more from each high-demand consumer than with the plan in Figure 18.11.

will buy 90 minutes. His consumer surplus before paying the fixed fee will then equal $40.50, the sum of the green- and grey-shaded areas in Figure 18.12(b). To leave the high-demand consumer indifferent between the 10- and 20-cent-per-minute plans, Clearvoice can charge a fixed fee for the 10-cent-per-minute plan that is equal to the green-shaded region in Figure 18.12(b). This fixed fee will leave the consumer with a surplus from the 10-cent-per-minute plan equal to the grey-shaded region, just as in the 20-cent-per-minute plan.[11]

When Clearvoice offers this menu of two-part tariffs, consumers will choose the option designed for them. High-demand consumers will choose the 10-cent-per-minute plan shown in Figure 18.12(b), because its fixed fee ensures that this plan is their best option. Low-demand consumers will opt for the 20-cent-per-minute plan shown in Figure 18.12(a). Though that plan gives them zero surplus, they would earn a negative surplus from the 10-cent-per-minute plan. [At a price of 10 cents per minute, their surplus is smaller than the green-shaded area in Figure 18.12(b).]

Figure 18.12 also shows Clearvoice's profit with this menu of plans. Figure 18.12(a) shows the profit from a low-demand consumer, the sum of the green- and yellow-shaded areas, which is $7.50. This profit is exactly the same as in Figure 18.11(a), since the low-demand consumer chooses the same plan as before. Figure 18.12(b) shows the profit from a high-demand consumer. With a per-minute price of 10 cents, Clearvoice's profit from a high-demand consumer equals the fixed fee it charges that consumer, which is the green-shaded area. This fixed fee is $13. Notice that it equals the sum of the green- and yellow-shaded areas in Figure 18.11(b), equal to $12.50, plus a triangle with the area of $0.50 (its base is 10 minutes and its height is $0.10). That triangle represents the dead-weight loss that arose for a high-demand consumer from the 20-cent-per-minute plan. By setting the per-minute charge for high-demand consumers equal to its marginal cost (10 cents), Clearvoice has eliminated the deadweight loss for high-demand consumers and then extracted this extra surplus through the plan's fixed fee, earning a greater profit.

Can Clearvoice do even better by also eliminating the deadweight loss for the low-demand consumer? No. We've already seen that if it sets the per-minute price in the plan intended for low-demand consumers at 10 cents, the high-demand consumers will choose that plan instead. In contrast, Clearvoice is free to eliminate the deadweight loss in the high-demand plan because low-demand consumers are not tempted to choose that plan.[12]

Making the Low-Demand Plan Less Attractive to High-Demand Consumers
Clearvoice can increase its profit even more by making the low-demand plan less attractive to high-demand consumers. Why? Notice that the option to choose the plan intended for low-demand consumers determines the fixed fee that Clearvoice can charge a high-demand consumer: it is the level that makes the high-demand consumer indifferent between the two plans. If Clearvoice can reduce the surplus that a high-demand consumer enjoys from choosing the 20-cent-per-minute plan, it can increase the fixed fee for the 10-cent-per-minute plan.

How can it do that? The idea is to limit the number of minutes a consumer can purchase in the 20-cent-per-minute plan to the number that the low-demand consumer wants.

[11]To make sure that high-demand consumers choose the plan intended for them Clearvoice could charge a penny less than this amount for the high-demand plan's fixed fee. For simplicity, we'll assume here that a high-demand consumer chooses the plan intended for him if he is indifferent between the two plans.

[12]More generally, with more than two types of consumers, a monopolist always benefits from eliminating the deadweight loss in the plan intended for the consumers with the highest willingness to pay.

This limitation has no effect on the value that a low-demand consumer derives from the 20-cent-per-minute plan, but makes that plan less attractive to high-demand consumers. As a result, it increases the fixed fee Clearvoice can charge in the 10-cent-per-minute plan intended for high-demand consumers.

Let's see how this works. Suppose Clearvoice limits the number of minutes that consumers can buy in the 20-cent-per-minute plan to 30—the number a low-demand consumer wants to purchase at a per-minute price of 20 cents. (An equivalent way to limit the number of minutes purchased would be to charge a prohibitively high price for all minutes over 30.) With this limitation on minutes, the high-demand consumer buys the same number of minutes in the 20-cent-per-minute plan as does a low-demand consumer and also pays the same amount in total charges. Since the low-demand consumer enjoys zero surplus from this plan, the high-demand consumer's surplus from the plan must be the grey-shaded area in Figure 18.13(b), which equals the difference in the willingness to pay for those minutes between the high- and low-demand consumers. This amount is $15, equal to 30 minutes times the extra 50 cents that a high-demand consumer is willing to pay for each of those minutes. Clearvoice can now charge a fixed fee of $25.50 for the high-demand plan, equal to the green-shaded area in Figure 18.13(b). This fixed fee leaves the high-demand consumer with a surplus from the 10-cent-per-minute plan of exactly $15. Notice that the $25.50 fixed fee is larger than the $13 fixed fee shown in Figure 18.12(b).

Figure 18.13

Capping Minutes in the Low-Demand Plan. The figure shows Clearvoice's profit if it caps the number of minutes in the low-demand plan at 30. The profit from a low-demand consumer stays the same, but the cap allows Clearvoice to increase the fixed fee in the high-demand plan because high-demand consumers get less surplus from the low-demand plan due to the cap.

Finally, is 20 cents the best per-minute price for the low-demand plan? Worked-out problem 18.5 compares the profitability of four different per-minute prices in the plan intended for low-demand consumers. Add-On 18A shows how to find the profit-maximizing menu of two-part tariffs using algebra.

Intuitively, the higher the per-minute price in the low-demand plan, the fewer minutes low-demand consumers will use, and the lower will be Clearvoice's profit from them (since their deadweight loss is larger). On the other hand, the higher the per-minute price, the lower will be the surplus that high-demand consumers enjoy from choosing the low-demand plan—and thus the higher the fixed fee the monopolist can charge those high-demand consumers. The profit-maximizing per-minute charge in the low-demand plan therefore depends on the relative proportions of the two types of consumers. The higher the fraction of high-demand consumers, the more it makes sense to raise the per-minute price in the low-demand plan. Add-On 18A discusses this effect in greater detail.

This discussion illustrates three general points. First, a firm can often profit by offering a menu of choices, with different choices designed for different types of consumers. Second, to maximize its profit, the firm should try to make each plan attractive to those consumers for whom it is designed but unattractive to other consumers. Third, the firm can benefit from setting the per-minute price in the plan intended for the consumers with the highest willingness to pay equal to the marginal cost, thereby eliminating the deadweight loss for those consumers.

WORKED-OUT PROBLEM   18.5

The Problem   Suppose that Clearvoice serves 100 high-demand consumers, each of whose monthly demand curve for minutes of wireless service is $Q_H^d = 100 - 100P$, and 400 low-demand consumers, each of whose monthly demand curve is $Q_L^d = 50 - 100P$, where P is the per-minute price in dollars. Its marginal cost is 10 cents per minute. Suppose it sells to both types of consumers, using a pair of two-part tariffs, with the plan intended for the high-demand consumers having a per-minute price of 10 cents, and the plan intended for the low-demand consumers having its minutes capped at the number a low-demand consumer desires to purchase given the per-minute price in that plan. Which of the following per-minute prices in the plan intended for low-demand consumers is the most profitable: 10, 15, 20, or 25 cents? (For simplicity, assume that Clearvoice can set its fixed fees in units smaller than a penny.)

The Solution   Table 18.4 shows the quantities purchased by, fixed fees for, and profits from each type of consumer for the four different per-minute prices, as well as the total profits. The numbers in the column for the 10- and 20-cent-per-minute prices correspond to the amounts calculated above in the text. Those in the columns for the other two per-minute prices are calculated in the same way, where in each case the fixed fee for the low-demand plan leaves a low-demand consumer with zero surplus, while the fixed fee in the high-demand plan leaves a high-demand consumer indifferent between the high-demand plan (with a per-minute price of 10 cents) and the plan intended for low-demand consumers. (As an exercise, you should calculate these amounts for yourself.) Of these four possibilities, the 20-cent and 25-cent plans both yield the highest profit, which is $5550.

Table 18.4

Profits from Four Possible Menus of Two-Part Tariffs

(400 low-demand consumers and 100 high-demand consumers)

	Per-Minute Price in Low-Demand Plan			
	$0.10	$0.15	$0.20	$0.25
Minutes purchased				
Low-demand consumer	40	35	30	25
High-demand consumer	90	90	90	90
Fixed Fee ($)				
Low-demand plan	8.00	6.125	4.50	3.125
High-demand plan	8.00	23.00	25.50	28.00
Profits ($)				
Low-demand consumer	8.00	7.875	7.50	6.875
High-demand consumer	8.00	23.00	25.50	28.00
Total profit ($)	4,000	5,450	5,550	5,550

IN-TEXT EXERCISE 18.6 Suppose that Clearvoice serves 100 high-demand consumers, each of whose monthly demand curve for minutes of wireless service is $Q_H^d = 100 - 100P$, and 200 low-demand consumers, each of whose monthly demand curve is $Q_L^d = 50 - 100P$, where P is the per-minute price in dollars. Its marginal cost is 10 cents per minute. Suppose it sells to both types of consumers, using a pair of two-part tariffs, with the plan intended for the high-demand consumers having a per-minute price of 10 cents, and the plan intended for the low-demand consumers having its minutes capped at the number a low-demand consumer desires to purchase given the per-minute price in that plan. Which of the following per-minute prices in the plan intended for low-demand consumers is the most profitable: 10, 15, 20, or 25 cents? (For simplicity, assume that Clearvoice can set its fixed fees in units smaller than a penny.)

*18.5 BUNDLING

A firm that sells more than one product could set the price for each product separately, using the techniques described in Chapter 17 and in Sections 18.1–18.4. For a firm that sells more than one product, however, it is sometimes profitable to make the price or availability of one good dependent on the customer's purchase of another good.[13] One version of this tactic is the practice of selling goods together, as a package. This practice is called **bundling**.

Bundling is quite common. One reason that firms bundle their products is that it is technologically efficient to do so. For example, one can think of a car as a package

Bundling is the practice of selling several products together as a package.

---

[13]This general type of pricing policy is much like quantity-dependent pricing for a single product, but where the price depends on purchases of *other* products instead of (or in addition to) the amounts purchased of the particular product.

Table 18.5

Willingness to Pay for Spreadsheet and Word Processing Programs

Consumer Type	Number	Willingness to Pay		
		Spreadsheet	Word Processor	Both
A	1,000	200	0	200
B	1,000	175	25	200
C	1,000	100	100	200
D	1,000	25	175	200
E	1,000	0	200	200

consisting of an engine, brakes, headlights, and so forth. Toyota and General Motors sell cars that way because they can assemble the parts more efficiently than consumers can. Consumers are therefore willing to pay more for the manufacturer's assembly services than those services cost the company to provide. For similar reasons, shirts are sold with buttons and laptop computers are sold with screens and hard drives.

Bundling can be profitable for another reason: it can increase a firm's ability to extract consumer surplus. To grasp this point, consider a software firm that is a monopolist of both spreadsheet and word-processing programs. To simplify the analysis, we'll assume those programs are neither complements nor substitutes, so that a consumer's willingness to pay for one program is unaffected by the decision to buy the other. Table 18.5 shows the willingness to pay for the programs among five different types of consumers, labelled A through E. Consumer type A has the highest willingness to pay for a spreadsheet program ($200), but does not value a word-processing program at all. In contrast, consumer type E is willing to pay $200 for a word-processing program, but nothing for a spreadsheet program. Consumer types B, C, and D are willing to pay positive amounts for both types of program. The market includes 1000 consumers of each type.

How would the software monopolist price these two programs if they were sold independently, with a separate price for each one? We'll assume that the monopolist's marginal costs are zero (which is approximately true for software). Let's consider first the best price for the spreadsheet. From the table, we can see that the monopolist can sell 1000 copies at a price of $200, earning $200,000; 2000 copies at a price of $175, earning $350,000; 3000 copies at a price of $100, earning $300,000; and so on. Profit on the spreadsheet program is maximized at a price of $175. Similarly, the profit-maximizing price of the word-processing program is $175. At these prices, the monopolist earns $700,000.

Now let's think about selling these two programs as a bundle. The last column of Table 18.5 shows that every type of consumer has the *same* willingness to pay for a bundle that includes both programs: $200. So the monopolist can sell the bundle to everyone at a price of $200 and in doing so earns $1 million, which is $300,000 more than under the best independent pricing policy.

Why does bundling increase profit in this example? Bundling is a very effective tool for extracting consumer surplus here because different consumers' willingness to pay for the two programs are perfectly negatively related. In this special example, a consumer

Table 18.6

Another Example of Willingness to Pay for Spreadsheet and Word Processing Programs

Consumer Type	Number	Willingness to Pay Spreadsheet	Willingness to Pay Word Processor	Both
A	1,000	100	100	200
B	1,000	100	200	300
C	1,000	200	100	300
D	1,000	200	200	400

who values a spreadsheet at $75 more than another consumer, values a word processor at $75 less than the other consumer. With independent pricing, the monopolist can't extract all the consumer surplus from a single program, because the demand curve for that program is downward sloping. As a result, some consumers end up earning a positive surplus, while others choose not to buy at the $175 price. Bundling eliminates this variation in consumer valuations, allowing the monopolist to extract all of aggregate surplus as profit.

In fact, bundling can be a profitable strategy in a much wider range of circumstances than this simple example suggests. Consumers' willingness to pay for different products need not be negatively related, as in Table 18.5. Table 18.6 shows an example in which the willingness to pay for the spreadsheet and word-processing programs are unrelated (formally, they are statistically independent). There are four types of consumers, labelled A–D, with 1000 consumers of each type. A consumer's willingness to pay for each product is either $100 or $200. Of those consumers whose willingness to pay for the spreadsheet is $100, exactly half are willing to pay $100 for the word processor and half are willing to pay $200. The same is true of those consumers whose willingness to pay for the spreadsheet is $200. So a consumers' willingness to pay for the spreadsheet tells you nothing about their willingness to pay for the word processor, unlike in Table 18.5.

Suppose the monopolist sells the two programs independently. Consider the spreadsheet. The monopolist (whose marginal cost is again zero) is indifferent between prices of $100 and $200: either one yields a profit of $400,000. The same is true of the word processor. So the total profit from independently selling the two goods is $800,000.

Now suppose the monopolist sells only a bundle. As Table 18.6 shows, 1000 consumers are willing to pay $200 for the bundle, 2000 are willing to pay $300, and 1000 are willing to pay $400. The profit-maximizing bundle price is $300, which results in a profit of $900,000. Bundling increases the monopolist's profit by $100,000.

When the willingness to pay for two goods has the special feature that a dollar-higher willingness to pay for one good implies a dollar-lower willingness to pay for the other, as in Table 18.5, bundling always yields higher profits (provided marginal cost is zero). More generally, bundling need not be a multiproduct monopolist's profit-maximizing pricing policy. In-text exercise 18.7 provides an example in which consumers' willingness to pay for two goods is unrelated (they are statistically independent) and independent pricing is more profitable than bundling.

> IN-TEXT EXERCISE 18.7   **Suppose that a monopolist seller of spreadsheet and word processor programs faces four types of consumers, A–D. The willingness to pay for a spreadsheet is $0 for types A and B, and $100 for types C and D. The willingness to pay for a word processor is $0 for types A and C, and $100 for types B and D. The marginal cost of producing either good is zero. There are 1000 consumers of each type. Compare the profits from independently selling the two goods and selling a bundle. Which is more profitable?**

Mixed Bundling

Mixed bundling is the practice of selling several products together as a package while also offering those products for sale individually.

A firm can also sell *both* a bundle *and* individual products. This is called **mixed bundling**. For example, hockey teams sell both season tickets and tickets to individual games.

To see one reason why mixed bundling can be a firm's most profitable pricing policy, consider again Table 18.5. Now, however, imagine that the cost of producing and distributing either of the programs is $20. As before, the monopolist could only sell a bundle at a price of $200, which is better than selling the two goods independently (you should check this for yourself). But, when it does so, the monopolist incurs the $20 production cost to sell a spreadsheet to consumer type E, who derives no value from it at all. Likewise, it incurs the $20 production cost to sell a word processor to consumer type A, who derives no value from that program at all.

Mixed bundling provides a way to avoid that waste. To see how, imagine that in addition to selling the bundle for $200 the monopolist offers to sell either program alone for $190. This is less than the price of the bundle, but the price reduction is less than the $20 cost the monopolist saves by omitting one program. As a result, the monopolist earns $10 more when a consumer buys a single good rather than the bundle. With this new pricing policy, the outcome is that consumer types B, C, and D still buy the bundle, consumer type A buys only the spreadsheet, and consumer type E buys only the word processor. (For example, type E's surplus is $10 from buying the word processor and zero from buying the bundle.) The monopolist's profits increase from $800,000 when it offers only the bundle to $820,000. The $20,000 difference represents the extra $10 the monopolist makes selling only one program to the 2000 consumers of types A and E. If the price the bundle were $200 and the price of each program were set to $195 the monopolists profits would increase from $800,000 to $830,000. This is still not the profit maximizing strategy. Keeping the bundled price at $200 and setting the price of an individual program to $199.99 would increase profits to $839,980.

Application 18.5

Mixed Bundling at McDonald's

Mixed bundling is a familiar practice at most fast-food restaurants. Table 18.7, for example, shows the prices of various "value meals," as well as the cost of their individual components, at a McDonald's restaurant in Guelph, Ontario in 2010. A value meal includes a sandwich, medium fries, and a medium drink. Purchased separately, medium fries cost $2.29 and a medium drink costs $1.89. The two columns in the table provide a comparison of the price of each value meal to the price of its three components sold separately. In each case, the cost of the value meal was less than the sum of the individual prices of its three components. However, as the last column shows, the discounts offered in the bundle varied widely across the different meals.

McDonald's allows customers to "Super Size" their value meals receiving a large drink and large fries for an additional 70 cents increasing the size of the discount. Is this form of mixed bundling the most profitable way for McDonald's to price? For example, why not also sell a fries/soft drink combo for less than $4.18, the sum of those two items' individual costs? Or also offer a Big Mac/medium soft drink "slightly less value" meal that omits the fries? It could be that consumer valuations are such that doing so is less profitable (only McDonald's would know this). But another reason why, in practice, bundled combinations are limited in number is that it can be costly (and confusing) to maintain many different prices.

A variation on mixed bundling is practised by many restaurants. Less than a kilometre away at the Other Brother's restaurant in Guelph, a three-course prix fixe dinner is $36 and includes an appetizer, principal plate, and dessert. Purchased separately the three courses would total anywhere from $38 to $41 so that purchasing them as a bundle gives the diner a 5.3 to 12.2 percent discount. In addition the restaurant lowers the price of a three-course meal to $30 if ordered before 6:00 p.m., giving the diner a 21.1 to 26.8 percent discount.

Table 18.7
Prices at McDonald's near the University of Guelph

Value Meal	Price	Cost of Components Purchased Separately	Discount
Big Mac	$6.69	$ 8.47	21.0%
Chicken McNuggets (10)	8.19	10.17	19.6
Fillet-O-Fish	6.19	7.97	22.3
Quarter Pounder	6.59	8.37	21.3
Angus Burger with Bacon and Cheddar	8.28	10.36	20.1

CHAPTER SUMMARY

1. **Price discrimination: pricing to extract surplus (LO1, 2)**

   a. Under certain conditions, a firm with market power can increase its profit by charging different amounts for different units of the same good.

   b. To do so, the firm must be able to distinguish purchases that involve a high willingness to pay from purchases that involve a low willingness to pay.

   c. A firm engages in quantity-dependent (or volume-sensitive) pricing when the price a consumer pays for an additional unit depends on how many units the consumer has bought.

2. **Perfect price discrimination (LO3)**

   a. When a monopolist knows the customer's willingness to pay for every unit and can charge a different price for each unit, it can perfectly price discriminate. Perfect price discrimination maximizes aggregate surplus (there is no deadweight loss), but consumers receive no surplus at all.

   b. A monopolist that can perfectly discriminate can also maximize its profit using a two-part tariff in which the per-unit price equals the marginal cost and each consumer pays a fixed fee that reduces consumer surplus to zero.

3. **Price discrimination based on observable customer characteristics (LO4)**

   a. Sometimes a firm that can't perfectly price discriminate can nonetheless distinguish between two or more distinct groups of customers.

   b. In that case, the firm can set a different price for each group, using the methods described in Section 17.2. When the firm does so, it sets a higher price for groups whose demand is less elastic than for groups whose demand is more elastic.

   c. Compared to simple monopoly pricing (see Section 17.2), price discrimination based on observed customer characteristics may either raise or lower consumer surplus and aggregate surplus.

d. Price discrimination can't occur in a perfectly competitive market, but it can exist in markets that are nearly perfectly competitive. It can also be greater in oligopoly markets than in monopoly markets.

4. **Price discrimination based on self-selection (LO5)**

   a. Sometimes a monopolist knows that different customers belong to different groups, but can't distinguish among them. In such cases, it may be able to price discriminate by offering each customer a menu of alternatives, designed so that different customers will make different choices. One tool that firms often use to price discriminate based on self-selection is quantity-dependent pricing.

   b. When a monopolist offers a single two-part tariff to more than one group of consumers, it can extract more of the high-demand consumers' surplus by raising the per-unit price above the marginal cost. The degree to which it is worthwhile to do this depends on the relative proportions of the different types of consumers.

   c. The monopolist can further increase its profit by offering a menu of two-part tariffs, each one targeted at a different group of consumers. In designing the menu, the monopolist should try to make each plan attractive to the group it is intended for but unattractive to the other groups. Doing so involves capping the quantity that can be purchased in the low-demand plan at the level that low-demand consumers desire to buy given the per-minute price in that plan. It should also offer high-demand consumers a plan with a per-unit price equal to its marginal cost to eliminate their deadweight loss.

*5. **Bundling (LO6)**

   a. For a firm that sells more than one product, it is sometimes profitable to make the price or availability of one good dependent on the customer's purchase of another good. One version of this tactic is the practice of selling goods together as a bundle.

   b. Bundling always increases a multiproduct monopolist's profit whenever an increase of a dollar in the willingness to pay for one good implies a reduction of a dollar in the willingness to pay for another good and the marginal cost is zero. In that case, there is no variation in consumers' willingness to pay for the bundle, and the monopolist can extract all of aggregate surplus as profit by bundling. However, bundling can also increase the monopolist's profit in other circumstances.

   c. A firm can sometimes profit by engaging in mixed bundling, where it sells a bundle but also sells the products in the bundle individually.

ADDITIONAL EXERCISES

Exercise 18.1: Give one example each of price discrimination based on observable customer characteristics and price discrimination based on self-selection. (LO1, 2, 3)

Exercise 18.2: If the Ice Cream Monopoly Company from Figure 18.2 (page 661) sells to Juan (whose demand curve is shown in Figure 14.16(b) on page 519) using a two-part tariff with a per-cone price of $1.50, what is the largest fixed fee it can charge Juan and still persuade Juan to make a purchase? How does its total revenue from Juan under this two-part tariff compare to its total revenue from Juan when it sells Juan four cones, each priced at Juan's willingness to pay for it? What is its total profit from Juan? (LO3)

Exercise 18.3: Suppose the wireless telephone monopolist in worked-out problem 18.1 (page 663) charges 40 cents per minute. How large a fixed fee can it charge and still persuade consumers to buy? What is its profit from each consumer? Its total profit? How does its total profit compare to its profit with a per-minute charge of 10, 20, and 30 cents per minute? (LO3)

Exercise 18.4: Suppose moviegoers' demand functions are the same as in worked-out problem 18.2 (page 665), but marginal cost is instead $3 per ticket. What prices will the monopolist set when she can discriminate and when it cannot? How will discrimination affect her profit? (LO4)

Exercise 18.5: Suppose the demand function of student moviegoers is the same as in worked-out problem 18.2 (page 665), but the demand function of other adults is instead $Q_A^d = 1800 - 100P$. Marginal cost is still $2 per ticket. What prices will the monopolist set when she can discriminate and when she cannot? How will discrimination affect her profit? (LO4)

Exercise 18.6: Suppose that the demand function of student moviegoers is the same as in worked-out problem 18.2 (page 665), but the demand function of other adults is instead $Q_A^d = 3000 - 100P$. Marginal cost is still $2 per ticket. What prices will the monopolist set when she can discriminate and when she cannot? How will discrimination affect her profit? (LO4)

Exercise 18.7: Verify the claims on pages 672–673 of the text about the welfare effect of discrimination in Figure 18.9. (The student demand function is $Q_s^d = 400 - 100P$; the demand function of other adults and the monopolist's marginal cost are the same as in worked-out problem 18.2 on page 665.) (LO4)

Exercise 18.8: What is the effect of discrimination on consumer and aggregate surplus in exercise 18.4? (LO4)

Exercise 18.9: What is the effect of discrimination on consumer and aggregate surplus in exercise 18.5? (LO4)

Exercise 18.10: What is the effect of discrimination on consumer and aggregate surplus in exercise 18.6? (LO4)

Exercise 18.11: Suppose the marginal cost in worked-out problem 18.2 (page 665) is $MC = 1 + 0.01Q$, where Q is the total number of tickets sold (equal to the sum of student tickets and other adult tickets). How would the answer to the problem change? What will happen to the student price under price discrimination if the demand of other adults increases to $Q_A^d = 1,800 - 100P$? Why? (LO4)

Exercise 18.12: Air Shangrila sells to both tourist and business travelers on its single route. Tourists always stay over on Saturday nights, while business travelers never do. The weekly demand function of tourists is $Q_T^d = 6000 - 10P$, and the weekly demand function of business travelers is $Q_B^d = 1000 - P$. If the marginal cost of a ticket is $200, what prices should Air Shangrila set for its tourist ticket and its business ticket? If the government passes a law that says all tickets must cost the same amount, what price will Air Shangrila set? What would be the elasticities of demand for the two groups at that price? (LO5)

Exercise 18.13: Suppose that in exercise 18.12, Air Shangrila has scheduled only 1300 seats per week on its route. How many of those seats should it sell to tourists and business travelers, respectively? What will its prices be? (LO5)

Exercise 18.14: Suppose the demand functions facing the wireless telephone monopolist in worked-out problem 18.4 (page 681) are $Q_L^d = 40 - 100P$ for each low-demand consumer and $Q_H^d = 120 - 100P$ for each high-demand consumer, where P is the per-minute price in dollars. The marginal cost is 10 cents per minute. Suppose the monopolist offers only a single two-part tariff. What will be the monopolist's profit from each type of consumer if it charges a per-minute price of 10 cents and a fixed fee that causes both types of consumer to make a purchase? What if it charges a per-minute price of 20 cents? If there are 100 high-demand consumers, how many low-demand consumers can the

monopolist serve and find the 20-cent-per-minute price more profitable? (LO5)

Exercise 18.15: Suppose the monopolist in exercise 18.14 offers a menu of two-part tariff plans, with one plan intended for each type of consumer. Suppose too, as in our discussion in the text, that for any per-minute price P_L in the low-demand plan, the fixed fee in the low-demand plan leaves a low-demand consumer with zero surplus; that the number of minutes in the low-demand plan is capped at the number of minutes desired by a low-demand consumer at that plan's per-minute price; and that the high-demand plan has a per-minute price of 10 cents and a fixed fee that leaves the high-demand consumer (approximately) indifferent between the low- and high-demand plans. Suppose that there are 100 high-demand consumers and 300 low-demand consumers. (The marginal cost is 10 cents per minute and the demand functions are the same as in exercise 18.14.) Will the monopolist's profit be higher when the per-minute price in the low-demand plan is 20 cents or 15 cents? (LO5)

Exercise 18.16: Redo exercise 18.15 assuming that the marginal cost is 5 cents per minute (and the per-minute charge in the high-demand plan is now 5 cents). (LO5)

*Exercise 18.17: Suppose that in Table 18.5 (page 688), consumer types B, C, and D instead have valuations of $75, $50, and $25, respectively, for a spreadsheet program, and $25, $50, and $75, respectively, for a word-processing program. What will be the profit-maximizing bundle price? How will profit from this pricing policy compare to profit under independent pricing of the two goods? (As in the text, assume the programs' marginal cost is zero.) (LO6)

*Exercise 18.18: Reconsider exercise 18.17, but assume instead that the marginal cost of each program is $25. Will bundling or independent pricing be more profitable? Now consider the possibility of offering a bundle and selling the two programs separately. Can you find prices for the bundle and the two individual products that will yield a greater profit than selling either the bundle alone or the individual products alone? (LO6)

19

Oligopoly

LEARNING OBJECTIVES

After reading this chapter, students should be able to

LO1 Discuss the relationship between oligopoly and game theory.

LO2 Describe the Bertrand model and the Cournot model, and identify the Nash equilibrium in each model.

LO3 Explain why product differentiation makes price competition less intense and identify the Nash equilibrium in a market with product differentiation.

LO4 Analyze whether or not collusion is sustainable in a setting of repeated price competition.

LO5 Determine the number of firms that will enter a market, discuss the factors that affect this number, and explain its relation to the socially optimal number.

LO6 Explain how strategic investments in R&D, advertising, production capacity, and even political lobbying can impact future competition.

LO7 Describe the main Canadian competition statutes and discuss their rationale.

Introduced to Canada in 1954, General Mills' Cheerios is one of the world's best-selling cereals.

Canadians eat a lot of cereal. Counting every man, woman, and child in Canada, Statistics Canada estimated that the average consumption was 4.1 kilograms per person in 2008. This represents a 38 percent increase from just 20 years ago. Each of those bowls of cereal costs consumers more—*way* more—than it costs the cereal maker who manufactures it. Historically, retail prices in this industry have reflected markups of between 40 and 50 percent.

Though the cereal industry isn't a monopoly, the four largest firms—Kellogg's, General Mills, Post (Ralcorp), and Quaker Oats (Pepsico)—accounted for most of the industry's nearly $500 million in Canadian sales. Consistently, these industry leaders have been among the most profitable firms. What is the cause of their high cereal prices? When and how can oligopolists maintain high prices and profits?

In this chapter we'll study competition in oligopoly markets. We'll cover eight topics:

1. *Oligopoly and game theory.* In oligopolies, a firm's best actions and profit depend on how its rivals behave. To analyze such situations, economists use game theory. We'll provide a brief discussion of this tool, which was covered in more detail in Chapter 12.

2. *The Bertrand model: price competition with homogeneous products.* In this simple model of oligopoly, firms sell identical products and compete by naming their prices simultaneously. Price undercutting drives prices down to marginal cost, just as in a perfectly competitive market. Unfortunately, conditions in many oligopoly markets do not conform to the Bertrand model's assumptions.

3. *Cournot quantity competition.* In many markets, firms make decisions that affect the quantity they can sell at any given moment. In those cases, quantity choices rather than price choices drive the competitive outcome. With quantity competition, the market price will be greater than marginal cost but below the monopoly price.

4. *Price competition with differentiated products.* In contrast to the Bertrand model's assumption, firms' products often are not identical. We'll see that when this is so, price competition is less intense than the Bertrand model predicts.

5. *Collusion.* Even if firms' products are identical, they may charge prices that are above marginal cost when they compete repeatedly. With repeated competition, firms may refrain from undercutting one another's prices for fear of setting off a price war.

6. *Market entry and monopolistic competition.* We'll examine the factors that determine the number of firms that enter an oligopolistic market and how that number compares with the number that maximizes aggregate surplus. We'll also discuss markets in which many firms enter with slightly differentiated products, a situation known as *monopolistic competition.*

*7. *Strategic behaviour that shapes future competition.* Among a firm's most important strategic decisions are those that shape its long-term competition with rivals. We'll discuss those actions and study how an early entrant in a market can sometimes commit to actions that increase its profit from competing with later entrants, or even deter others' entry altogether.

8. *Competition policy.* Competition policy maintains certain basic rules of competition that promote satisfactory market outcomes. We'll discuss the major competition statutes in Canada and their application.

19.1 OLIGOPOLY AND GAME THEORY

In Chapters 17 and 18, we discussed monopoly markets. Because a monopolist faces no rivals, its profit-maximizing price and profit are unaffected by the actions of other firms. Things are not so simple for oligopolists.

To illustrate, Figure 19.1 shows a stylized oligopoly situation. Imagine that each week Coke and Pepsi choose their prices for a 355-millilitre can of pop in a small city (assume that each produces only this one product and there are no other competitors). Suppose, for simplicity, that each has two possible prices it can choose: a high price and a low price. Each cell in Figure 19.1(a) represents a pair of price choices. For example, the top left cell, shaded yellow, corresponds to both firms choosing the high price; the cell just below this one corresponds to Coke choosing the low price and Pepsi choosing the high price. Within

Figure 19.1

An Oligopoly Pricing Game. Figure (a) shows the profits for Coke and Pepsi for each potential pair of price choices. The row corresponds to Coke's price and the column corresponds to Pepsi's. Coke's weekly profit is shown in the southwest half of each cell, while Pepsi's profit is shown in the northeast half. Figure (b) shows each firm's best responses. Coke's largest profit in each column is shaded green. Pepsi's largest profit in each row is shaded red. The Nash equilibrium involves each firm charging the low price, corresponding to the cell that is shaded half green and half red. The firms' joint profit is lower than if both charged the high price.

each cell, the figure shows the two firms' weekly profits for that pair of prices. The cell is divided into two halves. The number in the southwest half shows Coke's weekly profit; the number in the northeast half shows Pepsi's. For example, when Coke charges the low price and Pepsi charges the high price, Coke earns a weekly profit of $1700, and Pepsi earns $500. (Figure 19.1(a) is just like the game tables drawn in Chapter 12.)

In Figure 19.1(a), Coke and Pepsi's joint profit is highest if they both charge the high price. In that case, each earns $1500 and their joint profit is $3000. So, if the two firms could perfectly collude, acting like a monopolist, they would both charge the high price. Notice, however, that if a firm wants to maximize its own profit, then choosing the high price may not be in its best interest. For example, suppose Pepsi charges the high price. Is charging the high price best for Coke? If it does, it earns $1500. But if it instead charges the low price, its profit is $1700. Because Coke is concerned with only its own profit, it has an incentive to undercut Pepsi's price.

Coke's incentive to undercut Pepsi reflects a fundamental problem facing oligopolists. The higher its rival's price, the better each firm will do. But, because each is concerned only with its own profit, and not with its rival's, it may be tempted to lower its price to expand its sales. (In the language we will encounter in Chapter 20, each firm imposes an externality on the other.) If both firms do this, the resulting competition lowers their profits.

Economists determine the outcome of oligopoly competition by applying game theory, which we studied in detail in Chapter 12. For the purposes of this chapter, the key insight from game theory is fairly simple. Our goal is to find a market equilibrium. In Chapters 2, 14, and 15, we saw that in a competitive market equilibrium, each firm is doing as well as it can given the market price. Game theory extends this idea by looking for price or quantity choices at which each firm is doing as well as it can given the prices charged or quantities produced by its rivals. This is the concept of a **Nash equilibrium**, introduced in Section 12.3.

To illustrate, consider Coke's best price choices first. As we've seen, if Pepsi charges the high price, Coke's profit is largest if it undercuts Pepsi's price by charging the low

> In a **Nash equilibrium** of an oligopoly market, each firm is making a profit-maximizing choice given the choices of its rivals.

price. What if Pepsi charges the low price? In this case, Coke's most profitable choice is again the low price: its payoff of $1000 is greater than the payoff of $500 it gets if it charges the high price. In game theory, a firm's most profitable choice given the actions of its rivals is called its *best response*. (So, in a Nash equilibrium, each firm is choosing a best response to the actions of its rivals.)

Figure 19.1(b) shows Coke's best responses. In each column of the figure—corresponding in each case to a particular price choice for Pepsi—the half-cell containing Coke's largest profit is shaded green, indicating that a low price is Coke's best response to Pepsi's price.

Figure 19.1(b) also shows Pepsi's best responses. This time, in each row (corresponding to a particular price choice for Coke), the half-cell containing Pepsi's largest payoff is shaded red. Pepsi does best charging the low price regardless of Coke's price.

In a Nash equilibrium, each firm is choosing a best response to the price choice of its rival. This means that in Figure 19.1(b) the Nash equilibrium corresponds to the cell for which *both* halves are shaded. In the Nash equilibrium, both firms charge the low price. Given that Pepsi charges the low price, it is best for Coke to do the same. Likewise for Pepsi.

Notice that the two firms' joint profit in the Nash equilibrium is below the level they would achieve if they were colluding, acting like a monopolist. The incentive to undercut each other has led to lower prices than would exist in a monopoly market. (This outcome resembles the equilibrium of the Prisoners' Dilemma game in Example 12.2 on page 409.)

In the rest of the chapter, we'll look in more detail at competition in oligopoly markets. One of our central objectives will be to identify the factors that determine whether the equilibrium prices and quantities in an oligopoly are closer to those in perfect competition or monopoly.

The game in Figure 19.1 is special in one respect: each firm's most profitable choice is the same regardless of its rival's action. (In the language of Chapter 12, choosing the low price is each firm's *dominant strategy*.) More often, an oligopolist's most profitable price or quantity depends on its rivals' behaviour. We'll see many examples with that feature in the rest of the chapter. Still, in each of those cases the basic idea used to find a Nash equilibrium is the same as in Figure 19.1: identify each firm's best responses for the various possible actions of its rivals and find an outcome at which each firm is choosing a best response to what its rivals are doing.

19.2 THE BERTRAND MODEL: PRICE COMPETITION WITH HOMOGENEOUS PRODUCTS

Let's begin by considering the simplest possible oligopoly market: one with just two firms that produce identical products. This is called a **duopoly** market with **homogeneous** products (goods that are identical in the eyes of consumers). As an example, consider two ready-mix concrete manufacturers, Joe's Concrete Co. and Rebecca's Concrete Co., operating in a small town. Figure 19.2(a) shows the market demand curve. Both Joe's and Rebecca's marginal cost is $40 per cubic metre. As Figure 19.2 shows, the monopoly price in this market is $70 per cubic metre.

What prices are these firms likely to charge when they compete? To answer this question, we'll imagine a simple process in which the firms set their prices simultaneously. Buyers then observe those prices and decide how much to buy from each firm. Since the products are homogeneous, buyers will purchase from the firm with the lower price.

A market with two sellers is called a **duopoly**.

In a market for **homogeneous goods**, firms sell identical products.

Figure 19.2

Market Demand and Joe's Demand Curves. Figure (a) shows the demand and marginal cost curves, labelled D and MC, in a duopoly market for concrete. If the firms colluded perfectly and acted like a monopolist, the amount bought and sold (where the MR and MC curves intersect) would be 3000 cubic metres per year, and the price would be $70 per cubic metre. Figures (b) and (c) show Joe's demand curves when Rebecca charges $70 and $50 per cubic metre, labelled D_{70} and D_{50}, respectively. In each case, Joe sells nothing if his price is greater than Rebecca's, sells to half of the market demand if his price equals Rebecca's, and sells to all of the market demand if his price is less than Rebecca's.

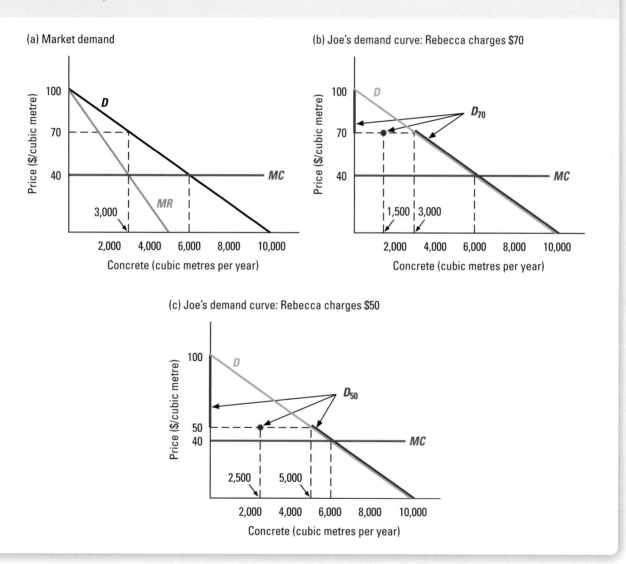

(a) Market demand

(b) Joe's demand curve: Rebecca charges $70

(c) Joe's demand curve: Rebecca charges $50

In the Bertrand model of oligopoly, firms produce homogeneous products and set their prices simultaneously.

If both firms charge the same price, each firm will sell to half the market at that price. This market model is known as the **Bertrand model of oligopoly**, after Joseph Bertrand, who published his analysis in 1883.

In this model, each firm's most profitable choice depends on what the other does. For example, if Rebecca charges $70, then charging $65 will be better for Joe than charging $45.

In either case, Joe's sales will equal the market demand at his announced price, but he will make more money by charging $65 than by charging $45. (With this demand curve, a price that is closer to the monopoly price results in a greater profit.) On the other hand, if Rebecca charges $50, then charging $45 will be better for Joe than charging $65, since he will make no sales at the higher price.

What is the outcome of this competition? Intuitively, we know that the firms in this market have an incentive to undercut each other's prices in order to win sales. Could both firms charge $70 per cubic metre—the monopoly price—in a Nash equilibrium? The answer is no; either firm could do better by lowering its price just a penny. Why? Because the goods are identical, each buyer just wants the lowest price. As a result, with a price that is just a penny lower, a firm steals all its rival's customers, doubling its demand. So lowering the price by only a penny approximately doubles its profit. The same would be true if both firms were charging $69, $60, $45, or even $40.25. This kind of undercutting behaviour drives prices down to marginal cost.

French mathematician Joseph Bertrand (1822–1900)

Let's go through this argument again, more carefully. To identify the Nash equilibrium in this Bertrand game, it's helpful to think about each firm's demand curve. A firm's demand curve shows the relationship between the firm's price and the quantity it sells given the price of its rival (or prices of its rivals, if there are more than one). A firm has many demand curves, each one corresponding to a different choice by its rival. Figure 19.2(b) shows Joe's demand curve if Rebecca charges $70, labelled D_{70} and drawn in blue. Figure 19.2(c) shows Joe's demand curve if Rebecca charges $50, labelled D_{50}.

In Figures 19.2(b) and 19.2(c), the market demand curve, labelled D, is shown in grey. (Where Joe's demand curve and the market demand curve coincide, the blue and grey curves are combined.) Notice that in each case, if Joe charges a higher price than Rebecca, he sells nothing. If he sets the same price as Rebecca, his sales equal half the market demand at that price. (For example, if he and Rebecca each charge $70, he sells 1500 cubic metres.) And if Joe charges a lower price than Rebecca's, his sales equal the market demand at his price. For example, if Rebecca charges $70 and Joe charges $40, Joe sells 6000 cubic metres of concrete.

First, let's show that if both firms charge $40—equal to their marginal cost—a Nash equilibrium results. Figure 19.3 shows Joe's demand curve when Rebecca charges $40, labelled D_{40}. If Joe charges $40, he sells 3000 cubic metres of concrete and earns a profit of zero. Can he do better by charging a different price? If he charges a price *above* $40, he makes no sales at all, and again earns zero. If he charges a price *below* $40, he makes more than twice as many sales (more than 6000 cubic metres), but he loses money because his price is lower than his marginal cost. So charging $40 is the best Joe can do given that Rebecca is charging $40. And because Rebecca is in the same situation as Joe, she can't do better than charging $40 either, as long as Joe is charging $40. Thus, when both charge $40 we have a Nash equilibrium.

Might there be some Nash equilibrium in which sales take place at a price other than $40? The answer is no. Suppose, for example, that Rebecca is making sales charging $50. Since Joe's price cannot be lower than Rebecca's, either he is charging $50 himself, supplying half the market demand [2500 cubic metres—see Figure 19.2(c)] and earning $25,000 in profit, or he is charging more than $50, making no sales and earning zero profit. In either case, he can earn more by slightly undercutting Rebecca's price of $50 (he'll earn almost $50,000). So this can't be a Nash equilibrium. The same argument would apply at any price above $40 at which Rebecca might be making sales.

Can sales occur at a price *below* $40? In that case, the firm that charged that price would be losing money. It would do better charging $40, which would guarantee that it breaks even. So prices below $40 can't happen in a Nash equilibrium, either.

Figure 19.3

Nash Equilibrium in the Bertrand Model. The figure shows Joe's demand curve when Rebecca charges $40, labelled D_{40}. If Joe charges $40, he sells 3000 cubic metres and earns a zero profit. If he charges more than $40, he makes no sales, also earning a zero profit. If he charges less than $40, he makes sales, but loses money. So Joe can't do better than charging $40 if Rebecca charges $40. Similarly, Rebecca can't do better than charging $40 if Joe is charging $40. So both firms charge $40, a price equal to their marginal cost. This outcome is a Nash equilibrium.

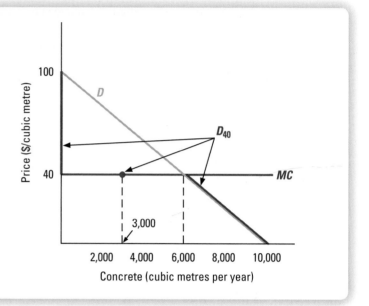

The Bertrand model yields a startling result. If this market were a monopoly, the price would be $70. But the Bertrand model tells us that with two firms, the price equals the marginal cost ($40)—the same as the perfectly competitive outcome! In a Bertrand market, firms find themselves in a position much like Coke and Pepsi in Figure 19.1. To maximize their joint profit, each would need to charge $70, but each is tempted to undercut that price to increase its own profit. In doing so, each firm ignores the negative effect of its behaviour on its rival's profit. In a Bertrand market, this temptation to undercut is very strong; so much so that prices are driven all the way down to marginal cost.

According to the Bertrand model, welfare losses due to market power are limited to monopoly markets. Unfortunately, this model paints an overly optimistic picture of what happens in most oligopoly markets. The reason has to do with some of the model's assumptions, which are often at odds with reality. We'll explain why, and discuss the effects of changing those assumptions, in the next three sections.

19.3 COURNOT QUANTITY COMPETITION

According to the Bertrand model of competition (Section 19.2), if Rebecca sets her price above marginal cost ($40), Joe will undercut her price and steal all her customers. To do so, though, Joe must be able to serve the entire market. In many settings, however, a firm can sell only a limited quantity at any point in time. It may, for example, have a limited inventory, or it may face constraints on its capacity. As a result, the Bertrand model may overstate the extent to which one company can steal business from another company, even when the two companies' products are homogeneous.

The conditions that often limit a firm's sales result from *choices* that the Bertrand model ignores. In reality, firms make decisions that influence the quantity of a product they can sell—for instance, by building new capacity or adding to their inventory. As a result, in some situations, quantities rather than prices drive the market outcome.

In this section, we'll study a model of competition that focuses on output decisions rather than on price decisions. As in the Bertrand model, we'll assume that the firms produce identical goods. However, in contrast to the Bertrand model, we'll assume that they decide how much to produce, rather than how much to charge, simultaneously. Given their chosen quantities, the price (which is the same for all firms) clears the market equating the quantity demanded to the supply. This model is known as the **Cournot model of oligopoly**, after the French mathematician Augustin Cournot, who introduced it in 1838.

Think, for example, about a small-town farmers' market that operates every Saturday morning. Early each Saturday, each farmer must decide how many vegetables to bring to market. Once the farmers have set up their stalls and the buyers have arrived, the price of the vegetables adjusts to equate the quantities supplied and demanded. In this case, the key decision for the farmer is how many vegetables to bring to market. By varying that quantity, a farmer can affect the market price. More generally, the Cournot model provides useful insights in any setting in which firms make capacity or inventory decisions that determine their sales capabilities.

Figure 19.4 shows how the price is determined in a Cournot market. The market demand curve is labelled D, and the marginal cost curve, labelled MC, is horizontal at $40. Suppose that Joe's output, denoted Q_{Joe}, is 1000 cubic metres per year, and Rebecca's, denoted $Q_{Rebecca}$, is 3000, so that total output is 4000 cubic metres per year. Given these quantities, the Cournot model assumes that the price will clear the market, so that the quantity demanded equals the total quantity produced. As the figure shows, the market-clearing price is $60 per cubic metre. If, instead, Rebecca's output is 5000 cubic metres per year and Joe's remains 1000, so that the total output is 6000 cubic metres, the market-clearing price will be $40.[1]

> In the **Cournot model of oligopoly,** firms choose how much to produce (their quantities) simultaneously, and the price clears the market given the total quantity produced.

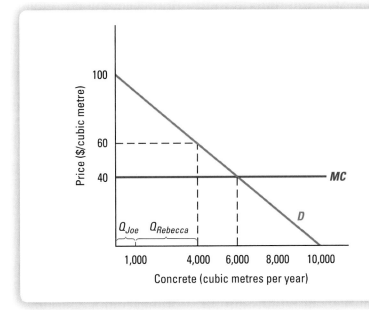

Figure 19.4
Price Determination in the Cournot Model. Given the outputs of the two firms, the price clears the market, so that the amount demanded equals the total output. Here Joe's output, Q_{Joe}, is 1000 cubic metres, and Rebecca's output, $Q_{Rebecca}$, is 3000. The price is therefore $60.

[1]To focus on firms' quantity choices, the Cournot model adopts a simple model of price determination in which the market price adjusts to equate the quantities demanded and supplied. Is this assumption—that oligopolists charge the market-clearing price—reasonable? Notice that at the market-clearing price, neither Joe nor Rebecca has an incentive to undercut the other's price because each is selling all of his or her output: neither can gain any sales by undercutting the other's price and would only lower his or her profit by doing so. What about raising the price? That is a more complicated issue, which we won't go into here. However, it can be shown that in the setting described here, neither Joe nor Rebecca will want to charge a price above the market-clearing price, provided that neither has drastically overproduced.

Antoine Augustin Cournot
(1801–1877)

Nash Equilibrium in a Cournot Market

Equilibrium in a Cournot market differs from equilibrium in a Bertrand market in an important way. In a Cournot market, the equilibrium price is always above marginal cost. To see why, suppose the firms produce a total of 6000 cubic metres of concrete per year, so that the price equals the marginal cost ($40). Each firm will earn zero profit. But that can't be an equilibrium, because Joe could do better by reducing his output, which would raise the market-clearing price above the marginal cost, yielding him a positive profit. (For example, if Joe and Rebecca were each producing 3000 cubic metres, Joe could reduce his output to 1000 cubic metres, raise the price to $60, and earn a $20,000 profit.) The same is true for Rebecca.

Let's take a closer look at the outputs that will be chosen in a Cournot market. In a Nash equilibrium, each firm's output choice maximizes its profit given its rival's output choice. To derive the Nash equilibrium outputs, then, we need to find each firm's profit-maximizing output choice—its best response—for each possible output level for its rival. We'll start by focusing on Joe's profit-maximizing output choices.

Residual Demand Curves   The first step is to derive Joe's residual demand curves. A **residual demand curve** shows the relationship between a firm's output and the market price given the outputs of the firm's rivals. Figure 19.5(a) shows Joe's residual demand curve when Rebecca's output is 2000 cubic metres per year. In the figure, D is again the market demand curve and RD_{2000} is Joe's residual demand curve. Joe's residual demand curve is found by shifting the market demand curve to the left by 2000 cubic metres, equal to Rebecca's output. Why? Consider a price of $80. The market demand curve tells us that the *total* output must be 2000 cubic metres for this price to clear the market. Since Rebecca is producing 2000 cubic metres, Joe's output at that price must be zero. What must Joe's output be for the price to be $40? The price is $40 when total output equals 6000 cubic metres, so Joe's output must be 4000. More generally, at each price, Joe's output must be less than the amount demanded by exactly the amount of Rebecca's output (2000 cubic metres). Similarly, Figure 19.5(b) shows Joe's residual demand curve when Rebecca's output is 4000 cubic metres.[2] Because this output is larger than the one shown in Figure 19.5(a), Joe's residual demand curve is located farther to the left than in Figure 19.5(a).

Best Responses   Joe's profit-maximizing output level for a given level of Rebecca's output, his best response, is the quantity that equates his marginal revenue with his marginal cost. Figures 19.6(a) and (b) show Joe's marginal revenue and marginal cost curves along with the residual demand curves from Figures 19.5(a) and (b). In each case, the marginal revenue curve is derived from Joe's residual demand curve. Joe's profit-maximizing production levels, where $MR = MC$, are 2000 cubic metres when Rebecca's output is 2000 cubic metres, and 1000 cubic metres when Rebecca's output is 4000 cubic metres. So Joe produces less output when Rebecca produces more.

By graphing Joe's best response at each of Rebecca's possible output levels, we obtain Joe's **best-response curve**, labelled BR_{Joe} in Figure 19.7(a). It includes the two best responses shown in Figure 19.6, as well as Joe's best responses at all other possible output levels for Rebecca. For example, if Rebecca were to produce no output, then Joe would produce 3000 cubic metres, the monopoly quantity. If instead Rebecca were to

A **residual demand curve** shows the relationship between a firm's output and the market price given the outputs of the firm's rivals.

A firm's **best-response curve** shows its best choice in response to each possible action by its rival.

---

[2]Note that a firm has many residual demand curves, each corresponding to a different output level of its rivals.

Figure 19.5

Joe's Residual Demand Curves. Figures (a) and (b) show Joe's residual demand curves when Rebecca's output is 2000 and 4000 cubic metres, respectively. In each case, the residual demand curve is shifted leftward from the market demand curve by an amount equal to Rebecca's output at every price.

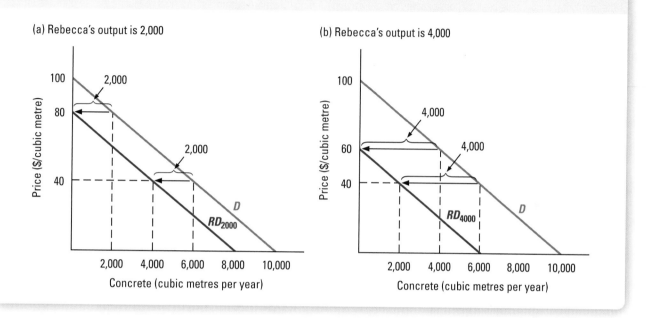

(a) Rebecca's output is 2,000

(b) Rebecca's output is 4,000

Figure 19.6

Best Responses in the Cournot Model. Figures (a) and (b) show Joe's profit-maximizing output levels when Rebecca's output is 2000 and 4000 cubic metres, respectively. Joe's best choices (2000 and 1000 cubic metres, respectively) are the quantities at which Joe's marginal revenue equals his marginal cost. The figures also show the resulting market prices given those best responses ($60 and $50 per cubic metre, respectively).

(a) Rebecca's output is 2,000

(b) Rebecca's output is 4,000

Figure 19.7

Best-Response Curves in the Cournot Model. Figure (a) shows Joe's best-response curve. It graphs Joe's best responses when Rebecca's output is 2000 and 4000 cubic metres from Figure 19.6(a), as well as Joe's best responses to every other possible output level for Rebecca. Figure (b) shows Rebecca's best-response curve, graphed with Joe's output on the vertical axis and Rebecca's on the horizontal axis. These best-response curves are downward-sloping: the more output a firm's rival produces, the smaller the firm's profit-maximizing output level.

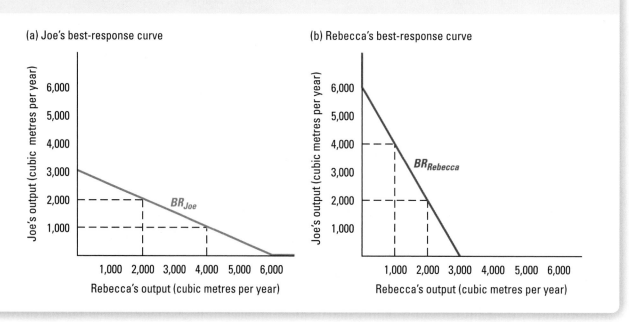

produce 6000 cubic metres of output, Joe would produce nothing. At that level, any production by Joe would drive the price below $40, and Joe would lose money. Joe's best-response curve slopes downward, indicating that the more output Rebecca produces, the less Joe wants to produce.

We can determine Rebecca's best responses in a similar way. Figure 19.7(b) shows Rebecca's best-response curve, labelled $BR_{Rebecca}$. It is drawn with Joe's output on the vertical axis and Rebecca's on the horizontal axis. Like Joe's best-response curve, Rebecca's slopes downward: the more output Joe produces, the less Rebecca wants to produce.

Nash Equilibrium   Figure 19.8 puts these two best-response curves together to find Joe and Rebecca's Nash equilibrium output choices. The Nash equilibrium occurs where the two curves cross. (The point where the best-response curves cross is like the cell in Figure 19.1(b) that is shaded half green and half red—at that pair of outputs, each firm is choosing a best response to its rival's output level; see Section 12.3.) In the Nash equilibrium, both Joe and Rebecca produce 2000 cubic metres of concrete per year. Looking back at Figure 19.4, at 4000 cubic metres of output, the market price in this equilibrium is $60 per cubic metre.

We can also find these equilibrium output choices using algebra; worked-out problem 19.1 shows how.

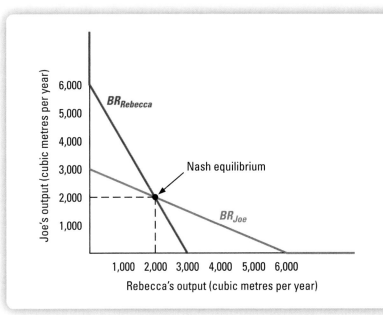

Figure 19.8

Nash Equilibrium in the Cournot Model. The figure shows the Nash equilibrium outputs in the Cournot Model. Joe and Rebecca both produce 2000 cubic metres per year, which is the point where their best-response curves cross. Each firm is therefore choosing its profit-maximizing output level given its rival's output.

WORKED-OUT PROBLEM   19.1

The Problem   Joe and Rebecca are small-town ready-mix concrete duopolists. The market demand function is

$$Q^d = 10{,}000 - 100P$$

where P is the price of a cubic metre of concrete and Q^d is the number of cubic metres demanded per year. Marginal cost is \$40 per cubic metre. Competition in this market is described by the Cournot model. What are Joe and Rebecca's Nash equilibrium outputs? What is the resulting price? What do they each earn as profit? How does the price compare to the marginal cost? How do the price and the two firms' joint profit (the sum of their individual profits) compare to the monopoly price and profit?

The Solution   The market inverse demand function is

$$P = 100 - 0.01Q$$

which corresponds to the demand curve in Figure 19.4. Given Joe and Rebecca's outputs, Q_{Joe} and $Q_{Rebecca}$, the price is therefore

$$P = 100 - 0.01(Q_{Joe} + Q_{Rebecca})$$

Rewriting this expression gives us each of their inverse *residual* demand functions. For Joe, it is

$$P = (100 - 0.01Q_{Rebecca}) - 0.01Q_{Joe}$$

and for Rebecca, it is

$$P = (100 - 0.01Q_{Joe}) - 0.01Q_{Rebecca}$$

Observe that at any output level for Rebecca, the term in parentheses in Joe's inverse residual demand function is constant from Joe's perspective (since he doesn't choose Rebecca's quantity). For example, if Rebecca produces 2000 cubic metres per year, then Joe's inverse residual demand function is $P = 80 - 0.01Q_{Joe}$. If instead she produces 4000 cubic metres of output, then his inverse residual demand function is $P = 60 - 0.01Q_{Joe}$.

Once we have these inverse residual demand functions, we can find the Nash equilibrium in three steps: the first two steps derive Joe's and Rebecca's best-response functions; the third step uses these best-response functions to find the Nash equilibrium.

Step 1: Finding Joe's best-response function.

Two steps are involved to derive Joe's best-response function:

Step 1A: Derive Joe's marginal revenue function. Joe's marginal revenue given Rebecca's output $Q_{Rebecca}$ is derived from his inverse residual demand function in the same way that a monopolist's marginal revenue is derived from the market inverse demand function. From formula (1) for marginal revenue in Section 17.2 (page 619) we know that $MR_{Joe} = P + (\Delta P/\Delta Q)Q_{Joe}$. Substituting for P and $(\Delta P/\Delta Q)$ using Joe's inverse residual demand function gives

$$MR_{Joe} = (100 - 0.01Q_{Rebecca} - 0.01Q_{Joe}) - (0.01)Q_{Joe}$$
$$= 100 - 0.01Q_{Rebecca} - 0.02Q_{Joe}$$

Step 1B: Derive Joe's profit-maximizing output at each possible output level for Rebecca. To find Joe's profit-maximizing output at a given output level for Rebecca, we look for the point at which Joe's marginal revenue equals his marginal cost. So we want to find the output Q_{Joe} at which

$$100 - 0.01Q_{Rebecca} - 0.02Q_{Joe} = 40$$

Rearranging terms, we find that the profit-maximizing output level is

$$Q_{Joe} = 3000 - 0.5Q_{Rebecca} \tag{1}$$

Notice that Joe's profit-maximizing output depends on Rebecca's output. For each additional cubic metre of output that Rebecca produces, Joe reduces his output by 0.5 cubic metres. This result is reflected in the best-response curve in Figure 19.7(a).

Step 2: Finding Rebecca's best-response function.

We can follow the same two steps to find Rebecca's best-response function. It turns out to be[3]

$$Q_{Rebecca} = 3000 - 0.5Q_{Joe} \tag{2}$$

This result corresponds to the best-response curve in Figure 19.7(b). (You should check this formula.)

Step 3: Deriving the Nash equilibrium quantities from the best-response functions.

To find the Nash equilibrium prices, we need to solve formulas (1) and (2) for Joe and Rebecca's outputs. To do so, we substitute for Q_{Joe} in formula (2) from formula (1) to obtain the equation.

Optional. Joe's best-response function can be found using calculus by setting the derivative of the profit function, $\Pi(Q_{Joe}) = PQ_{Joe} - MC_{Joe}Q_{Joe}$, equal to 0 taking Rebecca's output choice as fixed. This yields formula (1) when $P = 100 - 0.01(Q_{Joe} + Q_{Rebecca})$ and $MC_{Joe} = 40$.

---

[3]This is the same best-response function as Joe's, but with the labels for Joe and Rebecca's outputs reversed. The reason is that, in this particular example, Joe and Rebecca have the same cost function. See end-of-chapter exercise 19.4 for an example in which the two cost functions differ.

$$Q_{Rebecca} = 3000 - 0.5(3000 - 0.5Q_{Rebecca})$$

Solving for $Q_{Rebecca}$, we find that Rebecca's output in the Nash equilibrium is 2000 cubic metres per year. Substituting this value into formula (1) tells us that Joe's output is also 2000 cubic metres per year. This is the Nash equilibrium shown in Figure 19.8. The price is $60. Each producer earns a profit of $40,000 per year (each sells 2000 cubic metres, earning a profit of $20 on each).

Notice that the equilibrium price is greater than the marginal cost of $40, which would be the price if this were a competitive market. At the same time, the duopoly price is lower than the $70 price a monopolist would set, and the two firms' joint profit is less than the monopoly profit of $90,000 per year (you should verify this monopoly price and profit yourself).

 IN-TEXT EXERCISE 19.1 **Repeat worked-out problem 19.1, but assume instead that Joe and Rebecca each face a marginal cost of $25 per cubic metre. Then repeat assuming Joe's marginal cost is $10 and Rebecca's marginal cost is $40.**

Oligopoly versus Monopoly Deadweight Loss

Figure 19.9 compares the deadweight loss under oligopoly to the deadweight loss of monopoly. Joe and Rebecca produce a total of 4000 cubic metres per year. The resulting deadweight loss is the area of the light red triangle in the figure, which equals $20,000 per year. (See Sections 14.5 and 17.3 for discussions of deadweight loss.) If, instead, there was a monopolist in this market (or if Joe and Rebecca were to collude perfectly and act like a monopolist instead of competing as Cournot duopolists) the deadweight loss would be the sum of the dark and light red-shaded areas in the figure, which equals $45,000 per year. Because the price is closer to marginal cost in an oligopoly, the deadweight loss is smaller in an oligopoly than in a monopoly.

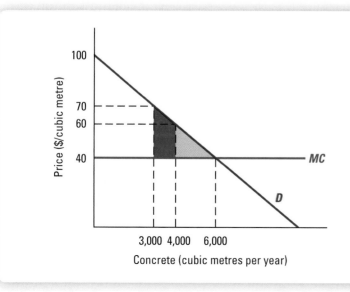

Figure 19.9

Deadweight Loss from Duopoly versus Monopoly. The deadweight loss with oligopoly equals the area of the light red triangle ($20,000 per year). The deadweight loss of monopoly, equal to the total of the light and dark red-shaded areas ($45,000 per year), is larger because the monopoly price is further above marginal cost than is the oligopoly price.

Oligopoly and Perfect Competition

What if there are more than two firms in the market? Intuitively, when the number of competitors in a market grows very large, so that each firm is supplying just a small fraction of the total output, we expect firms to begin acting like price takers. If so, the market outcome should approach a competitive equilibrium. And that is exactly what happens in a Cournot market.

Let's examine this point more closely. Think about Joe's situation if he faces several rivals—say, Rebecca, Louie, and Alex. When Joe decides how much to produce, he doesn't care who is producing the rest of the output in the market, whether it is Rebecca or someone else. The effect on the price he receives is the same. So when Joe faces more than one rival, only their total output matters in determining his best response. Given this fact, his best-response function will take the same form as in formula (1), but with Q_{Rivals}, the total output of his rivals, replacing $Q_{Rebecca}$. The same idea applies to Rebecca and every other firm in the market. So each firm's best response can be described with the following formula, where Q_i is firm i's profit-maximizing quantity.

$$Q_i = 3000 - 0.5Q_{Rivals} \qquad (3)$$

This formula says that a firm will produce 3000 cubic metres if its rivals produce nothing (this is the monopoly quantity) and will reduce its output by 0.5 cubic metres for every additional cubic metre of output that its rivals produce.

Suppose there are N firms in the market. Let's consider a Nash equilibrium in which each firm produces the same amount of output. In that case, if the total output in the market is Q, each individual firm's output is Q/N cubic metres, and the firm's $N - 1$ rivals produce a total of $(N - 1)(Q/N)$ cubic metres. Since formula (3) must hold in a Nash equilibrium, it must be that

$$(Q/N) = 3000 - 0.5(N - 1)\left(\frac{Q}{N}\right)$$

Multiplying both sides of this formula by two, and bringing terms involving the output Q over to the left-hand side, we can rewrite this formula as

$$Q\left[\left(\frac{2}{N}\right) + \left(\frac{N-1}{N}\right)\right] = 6000$$

Solving this equation for the equilibrium value of Q, we find that

$$Q = 6000\left(\frac{N}{N+1}\right) \qquad (4)$$

And substituting this expression into the demand curve, we find that the price is

$$P = 100 - 60\left(\frac{N}{N+1}\right) \qquad (5)$$

When $N = 1$, we have a monopoly: the price is $70 and 3000 cubic metres are produced and sold. When $N = 2$, we have a duopoly: as we've seen, the price is $60 and 4000 cubic metres are bought and sold. Table 19.1 shows the price, the difference between the price and marginal cost, the total output, the output per firm, and the profits for the industry as a whole and for each individual firm (each rounded to the nearest dollar or cubic metre) given different numbers of firms, based on formulas (4) and (5).

Table 19.1

Nash Equilibrium Outcomes for Various Numbers of Firms in the Cournot Market of Worked-Out Problem 19.1

Number of Active Firms	Price	(P – MC)	Total Output (Cubic metres per year)	Output per Firm (Cubic metres per year)	Industry Profit	Profit per Firm
1	$70	$30	3,000	3,000	$90,000	$90,000
2	60	20	4,000	2,000	80,000	40,000
3	55	15	4,500	1,500	67,500	22,500
4	52	12	4,800	1,200	57,600	14,400
5	50	10	5,000	1,000	50,000	10,000
10	45.45	5.45	5,455	545	29,752	2,975
20	42.86	2.86	5,714	286	16,327	816
50	41.17	1.17	5,882	118	6,920	138
100	40.59	0.59	5,941	59	3,529	35

Formulas (4) and (5) imply, and Table 19.1 shows, that as the number of firms increases, the price falls and the total quantity produced increases. With four firms the price is $52; with 10 firms it's $45.45; with 20 it's $42.86; and with 100 it's $40.59. Since $N/(N + 1)$ approaches 1 as N grows larger, formula (5) implies that the price approaches $40, the marginal cost. That is, as the number of firms grows large, the outcome of a Cournot oligopoly approaches the perfectly competitive outcome.

Markups in a Cournot Market

In Section 17.2 we saw that a monopolist's markup, $(P - MC)/P$, can be related to the elasticity of demand (see formula (4) on page 625 of chapter 17). A similar formula holds in a Cournot market and helps to clarify the factors that affect markups in those markets. Consider one of N identical Cournot competitors whose marginal cost is MC. We can write its marginal revenue as

$$MR = P + \left(\frac{\Delta P}{\Delta Q}\right)\left(\frac{Q}{N}\right) \tag{6}$$

This formula is just like the expression for a monopolist, but now the price reduction effect we discussed in Section 17.2 lowers the amount the firm receives only on its own output, which is Q/N rather than Q. In a Nash equilibrium, each firm's marginal revenue equals its marginal cost

$$P + \left(\frac{\Delta P}{\Delta Q}\right)\left(\frac{Q}{N}\right) = MC$$

Dividing by P and rearranging, we can write

$$\frac{P - MC}{P} = -\left[\left(\frac{\Delta P}{\Delta Q}\right)\left(\frac{Q}{P}\right)\right]\left(\frac{1}{N}\right)$$

Letting E^d denote the elasticity of market demand, we can rewrite this formula as

$$\frac{P - MC}{P} = -\left(\frac{1}{N \times E^d}\right) \tag{7}$$

So the elasticity of market demand affects the size of the markup, as does the number of firms. Formula (7) says that for a given number of firms, the less elastic the demand (the less negative is E^d), the greater the markup. The reason is the same as for a monopolist: the less elastic the demand, the greater the increase in price that results from a given reduction in a firm's output—and therefore the larger the gains from restricting output. Formula (7) also says that, for a given demand elasticity, the larger the number of firms, the lower the markup. The reason can be seen in formula (6): the greater the number of firms, the smaller each firm's output, Q/N, and thus the smaller the profit loss from the price reduction effect when a firm increases its output. Formula (7) also confirms that as N grows larger, the markup falls to zero, so the price approaches marginal cost.

> **IN-TEXT EXERCISE 19.2** **Given N identical firms with marginal costs of \$40 and market demand $Q^d = 10{,}000 - 100P$ find the price elasticity of demand when there are 2, 5, and 59 firms. What is the size of the markup in each case?**

Application 19.1

Price Spikes and Market Power in the Electricity Market

Across North America, electricity-market restructuring began in earnest in the 1990s. Alberta first began to restructure its electricity market in 1995 while in Ontario the Electricity Act of 1998 set the framework for electricity reform. In the United States deregulation in the largest state market, California, began in 1998. Prior to this time the prices that power producers received were regulated (see Section 17.7 for a discussion of price regulation). The motivation for restructuring in Ontario was due in part to the dismal financial position of one of North America's largest government-owned monopolies, Ontario Hydro. In 1999 Ontario Hydro had liabilities of \$38.1 billion, which constituted fully one third of the provincial debt, but had assets valued at only \$17.2 billion.[4] Ontario took the bold step of separating the transmission, distribution, and generation components of Ontario Hydro into three independent firms.

Electricity restructuring got off to a rocky start both in Canada and the United States. In Alberta the average wholesale price of electricity in 1999 was \$42.74 per MWh (megawatt hour) but in 2000 spiked to an average price of \$133.22 per MWh. The government of Alberta was forced to give rebates of \$40 a month in 2001 and to add new generation capacity in order to avoid a political revolt. Ontario opened the electricity market to price competition in May of 2002,

almost two years after its scheduled opening, and almost immediately wholesale and retail prices soared. In May 2002 the average wholesale price was \$30.1 per MWh. As the summer progressed prices started to increase. In June the price was \$37.1 per MWh with July seeing an average price of \$62 per MWh. By the end of the summer the price had peaked at \$83.1 per MWh. By November an increasingly unhappy electorate forced the province to announce both a price freeze and a rebate. South of the border in California the situation was even worse. Almost before the deregulation process began it ended in disaster with rolling blackouts, the bankruptcy of the state's largest electric utility, Pacific Gas and Electric, and the recall of Governor Gray Davis.

Although the price of oil was rising toward the end of the 1990s this was the not the primary reason for the price spikes. The main reason for the price increases was the lack of generation capacity and the market power exercised by even relatively small electric generators. The dramatic price increase in California has been extensively studied and the lessons learned have led to improvements in electricity reform efforts throughout the world.

In California, the state set up a wholesale market in which buyers and sellers of electricity could trade electricity one day ahead of its actual use.[5] The buyers were primarily

---

[4]Edward Iacobucci, Michael Trebilcock, and Ralph A. Winter, "The Canadian Experience With Deregulation." *University of Toronto Law Journal* 52, Winter 2006, pp. 1–74.

[5]Although there were other electricity markets in operation as well, most transactions took place in this one-day-ahead market, and prices were similar across different markets.

three electric utilities, Pacific Gas and Electric, Southern California Edison, and San Diego Gas & Electric, which served retail customers at regulated prices. The sellers were primarily five large independent electricity producers (Duke, Dynegy, Reliant, AES/Williams, and Mirant), plus smaller in- and out-of-state suppliers. The rules of the wholesale market allowed each producer to choose the amount of its capacity that would be available to supply electricity to the buyers. Unfortunately, in periods of high demand and low supply from other sources, the five large producers had strong incentives to limit their available capacity because of the effect this could have in raising the market price, just as in the Cournot model.

Let's take a closer look at a large producer's decision to limit capacity. For a given hour on a particular day, the blue curve in Figure 19.10(a) represents the market demand curve. The quantity demanded is very unresponsive to the wholesale price both because electricity is essential in many of its uses, and also because utilities were required

to satisfy the demands of households and businesses, which faced regulated retail prices for electricity that did not vary at all with changes in the wholesale price. The figure also shows in red the supply curve of smaller in- and out-of-state producers (we assume they are price takers). That supply curve is fairly flat, but rises steeply as it approaches the limit of these producers' combined capacity.

The curve labelled RD in Figure 19.10(b) is the residual demand curve that the five large producers faced (as a group). It shows the total market demand less the smaller in- and out-of-state producers' supply at each price. Because of the shape of that supply curve, the residual demand curve is very steep at high prices, when smaller in- and out-of-state producers are running at or near their capacity, and fairly flat at low prices, when they are running well below capacity. It becomes steep again when the price falls so low that the smaller in- and out-of-state producers supply nothing.

Figure 19.10

The Residual Demand Curve Facing California's Five Large Electricity Producers. Figure (a) shows the overall market demand curve, labelled *D*, and the supply curve of smaller in- and out-of-state producers, labelled *S*. Figure (b) shows the residual market demand curve facing the five large electricity producers, labelled *RD*. At each price it equals the difference between the total market demand and the small producer supply.

(a) Market demand and small producers' supply   (b) Residual market demand

Figure 19.11 illustrates the potential for the large producers to exercise market power by reducing supply. Figure 19.11(a) shows the residual demand curve facing the five large producers for an hour in which residual demand is low (say, from 2:00–3:00 a.m. on a weekend in March when a lot of out-of-state supply is available). The figure also shows the marginal cost curve of the five large producers in red. At the competitive price (which corresponds to the intersection of those two curves) the residual demand curve is fairly elastic (flat) because the smaller in- and out-of-state suppliers are producing much less than their capacity. In this case, none of the five large producers can increase the price very much by withholding output.

In contrast, Figure 19.11(b) shows an hour in which the residual demand facing the five large producers is very high (say, from 4:00–5:00 p.m. on a weekday in August when not much out-of-state supply is available). In this case, the competitive price corresponds to a point at which the large producers' residual demand curve is very inelastic (steep), because the smaller in- and out-of-state suppliers are running near full capacity. As a result, the large firms have significant incentives to withhold output to increase the market price.

In the summer of 2000, when demand was high and out-of-state sources of supply withered (low snowfall the previous winter in the Pacific Northwest reduced hydroelectric generation there), the five large producers exercised their market power with a vengeance. Table 19.2 shows the actual wholesale prices from January to September of 2000 along with estimates by economists Severin Borenstein, James Bushnell, and Frank Wolak of the prices that would have prevailed in a competitive market.[6] The actual and competitive prices are close during the spring, but diverge greatly in the summer. Even if the

Figure 19.11

Incentives to Reduce Output. In figure (a) the residual demand for the five large producers is low. Because their residual demand curve is relatively flat (elastic) where it intersects their marginal cost curve, their incentives to reduce output are low. In figure (b) their residual demand is high. Because their residual demand curve is steep (inelastic) where it intersects their marginal cost curve, their incentives to reduce output are high.

(a) Low residual demand

(b) High residual demand

[6]Severin Bornstein, James B. Bushnell, and Frank A Wolak, "Measuring Market Inefficiencies in California's Restructured Wholesale Electricity Market," *American Economic Review* 92, December 2002, pp. 1376–1405.

market had been perfectly competitive, the price would have risen by approximately 275 percent between January and August because of the lower hydroelectric supply (a cheap source of power) and higher natural gas costs. However, the actual prices increased by 533 percent during this time period, from \$31.18 per megawatt hour to \$166.24.[7] In an independent study, economists Paul Joskow and Edward Kahn confirmed this conclusion, and also documented the decisions of the five large producers to withhold capacity.[8]

Table 19.2

Actual versus Competitive Wholesale Prices for Electricity in California, January–September 2000

Month	Actual Price (U.S.\$/Megawatt hour)	Competitive Price (U.S.\$/Megawatt hour)
January	31.18	27.66
February	30.04	29.52
March	28.80	31.38
April	26.60	32.38
May	47.22	40.43
June	120.20	53.59
July	105.72	59.37
August	166.24	76.19
September	114.87	76.86

19.4 PRICE COMPETITION WITH DIFFERENTIATED PRODUCTS

Often, the products that firms in an oligopoly market sell are not homogeneous. Though Coke and Pepsi compete against each other, for example, they are not identical. At the same price, most consumers would prefer one of them over the other. When consumers do not view similar products as perfect substitutes, those products are called **differentiated products**.

When consumers do not view similar products as perfect substitutes, those products are called **differentiated products**.

In the Bertrand model of price competition with homogeneous products, described in Section 19.2, all consumers would buy from the firm with the lowest price. As a result, firms engaged in cutthroat competition, driving prices down to marginal cost in an attempt to steal each other's business. That does not happen in the markets for differentiated products, however. Let's think about the soft drink market in a small city, for example. For the sake of simplicity, we'll ignore all products other than Coke and Pepsi (*regular* Coke and Pepsi, that is) and assume that it costs \$0.30 to produce a can of either brand. Suppose Pepsi charges \$0.30 per can. If Coke also charges \$0.30, its profit will be zero. If instead Coke raises its price a little, it will lose some customers, but not all of them. As a result, Coke can make a positive profit by raising its price above its marginal cost.

Let's find the equilibrium prices when Coke and Pepsi choose their prices simultaneously. To do so, we must first identify Coke's most profitable price (its best response)

---

[7]By way of contrast, consumers were paying regulated retail prices averaging about \$60. This is why Pacific Gas and Electric declared bankruptcy.

[8]Paul Joskow and Edward Kahn, "A Quantitative Analysis of Pricing Behavior in California's Wholesale Electricity Market During Summer 2000," *The Energy Journal* 23, October 2002, pp. 1–35.

Figure 19.12

Coke's Demand Curves. Figures (a) and (b) show Coke's demand curves when Pepsi's price is $0.60 and $0.40 per can, respectively. A lower price for Pepsi shifts Coke's demand curve to the left, since Coke sells less at any given price.

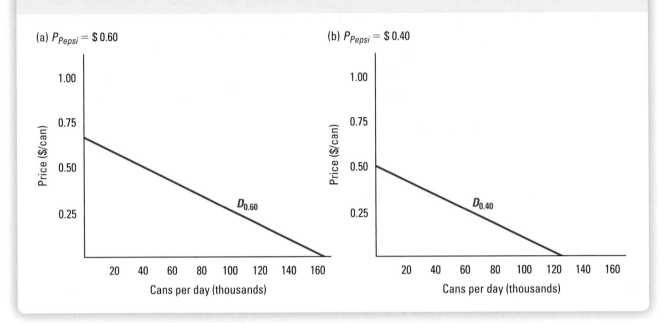

for each possible price for Pepsi. Figure 19.12(a) shows Coke's daily demand curve when Pepsi costs $0.60 per can, labelled $D_{0.60}$. Unlike the demand for a homogeneous product (see Figure 19.2 on page 698), Coke's demand decreases gradually as its price rises. Figure 19.12(b) shows Coke's demand curve when the price of Pepsi is instead $0.40, labelled $D_{0.40}$. Because the price of Pepsi is lower here than in Figure 19.12(a), and because Coke and Pepsi are substitutes (see Section 2.1), Coke sells fewer cans per day than in Figure 19.12(a) at each possible price.

Figure 19.13(a) adds to Figure 19.12(a) Coke's marginal revenue curve (derived from its demand curve) when Pepsi's price is $0.60 per can, as well as its marginal cost curve, a horizontal line at $0.30. Coke's profit-maximizing sales quantity occurs at the intersection of the marginal revenue and marginal cost curves: it is 45,000 cans per day. The price required to sell that many cans may then be found from Coke's demand curve: it is $0.48 per can.

Figure 19.13(b) shows the corresponding information when Pepsi's price is $0.40 per can. With a lower demand curve, Coke has a lower marginal revenue curve than in Figure 19.13(a). As a result, its profit-maximizing sales quantity, 25,000 cans, is lower than before. Its profit-maximizing price is now $0.40.

By graphing Coke's best response at each possible price that Pepsi might charge, we obtain Coke's best-response curve, shown in green in Figure 19.14. Coke's best-response curve is upward sloping: the more Pepsi charges, the more Coke should charge. By following the same steps, we can find Pepsi's profit-maximizing price at each possible price that Coke might charge. Figure 19.14 shows Pepsi's best-response curve in red, graphed with Coke's price on the vertical axis and Pepsi's price on the horizontal axis. The Nash

Figure 19.13

Coke's Best Responses. Figures (a) and (b) show Coke's profit-maximizing prices when Pepsi's price is $0.60 and $0.40 per can, respectively. They are found by first identifying Coke's profit-maximizing sales quantity [45,000 in (a) and 25,000 in (b)] which occurs where $MR = MC$, and then finding the corresponding profit-maximizing price [$0.48 in (a) and $0.40 in (b)] from the demand curve.

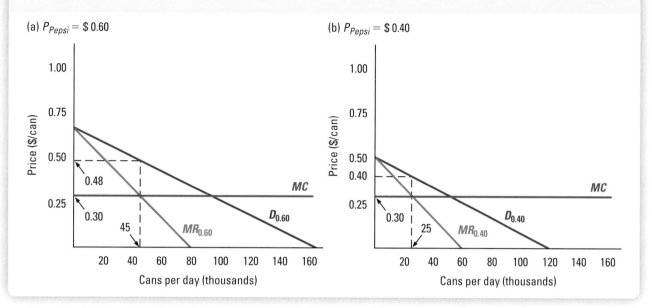

Figure 19.14

Nash Equilibrium with Differentiated Products. The figure graphs Coke and Pepsi's best-response curves. The Nash equilibrium is the point where they cross, with both firms charging $0.40 per can, more than their marginal cost of $0.30. At the Nash equilibrium, each firm's price maximizes the firm's profit given the price of its rival.

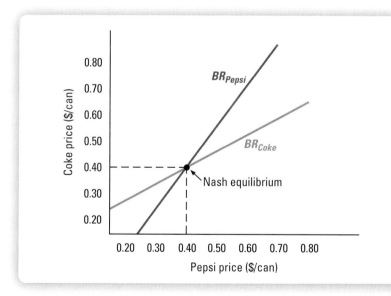

equilibrium occurs where the two curves cross, with each firm charging $0.40 per can, a price above the marginal cost. At the Nash equilibrium, each firm is choosing the price that maximizes its profit given its rival's price.

Worked-out problem 19.2 shows how to solve for the Nash equilibrium using algebra.

The Problem   Suppose the daily demand functions for Coke and Pepsi in a small city are given by

$$Q_{Coke} = 45 - 50P_{Coke} + 200(P_{Pepsi} - P_{Coke}) \qquad (8)$$

$$Q_{Pepsi} = 45 - 50P_{Pepsi} + 200(P_{Coke} - P_{Pepsi}) \qquad (9)$$

where Q_{Coke} and Q_{Pepsi} are the number of cans Coke and Pepsi sell, respectively, in thousands per day, and P_{Coke} and P_{Pepsi} are the prices of a can of Coke and Pepsi, respectively, measured in dollars. (These are the demand functions used to generate Figures 19.12 through 19.14.) Marginal cost is $0.30 per can. What are the Nash equilibrium prices when the two firms set their prices simultaneously?

The Solution   We can rewrite the demand functions (8) and (9) as

$$Q_{Coke} = (45 + 200P_{Pepsi}) - 250P_{Coke}$$

$$Q_{Pepsi} = (45 + 200P_{Coke}) - 250P_{Pepsi}$$

Notice that at any given price for Pepsi, the term in parentheses in Coke's demand function is a constant from Coke's perspective. For example, if $P_{Pepsi} = 0.60$, then Coke's demand function is $Q_{Coke} = 165 - 250P_{Coke}$. This is the demand function for the demand curve graphed in Figure 19.12(a). From these demand functions, we can also derive the two firms' *inverse* demand functions, which give the price the firms must charge for each amount they want to sell given their rival's price. Those inverse demand functions are

$$P_{Coke} = \left(\frac{45 + 200P_{Pepsi}}{250}\right) - \left(\frac{1}{250}\right)Q_{Coke} = (0.18 + 0.8P_{Pepsi}) - 0.004\,Q_{Coke}$$

$$P_{Pepsi} = \left(\frac{45 + 200P_{Coke}}{250}\right) - \left(\frac{1}{250}\right)Q_{Pepsi} = (0.18 + 0.8P_{Coke}) - 0.004\,Q_{Pepsi}$$

Once we have these inverse demand functions, we can find the Nash equilibrium prices in three steps. The first two steps derive each of the firm's best response functions. The third step uses these best response functions to find the Nash equilibrium prices.

Step 1: Finding Coke's best-response function.
Derive Coke's best-response function as folllows:

Step 1A: Derive Coke's marginal revenue function. Coke's marginal revenue given Pepsi's price is derived from Coke's inverse demand function in the same way that a monopolist's marginal revenue is derived from the inverse market demand function. From formula (1) for marginal revenue in Section 17.2 (page 620) we know that $MR_{Coke} = P + (\Delta P/\Delta Q)Q_{Coke}$. Substituting for P and $(\Delta P/\Delta Q)$ using Coke's inverse demand function gives

$$MR_{Coke} = (0.18 + 0.8P_{Pepsi} - 0.004Q_{Coke}) - 0.004Q_{Coke}$$

$$= 0.18 + 0.8P_{Pepsi} - 0.008Q_{Coke}$$

Step 1B: Derive Coke's profit-maximizing sales quantity at each possible price for Pepsi. Coke's profit-maximizing sales quantity sets its marginal revenue equal to its marginal cost: $MR_{Coke} = 0.30$. So we want to find the quantity Q_{Coke} at which

$$0.18 + 0.8P_{Pepsi} - 0.008Q_{Coke} = 0.30$$

Rearranging these terms, we find that Coke's profit-maximizing sales quantity is

$$Q_{Coke} = \left(\frac{-0.12 + 0.8P_{Pepsi}}{0.008}\right)$$

$$= -15 + 100P_{Pepsi}$$

Notice that the profit-maximizing sales quantity depends on Pepsi's price. The higher Pepsi's price, the more cans Coke should sell.

Step 1C: Derive Coke's profit-maximizing price at each possible price for Pepsi. We can find Coke's profit-maximizing price by substituting its profit-maximizing sales quantity into its inverse demand function

$$P_{Coke} = (0.18 + 0.8P_{Pepsi}) - 0.004(-15 + 100P_{Pepsi})$$

or equivalently

$$P_{Coke} = 0.24 + 0.4P_{Pepsi} \tag{10}$$

This best-response function tells us that when Pepsi's price is 10 cents higher ($0.10), Coke's profit-maximizing price increases by four cents ($0.04). For example, it is $0.40 when Pepsi charges $0.40 per can, but $0.48 when Pepsi charges $0.60 per can, exactly as shown in Figure 19.13. Coke's best-response function is shown in Figure 19.14.

Step 2: Find Pepsi's best-response function.
We can follow the same three steps to find Pepsi's best-response function. It turns out to be[9]

$$P_{Pepsi} = 0.24 + 0.4P_{Coke} \tag{11}$$

(You should check this for yourself.)

Step 3: Derive the Nash equilibrium prices from the best-response functions.
To find the Nash equilibrium prices, we need to solve formulas (10) and (11) for the two prices. To do so, we can substitute for P_{Pepsi} from formula (11) into formula (10).

$$P_{Coke} = 0.24 + 0.4(0.24 + 0.4P_{Coke})$$

Solving for P_{Coke}, we find that in the Nash equilibrium, the price of Coke is $0.40 per can. Substituting this value into formula (11) tells us that in the Nash equilibrium, the price of Pepsi is also $0.40 per can. This is the Nash equilibrium shown in Figure 19.13.

Optional. Coke's best-response function can be found using calculus by setting the derivative of the profit function, $\Pi (P_{Coke}) = P_{Coke}Q_{Coke} - MC_{Coke}Q_{Coke}$, equal to 0 taking Pepsi's price as fixed. This yields formula (10), since $Q_{Coke} = (45 + 200P_{Pepsi}) - 250P_{Coke}$ and $MC_{Coke} = 0.30$.

IN-TEXT EXERCISE 19.3 **Suppose the demands for Coke and Pepsi in a small city are given by formulas (8) and (9), but with 500 replacing 200. Find the Nash equilibrium prices. How do they compare with the Nash equilibrium prices in worked-out problem 19.2?**

---

[9]This is the same best-response function as Coke's, but with the labels for Pepsi's and Coke's prices reversed. In this particular example, Coke's and Pepsi's positions are completely symmetric; they have the same cost function and symmetric demand functions. In general, however, that need not be so; end-of-chapter exercise 19.7 provides an example.

Worked-out problem 19.2 and in-text exercise 19.3 illustrate an important lesson: as products become less differentiated, making consumers more willing to switch in response to price differences, competition becomes more intense. In those two problems, the demand functions for Coke and Pepsi had the forms

$$Q_{Coke} = 45 - 50P_{Coke} + D(P_{Pepsi} - P_{Coke}) \tag{12}$$

$$Q_{Pepsi} = 45 - 50P_{Pepsi} + D(P_{Coke} - P_{Pepsi}) \tag{13}$$

where D was 200 in worked-out problem 19.2 and 500 in in-text exercise 19.3. The larger D is, the more consumers will respond to a price difference by switching to the other product, and the greater each firm's incentive will be to undercut its rival. For example, when $D = 200$, holding the price of Coke fixed, Coke sells 2000 more cans each day for each cent that Pepsi's price exceeds its own (since $2 = 200 \times 0.01$ and Q_{Coke} and Q_{Pepsi} are measured in thousands). When $D = 500$, it sells 5000 more cans with this same price difference. Comparing the Nash equilibrium prices in worked-out problem 19.2 and in-text exercise 19.3 shows that the larger D is, the lower are equilibrium prices.

Because of this effect, a firm has an incentive to differentiate its products from those of its rivals. Indeed, product differentiation is one of the most important strategies firms use to ensure themselves a profit. Application 19.2 discusses one example of this powerful strategy.

Application 19.2

Product Differentiation Strategies: Canada's Bombardier and Brazil's Embraer

Competition in the commercial aircraft market can be brutal. For years, the Boeing Corporation and Airbus have slugged it out, trying to win airlines' business through aggressive pricing. In the midst of the battle two smaller companies, Canadian Bombardier and Brazilian Embraer, have competed in the market for smaller commercial planes. How are they doing?

Embraer has carefully avoided what CEO Maurico Botelho calls the "big dogs' yard."[10] In 1999, when the firm began to design its new 170/190 series, executives decided to exploit the "70–110 seat gap" in commercial airplane sizes. Planes in Embraer's new series would be larger than the 50–70 seat regional jets produced by Embraer and arch-rival Bombardier of Canada, but smaller than the smallest Boeing and Airbus jets. Embraer foresaw a growing demand for such planes, but there was another big

Embraer CEO Maurico Botelho standing before the Embraer 170

advantage to filling the gap: less intense price competition. The strategy paid off. In 2002, following the introduction of the 170/190 series, orders for the new planes climbed and Embraer's profits soared. In 2005 Embraer made a $446 million profit on revenues of $3.83 billion.

Bombardier's CEO Pierre Beaudoin has taken a different approach. Bombardier is the market leader in the production of executive aircraft with the Learjet but faces much stiffer competition with its larger aircraft. At the same time that Embraer announced its 170/190 series, Bombardier announced its new C-series, which were to have between 110 and 130 seats—at the low end of the Boeing and Airbus range. (At the time, the Airbus 318 and the Boeing 717, the smallest of the two companies' planes, could each carry about 108 passengers.) Going head-to-head with these two large companies made it much tougher for

---

[10]See "Brazilian Plane Maker Getting Big Orders for Smaller Jets," *New York Times*, March 18, 2005.

Bombardier to win profitable new business. On January 31, 2006, after two years of development efforts and an expenditure of hundreds of millions of dollars, Bombardier announced it was suspending its plans for the C-series. Exactly one year later Bombardier resurrected the C-series and as of 2009 has firm orders for 50 planes from its assembly plant in Montreal. It remains to be seen if the strategy of going head to head with Boeing and Airbus will pay off for Bombardier when the C-series goes into service in 2013.

19.5 COLLUSION

In the Bertrand and Cournot models, firms compete against one another only once. But in the real world, firms compete against one another over and over again. This repetition can make a big difference in the outcome of oligopolistic competition. When firms compete repeatedly, the incentive to undercut one another is often reduced.

Consider again Joe and Rebecca's Bertrand competition in the ready-mix concrete market of Section 19.2. Suppose the price is $50 per cubic metre, $10 above the marginal cost. Suppose, too, that the two producers are competing repeatedly. If Joe is thinking of undercutting Rebecca's price in order to steal her customers, he will face a question that did not arise in the Bertrand model: what effect will his action have on their future competition? If his undercutting Rebecca leads to a price war with her, it may not be such a good idea.

Let's examine this point more closely. Imagine that Joe and Rebecca play the Bertrand game over and over, with no definite end. In this variation, known as the **infinitely repeated Bertrand model**, Joe and Rebecca choose their prices simultaneously each market period, and customers buy from the firm with the lower price, exactly as in the original model. By the end of each period, the two have observed each others' price choices. The next period, they repeat the process. The infinitely repeated Bertrand model is an example of an infinitely repeated game of the type discussed in Section 12.4. In an equilibrium, at each point in the game each firm chooses a price that maximizes the firm's profit given the behaviour of its rival, accounting for its rival's current choices and future reactions. (For a discussion of this notion of equilibrium for games with multiple stages, called a *subgame perfect Nash equilibrium*, see Add-On 12A.)

> In the **infinitely repeated Bertrand model**, firms play the Bertrand pricing game over and over, with no definite end.

The length of a period in this model captures the amount of time a firm needs to observe its rival's price, formulate its response, and implement a price change. Here, we'll suppose this process takes a month, and that the monthly market demand function is $Q^d = 1000 - 10P$ (the marginal cost is still $40). You can check that the monopoly price is therefore $70 per cubic metre, and the monopoly profit is $9000 per month.

When firms compete repeatedly, one equilibrium outcome—known as the **noncooperative outcome**—involves the repetition in each period of the Nash equilibrium outcome that would arise were the firms to compete just once. Why? Think of a Bertrand market. If a firm's rival charges a price equal to marginal cost in every period, then the firm's best response is to set its own price equal to marginal cost every period; there is simply no way for the firm to make a positive profit. (See Section 12.4 for a further discussion of this point.)

> In a setting of repeated competition, the **noncooperative outcome** is the repetition in each period of the Nash equilibrium outcome that would arise were the firms to compete just once.

There may be other equilibrium outcomes, however. In fact, sometimes it is even possible for firms to sustain the monopoly price. Let's see how. Suppose Joe and Rebecca

PRICE WAR

both adopt the following strategy (for the definition of a strategy and its application in repeated games, see Section 12.4):

> Charge the monopoly price of $70 if no one has yet undercut that price; otherwise, charge $40 (equal to the marginal cost).

With this strategy, firms cooperate by charging the monopoly price so long as everyone has cooperated in the past. If not, firms engage in a price war, setting the price equal to marginal cost. We can think of this strategy as a threat: "I'll keep my price high if you do, but undercut me and a price war will result!" (This strategy is an example of a *grim strategy*, discussed in Section 12.4.)

If Joe and Rebecca both follow this strategy, they will end up charging $70 every period. Both will charge $70 in the first month of competition; in the second month, both will again charge $70, since they charged $70 in the first month; and so on. But do Joe and Rebecca have an incentive to follow this strategy? There are two issues to consider. First, will each want to charge $40 once either of them has undercut the other? The answer is yes. Once someone has undercut, charging $40 every period thereafter is a Nash equilibrium: for each firm, charging a price equal to marginal cost every subsequent period is a best response given that its rival will do the same. So the threat of a price war is credible.

Second, will either firm want to undercut the monopoly price, given that doing so will start a price war? The answer to this question involves a comparison of the benefits and costs of undercutting. Suppose Joe lowers his price very slightly, say to $69.99. He will steal all of Rebecca's business that month—all 150 cubic metres—earning (approximately) $30 on each of them. So he will gain $4500 that month. On the other hand, if he hadn't undercut Rebecca, he would have earned $4500 per month every subsequent period; when he undercuts her, he loses those future profits (since the price will be $40 in every subsequent month).

How much are those lost profits worth? In Section 10.1 we learned how to value future cash flows using the notion of *present discounted value*. If the monthly interest rate is R (for example, 0.005 each month, or roughly 6 percent per year, ignoring compounding) then $1 received every month starting a month from today is worth $1/R$ dollars today (see Section 10.1). Since undercutting Rebecca's price even slightly means that Joe will lose $4500 starting next month, his loss is worth $4500(1/R)$ dollars to him today. That means Joe will *not* undercut provided that

$$\underbrace{4500}_{\text{This month's gain}} \quad \leq \quad \underbrace{4500\left(\frac{1}{R}\right)}_{\text{Present discounted value of future loss}}$$

or equivalently, $R \leq 1$. ($R = 1$ corresponds to an interest rate at which money in the bank doubles each month.) The same is true for Rebecca. Thus, Joe and Rebecca can successfully charge the monopoly price provided that R is no greater than one. The key idea is that successful collusion relies on the credible threat of a future price war to keep firms from undercutting each other's prices. If future profits are important enough, firms will not want to jeopardize them by risking a price war. Such will be the case provided that the interest rate is not too high, so that the future losses from a price war are significant from today's perspective.

> **IN-TEXT EXERCISE 19.4** Determine the interest rates for which it is an equilibrium for Joe and Rebecca both to adopt the following strategy: charge **\$60 if no one has yet undercut that price; otherwise, charge \$40 (equal to the marginal cost).**

Since the typical monthly interest rate ranges from a half to one percent (R between 0.005 and 0.01), the condition $R \leq 1$ will almost always be satisfied. Indeed, collusion appears very easy to sustain. In practice, however, several considerations can make collusion more difficult than suggested by this simple model.

Factors that Inhibit Collusion

Consider, first, the effect of having more than two firms in the market. Suppose N firms are competing in repeated Bertrand fashion. If those firms do not undercut the monopoly price, each will sell to $1/N$ of the market. By undercutting the monopoly price, then, a firm would steal the business of all its rivals, gaining an $(N-1)/N$ share of the \$9000 monthly monopoly profit. The firm's future loss from this strategy would be the present discounted value of $1/N$ times \$9000 received every month, starting the following month. So a firm will refrain from undercutting if

$$\underbrace{\left(\frac{N-1}{N}\right)9000}_{\text{This month's gain}} \leq \underbrace{\left(\frac{1}{N}\right)9000\left(\frac{1}{R}\right)}_{\text{Present discounted value of future loss}}$$

or equivalently, if

$$R \leq \left(\frac{1}{N-1}\right)$$

With two firms, R must be less than 1, as we've already concluded. With five firms, it must be less than 0.25; with 11, it must be less than 0.10. The greater the number of firms, the harder it becomes to sustain collusion because as more firms operate in the industry, the gain from undercutting grows larger (the firm steals more business from its rivals). At the same time, the future loss from a price war grows smaller (the firm's market share, and hence its profit from collusion, shrinks). So, with more firms, there is more to gain today and less to lose in the future from undercutting.

Second, in this model firms observe their rivals' prices perfectly. But in many real-world settings, prices may be negotiated privately by buyers and sellers rather than posted publicly. In that case, a firm observes its rivals' prices only imperfectly, if at all. It may then have to infer indirectly if a rival has abided by the collusive agreement: Did it lose some important customers because the customers liked its rival's product better or because the rival firm cut its price? Not knowing the answer with certainty, the firm won't know whether or not to retaliate by lowering its price. Retaliation reduces profit, but if the firm doesn't retaliate in such circumstances, rivals may well decide that it pays to undercut in the future.

Third, we've assumed that Joe and Rebecca produce a single homogenous product with identical marginal costs. When this is not true, reaching a collusive agreement can be difficult. When firms' marginal costs of production differ, they will not agree on what price should be set (since each will have a different monopoly price). If firms also produce differentiated products, they may need to agree on many different prices rather than just one, which can be difficult.

Finally, the price war that follows undercutting may not be as bad as suggested in the repeated Bertrand model, which predicts that future profits will be driven to zero. Even under Bertrand competition, firms may choose not to lower the price all the way to marginal cost or may do so only for a limited amount of time. And if competition takes a different form—if firms fix their quantities instead of their prices or offer products that are differentiated—then reverting to the noncooperative outcome following undercutting no longer reduces future profit to zero.

For these reasons and others, collusion is likely to be more difficult than our simple model indicates. Nonetheless, even allowing for these difficulties, firms may sometimes be able to sustain collusive prices when they care enough about future profits.

Tacit versus Explicit Collusion

We've seen that when firms compete repeatedly, more than one outcome is possible. For example, provided that $R \leq 1$, Joe and Rebecca could collude successfully, charging the monopoly price ($70), or they could compete fiercely, charging a price that is equal to marginal cost ($40). In-text exercise 19.3 showed that other outcomes, such as charging $60, are also possible. In such cases, what determines which equilibrium prevails?

One possibility is that firms might communicate with one another and reach an agreement about what price to charge (or, more generally, about what kind of equilibrium to follow). This kind of activity is called **explicit collusion**. Under Canadian competition laws, as well as those of many other nations, explicit collusion is illegal. (We'll discuss competition law further in Section 19.8.) Nonetheless, firms sometimes do collude explicitly. Indeed, Adam Smith, whose views on the division of labour and the efficiency of competitive markets we discussed in Chapters 7 and 14, noted in his work *The Wealth of Nations* (1776) that "People of the same trade seldom meet together, even for merriment and diversion, but the conversation ends in a conspiracy against the public, or some contrivance to raise prices."[11] Application 19.3 discusses one recent example of explicit collusion. When firms explicitly collude, we might expect them to follow the most profitable collusive strategy that does not give anyone an incentive to deviate from the agreement. For example, in the simple repeated Bertrand model described earlier, when $R \leq 1$, we might expect the firms to agree to charge $70 rather than $60.[12]

Another possibility is that firms may manage to arrive at a shared understanding that they will price collusively without ever discussing the matter. This kind of activity is known as **tacit collusion**. Over time, the firms may have seen price wars break out following undercutting and may have tempered their competitive behaviour as a result. Or if the

Firms engage in **explicit collusion** when they communicate to reach an agreement about the prices they will charge.

Firms engage in **tacit collusion** when they collude without communicating, sustaining a price above the noncooperative price that would arise in a single competitive interaction.

---

[11]Adam Smith, *An Inquiry into the Nature and Causes of the Wealth of Nations*, Book I, Chapter X. London: Methuen and Co., Ltd., ed. Edwin Cannan, 1904. Fifth edition. First published: 1776.

[12]However, they might decide to charge the lower price if they thought that doing so would reduce the likelihood of their collusion being discovered.

firms have been charging a price equal to marginal cost, one firm may raise its price (giving up current sales) and in the process tacitly signal other firms to raise their prices. Tacit collusion generally is *not* illegal. However, it is less likely than explicit collusion to be successful. With tacit collusion, firms need to arrive at a mutual understanding without talking. Even if they are successful, they may converge to a collusive outcome that is less profitable than one that might prevail under explicit collusion.

Application 19.3

The Lysine Cartel

"They [customers] are not your friend. They are not my friend…You're my friend. I wanna be closer to you than I am to any customer. And all I wanna is ta tell you again is let's—let's put the prices on the board. Let's all agree that's what we're gonna do then walk out of here and do it."

With these words, Archer Daniels Midland (ADM) executive Terrence Wilson exhorted his fellow conspirators in the lysine cartel to abide by their cartel agreements from 1992 to 1995. Lysine is a feed additive that promotes the growth of lean muscle in animals. The sales of lysine in Canada over the period of the cartel were $89 million and exceeded $960 million worldwide. From 1992 to 1995, the producers of lysine engaged in a secret conspiracy to raise its price, in violation of Canadian competition laws as well as those of other countries. Unbeknownst to the conspirators, one of them—ADM executive Mark Whitacre—had squealed to the U.S. Department of Justice in return for immunity from prosecution. During the resulting investigation, the FBI secretly recorded the cartel's meetings. In May of 1998 Canada's Competition Bureau levied its largest fine ever, $16,000,000, against ADM from its role in the cartel.

Figure 19.15 shows the price of lysine from January 1990 to December 1995. Prior to 1991, the lysine industry included only a small number of firms, all of them foreign. Early in 1991, Archer Daniels Midland entered the industry with a new production facility that massively increased the industry's capacity from 390 million pounds per year to 640 million. By mid-1992, with the new plant producing at just 40 percent of capacity, lysine prices had fallen dramatically, to the point

where ADM could no longer cover its variable costs. When the cartel formed in June 1992, members agreed to raise the price from its 69-cent level to over $1. Prices rose at first, but in early 1993 adherence to the cartel began to unravel and the price began to fall.

In October 1993, cartel members reached a new agreement to fix their market shares and adopted a compensation scheme designed to eliminate the incentive to cheat on the agreement. Any firm that sold more than its allotted amount would buy lysine from firms that sold less than their allotted amounts at the cartel price they had agreed on. Under this scheme, provided that sales levels could be monitored accurately, a firm would end up worse off by secretly cutting prices to gain market share, since it would pay more in compensation for the extra units than it received for them from buyers. After this scheme was put in place, prices rose to over a dollar and remained at that point until the cartel was broken up by an FBI raid in June 1995. According to one estimate by economist John Connor, from July 1992 to June 1995 the lysine cartel elevated prices an average of 17 percent.[13]

For his part in the conspiracy, Wilson drew a two-year prison sentence in the United States and a $350,000 fine, as did ADM's CEO Dwayne Andreas. What about the informant, Whitacre? Unfortunately for him, it was discovered that he had embezzled millions of dollars from ADM, confirming the adage that there is rarely honour among thieves. Because this second crime violated his immunity agreement, he ended up with a two-and-a-half-year sentence for price fixing in addition to a nine-year sentence for embezzlement.

---

[13]John N. Connor, *Global Price Fixing: Our Customers Are the Enemy*, Boston, MA: Kluwer Academic Publishers, 2001.

Figure 19.15

Prices of Lysine, January 1990–December 1995. The figure shows the price of lysine before, during, and shortly after the lysine price-fixing conspiracy.

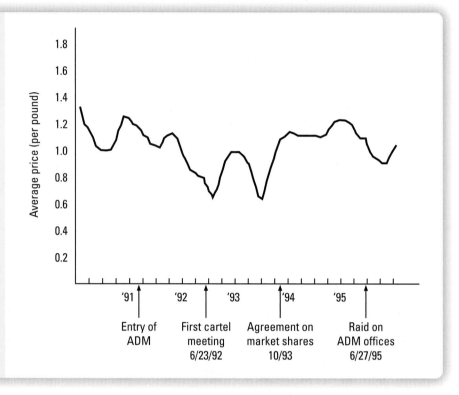

Application 19.4

Is There Something Fishy about Snow Crab Processing?

In recent years the Competition Bureau has investigated several allegations that seafood processors violated the Competition Act in the snow crab fishery. In New Brunswick and Nova Scotia processors were alleged to have conspired to fix the shore price paid to fishers for snow crabs during the 2001 season. The Bureau found that price fixing had occurred but concluded that the processors had insufficient control over the market to result in a reduction in competition. During the 1994 to 2002 fishing seasons, processors in Newfoundland and Labrador were investigated for alleged violations of the conspiracy provision of the Competition Act in their purchase of snow crabs. The allegation was that over an eight-year period processors conspired to fix or eliminate bonus payments to fishers and to allocate snow crab quotas among themselves.

(Snow crab harvesters receive bonus payments above the minimum price for snow crab established under provincial legislation.) The Bureau determined in this case that processors had not violated the Competition Act as there was excess capacity in the industry that resulted in an adequate level of competition.

In order for there to be an offense under the Competition Act evidence must show that there has been an agreement among processors to restrict competition *and* that the implementation of the agreement would unduly lessen competition. In both cases cited above the second criterion was not met. The Competition Bureau investigates dozens of allegations of non-competitive behaviour each year but only a few investigations result in fines and penalties imposed by the courts.

19.6 MARKET ENTRY AND MONOPOLISTIC COMPETITION

So far, we've taken the number of firms in an oligopolistic market as given. What determines their number? Just as in a perfectly competitive market, firms enter an oligopolistic market in response to profit opportunities.

Consider, for example, the Cournot ready-mix concrete market that we studied in Section 19.3 (see worked-out problem 19.1, page 705). If a firm must incur a fixed cost to enter the market, it will enter if, and only if, the future profits it anticipates more than compensate for the fixed cost it incurs by entering. Suppose that by entering the market, the firm commits to a yearly fixed cost of $34,000. (In Section 10.1 we learned that if the annual interest rate is R, this amount is equivalent to a one-time entry expense of $34,000/R$ dollars.) Figure 19.16 shows the relationship between the number of firms in the market and each firm's yearly profit exclusive of this fixed cost (the number of firms is shown on the horizontal axis and a firm's profit is shown on the vertical axis). The data are taken from the last column of Table 19.1 on page 709. The profit falls as the number of firms grows larger. The horizontal line drawn at $34,000 shows the amount of the fixed cost.

The figure shows that only two firms enter the market when the fixed cost is $34,000 per year. Why? Two is the largest number of firms at which an individual firm's profit remains above the fixed cost. If only one firm were to enter, a second firm would find it profitable to enter. Once two firms have entered the market, any additional firm that enters will lose money.[14]

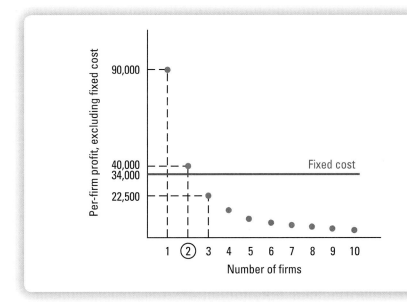

Figure 19.16
The Number of Firms Entering a Cournot Market. The blue dots show the relationship between the yearly profit of an active firm, excluding fixed costs, and the number of active firms. The red line shows the fixed cost on an annual basis. Two firms will enter this market.

[14]To be more specific, we can think of a game in which a large number of firms decide in sequence whether or not to enter the market after observing how many firms have already entered. Once no further firms want to enter, those firms that have entered play a Cournot game against each other. The equilibrium can be deduced by solving the game backward, as described in Section 12.4 (which is equivalent to finding the subgame perfect Nash equilibrium, discussed in Add-On 12A). Alternatively, we can think of a game in which a large number of firms choose simultaneously whether to be in or out of the market and identify the Nash equilibrium in that game. Both games yield the outcome described in the text.

Factors That Affect the Number of Firms Entering a Market

Several factors affect the number of firms that will enter a market. Most obvious is the fixed cost associated with becoming active in the market. We've seen that two firms will enter when the fixed cost is $34,000 per year. Suppose the fixed cost falls by 50 percent, to $17,000. As Figure 19.17(a) shows, a third firm will enter the market. The entry of the third firm reduces the price (see Table 19.1 on page 709). If the fixed cost were to fall to $12,000, a fourth firm would enter. Table 19.1 shows that with a fixed cost as low as $25, more than 100 firms would enter the market, and the price would fall below $40.59—close to the competitive market level.

Notice that, in an oligopolistic market, entry need not drive active firms' profits down to zero. For example, any entry cost between $40,000 and $22,500 per year will result in two firms entering the market. So the profit of an active firm in a duopoly could be anywhere between zero and $17,500 per year. However, as the fixed cost shrinks and the number of firms grows, the possible profits of an active firm approach zero.

Another important factor is the size of the market. Suppose that demand doubles at every price. In end-of-chapter exercise 19.15, you'll see that for any given number of firms, each firm's profit will double. As Figure 19.17(b) shows, each profit point doubles in height. Holding the entry cost fixed, this change causes a third firm to enter the market.

Figure 19.17

Factors Affecting the Number of Firms. Figure (a) shows that if the fixed cost is reduced by 50 percent, falling to $17,000, three firms enter the market rather than two. Figure (b) shows that the same is true if demand doubles, doubling the per-firm profit for any given number of firms, from the dark blue to the light blue dots.

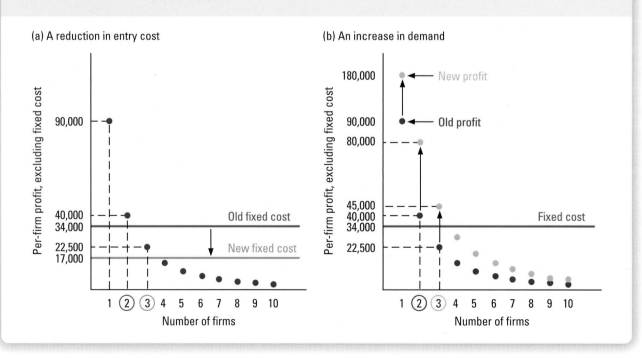

If demand skyrockets, the number of firms entering the market grows very large, and again, the price is driven down almost to marginal cost.

It's important to remember that this last conclusion holds if the level of the fixed cost is held constant as the market grows. Sometimes fixed costs rise as the market grows larger. For example, land and building costs are typically higher in a city than in a small town. Likewise, the cost of informing buyers of the firm's entry may well be higher in large markets with many buyers than in small markets with fewer buyers. When fixed costs increase with market size, the conclusion that the number of firms grows larger as a market's size grows larger need not hold. For example, the number of newspapers in a small town is typically about the same as the number of newspapers in a large city (one or two). You have probably noticed, however, that the newspapers in large cities look very different from those in small towns: they have many more pages and sections and employ many more editors and reporters, which means that their fixed costs are much higher.

A third factor that affects the number of firms that will enter a market is the intensity of competition. Economists say that competition is more intense in one market than in another if, given any *fixed* number of firms, the equilibrium price is lower in the first market than in the second. For example, a Bertrand market has more intense competition than a Cournot market. Because profits are lower in a market with more intense competition, fewer firms will enter. In fact, this effect can be so strong that the more intensely competitive market may end up with a *higher* price once the difference in the number of entering firms is taken into account. To illustrate, Figure 19.18 shows the profits in a Cournot market as blue dots (redrawn from Figure 19.16), and the profits in a Bertrand market as red dots. Only one firm enters the Bertrand market, because the profit in a Bertrand market is zero whenever there is more than one firm. In contrast, two firms enter with Cournot competition. As a result, the equilibrium price is *higher* in the Bertrand market ($70) than in the Cournot market ($60).

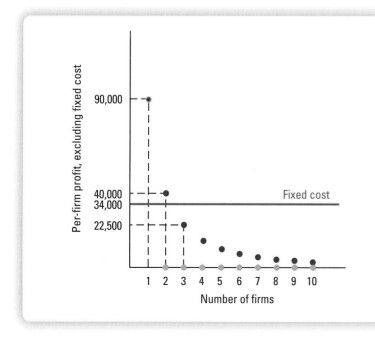

Figure 19.18

Entry in the Bertrand versus Cournot Models. The blue dots are the profits of an active firm with Cournot competition (from Figure 19.16). The red dots are profits with Bertrand competition. With Bertrand competition, only one firm enters, and the price is higher than with Cournot competition.

Application 19.5

How Many Tire Dealers in Hudson Bay, SK?

With no other towns nearby, the residents of Hudson Bay, Saskatchewan, rely heavily on their local businesses. But in a town of only one and a half thousand people, their choices are fairly limited. How many tire dealers can a market that size support? How many plumbers or dentists? How much would Hudson Bay's population have to grow to entice another tire dealer, plumber, or dentist to set up shop there?

These were the kinds of questions that economists Timothy Bresnahan and Peter Reiss wanted to answer when they put together a dataset on the number of firms in 202 geographically isolated local markets for retail and professional services.[15] The towns and cities ranged in size from 120 to 45,000 residents; their average population was 3740. Table 19.3 shows the results for tire dealers: the larger the market, the greater the number of firms. The first row of the second column shows that in the typical market, approximately 490 residents must be present to entice the first dealer to enter. The second row shows that the second tire dealer enters once there are about 1780 residents. Three dealers enter when there are approximately 3410 residents, four when there are 4740 residents, and five when there are 6100 residents. So the number of firms increases with the number of residents.[16]

Hudson Bay, Saskatchewan

Table 19.3
Market Size and the Number of Tire Dealers

Number of Tire Dealers	Necessary Town Population
1	490
2	1,780
3	3,410
4	4,740
5	6,100

Market Entry and Social Welfare

With perfect competition, the number of firms that enter a market maximizes aggregate surplus (see Sections 14.3 and 14.4). That is, firms' individual entry decisions correctly balance the social benefits of their entry with their social costs. Such is not necessarily the case in monopoly and oligopoly markets, however. Figure 19.19 illustrates this point for the ready-mix concrete market of Figure 19.4 (page 701). Consider the first firm to enter the market: Figure 19.19(a) shows its profit in green. The aggregate surplus that its entry

---

[15]Timothy F. Bresnahan and Peter C. Reiss, "Entry and Competition in Concentrated Markets," *Journal of Political Economy* 99, October 1991, pp. 977–1009.

[16]Table 19.2 reveals another interesting fact: notice that persuading the second tire dealer to enter requires more than twice as many residents as are required to get the first dealer to enter. The reason is that entry of a second firm will lower the price of tires (recall Table 19.1). If the first dealer requires 490 residents to break even at a monopoly price, the second will require more than 980 residents in a market (so that there are more than 490 residents available *for each firm*) to break even at the lower duopoly price.

Figure 19.19

Entry and Welfare. Figure (a) shows that the first entrant has too little incentive to enter given annual fixed costs despite the fact that aggregate surplus would increase with entry: the entrant's profit (excluding the cost of entry) equals the green-shaded area, but entry increases aggregate surplus by the sum of the yellow- and green-shaded areas. Figure (b) shows a situation in which the second entrant has too much incentive to enter: that entrant's profit (excluding the cost of entry) equals the sum of the green- and blue-shaded areas, while the increase in aggregate surplus equals the sum of the green-and yellow-shaded areas. Since the blue-shaded area is larger than the yellow-shaded area, there is an excessive incentive to enter and aggregate surplus falls.

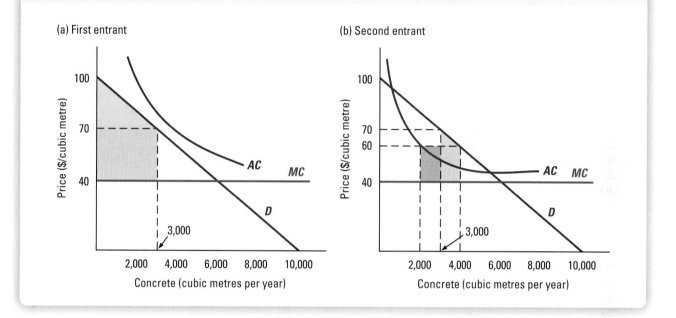

creates, however, is larger: it is the sum of the green-shaded profit and the yellow-shaded consumer surplus created by the firm's entry. So if the fixed cost of the firm's entry (on an annual basis) is greater than the green area but smaller than the sum of the green and yellow areas, the firm won't enter the market even though by doing so it would increase aggregate surplus. In this case the average cost curve of the firm would lie above the demand curve. In principle, the government might want to subsidize the entry of the first firm in this market to increase aggregate surplus. (See end-of-chapter exercise 19.17 for an example.)

On the other hand, if the fixed cost is low enough to permit entry, too many firms may enter. That is, the social benefits of a profitable firm's entry may be lower than the social costs. To see why, look at Figure 19.19(b), which concerns the entry decision of a second ready-mix concrete firm. That entry causes the price to fall from $70 per cubic metre to $60, and the amount bought and sold to increase from 3000 cubic metres to 4000. The increase in aggregate surplus, not including the fixed cost, is the sum of the yellow- and green-shaded areas. The second firm's profit, however, is the sum of the green- and blue- shaded areas (that is, the $60 duopoly price less the $40 marginal cost times the 2000 cubic metres a duopolist sells). If the blue area is larger than the yellow area, as shown in the figure, then the private benefit from entry is *larger* than the social benefit. And if the cost of the second firm's entry is larger than the sum of the yellow and green areas, but smaller than the sum of the green and blue areas, then the second firm will enter even though its entry lowers aggregate surplus.

Business stealing arises when some of a new entrant's sales come at the expense of existing firms, whose sales contract after the new firm enters the market.

What accounts for the possibility of excessive entry once a firm has already entered the market? The answer is **business stealing**: once one firm (or more than one firm) has entered the market, a new entrant's sales will come partly at the expense of the existing firm (or firms), whose output will contract after the new firm enters. In Figure 19.19(b), for example, the second firm's entry causes total output to increase by 1000 cubic metres. But the new entrant sells 2000 cubic metres, 1000 of which come at the expense of the first firm, whose output in the Cournot equilibrium shrinks from 3000 to 2000 cubic metres. The social benefit of the second firm's entry comes from the increase in total output, but the entrant earns a profit not only on those sales but also on the sales it takes from the first firm. As a result, a prospective entrant can have too much of an incentive to enter.

IN-TEXT EXERCISE 19.5   **Suppose that annual fixed costs of a potential market entrant are equal to $100,000. Figure 19.16 indicates that even the first entrant will choose not to enter (the situation in Figure 19.19a). If fixed annual costs are $36,000 Figure 19.16 indicates that two firms will enter the market (the situation depicted in Figure 19.19b). Calculate the change in aggregate surplus when the second firm enters the market. If fixed annual costs are $18,000 how many firms will enter? Calculate the change in aggregate surplus when the last firm enters.**

Application 19.6

The Welfare Effects of Free Entry in Radio Broadcasting

How significant are the welfare losses from free entry into oligopoly markets? Economists Steven Berry and Joel Waldfogel examined this question in the context of radio broadcasting, using data on the number of radio stations, the listenership, and the advertising prices in 135 metropolitan markets in the United States in 1993. (Their study predated the availability of satellite radio.)[17]

Radio broadcasting is an unusual market, in that a station makes its signal available to listeners for free. In essence, radio broadcasters sell listeners to advertisers. Thus, we can think of radio advertisers as the buyers and the listeners a station attracts as its output.

Berry and Waldfogel first estimated the demand curve for advertising and then used information on listening behaviour to infer how much additional listening occurred after the entry of a new station. If that station didn't expand total listening, its entry involved only business stealing. The two researchers found a substantial amount of business stealing in the markets they examined. Using this information, along with estimates of fixed costs inferred from stations'

entry behaviour, Berry and Waldfogel compared the number of stations that would have maximized the sum of the stations' and advertisers' surpluses with the actual number of stations in those markets. In total, 2509 stations were active, though the sum of the advertisers' surplus and the stations' profit would have been maximized with only 649 stations. The resulting deadweight loss was $2.3 billion per year.

As we've noted, radio broadcasting is unusual because the buyers and sellers (advertisers and stations) aren't the only ones who benefit from the market. Listeners derive an important benefit, because they can listen to radio broadcasts for free. (This benefit is an example of an externality, which we'll study in Chapter 20.) Thus, this calculation of advertisers' surplus and stations' profit omits an important consideration in judging the socially optimal level of market entry in radio broadcasting: listeners' benefits increase when new stations enter. Berry and Waldfogel calculated that if a typical listener valued the additional listening generated by new entrants at 13.5 cents per hour, then the actual level of entry in these markets was not socially excessive.

---

[17]Steven T. Berry and Joel Waldfogel, "Free Entry and Social Inefficiency in Radio Broadcasting," *RAND Journal of Economics* 30, Autumn 1999, pp. 397–420.

Market Entry, Product Differentiation, and Monopolistic Competition

Up to this point we've examined entry only in markets with homogeneous products. Indeed, many of the factors that affect market entry are the same with or without product differentiation. In both cases, market entry is motivated by the profit incentive, and encouraged by low entry costs and high demand. But in markets with product differentiation, we must consider a new factor: firms must decide what kind of product to produce.

As Application 19.2 (page 718) indicated, firms will often try to differentiate their products from those of other firms in order to avoid intense price competition. In some cases, this strategy is not practical, particularly if the market is so large that many firms enter. Think of a case in which there are a limited number of products that consumers may be interested in. With enough entrants, many firms will end up producing each of those products and the price of each will approach its marginal cost.

In other cases, the number of products that consumers may want to buy can be very large. As new firms enter the market, each can produce a unique product. In such cases, we can end up with many products, each of which is a little different from the others and sells for a price that is above marginal cost. Think of the gas stations or convenience stores in a large city. Each has a unique location, as well as some other characteristics that make it more convenient or attractive to a particular set of consumers. Though the entry process drives their profits net of fixed costs down to zero, or close to it, each firm can still price its wares above marginal cost. This situation is known as **monopolistic competition**.

> **Monopolistic competition** occurs in a market with free entry when there is a large number of firms, each of which produces a unique product, prices above marginal cost, and earns (close to) zero profit net of its fixed costs.

Figure 19.20 illustrates the outcome for each firm in a monopolistically competitive market. The firm's demand curve is labelled D. It is downward sloping because the firm's product is differentiated from those of other firms. The figure also shows the firm's average cost, marginal cost, and marginal revenue curves. Entry of other firms has shifted the firm's demand curve down to the point where, at the firm's profit-maximizing price and quantity, the firm's price exactly equals its average cost so that it breaks even.

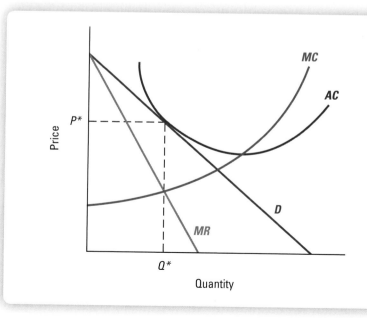

Figure 19.20

Monopolistic Competition. In monopolistic competition, each firm faces a downward-sloping demand curve for its differentiated product. Entry occurs until each firm's profit is (approximately) zero, which means that the firm's average cost curve lies above its demand curve and touches it at the firm's profit-maximizing output level.

In general, entry in monopolistically competitive markets may be either excessive or insufficient relative to the level that maximizes aggregate surplus. As Figure 19.20 shows, the firm operates below its efficient scale (the quantity at which average cost is lowest). While this entails some inefficiency in production, it may be counterbalanced by the unique benefits its differentiated product brings to consumers.

*19.7 STRATEGIC BEHAVIOUR THAT SHAPES FUTURE COMPETITION

Among a firm's most important strategic decisions are those that shape its long-term competition with rivals. In Application 19.2 (page 718), for example, we saw that Embraer chose to differentiate the seating capacity of its new planes from those of Boeing and Airbus while Bombardier directly competed with them. The company's decision meant that Boeing and Airbus would be less likely to lower their prices in response to Embraer's new series of planes, since it wouldn't pose a direct threat to those firms, while the competition for Bombardier's C-series planes could well engender price competition. More generally, investments in capacity, research and development, advertising, and product quality all shape future competition. By carefully thinking through these effects, firms can more effectively maximize their profit.

We provide here only an introduction to the topic of how firms can make decisions that increase their future competitive profit. While many decisions by firms can alter future competition in this way, we'll focus on two general types: those that raise rivals' costs and those that involve strategic precommitment.

Raising Rivals' Costs

Sometimes a firm can alter future competitive conditions to its advantage by taking actions that induce its rivals to behave less aggressively—for example, to raise their prices or reduce their output. One way to do so is to raise their marginal costs. (For another way, see Application 19.7.) For example, Figure 19.21(a) shows that in the Cournot ready-mix concrete market of Figure 19.8 (page 705), if Rebecca takes actions that raise Joe's marginal cost to $55 from $40 per cubic metre, she will shift his best response curve downward and Joe's equilibrium output will fall. (Joe's best-response curve shifts downward because the higher his marginal cost is, the less he will want to produce, given any possible quantity Rebecca produces.) Joe's output reduction necessarily raises Rebecca's profit, since at each possible quantity Rebecca might produce the market price will be higher. Figure 19.21(b) shows a similar effect with differentiated price competition: if Pepsi can take actions that raise Coke's marginal cost, Pepsi will shift Coke's best-response curve upward (meaning that Coke charges a higher price for each of Pepsi's prices), and Coke's equilibrium price will rise, increasing Pepsi's profit.

How can a firm raise its rival's marginal cost? Sometimes clever lobbying will do the trick. For example, if the rival uses a different production process, lobbying the government to impose stringent environmental regulations on that process might work. If the rival is a foreign company, convincing the government to impose a tariff on imports of the rival's product could prove effective. Finding a way to increase the cost of a rival's inputs is another possibility. In one instance, some large mining firms joined forces with the United Mine

Figure 19.21

Raising Rival's Costs. Figure (a) shows that if Rebecca can take actions that raise Joe's marginal cost, his equilibrium output in a Cournot market will fall. This raises Rebecca's profit. Figure (b) shows that in differentiated price competition, Coke's price will rise if Pepsi can take actions that raise Coke's marginal cost. This increases Pepsi's profit.

(a) Cournot competition

(b) Differentiated price competition

Workers union in a campaign to raise wages at small mines, with the aim of forcing those mines' exit from the market (the firms were found guilty of violating competition laws). Another tactic would involve buying much of the supply of a critical input, a strategy that the dominant aluminum producer, Alcoa, pursued in the early twentieth century.

Strategic Precommitment

Another way for a firm to alter future competition is to commit to certain actions before rivals can take theirs. Such behaviour is known as **strategic precommitment**. The benefits of such commitments in rivalrous situations have long been understood. In 1519, for example, the Spanish conquistador Cortés prepared for his invasion of the Aztec city of Tenochtitlan by burning most of his ships, thus committing his army not to retreat. His act brought the desired response when the Aztecs, understanding his soldiers' incentives, chose not to resist the invasion. Similar though less deadly commitment opportunities often present themselves in market settings.

A **strategic precommitment** occurs when a firm commits to some actions before rivals take theirs, with the aim of increasing its future competitive profit.

Output Choice by a First-Mover   Think back on our discussion of market entry in Section 19.6. In that discussion, we assumed that firms decide first whether to enter a market and then choose their outputs simultaneously (in the case of a Cournot market). In reality, however, entry may not be simultaneous, and the first firm to enter the market may

Heinrich von Stackelberg
(1905–1946)

In the **Stackelberg model of quantity competition,** two firms choose their outputs sequentially.

be able to take advantage of its position to increase its profit. By committing to its output choice first, before other firms have entered the market and chosen their outputs, the firm may be able to reduce rivals' production (we'll see how later in this section). Sometimes, the first firm may even be able to deter their entry altogether.

To examine this idea, let's consider again the Cournot ready-mix concrete market of Section 19.3. We'll suppose for the sake of simplicity that Joe and Rebecca are the only possible entrants into this market (or that the entry cost is high enough that a third entrant could never make a profit). In contrast to Section 19.3, however, we'll suppose that Rebecca has entered this market before Joe and can choose her output first. For example, Rebecca might sign a labour contract that commits her to a certain level of production. Or she might build a plant with a production process that must be run at full capacity. This model of sequential output choices is known as the **Stackelberg model of quantity competition**, after economist Henrich von Stackelberg, who introduced it in 1934.

To begin, notice that Rebecca has to do at least as well by moving first as she does by choosing her output at the same time as Joe. After all, if she moves first, she is free to commit to producing 2000 cubic metres of concrete, her Cournot equilibrium output. If she did, Joe would respond by choosing an output of 2000, since that would be his best response. Rebecca would end up with her Cournot profit.

But Rebecca may be able to do better. Imagine that Joe will definitely enter this market. In that case, what output should Rebecca choose? Figure 19.22 illustrates her choice.

Figure 19.22

Rebecca's Profit-Maximizing Output as a First Mover. When Rebecca can choose her output before Joe and Joe will certainly enter, she maximizes her profit by producing 3000 cubic metres, 1000 more than in a Cournot equilibrium. By expanding her output, she induces Joe to reduce his to 1500 cubic metres. The equilibrium outcome is point C. If instead Joe may not enter, Rebecca can expand her output further to deter his entry. This is worthwhile if his entry cost is $15,000 (she produces 4000 cubic metres) but not if his entry cost is $2000.

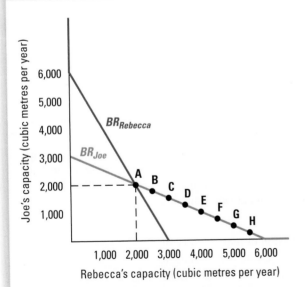

Point	Rebecca's output (cubic metres/year)	Joe's best response (cubic metres/year)	Joe's profit if he enters and chooses his best response ($/year)	Rebecca's profit if Joe enters ($/year)	Rebecca's profit if Joe doesn't enter ($/year)
A	2,000	2,000	$40,000	$40,000	$80,000
B	2,500	1,750	30,625	43,750	87,500
C	3,000	1,500	22,500	45,000	90,000
D	3,500	1,250	15,625	43,750	87,500
E	4,000	1,000	10,000	40,000	80,000
F	4,500	750	5,625	33,750	67,500
G	5,000	500	2,500	25,000	50,000
H	5,500	250	625	13,750	27,500

The figure and accompanying table show that if Rebecca chooses her Cournot equilibrium output the outcome ends up, after Joe responds, at point A, and Rebecca earns her Cournot equilibrium profit of $40,000. But other choices are possible.

What if Rebecca produces 3000 cubic metres? When Joe enters, he'll produce only 1500 cubic metres, the amount indicated by his best-response curve (see the table in Figure 19.22). In fact, for every additional cubic metre Rebecca produces, Joe's output falls by 0.5 cubic metres. As a result, Rebecca's decision is fundamentally different from when she chooses her output at the same time as Joe, because in this setting she can cause Joe to reduce his output. In essence, she needs to find the point on Joe's best-response curve that will maximize her profit.

The table in Figure 19.22 lists Rebecca's profits at various points along Joe's best-response curve, labelled A–H. From the fifth column of the table (labelled "Rebecca's profit if Joe enters"), the most profitable point is C, where Rebecca produces 3000 cubic metres and Joe responds by producing 1500. At that point Rebecca's profit is $45,000 (see the circled amount in the fifth column), compared to $40,000 at point A, the equilibrium point in the Cournot model with simultaneous output choices. Joe's profit at that point, shown in the fourth column, is $22,500, compared to $40,000 at point A. Worked-out problem 19.3 shows how to solve Rebecca's problem using algebra.

WORKED-OUT PROBLEM 19.3

The Problem The market demand function in a ready-mix concrete market is

$$Q^d = 10,000 - 100P$$

where P is the price of a cubic metre of concrete and Q^d is the number of cubic metres demanded per year. The marginal cost is $40 per cubic metre. Suppose Rebecca enters this market first and chooses her output before Joe. What is Rebecca's profit-maximizing output? What is her profit at that output? How much larger is her profit compared to the case in which she and Joe choose their outputs simultaneously, as in the Cournot model? How do Joe's profits in the two cases compare?

The Solution Recall Rebecca's inverse residual demand function from the solution to worked-out problem 19.1 (page 705).

$$P = (100 - 0.01Q_{Joe}) - 0.01Q_{Rebecca}$$

Formula (1) of that solution described Joe's best response at each level of output that Rebecca might choose.

$$Q_{Joe} = 3000 - 0.5Q_{Rebecca}$$

By substituting Joe's best response into Rebecca's inverse residual demand function, we get a formula that describes the price Rebecca receives at each level of output she might produce, taking into account Joe's response to her choice:

$$P = [100 - 0.01(3000 - 0.5Q_{Rebecca})] - 0.01Q_{Rebecca}$$

$$= 70 - 0.005Q_{Rebecca}$$

From this relationship, Rebecca can derive her marginal revenue, which is

$$MR = P + (\Delta P/\Delta Q)Q_{Rebecca}$$

$$= (70 - 0.005Q_{Rebecca}) + (-0.005)Q_{Rebecca}$$

$$= 70 - 0.01Q_{Rebecca}$$

She will maximize her profit by choosing the output level $Q_{Rebecca}$ that equates her marginal revenue with her marginal cost.

$$70 - 0.01Q_{Rebecca} = 40$$

That output is $Q_{Rebecca} = 3000$. Joe's best response is $Q_{Joe} = 3000 - 0.5(3000) = 1500$. At a total output of 4500 cubic metres, the market price is $55. This result implies that Rebecca's profit is $45,000 per year, while Joe's is $22,500. Rebecca makes $5000 more, and Joe $17,500 less, than when the two choose their outputs simultaneously as in the Cournot model.

 IN-TEXT EXERCISE 19.6   Repeat worked-out problem 19.3, but assume that Rebecca's marginal cost is $25 per cubic metre.

Entry Deterrence   Now let's consider how the situation changes when, depending on Rebecca's choice, Joe may not find it profitable to enter the market. In that case, a new strategic incentive arises. By expanding her output sufficiently, Rebecca may reduce the profit Joe foresees enough to deter him from entering the market.

Suppose Joe's fixed cost is $15,000 per year. If Rebecca produces 3000 cubic metres of concrete, as she would if Joe were certain to enter the market, Joe's profit will be $22,500. In that case, Joe would want to enter. But, as the table in Figure 19.22 shows, if Rebecca were to produce 4000 cubic metres or more, Joe's profit would be less than $15,000, and he would decide to stay out of the market (see the fourth column, where Joe's profits when Rebecca produces 4000 cubic metres or more are shaded yellow). So Rebecca has a choice: produce 3000 cubic metres as before and accept that Joe will enter the market, or build enough capacity so that Joe won't enter the market.

Is it profitable for Rebecca to prevent Joe's entry? If Rebecca deters his entry, she'll receive the profits listed in the last column of the table. The profits from output choices that deter Joe's entry are shaded in green. Her best choice among those is producing 4000 cubic metres, which gives her a profit of $80,000 (since Joe doesn't enter, the price is $60). Since this amount is much more than the $45,000 she will earn by producing 3000 cubic metres, deterring Joe's entry is her best choice.

Deterring a competitor's entry isn't always the best choice, though. If Joe's fixed cost were only $2000, then Rebecca would need to produce 5500 cubic metres to deter him from entering the market. (Producing 5500 cubic metres would leave Joe with a profit of $625 from entry.) Her profit from doing so would be only $27,500 per year (see the last row of the last column). In that case, she would be better off accepting Joe's entry and using her first-mover position to reduce his output by producing 3000 cubic metres.

Credible Entry Deterrence   Up to this point we've assumed that Rebecca can commit to her output choice. Sometimes that assumption is a reasonable one. In alumina refining, for example, a plant must be run continuously at close to full capacity or the firm will face a severe cost penalty. So the firm's capacity decision essentially commits it to an output level.

Usually, however, a firm can commit only imperfectly to its output level. For example, Rebecca might build a high-capacity manufacturing facility, capable of producing a lot of output at a low marginal cost, to try to deter Joe's entry. In effect, she is saying "With this factory, if you enter, I'll produce a lot." This threat, however, will deter Joe's entry only if it is credible that Rebecca will actually use the plant's high capacity should he enter. Add-On 19A discusses how to determine the credibility of her threat in this case.

Playing Tough versus Playing Soft   In choosing her output or capacity first, Rebecca took advantage of her first-mover position by committing to be *tough*. That is, she committed to producing more output than she would have if she and Joe were choosing quantity simultaneously. Doing so was worthwhile to her because it would cause Joe to reduce his output—or in the extreme, to forgo entering the market.

Sometimes there is instead a strategic benefit to being *soft*. In Figure 19.14 (page 715) we saw that Coke and Pepsi's best-response curves both slope upward. So the higher one firm's price, the higher its rival's profit-maximizing price. As a result, firms in such markets have an incentive to commit to price higher than if prices were chosen simultaneously— that is, to play *soft*—so as to induce their rivals to do the same. Application 19.7 illustrates the use of this type of strategy.

Commitment versus Flexibility

Though a firm can sometimes gain by precommitting to future actions, there is a potential downside to the strategy if market conditions are uncertain. Put simply, precommitting limits the firm's ability to respond to changing market conditions. For example, DuPont once tried to deter rivals from producing titanium dioxide (a whitener used in paints and plastics) by committing to an extensive expansion of its facilities. Unfortunately for DuPont, because of a recession, market demand turned out to be much lower than DuPont forecasted, causing the firm's clever strategy to yield a disappointing loss.

Application 19.7

Food Fights in Alberta

In October 1972 the Attorney General of Canada charged Canada Safeway with being a monopoly in grocery retailing in the cities of Edmonton and Calgary from 1965 to 1972. Canada Safeway was prohibited from expanding in the two cities for a period of five years and prohibited from excessive advertising and price cutting. Von Hohenbalken and West have explained Safeway's dominant position as a predatory location strategy that effectively forestalled entry into the two markets.[18] Von Hohenbalken and West described a predatory location strategy as one in which "(a) new stores of an entering firm are challenged by stores of the established

firm built in their neighbourhood, (b) the predator's plants are located so as to force losses on the entrant's plants, (c) the entrant ceases to construct new plants, (d) the entrant eventually withdraws from the market."

Using supermarket location data from 1959–1973 the authors of the study found the data were consistent with Canada Safeway practicing locational predation against the Dominion, Loblaws, and Tom Boy supermarket chains. As a result of being able to successfully deter entry in the market Safeway was able to avoid having to incur the costs of opening new stores and engaging the competition in an outright food fight.

---

[18]Balder Von Hohenbalken and Douglas S. West "Predation among Supermarkets: An Algorithmic Locational Analysis," *Journal of Urban Economics* 15, 1984, pp. 244–257.

19.8 COMPETITION POLICY

What can government do to limit the welfare losses resulting from the existence of market power? In Section 17.7 we discussed one possibility: price regulation. In this section we'll discuss another form of regulation: competition policy.

While competition law regulates economic activity, it differs from price regulation in some important ways. Price regulation, which tends to be industry-specific, typically involves regular, often extensive hearings to determine the regulated firm's prices. In contrast, competition legislation enables markets to produce good outcomes. Investigation and intervention are exceptional events that occur only when the rules are thought to have been violated.

Canadian Competition Law

In 1889 Canada passed the world's first antitrust law. In that year An Act for the Prevention and Suppression of Combinations Found in Restraint of Trade was passed. Section 1 of the Act stated that

> Every person who conspires, agrees or arranges with any other person, or with any railway, steamship, steamboat or transportation company,
>
> (a) to unduly limit the facilities for transporting, producing, manufacturing, supplying, storing or dealing in any article or commodity which may be a subject of trade or commerce or -
>
> (b) to restrain or injure trade or commerce in relation to any such article or commodity or -
>
> (c) to unduly prevent, limit, or lessen the manufacture or production of any such article or commodity, or to unreasonably enhance the price thereof; or -
>
> (d) to unduly prevent or lessen competition in the production, manufacture, purchase, barter, sale, transportation or supply of any such article or commodity, or in the price of insurance upon person or property.
>
> Is guilty of a misdemeanour and liable, on conviction, to a penalty not exceeding four thousand dollars and not less than two hundred dollars, or to imprisonment for any term not exceeding two years; and if a corporation, is liable on conviction to a penalty not exceeding ten thousand dollars and not less than one thousand dollars.

Enforcement of the Act was left up to the Attorneys General of the provinces and no investigatory powers were created to enforce the Act.

The Combines Investigation Act passed in 1910 did provide the investigative machinery that the original Act of 1889 was lacking. The Act was amended in 1923 and on several additional occasions ultimately leading to its renaming as the Competition Act in 1986.

Today, the Competition Bureau, headed by the Competition Commissioner, is charged with the enforcement and administration of the Competition Act. The Competition Bureau investigates complaints and files applications with the Competition Tribunal which is the federal adjudicative body that rules on filings by the Bureau. The Competition Bureau's functions can be broadly categorized as investigating collusive behaviour by cartels, reviewing mergers, and preventing abuse of market power to exclude rival firms.

Competition Violations

Competition laws can be divided into two categories: those concerned with collaboration among competitors either through collusion or merger, and those concerned with exclusion from the market. Let's consider each of these categories.

Collaboration among Competitors

The first category, collaboration among competitors, is the focus of the collusion and merger provisions of the Competition Act. This body of law concerns the ways in which competitors attempt to reduce the intensity of competition among themselves. There are two main ways that firms try to do this: by explicitly colluding and by merging their operations.

Collusion   We discussed explicit collusion in Section 19.5. Put simply, if competitors are found to have reached an agreement with one another about the prices they will charge or the quantities they will produce—called **price fixing**—they will be found guilty and sentenced to jail time, monetary fines, or both. We saw an example of such an enforcement action in Application 19.3 (page 723), which described how members of the lysine cartel came to be charged with price fixing.

> Firms engage in **price fixing** when they agree on the prices they will charge or quantities they will produce.

Sometimes firms attempt to raise prices through agreements that do not fix prices or output levels directly, but are intended to have that effect. For example, a pair of duopolists might decide on a market division scheme, whereby one will sell west of the Manitoba-Ontario border and the other east of it. By creating two regional monopolies free from each other's competition, they can raise prices. Such a scheme would also be illegal under Section 45 of the Competition Act which is known as the conspiracy section. The collusive provisions of the Competition Act also outlaw bid rigging, collusive behaviour by financial institutions regarding the setting of interest rates or service charges, restrictions on player mobility in professional sports, and the implementation of collusive behaviour agreed upon outside of the country. Many of the most prominent anticompetitive rulings by the Competition Tribunal have been grounded in the conspiracy section of the Act.

As we mentioned in Section 19.5, rather than colluding explicitly, sometimes firms manage to collude tacitly, that is, without ever communicating with each other. Under Canadian competition law, tacit collusion is generally not considered a competition violation. Part of the reason is that it would often be difficult to prove that firms are tacitly colluding, as opposed to pricing high for other reasons, such as the presence of differentiated products. Proposals have been advanced to amend the Competition Act to restrict practices that would facilitate collusive behaviour such as the advance announcement of prices, the use of pricing manuals, and price matching in purchase agreements.

Horizontal Mergers   The other main form of collaboration among competitors, **horizontal mergers**, occurs when two or more competing firms combine their operations. In Canada today, large companies that wish to merge must notify the Commissioner of Competition prior to their action, to give the Competition Bureau time to review the merger.

> In a **horizontal merger**, two or more competing firms combine their operations.

The concern with horizontal mergers among competing sellers is that they may raise market prices by reducing the number of competitors (recall Table 19.1 on page 709). Indeed, a horizontal merger is even more effective than price fixing in coordinating firms' prices since, once firms have merged, their interests are perfectly aligned. (With a merger among competing buyers, the concern is instead that the merger might increase the

Figure 19.23
Welfare Effects of a Horizontal Merger. The figure shows the welfare effect of a horizontal merger that lowers marginal cost per cubic metre from $40 to $20 but increases the price from $40 to $60. The merger increases aggregate surplus because the red deadweight loss triangle is smaller than the green cost-reduction rectangle.

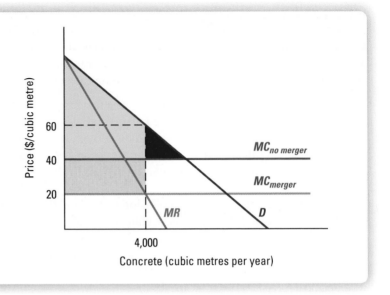

buyers' exercise of market power, as with Suncor's acquisition of Petro-Canada discussed in Application 17.6 on page 644.)

But horizontal mergers can have beneficial effects as well; for example, they can lead to cost reductions as the two firms find ways to reorganize their production process in a more efficient way. Indeed, in most announced mergers, the firms' executives assert that large cost reductions will result from combining operations. These cost reductions can increase aggregate surplus and even lead market prices to fall.

In deciding whether to allow a specific merger, the competition agencies and the courts need to weigh these two effects. Section 96 of the Competition Act instructs the Competition Tribunal not to dissolve or prohibit the merger if the merger results in efficiency gains that more than offset the reduction in competition from the merger. The Tribunal may require the merging firms to divest themselves of some assets so that there is not a substantial lessening of competition as a result of the merger. Figure 19.23 illustrates this trade-off for a government agency concerned with maximizing aggregate surplus. Imagine that Joe and Rebecca are initially duopolists competing in a Bertrand fashion, pricing at their marginal cost of $40. If they merge, their marginal cost will fall to $20, but they will raise their price to $60, the monopoly price given their post-merger marginal cost. Aggregate surplus before the merger equals the sum of the yellow- and red-shaded areas; after the merger it equals the sum of the yellow- and green-shaded areas. So the merger increases aggregate surplus if the green rectangle is larger than the red triangle, as in the figure. If, instead, the marginal cost had fallen only to $30, the red triangle would have been larger (the post-merger price would have been higher) and the green rectangle smaller, and the merger would have reduced aggregate surplus.

Exclusionary Behaviour   The second category of competition violation, exclusion, is the concern of the sections of the Competition Act dealing with predatory behaviour (Section 50), abuse of dominant position (Sections 78–79), exclusive dealing or tied selling (Section 77), or a refusal to deal with a business (Section 75). This body of law focuses on the ways in which a dominant firm may reduce competition by excluding rivals from the marketplace, either fully or by impairing their competitiveness. While the law does not make *being* a monopolist illegal, it does require that dominant firms not attempt to *monopolize* markets through tactics designed to exclude rivals.

Most competition enforcement actions involve either price fixing or horizontal mergers. However, many of the most publicized cases, such as the Microsoft case discussed in Chapter 17 or the predatory pricing case against Air Canada in Application 19.8 below, involve exclusionary behaviour. Such cases make for exciting newspaper and magazine articles because they usually involve allegations that the dominant firm in a market has intentionally tried to crush a smaller rival.

Firms can engage in many kinds of exclusionary behaviours. These include: (1) predatory pricing, the practice of pricing below cost to drive a less financially strong rival out of the market by making it incur losses; (2) exclusive contracts, the signing of contracts with buyers or suppliers that commit them not to deal with a rival; and (3) bundling, the practice of selling a competitive good only in conjunction with the dominant firm's monopolized product to prevent customers from buying the competitive product from rivals. In the Microsoft case, for example, Microsoft was accused (and found partially guilty) of having signed exclusionary contracts with computer manufacturers, Web sites, and other software manufacturers that placed its upstart rival, Netscape, and its Navigator Web browser at a disadvantage. It was also accused (but not found guilty) of illegally bundling its Internet Explorer® Web browser into the Windows operating system to disadvantage Netscape.

The problem with exclusionary cases is that it can be difficult to restrain dominant firms from disadvantaging their rivals without limiting their beneficial, surplus-enhancing actions. For example, in the Microsoft case, Microsoft's bundling of its Internet Explorer into Windows may have brought real benefits to consumers, through increased ease of use. But it may have also made it difficult for Netscape to compete profitably for reasons unrelated to those benefits. Balancing these two concerns is a challenge.

This difficulty makes the appropriate policy stance toward exclusionary behaviour the subject of contentious debate. Some believe that the competition agencies and courts are likely to do more harm than good in trying to limit these behaviours. Others think that it is possible to effectively restrain anticompetitive exclusionary behaviours without restricting other, efficiency-enhancing behaviours.

Application 19.8

When 100 Percent of a Market Is Not Enough

In March of 2001 the Competition Bureau asked the Competition Tribunal, the court that rules on antitrust matters, to issue an order prohibiting Air Canada from setting fares below its avoidable cost in seven markets in Eastern Canada. When Calgary-based WestJet announced a new route from Hamilton, Ontario, to Moncton, New Brunswick, Air Canada responded by adding capacity and matching or undercutting WestJet's fares. CanJet, with six aircraft in September of 2001 compared to Air Canada's 374 aircraft, announced new routes in Eastern Canada only to find that Air Canada slashed fares on the same routes. Air Canada in 2001 accounted for 90 percent of Canada's air passenger revenue and its market share on routes between Toronto, Saint John, Moncton, and Charlottetown approached 100 percent in 2001. Royal Airlines agreed with WestJet and CanJet that Air Canada was practicing predatory pricing and also complained that Air Canada was pressuring travel agents.

The Competition Bureau believed that Air Canada's pricing strategy would drive CanJet and WestJet out of the market in Eastern Canada. The Bureau claimed that Air Canada was abusing its position of dominance in the industry to deter prospective competitors. Although the tribunal found evidence that Air Canada was pricing below avoidable cost it did not rule on whether Air Canada was abusing its dominant position in the industry as Air Canada filed for protection under the Companies' Creditors Arrangement Act in April of 2003. The Commissioner of Competition withdrew the application based on the fact that Air Canada would not contest the ruling that it had priced below avoidable cost.

Since the Competition Bureau order in March of 2001, WestJet has made significant inroads into Air Canada's market share for domestic routes. By March of 2010 WestJet had captured 38 percent of the domestic market. CanJet ceased offering scheduled flights in September of 2006 and now offers only charter flights.

CHAPTER SUMMARY

1. **Oligopoly and game theory (LO1)**

   a. In oligopolies, a firm's best actions and profit depend on how its rivals behave. To analyze such situations, economists use game theory.

   b. In a Nash equilibrium of an oligopoly market, each firm is choosing a best response to the choices of its rivals.

   c. A fundamental problem facing oligopolists is that each cares only about its own profit and ignores the effects of its actions on rivals' profits. Because each has an incentive to lower its price or increase its quantity to expand its sales, joint profits in the Nash equilibrium are lower than they would be if the firms colluded and acted like a monopolist.

2. **The Bertrand model: price competition with homogeneous products (LO2)**

   a. In the Bertrand model of oligopoly, firms produce homogeneous products and set their prices simultaneously.

   b. At the equilibrium point in a Bertrand oligopoly, all sales occur at a price equal to marginal cost.

   c. The Bertrand model's assumptions are often unrealistic.

3. **Cournot quantity competition (LO2)**

   a. In the Cournot model of oligopoly, firms produce homogeneous products and choose their quantities simultaneously.

   b. In a Cournot market, the equilibrium price is lower than the monopoly price but higher than the marginal cost. The deadweight loss is therefore positive but smaller than in a monopoly.

   c. As the number of firms in a Cournot market grows larger the price falls, approaching marginal cost as the number of firms grows very large.

   d. In a Cournot market with N identical firms, the markup equals negative one divided by the product of the number of firms and the elasticity of market demand: $(P - MC)/P = -1/(N \times E^d)$.

4. **Price competition with differentiated products (LO3)**

   a. When a firm's products are differentiated, the firm won't lose all its customers if it raises the price a little above marginal cost. As a result, the equilibrium price exceeds marginal cost in a market for differentiated goods.

   b. The more willing consumers are to switch between different firms' differentiated products in response to a price difference, the lower the equilibrium price.

5. **Collusion (LO4)**

   a. When firms compete repeatedly with no definite end, the noncooperative outcome is the repetition in each period of the outcome when they compete just once. In the repeated Bertrand model, this means that the firms charge a price equal to marginal cost in every period.

   b. Sometimes other outcomes are possible, including in some cases the monopoly outcome. Firms manage to sustain a collusive price by adopting strategies that call for future competition to become more intense (a price war) if anyone deviates from the collusive price.

   c. The more important future profits are, the more likely that firms will be able to sustain collusive pricing. Firms compare the current gain from undercutting the collusive price to the loss of future profits. When the future losses (discounted to their present value) exceed the current gains, firms will refrain from undercutting the collusive price.

d. Several factors can make collusion difficult to achieve, including a large number of firms, imperfectly observable prices, a large number of products, and differing marginal costs.

e. Firms engage in explicit collusion when they communicate about the prices or strategies they plan to adopt. Firms engage in tacit collusion when they manage to collude without communicating with one another. Explicit collusion is illegal but is more likely to be successful (barring discovery by antitrust authorities) than tacit collusion.

6. Market entry and monopolistic competition (LO5)

a. Firms respond to profit opportunities in deciding whether to enter an oligopolistic market. They will enter only if the profits they anticipate more than compensate for the fixed costs of entry.

b. When the fixed cost associated with participating in a market falls, more firms will enter the market. As the fixed cost approaches zero, the number of firms grows very large, and the price falls close to the level of marginal cost.

c. When the size of the market increases, holding fixed costs constant, more firms will enter the market. As the size of the market grows very large, holding fixed costs constant, the number of firms grows large, and the price approaches marginal cost.

d. Economists say that competition is more intense in one market than in another if, given any fixed number of firms, the equilibrium price is lower in the first market than in the second. A market with more intense price competition will have fewer firms than a market with less intense price competition. It may even end up with a higher price, once the difference in the number of entering firms is taken into account.

e. The number of firms that choose to enter an oligopoly market may differ from the socially optimal number. The first entrant into a market has too little incentive to enter, because that firm does not capture the entire consumer surplus that its entry generates. Additional entrants often have too much incentive to enter, because part of their profit comes from stealing business from existing firms.

f. Monopolistic competition occurs in a market with free entry when there is a large number of firms, each of

which produces a unique product, prices above marginal cost, and earns (close to) zero profit net of its fixed costs.

*7. Strategic behaviour that shapes future competition (LO6)

a. Among a firm's most important strategic decisions are those that shape its future competition with rivals.

b. One way for a firm to raise its future competitive profit is to cause rivals to become less aggressive in their pricing by raising those rivals' marginal costs.

c. Another way for a firm to raise its future competitive profit is to commit to certain actions before rivals can commit to theirs.

d. In some cases, the first entrant into a market can commit to an output level before its rivals, forcing them to reduce their production or to forgo entering the market.

e. Through strategic precommitments, firms sometimes commit themselves to "play tough" and at other times commit themselves to "play soft" in order to reduce rivals' aggressiveness.

f. The downside of strategic precommitments is that they limit a firm's flexibility in responding to changing market conditions.

8. Competition policy (LO7)

a. Competition law is a form of regulation that applies quite broadly. The goal is to maintain certain basic rules of competition that enable markets to achieve good outcomes.

b. Competition concerns can be divided into two categories: those that apply to collaboration among competitors and those that apply to exclusion of rivals.

c. Agreements by competitors about the prices they will charge or quantities they will produce—called *price fixing*—are illegal.

d. Horizontal mergers can both increase market power and reduce costs. In deciding whether to allow a merger, antitrust authorities must weigh those two opposing effects on social welfare.

e. Dominant firms can engage in tactics such as predatory pricing, exclusive contracting, and bundling to disadvantage rivals and monopolize markets. However, distinguishing between anticompetitive exclusionary behaviour and efficiency-enhancing behaviour can be difficult.

ADDITIONAL EXERCISES

Exercise 19.1: Suppose Joe, Louie, and Rebecca compete in the Bertrand ready-mix concrete market described in Section 19.2. Show that in any Nash equilibrium, all sales must occur at a price of $40 per cubic metre (equal to marginal cost). Extend your argument to show that this statement will be true as long as two or more firms are competing in the market. (LO2)

Exercise 19.2: Suppose that in the Bertrand ready-mix concrete market described in Section 19.2, Joe's marginal cost is $35 and Rebecca's is $40. Their prices must be quoted in pennies. Show that it is a Nash equilibrium for Rebecca to set a price of $40 and Joe to set a price of $39.99. Show that it is also a Nash equilibrium for Rebecca to set a price of $40.01 and Joe to set a price of $40. Finally, show that there is no Nash equilibrium in which sales will occur at a price above $40.01. Notice that Joe's profit on each unit approximates his cost advantage. (LO2)

Exercise 19.3: Repeat worked-out problem 19.1 (page 705), but assume instead that Joe and Rebecca both have a marginal cost of $55 per cubic metre. What is the deadweight loss in this market? (LO2)

Exercise 19.4: Repeat worked-out problem 19.1 (page 705), but assume instead that Joe's marginal cost is $25 per cubic metre; Rebecca's remains at $40. What are the equilibrium quantities, price, and profits in this market? How do they compare to the market in which both firms face a marginal cost of $40? Graph the best responses in the two cases, showing the Nash equilibrium in each. Is the total output produced at the lowest possible cost? (LO2)

Exercise 19.5: Consider the Cournot market in worked-out problem 19.1 (page 705). Suppose the demand function in that market changes to $Q^d = 5500 - 25P$. Draw the old and new demand curves. Notice that the change in demand rotates the demand curve, making it less elastic at the initial equilibrium. What are the new equilibrium quantities and price? How does your answer relate to the discussion in Section 17.4? (LO2)

Exercise 19.6: Suppose the demand for Coke and Pepsi in a small city are given by formulas (12) and (13) on page 718, with $D = 50$. The marginal cost is $0.30 per can. Find the Nash equilibrium prices. How does a change in D affect competition? Why? (LO3)

Exercise 19.7: Consider again worked-out problem 19.2 (page 716), but assume that Coke's marginal cost is now $0.24 (Pepsi's is still $0.30). What are the equilibrium prices (to the nearest penny) and sales quantities when the firms set their prices simultaneously? (LO3)

Exercise 19.8: Suppose a single monopolist controls the market for Coke and Pepsi in worked-out problem 19.2 (page 716). If the monopolist sets the same price for Coke and Pepsi, what price would maximize its profit? How does that price compare to the equilibrium prices in worked-out problem 19.2? (LO3)

Exercise 19.9: Suppose 100 consumers live along a one-mile road, with a coffee shop at each end. Because consumers dislike having to travel for their coffee, each consumer buys his coffee at the shop with the lowest "distance-adjusted price." The distance-adjusted price for a particular consumer at a given coffee shop is the shop's price plus a positive number t times the distance to the shop: $P + (t \times distance)$. Let the price of the coffee shop on the south end of the road be P_{South} and the price of the shop on the north end be P_{North}. Write a

formula for the location of the consumer who is indifferent between the two shops. Assume that all consumers want to buy one cup a day, that their homes are evenly spaced along the road, and that $t = 0.5$. Write the demand function for each shop, expressed in terms of the share of consumers the shop sells to, given the prices. Suppose that the marginal cost of a cup of coffee is $0.50. Find the equilibrium price of a cup of coffee. What if $t = 0.25$? What if $t = 0$? (LO3)

Exercise 19.10: Suppose that in the repeated Bertrand model discussed in Section 19.5, each period is a month, the monthly demand function is $Q^d = 1000 - 10P$, and the marginal cost is $50. At what monthly interest rates can the firms sustain the monopoly price by charging the monopoly price if no one has yet undercut it, and $50 if someone has undercut it? (LO4)

Exercise 19.11: In 1983 Environment Canada announced a phase-out of leaded gasoline. Prior to that time, three producers had been selling a very profitable lead-based additive, tetraethyl lead, which gasoline producers used to boost their gasoline's octane. If those three producers were trying to sustain collusive pricing for this additive, what effect would you expect Environment Canada's announcement to have on their ability to sustain the monopoly price? (LO4)

Exercise 19.12: Suppose that in the repeated Bertrand model of Section 19.5, Joe and Rebecca take only a week instead of a month to observe and respond to each other's prices. Derive the largest weekly interest rate for which the two producers have an incentive to follow this strategy. Charge the monopoly price of $70 if no one has yet undercut that price; otherwise, charge $40 (equal to marginal cost). What is the largest weekly interest rate when price changes take a month? (LO4)

Exercise 19.13: Suppose Joe and Rebecca engage in a repeated Cournot competition in which they can change their quantity decisions only once a year. The yearly demand function and costs are the same as in worked-out problem 19.1 (page 705). Derive the largest yearly interest rate for which each has an incentive to adopt the following strategy: produce half the monopoly output of 1500 cubic metres if no one has yet deviated from that output level; otherwise, produce the Cournot output of 2000 cubic metres. (*Hint:* You will need to figure out a firm's most profitable deviation from the monopoly output in order to see when deviating from it is profitable. The most profitable deviation involves the firm playing its best response to its rival's output of 1500 cubic metres.) (LO4)

Exercise 19.14: Suppose research and development efforts are a critical part of the competition between the two firms in an industry. If the firms could curtail their R&D efforts, each could earn a greater profit. Would you expect that sustaining this type of collusion would be easy or hard? (LO4)

Exercise 19.15: Suppose that in the Cournot market of worked-out problem 19.1 (page 705), the demand doubles at each price. What are the new equilibrium quantities and market price? How do profits change when the demand doubles? (LO2)

Exercise 19.16: Consider the setting of in-text exercise 19.1 (page 707). If the fixed costs associated with being active in this market are $30,000 per year, how many firms will enter the market? (LO5)

Exercise 19.17: In 1983 the United States Congress passed the Orphan Drug Act, which gave special tax credits to pharmaceutical manufacturers that develop drugs for treating rare diseases, and delayed the date at which generic drug manufacturers can enter the market for those drugs. Why might this legislation increase aggregate surplus? Why might it lower it? Might your answer to the last question explain why Canada does not have an orphan drug policy? (LO5)

Exercise 19.18: An economist has found that patients who suffer from diseases that are more prevalent than other diseases are more likely than other patients to take the medicine their doctors prescribe. Why might this be so? (LO5)

Exercise 19.19: In exercise 19.16, would reducing by one the number of firms that enter the market raise or lower aggregate surplus? (LO5)

Exercise 19.20: When Sam Walton started Walmart in 1969, he decided to open his large discount stores in relatively small towns, even though the potential demand in those towns was lower than in some larger cities. Why was his plan a good idea? (LO6)

*Exercise 19.21: Repeat worked-out problem 19.3 (page 735), but assume that Rebecca's marginal cost is $25 per cubic metre while Joe's is $40 per cubic metre. (LO6)

*Exercise 19.22: If Joe's fixed cost in exercise 19.21 is $15,000 per year, will Rebecca choose to deter Joe's entry? (LO6)

20

Externalities and Public Goods

LEARNING OBJECTIVES

After reading this chapter, students should be able to

LO1 Explain why competitive markets may not allocate resources efficiently when externalities are present.

LO2 Discuss the nature and limitations of private negotiation as a remedy for market failures associated with externalities.

LO3 Evaluate various public policies that are designed to address externalities.

LO4 Understand why common property resources tend to be overused, and analyze ways that such problems can be corrected.

LO5 Identify the characteristics of a good that can justify public provision.

During the late twentieth century, compounds known as *chlorofluorocarbons* (CFCs) were widely used as refrigerants, aerosol spray propellants, and cleaning solvents. Since the mid-1970s, scientists had known that artificial CFCs could reach the stratosphere, where exposure to ultraviolet (UV) radiation would cause them to release chlorine atoms; they also knew that chlorine atoms could serve as a catalyst for chemical reactions that destroy ozone molecules. Because the stratospheric ozone protects the surface of the earth from harmful UV radiation, its destruction could be potentially catastrophic. Concern over the fate of the ozone layer led a few countries to limit the use of CFCs in the late 1970s. Progress toward more comprehensive regulation was slow, however. Evidence concerning the rate of ozone depletion was mixed, and advocates for the CFC industry characterized the threat as science fiction.

In 1985, three scientists working for the British Antarctic Survey jolted the world by announcing the discovery of an "ozone hole" over the Antarctic. Their findings implied that the rate of ozone depletion far exceeded even the most pessimistic estimates. Indeed, roughly contemporaneous satellite measurements that pointed toward the same conclusion

The ozone hole

had been automatically rejected as measurement error on the grounds that they were not believable. Two years later, representatives from 43 nations signed an international treaty known as the Montreal Protocol, which was designed to phase out the production and use of CFCs. The phase-out was largely completed by 1996. Former United Nations Secretary General Kofi Annan has called the Montreal Protocol "perhaps the single most successful international agreement to date."

Fortunately, the world did not leave the fate of the ozone layer to free markets. Since each individual's contribution to ozone depletion was negligible, no one would have had a personal incentive to adopt more costly alternatives to CFCs. And yet, the world's population is collectively better off now that everyone uses those alternatives. The absence of individual incentives to refrain from using CFCs exemplifies a class of market failures known as *externalities*. This chapter is devoted to the study of externalities and related phenomena. It covers the following five topics:

1. *Externalities and inefficiency*. Sometimes our choices directly affect the well-being of others. We'll explain why competitive markets may not allocate resources efficiently when such effects are present.

2. *Remedies for externalities: the private sector*. Whenever the allocation of resources is inefficient, it is always possible to arrange mutually beneficial trades. Private parties therefore have strong incentives to identify inefficiencies and negotiate solutions. We'll explore the nature and limitations of private negotiation as a remedy for the market failures associated with externalities.

3. *Remedies for externalities: the public sector.* When private negotiations fail to remedy the market failures associated with externalities, appropriate government policies can potentially improve economic efficiency. We'll describe and evaluate various public policies that are designed to address externalities.

4. *Common property resources*. Sometimes people are free to use a resource without payment, even though their use reduces the resource's value to others. We'll apply what we've learned about externalities to understand why those resources tend to be overused, and how that problem can be corrected.

5. *Public goods*. Governments provide some types of goods and services directly to the public. We'll identify the characteristics of a good that can justify public provision.

20.1 EXTERNALITIES AND INEFFICIENCY

In Chapters 14 and 16, we saw that perfectly competitive markets can generate efficient social outcomes, even though individuals ignore the greater good and pursue their own narrow self-interest. However, in reaching the conclusion that the invisible hand of the market promotes efficiency, we assumed that consumers' well-being depends only on their own consumption, and that each firm's output depends only on its own production decisions. In practice, those assumptions are often violated. Sometimes, our choices create annoyances for others, as when university students disturb their neighbours by playing loud music. In other cases, choices can profoundly affect the well-being of others, as when a power generator pollutes the air by burning coal, thereby contributing to respiratory disease, acid rain, and global warming. In such cases, competitive markets may not allocate resources efficiently. In this section, we'll learn why.

What Is an Externality?

When an action affects someone with whom the decision maker has not engaged in a related market transaction, that effect is called an **externality**.[1] Externalities can be either harmful or beneficial. A decision that harms someone else creates a **negative externality**. Examples include activities that pollute the air or water. In contrast, a decision that benefits someone else creates a **positive externality**. When homeowners carefully tend their gardens, the value of surrounding homes is increased, thereby generating positive externalities for other homeowners. Notice, however, that the abatement of pollution creates positive externalities, while neglecting a garden creates negative externalities. Thus, depending on how we describe an activity (polluting versus abating, tending versus neglecting), the associated externality can be either positive or negative.

Externalities can involve producers, consumers, or both. When a paper mill releases toxic chemicals into a river, it imposes externalities on consumers who use the river for recreation, as well as on downstream farmers who rely on the river as a source of water for irrigation. Similarly, when a restaurant patron lights up a cigarette during a meal, that imposes externalities on other diners and on the restaurant's employees.

While many of our decisions affect others, only some of those effects are externalities. For example, a diner benefits from a restaurant owner's decision to provide food, and the restaurant owner benefits from the diner's decision to buy food. However, since both of those effects are associated with a market transaction between the diner and the restaurant owner, neither qualifies as an externality. Why is that distinction important? The competitive price of the meal equals both the diner's marginal benefit and the restaurant owner's marginal cost. Because diners have to pay that price, they account for the restaurant owner's costs when deciding whether or not to order a meal. Likewise, because restaurant owners receive that price, they account for the diner's benefits when deciding whether to supply a meal. In contrast, when a decision creates an externality, the decision maker does not account for the effects on others. As we'll see in the next section, the failure to do so leads to inefficient resource allocation.

Application 20.1

Externalities from Second-hand Smoke

When a smoker lights up a cigarette near a non-smoker, the non-smoker experiences negative externalities. Those externalities can cause a great deal of tension between smokers and non-smokers. Many non-smokers feel that they should have the right to breathe clean air. They often show their displeasure by grimacing, moving, complaining, or politely asking smokers to extinguish their cigarettes. Smokers' responses vary from apologetic co-operation to strident insistence on their right to smoke.

Economic analysis cannot reveal whose right should take precedence as a matter of ethics. However, it does tell us that a smoker's failure to account for costs to non-smokers will lead to inefficient resource allocation. The severity of the market failure will depend on the magnitude of the externality. From an economist's perspective, it is therefore important to determine whether second-hand smoke is a minor annoyance or a major concern.

---

[1]Externalities are also known as *external effects*.

A large body of scientific research concludes that regular exposure to second-hand smoke has serious medical consequences. For example, according to one study, it leads to a 22 percent increase in the risk of lung cancer, a 41 percent increase in the risk of cervical cancer, a 44 percent increase in the risk of asthma, and an 83 percent increase in the risk of chronic pulmonary disease.[2] The Canadian Cancer Society reports that second-hand smoke results in at least 1000 deaths per year while the Heart and Stroke Foundation estimates deaths at 6300. In addition to human suffering, these conditions generate substantial economic costs. The Canadian Centre on Substance Abuse estimated the cost of tobacco use at $17 billion in 2002.[3] In the United States the annual direct costs of second-hand smoke, including expenses involving the treatment of medical conditions and disabilities, are estimated at U.S.$4.98 billion. In addition, the annual indirect costs, including wages, fringe benefits, and services lost due to early mortality and disability, are estimated at U.S.$4.68 billion. Considering the various categories of costs that the study did not quantify (such as the opportunity costs of unpaid caregivers), the total annual direct and indirect costs of second-hand smoke likely exceed U.S.$10 billion. In contrast, for the smokers themselves, the annual direct and indirect costs total roughly U.S.$150 billion.[4] Assuming the ratio of costs attributed to tobacco users to second-hand smoke costs is the same in Canada as in the U.S., the second-hand smoking costs in Canada could be estimated at approximately $1.1 billion.

Negative Externalities and Inefficiency in Competitive Markets

When a consumption or production activity creates a negative externality, competitive markets will usually allocate economic resources inefficiently. To see why, let's assume that the paper market is perfectly competitive and that paper production generates harmful water pollution. To keep things simple, we'll also assume that there is a fixed relationship between the amount of paper produced and the economic harm suffered by consumers and other producers; in other words, paper mills cannot abate their pollution by using more environmentally friendly production methods, and the affected parties cannot mitigate the harms of pollution by relocating.

Figure 20.1 shows a short-run competitive equilibrium in the paper market. Each of 200 paper mills produces 250,000 tonnes of paper per year, for an industry total of 50 million tonnes, and paper sells at a price of $1000 per tonne. In Figure 20.1(a), each paper mill produces up to the point at which its marginal cost curve, labelled MC^{mill} and shown in red, intersects a horizontal line drawn at the market price (shown in blue). The industry supply curve, labelled S^{market} in Figure 20.1(b) and shown in red, is simply the horizontal sum of 200 identical marginal cost curves. Notice that the market demand curve, labelled D^{market} in Figure 20.1(b) and shown in blue, intersects the market supply curve at the equilibrium price of $1000 per tonne. In the absence of externalities, this competitive equilibrium would be efficient. However, it is not efficient if paper production creates negative externalities. Let's see why.

We'll assume for the sake of simplicity that each paper mill pollutes a different river, so that the **external cost** of production—that is, the economic harm imposed on others—

An **external cost** is the economic harm that a negative externality imposes on others.

[2]Donald F. Behan, Michael P. Eriksen, and Yijia Lin, *Economic Effects of Environmental Tobacco Smoke,* Society of Actuaries, March 2005.

[3]J. Rehm et al., "Calculating the Costs of Substance Abuse in Canada 2002: Highlights," Canadian Centre on Substance Abuse, Ottawa, 2006.

[4]Donald F. Behan et al., ibid.

Figure 20.1

A Competitive Equilibrium with a Negative Externality. Figure (a) shows that, at a price of $1000 per tonne, a mill would produce 250,000 tonnes of paper. If the mill took external costs into account, it would produce only 100,000 tonnes of paper. Figure (b) shows the competitive equilibrium with 200 mills: a total of 50 million tonnes of paper is produced and sold for $1000 per tonne. It also shows that the socially efficient level of paper production is 30 million tonnes. The area of the red triangle represents the deadweight loss created by the externality.

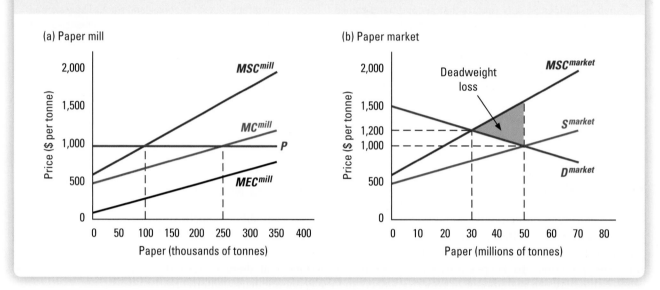

does not depend on the production level of any other mill. We can then write that external cost as a function of the mill's output.

$$External\ cost = EC(Q^{mill})$$

Optional Using calculus, the marginal external cost can be calculated by taking the derivative of the external cost function with respect to output. That is, $MEC = dEC(Q)/dQ$.

We can derive the marginal external cost of production from the external cost function exactly as we derived the marginal cost of production from a firm's cost function in Section 8.5. Figure 20.1(a) shows, in black, the marginal external cost curve (labelled MEC^{mill}) for a typical paper mill. The fact that the curve slopes upward implies that the harm caused by the pollution associated with an extra tonne of paper increases along with the level of pollution. This pattern is fairly typical of pollutants, but it is unimportant for our purposes; our analysis of market efficiency would be essentially unchanged if the curve were flat or sloped downward.

What is the socially efficient level of paper production for a single mill, assuming that the value of paper to consumers is $1000 per tonne, the price in the competitive equilibrium? The efficient level of paper production for any particular mill equates marginal social cost and marginal social benefit (recall Section 3.2). To determine the marginal social cost (MSC) of production, we sum the marginal cost to the producer and the marginal external cost: $MSC = MC + MEC$. In Figure 20.1(a), the mill's marginal social cost curve (shown in brown and labelled MSC^{mill}) is the vertical sum of the MC^{mill} and MEC^{mill} curves. The marginal social benefit of paper is just the consumer's marginal benefit, $1000, as there are no marginal external benefits from the consumption of paper. Therefore, in Figure 20.1(a), the socially efficient level of paper production for a single mill is 100,000 tonnes; this is the level at which marginal social cost equals marginal social benefit. The mill's equilibrium production level—250,000 tonnes—is therefore excessive and inefficient. For each of the last 150,000 tonnes, the marginal social cost exceeds the marginal social benefit. The mill chooses to produce that paper because it considers only its own costs, and ignores the social costs borne by others.

What is the socially efficient level of paper production for the entire market? One way to address this question is to determine the level of production that would prevail in a competitive market if there were no externalities—that is, if the external costs of production were instead costs to the mill rather than to others.[5] For the reasons discussed in Section 14.4, that competitive outcome would definitely be efficient. If a mill bore all the social costs of paper production, then the MSC^{mill} curve in Figure 20.1(a) would be its supply curve. At a price of $1000 per tonne, it would produce only 100,000 tonnes. The market supply curve would be the horizontal sum of the MSC^{mill} curves for the 200 mills, shown as the brown curve in Figure 20.1(b). We have labelled that curve MSC^{market} because it also measures the marginal social cost of total paper production. In equilibrium, mills would sell 30 million tonnes of paper at a price of $1200 per tonne. We know that outcome is efficient because it arises in a competitive equilibrium without externalities. We can confirm that it's efficient simply by remembering that the height of the demand curve measures the marginal social benefit of paper (equivalently, marginal willingness to pay). As shown in the figure, at 30 million tonnes the marginal social cost of paper production equals the marginal social benefit.

Thus, when mills ignore external costs, they are willing to produce too much paper at any given price. As a result, paper is priced too cheaply in equilibrium ($1000 per tonne instead of $1200). Normally, competition promotes efficient consumption because equilibrium prices force consumers to weigh the benefits of extra paper against all the social costs of production. In this example, however, the equilibrium price forces consumers to weigh their benefits only against the marginal costs borne by mills, and not against other marginal social costs. Because paper is priced incorrectly when the mills' production creates an externality, consumers demand too much (50 million tonnes instead of 30 million).

Figure 20.1(b) also shows the deadweight loss created by the externality. For each tonne of paper produced beyond 30 million tonnes, society's net loss equals the vertical distance between the demand curve (which measures marginal benefit) and the marginal social cost curve. Therefore, when the market produces 50 million tonnes instead of 30 million, the total deadweight loss is the area of the red-shaded triangle.

So far, our analysis has taken the number of mills as given. Negative externalities also lead to long-run inefficiency when mills can enter and exit the paper market. In Section 14.3, we learned that a good's long-run competitive equilibrium price equals its minimum long-run average cost of production. With negative externalities, the average *social* cost of producing paper must therefore exceed its long-run competitive price. If mills had to absorb those external costs, they would earn negative profits, and some would leave the market. The price of paper would gradually rise to a new long-run competitive equilibrium level, equal to the minimum long-run average social cost of production, leading consumers to purchase less paper. Therefore, with negative externalities, the industry produces too much paper in the long run.

---

[5]We would reach exactly the same conclusions if the marginal external costs were borne directly by the consumers instead of by the mill.

WORKED-OUT PROBLEM   20.1

The Problem   Two hundred paper mills compete in the paper market. The total cost of production (in dollars) for each mill is given by the formula

$$TC = 500Q^{mill} + (Q^{mill})^2$$

where Q^{mill} indicates the mill's annual production in thousands of tonnes. The marginal cost of production is[6]

$$MC = 500 + 2Q^{mill}$$

The external cost of a mill's production (in dollars) is given by the formula

$$EC = AQ^{mill} + (Q^{mill})^2$$

and the marginal external cost of production is

$$MEC = A + 2Q^{mill}$$

where A is a constant. (We'll supply values for A later.) Finally, annual market demand (in thousands of tonnes) is given by the formula

$$Q^d = 150,000 - 100P$$

where P is the price of paper per tonne.

Assume that $A = 100$. Using algebra, find the competitive equilibrium price and quantity, as well as the efficient quantity. Calculate the magnitude of the deadweight loss resulting from the externality. Illustrate your solution with graphs.

The Solution   First we'll find the competitive equilibrium. Each mill produces the quantity for which price equals marginal cost: $P = MC = 500 + 2Q^{mill}$. It follows that, at any price P, each mill supplies the quantity $Q^{mill} = P/2 - 250$. Multiplying that quantity by 200 (the number of mills), we obtain the market supply curve

$$Q^s = 100P - 50,000$$

In equilibrium, the quantities supplied and demanded must be equal: $100P - 50,000 = 150,000 - 100P$. Solving that equation, we obtain the competitive price: $P = 1000$. Substituting that price into either the market supply or demand function, we obtain the market quantity: $Q^{market} = 50,000$.

Next we'll find the efficient level of production. If the external costs of production were borne directly by the mills, each mill would produce the quantity for which price equals marginal social cost: $P = MSC = MC + MEC = 600 + 4Q^{mill}$. It follows that, at any price P, each mill would supply the quantity $Q^{mill} = P/4 - 150$. Multiplying that quantity by 200 (the number of mills), we obtain a new formula for market supply.

$$\hat{Q}^S = 50P - 30,000$$

In equilibrium, the quantities supplied and demanded must be equal: $50P - 30,000 = 150,000 - 100P$. Solving that equation, we find the competitive price that would prevail without externalities: $P = 1200$. Substituting that price into either the new

---

[6]If you know calculus, you can check that the formula for marginal cost is the derivative of the formula for total cost. You can also check that the formula for marginal external cost, which follows, is the derivative of the formula for external cost.

market supply function or the demand function, we obtain the efficient quantity: $Q^{efficient} = 30,000.$[7]

Notice that the formulas for each mill's marginal cost, marginal external cost, and marginal social cost correspond to the curves drawn in Figure 20.1(a). Likewise, the formulas for Q^s and Q^d correspond to the market supply and demand curves drawn in Figure 20.1(b), while the formula for $\hat{Q}^S$ (the market supply curve when firms are forced to internalize the external costs of production) corresponds to the curve labelled MSC^{market}. Therefore, Figure 20.1 illustrates the competitive equilibrium and efficient allocation for which we solved algebraically.

The deadweight loss created by the externality equals the area of the red triangle in Figure 20.1. Looked at sideways, the base of that triangle—that is, the vertical distance between the red and brown lines—equals the magnitude of the marginal external cost of production when the market output is 50 million tonnes. With 200 mills, production per mill is 250,000 tonnes. Substituting that value into our formula for marginal external cost (and remembering that Q^{mill} measures thousands of tonnes) we find that $MEC(250) = \$600$ per tonne. The height of the triangle, 20 million tonnes, equals the difference between the competitive quantity (50 million tonnes) and the efficient quantity (30 million tonnes). To find the deadweight loss, we compute the area of the triangle: ($\$600$ per tonne $\times$ 20,000,000 tonnes)/2 = $\$6$ billion per year.

IN-TEXT EXERCISE 20.1   Repeat worked-out problem 20.1 assuming that $A = 40$. Repeat the problem again assuming that $A = 130$. Based on your answers, explain what happens to the socially efficient level of production and the deadweight loss as the external cost becomes larger at any given level of production.

Positive Externalities and Inefficiency in Competitive Markets

It's natural to think that *positive* externalities might be good for society: choices that create benefits for others confer social bonuses. And yet, competitive equilibria are inefficient when *either* positive or negative externalities are present. To understand why, remember that we classify an externality as positive or negative depending on how we describe the activity with which it's associated. If neglecting a garden creates a negative externality, then caring for the garden creates a positive externality. Just as the negative externality from neglect encourages too much neglect, the positive externality from care encourages too little care; these observations are simply two sides of the same coin.

Education is widely thought to create important positive externalities. As a society's population becomes more educated, social ills such as crime and communicable disease decline, and democratic institutions function more effectively. As we'll see in Section 20.3, those externalities can justify government intervention, including compulsory schooling laws, student loans, and subsidies to educational institutions. What would happen if, instead, educational decisions were left entirely to families and profit-seeking firms in competitive markets? Because of the positive externalities, the level of educational attainment would be inefficiently low.

---

[7]Here's another way to reach the same conclusion. First, solve for the marginal social cost of paper as a function of industry production. Next, use the demand function to derive the inverse demand function, which expresses the marginal benefit of consumption (equivalently, the price) as a function of total consumption. Finally, find the quantity that equates the marginal social cost and the marginal benefit.

Figure 20.2

A Competitive Equilibrium with a Positive Externality. In a competitive equilibrium, 750 thousand students would each pay $8000 per year in tuition to attend university. Because education creates positive externalities, it is socially efficient for one million students to attend university. The area of the red triangle represents the deadweight loss created by the externality.

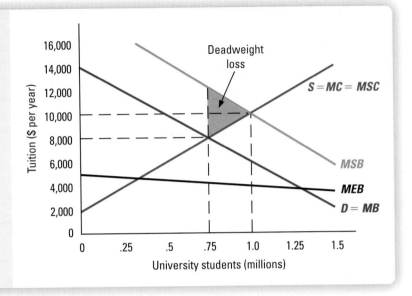

Figure 20.2 shows a competitive equilibrium in the market for university education. The industry supply curve, labelled S and shown in red, indicates the number of students that profit-maximizing universities would be willing to educate at each possible level of annual tuition. The industry demand curve, labelled D and shown in blue, indicates the number of students seeking a university education at each tuition level. The intersection of the supply and demand curves determines the competitive market equilibrium. In that equilibrium, 750,000 university students each pay $8000 in annual tuition.

Because education creates positive externalities, the competitive equilibrium shown in Figure 20.2 is inefficient. Let's assume that the **external benefit** of education—that is, the economic gain enjoyed by others—depends on the number of students who receive university degrees, Q.

> An **external benefit** is the economic gain that a positive externality provides to others.

$$\textit{External benefit} = EB(Q)$$

> *Optional* Using calculus, the marginal external benefit can be calculated by taking the derivative of the external benefit with respect to output. That is, $MEB = dEB(Q)/dQ$.

We can derive the marginal external benefit from the external benefit function exactly as we derived the marginal benefit from a total benefit function in Section 3.2.[8] Figure 20.2 shows, in black, the marginal external benefit curve (labelled *MEB*) for university degrees.

The efficient number of university degrees equates marginal social cost and marginal social benefit. The height of the supply curve indicates the marginal social cost of university degrees.[9] (In the figure, notice that the supply curve is also labelled *MSC*.) What about benefits? The height of the demand curve indicates the marginal benefit of university degrees to students; therefore, the curve is also labelled *MB*. To determine the marginal social benefit (*MSB*) of university degrees, we sum the marginal benefit to students and the marginal external benefit: $MSB = MB + MEB$. In Figure 20.2, the marginal social benefit curve (shown in green and labelled *MSB*) is therefore simply the vertical sum of the *MB* and *MEB* curves.

---

[8]The marginal external benefit is the extra external benefit resulting from a very small increase in the number of university degrees, divided by the change in the number of degrees, $MEB = \Delta EB/\Delta Q$.

[9]This statement assumes that education is provided by competitive, profit-maximizing universities, and that universities create no external costs.

By inspecting the intersection of the marginal social benefit and marginal social cost curves, we learn that it is socially efficient for one million students to earn university degrees. If there were no externalities—that is, if the external benefits of education were instead enjoyed directly by students—the demand for university education would be given by the green curve instead of the blue curve, and the equilibrium would be efficient: one million students would each pay $10,000 in annual tuition to earn their degrees. Because students ignore the external benefits of their education, too few students go to university (750,000 instead of one million), and annual tuition is lower in equilibrium ($8000 instead of $10,000).

Figure 20.2 also shows the deadweight loss created by the externality. For each university graduate beyond 750,000, society's net gain equals the vertical distance between the marginal social benefit curve and the supply curve (which measures marginal social cost). Therefore, when the market produces 750,000 university graduates instead of one million, the total deadweight loss is the area of the red triangle.

Externalities in Imperfectly Competitive Markets

Up to this point in our discussions of externalities and market power (Chapters 17 through 19), we have examined the effects of particular market failures in isolation. In practice, economists sometimes encounter markets with multiple failures—for example, monopolists or oligopolists who generate pollution. As we'll see in this section, some of the lessons we've learned concerning the efficiency effects of market failures may not be valid when there is more than one failure.

In Chapter 17, we learned that monopoly is less efficient than competition, and that a monopolist's output is inefficiently low. Neither conclusion necessarily follows if the production of the good in question creates a negative externality. To illustrate this possibility, we'll modify our analysis of the market for paper. Let's suppose that a single monopolistic firm purchases all 200 paper mills, and that new mills are unable to enter the market. Figure 20.3(a) illustrates the monopolist's decision; it is identical to Figure 20.1(b), except that we have added a marginal revenue curve, labelled *MR*. As shown in the figure, the monopolist chooses the output level, 33 million tonnes, at which its marginal revenue equals its marginal cost. The socially efficient level of production is 30 million tonnes, just as in Figure 20.1(b). Therefore, the monopolist's production is inefficiently high, rather than inefficiently low. The deadweight loss created by the monopolist's inefficient production decision corresponds to the area of the grey triangle. Notice that this deadweight loss is smaller than the one associated with the competitive equilibrium (the grey triangle plus the red-shaded area). Thus, monopoly is more efficient than competition in this example.

Figure 20.3(a) illustrates the general principle that a market failure can be beneficial if its effects offset another market failure. Because of the negative externality associated with paper production, competitive firms will produce too much paper. In contrast, a monopolist will restrict the supply of paper, thereby reducing the magnitude of the external costs.

However, we should not jump to the conclusion that monopoly is necessarily better than competition when production creates negative externalities. A monopolist's interests will coincide with society's only by chance. Indeed, the monopolist's tendency to restrict supply can overcompensate for the external costs, in which case monopoly can be less efficient than competition. Certainly, the external costs won't make much of a difference if they are very small, and standard conclusions concerning the efficiency implications of competition (Section 14.3) and monopoly (Section 17.3) will be approximately correct. Figure 20.3(b) illustrates such a case. All of the curves are the same as

Figure 20.3

Monopoly with a Negative Externality. In both figures, the monopolist produces 33 million tonnes. That production level is inefficiently high in figure (a) and inefficiently low in figure (b). A comparison of the sizes of the triangles that correspond to the deadweight losses reveals that monopoly is more efficient than competition in figure (a) but less efficient in figure (b).

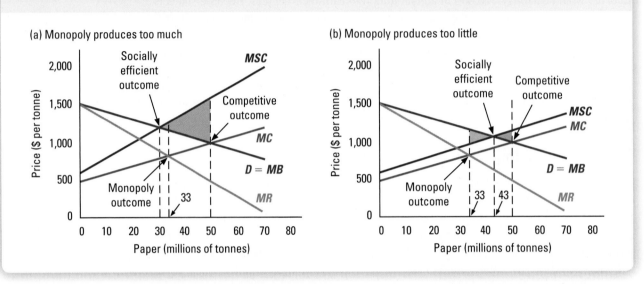

in Figure 20.3(a), except that the marginal social cost curve (labelled *MSC*) is closer to the marginal cost curve (labelled *MC*), which implies that external costs are smaller. At 43 million tonnes, the marginal social benefit of paper (as indicated by the height of the demand curve) equals the marginal social cost; this is the efficient social outcome. Notice that the monopolist's output is inefficiently low while the competitive output is inefficiently high. The deadweight losses equal the area of the grey triangle with monopoly, and the area of the red triangle with competition. Since the grey triangle is larger than the red one, competition is more efficient than monopoly.

Application 20.2

The Deadweight Loss from Overuse of Antibiotics

Prior to the discovery of penicillin and the development of antibiotics during the first half of the twentieth century, medical science was powerless to treat a wide range of bacterial infections. Even minor wounds that became infected, and common diseases such as strep throat, were potentially life-threatening. Today, we take our miracle cures for granted; we pop a few pills, and the infection vanishes.

However, there is increasing concern that antibiotics are overused. In Canada antibiotic prescriptions were 63.5 per 100 individuals in 2005, one of the highest rates in the world.[10] The rates of use by children is even higher. Over one

---

twelve-month period approximately four million antibiotic prescriptions were filled for one million paediatric claimants aged 18 or younger.[11] Unfortunately, over time, widely used antibiotics become progressively less effective at treating diseases. One leading explanation for this phenomenon is that an antibiotic eliminates competition for resistant strains of bacteria by killing off susceptible strains. The potential and actual consequences for public health are alarming. For example, in the 1940s, almost all strains of *Staphylococcus aureus*, the bacteria that causes staph infections (an increasingly common problem among hospital patients), were susceptible to penicillin; today, fewer than 10 percent remain susceptible, and some have even shown resistance to more recently developed antibiotics, including the drugs of last resort. The cost to the Canadian health care system of antibiotic resistance has been estimated to be as high as $200 million per year.[12]

The overuse of antibiotics results from a negative externality. When deciding whether to use an antibiotic, a patient and doctor consider the likely impact on the patient's health and well-being. They often do not consider the fact that the patient's use of the antibiotic promotes the development of resistant strains of bacteria, and thereby

"Don't forget to take a handful of our complimentary antibiotics on your way out."

© The New Yorker Collection 1998 Mick Stevens from cartoonbank.com. All Right Reserved.

harms others who might need an effective antibiotic in the future.

How large is the deadweight loss resulting from the overuse of antibiotics? In all likelihood, the answer to this question differs considerably from one drug to another. Health economist Elamin Elbasha has estimated the size of the deadweight loss for amoxicillin, a common antibiotic.[13] Elbasha constructed the demand curve for amoxicillin using information concerning prices, quantities, and the elasticity of demand. He estimated the external costs of amoxicillin use from information on the rate of resistance, the relationship between resistance and the drug's use, and the relative economic costs of infections with susceptible and resistant strains of bacteria. Finally, he assumed that the pharmaceutical industry is imperfectly competitive, and used a simple model of oligopolistic pricing to describe the supply of amoxicillin. Despite the tendency for oligopolies to restrict supply relative to perfect competitors, Elbasha found that amoxicillin is significantly overused due to the negative externality it generates. According to Elbasha, in 1996 the socially efficient level of amoxicillin use was roughly half its actual level in the United States, and the deadweight loss from overuse totalled more than U.S.$223 million.

20.2 REMEDIES FOR EXTERNALITIES: THE PRIVATE SECTOR

Whenever the allocation of resources is inefficient, it is always possible to arrange mutually beneficial trades (recall Sections 16.4 and 16.5). Private parties therefore have strong incentives to identify inefficiencies and negotiate solutions. In this section, we will explore the nature and limitations of private negotiation as a remedy for the market failures associated with externalities.

[11]L. Abi Khaled et al., "Prescription medicine use by one million Canadian children," *Paediatric Child Health,* April 2003, Supplement A:6A-56A.

[12]John Conley, "Antimicrobial Resistance in Canada," *Canadian Medical Association Journal* 167(8), October 2002, pp. 885–891.

[13]Elamin H. Elbasha, "Deadweight Loss of Bacterial Resistance Due to Overtreatment," *Health Economics* 12, February 2003, pp. 125–138.

Property Rights and Negotiation

The outcome of any negotiation depends on the parties' property rights. As we explained in Chapter 1, a property right is an enforceable claim on a good or resource. In any negotiation, the party who holds the relevant property rights is in a stronger bargaining position and will ordinarily emerge with a more favourable deal.

A numerical example helps to clarify this point. We'll suppose that a paper mill earns $600,000 in profits when it pollutes a river, and that it can abate pollution at a cost of A. To keep the example simple, we'll assume that the effects of the pollution are confined to a single farmer. The farmer is free to use the river water for irrigation, but pollution hurts his crops. He'll earn $370,000 if the water is clean, but only $250,000 if it's polluted. The combined profits of both businesses are $(600,000 + 250,000) = $850,000 without abatement, and $(600,000 - A + 370,000) = $(970,000 - A)$ with abatement. Therefore, if $A <$ $120,000, the benefits of abatement exceed the costs, and abatement is efficient; if $A >$ $120,000, the costs of abatement exceed the benefits, and pollution is efficient.

Now let's see how the assignment of property rights affects the nature of the agreement that the paper mill and the farmer will reach in negotiating a remedy for the market failure associated with the mill's pollution. First we'll assume that the abatement cost is low (less than $120,000), so that abatement is efficient. If the law guarantees the farmer access to clean water, then the farmer holds the relevant property rights. Any payment sufficient to compensate the farmer for pollution (that is, at least $120,000) will exceed the mill's cost of abatement. As a result, the farmer will insist on abatement and no further negotiation will take place. If abatement costs $50,000, for example, the mill will earn $550,000 and the farmer will earn $370,000.

What if there is no law that prevents the mill from polluting the river? In that case, the mill holds the relevant property right by default: it has the right to pollute the river. But since pollution is inefficient, the parties have an incentive to negotiate. Suppose that abatement costs $50,000. Then the combined profits of the mill and the farmer will be $70,000 higher with abatement than with pollution ($920,000 versus $850,000, as shown in Table 20.1). As long as both parties share in that $70,000 gain, both will be better off. For example, to split the gain equally, the farmer would pay the mill $85,000 in exchange for a binding promise not to pollute.[14] As shown in Table 20.1, the mill would then earn

Table 20.1
Bargaining with a Low Abatement Cost When the Mill Has the Right to Pollute
Assumes abatement cost is $50,000

| | Mill Pollutes Profits ($) | Mill Abates | | | |
		Profits before Payment ($)	Negotiated Payment ($)	Profits with Payment ($)	Gain ($)
Mill	600,000	550,000	+85,000	635,000	+35,000
Farmer	250,000	370,000	-85,000	285,000	+35,000
Total	850,000	920,000	0	920,000	+70,000

[14]If the payment is P, then the mill's gain from abatement is $(550,000 + P - 600,000)$ and the farmer's gain is $(370,000 - P - 250,000)$. Setting those two expressions equal (so that their gains are the same) and solving for P, we find that $P = $85,000.

Table 20.2

Bargaining with a High Abatement Cost When the Farmer Has the Right to Clean Water

Assumes cost of abatement is $200,000

| | Mill Abates | Mill Pollutes | | | |
	Profits ($)	Profits before Payment ($)	Negotiated Payment ($)	Profits with Payment ($)	Gain ($)
Mill	400,000	600,000	−160,000	440,000	+40,000
Farmer	370,000	250,000	+160,000	410,000	+40,000
Total	770,000	850,000	0	850,000	+80,000

$635,000 in total ($550,000 plus the farmer's $85,000 payment), $35,000 more than if it chose to pollute. Similarly, the farmer would earn $285,000 in total ($370,000 minus the $85,000 payment), $35,000 more than if the mill chose to pollute. Thus, the agreement increases each party's profits by $35,000, for a total gain of $70,000.

Notice that the assignment of property rights does not affect the level of pollution; since abatement is efficient, the mill will abate regardless of how property rights are assigned. However, property rights do affect profits. The mill's profits are higher when it holds the relevant property rights than when the farmer holds those rights ($635,000 versus $550,000 when abatement costs $50,000), while the farmer's profits are lower ($285,000 versus $370,000).

Next we'll assume that the abatement cost is high (more than $120,000), so that abatement is inefficient. If the farmer holds the relevant property rights and can insist on abatement, the parties will have an incentive to negotiate. Suppose that abatement costs $200,000. Then the combined profits of the mill and the farmer will be $80,000 higher with pollution than with abatement ($850,000 versus $770,000, as shown in Table 20.2). As long as both parties share in that $80,000 gain, both will be better off. For example, to split the gain equally, the mill would pay the farmer $160,000 in exchange for the right to pollute.[15] As shown in Table 20.2, the mill would then earn $440,000 in total ($600,000 minus the $160,000 payment), $40,000 more than if it chose to abate. Similarly, the farmer would earn $410,000 in total ($250,000 plus the $160,000 payment), $40,000 more than if the mill chose to abate. Thus, the agreement increases each party's profits by $40,000, for a total gain of $80,000.

What if the mill holds the relevant property rights? Any payment sufficient to compensate the mill for abatement (that is, at least $200,000) will exceed the farmer's benefits from clean water. As a result, the mill will insist on polluting and no further negotiation will take place; the mill will earn $600,000 and the farmer will earn $250,000.

Once again, the assignment of property rights does not affect the level of pollution; since abatement is inefficient, the mill will pollute regardless of how property rights are assigned. However, as we noted for the case of low abatement costs, property rights do affect profits. The mill's profits are higher when it holds the relevant property rights than when the farmer holds those rights ($600,000 versus $440,000 when abatement costs $200,000), while the farmer's profits are lower ($250,000 versus $410,000).

So far, we have assumed that a deal between the mill and the farmer would take the form of a payment from one party to the other in exchange for an agreement concerning

Ronald Coase (1910–) received the 1991 Nobel Prize in Economics for his path-breaking analysis of the ways in which property rights, transactions costs, and institutions affect the allocation of economic resources.

---

[15]If the payment is P, then the mill's gain from pollution is $(600,000 − P − 400,000)$ and the farmer's gain is $(250,000 + P − 370,000)$. Setting those two expressions equal (so that their gains are the same) and solving for P, we find that $P = 160,000$.

abatement. Alternatively, one party could simply negotiate to buy the other out. If the owner of the mill also owned the farm, his objective would be to maximize the total profits of both firms. Therefore, he would "internalize" the externality and always make efficient choices concerning abatement.

Throughout the preceding discussion, we have also implicitly assumed that bargaining is *frictionless*, in the sense that the paper mill and the farmer can costlessly reach an agreement whenever a mutually beneficial alternative is available. Our simple example illustrates a general point: if bargaining is frictionless, then regardless of how property rights are assigned, voluntary agreements between private parties will remedy the market failures associated with externalities and restore economic efficiency. This principle is often attributed to Nobel Laureate Ronald Coase and is widely known as the **Coase Theorem**.

Some free market advocates have argued that the Coase Theorem justifies a policy of laissez-faire even when externalities are present. Ironically, Coase himself did not believe that bargaining is actually frictionless. Coase was suspicious of the government's ability to remedy externalities more efficiently than private markets, but his reasons were more subtle. We will discuss some of those reasons later, in Section 20.3. First, however, it is important to understand why the assumption of frictionless bargaining is often unreasonable.

> The **Coase Theorem** states that if bargaining is frictionless, then regardless of how property rights are assigned, voluntary agreements between private parties will remedy the market failures associated with externalities and restore economic efficiency.

Application 20.3

Two Approaches to Environmental Protection

The Nature Conservancy and Ecojustice are both dedicated to protecting the natural environment. However, they have sharply contrasting approaches. This contrast reflects the fact that the negotiation strategies used by private parties who seek remedies for negative externalities depend on the assignment of property rights.

The Nature Conservancy operates a conservation land trust. The purpose of the trust is to protect vulnerable natural areas through outright acquisition, or by negotiating agreements with property owners, known as *conservation easements*, that place restrictions on the ways in which the property can be used. In 2008 the Nature Conservancy announced the largest single private conservation effort, 55,000 hectares, in Canadian history. The protected area of temperate rain forest, dubbed Darkwoods, is critical habitat for a variety of threatened species in British Columbia's Selkirk Mountains. Altogether, the Nature Conservancy has helped to protect roughly 800,000 hectares of land in Canada since 1962.[16]

In contrast, Ecojustice pursues and promotes litigation to enforce antipollution laws. In some cases, it seeks court injunctions that stop pollution from occurring, as well as compensation for past pollution. In other cases, it uses the threat of litigation to negotiate binding agreements with polluters. These out-of-court settlements sometimes require polluters to reduce emissions and pay for other conservation activities. For example, in March 2007 Ecojustice challenged Imperial Oil's tar sands project in northern Alberta. Imperial planned an open-pit mine that, if approved, would strip mine on approximately 200 square kilometres of boreal forest and wetlands. Ecojustice went to court in 2008 arguing that a proper environmental review had not been done and that a joint federal-provincial panel's finding that the environmental impact would be "insignificant" was in error. The Federal Court ruled in March 2008 that critical legal errors had been made in the panel's assessment, the first time a tar sands joint panel assessment had been successfully challenged.[17]

When the Nature Conservancy negotiates the purchase of land or a conservation easement, it bargains from a relatively weak legal position. The existing land owner holds the relevant property rights and can choose to use the land for other purposes. The Nature Conservancy cannot obtain

[16]Nature Conservancy Canada, *Annual Report 2008*.

[17]Information on Ecojustice's litigation can be found at www.ecojustice.ca.

environmental concessions through threats of litigation; instead, it must pay for concessions. In contrast, when Ecojustice negotiates a legal settlement with a polluter, it bargains from a relatively strong legal position. Because of environmental laws, the public arguably holds the relevant property rights. Therefore, Ecojustice can (and does) obtain environmental concessions through threats of litigation without paying for them. In March of 2007 Ecojustice, in conjunction with the Department of Fisheries and Oceans, was able to halt seismic testing off the coast of British Columbia by providing evidence that the humpback whale population was at risk. The Batholiths Project which would have used air guns to conduct seismic tests was terminated by Canada's Natural Sciences and Engineering Research Council.

Limitations of Bargaining

When the mill and the farmer negotiate an efficient agreement concerning pollution abatement, they are in effect creating a market for exchanging the property right to a good; either the mill buys the farmer's right to clean water or the farmer buys the mill's right to pollute. Prior to their negotiation, an externality was present because those markets didn't exist. If there had been markets for the various uses of the river—if the mill had paid for the right to pollute and the farmer had paid for water—there would have been no market failure. In fact, every externality can be traced to missing markets. Private negotiations remedy the market failures associated with externalities because they lead to the transactions that the parties would have made if the required markets hadn't been missing.

Why might two or more parties fail to address an externality through voluntary negotiation, despite the promise of mutual benefit? Not surprisingly, many of the same factors that cause markets to disappear, and thereby give rise to externalities, can also cause bargaining to break down. In this section, we discuss four important barriers to negotiating efficient remedies for externalities.

First, bargaining can be impractical. It can require substantial time and effort, as well as the services of highly paid attorneys and professional negotiators. For certain types of externalities, the logistics of the negotiations envisioned by the Coase Theorem are difficult to imagine. Consider the problem of air pollution in the Greater Toronto Area (GTA). If the public has the legal right to clean air, then a driver would need to buy that right from each of the GTA's roughly 6 million residents before operating a vehicle. Moreover, because each of those residents could separately forbid any driving, every one of them would have a powerful bargaining position. By way of analogy, if drivers were required to fill their tanks with drops of fuel from each of 6 million different gas stations, driving would be impractical. The private sector is therefore unlikely to achieve an efficient remedy for air pollution.

Second, the assignment of property rights may be ambiguous. Based on conflicting legal precedents, the owner of the mill may believe that she has the right to pollute and the farmer may believe that he has the right to clean water. In such cases, neither party may be willing to make a concession. Instead of bargaining efficiently, they may find themselves in a protracted and costly legal battle.

Third, parties to a negotiation may have limited information about each others' costs and benefits. Sometimes, this limitation can lead them to an impasse. For example, suppose the mill has the right to pollute and that abatement is efficient. To justify a demand for a large payment, the mill's owner may try to exaggerate the cost of abatement. To justify a smaller offer, the farmer may try to understate the benefits of clean water. If this process leads the parties to conclude incorrectly that the costs of abatement exceed the benefits, they may fail to reach an efficient agreement.

Finally, efficient contracts may be difficult to enforce. In some situations, the parties may not be able to monitor compliance with the terms of an agreement, or monitoring may be prohibitively costly. In our example, the farmer may have difficulty measuring effluent produced by the paper mill. Even if he suspects that the mill has violated an agreement to reduce pollution, he may be unable to prove his suspicion in court. In other situations, the parties to a negotiation may fear that the legal system will fail to enforce the terms of a contract. That concern is particularly acute in some developing countries where the rule of law is not well established.

20.3 REMEDIES FOR EXTERNALITIES: THE PUBLIC SECTOR

When private negotiations fail to remedy the market failures associated with externalities, appropriate government policies can potentially improve economic efficiency. In this section, we describe various public policies that are designed to address externalities. We also discuss their advantages and disadvantages.

Policies That Support Markets

We learned in Section 20.2 that externalities arise because of missing markets. In some situations, governments can address those externalities through policies that help the private sector create the necessary markets. For example, the government can establish clear property rights, provide a legal framework that protects those rights, and enforce contracts. If necessary, the government can even create and operate a market.

Consider how the Canadian government has handled the externalities associated with the use of the electromagnetic spectrum, known informally as the airwaves. As mentioned in Application 1.3 (page 22), all wireless electronics, including cell phones, television, and radio, make use of the spectrum. If two radio stations in the same locality tried to use the same portion of the spectrum, their signals would interfere with each other, reducing the quality of the broadcast services. In other words, the stations would impose negative externalities on each other. Consequently, if everyone were free to use any or all portions of the spectrum, the airwaves would become inefficiently crowded. Indeed, during the early days of radio broadcasting, the use of the airwaves was chaotic, and interference between competing stations led to widespread dissatisfaction with the quality of radio reception.

To remedy the externalities associated with spectrum overuse, Parliament passed the Canadian Radio Broadcasting Act of 1932, which allocated spectrum through a restrictive licensing system, in effect providing broadcasters with narrowly limited property rights to portions of the spectrum. Broadcasters did not, however, have the ability to freely trade their spectrum rights as in a private market. Starting in the 1990s, public policy has increasingly relied on markets to allocate the spectrum. As discussed in Application 1.3, Industry Canada has created and operated markets (auctions) for allocating initial spectrum property rights. It has also granted companies greater freedom to trade those rights, thereby encouraging the growth of a private spectrum market. Thus, current economic policy addresses the potential externalities associated with spectrum use by creating and encouraging markets.

Often, market remedies for externalities are impractical. For example, it is difficult to imagine a functioning market in which each person who drives a car in Vancouver would separately buy the right to pollute the air breathed by every one of the city's residents. Partly for reasons of practicality, and partly for other reasons such as perceptions that market solutions would be inequitable, policy makers often turn to nonmarket remedies.

Quantity Controls

Sometimes the government attempts to remedy an externality by regulating the level of the activity that produces it. For example, in many jurisdictions, **emissions standards** govern the amount of pollution generated by vehicles, various types of equipment, power plants, and other industrial enterprises. An emissions standard is a legal limit on the amount of pollution that a person or company can produce when engaged in a particular activity.

To illustrate this regulatory approach, we'll consider an example involving aircraft noise abatement. Suppose an airline uses a passenger plane to make one flight per day. Unfortunately, the noise from takeoffs can be extremely unpleasant and potentially harmful to people living or working near the airport. (To keep the example simple, we'll focus on residents and ignore workers. We'll also assume that landings are relatively quiet and not a source of concern.) Noise abatement is technologically feasible, but costly. Left to its own devices, the airline has no incentive to reduce aircraft noise.

Figure 20.4 illustrates the marginal costs and benefits of noise abatement. We've assumed that with no abatement an airplane generates 150 decibels of sound on takeoff. Below 150 decibels, more noise means less abatement. Therefore, an increase in noise benefits the airline by reducing the cost of abatement. In fact, the airline's marginal benefit of noise equals the marginal cost of abatement (MCA). In the figure, the blue curve labelled $MB = MCA$ shows the airline's marginal benefit of noise (equivalently, its

> An **emissions standard** is a legal limit on the amount of pollution that a person or company can produce when engaged in a particular activity.

Figure 20.4

Achieving Aircraft Noise Abatement through a Noise Limit. The socially efficient level of aircraft noise is 80 decibels. At that level, the marginal benefit of noise (equivalently, the marginal cost of abatement) equals the marginal social cost of noise. To achieve the socially efficient outcome, the government could either impose a noise limit of 80 decibels or require noise reduction of at least 70 decibels.

marginal cost of abatement). The fact that the curve slopes downward indicates that, as the airline reduces noise (moving to the left in the figure), additional reductions become more costly. For example, the MCA rises from $1250 with no abatement (equivalently, at a noise level of 150 decibels), to $7500 per decibel with an abatement level of 50 decibels (equivalently, a noise level of 100 decibels), and to $13,250 per decibel at an abatement level of 100 decibels (equivalently, a noise level of 50 decibels). Because the airline's marginal benefit of noise is positive at all levels of abatement, it will not of its own accord reduce the level of noise below 150 decibels.

The red curve in Figure 20.4 shows the marginal social cost (MSC) of noise, which includes the economic value of the discomfort and adverse health effects experienced by residents.[18] The fact that the curve slopes upward indicates that the MSC of additional noise rises with the amount of noise exposure.

Notice that the two curves intersect at point A. The socially efficient level of noise is therefore 80 decibels. At that level, the marginal benefit of noise (equivalently, the marginal cost of abatement) equals the marginal social cost of noise. To achieve the socially efficient outcome, the government could either impose a noise limit of 80 decibels, or require noise reduction of at least 70 decibels. Because abatement is costly, the airline will abate just enough to comply with the regulatory requirement, shown as the vertical line through point A.

Of course, to set a socially efficient noise abatement standard, the government needs to have a great deal of information about the airline's costs of abatement and the social cost of noise, so that it can determine the location of point A. That is a demanding requirement. If the government sets the standard based on information supplied by private parties, the airline may have an incentive to exaggerate the cost of abatement (so that the noise standard will be higher), and local residents may have an incentive to exaggerate the cost of noise (so that the standard will be lower). Therefore, the government may have trouble learning the truth, leading it to set an inefficient standard and create a deadweight loss.

Policies That Correct Private Incentives

When externalities are present, inefficiencies arise because people fail to account for all the social costs and benefits of their actions. Some policies attempt to remedy externalities by forcing people to *internalize* external costs and benefits. They accomplish this objective by imposing taxes or fees, providing subsidies, or exposing decision makers to legal liability for the harms that result from their choices.

British economist Arthur Cecil Pigou (1877–1959) originated the idea that governments can correct externalities through taxes and subsidies.

Pigouvian taxation involves the use of taxes or fees to remedy negative externalities.

Taxes, Fees, and Subsidies   In the early 1900s, a famous economist named Arthur Cecil Pigou hit upon a simple but powerful idea: if an activity creates an external cost that the decision makers ignore, the government can induce them to act as if they bear *all* of the activity's social costs by imposing a tax (or fee) equal to the magnitude of the marginal external cost at the efficient outcome. In recognition of Pigou's contribution, the use of taxes (or fees) to remedy negative externalities is known as **Pigouvian taxation**.

Let's see how the government can use taxation to remedy the negative externality associated with aircraft noise. Figure 20.5 reproduces the marginal social cost and marginal cost of abatement curves from Figure 20.4. When the noise level is socially efficient (80 decibels), the marginal social cost of noise is $10,000 per decibel. All of those social

---

[18]We can place a monetary value on nonmonetary consequences using the concept of compensating variation, introduced in Section 6.2.

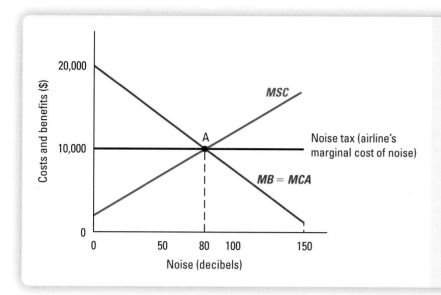

Figure 20.5

Achieving Aircraft Noise Abatement through a Noise Tax. The socially efficient level of aircraft noise is 80 decibels. To achieve that outcome, the government could impose a noise tax of $10,000 per decibel, equal to the MSC at 80 decibels. The airline would produce noise up to the point at which its marginal benefit of noise (the marginal cost of abatement) equals its marginal cost of noise (the tax).

costs are external. Therefore, to correct the externality through Pigouvian taxation, the government would tax aircraft noise at the rate of $10,000 per decibel. With that tax in place, the airline's marginal cost of noise would also be $10,000 per decibel (as indicated by the horizontal line running through point A). To maximize profits, the airline would generate noise up to the point at which its marginal cost of noise equals its marginal benefit, which occurs at 80 decibels. Because of the tax, the airline would internalize the marginal external cost of noise associated with the efficient level of abatement, weigh it against the marginal benefit of noise, and make a socially efficient decision.

To understand why Pigouvian taxation can promote efficiency, remember that every externality arises because the market for some good is missing. The ideal Pigouvian tax simply reproduces the price that the good in question would command in an efficient competitive equilibrium if its market were not missing. Since no private party charges that price, the government charges it instead. In our example, the right to generate noise would sell for $10,000 per decibel in a competitive equilibrium. Therefore, when there is no market for that right, $10,000 per decibel is the ideal Pigouvian tax rate.

An ideal noise tax and an ideal noise standard have different distributional implications: the government raises revenue from the polluter with the tax but not with the standard. However, they lead to the same noise level and are equally efficient. They are also similar in other respects. For example, we noted previously that the government would need to have a great deal of information about the airline's cost of abatement and the social cost of noise to set an efficient noise standard. It would require the same information to set a socially efficient Pigouvian noise tax. Later in this section, we will explain why the efficiency effects of these two approaches may differ in practice, and we'll discuss the advantages and disadvantages of each.

Pigou's insight is also applicable to activities that create positive externalities. In those cases, the object is to induce decision makers to act as if they receive all of the activity's social benefits by providing a subsidy equal to the magnitude of the marginal external benefit. The use of subsidies to remedy positive externalities is known as **Pigouvian subsidization**. We'll discuss an example of this approach in Application 20.5.

Pigouvian subsidization involves the use of subsidies to remedy positive externalities.

WORKED-OUT PROBLEM   20.2

The Problem   Your neighbour likes to play loud music—the louder the better. Because you like to study, her music imposes a cost on you. Let's use D to stand for the volume of her music in decibels, B for her benefit, and C for your costs (where we've measured benefits and costs in dollars). For any given volume D, your neighbour's benefit is

$$B = 0.53D - 0.002D^2$$

which means her marginal benefit is

$$MB = 0.53 - 0.004D$$

Your cost is

$$C = A \times D + 0.001D^2$$

which means your marginal cost is

$$MC = A + 0.002D$$

where A is a constant. Assuming that $A = 0.05$, what is the efficient noise limit? What is the efficient Pigouvian tax?

The Solution   Setting marginal benefit equal to marginal cost, we see that

$$0.53 - 0.004D = 0.05 + 0.002D$$

Solving for D, we obtain $D = 80$. Therefore, the efficient noise limit is 80 decibels. At that socially efficient level, your marginal cost is $\$[0.05 + (0.002 \times 80)] = \$0.21$. Therefore, the efficient Pigouvian tax is $\$0.21$ per decibel. With that tax, your neighbour will choose 80 decibels, paying $\$16.80$ in total.

IN-TEXT EXERCISE 20.2   **Repeat worked-out problem 20.2 assuming that $A = 0.11$. Repeat the problem again assuming that $A = 0.17$. Based on your answers, explain how the socially efficient noise limit and Pigouvian tax change as the cost of any given level of noise to you becomes larger.**

Liability rules   The government can also attempt to remedy negative externalities by establishing liability rules. Under a **liability rule**, a party who takes an action that harms others must compensate the affected parties for some or all of their losses. In an ideal legal system, liability rules induce decision makers to internalize all external costs, and therefore lead to efficient choices.

> A **liability rule** is a legal principle requiring a party who takes an action that harms others to compensate the affected parties for some or all of their losses.

Let's see how a liability rule can remedy the negative externality associated with aircraft noise. Figure 20.6 reproduces the marginal social cost and marginal cost of abatement curves from Figure 20.4. Let's assume that the government makes the airline liable for all external costs. In that case, the airline's marginal cost (MC) curve will coincide with the marginal social cost (MSC) curve. To maximize profits, the airline would generate noise up to the point at which its marginal cost of noise equals its marginal benefit, which occurs at 80 decibels. Because of the liability rule, the airline internalizes the

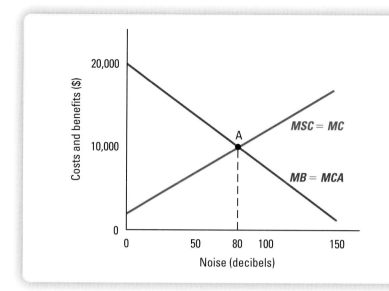

Figure 20.6

Achieving Aircraft Noise Abatement through a Liability Rule. The socially efficient level of aircraft noise is 80 decibels. To achieve that outcome, the government could make the airline liable for all harm caused to residents. In that case, the airline's marginal cost of noise would be equal to the marginal social cost of noise. The airline would produce noise up to the point at which its marginal benefit of noise (the marginal cost of abatement) equals its marginal cost.

marginal external cost of noise at *all* levels of abatement, weighs it against the marginal benefit of noise, and makes a socially efficient decision.

In this example, the government needs less information to remedy the externality through a liability rule than through an emissions standard or a Pigouvian tax. To implement the rule, courts need to be able to calculate the actual losses incurred by the residents after the fact. They do not need to determine the entire marginal social cost curve (which also indicates what losses would have been with other levels of abatement), measure the marginal cost of abatement, or identify the social efficient choice. The objective of the policy is simply to require full compensation for the actual losses incurred by the residents, so that the airline internalizes all external costs when making their choices. However, as we'll see next, the implementation of efficient liability rules isn't always as simple as in this example.

Liability rules also raise other difficulties. To recover damages, injured parties must file lawsuits. Real litigation is costly and time-consuming, and there is no guarantee that a court will reach the desired decision. Some injured parties may decide against legal action, and others may fail to collect full compensation for their losses. Uninjured parties may also file suit in the hope of obtaining a large award or settlement. As a result, decision makers may not fully or properly internalize all external costs, and their decisions may remain inefficient.

Pitfalls for Policies That Correct Private Incentives   The purpose of both a liability rule and a Pigouvian tax is to force a decision maker to internalize any harm caused to others. But as Coase and others have argued, harms often have multiple causes. In such cases, well-intentioned efforts to correct private incentives can go awry, leading to high levels of inefficiency.

Consider the case of aircraft noise. So far, we have implicitly assumed that residents have no choice other than to live near the airport. In fact, they do have choices. The harm they suffer is caused both by the airline's decision to fly a noisy airplane and by their own decisions to live nearby. If the costs of locating elsewhere are high and the costs of noise abatement are low, then it will be efficient for them to remain where they are. In that case,

Figure 20.7

A Pitfall for a Liability Rule or a Pigouvian Tax. Residents will choose to live near the airport if aircraft noise is less than 90 decibels, and far from the airport if aircraft noise exceeds 90 decibels. A liability rule that makes the airline responsible for all social costs regardless of the residents' location decisions will lead the residents to locate near the airport, even though it is efficient for them to move further away. A noise tax of $10,000 leads to the same problem, even though it forces the airline to internalize the residents' marginal costs, given where they choose to live.

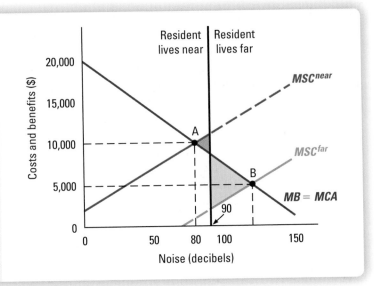

holding the airline responsible for all external costs leads to the efficient level of abatement. However, if the costs of locating elsewhere are low and the costs of noise abatement are high, then it will be efficient for the residents to move. In that case, a policy that induces the airline to abate noise, thereby keeping the residents nearby, may be highly inefficient.

To see how improperly designed liability rules and Pigouvian taxes can produce inefficient decisions, look at Figure 20.7. We have reproduced the blue marginal cost of abatement curve (labelled $MB = MCA$) from the previous figures, as well as the red marginal social cost curve (labelled MSC^{near}), which reflects the external costs that people incur when they live near the airport. We have also added a second marginal social cost curve (shown in light red and labelled MSC^{far}), which reflects the external costs that people incur when they live farther from the airport. For the purpose of this example we will assume that, without financial compensation for aircraft noise, people will live near the airport if the noise level is less than 90 decibels, and far from the airport if it exceeds 90 decibels. Accounting for the fact that people will move away from the airport when aircraft noise hits that threshold, the true marginal social cost of noise corresponds to the solid portions of MSC^{near} and MSC^{far}.

Notice that there are two points, A and B, at which the marginal benefit of additional noise to the airline equals the marginal social cost of additional noise. Which of these points is more efficient? The red triangle represents the net social cost of increasing the noise level from 80 to 90 decibels assuming that people live near the airport. At 90 decibels, people are indifferent between remaining near the airport or moving away (accounting for any moving costs); they can move with no impact on social welfare. The green triangle represents the net social gain obtained by increasing the noise level from 90 decibels to 120 decibels after people move further from the airport. Since the green triangle is significantly larger than the red triangle, increasing the noise level from 80 to 120 decibels produces a net social gain, even accounting for the fact that people will relocate. Therefore, point B is socially efficient while point A is not.

Now suppose the government adopts a liability rule stating that the airline must compensate residents for all harms resulting from aircraft noise. With no noise, the residents prefer to live near the airport. Regardless of where residents choose to live, full compensation makes them just as well off as with no noise. Therefore, even if there is noise, residents who anticipate receiving full compensation will choose to live near the airport. Knowing that it is liable for harm to residents who have chosen to live nearby, the airline will select point A and generate 80 decibels of noise. As we know, that outcome is inefficient.

The liability rule considered in the last paragraph is inefficient because it forces the airline to internalize all the costs of noise in all circumstances, even though residents' decisions contribute to those costs. Since the socially efficient outcome involves both avoidance on the part of residents and 30 decibels of abatement on the part of the airline, both parties should bear some portion of the social costs under some circumstances. Here, the best liability rule would award damages as if people had selected their places of residence efficiently, regardless of where they actually chose to live. In other words, it would require the airline to compensate residents based on the marginal cost curve labelled MSC^{far} even if residents chose to live near the airport. Under that rule, the airline would choose to generate 120 decibels of noise. Because the compensation residents receive would not depend on their locational choices, with that level of noise they would choose to live farther from the airport, just as social efficiency requires. Unfortunately, the ideal rule is difficult to implement because it requires courts to determine each resident's efficient location decision, as well as the harm the residents would have suffered had they made the efficient choice.

Pigouvian taxation potentially encounters similar pitfalls. Suppose that the residents chose to live near the airport before the airline's arrival. Upon learning that the airline has decided to offer flights, the government may be tempted to create a Pigouvian tax based on the external costs that the existing residents would incur. That policy would lead to point A: the airline would generate 80 decibels of noise, the residents would stay where they are, and the airline would pay a fee equal to the marginal social cost of noise to nearby residents, $10,000 per decibel. In contrast, the ideal Pigouvian tax would recognize that it is efficient for existing residents to move. The airline would generate 120 decibels of noise, paying a fee equal to the marginal social cost of noise to distant residents, $5000 per decibel.

Application 20.4

Pigouvian Taxation, Liability Rules, and the Accident Externality from Driving

When people choose to drive cars, they increase the risk that others will be involved in accidents. If they ignore those external costs, they will drive excessively from the perspective of social efficiency. In principle, liability rules could force drivers to internalize those costs. In practice, however, actual liability rules do not adequately remedy the accident externality from driving.

To understand the problem with existing liability rules, consider the following simple example. Two individuals must decide separately whether to go for a drive on a particular day. If both decide to drive, there is a chance they will collide, causing $1000 of damage to each car. Because the accident cannot happen unless both drivers are on the road, each individual's decision to drive literally causes *all* of the damages associated with the accident. The ideal liability rule would make each driver responsible for his marginal contribution to total damages, which is $2000. In other words, both drivers would be required to pay for the entire accident.

Real liability rules differ from jurisdiction to jurisdiction, but all of them have one important feature in common: they divide the responsibility for total damages between the parties. In our example, they would require the drivers to pay $2000 in total, rather than $2000 each. Therefore, with existing liability rules, either or both drivers will fail to internalize all the external costs of driving.

How large is the negative externality that remains after accounting for the external costs that drivers internalize because of liability rules? According to a study by economists Aaron Edlin and Pinar Karaca-Mandic, the answer depends on the volume of traffic.[19] Edlin and Karaca-Mandic used state-level data from 1987 through 1995 to estimate the effect of changes in traffic density on the amount of automobile accident costs for which the typical driver is responsible.[20] The study found that the addition of one driver increases the total accident costs for which all *other* drivers are responsible by $1725 to $3239 per year in California, a state with high traffic density, but by only $10 in North Dakota, a state with very low traffic density. The externalities in high-density states are so large that an efficient Pigouvian tax would have raised over $220 billion per year across the U.S. in 1996, and over $66 billion in California alone. To put these figures into perspective, all states combined raised only $163 billion from personal and corporate income taxes in 1996, and California's total tax revenues came to only $57 billion.

Controlling Quantities versus Correcting Incentives

In choosing between a policy that controls quantities, such as an emissions standard, and one that corrects private incentives, such as a Pigouvian tax or liability rule, many factors can come into play. In this section, we examine three important considerations: the consequences of errors in setting policies, the prospects for minimizing the costs of abatement, and the practical flexibility of competing approaches.

The Consequences of Policy Errors   Earlier in this chapter, we observed that an ideal noise standard and an ideal noise tax are equally efficient. However, neither the government's information nor its choices are ideal in practice. Errors in setting a noise tax and a noise standard may have different implications for efficiency, and this consideration can provide a reason for preferring one approach over the other.

Let's suppose the government can calculate the appropriate noise standard and noise tax with equal accuracy. Which policy is better? The answer depends on the slopes of the *MSC* and *MCA* curves. Figure 20.8(a) illustrates a case in which a noise standard is better than a noise tax. To see why, let's evaluate the deadweight loss resulting from a 20 percent error in setting the standard and compare it to the deadweight loss resulting from a 20 percent error in setting the tax. According to the figure, the socially efficient noise level is 80 decibels, and the efficient tax is $10,000 per decibel. If the government sets the standard at 96 decibels (a 20 percent error), the resulting deadweight loss will equal the area of the yellow triangle. If the government sets the tax at $8000 per decibel (also a 20 percent error), the resulting deadweight loss will equal the area of the yellow triangle plus the red area. Therefore, errors of comparable magnitude lead to a smaller loss with a noise standard than with a noise tax.

Figure 20.8(b) illustrates a case in which a noise tax is better than a noise standard. The socially efficient policies are the same as in Figure 20.8(a). The red triangle represents the deadweight loss of a 20 percent error in setting the noise tax ($8000 instead of

---

[19]Aaron S. Edlin and Pinar Karaca-Mandic, "The Accident Externality from Driving," *Journal of Political Economy* 114, October 2006, pp. 931–955.

[20]Because insurers pay most of the accident costs for which their policy holders are responsible, Edlin and Karaca-Mandic actually studied the effects of traffic density on insurer costs and insurance premiums.

Figure 20.8

The Consequences of Policy Errors for a Noise Standard and a Noise Tax. In figure (a), a 20 percent error in setting a noise standard leads to a deadweight loss equal to the area of the yellow triangle. A 20 percent error in setting a noise tax leads to a deadweight loss equal to the yellow triangle plus the red area. A noise standard is therefore more efficient. In figure (b) a 20 percent error in setting a noise tax leads to a deadweight loss equal to the area of the red triangle. A 20 percent error in setting a noise standard leads to a deadweight loss equal to the red triangle plus the yellow area. A noise tax is therefore more efficient.

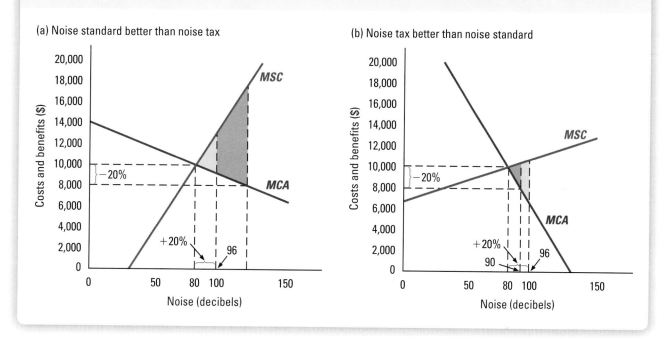

(a) Noise standard better than noise tax

(b) Noise tax better than noise standard

$10,000), while the red triangle plus the yellow area represents the deadweight loss of a 20 percent error in setting a noise standard (96 instead of 80 decibels). Therefore, errors of comparable magnitude lead to a smaller loss with a noise tax than with a noise standard. A comparison of Figures 20.8(a) and (b) reveals that a noise standard is superior when the *MCA* curve is relatively flat and the *MSC* curve is relatively steep. A noise tax is superior when the *MCA* curve is relatively steep and the *MSC* curve is relatively flat.

Minimizing the Total Cost of Abatement Sometimes, the external costs of pollution depend on the *total* emissions of many parties. In such cases, an emission tax guarantees that polluters will collectively achieve any given reduction in the overall level of pollution at the lowest possible cost, while an emissions standard does not. To understand why, look at Figure 20.9. For simplicity, we'll assume that two power-generating firms are responsible for all sulfur dioxide (SO_2) emissions. While their emissions are equally harmful, their abatement costs differ. As shown in the figure, at any given level of emissions, firm 1's marginal cost of abatement is lower than firm 2's.

With a tax on SO_2 emissions, each firm will pollute up to the point at which the marginal cost of abatement equals the tax rate. While the firms will produce different amounts of pollution, they will share the same marginal cost of abatement. Consequently, any change in their emissions that leaves total pollution unchanged will increase overall abatement

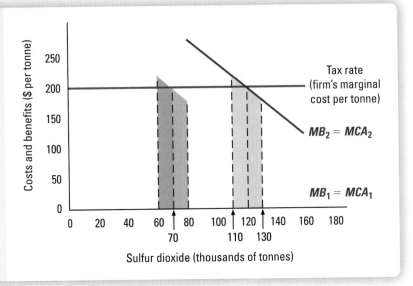

Figure 20.9

An Emissions Tax Minimizes the Cost of Achieving a Fixed Level of Emissions.
With a \$200-per-tonne tax on SO_2 emissions, each firm will pollute up to the point at which the marginal cost of abatement equals \$200. While the firms will produce different amounts of pollution, they will share the same marginal cost of abatement. Consequently, any change in their emissions that leaves total pollution unchanged will increase overall abatement costs.

costs. Suppose, for example, that the tax is \$200 per tonne. As shown in Figure 20.9, firm 1 will generate 70 tonnes and firm 2 will generate 120 tonnes. Consider the effect of shifting 10,000 tonnes of SO_2 production from firm 1 to firm 2. The red-shaded area represents the increased abatement cost for firm 1, and the green-shaded area represents the reduced abatement cost for firm 2. Since the red-shaded area is larger than the green-shaded area, overall abatement costs rise. Alternatively, consider the effect of shifting 10,000 tonnes of SO_2 production from firm 2 to firm 1. The yellow-shaded area represents the increased abatement cost for firm 2, and the blue-shaded area represents the reduced abatement cost for firm 1. Since the yellow-shaded area is larger than the blue-shaded area, overall abatement costs rise in this case as well. (Worked-out problem 8.5 on page 279 made a similar point.)

The government could achieve the same outcome by setting an emissions standard of 70,000 tonnes for firm 1 and a standard of 120,000 tonnes for firm 2. However, it may not know enough about the firms' abatement costs to determine the cost-minimizing emissions standards. Any other choice of standards that permits the firms to emit a total of 190,000 tonnes of SO_2 would necessarily lead to higher overall abatement costs. In particular, setting the same emissions standard for both firms (95,000 tonnes) would be extremely inefficient. With equal emissions, firm 2's marginal costs of abatement would be much higher than firm 1's, so shifting emissions from firm 2 to firm 1 would reduce costs.

Flexibility   The choice between a quantity standard and a tax can also depend on the flexibility of each policy. As a practical matter, a quantity standard sometimes offers greater flexibility than a tax. The government can ban smoking in the workplace while permitting it in bars, but would have great difficulty taxing cigarettes differently according to where smokers consume them. Similarly, a tax sometimes offers greater practical flexibility than a quantity standard. The government would have difficulty monitoring compliance with a limit on the number of cigarettes that a person can smoke (aside from a limit of zero), but can easily vary the tax rate

"If you wanted the no-smoking section, you should have said so."

on cigarettes. Since quantity standards can be more flexible in some dimensions while taxes can be more flexible in others, government policy sometimes involves a mix of standards and taxes. Many jurisdictions tax cigarettes and forbid smoking in some settings (a quantity standard). Application 20.5 discusses another context in which governments typically use a mixed approach.

Application 20.5

Public Policy toward Educational Attainment

As we explained in Section 20.1, education generates important positive externalities. Consequently, the governments of all developed countries regularly intervene in decisions regarding educational attainment. Canada's Constitution Act of 1867 gives provinces the exclusive right to develop educational institutions and legislation. In Canada, school attendance is compulsory up to an age set by the provincial government. Depending on the jurisdiction, the age to which education is mandatory varies from 15 to 18. Public primary and secondary education is provided free of charge; the associated cost to taxpayers totalled $48 billion during 2009. Various levels of government also subsidize higher education by supporting public universities and colleges, sponsoring low-cost student loans, providing educational grants and scholarships, and offering tax credits

for educational expenses. In total, taxpayers paid $21 billion to support higher education during 2008.

Compulsory schooling laws are quantity restrictions. In contrast, the various subsidies listed above provide private incentives for educational attainment. Why are different approaches used in different circumstances? Let's begin with higher education. Figure 20.10 reproduces the various curves from Figure 20.2. Recall that, in the competitive equilibrium, 750,000 students would pay $8000 per year in tuition. However, it is socially efficient for one million students to attend university. As shown in the figure, the government can achieve the socially efficient outcome through a Pigouvian tuition subsidy of $4000 per year. We determined the size of this subsidy by examining the marginal external benefit of an additional student when one million students

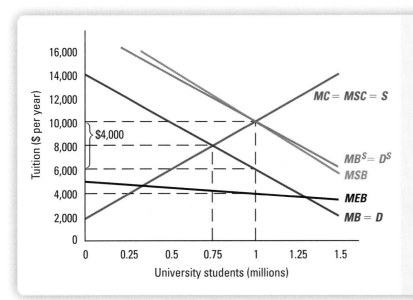

Figure 20.10

A Pigouvian Subsidy for University Tuition. With the socially efficient number of university students, the marginal external benefit of an additional student is $4000 per year. With a $4000 per year Pigouvian tuition subsidy, the marginal benefit curve for university students shifts upward from *MB* to *MB^S*. Because marginal benefit curves are also demand curves, in the new equilibrium one million students pay $10,000 per year in tuition before receiving their $4000 subsidies.

attend university. The subsidy increases the marginal benefit of attending university by $4000 per year. The new marginal benefit curve, labelled MB^S in the figure, is exactly $4000 higher than the original marginal benefit curve, labelled MB. Since the marginal benefit curves are also demand curves, in the new equilibrium one million students pay $10,000 per year in tuition before receiving their $4000 subsidies.

In principle, the government could also achieve the socially efficient outcome by requiring one million students to attend university. In practice that solution is fraught with difficulties because government officials would need to identify the one million students for whom university education is efficient. Because those officials lack detailed information on each individual's abilities, preferences, and circumstances, they are likely to make many errors when deciding who will and will not attend university.

In contrast, if it is socially efficient for *all* students to receive some minimum amount of basic education, then compulsory schooling is an attractive alternative. To understand why, look at Figure 20.11. The horizontal axis measures years of basic education for a particular individual while the vertical axis measures economic costs and benefits. The demand curve shown in the figure corresponds to the individual (or family) who attaches the least value to education. Once again, the marginal social benefit curve (labelled MSB) is the vertical sum of the demand curve (labelled $D = MB$) and the marginal external benefit curve (labelled MEB). We've assumed for simplicity that the marginal cost of additional schooling is constant (that is why the curve labelled $MC = MSC = S$ is flat). The competitive market solution corresponds to the intersection of the demand curve and the marginal cost curve; the student receives only three years of schooling. Even with free education, the student would attend school for only seven years. Because the marginal external benefit of education exceeds the marginal social cost at seven years, the socially efficient choice, 10 years, is even larger. And because we've assumed that other individuals (families) attach even greater value to education than the one depicted in the figure, the socially efficient choice exceeds 10 years for them. As shown in the figure, the Pigouvian subsidy required to achieve the socially efficient outcome is $14,000 per year, which exceeds the cost of education, $8000 per year. In effect, the government would have to pay families steep "bribes" to keep children in school. Because at least 10 years of education is socially efficient for virtually everyone, it is both simpler and less expensive to make it compulsory and provide it free of charge.

Hybrid Market Approaches

As we have seen, an emission tax guarantees that polluters will collectively achieve any given reduction in the overall level of pollution at the lowest possible cost, while an emissions standard does not. If the government favours emissions standards over taxes for other reasons—for example, if it is uncertain about the tax rate required to bring the overall level of emissions below some desired limit—it needn't give up on minimizing the total cost of abatement. Instead, it can issue **tradable emissions permits**. A permit of this type entitles a firm to generate a specified amount of a given pollutant. It is also transferrable; one firm can sell a permit to another. Each firm is forbidden to generate more pollution than the total amount to which it is entitled based on the permits that it either retains or purchases from other firms. Firms that violate the restriction face severe financial penalties.

A **tradable emissions permit** entitles a firm to generate a specified amount of a given pollutant. It is also transferrable; one firm can sell it to another.

Under a system of tradable emissions permits, total emissions are limited by the number of permits the government chooses to issue. Therefore, just like fixed emissions standards, tradable permits enable the government to reduce the level of pollution to any desired target. However, just like an emissions tax, tradable permits can also achieve any given reduction in total emissions at the lowest possible abatement cost.

To understand why tradable permits promote least-cost abatement, let's return to our example, in which two power-generating firms are responsible for all SO_2 emissions. Figure 20.12 reproduces the marginal cost of abatement curves from Figure 20.9. Suppose

Figure 20.11

An Economic Justification for Compulsory Schooling. The demand curve shown below corresponds to the individual (or family) who attaches the least value to education. In a competitive market, the student would receive only three years of schooling. Even with free education, the student would attend school for only seven years. As shown in the figure, the Pigouvian subsidy required to achieve the socially efficient outcome, 10 years, would exceed the cost of education ($14,000 versus $8000). It is therefore both simpler and less expensive to make it compulsory and provide it free of charge.

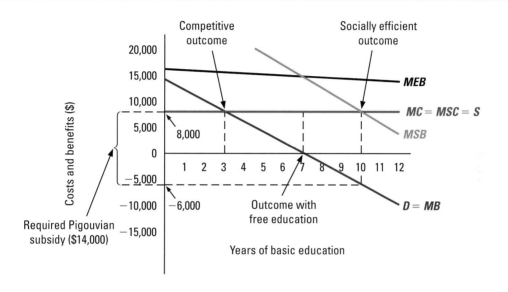

Figure 20.12

Tradable Permits Promote Low-Cost Abatement. Suppose the government issues 190 one-thousand-tonne SO_2 emissions permits and splits them equally between firm 1 and firm 2, giving each 95 permits. If each firm retains its permits, abatement costs will be inefficiently high. However, there are potential gains from trade. The green-shaded area reflects firm 2's maximum willingness to pay for 25 permits. The red-shaded area reflects the minimum amount firm 1 would be willing to accept for 25 permits. Since firm 2's maximum willingness to pay is greater than the minimum amount firm 1 is willing to accept, the firms should be able to negotiate a trade.

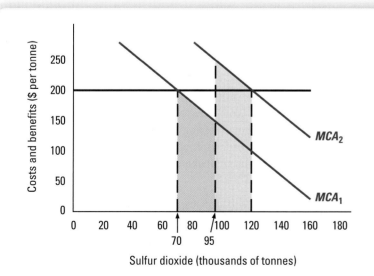

the government issues 190 one-thousand-tonne SO_2 emissions permits and splits them equally between firm 1 and firm 2, giving each 95 permits. If each firm retains its permits, abatement costs will be inefficiently high. However, as is always the case, inefficiency implies the existence of gains from trade. To achieve the same level of total abatement at minimum cost, firm 1 would transfer 25 permits to firm 2. The green-shaded area reflects the reduction in firm 2's abatement costs: that is, firm 2's maximum willingness to pay for the 25 permits. The red-shaded area reflects the increase in firm 1's abatement costs: that is, the minimum amount firm 1 would be willing to accept for the 25 permits. Since firm 2's maximum willingness to pay is greater than the minimum amount firm 1 is willing to accept, the firms should be able to negotiate a trade.

If there are many polluting firms, and if the government avoids issuing too many permits either to a single firm or to a small group of firms, it is likely that a competitive market for emissions permits will emerge. Each firm will act as a price taker and generate pollution up to the point at which the marginal cost of abatement equals the market price of a permit. Just as with an emissions tax, every firm's marginal cost of abatement will be the same, which implies that the firms will collectively achieve the overall emissions target at the lowest possible abatement cost. Firms with low marginal abatement costs, like firm 1 in our example, will sell some of their permits and generate relatively little pollution. In contrast, firms with high marginal abatement costs, like firm 2 in our example, will buy additional permits and generate relatively high levels of pollution.

In short, a system of tradable permits harnesses the power of the market to achieve one aspect of economic efficiency: abatement cost minimization. It does not, however, rely on markets to determine the overall level of pollution. Rather, it is a hybrid approach. The genius of the approach is the recognition that, while it may not be practical to remedy an externality completely by bringing a missing market into existence, it is possible to distinguish between different components of the market failure, and to remedy one of them by fostering a viable market. To learn more about the use of tradable emissions permits in practice, reread Application 14.2 (page 517). As we explained in that application, the market for tradable SO_2 permits has worked remarkably well, lowering the cost of achieving SO_2 abatement targets by U.S.$225–375 million per year.

WORKED-OUT PROBLEM   20.3

The Problem   Suppose that the government wants to reduce carbon dioxide emissions generated by two types of firms, classed according to their costs of CO_2 abatement, by issuing marketable permits. Assume that there is a large equal number of each type of polluting firm so that each firm acts as a price taker; a competitive market for CO_2 permits will emerge. Marginal abatement costs for the high-cost firms are given by

$$MAC_H = 100 - E_H$$

while marginal abatement costs for the low-cost firms are given by

$$MAC_L = 50 - (1/2)E_L$$

In the absence of any permits being issued each type of firm will choose to emit 100 tonnes of carbon dioxide where marginal abatement costs are zero. Suppose the government gives marketable emission permits for 70 tonnes of CO_2 to each firm which is a reduction of 30 percent from current levels. Determine the market price of a permit and the emission levels of each type of firm.

The Solution   To determine the market price and the emission levels of each type of firm we use two conditions. The first is that the sum of emissions by the two firm types total 140.

$$E_H + E_L = 140$$

The second condition is that in a competitive market the marginal abatement costs for each firm equal the market price of a permit so that marginal abatement costs for each firm type are equal.

$$MAC_H = 100 - E_H = 50 - (1/2)E_L = MAC_L$$

Together the two conditions give the result that the high-cost firm emits 80 tonnes of CO_2 and the low-cost firm emits 60 tonnes of CO_2. Marginal abatement costs and the permit price are $20. Total abatement costs are given by the area under the marginal abatement cost curve for each firm type and are $200 for the high-cost firm and $400 for the low-cost firm. The low cost firm sells 10 permits to the high-cost firm for $200 in total. It is interesting to note that a Pigouvian tax of $20 would achieve the same emission reduction as giving 30 marketable permits to each firm.

   If the government required a 30 percent emission reduction by each firm but did not allow them to be traded each firm would emit 70 tonnes of CO_2. The high-cost firm would incur abatement costs of $450 and the low-cost firm would incur abatement costs of $225 for a total cost of $675. Marketable permits achieve the same reduction of CO_2 for a total cost of $600.

IN-TEXT EXERCISE 20.3   **Suppose that the situation described in worked-out problem 20.3 continues to hold and let the marginal social costs from emissions be $MSC = (1/2)[E_H + E_L]$ given all firms of each type have the same emissions. Show that the socially efficient emission level is 20 for the low-cost firm and 60 for the high-cost firm. Determine the number of marketable permits that must be given to each firm to reach the socially desirable level of emissions.**

20.4 COMMON PROPERTY RESOURCES

Sometimes more than one person is free to use the same resource without payment. Familiar examples of these **common property resources** include lakes, rivers, oceans, beaches, parks, air, and populations of wild animals that are valued for food or other purposes. In many cases, each person's use of a common property resource reduces its value to others, thereby creating a negative externality. Therefore, people tend to over use such resources. The externality manifests itself in a variety of ways. Public recreational areas become unpleasantly crowded, species of fish and wildlife are caught or hunted to the brink of extinction, and waterways grow polluted. Canadian history is replete with examples of overused common property resources. The devastation of the Atlantic cod fishery and the west coast salmon fishery in recent years, and the dumping of sewage in the Great

A **common property resource** is a resource that more than one person is free to use without payment.

Figure 20.13

Common Property Resources and Overfishing. In the competitive equilibrium, $Q^{equilib}$ kilograms of fish are caught and consumed. Unfortunately, the marginal social cost of fishing exceeds the marginal private cost. Each fisher fails to account for the fact that his decision to catch fish reduces the fish population, thereby raising the cost of fishing for future fishers. The socially efficient level of fish consumption, $Q^{efficient}$, equates the marginal social cost of fishing with the marginal social benefit; it corresponds to the intersection of the *MSC* and market demand curves. Because fishing generates a negative externality, the competitive equilibrium level of fishing is socially excessive.

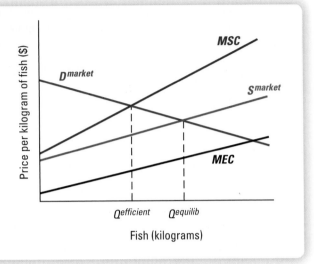

Lakes until the 1970s are just a few examples. In this section, we'll apply what we've learned about negative externalities to obtain a better understanding of common property resources.

Let's assume that a large lake is the only source of fresh fish for nearby towns. Because access to the lake is unrestricted, anyone can become a fisher free of charge. The market supply of fish, shown in Figure 20.13 as a red line labelled S^{market}, reflects the marginal private cost of fishing. Assuming that fishing is competitive, fishers will catch fish up to the point at which the market supply curve intersects the blue market demand curve, labelled D^{market} in Figure 20.13. In the competitive equilibrium, $Q^{equilib}$ kilograms of fish are caught and consumed. Because the height of the demand curve indicates consumers' marginal benefit of fish, the marginal private cost of catching fish equals that marginal benefit at $Q^{equilib}$.

Unfortunately, the marginal social cost of fishing exceeds the marginal private cost. Each fisher fails to account for the fact that the decision to catch fish reduces the fish population, thereby raising the cost of fishing for future fishers. In Figure 20.13, the black curve labelled *MEC* shows those future marginal external costs. The brown curve labelled *MSC* shows the marginal social costs; it is the vertical sum of the market supply curve (which measures marginal private costs) and the *MEC* curve. The socially efficient level of fish consumption, $Q^{efficient}$, equates the marginal social cost of fishing with the marginal social benefit; it corresponds to the intersection of the *MSC* and market demand curves. Because fishing generates a negative externality, $Q^{efficient}$ is less than $Q^{equilib}$. In other words, the competitive level of fishing is socially excessive.

The remedies for the market failures associated with common property resources are the same as for negative externalities. The local authority can create markets by selling the lake to a private owner. The owner would have an incentive to restrict access to the lake and charge fishers fees that reflect the negative externality of fishing. However, if the demand curve for the lake's fish is downward sloping (as it is in our example), there is a danger that the owner will exercise market power, possibly creating even greater inefficiency. Alternatively, the local authority can impose quantity restrictions. It can control the number of fishers by requiring them to be licensed, and it can limit the number of fish taken by an individual on any given day. It can also attempt to correct private incentives by charging licensing fees, or by imposing a sales tax on fish that are caught locally.

Political scientist Elinor Ostrom has challenged the notion that common property requires regulation or market-based solutions. Her research indicates that communities are frequently able to develop decision-making mechanisms for the management of the commons and formulate rules to minimize conflicts between users. In 2009 she became the first woman to be awarded the Nobel Memorial Prize in Economics for her research on the development of institutions to manage common property.

Political scientist Elinor Ostrom was awarded the 2009 Nobel Memorial Prize in Economic Sciences for her work in demonstrating that common property can be successfully managed by user groups.

> **IN-TEXT EXERCISE 20.4** **Suppose the market demand and supply for fish are given by $Q^d = 120 - 2P$ and $Q^S = 4P$, respectively, where quantity is measured in kilograms. If marginal external costs (MEC) are given by $MEC = (3/4)Q$, determine the competitive equilibrium and the socially efficient level of catch. Calculate the Pigouvian tax per kilogram of fish caught that the local authority would need to impose to correct private incentives to overfish.**

Application 20.6

Traffic Jams and Congestion Fees

Historically, most roads and highways have been treated as common property resources. Each individual's decision to drive imposes negative externalities on other drivers. As we discussed in Application 20.4, one type of externality results from the effect that each additional driver has on the likelihood of accidents. A second type of externality results from congestion. As traffic density increases, all drivers must slow down. At first, vehicle throughput—the number of cars and trucks traveling a short distance during a fixed period of time—continues to rise despite the slower speeds. However, severe congestion during rush hours can actually reduce vehicle throughput; the negative externality becomes so severe that the total amount of services a highway delivers (measured in vehicle miles per hour) declines.

When drivers have free access to roads and highways, they lack incentives to consider the costs they impose on others by contributing to congestion. Roadways are therefore overused and congestion is socially excessive. A 2007 study commissioned by Transport Canada estimated the cost of congestion in nine major metropolitan areas of Canada at

$3.7 billion.[21] Approximately 90 percent of the costs incurred by congestion represent the value of lost time; the remaining 10 percent of the costs can be attributed to the value of wasted fuel plus damage from associated pollutants. The study only considered costs of recurrent congestion and did

---

[21] *The Cost of Urban Congestion in Canada*, Transport Canada Environmental Affairs, March 2006 (revised July 2007).

not attempt to measure costs of non-recurrent congestion due to accidents, weather, or construction.

If people took the external costs of driving into account, they might relieve congestion by avoiding unnecessary rush-hour driving, joining car pools, using public transportation, or choosing alternative routes. To correct drivers' private incentives, the government can impose tolls, a practice known as *congestion pricing*. Efficient congestion pricing requires tolls that vary with the size of the external cost of driving, which in turn depends on the degree of congestion. Most road, highway, and bridge tolls do not vary; historically, their purpose was to generate revenue, often to cover the costs of construction and maintenance. However, the use of variable tolls to address congestion has become increasingly common. Several major cities, including London, Singapore, and Stockholm combat congestion by charging fees to drive within high-density zones during peak commute hours. In the United States, local traffic authorities have implemented variable tolls for special lanes on several major highways,

including I-15 in San Diego and SR 91 in Orange County, California. Congestion pricing has proven effective at reducing traffic density. Traffic has fallen by 15 percent in central London, 13 percent in Singapore, and 22 percent in central Stockholm. The variable toll lanes on Orange County's SR 91 achieve twice as much vehicle throughput as the free lanes.

Advances in technology have opened the door to efficient corrective tolling. Traditional tolling methods rely on toll booths, which require traffic to stop, adding to delays. Modern electronic tolling methods can collect tolls automatically while cars move at highway speeds. On Toronto's Highway 407 tolls are assessed electronically depending on the time of day. Newer technologies allow traffic authorities to vary tolls by lane, and even current traffic conditions. Tolls for the use of the high-occupancy toll (HOT) lanes on San Diego's I-15 can change as often as every six minutes in 25-cent increments. Drivers can decide whether to use those lanes based on the prevailing fees and their need for speed.[22]

20.5 PUBLIC GOODS

In some cases, governments provide certain goods and services directly to the public. For example, the United States government spent roughly half a trillion dollars on national defence in 2006. Virtually all economists agree that there are circumstances in which the public sector could, in principle, meet the needs of consumers more effectively than the private sector. (Whether public provision *actually* improves upon private provision is another matter; we will return to that issue at the end of this section.) For certain types of goods, including *public goods*, the case for public provision is particularly strong.

A **public good** has two defining characteristics: it is *nonrival* and *nonexcludable*. A good is **nonrival** if more than one person can consume it (or more than one firm can use it) at the same time without affecting its value to others. Once a nonrival good has been produced, the marginal cost of providing it to additional consumers or firms is zero. A good is **nonexcludable** if there is no way to prevent a person from consuming it (or in the case of a firm, from using it). National defence is a classic example of a public good. Because one citizen's enjoyment of national security does not reduce its value to others, defence is nonrival. And because there is no way to withhold the benefits of national security from any particular person, defence is nonexcludable. The construction of a lighthouse is also a public good, as is the control of an agricultural pest that threatens crops within a wide geographic area. (Can you explain why those activities are public goods?)

In contrast, the typical goods that people buy and sell through private markets involve rivalry. Once someone eats a sandwich or drinks a can of pop, neither the sandwich nor the pop has any remaining value to anyone else. Even the consumption of a reusable good,

A **public good** is a good that is nonrival and nonexcludable.

A good is **nonrival** if more than one person can consume it (or more than one firm can use it) at the same time without affecting its value to others.

A good is **nonexcludable** if there is no way to prevent a person from consuming it (or in the case of a firm, from using it).

---

[22]See *Congestion Pricing: A Primer*, U.S. Department of Transportation, Federal Highway Administration, Publication No. FHWA-HOP-07–074, December 2006.

like a car, involves rivalry. Two people can drive the same car to different locations at different times without affecting each other's benefits, but they can't do so at the *same* time. Rivalry implies that society must somehow allocate the good in question among individuals. That same imperative does not arise with a nonrival good; instead, society can allow everyone to benefit from it, without sacrificing anyone's enjoyment.

The typical goods that people buy and sell through private markets are also excludable. For example, there are many ways to prevent someone from consuming a particular sandwich or can of pop, or from driving a particular car. The threat of exclusion is what makes someone willing to pay for the sandwich, pop, or car. In contrast, a self-interested individual will never voluntarily pay for a nonexcludable good that someone else has provided. A good for which consumption involves perfect rivalry (in the sense that only one person can consume it) and that is completely excludable is called a **private good**.

> A **private good** is a good for which consumption involves perfect rivalry and that is completely excludable.

Some goods are nonrival but excludable. Those are not public goods. The digital code for a recording of a popular song is nonrival. When people load the code into an MP3 player and listen to the song, they have no effect on the code's value to others. However, because anti-copying technologies are available, digital code is excludable, at least to some degree. That is why a private market for digital music recordings is viable. Television and radio signals, which are accessible to all but can be scrambled for the purpose of establishing excludability, fall into the same category.

Other goods are nonexcludable but involve rivalry. Those also are not public goods. For example, because all countries have access to the ocean, each country's investments in the renewal of ocean fisheries have nonexcludable benefits. However, because aggressive fishing by the citizens of any country can diminish the value of fishery renewal to others, those benefits involve rivalry.

Strictly speaking, goods that are completely nonrival and absolutely nonexcludable are relatively rare. There are, however, many more goods for which rivalry is low and exclusion is difficult, costly, or inherently limited. Police protection falls into that category. Because an officer cannot look into several matters at the same time, there is some rivalry. And because the police can selectively answer calls, there is some ability to exclude. However, a general reduction in the crime rate creates nonrival, nonexcludable benefits. Though we will only examine *pure* public goods in this section, our analysis also applies to goods that are nearly public.

The Efficient Provision of Public Goods

Whether a good is public or private, social efficiency is achieved at a level of production for which its marginal social benefit equals its marginal cost of production.[23] What is the marginal social benefit of a public good? To determine the total social gain from a small increase in the level of the good (the marginal social benefit), we would add up the gains to all the affected individuals (their private marginal benefits). Therefore, at the socially efficient level of production, the *sum* of the individuals' marginal benefits must equal the marginal cost of production.

Let's consider an example. Three department stores, Holt Renfrew, Sears, and the Bay, are located on the same city block. All have problems with theft. They can reduce theft by hiring security guards to patrol the street. (They can also hire guards to patrol their premises, but that's not the focus of this example.) Street patrols would provide

---

[23]This statement assumes that some of the good should be produced.

Figure 20.14

Efficient and Inefficient Provision of a Public Good. The light blue curves show the marginal benefit of street security patrols for three department stores. The dark blue curve is the marginal social benefit for the three stores (the vertical sum of their individual marginal benefit curves). To find the socially efficient level of street patrols, we look for the intersection of the marginal social benefit and marginal cost curves. Here, social efficiency requires 270 person-hours of street patrols. If security is left entirely to the independent actions of the three stores, only 200 person-hours of patrols will be provided due to free-riding.

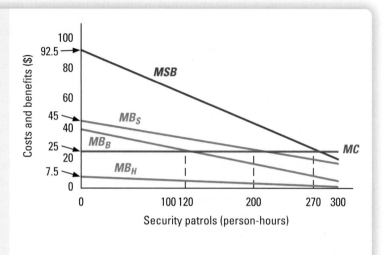

thieves with incentives to stay out of the area, thereby creating nonexcludable benefits for the stores. Because a reduction in theft at one store would not affect the value of a reduction in theft at another store, the benefits of the patrols are nonrival. From the perspective of the stores, this form of security protection is therefore a public good.

For each store, the marginal benefit of street patrols corresponds to the resulting reduction in economic losses due to theft. Let's measure the level of street patrols in person-hours per week. Figure 20.14 shows (in light blue) the marginal benefit curves of the three stores. They are labelled MB_H (for Holt Renfrew), MB_S (for Sears), and MB_B (for the Bay). The marginal social benefit curve, MSB, is the vertical sum of those three curves. For example, the vertical intercepts of the stores' marginal benefit curves imply that the first hour is worth $7.50 to Holt Renfrew, $45 to Sears, and $40 to the Bay. Therefore, the marginal social benefit of the first hour is $7.50 + $45 + $40 = $92.50, the vertical intercept of the MSB curve. We've assumed that the stores can hire security guards for $25 per hour, so the marginal cost curve is the horizontal red line labelled MC.

To find the socially efficient level of street patrols, we look for the intersection of the marginal social benefit and marginal cost curves. According to the figure, social efficiency requires 270 person-hours of street patrols. Starting from any other alternative, it would be possible to make all three stores better off.

There is an important qualitative difference between the methods we use to identify the socially efficient levels for public and private goods. In either case, we look for the intersection of a marginal benefit curve and a marginal cost curve (equivalently, a supply curve). However, we construct the marginal benefit curve by summing the individual demand curves (equivalently, the marginal benefit curves) *horizontally* for a private good and *vertically* for a public good.

Public Goods and Market Failure

If someone decides to contribute to a public good, such as national defence, the control of an agricultural pest, or the construction of a lighthouse, other people will benefit. In other words, the contribution creates a positive externality. As we learned in Section 20.1, competitive markets tend to produce too little output when positive externalities are present. Therefore, if the provision of a public good is left entirely to the independent actions of private parties, the level of production will be inefficiently low.

Look again at Figure 20.14. If the provision of security were left to the independent decisions of the stores, how many hours would they purchase? If one of the stores had sole responsibility for security, it would choose the number of hours at which its private marginal benefit, rather than the marginal social benefit, equals the marginal cost of patrols. Sears would choose 200 hours and the Bay would choose 120 hours. Because the marginal cost of security exceeds Holt Renfrew's marginal benefit at all levels of provision, Holt Renfrew would spend nothing on security (a boundary solution).

Of course, if Sears provides 200 hours of patrols, the Bay's marginal benefit will be less than the marginal cost of additional security. Therefore, given Sears' decision to provide 200 hours, the Bay's best choice is to provide nothing (as is Holt Renfrew's). That outcome—200 hours provided by Sears, and nothing provided by either the Bay or Holt Renfrew—is a Nash equilibrium (see Sections 12.3 and 19.1): the choice made by each store provides it with the highest possible payoff, given the choices of the other stores. Notice that the total level of security provided by the stores is less than the socially efficient level (200 versus 270 hours).

The market failure associated with public goods arises from a phenomenon known as *free riding*. A **free rider** contributes little or nothing to a public good while benefitting from others' contributions. In our example, the Bay and Holt Renfrew are free riders on Sears' security measures.

> A **free rider** contributes little or nothing to a public good while benefitting from others' contributions.

In some situations, the private sector offers solutions for free riding. If Holt Renfrew, Sears, and the Bay were to encounter the problem described in this section, they would probably reach a cooperative solution. They might sign a contract requiring each to pay amounts sufficient to provide 270 person-hours of weekly security patrols. However, when the number of affected parties is extremely large, negotiations become unwieldy. It is hard to imagine all of the households in Canada engaging in a comprehensive private negotiation to determine contributions to national defense. Even if the parties reached an agreement, it might be difficult or costly to monitor compliance.

WORKED-OUT PROBLEM   20.4

The Problem   Five stores have a problem with theft, and security is a public good. Let's use S to stand for the number of person-hours of security patrols per week. The marginal benefit of security patrols to each of the stores is given by the formula[24]

$$MB = \frac{100}{1 + S}$$

Patrols cost $20 per hour. What is the socially efficient level of security? If security is left to the independent decisions of the stores, what will they choose?

The Solution   First we compute the marginal social benefit of security.

$$MB = 5 \times MB = \frac{500}{1 + S}$$

---

[24]The corresponding total benefit formula is $B = 100 \ln(1 + S)$.

The marginal social benefit equals marginal cost at the value of S that satisfies

$$\frac{500}{1 + S} = 20$$

Solving for S, we obtain $S = 24$. Therefore, the socially efficient level of security is 24 person-hours of patrols per week.

If one store provided all of the security by itself, it would set its marginal benefit equal to the marginal cost.

$$\frac{100}{1 + S} = 20$$

Solving for S, we obtain $S = 4$. A store's marginal benefit is greater than marginal cost when $S < 4$ and less than marginal cost when $S > 4$.

If security is left to the independent decisions of the stores, they will provide four hours of security patrols in total. If the total were less than four hours, marginal benefit would exceed marginal cost for all of the stores, and they would all have an incentive to spend more on security. If the total were greater than four hours, marginal cost would exceed marginal benefit for all of the stores, and any store that was providing security would have an incentive to reduce the amount provided.

IN-TEXT EXERCISE 20.5   **Repeat worked-out problem 20.4, assuming that there are three stores, the marginal benefit to each store is given by the formula $MB = 100 - 2S$, and the cost of patrols is \$30 per hour.[25] How would your answer change if there were 5 stores? 10 stores? 100 stores?**

Public Policy toward Public Goods

Governments address the market failures associated with public goods in a variety of ways. They provide some public goods, such as national defence. They contribute to non-profit organizations that provide other public goods, such as public radio and television broadcasting (see Application 20.7). And they subsidize private contributions to many public goods, such as environmental protection. Subsidization often takes the form of tax deductibility for contributions to charitable causes that support public goods.[26]

We've seen that the private provision of public goods is inefficient because of positive externalities. Not surprisingly, the remedies mentioned in the last paragraph are variants of the ones discussed in Section 20.3. By providing a public good or by contributing to its provision, the government directly controls or attempts to control the good's quantity, as well as the levels of citizens' contributions (through taxes). In contrast, the subsidization of private contributions to public goods adjusts private incentives.

Subsidization offers fewer advantages relative to quantity controls than in other contexts with positive externalities. For example, in Application 20.5, we saw that subsidies for higher education may be more efficient than quantity restrictions because they allow

---

[25]The corresponding total benefit formula is $B = 100S - S^2$.

[26]Suppose the government taxes earnings at the rate of 50 percent but allows taxpayers to deduct charitable contributions. Then a \$100 contribution reduces before-tax income by \$100, causing tax payments to fall by \$50. In effect, the individual contributes \$50 from after-tax income, and the government matches that contribution dollar for dollar, bringing the total to \$100.

different people to make different choices based on their abilities, preferences, and circumstances. In contrast, the level of a public good must be the same for everyone. Though subsidization would allow people to choose different contributions to a public good, that is a matter of distributional equity, not efficiency. In addition, Pigouvian subsidization may not be practical. For public goods that benefit large populations, the Pigouvian approach can require subsidization at astronomical rates. For example, in a country of 30 million identical people, the marginal external benefit of a contribution to national defence would be 30 million times the private benefit. Therefore, to correct private incentives, the government might need to match voluntary contributions at the rate of $30 million per dollar contributed.

Notably, the efficient public provision of a public good need not entail public *production*. The market failure associated with a public good pertains to demand, not production; unless there is some other market failure, there is no reason to think that the private sector would produce that good inefficiently. In practice, governments often rely on the private sector to produce public goods in the expectation that private firms will be more efficient than a public enterprise. For example, the Canadian Department of National Defence (DND) obtains military equipment from private defence contractors. However, the DND also produces defence services by managing the armed forces. The potential reasons for preferring public production over private production involve other types of market failures, and are therefore beyond the scope of our discussion.

Application 20.7

Financing Commercial-Free Radio Broadcasting

When someone tunes in to an AM or FM radio station, the value of the broadcast signal to others is unaffected. In addition, an individual station has essentially no ability to exclude listeners. While it could scramble its signal, reception would then require the use of specialized equipment, rather than the standard radios owned by existing listeners. From a practical perspective, a station's broadcast signal is therefore both nonrival and nonexcludable; it is a public good.

Long ago, the private sector hit upon a creative solution to the public goods problem. Since stations are unable to sell programming to listeners, most of them provide the listeners with free programming and sell the "ears" to advertisers. The solution is not ideal, however. Advertisers' commercial messages interrupt scheduled programming, which usually irritates listeners. Most listeners would be willing to pay for commercial-free radio broadcasts.

Public commercial-free radio represents an alternative solution to the public goods problem. Through the Canadian Radio Broadcasting Act, the Canadian Broadcasting Corporation (CBC) was established in 1936. In 1972 the CBC

decided that it would not air commercials on its radio broadcasts, a decision that was made easier by the fact that most advertisers had already departed for television. The CBC's expenditures for CBC radio and the radio division of Radio-Canada totalled $329 million in 2009.

Although CBC radio is commercial free, CBC television is not. Advertising revenue in 2008–2009 was over $350 million. The CBC can be thought of as a public-private hybrid. In the United States, National Public Radio raises about two-thirds of its budget from private sources. Listeners voluntarily contribute about half of that amount, typically during pledge drives; corporations and other local organizations add the rest. Grants from the Corporation for Public Broadcasting, state governments, and universities cover the remaining third of the typical station's budget. Therefore, commercial-free public radio in the United States represents a hybrid solution to the public goods problem, one that involves both public and private funding. This solution makes good sense: a degree of public support is necessary to make the operation financially viable, but full public support would reduce a station's accountability and responsiveness to listeners. CBC radio has recently been considering whether to accept advertising revenue or to explore other sources of funding. CBC television and other broadcasters recently petitioned the CRTC to mandate payments from cable and satellite companies for the distribution of their programs. Application 17.7 discusses the recent CRTC ruling on compensation and the exclusion of the CBC from that process.

Recent technological advances have enabled the private sector to offer a new solution to the public goods problem. Through satellite-based radio broadcasting, a company like Sirius can offer nationwide (or worldwide)

access to a large collection of commercial-free stations, including several of the CBC stations. Because this package of services is much more valuable than the ability to receive a single station in a single location, many consumers are willing to pay for specialized reception equipment. Therefore, the company can make the signal excludable by scrambling it, and offer access on a subscription basis. Even this solution is not ideal, however. Since satellite radio signals are nonrival, it would be costless (and therefore efficient) to unscramble them, providing access to everyone. But then the enterprise would not be commercially viable.

The Problem of Gathering Reliable Information

To provide a public good efficiently, the government must have a great deal of information concerning the preferences of private citizens. Gathering that information presents challenges. The government cannot simply ask people to report their preferences. Answers to such questions will depend on who expects to foot the bill. Someone who expects to pay a disproportionately small share will exaggerate the good's benefits to encourage a high level of provision; someone who expects to pay a disproportionately large share will do the opposite. Can the government adopt a procedure for setting the level of the public good that will induce everyone to report their preferences correctly, and that produces a socially efficient outcome? Surprisingly, it can, at least in principle. One approach involves a policy known as a **Groves mechanism**, named after the economist who first proposed it, Theodore Groves.

> A **Groves mechanism** is a procedure for setting the level of the public good that induces everyone to report their preferences correctly, and that produces a socially efficient outcome.

To operate a Groves mechanism, the government would ask all citizens to report the total benefit they would receive from the public good at each possible level of provision. From that information, it would calculate each individual's reported marginal benefit (RMB). For the purpose of determining the level of the public good, the government would act as if everyone reported their true marginal benefit, (MB). In Figure 20.15, the chosen quantity would be Q^{tot}, at which the total reported marginal benefit curve (shown in dark blue and labelled RMB^{tot}) intersects the marginal cost curve (shown in red and labelled MC).[27] The same figure also shows how the contribution of a typical individual, Ted, would be calculated. Without Ted, the government would set the level of the public good at Q^{others}, the quantity at which the vertical sum of the RMB curves for all other individuals (shown in light blue and labelled RMB^{others}) intersects the marginal cost curve. The area of the red-shaded triangle measures the deadweight loss of increasing the quantity of the public good from Q^{others} to Q^{tot} based on the others' reported RMBs, ignoring Ted. The Groves mechanism sets Ted's contribution equal to the area of that triangle.[28]

With a Groves mechanism, each individual has an incentive to report his benefits truthfully, regardless of what he expects others to report. To understand why, look at Figure 20.15(b). If Ted reports his true benefits, total reported marginal benefits will

Economist Theodore Groves devised a method for setting the level of a public good efficiently, known as the Groves mechanism.

---

[28]The total reported marginal benefit curve, RMB^{tot}, is the vertical sum of all the individual RMB curves.

[29]There is no guarantee that these contributions would, in total, cover the cost of the public good. To balance its budget, the government might have to use lump sum taxes or subsidies.

Figure 20.15

The Groves Mechanism. A Groves mechanism requires each citizen to report the benefit received from the public good at each possible level of provision. As shown in figure (a), the chosen quantity would be Q^{tot}, at which the total reported marginal benefit curve (shown in dark blue and labelled RMB^{tot}) intersects the marginal cost curve (shown in red and labelled MC). The area of the red-shaded triangle indicates the mandatory contribution for an individual whose reported benefits causes the government to increase the quantity of the public good from Q^{others} to Q^{tot}. Figure (b) shows that each individual has an incentive to report his benefits truthfully.

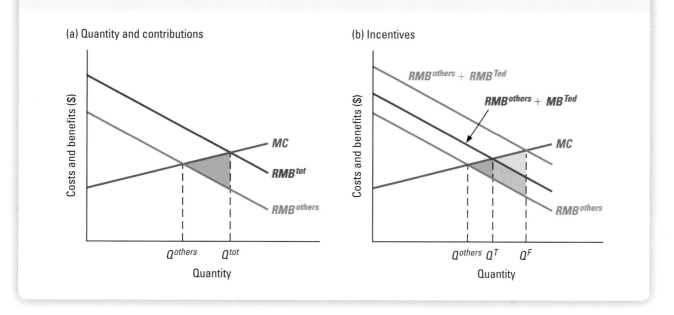

(a) Quantity and contributions

(b) Incentives

be given by the dark blue curve labelled $RMB^{others} + MB^{Ted}$. The quantity of the public good will be Q^T and Ted's contribution will equal the area of the red triangle. Let's see if it's worthwhile for Ted to exaggerate his benefits. Assuming he does so, total reported marginal benefits will be given by the light blue curve labelled $RMB^{others} + RMB^{Ted}$. The quantity of the public good will be Q^F and Ted's contribution will equal the area of the large triangle formed by the red, yellow, and green areas. Notice that he will pay more when he exaggerates his benefits than when he tells the truth; his incremental contribution will equal the size of the yellow and green areas. How does his benefit change? His marginal benefit equals the vertical distance between the curve labelled RMB^{others} and the one labelled $RMB^{others} + MB^{Ted}$. Therefore, if the quantity of the public good increases from Q^T to Q^F, his incremental benefit will equal the size of the green-shaded area. Notice that Ted's incremental contribution will be larger than his incremental benefit; the area of the yellow triangle measures his net loss. In other words, Ted will be worse off if he exaggerates his benefits than if he tells the truth. For similar reasons, Ted would also be worse off if he understated his benefits. [Try showing this by drawing a picture similar to Figure 20.15(b)]. Therefore, the Groves mechanism provides him with a strong incentive to tell the truth. With everyone reporting their benefits truthfully, the government will choose the efficient level of the public good.

Public Decision Making.

When markets fail, the public sector may be able to improve the allocation of resources *in principle*. But will government officials make efficient decisions *in practice*? When markets work well, selfish decisions lead to efficient outcomes. In contrast, there is no reason to think that the selfish interest of a government official will coincide with the social interest. Some officials may respond to pressure and promises from special interests. Others may be corrupt, power-hungry, or simply lazy. To determine whether public intervention is justified, we must therefore weigh the consequences of a market failure against the likely consequence of a government failure. For this purpose, we use tools from the field of **political economy**, which examines the economic consequences of public sector decision making.

The field of **political economy** examines the economic consequences of public sector decision making.

Democratic institutions make government officials accountable to the public, at least to some degree. Elected officials must please voters to win and retain their positions. Also, in many jurisdictions, voters can constrain officials through direct referendums on budgets and other aspects of public policy. Do these democratic mechanisms promote socially efficient government decision making? As a first step toward answering that question, we'll assume that democratic institutions are *completely* effective in making public officials accountable to the will of the majority. Consequently, a policy will be overturned if more than 50 percent of voters prefer an alternative.

Let's examine the implications of majority rule in the context of a simple example. Suppose an agricultural pest threatens the crops grown in a farming community. No single farm can adequately address the problem because the effects of pesticides are short-lived; once they wear off, pests can spread from other farms. The farmers want the county government to eradicate the pests by spraying the entire area. The county will pay for spraying by taxing the farms. We'll assume for the moment that each farm will pay a fixed fraction of the spraying costs. Because the benefits of spraying will differ from one farm to another, and because farmers will bear different shares of the costs, they have different opinions concerning the best level of spraying.

Figure 20.16 shows the net benefits of spraying for three farmers, Joe Average (in blue), Minnie (in red), and Maxine (in yellow). To maximize Joe Average's net benefit, the county would use 15 kilograms per hectare. We'll call that level of spraying Joe's *ideal policy*. Similarly, Minnie's ideal policy is six kilograms per hectare and Maxine's is 18 kilograms per hectare. Notice that more intensive spraying increases a farmer's net benefit until his or her ideal policy is reached; beyond that level, the farmer's net benefit declines. When a voter's preferences have that property, we call them **single-peaked**. Joe Average is special because half of the other farmers (like Minnie) have lower ideal policies, and half (like Maxine) have higher ideal policies. In other words, among all the farmers, Joe's ideal policy is the median.[29] For that reason, Joe is known as the **median voter**.

A voter's preferences are **single-peaked** if her net benefit from an activity increases with the activity's level until her ideal is reached, and declines thereafter.

The **median voter** is the voter who has the median ideal policy among all voters.

If the county government is perfectly constrained by majority rule, it will adopt Joe's ideal policy. Why? For every alternative policy, there is a majority that prefers 15 kilograms per hectare. Consider any lower level of spraying, such as 10 kilograms per hectare. Joe obviously prefers 15 kilograms to 10 kilograms. So does Maxine. Indeed, so does every other voter whose ideal policy, like Maxine's, exceeds 15 kilograms per hectare. Altogether, those voters form a majority. Similarly, a majority of voters, including Joe, Minnie, and every other voter whose ideal policy (like Minnie's) is less than 15 kilograms per hectare prefer 15 kilograms to any higher level of spraying, such as 17 kilograms.

---

[29]To find the median of a list of numbers, we arrange them from lowest to highest and pick the one in the middle.

Figure 20.16

Majority Rule and the Level of a Public Good. The red, blue, and yellow curves represent the net benefits of a pest eradication program for three farmers. Among all farmers, Joe Average's ideal policy is the median. If the county government is perfectly constrained by majority rule, it will adopt Joe's ideal policy. That policy does not necessarily maximize the net social benefit to all farmers. Instead, the net social benefit is maximized at the peak of the green curve labelled "Total."

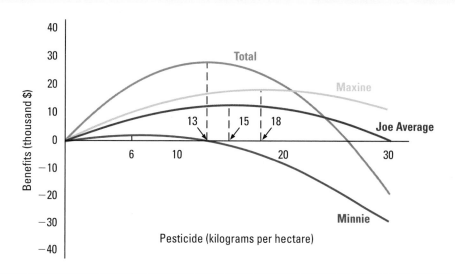

Our example illustrates a general principle known as the **median voter theorem**. This important result tells us that, if voters have single-peaked preferences, a majority of them prefer the median ideal policy to all other policies. Therefore, majority rule leads to the selection of the median ideal policy.

Does majority rule lead to a socially efficient outcome? Because everyone will vote in favour of a policy that makes everyone better off, majority rule can never lead to a Pareto inefficient choice, given the available policies. Indeed, in our example, 15 kilograms per hectare is Pareto efficient; any other choice would make Joe Average and either Minnie or Maxine worse off.

Despite the preceding observation, the ideal policy of the median voter usually differs from the policy that maximizes the net social benefit. Intuitively, the policy that maximizes the net social benefit depends on the intensity and extremity of every voter's preferences, while the ideal policy of the median voter does not. The two policies can coincide, but only by accident. To illustrate this point, let's assume that there are no farmers other than Joe Average, Minnie, and Maxine. Figure 20.16 includes a green curve showing net social benefits; it is the vertical sum of the three farmers' net benefit curves. To maximize the net social benefits, the county should choose 13 kilograms per hectare instead of 15 kilograms.

How can the ideal policy of the median voter be Pareto efficient if it doesn't maximize the net social benefit? This apparent puzzle is easily resolved. The ideal policy of the median voter is only Pareto efficient among the policies from which the voters could choose in our example. Those alternatives were limited by the county's fixed tax system.

The **median voter theorem** states that, if voters have single-peaked preferences, a majority of them prefer the median ideal policy to all other policies.

If the cost savings of a reduction in spraying from 15 to 13 kilograms were distributed appropriately, all three farmers would be better off. However, that alternative was not available to the voters.

Unfortunately, the principle of majority rule has clear implications only in simple settings like the one discussed above. If we make our example just a bit more complicated, no policy will be a clear majority winner. Let's suppose that the county has to choose both the level of spraying and each farmer's contribution to the costs of spraying. In that case, for every possible policy, there is an alternative that a majority prefers, which implies that every policy would be overturned. Suppose a policy prescribes a level of spraying S and tax burdens X for Minnie, Y for Joe Average, and Z for Maxine. Compare that policy with one that prescribes the same level of spraying and tax burdens $X - 1$ for Minnie, $Y - 1$ for Joe Average, and $Z + 2$ for Maxine.[30] Notice that the alternative raises the same amount of revenue ($X + Y + Z$), and that a majority (Minnie and Joe) prefer it to the original policy.

With no clear majority winner, the outcome will depend on the specific rules and procedures that the county uses to make decisions—for example, who is entitled to make proposals, whether proposals can be amended, whether people vote sequentially or simultaneously, and so forth. The field of political economy has shown that different procedures for implementing the principle of majority rule can lead to dramatically different outcomes.

CHAPTER SUMMARY

1. **Externalities and inefficiency (LO1)**

    a. When an activity creates an externality, competitive markets will allocate resources inefficiently. The level of the activity tends to be too high if the externality is negative and too low if it's positive. Markets fail because prices diverge from marginal social costs or benefits.

    b. If the production of a good creates negative externalities, monopoly can be either more or less efficient than competition, and the monopolist's output can be either inefficiently high or low, depending on the size of the externality.

2. **Remedies for externalities: the private sector (LO2)**

    a. If bargaining is frictionless, then regardless of how property rights are assigned, voluntary agreements between private parties will remedy the market failures associated with externalities and restore economic efficiency. The assignment of property rights affects the distribution of economic benefits.

    b. Private parties can achieve efficient solutions for externalities either through contracts or through common ownership.

    c. Externalities result from missing markets. Negotiations can substitute for those markets.

    d. Negotiations can fail to address an externality if bargaining is impractical, the assignment of property rights is ambiguous, different parties have limited information about each others' costs and benefits, or contracts are difficult to enforce.

3. **Remedies for externalities: the public sector (LO3)**

    a. Governments can remedy some externalities through policies that help the private sector create the necessary markets, or by creating and operating those markets.

    b. Another remedy for externalities is to regulate the level of the activities that produce them. This strategy requires a great deal of information concerning private costs and benefits.

    c. Another remedy for externalities is to correct private incentives through taxes, fees, subsidies, or liability rules.

    d. Ideal quantity controls and ideal corrective taxes have different distributional implications, but are equally efficient and require similar information.

---

[30]We are allowing for the possibility that taxes are negative (in other words, that the county pays subsidies).

e. When external harms have multiple causes, well-intentioned efforts to correct private incentives can go awry, leading to inefficiency.

f. If the government errs when setting quantity controls and corrective taxes, those two approaches need not be equally efficient.

g. If the external costs of pollution depend on the total emissions of many parties, an emissions tax leads to efficient abatement, while quantity controls generally do not.

h. As a practical matter, either a quantity standard or a tax can be more flexible, and therefore more desirable.

i. A system of tradable emissions permits allows the government to set overall quantity standards without sacrificing efficient abatement.

4. **Common property resources (LO4)**

a. People tend to overuse common property resources due to the presence of negative externalities.

b. Possible remedies for common property resource problems include transferring the resource to an owner, limiting access, and charging user fees.

5. **Public goods (LO5)**

a. Goods differ in their degrees of rivalry and excludability.

b. To determine the efficient level of a public good, we sum all parties' marginal benefit curves vertically and then find the intersection of the resulting marginal social benefit curve with the marginal cost curve.

c. Providing public goods creates positive externalities. The private sector under-provides public goods due to the free rider problem.

d. Possible remedies for public goods problems include public provision, contributions to nonprofit providers, and subsidies for private contributions.

e. Subsidization offers fewer advantages than in other contexts involving positive externalities because the level of the public good must be the same for everyone. Efficient subsidization may also be impractical.

f. The efficient provision of a public good need not entail public production.

g. There are procedures for setting the level of a public good that provide people with incentives to report their preferences correctly and that produce socially efficient outcomes.

h. To determine whether public intervention is justified, we must weigh the consequences of market failure against the likely consequence of government failure arising from the self-interested actions of government officials.

i. Assuming that the public sector is constrained by majority opinion and that voters have single-peaked preferences, majority rule leads to the selection of the median ideal policy. That policy is Pareto efficient among the available policies but need not maximize net social benefits (in which case it is not Pareto efficient within a broader class of policies).

j. The principle of majority rule has clear implications only in simple settings. Often there is no clear majority winner, and the outcome depends on the specific rules and procedures used to make public decisions.

ADDITIONAL EXERCISES

Exercise 20.1: Give three examples of negative externalities and three examples of positive externalities. (LO1)

Exercise 20.2: Students receive two types of benefits from standardized test preparation services: first, they learn useful material; second, they score better on the test relative to other students. Because relative performance matters, their improved performance creates a negative externality for other students. Suppose that the market demand function for test preparation services is $Q^d = 30 - P/2$, where Q^d is millions of hours of services and P is the price per hour. Suppose also that the market for these services is competitive and that the market supply function is $Q^s = 2P - 30$. Finally, suppose that the marginal external cost of test preparation is given by $MEC = 5 + 1.5Q$. Find the socially efficient level of test preparation,

the competitive equilibrium, and the deadweight loss created by the externality. Draw a figure to illustrate your answer. (LO1)

Exercise 20.3: Consider the same market described in exercise 20.2, but now assume that test preparation services are monopolized. Also assume that the monopolist's marginal cost curve coincides with the market supply curve in the last problem. How does the monopoly output compare with the socially efficient output? Calculate the deadweight loss of monopoly. Draw a figure to illustrate your answer. (LO1)

Exercise 20.4: Suppose that a paper mill earns $400,000 when it pollutes a river, and that it can abate pollution at a cost of $80,000. The effects of pollution are confined to a single farmer, who earns $530,000 if the water is clean and $330,000 if it is polluted. Assume that bargaining is frictionless and that the parties will split the gains from any agreement equally. What agreement will the mill and the farmer negotiate if the mill has the right to pollute? What if the farmer has the right to clean water? (LO2)

Exercise 20.5: In Section 20.3, you learned that Parliament passed the Canadian Radio Broadcasting Act of 1932 to coordinate the use of the radio spectrum. Why do you think private negotiation failed to solve the problem of allocating the airwaves efficiently? (LO2)

Exercise 20.6: For each of the externalities you listed in your answer to exercise 20.1, identify the missing market or markets that are responsible for the externality. Would it be possible to create such a market? If so, how? If not, why not? (LO3)

Exercise 20.7: Calculate the efficient Pigouvian tax to correct the externality in worked-out problem 20.1 (page 752). Show graphically and algebraically that, with this tax, the competitive equilibrium will be efficient. (LO3)

Exercise 20.8: Inoculations create external benefits by reducing other people's exposure to communicable diseases. Suppose the market demand curve for inoculations is $Q^d = 100 - 10P$, where Q^d is millions of inoculations and P is the price per inoculation. Suppose also that the market for inoculations is competitive and that the market supply curve is $Q^s = 2P - 8$. Finally, suppose that the marginal external benefit of inoculations is $MEB = 8 + 1.5Q$. Find the socially efficient level of inoculations, the competitive equilibrium, the deadweight loss created by the externality, and the optimal Pigouvian subsidy. Draw a figure to illustrate your answer. (LO3)

Exercise 20.9: Many people think that liability for accidents should be based in part on negligence. For example, a negligence rule might state that if two cars collide while one driver is following traffic laws while the other is not, the second driver should bear full responsibility, while the first should bear none. Does that rule make sense from the perspective of economic efficiency? Why or why not? (LO3)

Exercise 20.10: For each of the externalities you listed in your answer to exercise 20.1, do you think there is a reason to prefer a remedy designed to control quantities, or one designed to correct private incentives? Justify your answers. (LO3)

Exercise 20.11: A politician is concerned that Canadians create too much pollution by driving excessively. She proposes issuing a fixed number of tradable driving permits each month. Each permit would be good for 100 miles during that particular month. Each adult citizen would receive the same number of permits. People would be free to buy and sell their permits. Those who drive more than the amount allowed by the permits they retain or purchase would face stiff penalties. Enforcement would involve periodic odometer checks. What are the advantages and disadvantages of this proposal? Is it workable? How does it compare to a gasoline tax? (LO3)

Exercise 20.12: Give three examples of common property resources other than the ones listed in the text. In each case, how is overuse addressed in practice, if at all? How could it be addressed? (LO4)

Exercise 20.13: Give three examples of public goods, other than the ones discussed in the text. Explain why they are nonrival and nonexcludable (or at least approximately so). (LO5)

Exercise 20.14: Fifty residents of a university dorm all like espresso. An espresso machine costs $1000. Each dorm resident is willing to pay up to $50 for the machine. One resident, Eugene, decides to take up a collection. Assuming there is no way to make other residents contribute, is Eugene likely to raise the necessary $1000? Why or why not? What could he do to improve his chances of success? (LO5)

Exercise 20.15: Using a graph like the one shown in Figure 20.15(b) (page 787), explain why an individual has no incentive to understate his benefits from a public good if the good is provided through a Groves mechanism. (LO5)

Exercise 20.16: Suppose as in the text that the red, blue, and yellow curves in Figure 20.16 (page 789) represent the net benefits of a pest eradication program for three farmers, Minnie, Joe Average, and Maxine. No one else is affected by the program. The county has established a default policy, X kilograms per hectare, which it will follow unless a majority of the farmers agree to an alternative. Minnie is the president of the local farmers' association, a position that gives her the authority to make a proposal to the others. The three will then vote on Minnie's proposal. If a majority approves, the county will follow it. If a majority does not approve, the county will follow the default policy. What will Minnie propose, and how much spraying will occur if $X < 6$? If X is between six and 15? If X is above 15? (LO5)

GLOSSARY

A

Actuarially fair An insurance policy is actuarially fair if its expected net payoff is zero.

Ad valorem tax An *ad valorem* tax is a tax that is stated as a percentage of the good's price.

Adverse selection Adverse selection is present if an informed individual is more willing to trade when trading is less advantageous to an uninformed trading partner.

Aggregate surplus Aggregate surplus equals consumers' total willingness to pay for a good less firms' total avoidable cost of production. It captures the net benefit created by the production and consumption of the good.

Anchoring Anchoring occurs when someone's choices are linked to prominent but patently irrelevant information.

Average cost A firm's average cost, $AC = C/Q$, is its cost per unit of output produced.

Average product of labour The average product of labour, denoted APL, equals the amount of output divided by the number of workers employed.

Avoidable A fixed cost is avoidable if it is not incurred when the firm decides to produce no output.

B

Backward induction Backward induction is the process of solving a strategic problem by reasoning in reverse, starting at the end of the tree diagram that represents the game, and working back to the beginning.

Bad A bad is an object, condition, or activity that makes a consumer worse off.

Benefit An insurance benefit is the amount of money a policyholder receives if a specific loss occurs.

Bertrand model of oligopoly In the Bertrand model of oligopoly, firms produce homogeneous products and set their prices simultaneously.

Best response The best response is a strategy that provides a game player with the highest possible payoff, assuming that other players behave in a specified way.

Best-response curve A best response function, also known as a reaction function, shows the relationship between one player's choice and the other's best response.

Best-response functions A best response function, also known as a reaction function, shows the relationship between one player's choice and the other's best response.

Boundary action A boundary action, or boundary choice, is an action at which it is possible to change the activity level in only one direction.

Boundary choice At a boundary choice there are no affordable bundles that contain either a little bit more or a little bit less of some good. When the consumer's best choice is a boundary choice, we call it a boundary solution.

Boundary solution At a boundary choice there are no affordable bundles that contain either a little bit more or a little bit less of some good. When the consumer's best choice is a boundary choice, we call it a boundary solution. Also, if the least-cost input combination excludes some inputs, it is a boundary solution.

Budget constraint A budget constraint identifies all of the consumption bundles a consumer can afford over some period of time.

Budget line A budget line shows all of the consumption bundles that just exhaust a consumer's income.

Bundling Bundling is the practice of selling several products together as a package.

Business stealing Business stealing arises when some of a new entrant's sales come at the expense of existing firms, whose sales contract after the new firm enters the market.

C

Capitalist economy A capitalist economy is one in which the means of production are mostly owned and controlled by and for the benefit of private individuals, and the allocation of resources is governed by voluntary trading among businesses and consumers.

Captured Regulators have been captured when they promote the regulated firm's agenda.

Cardinal Information about preferences is ordinal if it allows us to determine only whether one alternative is better or worse than another. Cardinal information tells us something about the intensity of those preferences— it answers the question "How much worse?" or "How much better?"

Certainty equivalent The certainty equivalent of a risky bundle is the amount of consumption which, if provided with certainty, would make the consumer equally well off.

Coase Theorem The Coase Theorem states that if bargaining is frictionless, then regardless of how property rights are assigned, voluntary agreements between private parties will remedy the market failures associated with externalities and restore economic efficiency.

Cobb-Douglas production function The Cobb-Douglas production function is $Q = F(L, K) AL^\alpha K^\beta$.

Common property resource A common property resource is a resource that more than one person is free to use without payment.

Communist economy A communist economy is one in which the state owns and controls the means of production and distribution.

Compensated demand curve A compensated demand curve, or Hicksian demand curve, shows the effect of a compensated change in a good's price on the amount consumed. In other words, it describes the relationship between the price and the amount consumed holding the consumer's well-being fixed and allowing income to vary.

Compensated price change An uncompensated price change consists of a price change with no change in income. A compensated price change consists of a price change and an income change which, together, leave the consumer's well-being unaffected.

Compensating variation A compensating variation is the amount of money that exactly compensates the consumer for a change in circumstances.

Complements   Two products are complements if, all else equal, an increase in the price of one of the products causes consumers to demand less of the other product.

Compounding   Compounding refers to the payment of interest on loan balances that include interest earned in the past, a practice that causes the loan balance to grow faster as time passes.

Constant elasticity demand curve   A constant elasticity (or isoelastic) demand curve has the same elasticity at every price.

Constant expected consumption line   A constant expected consumption line shows all the risky consumption bundles with the same level of expected consumption.

Constant returns to scale   A firm has constant returns to scale if a proportional change in all inputs produces the same proportional change in output.

Consumer surplus   (Aggregate) consumer surplus equals the sum of consumers' total willingness to pay less their total expenditure.

Consumption bundle   A consumption bundle is the collection of goods that an individual consumes over a given period, such as an hour, a day, a month, a year, or a lifetime.

Contract curve   The contract curve shows every efficient allocation of consumption goods in an Edgeworth box.

Cost function   A firm's cost function describes the total cost of producing each possible level of output. It is a function of the form *Total cost = C(Output)*.

Cost-of-living index   A cost-of-living index measures the relative cost of achieving a fixed standard of living in different situations.

Cournot model of oligopoly   In the Cournot model of oligopoly, firms choose how much to produce (their quantities) simultaneously, and the price clears the market given the total quantity produced.

Cross-price elasticity of demand   The cross-price elasticity of demand with another product equals the percentage change in the amount demanded of the product for each one percent increase in the price of the other product.

Cross-subsidization   In an insurance market, cross-subsidization occurs when one type of policy generates losses, while another type of policy generates profits, and all policies collectively break even.

D

Deadweight loss   A deadweight loss is a reduction in aggregate surplus below its maximum possible value.

Deadweight loss from monopoly pricing   The deadweight loss from monopoly pricing is the amount by which aggregate surplus falls short of its maximum possible level, which is attained in a perfectly competitive market.

Deadweight loss of taxation   The deadweight loss of taxation is the lost aggregate surplus due to a tax.

Declining marginal rate of technical substitution   An isoquant for a production process using two inputs, X and Y, has a declining marginal rate of technical substitution if $MRTS_{XY}$ declines as we move along the isoquant, increasing input X and decreasing input Y.

Declining MRS   An indifference curve has a declining MRS if it becomes flatter moving along the curve from the northwest to the southeast.

Decreasing returns to scale   A firm has decreasing returns to scale if a proportional change in all inputs produces a less than proportional change in output.

Default   Default is the failure to pay back borrowed money.

Default effect   The default effect refers to the fact that when confronted with many alternatives, people sometimes avoid making a choice and end up with the option that is assigned as a default.

Demand curve   A product's demand curve shows how much buyers of the product want to buy at each possible price, holding fixed all other factors that affect demand.

Demand function   A product's demand function describes the amount of the product that is demanded for each possible combination of its price and other factors.

Dependent variable   In econometrics, the variable whose movements we are trying to explain is called the dependent variable. The variables that explain the changes in the dependent variable are called the explanatory variables.

Deviation   A deviation is the difference between the actual payoff and the expected payoff.

Dictator game   In the dictator game, one player (the dictator) divides a fixed prize between himself and another player (the recipient) who is a passive participant.

Differentiated products   Products are homogeneous when they are identical in the eyes of purchasers. They are differentiated when some purchasers view the products as different.

Diminishing sensitivity   The property of diminishing sensitivity holds when the marginal impact of enlarging a change from the status quo declines with the size of the change.

Diseconomies of scale   A firm experiences diseconomies of scale when its average cost rises as it produces more.

Diseconomies of scope   Diseconomies of scope occur when producing two products in a single firm is more expensive than producing them separately, in different firms.

Diversification   Diversification is the practice of undertaking many risky activities, each on a small scale, rather than a few risky activities (or just one) on a large scale.

Domestic aggregate surplus   Domestic aggregate surplus is the sum of consumer surplus, domestic producer surplus, and government revenue.

Dominant   A strategy is dominant if it is a player's only best response, regardless of other players' choices.

Dominated   A strategy is dominated if there is some other strategy that yields a strictly higher payoff regardless of others' choices.

Duopoly   A market with two sellers is called a duopoly.

Dynamically consistent   A person is dynamically consistent if his preferences over the alternatives available at some future date don't change as that date approaches or once it arrives. When this condition doesn't hold, preferences are dynamically inconsistent.

Dynamically inconsistent   A person is dynamically consistent if his preferences over the alternatives available at some future date don't change as that date approaches or once it arrives. When this condition doesn't hold, preferences are dynamically inconsistent.

E

Econometrics   Econometrics is the application of statistical methods to empirical questions in the field of economics.

Economies of scale   A firm experiences economies of scale when its average cost falls as it produces more.

Economies of scope   Economies of scope occur when a single firm can produce two or more products more cheaply than two separate firms.

Edgeworth box   The Edgeworth box is a diagram that shows two consumers' opportunities and choices in a single figure.

Efficient   A production method is efficient if there is no other way for the firm to produce a larger amount of output using the same amounts of inputs.

Efficient production frontier   A firm's efficient production frontier contains the combinations of inputs and outputs that a firm can achieve using efficient production methods.

Efficient scale of production   A firm's efficient scale of production is the output level at which its average cost is lowest.

Egalitarianism   According to the principle of egalitarianism, equal division of society's resources among all members of the population is the most equitable outcome.

Elastic demand   Demand is elastic when the elasticity of demand is less than -1. It is inelastic when the elasticity of demand is greater than -1 (that is, between -1 and 0).

Elasticity   The elasticity of Y with respect to X, denoted E_X^Y, equals the percentage change in Y divided by the percentage change in X, or equivalently, the percentage change in Y for each one percent increase in X.

Elasticity of demand   The (price) elasticity of demand at price P, denoted E^d, equals the percentage change in the amount demanded for each one percent increase in the price.

Elasticity of supply   The (price) elasticity of supply at price P, denoted E^s, equals the percentage change in the amount supplied for each one percent increase in the price.

Elastic supply   Supply is elastic at price P when the elasticity of supply is greater than one, and inelastic when the elasticity of supply is between zero and one.

Emissions standard   An emissions standard is a legal limit on the amount of pollution that a person or company can produce when engaged in a particular activity.

Endowment   An endowment is the bundle of goods an individual starts out with before trading.

Endowment effect   The endowment effect refers to the observation that people tend to value something more highly when they own it than when they don't.

Engel curve   The Engel curve for a good describes the relationship between income and the amount consumed, holding everything else fixed (including prices and the consumer's preferences).

Equilibrium price   The equilibrium price is the price at which the amounts supplied and demanded are equal.

Equity share   An equity share is a proportional claim on the ownership of a company.

Exchange economy   In an exchange economy, people own and trade goods, but no production takes place.

Exchange efficiency condition   The exchange efficiency condition holds if every pair of individuals shares the same marginal rate of substitution for every pair of goods.

Expected payoff   The expected payoff of a risky financial choice is a weighted average of all the possible payoffs, using the probability of each payoff as its weight.

Expected utility function   An expected utility function assigns a benefit level to each possible state of nature based only on what is consumed, and then takes the expected value of those benefits.

Explanatory variables   In econometrics, the variable whose movements we are trying to explain is called the dependent variable. The variables that explain the changes in the dependent variable are called the explanatory variables.

Explicit collusion   Firms engage in explicit collusion when they communicate to reach an agreement about the prices they will charge.

External benefit   An external benefit is the economic gain that a positive externality provides to others.

External cost   An external cost is the economic harm that a negative externality imposes on others.

Externality   An action creates an externality if it affects someone with whom the decision-maker has not engaged in a related market transaction. It creates a negative externality if it harms someone else and a positive externality if it benefits someone else.

F

Factor market   A factor market is a market for an input.

Factor-neutral technical change   A factor-neutral technical change has no effect on the MRTS at any input combination. It simply changes the output level associated with each of a firm's isoquants.

Family of indifference curves   A family of indifference curves is a collection of indifference curves that represents the preferences of the same individual.

Family of isocost lines   A family of isocost lines contains, for given input prices, the isocost lines for all of the possible cost levels of the firm.

Family of isoquants   A firm's family of isoquants consists of the isoquants corresponding to all of its possible output levels.

Finitely repeated game   A finitely repeated game is formed by repeating a simpler game a fixed number of times, after which the game ends.

First welfare theorem   The first welfare theorem tells us that, in a general equilibrium with perfect competition, the allocation of resources is Pareto efficient.

Fixed costs   Fixed costs are the costs of inputs whose use does not vary as the firm's level of output changes, with the possible exception that the cost might not be incurred if the firm decides to produce nothing.

Fixed input   A variable input can be adjusted over the time period being considered, while a fixed input cannot.

Fixed proportions   Two inputs are used in fixed proportions when they must be combined in a fixed ratio. They are then known as perfect complements.

Fixed-weight price index   A fixed-weight price index measures the percentage change in the cost of a fixed consumption bundle.

Free entry   There is free entry in a market when technology is freely available to anyone who wishes to start a firm and entry is unrestricted. In that case, the number of potential firms is unlimited.

Free market system   In a free market system, the government mostly allows markets to operate as they will, with little regulation or other intervention.

Free rider   A free rider contributes little or nothing to a public good while benefitting from others' contributions.

Full insurance   With full insurance, the promised benefit equals the potential loss.

G

Gambler's fallacy   The gambler's fallacy is the belief that once an event has occurred, it is less likely to repeat.

Game   A game is a situation in which a number of individuals make decisions, and all care both about their own choices and about others' choices.

General equilibrium analysis   General equilibrium analysis is the study of competitive equilibrium in many markets at the same time.

Giffen good   A product is called a Giffen good if the amount purchased increases as the price rises.

Grim strategies   With grim strategies, the punishment for selfish behaviour is permanent.

Groves mechanism   A Groves mechanism is a procedure for setting the level of the public good that induces everyone to report their preferences correctly, and that produces a socially efficient outcome.

Guaranteed consumption line   The guaranteed consumption line shows the consumption bundles for which the level of consumption does not depend on the state of nature.

H

Hedging   Hedging is the practice of taking on two risky activities with negatively correlated financial payoffs.

Hicksian demand curve   A compensated demand curve, or Hicksian demand curve, shows the effect of a compensated change in a good's price on the amount consumed. In other words, it describes the relationship between the price and the amount consumed holding the consumer's well-being fixed and allowing income to vary.

Higher productivity   A firm has higher productivity (is more productive) when it can produce more output using the same amounts of inputs. Equivalently, its production function shifts upward at each combination of inputs.

Homogeneous   Products are homogeneous when they are identical in the eyes of purchasers. They are differentiated when some purchasers view the products as different.

Horizontal merger   In a horizontal merger, two or more competing firms combine their operations.

Hot-hand fallacy   The hot-hand fallacy is the belief that once an event has occurred several times in a row, it is more likely to repeat.

Human capital   Human capital consists of marketable skills acquired through investments in education and training.

I

Incentive scheme   An incentive scheme is a contract or compensation policy that ties rewards or punishments to performance, designed in a manner to induce desirable behaviour.

Incidence   The incidence of a tax indicates how much of the tax burden is borne by various market participants.

Income   A consumer's income consists of the money received during some fixed period of time.

Income-consumption curve   The income-consumption curve shows how the best affordable consumption bundle changes as income changes, holding everything else fixed (including prices and the consumer's preferences).

Income effect   An income effect is the change in the consumption of a good that results from a change in income.

Income effect of a price change   The effect on consumption of removing the compensation after creating a compensated price change is known as the income effect of a price change.

Income elasticity of demand   The income elasticity of demand equals the percentage change in the amount demanded for each one percent increase in income.

Increasing returns to scale   A firm has increasing returns to scale if a proportional change in all inputs produces a more than proportional change in output.

Independent variable   In econometrics, the variable whose movements we are trying to explain is called the dependent variable. The variables that explain the changes in the dependent variable are called the explanatory variables.

Indifference curve   Starting with any alternative, an indifference curve shows all the other alternatives that a consumer likes equally well.

Indifferent   A consumer is indifferent between two alternatives when liking (or disliking) them equally.

Individual demand curve   An individual demand curve describes the relationship between the price of a good and the amount a particular consumer purchases, holding everything else fixed (including the consumer's income and preferences, as well as all other prices).

Individual sovereignty   The principle of individual sovereignty holds that each person knows what's best for him or her.

Inelastic   Demand is elastic when the elasticity of demand is less than -1. It is inelastic when the elasticity of demand is greater than -1 (that is, between -1 and 0).

Inferior good   If the demand for a product increases when income grows larger, the product is called a normal good. If it instead decreases, it is called an inferior good.

Infinitely repeated Bertrand model   In the infinitely repeated Bertrand model, firms play the Bertrand pricing game over and over, with no definite end.

Infinitely repeated game   An infinitely repeated game is formed by repeating a simpler game indefinitely.

Informational asymmetry   An informational asymmetry is present when one party to a transaction has more information than another about the characteristics of the good or service to be traded.

Inframarginal units   The inframarginal units are the units the firm sells other than the ΔQ marginal units.

Input efficiency   Input efficiency means that holding constant the total amount of each input used in the economy, there is no way to increase any firm's output without decreasing the output of another firm.

Input efficiency condition   The input efficiency condition holds if, for every pair of inputs, every pair of firms share the same marginal rate of technical substitution.

Inputs   Outputs are the physical products or services a firm produces. Inputs are the materials, labour, land, or equipment that firms use to produce their outputs.

Insurance policy   An insurance policy is a contract that reduces the financial loss associated with some risky event, like a burglary, an accident, an illness, or death.

Interest   Interest is the amount of money a borrower is obliged to pay a lender, over and above the principal.

Interest rate   The interest rate is the amount of interest paid on a loan during a particular period (usually a year), stated as a percentage of the principal.

Interior action   An interior action, or interior choice, is an action at which it is possible to marginally increase or decrease the activity level.

Interior choice   An affordable bundle is an interior choice if, for each good, there are affordable bundles containing a little bit more of that good and affordable bundles containing a little bit less of it. When the best affordable choice is an interior choice, we call it an interior solution.

Interior solution   An affordable bundle is an interior choice if, for each good, there are affordable bundles containing a little bit more of that good and affordable bundles containing a little bit less of it. When the best affordable choice is an interior choice, we call it an interior solution.

Internal rate of return   A project's internal rate of return (or IRR) is the rate of interest at which its NPV is exactly zero.

Inverse demand function   The inverse demand function for a firm's product describes how much the firm must charge to sell any given quantity of its product. It takes the form *Price = P(Quantity demanded)*.

Isocost line   An isocost line contains all the input combinations with the same cost.

Isoquant   An isoquant identifies all the input combinations that efficiently produce a given amount of output.

Iterative deletion of dominated strategies   The iterative deletion of dominated strategies refers to the following process: Remove the dominated strategies from a game. Inspect the simplified game to determine if it contains any dominated strategies. If it does, remove them. Repeat this procedure until there are no more dominated strategies left to remove.

L

Labour supply   Labour supply refers to the sale of a consumer's time and effort to an employer.

Laissez-faire   The doctrine of laissez-faire holds that the government should adopt a "hands off" approach to private commerce.

Laspeyres price index   A Laspeyres price index is a fixed-weight index that is based on the consumption bundle actually purchased in the base period. It tells us whether the cost of the base-period consumption bundle has risen or fallen, and by how much.

Law of Demand   The Law of Demand states that demand curves usually slope downward.

Law of Diminishing Marginal Returns   The Law of Diminishing Marginal Returns states the general tendency for the marginal product of an input to eventually decline as its use is increased, holding all other inputs fixed.

Law of Supply   The Law of Supply says that when the market price increases, the profit-maximizing sales quantity for a price-taking firm never decreases.

Lerner Index   A firm's markup, price-cost margin, or Lerner Index equals the amount by which its price exceeds its marginal cost, expressed as a percentage of its price.

Liability rule   A liability rule is a legal principle requiring a party who takes an action that harms others to compensate the affected parties for some or all of their losses.

Long run   The short run is a period of time over which one or more inputs is fixed. The long run is a period of time over which all inputs are variable.

Loss aversion   Loss aversion occurs when the consumer's valuation of an outcome is more sensitive, per dollar, to small losses than to small gains.

Loss leader   A loss leader is a product that is sold at a price below its direct marginal cost to encourage sales of a complementary product.

Lump-sum transfer   With a lump-sum transfer, the amount of resources received or surrendered by each consumer is fixed; it doesn't depend on the consumer's choices.

M

Marginal benefit of an action   The marginal benefit of an action at an activity level of X units is equal to the extra benefit produced by the marginal units, $B(X) - B(X - \Delta X)$, divided by the number of marginal units, ΔX.

Marginal change   A marginal change is a small adjustment of a choice.

Marginal cost   A firm's marginal cost, MC, measures how much extra cost the firm incurs to produce the marginal units of output, per unit of output added.

Marginal cost of an action   The marginal cost of an action at an activity level of X units is equal to the extra cost incurred due to the marginal units, $C(X) - C(X - \Delta X)$, divided by the number of marginal units, ΔX.

Marginal expenditure   A monopsonist's marginal expenditure, ME, is the extra cost incurred to hire or purchase the marginal units of an input, per marginal unit.

Marginal product of labour   The marginal product of labour with L workers, denoted MP_L, equals the extra output produced due to the ΔL marginal units of labour, per unit of labour added.

Marginal rate of substitution   The marginal rate of substitution for X with Y, written MRS_{XY}, is the rate at which a consumer must adjust Y to maintain the same level of well-being when X changes by a tiny amount, from a given starting point. Mathematically, if ΔX is the tiny change in X and ΔY is the adjustment to Y, then $MRS_{XY} = -\Delta Y/\Delta X$.

Marginal rate of technical substitution (MRTS) for labour with capital   The marginal rate of technical substitution (MRTS) for input X with input Y, written as $MRTS_{XY}$, is the rate ($\Delta Y/\Delta X$) at which a firm must replace units of X with units of Y to keep output unchanged starting at a given input combination, when the changes involved are tiny. It equals the slope of the firm's isoquant at this input combination, times -1.

Marginal rate of transformation   The marginal rate of transformation from good X to good Y is the additional amount of Y that can be produced by sacrificing one unit of X (where the units involved are very small).

Marginal revenue   A firm's marginal revenue at Q units equals the extra revenue produced by the ΔQ marginal units sold, measured on a per unit basis.

Marginal units   The marginal units of action choice X are the last ΔX units, where ΔX is the smallest amount you can add or subtract.

Marginal units of labour   The marginal units of labour are the last ΔL units hired, where ΔL is the smallest amount of labour an employer can add or subtract.

Marginal units of output   The marginal units of output are the last ΔQ units, where ΔQ is the smallest amount of output the firm can add or subtract.

Market clearing curve   The market-clearing curve for a good shows the combinations of prices (both for that good and for other related goods) that bring supply and demand for the good into balance.

Market demand   The market demand for a product is the sum of the demands of all the individual consumers. Graphically, the market demand curve is the horizontal sum of the individual demand curves.

Market demand curve   Graphically, the market demand curve is the horizontal sum of the individual demand curves.

Market economy   A market economy allocates scarce resources primarily through markets.

Market failure   A market failure is a source of inefficiency in an imperfectly competitive economy.

Market power   A firm has market power when it can profitably charge a price that is above its marginal cost.

Markets   Markets are economic institutions that provide people with opportunities and procedures for buying and selling goods and services.

Market supply   The market supply of a product is the sum of the supply of all the individual sellers. Graphically, the market supply curve is the horizontal sum of the individual supply curves.

Market supply curve   Graphically, the market supply curve is the horizontal sum of the individual supply curves.

Market unravelling   Market unravelling occurs in settings with adverse selection when the presence of unattractive trading partners drives attractive trading partners out of the market by altering the prices at which they can trade.

Markup   A firm's markup, price-cost margin, or Lerner Index equals the amount by which its price exceeds its marginal cost, expressed as a percentage of its price.

Marshallian demand curve   An uncompensated demand curve, or Marshallian demand curve, shows the effect of an uncompensated change in a good's price on the amount consumed. In other words, it describes the relationship between the price and the amount consumed holding the consumer's income fixed and allowing well-being to vary.

Median voter   The median voter is the voter who has the median ideal policy among all voters.

Median voter theorem   The median voter theorem states that, if voters have single-peaked preferences, a majority of them prefer the median ideal policy to all other policies.

Mixed bundling   Mixed bundling is the practice of selling several products together as a package while also offering those products for sale individually.

Mixed strategy   When a player uses a rule to randomize over the choice of a strategy, we call it a mixed strategy.

Mixed strategy equilibrium   In a mixed strategy equilibrium, players choose mixed strategies, and the mixed strategy chosen by each is a best response to the mixed strategies chosen by the others.

Model   A model is a simplified representation of a phenomenon.

Monopolist   A monopoly market is a market with a single seller, who is called a monopolist.

Monopolistic competition   Monopolistic competition occurs in a market with free entry when there is a large number of firms, each of which produces a unique product, prices above marginal cost, and earns (close to) zero profit net of its fixed costs.

Monopoly market   A monopoly market is a market with a single seller, who is called a monopolist.

Monopsonist   A monopsony market is a market with a single buyer, who is called a monopsonist.

Monopsony market   A monopsony market is a market with a single buyer, who is called a monopsonist.

Moral hazard   Moral hazard is present when one party to a transaction takes actions that a trading partner cannot observe, and that affect the benefits the partner receives from the trade.

More productive   A firm is more productive or has higher productivity when it can produce more output using the same amounts of inputs. Equivalently, its production function shifts upward at each combination of inputs.

Multiple-stage game   In a multiple-stage game, at least one participant observes a choice by another participant before making some decision.

N

Narrow framing   Narrow framing is the psychological tendency to group related items into categories, and, in making a choice, to consider other items in the same category while ignoring items in different categories.

Nash equilibrium   In a Nash equilibrium, the strategy played by each individual is a best response to the strategies played by everyone else.

Nash equilibrium of an oligopoly market   In a Nash equilibrium of an oligopoly market, each firm is making a profit-maximizing choice given the choices of its rivals.

Natural experiment   In a natural experiment, the circumstances of otherwise identical people differ entirely by chance. An economist attributes differences in the average outcomes for those people to the differences in their circumstances.

Natural monopoly   A market is a natural monopoly when a good is produced most economically by a single firm.

Negative externality   An action creates an externality if it affects someone with whom the decision-maker has not engaged in a related market transaction. It creates a negative externality if it harms someone else and a positive externality if it benefits someone else.

Negatively correlated   Two variables are negatively correlated if they tend to move in the opposite direction.

Net benefit   Net benefit equals total benefit less total cost.

Net cash flows   A net cash flow (NCF) is the difference between revenue and cost during a single year of a project's life.

Net present value   The net present value (NPV) of an investment project is the difference between the PDV of the revenue stream and the PDV of the cost stream.

Neuroeconomics   Neuroeconomics studies the human neural system, including brain processes, with the object of discovering new principles of economic decision making.

Nominal income   Nominal income is the amount of money actually received in a particular period. Real income is the amount of money received in a particular period adjusted for changes in purchasing power that alter the cost of living over time.

Nominal interest   Nominal interest is the compensation received by the lender over and above the principal, measured in nominal dollars (that is, without adjusting for inflation).

Noncooperative outcome   In a setting of repeated competition, the noncooperative outcome is the repetition in each period of the Nash equilibrium outcome that would arise were the firms to compete just once.

Nonexcludable   A public good is a good that is nonrival and nonexcludable. A good is nonrival if more than one person can consume it (or more than one firm can use it) at the same time without affecting its value to others. A good is nonexcludable if there is no way to prevent a person from consuming it (or in the case of a firm, from using it).

Nonrival   A public good is a good that is nonrival and nonexcludable. A good is nonrival if more than one person can consume it (or more than one firm can use it) at the same time without affecting its value to others. A good is nonexcludable if there is no way to prevent a person from consuming it (or in the case of a firm, from using it).

Normal   If the demand for a product increases when income grows larger, the product is called a normal good. If it instead decreases, it is called an inferior good.

Normative economic analysis   Normative economic analysis addresses questions that involve value judgments, also known as normative questions. It concerns what ought to happen rather than what did, will, or would happen.

NPV criterion   The NPV criterion states that an investment project is profitable when its NPV is positive, and unprofitable when its NPV is negative.

O

Objective probability   An objective probability is a measure of the likelihood that a specific state of nature will occur based on the frequency with which it has occurred in the past, under comparable conditions.

Observable customer characteristics   Price discrimination is based on observable customer characteristics when a firm can distinguish, even if imperfectly, consumers with a high versus a low willingness to pay.

Oligopolists   An oligopoly market is a market with a few (but not many) sellers, who are called oligopolists.

Oligopoly market   An oligopoly market is a market with a few (but not many) sellers, who are called oligopolists.

One-stage game   In a one-stage game, participants make all of their choices before observing any choice by any other participant.

Opportunity cost   An opportunity cost is the cost associated with forgoing the opportunity to employ a resource in its best alternative use.

Opportunity cost of funds   The time value of money (also called the opportunity cost of funds) is the opportunity cost associated with the economic benefit an investor could receive by lending money at the prevailing interest rate.

Ordinal   Information about preferences is ordinal if it allows us to determine only whether one alternative is better or worse than another. Cardinal information tells us something about the intensity of those preferences— it answers the question "How much worse?" or "How much better?"

Outcome-oriented   Outcome-oriented notions of equity focus on whether the process used to allocate resources yields fair results.

Output efficiency   Output efficiency means that, among allocations satisfying exchange efficiency and input efficiency, there is no way to make one consumer better off without harming anyone else by shifting production from one good to another.

Output efficiency condition   An allocation satisfies the output efficiency condition if, for every pair of goods, every consumer's marginal rate of substitution equals the marginal rate of transformation.

Output expansion path   A firm's output expansion path shows the least-cost input combinations at all possible levels of output for fixed input prices.

Outputs   Outputs are the physical products or services a firm produces. Inputs are the materials, labour, land, or equipment that firms use to produce their outputs.

P

Pareto efficient   An allocation of resources is Pareto efficient if it's impossible to make any consumer better off without hurting someone else.

Partial equilibrium analysis   Partial equilibrium analysis concerns competitive equilibrium in a single market, considered in isolation.

Partial insurance   With partial insurance, the promised benefit is less than the potential loss.

Pass-through rate   The pass-through rate is the ratio $\Delta P/\Delta MC$, the increase in price that occurs in response to a small increase in marginal cost, measured per dollar of increase in marginal cost.

Payback period   The payback period is the amount of time before a project's total inflows match its total outflows.

Perfect complements   Two products are perfect complements if they are valuable only when used together in fixed proportions.

Perfect information   In a game with perfect information players make their choices one at time, and nothing is hidden from any player.

Perfectly correlated   Two variables are positively correlated if they tend to move in the same direction. Two variables are negatively correlated if they tend to move in the opposite direction. Two variables are uncorrelated if their movements tend to be unrelated. Finally, two variables are perfectly correlated if one is simply a multiple of the other.

Perfectly elastic demand   Demand is perfectly elastic when the demand curve is horizontal so that the elasticity of demand equals negative infinity.

Perfectly inelastic demand   Demand is perfectly inelastic when the demand curve is vertical so that the elasticity of demand is zero.

Perfectly inelastic supply   Supply is perfectly inelastic when the supply curve is vertical so that the price elasticity of supply is zero, and perfectly elastic when the supply curve is horizontal so that the price elasticity of supply is infinite.

Perfect price discrimination A monopolist can perfectly price discriminate if it knows perfectly the customer's willingness to pay for each unit and can charge a different price for each unit.

Perfect substitutes Two products are perfect substitutes if their functions are identical, so that a consumer is willing to swap one for the other at a fixed rate.

Pigouvian subsidization Pigouvian subsidization involves the use of subsidies to remedy positive externalities.

Pigouvian taxation Pigouvian taxation involves the use of taxes or fees to remedy negative externalities.

Political economy A voter's preferences are single-peaked if her net benefit from an activity increases with the activity's level until her ideal is reached, and declines thereafter.

Pooling equilibrium In a separating equilibrium, people with different information choose different alternatives. In a pooling equilibrium, people with different information choose the same alternative.

Positively correlated Two variables are positively correlated if they tend to move in the same direction.

Positive economic analysis Positive economic analysis addresses factual questions, also known as positive questions, usually concerning choices or market outcomes. It concerns what did, will, or would happen.

Positive externality An action creates an externality if it affects someone with whom the decision-maker has not engaged in a related market transaction. It creates a negative externality if it harms someone else and a positive externality if it benefits someone else.

Precommitment A precommitment is a choice that removes future options.

Preferences Preferences tell us about a consumer's likes and dislikes.

Premium An insurance premium is the amount of money a policyholder pays for an insurance policy.

Present bias Present bias is a form of dynamic inconsistency involving a bias toward immediate gratification.

Present discounted value Present discounted value (or PDV) of a claim on future resources is the monetary value of that claim today.

Price A price is the rate at which someone can swap money for a good.

Price-consumption curve The price-consumption curve shows how the best affordable consumption bundle changes as the price of a good changes, holding everything else fixed (including the consumer's income and preferences, as well as all other prices).

Price-cost margin A firm's markup, price-cost margin, or Lerner Index equals the amount by which its price exceeds its marginal cost, expressed as a percentage of its price.

Price discrimination A firm engages in price discrimination when it charges different prices for different units of the same good.

Price fixing Firms engage in price fixing when they agree on the prices they will charge or quantities they will produce.

Price floor A price floor is the minimum price that sellers can charge.

Price support A price support program raises the market price by making purchases of the good, thereby increasing demand.

Price taker A firm is a price taker when it can sell as much as it wants at some given price P, but nothing at any higher price.

Principal Principal is the amount borrowed when one person (or firm) lends money to another.

Private good A private good is a good for which consumption involves perfect rivalry and that is completely excludable.

Probability Probability is a measure of the likelihood that a specific state of nature will occur.

Probability distribution The probability distribution of a set of payoffs tells us the likelihood that each possible payoff will occur.

Process-oriented Process-oriented notions of equity focus on the procedures used to arrive at an allocation of resources rather than on the allocation itself.

Producer surplus (Aggregate) producer surplus equals the sum of firms' revenues less their avoidable costs.

Production contract curve The production contract curve shows every efficient allocation of inputs between two firms in an Edgeworth box.

Production function A production function is a function of the form $Output = F(Inputs)$, giving the amount of output a firm can produce from given amounts of inputs using efficient production methods.

Production possibilities set A firm's production possibilities set contains all combinations of inputs and outputs that are possible given the firm's technology.

Production possibility frontier The production possibility frontier shows the combinations of outputs that firms can produce when inputs are allocated efficiently among them, given their technologies and the total inputs available.

Production quota A production quota program imposes limits on the quantity that individual firms can produce.

Production technology A firm's production technology summarizes all of its possible methods for producing its output.

Profit A firm's profit, π, is equal to its revenue, R, less its cost, C: that is, $\Pi = R - C$.

Projection bias Projection bias is the tendency to evaluate future consequences based on tastes and needs at the moment of decision making.

Property right A property right is an enforceable claim on a good or resource.

Prospect theory Prospect theory is an alternative to expected utility theory that may resolve a number of puzzles related to risky decisions.

Public good A public good is a good that is nonrival and nonexcludable. A good is nonrival if more than one person can consume it (or more than one firm can use it) at the same time without affecting its value to others. A good is nonexcludable if there is no way to prevent a person from consuming it (or in the case of a firm, from using it).

Pure strategy When a player chooses a strategy without randomizing, we call it a pure strategy.

 Q

Quantity-dependent pricing In a quantity-dependent (or volume-sensitive) pricing plan, the price a consumer pays for an additional unit depends on how many units the consumer has bought.

Quota A quota directly limits the total quantity of a good that can be imported.

Quota rent A quota rent per unit output is the difference between the marginal cost of production at the quota amount and the price that results from the imposition of the quota.

R

Rationed   When the government or a supplier limits the amount that each consumer can purchase, we say that the good is rationed.

Rawlsianism   According to the principle of Rawlsianism, society should maximize the well-being of its least advantaged member.

Reaction functions   A best response function, also known as a reaction function, shows the relationship between one player's choice and the other's best response.

Real income   Nominal income is the amount of money actually received in a particular period. Real income is the amount of money received in a particular period adjusted for changes in purchasing power that alter the cost of living over time.

Real interest   Real interest is the compensation received by the lender over and above the principal, measured in real dollars (that is, adjusted for inflation).

Rent seeking   Rent seeking is socially useless effort devoted to securing a monopoly position.

Repeated game   A repeated game is formed by playing a simpler game many times in succession.

Reputation   A reputation is a widely held belief about a characteristic of a person or company that predisposes them to act in a particular way.

Residual demand curve   A residual demand curve shows the relationship between a firm's output and the market price given the outputs of the firm's rivals.

Revealed preference approach   The revealed preference approach is a method of gathering information about consumers' preferences by observing their actual choices.

Revealed preferred   One consumption bundle is revealed preferred to another if the consumer chooses it when both are available.

Risk averse   A person is risk averse if, in comparing a riskless bundle to a risky bundle with the same level of expected consumption, he prefers the riskless bundle.

Risk loving   A person is risk loving if, in comparing a riskless bundle to a risky bundle with the same level of expected consumption, he prefers the risky bundle.

Risk management   The object of risk management is to make risky activities more attractive by taking steps to moderate the potential losses while preserving much of the potential gains.

Risk neutral   A person is risk neutral if he is indifferent between all bundles with the same level of expected consumption.

Risk premium   The risk premium of a risky bundle is the difference between its expected consumption and the consumer's certainty equivalent.

Risk sharing   Risk sharing involves dividing a risky prospect among several people.

S

Scientific method   The scientific method is the general procedure used by scientists to learn about the characteristics, causes, and effects of natural phenomena.

Screening   Screening occurs when an uninformed party establishes a test that induces informed parties to self-select, thereby revealing what they know.

Second welfare theorem   The second welfare theorem tells us that every Pareto efficient allocation is a competitive equilibrium for some initial allocation of resources.

Self-enforcing agreement   In a self-enforcing agreement, every party to the agreement has an incentive to abide by it, assuming that others do the same.

Self-selection   Price discrimination is based on self-selection when the firm offers a menu of alternatives, designed so that different customers will make different choices based on their willingness to pay.

Separating equilibrium   In a separating equilibrium, people with different information choose different alternatives. In a pooling equilibrium, people with different information choose the same alternative.

Short run   The short run is a period of time over which one or more inputs is fixed. The long run is a period of time over which all inputs are variable.

Signalling   Signalling occurs when an informed individual undertakes a costly activity to convince others of particular facts.

Single-peaked   A voter's preferences are single-peaked if the net benefit from an activity increases with the activity's level until the voter's ideal is reached and declines thereafter.

Slutsky equation   The Slutsky equation is a precise mathematical statement of the principle that the effect of an uncompensated price change equals the effect of a compensated price change (the substitution effect) plus the effect of removing the compensation (the income effect).

Social insurance   Social insurance is insurance provided by the government.

Social welfare function   A social welfare function summarizes judgments about resource allocations. For each possible allocation, the function assigns a number that indicates the overall level of social welfare.

Specific tax   A specific tax is a fixed dollar amount that must be paid on each unit bought or sold.

Stable   A market equilibrium is stable if market pressures near the equilibrium point tend to push the price toward its equilibrium level; it is unstable if they tend to push it away.

Stackelberg model of quantity competition   In the Stackelberg model of quantity competition, two firms choose their outputs sequentially.

Standard deviation   The standard deviation is the square root of the variance.

State of nature   A state of nature is one possible way in which events relevant to a risky decision can unfold.

Strategic precommitment   A strategic precommitment occurs when a firm commits to some actions before rivals take theirs, with the aim of increasing its future competitive profit.

Strategy   A strategy is one player's detailed plan for playing a game. For every situation that might come up during the course of play, it tells us what the player will do.

Subjective probability   A subjective probability is a measure of the likelihood that an event will occur based on subjective judgment.

Subsidy   A subsidy is a payment that reduces the amount that buyers pay for a good or increases the amount that sellers receive.

Substitutes   Two products are substitutes if, all else equal, an increase in the price of one of the products causes buyers to demand more of the other product.

Substitution bias   The substitution bias of a Laspeyres price index involves a failure to capture the consumer's tendency to moderate the impact of a price increase by substituting away from goods that have become more expensive. As a result, the index overstates increases in the cost of living.

Substitution effect of a price change　The effect on consumption of a compensated price change is known as the substitution effect of a price change.

Sunk cost　A fixed cost is avoidable if it is not incurred when the firm decides to produce no output. It is sunk if it is incurred even when the firm decides not to operate.

Sunk cost fallacy　The sunk cost fallacy refers to the belief that if you paid more for something it must be more valuable to you.

Supply curve　A product's supply curve shows how much sellers of a product want to sell at each possible price, holding fixed all other factors that affect supply.

Supply function　The supply function of a price-taking firm tells us how much the firm wants to sell at each possible price P. It is a function of the form *Quantity Supplied = S(Price)*.

T

Tacit collusion　Firms engage in tacit collusion when they collude without communicating, sustaining a price above the noncooperative price that would arise in a single competitive interaction.

Tangency condition　A bundle on the budget line satisfies the tangency condition if, at that bundle, the budget line lies tangent to the consumer's indifference curve.

Tariff　A tariff is a tax on imports.

Technological change　Technological change occurs when a firm's ability to turn inputs into output changes over time.

Theory　A theory is a possible explanation for a natural phenomenon.

Time value of money　The time value of money (also called the opportunity cost of funds) is the opportunity cost associated with the economic benefit an investor could receive by lending money at the prevailing interest rate.

Total cost　A firm's total cost of producing a given level of output is the expenditure required to produce that output in the most economical way.

Tradable emissions permit　A tradable emissions permit entitles a firm to generate a specified amount of a given pollutant. It is also transferrable; one firm can sell it to another.

Trade　Trade occurs whenever two or more people exchange valuable goods or services.

Transferrable　Property rights are transferrable if the current owner of a good can reassign those rights to another consenting party.

Trust game　In the trust game, one player (the trustor) decides how much money to invest. A second party (the trustee) divides up the principal and earnings.

Two-part tariff　With a two-part tariff, consumers pay a fixed fee if they buy anything at all, plus a separate per-unit price for each unit they buy.

U

Ultimatum game　In the ultimatum game (also known as ultimatum bargaining), one player (the proposer) offers to give the second player (the recipient) some share of a fixed prize. The recipient then decides whether to accept or reject the proposal.

Uncompensated demand curve　An uncompensated demand curve, or Marshallian demand curve, shows the effect of an uncompensated change in a good's price on the amount consumed. In other words, it describes the relationship between the price and the amount consumed holding the consumer's income fixed and allowing well-being to vary.

Uncompensated price change　An uncompensated price change consists of a price change with no change in income. A compensated price change consists of a price change and an income change which, together, leave the consumer's well-being unaffected.

Uncorrelated　Two variables are uncorrelated if their movements tend to be unrelated. Finally, two variables are perfectly correlated if one is simply a multiple of the other.

Unstable　A market equilibrium is stable if market pressures near the equilibrium point tend to push the price toward its equilibrium level; it is unstable if they tend to push it away.

Utilitarianism　According to the principle of utilitarianism, society should place equal weight on the well-being of every individual.

Utility　Utility is a numeric value indicating the consumer's relative well-being. Higher utility indicates greater satisfaction than lower utility.

Utility function　A utility function is a mathematical formula that assigns a utility value to each consumption bundle.

Utility possibility frontier　The utility possibility frontier shows the utility levels associated with all efficient allocations of resources.

V

Variability　The variability of payoffs is an indication of risk. With little variability, the actual payoff is almost always close to the expected payoff. With substantial variability, the two amounts can differ significantly.

Variable cost function　A firm's variable cost function describes the variable cost of producing each possible level of output. It is a function of the form *Variable cost = VC(Output)*.

Variable costs　Variable costs are the costs of inputs that vary with the firm's output level.

Variable input　A variable input can be adjusted over the time period being considered, while a fixed input cannot.

Variance　The variance is the expected value of a squared deviation.

Volume-sensitive pricing　In a quantity-dependent (or volume-sensitive) pricing plan, the price a consumer pays for an additional unit depends on how many units the consumer has bought.

Voluntary contribution game　In a voluntary contribution game, each member of a group makes a contribution to a common pool. Each player's contribution benefits everyone, but the cost exceeds the contributor's benefit.

Voluntary production reduction　A voluntary production reduction program offers firms inducements to reduce their production voluntarily.

W

Weakly dominated strategy　A strategy is weakly dominated if there is some other strategy that yields a strictly higher payoff in some circumstances, and that never yields a lower payoff regardless of others' choices.

Winner's curse　The winner's curse is the tendency, in certain types of auctions, for unsophisticated bidders to overpay whenever they win.

CREDITS

Chapter 17

Page 614: © AP/Wide World Photos
Page 617: Photodisc/Getty Images
Page 644: Canadian Press/Frank Gunn

Chapter 18

Page 656: CPU Photo Library

Chapter 19

Page 694: © McGraw-Hill Companies/Jill Braaten, photographer
Page 699: © Roger-Viollet/The Image Works
Page 702: The Warren J. Samuels Portrait Collection at Duke University
Page 718: © Paolo Fridman/Corbis
Page 728: © Steven and Julie Golding-Page
Page 734: © Universität Bonn

Chapter 20

Page 746: NASA/Goddard Space Flight Center/Scientific Visualization Studio
Page 759: Courtesy of University of Chicago Law School
Page 764: © Mary Evans Picture Library/Alamy
Page 779: Courtesy of Indiana University and Dr. Elinor Ostrom
Page 786: Courtesy of Dr. Theodore Groves

Chapter 21

Page 21–1: Dynergy logo © 2007 Dynergy Inc.;
Enron logo © Enron Corporation.
Page 21–3: © G. Paul Bishop, Jr.
Page 21–12: Photo by Xiao Xuan/Photocome/Newscom
Page 21–21: © Bettmann/Corbis
Page 21–23: (**top**) © Colin McPherson/Corbis
Page 21–23: (**middle**) Office of Communications, Princeton University
Page 21–23: (**bottom**) Courtesy of Charles Wilson

INDEX